# DEBUNKING TEENAGERS

# DEBUNKING TEENAGERS

200 RESEARCH-BASED PARENTING STRATEGIES TO HELP YOUR ADOLESCENT SUCCESSFULLY NAVIGATE THE "TEMPTEEN" YEARS

DAPHNE ADLER

Cover and interior design by Danna Mathias Steele

Debunking Teenagers: 200 research-based parenting strategies to help your adolescent successfully navigate the "tempteen" years | First Edition / by Daphne Adler, BA, MBA
Includes notes, references and index.

Paperback ISBN: 979-8-218-41493-1

*Many thanks to all the individuals whose input was invaluable in helping refine early versions of this book, including Blythe Wilder, Kimberly Chase-Adler, Tom Adler, Claudio Siniscalco, Marina Siniscalco, Adrian Siniscalco, Julian Critchlow, Wendy Grad, Sharon AvRutick and Alicia Rouverol.*

# CONTENTS

# PROLOGUE

Parenting a teenager is not for the faint of heart. Modern parents have to grapple with alcohol and drugs, mental health problems, bullying, even technology overuse. Teenagers pose real challenges, and their mistakes can have full-blown adult ramifications.

Until now, there has not been a resource with fact-based advice on how to deal with these challenges. Yes, bookstore shelves are brimming with guides designed to help parents communicate with their teen better, understand the psychology of adolescents, or even discover how the teen brain functions. All of these books are interesting, and some are useful. But none answer the most important practical question — what should parents do? Can parents make any real difference in altering the trajectory of their teens' lives? Or is their role simply to step back, cross their fingers and watch as their child careens down the bumpy slope of adolescence?

The truth is that parents have many practical ways to erect barriers and guard rails to ensure their wild projectiles are hurtling in the right direction. This prologue provides the "Cliffs Notes." The strategies laid out below are not opinions from a pundit, tried and tested hacks from a parent who has raised a large brood, or epiphanies from a therapist who has spent time counseling teens. They are the product of a comprehensive review of the current academic research, augmented by proprietary data analysis of the key risks facing teenagers today. These are the strategies that have the best chance of steering your child away from the emergency room today, and away from lifelong regret tomorrow.

If any of these recommendations contradict your gut feelings, the following chapters of the book, which can be used as a reference guide, are there to convince you otherwise.

**The top 10 ways to protect your teen from harm:**

**1. Lock up the liquor**: When it comes to alcohol, a zero-tolerance policy is the way to go if you live in a society where alcohol is routinely abused (i.e., virtually everywhere except Italy). Don't condone sipping, or allow teens to drink in the "safety" of your own home under your supervision. Instead, lock up the alcohol cabinet, and collude with other parents to keep alcohol inaccessible. Many people who drink as teens turn out just fine (as perhaps you did yourself!), but if society as a whole were to adopt this more restrictive approach, rates of alcoholism and premature deaths from alcohol-related causes would drop.

**2. Ban smoking & vaping:** It's tempting to lecture your child about the dangers of smoking, but teens are typically impervious to this sort of logic. Instead, communicate your strong disapproval; explain that tobacco and vaping company executives are scheming to hook another customer for life; and enforce a firm no smoking or vaping policy inside your home (which applies to the adults too!).

**3. Script some refusals:** When peers offer your teen a substance, they typically do so in front of an audience of other peers, and rarely accept a simple no for an answer. Preparing some potential responses in advance will make it easier for your teen to say 'no' while saving face.

**4. Dispense sex protection:** Parents are almost always in the dark about the timing of their children becoming sexually active. Your child will most likely start down this path sooner than you think. Fortunately, providing protection doesn't encourage bad behavior, as long as you simultaneously clarify that you hope or expect your child to wait. Get your teen vaccinated for HPV as soon as possible, provide lots of condoms and a few STD test kits, and put girls on long-acting reversible contraception.

**5. Install telematics**: Fatal driving accidents spike in the first few months after teens get their license. Buying a vehicle with a monitoring system or installing a telematics device provided by an insurance company is the best way to ensure your novice driver is behaving sensibly on the road once you're no longer sitting in the passenger seat.

**6. Veto motorcycles**: This particular mode of transportation is deadly. Motorcycles are approximately 70–85 times more dangerous for teens to drive than cars. The thrill is not worth the risk.

**7. Suicide-proof your house**: Most suicidal thoughts are temporary, so removing the means can prevent tragedy. Even if your child isn't showing signs of being depressed, suicide-proofing can prevent substance abuse and accidents as well. Empty the medicine cabinet of non-essentials (including opioids); only keep small quantities of medicines and lock them away; and keep guns and bullets locked in separate locations or, better yet, out of the house.

**8. Discuss dominant males**: Counter-intuitively, the vast majority of assaults are perpetrated by male friends or acquaintances rather than strangers. Encourage your teen to look out for warning signs of controlling behavior, and to think carefully before going somewhere alone with any assertive male, no matter how seemingly trustworthy.

**9. Get struggling teens cognitive behavioral therapy:** Half of all teens will face a mental health issue at some point. The best option is to get professional help, specifically cognitive behavioral therapy, which works remarkably well across many different types of disorders, with the added bonus of having no side effects.

**10. Keep "tempteens" on a tight leash:** Puberty increases risk-taking, and many teens are now going through puberty earlier, so they crave risk before they are cognitively ready to handle it. Socializing is important, but early maturers need active adult supervision.

**The top 10 ways to help your teen thrive and become a good citizen:**

**1. Maximize sleep:** Three-quarters of American teens aren't getting enough sleep, which is affecting everything from school performance to mood to weight gain. To maximize your teen's sleep, keep all devices including phones out of the bedroom at night, limit caffeine, and encourage your adolescent to nap after lunch when feasible.

**2. Engineer exercise:** Half of girls and a third of boys and aren't getting exercise every day, nor a vigorous 20-minute workout at least three times a week. Exercise has huge benefits to physical health, mental health, and academic performance, so find an activity your teen can pursue with friends.

**3. Serve old-fashioned food:** Food companies have a profit motive to entice everyone to eat more, and their products are engineered to be irresistible, with little regard for health. Explain this reality, and to the extent practical, steer your teen away from processed foods and towards green-derived foods instead (vegetables; meat, fish and dairy raised on a diet of greens not grains, etc.). The best foods for everyone, including growing adolescents, are those a great-grandmother would recognize.

**4. Recommend flash cards:** Most teens use study methods that are ineffectual, like highlighting and re-reading. Flashcards, reviewed multiple times with nights of sleep in between, are by far the best method for retaining new information.

**5. Delay social media:** As Facebook co-founder Sean Parker has noted, social media "exploits a vulnerability in human psychology... God only knows what it's doing to our children's brains." Encourage your teen to watch the movie *The Social Dilemma*, and hold out as long as possible before giving your child a smart phone.

**6. Discuss misinformation:** Instead of worrying about spurious threats like online predators, we should instead be worrying about the morass of misinformation awaiting our children online. Even many adults are not savvy about getting their news from reputable sources (instead of social media) and spotting misleading content. Now is the time to teach your teen these critical life skills.

**7. Encourage brave bystander behavior:** Bystanders are the hidden key to the problem of bullying. Most bullying takes place in front of an audience of peers, and bullies are acutely aware of how their performance is going over with the crowd. If your teen is lucky enough to be popular, encourage your child to spend a bit of social capital standing up to the bully or coming to the defense of the victim.

**8. Emphasize that harassment isn't funny:** Sexual harassment is endemic amongst teens, and victims find it highly distressing. Yet nearly half of teens who admitted to harassing behavior assumed it wasn't a big deal. Encourage your child to consider the recipient's point of view, and to avoid being cavalier with others' privacy: forwarding nude photos for a laugh has the potential to ruin someone's life.

**9. Help your ugly duckling become a swan:** Teens are preoccupied with their appearance for good reason: how they look influences how their peers and even the adults in their lives treat them, impacting their confidence for life. So if you can afford it, pay for braces, contact lenses, and an appointment with a dermatologist.

**10. Keep calm and carry on:** Set out clear rules and consequences for rule breaking in advance, then calmly enforce them. Easy in theory, difficult in practice!

So there you have it: 20 strategies to help your child survive and thrive during the "terrible teens."

If there's a single common theme running through many of these suggestions, it's the following: don't be naïve. Surveys of parents and teens consistently show a stark disconnect between what parents think their teen is doing and what their teen is actually doing. No matter how angelic and obedient your darling appears to be on the surface, you can be sure your teen has a secret life hidden from you. This is normal and developmentally appropriate. But plan accordingly.

**An aside: juicy headlines**

You won't find any real-life examples of improbable threats like online predators in the following pages, even if a shocking anecdote would be more likely to captivate your attention. Juicy headlines are at fault for skewing our societal sense of the real sources of risk we face. It's simply too easy to freak out over incredibly rare but scary-sounding stories. We vividly remember the disasters at Chernobyl, Fukushima and Three-Mile Island so we're wary of nuclear energy, even though the pollution from coal-fired power plants kills more people each year than have ever died in nuclear meltdowns.[1] When it comes to the threats facing teens, serious dangers like car crashes never get enough press, so you'll find these types of important topics have been intentionally illustrated with graphic examples, as the shudder they elicit might serve a useful purpose.

Admittedly, it's easy to dish out parenting advice. It's far harder to put that advice into practice, especially when it pits you against not only your own teen, but perhaps also other parents in your community. However, parents often fall prey to the influence of "imaginary peers," for example by overestimating other parents' approval of underage drinking. So have confidence in your convictions, and consider sharing your copy of this book with other parents in your teen's sphere, so you can all collude to keep your adolescents in line. Someday, although perhaps not now, your child will thank you for it.

Let's turn now to the details of how, in practice, parents can keep their teens safe from harm and help them thrive, so they can blossom into the adults they were destined to be.

# 1. DRUGS

## Lock up the liquor

On the Caribbean islands of St. Kitts, Nevis and Barbados, tourists wearing flamboyant beachwear aren't the only ones over-indulging in fruity cocktails at sunset. Local troupes of vervet monkeys have also come to appreciate the allure of an after-dinner drink, and have become increasingly adept at stealing alcohol from the unwitting islanders.[1] While drunken monkeys make entertaining home video subjects to post on YouTube, these primates have also attracted the attention of scientists hoping to better understand our own hominid obsession with fermented beverages.

Vervet monkeys show a remarkable similarity to humans. 17 to 18 percent have a tendency to over-indulge, become aggressive and drink themselves to unconsciousness,[2] while the majority drink modestly or not at all.[3] Monkeys who are temporarily socially isolated tend to drink more.[4] Most revealingly for the purposes of this book, juvenile vervet monkeys of both sexes have a tendency to drink far more than their elders.[5]

Experts have offered up a variety of theories for why humans and our nearest primate kin have a specific weakness for alcohol. Our shared ancestors may have been attracted by rotting fruit because it was easier to digest; fermenting grain may have added nutrients that were missing from early diets; and ethanol kills microbes, making fermented drinks a potentially safer alternative to contaminated water.[6] But now that we no longer have to forage for rotten fruit and have learned how to convert our grains into 80-proof whiskey and vodka, our predilection for alcohol has morphed from an asset into a liability. About 10 percent of men and 5.5 percent of women in the US are alcoholics,[7] and it's estimated that 3.6 percent of all deaths in the US can be directly attributed to excessive drinking, with causes ranging from liver disease to traffic accidents.[8]

**Alcoholism is partially genetic**

Twin and adoption studies have shown that genes explain about half of the risk for alcoholism.[*9] If you're an alcoholic, your kids are four times more likely to be alcoholics as well.[10] Certain innate characteristics are also related to alcoholism. For example, people of Japanese, Chinese and Korean descent whose skin flushes in response to alcohol are at lower risk of becoming alcoholics, while teens with high impulsivity and various psychiatric conditions are at higher risk.

Another lesser-known risk factor is a low level of response to alcohol. Those who are relatively unaffected by alcohol have to drink more to achieve the same effects,[11] and may be able to continue drinking when others would have passed out already.[12] As a result, their capacity and tendency to imbibe more puts them at higher risk for alcohol addiction. One study observed that men with low responses to alcohol at age 20 were far more likely to be alcoholics at 40, even controlling for many other factors.[13] Similarly, a study of adolescents of both sexes in the UK also concluded that the ability to "drink others under the table" predicted problematic drinking.[14] Since "drinking others under the table" is rather non-specific, there's a brief quiz your adolescent can take to diagnose a low response to alcohol.[†15] Warning teens that they could be vulnerable to future alcohol problems has been shown to lower the risk.[16]

---

* Alcohol use disorder is defined by the Diagnostic and Statistical Manual of Mental Disorders, 5th Edition (DSM-5) as a problematic pattern of alcohol use leading to clinically significant impairment or distress, as manifested by at least two of the following, occurring within a 12-month period:

1. Alcohol is often taken in larger amounts or over a longer period than was intended.
2. There is a persistent desire or unsuccessful efforts to cut down or control alcohol use.
3. A great deal of time is spent in activities necessary to obtain alcohol, use alcohol, or recover from its effects.
4. Craving, or a strong desire or urge to use alcohol.
5. Recurrent alcohol use resulting in a failure to fulfill major role obligations at work, school, or home.
6. Continued alcohol use despite having persistent or recurrent social or interpersonal problems caused or exacerbated by the effects of alcohol.
7. Important social, occupational, or recreational activities are given up or reduced because of alcohol use.
8. Recurrent alcohol use in situations in which it is physically hazardous.
9. Alcohol use is continued despite knowledge of having a persistent or recurrent physical or psychological problem that is likely to have been caused or exacerbated by alcohol.
10. Tolerance, as defined by either of the following:
    a. A need for markedly increased amounts of alcohol to achieve intoxication or desired effect.
    b. A markedly diminished effect with continued use of the same amount of alcohol.
11. Withdrawal, as manifested by either of the following:
    a. The characteristic withdrawal syndrome for alcohol (refer to Criteria A and B of the criteria set for alcohol withdrawal, pp. 499–500).
    b. Alcohol (or a closely related substance, such as a benzodiazepine) is taken to relieve or avoid withdrawal symptoms.[1]

† For the first 5 times you ever drank:

1. How many drinks did it take for you to begin to feel different (where you could feel an effect)?
2. How many drinks did it take for you to feel a bit dizzy or to begin to slur your speech?
3. How many drinks did it take for you to begin stumbling or walking in an uncoordinated manner?
4. How many drinks did it take for you to pass out or fall asleep when you did not want to?

Then divide the total number of drinks recorded in the four possible questions by the number of questions with a response. Those with a low responsiveness to alcohol will have an answer over 4.5.[1]

Alcohol is at the top of our list of dangers facing teens because the earlier adolescents begin drinking, the higher the chance that they will subsequently become problem drinkers (see box).[17] For example, one study found that more than 40 percent of those who started drinking at age 14 or younger became alcoholics, vs. only approximately 10 percent of those who started at age 20 or older.[18] So there's a strong rationale for keeping teens away from booze as long as possible.

**Further detail on the case against early drinking**

Observational studies don't actually prove that early drinking is the cause of alcoholism. The same underlying personality characteristic, for example, a lack of impulse control, could be driving those who are destined to be problem drinkers to seek out alcohol at a younger age; or alcoholic parents might be more lenient with their kids about drinking but also passing along their genetic tendency. However, there are three sources of evidence that all suggest that early drinking itself is a big part of the problem.

Firstly, the negative effects of early drinking are apparent even after carefully controlling for genetics.[19] A study of 8,000 male twins in the US found that early regular drinking was associated with future alcoholism,[20] and another study of 6,000 twins in Australia reached similar conclusions.[21]

Secondly, animal studies, while imperfect, also suggest that the adolescent brain is more vulnerable to damage by alcohol.[22] High levels of alcohol exposure during adolescence can cause lasting memory problems in animals,[23] and juveniles are less likely than adults to be sedated by alcohol, allowing them to continue to drink more.[24] Furthermore, adolescent brains in animals are more sensitive to the pleasurable effects of alcohol,[25] and animals exposed to alcohol are more likely to take risks months after,[26] both of which could influence addiction potential.

Finally, experiments with humans above the legal drinking age also support the theory that younger brains are more susceptible to the effects of alcohol.[27] Memory impairment has been documented in young adults who volunteered to participate in an "acute alcohol challenge," with the 21- to 24-year-olds showing more impairment after recovering from a bout of drinking than those who were 25 and older.[28] So the longer you can keep your teen away from the liquor cabinet, the better.

**Other problems with early drinking**

According to the Surgeon General, early drinking is associated with a large assortment of other problems during adolescence, including risky sex (as referenced later in the section on sexual assault),[29] car crashes, unintentional injuries, physical fights, suicidal behavior, dating violence, and drug addiction.[30] Of course all of these studies on the dire effects of early drinking are discussing correlations. It's plausible that teens who relish breaking rules from a young age are drawn towards alcohol as a way to rebel, so the subsequent problems may reflect the risk-taking tendencies, rather than the effects of the alcohol itself.

Interestingly, people are also more susceptible to alcoholism in certain parts of the world. Here are the rates of alcoholism in several Western countries:[31]

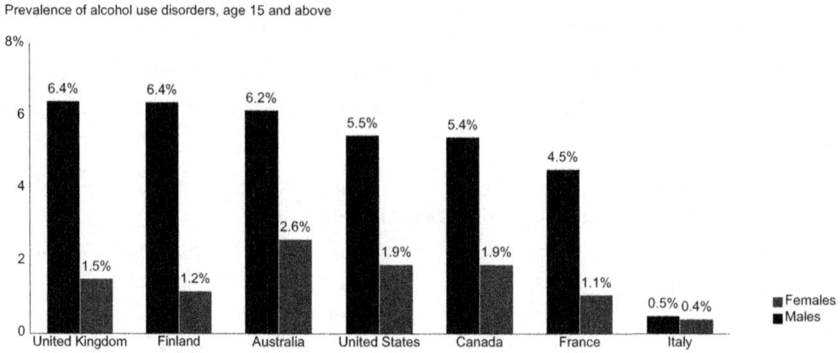


This chart contains a single striking outlier. Italy has dramatically fewer alcoholics than other countries. We can't definitively rule out the possibility that Italians are different in some important way from the rest of us, for example, genetically; but it's far more likely to be the result of their unique cultural relationship with alcohol (see box), which unfortunately has proven impossible to replicate outside Italy.

**Italy vs. Finland: a case study**

In Italy, wine is a part of everyday life, served in moderation at the typical family meal. Children are allowed small sips, and come to associate alcohol with positive family traditions. Looking back, most Italian adults can't distinguish when they first noticed or experienced alcohol, as wine is ubiquitous and embedded in family life.[32]

Finland, a country with much higher levels of alcoholism, provides a stark contrast. The Finns consider alcohol dangerous, and forbid their children from drinking. Most adults vividly recall both the first time they saw someone drinking, which was often an adult getting drunk at a special occasion, and the first time they themselves drank, which typically involved surreptitiously drinking to excess with peers somewhere outside the house.[33]

Why don't we all simply start behaving more like the Italians? Perhaps we should introduce wine at our dinner tables henceforth, and teach our teens to appreciate the merits of a fine cabernet? Unfortunately, the answer is not that straightforward. It turns out that it's virtually impossible to import an entire set of cultural behaviors into another cultural context. A child's perception of alcohol forms early in life.[34] Even your young tween has probably already absorbed all sorts of cultural messages about alcohol from television, books, movies, discussions with friends, etc.

In Finland, attempts to become more "Italian" have backfired. When parents let their children drink moderately at home to model good drinking behavior, the children simply go on to drink even more outside the home.[35]

In the US, up to 40 percent of parents think that allowing teens to sip alcohol at home like the Italians can protect their children from future problem drinking.[36] The unfortunate reality is that kids who sip under their parents' supervsion are more likely to develop a drinking problem (see box).[37]

**More on sipping at home**

In one study in the US, sixth graders who had been offered alcohol by an adult (usually a parent) were far more likely to drink heavily by ninth grade than non-sippers.[38] And another study found that in both the US and Australia, adult-supervised drinking predicted harmful alcohol consequences later.[39]

It's hard to prove that the permissive parental attitudes are the cause of the problem drinking, as no one has yet tried intervening with parents to discourage sipping.[40] It would make intuitive sense, however, that in a culture where drinking by young people is illegal and culturally frowned upon, parents who allow sipping may be perversely signalling to their children that they condone taboo behaviour, and may be unintentionally giving their children a free pass to over-indulge out of their eyesight.

Most parents would prefer not to be the stickler who socially handicaps their child with the strictest rules in the neighborhood, but it's easy to fall prey to assuming others are more lenient. As referenced in the prologue, parents significantly overestimate other parents' approval of teen drinking.[41] So don't be afraid to be firm on this subject — other parents are likely to appreciate it.

Similarly, don't fall into the trap of naiveté. Problematic teenage drinking is gradually decreasing in the US, but is still a significant problem (see box).

**Binge drinking**

The following chart shows the rate of binge drinking amongst teens, defined as five or more drinks in a row over the previous two weeks:[42]

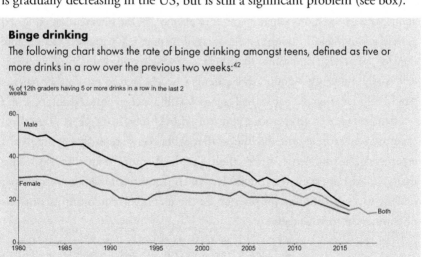

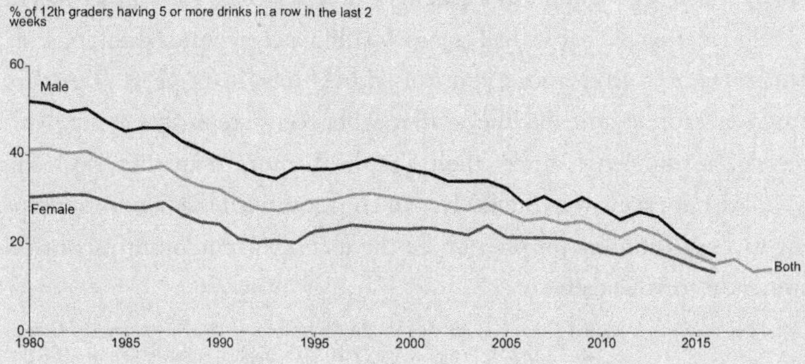

14 percent of teens currently binge drink frequently, which is considerably less than the 40 percent in 1980, but is still nowhere near zero.

Approximately 6-7 percent of teens will have developed a fully-fledged drinking problem by the time they reach age 18.* [43] Yet parents consistently underestimate whether and how much their teens drink.[44]

**The specific blind spots of parents**

In one large study, more than three quarters of kids who drank almost every day had mothers who thought their children drank less than once a month. The specific blind spots were particularly revealing:

- Mothers from religious families were more likely to underestimate their child's drinking
- Mothers who supervised their children more tended to underestimate their child's drinking
- Mothers reporting a good relationship with their teen were less likely to realise their child was a regular drinker
- The better an adolescent was doing in school, the less likely the mother was to realise her child was a regular drinker (adolescents who do well in school do tend to drink less, but there are still many who drink on a regular basis)[45]

Locking up the liquor is the most obvious first step to take to keep your child away from alcohol,[46] because about a quarter of young drinkers admit to sourcing their booze from the cupboards at home.[47] Many parents, when interviewed, admit that they keep their alcohol unlocked in easily accessible locations,[48] and rely primarily on memory and intuition, acknowledging that they wouldn't notice if small amounts of alcohol disappeared.[49]

It's also worth sitting your teen down at some point and being very clear about your expectations when it comes to alcohol.[50] One intervention educated parents about binge drinking and encouraged them to talk with their teens before they left for college, and found that those kids were less likely to drink excessively.[51] And another study found that parents who checked to see if other parents would be present at teen parties had teens who ultimately reported drinking less.[52]

In that same conversation, you can address imaginary peers. Teens frequently over-estimate the likelihood that other teens are misbehaving. Most erroneously assume that others their age drink more than they do,[53] and many will drink excessively themselves to conform with the false stereotype, leading to a self-fulfilling prophecy.[54] So there's no harm in pointing out this phenomenon to your teen.

* Calculated based on weighted average: Males Age 12-17 1.3%; Males Age 12-20 3.0%; Implied Males Age 18-20: 6.4%; Females Age 12-17 2.1%; Females Age 12-20 3.7%; Implied Females Age 18-20: 6.9%

**Where do imaginary peers come from?**
Teen misperceptions may arise because bad behavior attracts attention. At a party where most people are behaving sensibly, the one person who ends up vomiting in the bathroom will dominate memories and generate gossip well into the future, giving everyone a skewed sense of what took place that night. Another explanation could be that when discussing misbehavior in a group, teens can be reluctant to express their disapproval, and others in the group then misinterpret their silence as tacit approval.[55]

A whole field called "social-norms marketing" has been developed to counter such teen misperceptions, turning the "just say no" message into the much easier sell, "just act like everyone else."[56] One of the first campaigns at Northern Illinois University started out using newspaper ads, posters and handouts to spread the message that most students had fewer than five drinks when they partied.[57] Then two students were hired to dress up like the Blues Brothers, approach groups of students in the cafeterias, and offer money to the first individual to correctly guess how many drinks most students consumed at parties. Finally, students were promised $5 if a campaign poster was up on their wall when a student representative knocked on their door.

These campaigns succeeded in reducing binge drinking on campus,[58] and the concept quickly spread.[59] At one point, a survey of 1,000 colleges in the US found that half of all schools had conducted a social norms marketing campaign,[60] and similar experiments have also been run in high schools.[61] Unfortunately, the effects of these campaigns over the long term tend to be small.[62]

Another option is limiting your teen's exposure to alcohol advertising. Nine- to 10-year-olds in the US can identify the Budweiser frogs nearly as easily as Bugs Bunny,[63] and 75 percent of American fourth graders can recognize a Budweiser ferret ad.[64] A report from the American Academy of Pediatrics in 2010 concluded that advertising was likely responsible for up to 30 percent of adolescent alcohol use, pointing out that all of the top 15 teen-oriented TV shows at the time contained alcohol ads, with teenagers 400 times more likely to see an alcohol ad than a public service announcement discouraging underage drinking.[65]

The advertising mediums may have changed since 2010 from TV to YouTube and TikTok, but there's no doubt that alcohol companies are continuing to target teen eyeballs, wherever they're being pointed. Alcohol advertising both increases the likelihood that adolescents will start drinking and encourages them to drink more, which is unsurprising since alcohol companies would hardly throw their money away on advertising if it had no effect.[66] Yet parents pay very little attention to the content their children are viewing: most 8- to 18-year-olds say they don't have any rules about what content they can watch or how much time they can spend glued to a screen.[67]

**What if your child is already drinking?**
If you're a savvy parent and suspect your adolescent has an alcohol problem, a treatment called electronic screening and brief intervention (e-SBI), delivered over the internet, has shown promise in helping adults,[68] and is now recommended by the U.S. Department of Health and Human Services.[69] One such program currently available self-serve online* is effective for the general population[70] and has also reduced heavy drinking in young adults and college students,[71] although it has yet to be evaluated in adolescents.† [72] Another helpful intervention conducted by a health professional is called "BASICS."‡ [73]

Ultimately, our cultural traditions obscure an objective point about alcohol which is easy to overlook: "Alcohol is quite toxic. Indeed, if alcohol were a newly formulated beverage, its high toxicity and addiction potential would surely prevent it from being marketed as a food or drug."[74] Mothers Against Drunk Driving deserve the last word on this subject: "Alcohol use by those under the age of 21 isn't a rite of passage."[75]

## Ban smoking and vaping

Columbus first encountered "strange leaves" during his journey to the New World in the late 1400s. He could never have predicted that five centuries later, a third of adults globally would be hooked on this new drug.[76]

Nicotine is one of the most addictive drugs known to man, surpassed only by crack cocaine and heroin.[77] "Loss of autonomy," or being unable to quit smoking despite wanting to, can happen quickly. Among sixth graders who experimented with smoking, 10 percent lost autonomy within two days, and 25 percent within 30 days.[78] The most common initial symptom is a feeling of addiction or strong urge to smoke, accompanied by irritability, nervousness, restlessness or anxiousness when prevented from smoking.[79] Ultimately, around a third of people who try smoking go on to become dependent,[80] although most never intended to:[81] in one study, around two

* www.checkyourdrinking.net

† Many other programs have been or are currently being tested,[i] but none are yet available selfserve to the English-speaking public.

‡ The student fills out a questionnaire about alcohol consumption, personal beliefs about alcohol, understanding of social alcohol norms, and family history, and has two 50-minute interviews one week apart, which include personalized feedback on myths about alcohol's effects, facts on alcohol norms, ways to reduce future risks associated with alcohol use, and a menu of options to assist in making changes.

thirds of those who had been daily smokers in the twelfth grade were still daily smokers a decade later, although only 3 percent had thought they would still be smoking five years hence.[82]

The vast majority of people who start smoking end up regretting it: a full 85 percent.[83] Mary Beecham, a 62-year-old grandmother, speaks for many when she describes her experience:

> "I started smoking when I was 14 because I wanted to fit in. If I'd realized how hard it would be to stop, I would never have started in the first place. I've tried to give up several times but it's an addiction I can't break. I only wish I'd managed to stop myself having that first cigarette."[84]

Even adolescents themselves are actively trying but failing to quit: close to half of high school smokers have tried to give up smoking at some point in the previous year.[85] Quit they should; according to an estimate by the Surgeon General, 7.5 percent of all American children currently under 18 years old are destined to die prematurely as adults because of a smoking-related illness.[86]

**It's in the genes**

Genetics plays a prominent role in who gets hooked and how quickly.[87] Twin studies from multiple geographies all suggest that genes account for over half the variance in susceptibility to nicotine.[88] It's even possible to predict future smoking habits based on an individual's very first cigarette experience: those who feel a pleasurable rush or buzz and/or a sense of relaxation are many times more likely to become smokers than those who cough, splutter or feel sick.[89]

**How do we know teens are uniquely vulnerable?**

Animal studies suggest the teenage brain is particularly susceptible to nicotine.[90] The limbic system (the part of the brain that controls cognition, emotion and drug reward) is still maturing during the teen years, and animals exposed to even a single, very low dose of nicotine before reaching maturity show lasting changes in this part of the brain.[91] A review of animal studies by the Surgeon General has concluded that chronic nicotine exposure during brain development produces long-lasting, unique addiction effects not observed in mature adult animals.[92]

There is also evidence from human twin studies that younger smokers are uniquely vulnerable. One group of researchers tracked down 240 pairs of identical twins who had started smoking at different times at least two years apart, and found that the twins who had begun smoking earlier had significantly higher scores on a test for nicotine dependence and greater cravings for cigarettes when unable to smoke than their siblings who had started later.[93]

**Consequences now as well as later**

Beyond the obvious long-term health risks, smoking has short-term impacts as well. A study of approximately 2,600 identical twin pairs in which one twin smoked and the other had never started found that the smokers reported significantly more attention problems than their non-smoking siblings, although the scores equalized if and when their twins began to smoke too.[94] Attempting to quit also causes problems for adolescents. Those in the process of weaning themselves off nicotine suffer short-term impairments in verbal memory and working memory, and longer-term declines in cognitive performance, until their bodies finally adjust to being nicotine-free.[95]

Throughout our lifetimes, governments have been scrambling to contain the health scourge represented by tobacco. The UK National Health Service recently launched a series of "shockvertisements" with the tagline "Get Unhooked" (search for images online if you aren't put off by graphic photos),[96] continuing in the tradition established by the warning graphics required on US cigarette packs to counter the allure of this drug. Partly because of aggressive health measures such as these, tobacco use is gradually declining, but it remains a major issue. In 2019, 22 percent of twelfth graders had tried smoking.[97]

Tobacco companies count on snagging their customers early. Approximately three-quarters of adult tobacco users and 88 percent of those who ever smoked daily started before the age of 18.[98] The chart below shows when teens first begin to light up:[99]

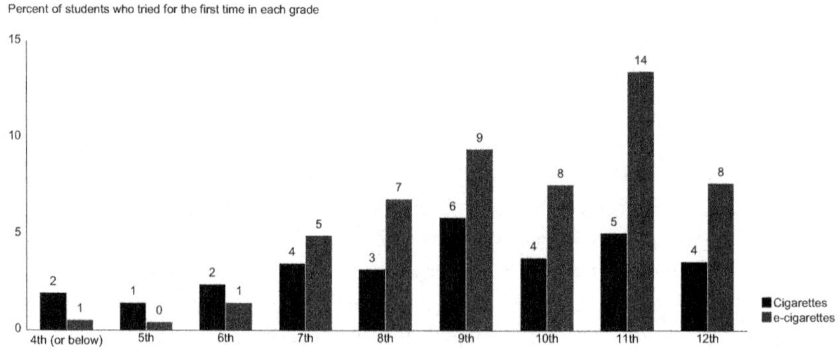


Over the years, tobacco companies in the US have increasingly been hamstrung by the government in their attempts to recruit new teen smokers. A 1998 Master Settlement Agreement (MSA) banned tobacco billboards, advertisements in many magazines, merchandise with tobacco logos and any other form of marketing targeting kids.[100] Yet, despite these restrictions, tobacco companies are still managing to attract almost a quarter of our teens before they leave high school. How do they accomplish this stealthy feat?

First, the products themselves are carefully tailored to appeal to teens, for example, with distinctive flavorings.[101] More importantly, the branding is designed to emphasize qualities teens find appealing (see box). Young women are also targeted specifically with ads recommending cigarettes for weight-control, even though there's no evidence that smoking actually affects weight.[102]

**Sneaky marketing**

An analysis of internal tobacco company documents obtained through litigation has revealed that to recruit children, brands seek to "communicate independence, freedom and peer acceptance. They portray smokers as attractive and autonomous, accepted and admired, athletic and at home in nature;"[103] "[t]o smoke Marlboro Lights represents having passed a rite of passage;" "[s]moking for [young] people is a badge, a sign of maturity, discernment and independence."[104]

Tobacco companies currently spend most of their marketing budget in stores where advertising isn't yet as restricted, at least in the US.[105] (Even this form of advertising is now banned in England, Wales and Northern Ireland and some Australian states, and bans are being considered in New Zealand, Finland and Brazil.)[106] In England, about a third of independent retailers get incentives from tobacco company representatives for selling their products, including pens, free packs of cigarettes, offers on products, and vouchers at discount stores. In the words of one independent retailer, "You just want to shift the stock, so if a kid comes in late at night you're tempted to sell to them."[107] These advertising tactics work; a survey of middle-school students in California found that the two-thirds of students who made at least weekly visits to small grocery, convenience, or liquor stores were 50 percent more likely to smoke.[108] Tobacco companies also spend money on direct marketing strategies, including direct mail, tobacco coupons, company websites and giveaway items.[109]

Movies and television are another important source of influence. Observing glamorous sirens or rebellious youths smoking on screen primes adolescents to be receptive to cigarettes.[110] Teens whose parents allow them to watch R-rated movies are twice as likely to start smoking as their more sheltered peers, and even having a television in the bedroom increases the risk of a teen becoming a smoker.[111] One study estimates that the portrayal of smoking in movies may be responsible for over a third of cases of kids choosing to light up.[112]

However the most important step teens take on the path towards becoming hooked on tobacco involves peers.[113] Subconsciously influenced by a variety of marketing messages, teens are less likely to resist, but it's their peers who ultimately pressure them into trying their first cigarette. More than 80 percent of smokers take their first drag in a friend's home when the parents are out.[114]

Parents typically have no idea that their children are being initiated into the secret society of smokers beneath their noses. Three-fourths of parents believe they're communicating an "anti-drug" message effectively to their children; but a recent survey of parents and their twelfth graders revealed a stark disconnect: only 5 percent of parents believed their kids had used tobacco in the past year, when the true figure was 39 percent.[115]

Short of banning visits to friends, how can you prevent your teen from starting down the path toward nicotine addiction? Appealing to an adolescent's rational brain is ineffectual. Many school programs beginning in the 1970s attempted to educate students about the risks associated with smoking, and none had any effect.[116] Mass-media campaigns, on the other hand, have successfully managed to lower teen smoking rates, not by lecturing about lung cancer in the distant future, but by cleverly appealing to adolescents' desire for autonomy.[117] Inform teens that smoking means falling prey to the manipulative desires of profit-hungry adult tobacco industry executives, and they suddenly become less inclined to pick up a cigarette.[118]

**The anti-smoking campaigns that work**

The Truth campaign,* funded in Florida by a settlement with the tobacco industry and positioned as a hip, rebellious, youth-led movement, cut rates of teen smoking dramatically.[119] The same group launched a subsequent campaign, dubbed "Truth FinishIt," at the MTV Video Music Awards, urging teens to use their social influence to become the generation that ends the tobacco epidemic.[120] The FDA's nationwide campaign, The Real Cost,† has reached many US adolescents, and successfully fostered negative attitudes toward tobacco products.‡[121] And if you happen to live in a school district which offers a peer-led, anti-smoking program, these have also been shown to be effective[122] (e.g. "Teens Against Tobacco Use").[123]

* www.thetruth.com

† https://therealcost.betobaccofree.hhs.gov

‡ There are also sub-campaigns currently being assessed which are aimed at specific demographics: "Fresh Empire" (https://freshempire.betobaccofree.hhs.gov) targets teens who identify with hip-hop culture,[1 2] and "This Free Life" is designed to appeal to those who are lesbian, gay, bisexual, and transgender (LGBT).[3 4] Such campaigns are part of a wider set of strategies focused on helping teens building the skills to resist negative influences, including recognising advertising tactics and peer influences, improving communication and decision-making skills, and cultivating assertiveness, collectively called "social influence resistance."[5 6]

There's also no harm in proactively expressing your disapproval of smoking. When asked, young people say that parental disapproval is the major reason they avoid tobacco and other drugs,[124] and teens who progress to smoking are more likely to have parents who are unconcerned. [125] Having an official home smoking policy ("smoking is not allowed in our house") also lowers the likelihood of teens smoking,[126] even when the parents themselves are smokers, as long as they too adhere to the rule.[127]

**How do we know parent attitudes matter?**
The most effective intervention for reducing smoking among teens whose parents smoke, called Smokefree Kids, included newsletters and mailed parenting tips, and successfully reduced teen smoking rates from 19 percent to 12 percent.[128] The materials are not available online, but the fact that the program worked reinforces the point that parents can make a difference in influencing their teens' future smoking behavior.

As a last resort, you can always buy your teen a vintage "smoking is very glamorous" poster featuring a hag with a cigarette butt dangling from her mouth.*

**What if your teen is smoking already?**
If your child has already been snared by tobacco's clutches, your best bet is the American Lung Association's N-O-T (Not on Tobacco) program.[129] Aimed specifically at adolescents, it's taught by an adult over ten sessions in a small group format.[130] (If the in-person sessions are not available where you live, there's also an online version.†)

Unfortunately, our problems with nicotine don't end with traditional cigarettes. Even as smoking rates are steadily declining in most of the Western world, a new frontier in the battle is rapidly emerging. When it comes to e-cigarettes, beware. Vaping has already arrived at a school near you:

> "It's not something that's limited to one social group," says a junior at Churchill High School in Potomac, Md. "It's not just the kids who are stoners. It's the athletes. It's the nerds. It's everybody. It's infiltrated every social clique. Every type of person knows someone — or maybe they are that person — who is vaping."[131]

* www.chisholm-poster.com/posters/CL44687.html

† https://notforme.org/

In his four years at Cape Elizabeth High School in Maine, vice principal Nate Carpenter says he can't recall seeing a single student smoke a cigarette, but vaping is suddenly everywhere. "It's our demon," he says. "It's the one risky thing they can do — with little consequence, in their mind — to show that they're a bit of a rebel." Howard Colter, the interim superintendent, adds, "They can pin them on to their shirt collar or bra strap and lean over and take a hit every now and then, and who's to know?"[132] According to Michael McAlister, principal of Northgate High School in California, "out of 53 suspensions last year, 40 were for vaping devices. We're losing a battle."[133] A freshman at Cornell University reports that JUUL, a popular brand of e-cigarette, has become so ubiquitous on campus that a popular late-night food truck now sells vaping devices and nicotine liquids.[134]

**The losing battle**

Traditional cigarette and e-cigarette trends are moving in tandem: vaping is becoming more common as traditional tobacco use declines. The delivery mechanism is shifting, but the levels of nicotine addiction in the next generation remain the same. According to the most recent figures from an annual pulse-check of American teens, 43 percent of twelfth graders have tried vaping, far more than cigarettes (24 percent), and the increase in vaping recorded in 2018 was the largest increase ever recorded for any substance in 44 years of tracking adolescent drug use.[135] Delays in rolling out regulatory requirements and inconsistencies in enforcing them haven't helped.[136] More than a dozen new JUUL-like nicotine delivery devices have come to market since August 2016, in defiance of the deadline set by the FDA banning the sale of new e-cigarette products without regulatory approval.[137]

A key difficulty is the perception among teens that vaping is harmless. Only 18 percent of teens think e-cigarettes pose a "great risk,"[138] and worse, only 37 percent of teens who vaped even knew that a popular brand (JUUL) contains nicotine.[139] Given that nicotine is extremely addictive, a decision to vape is likely to continue to haunt a teen later in life. And although e-cigarettes may be less harmful than traditional cigarettes, they pose health risks too (see box).

**How dangerous are e-cigarettes, anyway?**

E-cigarettes used in the standard way are moderately less harmful than ordinary cigarettes. The most comprehensive analysis of research on e-cigarettes[140] has concluded there's substantial evidence that e-cigarettes contain lower levels of toxic substances than ordinary cigarettes.[141] Nevertheless, e-cigarettes are not benign; they still emit numerous potentially toxic substances,[142] and may also have long-term health effects that haven't yet come to light.[143]

E-cigarettes certainly contain a cocktail of chemicals: one analysis of a variety of e-liquids identified approximately 120 different compounds.[144] These include aldehydes (e.g., formaldehyde, acetaldehyde, and acrolein), which are carcinogenic and increase the risk of heart disease and lung disease,[145] as well as toxic heavy metals (e.g. lead and cadmium).[146] Diacetyl, found in 75 percent of e-cigarettes and used to create artificial flavors like butter, strawberry, piña colada and butterscotch, was responsible a few years ago for a severe and irreversible lung disease, gruesomely dubbed "Popcorn Lung," among workers in a microwave popcorn packaging factory who inhaled too much of the butter flavoring.[147]

When it comes to nicotine, levels in e-cigarettes are comparable on average to normal cigarettes, although the amounts are highly variable depending on the device and how it's used.[148]

Perversely, e-cigarettes are also a gateway to future tobacco smoking.[149] For example, twelfth graders who had vaped were more than four times as likely to begin smoking cigarettes over the following year than their peers who hadn't tried an e-cigarette.[150] And researchers believe the experience with vaping is directly responsible for the transition to traditional smoking.[151]

As with cigarettes, adolescents are first being primed with plenty of advertising. Approximately 70 percent of middle and high school students have been exposed to e-cigarette advertisements in retail stores, on the internet, on TV and in movies.[152]

**Why do teens say they vape?**
The most common reasons given by teens are "to experiment – to see what it's like", "because it tastes good", and "to have a good time with my friends."[153] Most adolescents who vape own their own device (78 percent), but three quarters had also used someone else's in the previous month, suggesting vaping is a highly social habit.[154]

The vaping companies are currently winning the race against both the regulators and the researchers scrambling to identify ways of curbing the epidemic. There are no proven techniques yet for preventing teen vaping,[155] although presumably some of the lessons learned with regular cigarettes should apply to e-cigarettes, too.

Tipping off your teen that JUUL and other vaping devices, as well as the new Zyn pouches hitting the market, do indeed contain nicotine and various other harmful substances might be a good place to start. Each day, countless teens thoughtlessly accept their first puff of mango-flavored vapor from a friend, unaware that this seemingly innocuous, fleeting pleasure may be starting them down a life-long path.

# Script some refusals

"This is your brain. This is your brain on drugs. Any questions?"

If you were a teen in the US in the 1980s, you're likely to recall this classic ad, featuring a paternal figure frying an egg.[156] Back then, drugs all fell into a single category, and they all were bad.

Even today, most drug campaigns attempt to steer teens away from drugs as a broadly defined category. So while our tour of alcohol and cigarettes has included a few specific examples of ways to influence adolescents to steer clear, other insights can be gleaned from the research on drugs in general.[*] [157]

Sadly educational media campaigns, involving frying pans and eggs or otherwise, don't seem to help, despite their widespread use.[158] Arousing teens' fear by emphasizing risks, engaging their moral compass by implying drugs are evil, or appealing to their better selves by teaching self-esteem and responsible decision-making are all virtually useless.[159]

**School-based training?**
Certain school-based training programs have succeeded in reducing drug use, but it's not always obvious which components of these programs are the critical ones; there's no easily discernible pattern.[160] That only leaves the option of adopting one of these effective programs wholesale, for example by convincing your school to run one. A few programs have also made their content available self-serve to parents; for details, see Appendix I.

What does work? Firstly, reducing teens' access to drugs.[161] It's therefore a highly sensible precaution to empty or secure your medicine cabinets to remove the temptation of easy access to opioids, stimulant and sedative prescriptions, even cough syrup. This tip is also worth sharing with the parents of your teen's friends.

Providing your teen with information can also help in a limited fashion as long as the information is pitched correctly. Emphasizing only the negatives of a substance can backfire, as kids don't perceive a one-sided account as credible. In one study involving adolescent varsity football players, one group who were told only about the negative effects of using anabolic steroids did not change their views, while another group who were offered

* This section draws on a number of general sources, each of which have rigorously evaluated and compared various drug intervention programs.[1 2 3 4]

a balanced perspective of both the risks and benefits came away far more convinced that the adverse effects were real.[162]

However the most important action you can take as a parent is to help your teen craft some pre-formulated responses. Kids are most at risk of substance use when they're with their peers.[163] An important subtlety, however, is that when teens are propositioned, they frequently have an audience. For example, of a group of seventh grade students who were offered drugs, 89 percent said at least one additional friend, acquaintance or extended family member was present, while only 11 percent were alone with the offeror.[164]

In a social context, the idea that teens should "just say no" is naïve and inadequate. Another study of high school students found that peer pressure was involved in 72 percent of the offers, mostly after the initial offer had been refused.[165] In other words, teens frequently do "just say no" initially, but they have trouble doing so a second time, especially after a persuasive appeal in front of a peanut gallery of peers heckling from the sidelines.

**Why do peers pressure?**

Why do the teens who are making the offer continue to apply pressure and insist a second time, instead of taking no for an answer? There are thousands of studies, articles and books that address the topic of peer pressure and discuss in great detail why teens can be vulnerable to persuasion, why they often succumb, and how to help them resist. Yet not a single one of these examines the other side of the equation, i.e. the motivations of the one exerting the pressure. The offeror could theoretically have a profit motive: an informal, small-scale dealer might be wanting to hook a friend or acquaintance to gain a new customer. Yet one study of the "social supply" of drugs concluded that offers of drugs to friends and acquaintances are almost exclusively non-commercially motivated.[166] Another theory posits that humans are social creatures who are motivated to form cohesive groups. Groups use norms to control their members,[167] and develop a tendency to shun non-conformity. Therefore an individual abstaining from a substance in a social situation could be perceived as a challenge to the group which must be overcome.[168]

The fact that around 90 percent of offers take place in front of bystanders suggests a final obvious possibility: that the offeror is seeking to gain social status by publicly endorsing a taboo/rebellious/adult behavior, and then further establishing social dominance by insisting and successfully forcing the target to cave. No research appears to have examined this possibility, or tested whether teaching adolescents to be suspicious about the motivation of those offering drugs could help them to resist. It would also be illuminating to explore whether the teens who do continue to resist truly end up losing status in the eyes of bystanders, or instead gain status for confidently refusing to give in to the persuasion.

There is unquestionably an art to saying "no" gracefully. In a study of sixth graders, the non-smokers often proposed alternative activities to smoking, which enabled them to avoid their friends interpreting their refusal as a rejection of the friendship.[169] This is a sensible approach, as kids who simply say no assertively tend to be perceived as offensive and unlikeable,[170] while remaining conversational mitigates the harshness of the refusal.[171] The sixth grade non-smokers also used more facts in their successful refusals, e.g. smoking causes bad breath and smelly clothing, can lead to cancer, or interferes with sports performance.[172] Since not all teens will be able to invent a credible refusal on the spot, it's worth helping them plan a strategy in advance (see box for examples).[173]

**Refusal strategies**

1. Create an excuse to leave: download an app like "Gotta Go", or call a parent for an ostensibly credible reason (e.g. to ask to extend curfew, or because the parent insists on a check-in by phone at a specified time) with a pre-agreed code word or phrase that signals an uncomfortable or risky situation
2. Pretend to participate: fill a cup with just a mixer, or with a small amount of water (e.g. "vodka") in the bathroom; or refill an alcohol can/bottle with something non-alcoholic
3. Make an excuse about unreasonable parents, such as:
   a. My parents are really strict, so it's not worth the chance of being grounded
   b. My parents have bought a breathalyzer test / drug testing kit online (note: personal breathalyzers sell for as little as $30 on Amazon)
   c. If my parents knew I tried anything, they'd take all of my college money/put me in a rehab program/etc.; they're so unreasonable I can't take a chance
   d. My parents said they'll take away my cell phone if I do that
   e. My mother used to use X when she was younger and now she can smell it from a mile away — she checks my clothes every night
   f. I have to always come and say good night to my parents when I come in, even if it involves waking them, and they can tell immediately
4. Make an excuse about a personal experience with the risk, such as:
   a. Someone I know ended up in a dangerous/life-threatening situation (alcohol poisoning, drug overdose)
   b. Someone I know is an alcoholic/drug addict and has ruined his/her life
   c. I've tried it before and had a bad experience / that stuff makes me sick (works better when armed with some knowledge of the typical effects of the substance in question)
5. Make a health-related excuse, such as:
   a. My asthma or allergies make it dangerous (my doctor says I could end up in the hospital if I do X)
   b. I can't as I'm on medication (e.g. antibiotic)
   c. I need to stay healthy to achieve my sports goals / avoid letting down my team

(e.g. smoking will make me out of breath)

6. Claim it would interfere with what's happening next, for example:
    a. I have to be somewhere at a specific time
    b. I'm driving (offer to be the designated driver)
    c. I've got my eye on someone, and don't want to kiss him/her with horrible ash tray breath/have my clothes smell bad
    d. I'm hooking up with someone later and I want to remember all of it
    e. I have to get up early the next day
    f. I have to [study for a big test / go to a concert / play in a sports match etc.]. I can't do that after a night of X

One option besides simply showing this list to a teen would be to suggest drafting an "implementation intention," or a plan that explicitly lays out "If I encounter situation X then I will do Y." (see box)

**Implementation intentions**

One study attempting to reduce smoking rates offered a randomly selected group of students a template ('I can say _______ if I'm offered a cigarette'; 'I can say _______ if my friends want me to smoke'; 'I can say _______, even if I'm the only one in the group not smoking') with a few suggestions of answers ('No thanks, I don't want the habit; No cancer sticks for me; No thanks, smoking makes you smell bad; No, it's bad for your health'). Then they asked them to fill it out and sign it in order to say no to smoking that term. The adolescents involved were significantly less likely than their peers to have started smoking several years later.[174]

If embarking on such an exercise with your teen feels awkward, you could always suggest the concept to your local school. In a battle as important as this one, you need all the help you can get.

# Dig deeper

Humans have been using and abusing drugs for millennia. Magic mushrooms were utilized by the Aztec Indians for healing and divination well before the Spanish conquest;[175] cannabis was mentioned in a Chinese document dating from 2,700 BCE;[176] and the Chinese were making wine from rice, honey, and fruit some 9,000 years ago.[177]

In more recent times, humans have found inventive ways to make the drugs of yore more potent, and concomitantly more addictive. Distillation has increased alcohol content dramatically. Coca leaves, historically chewed by Andean miners to relieve their fatigue, have been processed into crack cocaine. Opium, previously used for pain relief and anesthesia, was first purified into morphine and then synthesized as heroin. And tobacco, formerly chewed or sniffed, was later rolled into cigarettes, allowing the inhaled nicotine to reach the brain in a few seconds.[178]

The modern era has spawned a further wave of innovation. In the types of clandestine laboratories glamorized by *Breaking Bad*, new drugs like "Spice" and "K2" (synthetic cannabinoids) are being invented every day. As a result, modern teenagers have access to a panoply of mind-altering substances that didn't even exist when their parents were coming of age. Yet many modern parents aren't worried about the onslaught of drugs their children will inevitably encounter as teens. Approximately 60 percent of parents say they're not concerned about their children's possible use or abuse of alcohol or other drugs.[179]

It's true that teens are somewhat better behaved than their counterparts a generation ago. Here are the trends for a variety of common drugs in the US:[180]

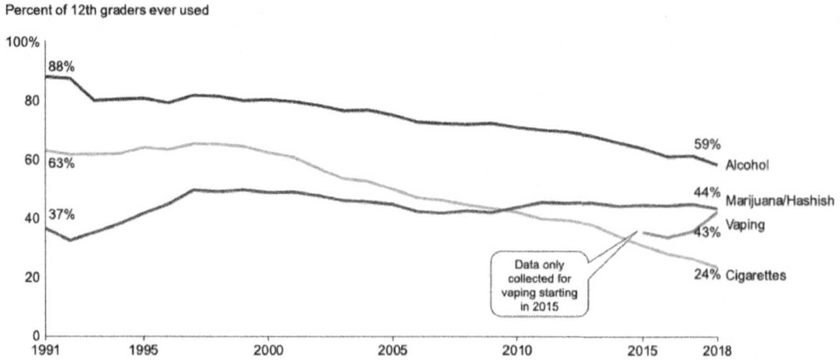


It's striking that 88 percent of American seniors were using alcohol in 1991, while only 59 percent drink today. Similarly, the 63 percent of teens smoking cigarettes in 1991 has declined to 24 percent today, although if you add in the 43 percent who vape, that's a similar number of teens hooked on nicotine. The pattern of decline holds for the less common drugs as well:[181]

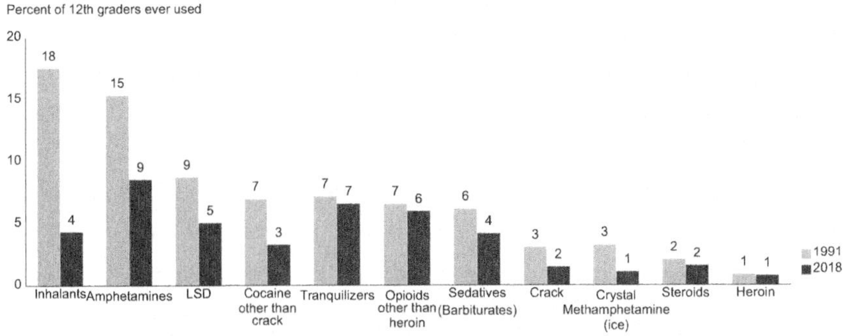


Nevertheless, a large number of teenagers are still using drugs, and most have easy access to substances of all kinds. For example, 83 percent of twelfth graders say it would be fairly or very easy to access alcohol, 82 percent to get hold of a vaping device, 78 percent to source marijuana, and 73 percent to procure cigarettes. Even the less common drugs are readily available to a significant minority of teens, including amphetamines (38 percent), LSD (29 percent), opioids (31 percent), other hallucinogens (28 percent), cocaine (27 percent), and ecstasy (24 percent).[182] A full 81 percent of older adolescents report they've had an opportunity at some point to use illicit drugs.[183]

In fact, many teens are secretly using drugs under their parents' noses. Studies of parent-teen pairs have found that 20 to 35 percent of parents who think their children don't drink have teens who are secretly imbibing.[184] Parents are even unaware of abuse and dependence problems in their children; another study found that parents and adolescents agreed only 27 percent of the time about diagnoses of alcohol abuse or dependence and 26 percent of the time on marijuana abuse or dependence.[185] In fact, by age 18, 14.5 percent of teens have suffered from alcohol dependence, and 16 percent from dependence on another substance.[186]

Furthermore, drug use is not a problem confined to the inner city like homicide — quite the opposite. Affluent students are more likely than their less affluent counterparts to use cigarettes, alcohol,[187] marijuana and other illegal drugs.[188] In one study of two academically-gifted groups of adolescents, one from an exclusive private, affluent school and the other from a magnet school with low-income students, the lower-income students reported much less substance use than the affluent students, despite similar levels of academic pressure.[189] Amongst affluent teens, popularity is correlated with substance use, so once a druggy peer culture is established in a community, the popular crowd will continue to suck in new users.[190] Affluent teen users are also more likely to suffer from depression and anxiety, suggesting some may be using the substances as a coping mechanism.[191]

Knowing our teens are surrounded by temptation, which substances should we be most worried about? This is a thorny question to answer. One study funded in part by the Gates foundation has estimated the "Disability Adjusted Life Years," or years of life lost due to death and disability, attributed to certain drugs. Their analysis suggests that for society as a whole, tobacco and alcohol cause by far the most harm:[192]

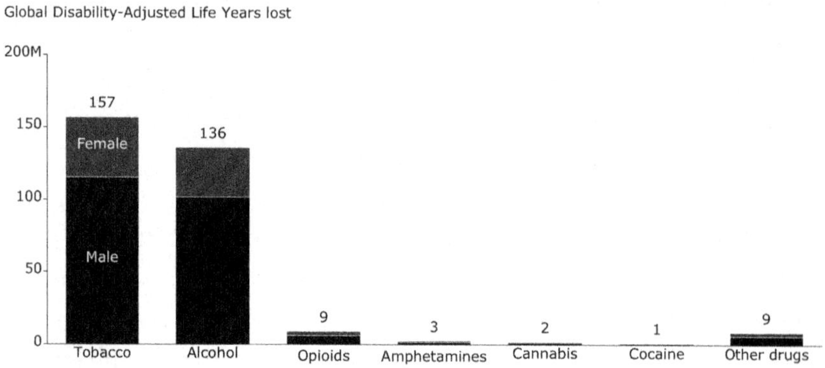


However, these figures are a cumulative view reflecting how many people use these drugs, not the risks facing a single teenager offered a range of options.

**How to assess harmfulness?**

From an individual's perspective, a drug has several different dimensions of harmfulness:

1. Physical harm, including immediate toxicity, long-term toxicity, and harm due to the method of use (e.g. contracting HIV from intravenous drug use)
2. Dependence, which can be a combination of psychological dependence, physical dependence/withdrawal, and pleasure/desire to repeat the experience
3. Anti-social behavior causing harm to others

The first factor, physical harm, is surprisingly hard to assess, because it isn't ethical to conduct experiments on humans. Findings in animals such as mice may not apply, and there are all sorts of problems with simply observing individuals who have chosen to take various drugs. If more people show up in the hospital with alcohol poisoning than with a heroin overdose, that's probably because more people drink than use heroin; without knowing how many people were abusing each in the first place, it's difficult to estimate the risk. Furthermore, people may not admit to taking something illegal, may not remember how much of a drug they consumed, or may have taken multiple substances in combination.[193]

As a result, the best options we have for comparing the physical harm of different drugs are only approximate. One metric used is the "margin of exposure," which compares the amount of the drug that causes negative effects with the amount people usually consume.[194] Another similar metric is the "safety ratio," which compares the lethal dose with the dose most commonly used. Heroin has a lethal dose less than 10 times the typical dose, which is why it's dangerously easy for addicts to get the dose wrong unintentionally and fatally overdose.[195]

The second element of harm is dependence. Identifying which drugs have the greatest potential to be addictive depends, in part, on how you define addiction. One option is to look at the "capture ratio," or proportion of people who will continue to use the drug despite sincerely intending not to do so. By this measure, tobacco would be ranked near the top. Another factor is the severity of withdrawal symptoms, which would rank alcohol and heroin first. A final measure is how strongly a user wants to repeat the experience to achieve euphoria, feelings of confidence, etc.; cocaine and opiates are the top drugs in this category.[196] * [197] It's also likely that some people are genetically more susceptible than others to becoming addicted to any drug.[198]

All of this complexity doesn't help parents untangle which drugs to worry about. Although certain broad principles do apply to steering kids away from drugs in general, there are also prevention techniques specific to individual substances. What we ideally need is a ranked list, somehow combining all the sources of harm.

Fortunately, two different research teams in the UK[199] and the Netherlands[200] have attempted to tackle this problem both separately and in collaboration[201] by asking panels of experts for harm ratings and consolidating their views. Although their methods have generated debate about the best way to combine harm into a single score, they rightly point out that having some sort of score is still useful.[202]

Here is a chart showing an estimate of harm to an individual user:† [203]

* Some studies have attempted to create a single metric of overall dependency.[1 2] For example one estimates that 68% of nicotine users, 23% of alcohol users, 21% of cocaine users, and 9% of cannabis users become dependent at some time in their life.[3]

† Butane used for solvents/inhalants

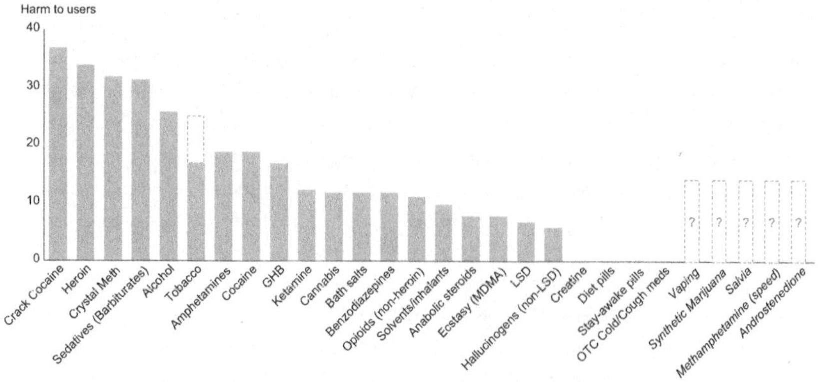


Crack cocaine, heroin and crystal meth all live up to their bad reputations. However alcohol is ranked fifth, placing it above a variety of drugs which are illegal in most countries, including cocaine, cannabis, ecstasy and LSD. This discrepancy with public policy has not gone unnoticed; Michael Pollan's book, *How to Change your Mind: What the New Science of Psychedelics Teaches Us About Consciousness, Dying, Addiction, Depression, and Transcendence*, documents the controversy arising from the chart above, which led the lead author of the study, Professor David Nutt, to be unceremoniously fired from his post as the chair of the UK government's Advisory Council on the Misuse of Drugs for adhering to his evidence-based convictions.

**Scoring tobacco**

Tobacco is ranked sixth for overall harm given it has very few short-term physical risks; no one keels over and dies of an overdose or attempts to jump out a window after smoking a cigarette. Yet it ranks #1 of all drugs for chronic harm, and #5 for physical dependence, a terrible combination if you care about the longevity of your child. Professor Nutt and colleagues have acknowledged that having a single, integrated score doesn't deal adequately with a substance like tobacco that's extremely harmful in only one respect.[204] The dotted box in the chart above has therefore been added to reflect this long-term harm.

Wringing our hands about the catastrophic effects of crystal meth may be pointless if teens show no interest in it. The chart below therefore provides a different ranking of drugs, according to the percent of teens who use each one (the bars),[205] with harm scores marked as horizontal lines:[206]

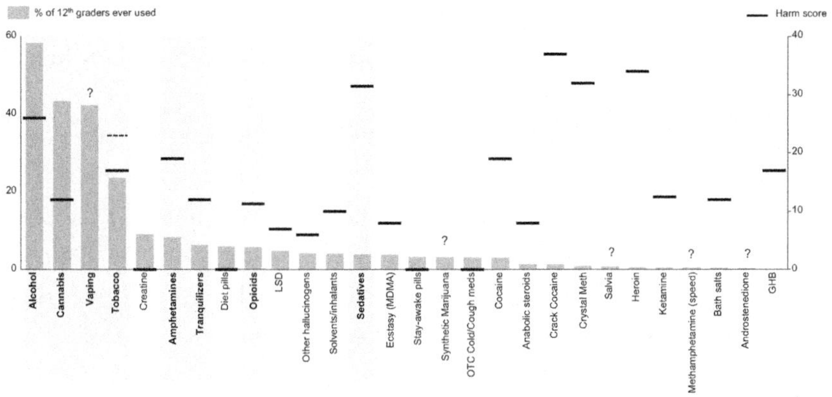


The drugs highlighted with their names in bold are those that are either very commonly used (a large bar), or somewhat commonly used (a medium bar) but particularly harmful (a high line). Those not yet covered will be discussed in greater detail here; the remaining drugs are covered in Appendix II.

## *Marijuana*

> Houseplant, the cannabis brand co-founded by comedian, actor, writer, producer, and director Seth Rogen, is introducing two new product lines: pre-rolled joints and soft gel capsules. Rogen said that Houseplant is not just about creating the highest-quality product possible, but also about helping consumers to "understand cannabis on a deeper level so that they can truly have the best experience possible."[207]

Rogen is the latest ambassador in a long line of marijuana afficionados from around the world, dating back to the late third or early second millennium BC in Turkmenistan; circa 1350 b.c. in Egypt; 2,500 years ago in China; 2,000 years ago in sub-Saharan Africa; and fourth century Israel/Palestine.[208] In the present day, marijuana is the most widely used drug worldwide,* with an estimated 188 million people having partaken in the last year.[209] Weed has become far more potent, not only since the time of the Egyptians, but also more recently.[210] In the early 1990s, the average THC† content of mar-

* "Drug" in this context refers to substances controlled under international drug control conventions; the definition therefore excludes alcohol.

† THC, or Tetrahydrocannabinol, is the main psychoactive compound in cannabis that produces the sensation of being "high."

ijuana was around 3.7 percent. In contrast, the average THC content of the marijuana now legally for sale in Colorado is more than five times higher (19 percent).[211]

Why do some adolescents become pot-heads while others are content to simply smoke a joint on rare occasions? As with alcohol, twin studies have demonstrated that some of us are genetically more susceptible to the pleasurable effects of marijuana than others. While family and social contexts influence which adolescents will sample the drug in the first place, it's their genes that determine whether they will go on to become heavy users.[212]

**Teens and weed**

As with alcohol and nicotine, adolescents appear to be particularly vulnerable to the effects of cannabis.[213] Once again, it wouldn't be ethical to run controlled experiments giving weed to a randomly-selected group of teens, so we're stuck with imperfect observational studies. However, one study which followed 1,000 individuals from birth to age 38 found that those who started smoking weed as teens began to show a variety of cognitive problems over time, with greater use associated with greater decline. Furthermore, giving up the drug didn't fully restore the frequent users' levels of cognitive functioning.[214] Researchers believe the drug itself is the cause of the impairment, because THC interferes with the exchange of information between neurons, and regular exposure to THC in adolescents permanently changes the neuropathways that are related to learning, attention and emotional responses.[215]

Marijuana isn't great for teens (see box). It can impair their short-term memory, decrease their concentration, attention span, and problem solving abilities, and harm their lungs.[216] On the positive side, unlike alcohol and tobacco, even heavy users aren't more likely to die prematurely.[217]

It won't be easy to keep your teen away from marijuana, as weed is ubiquitous. Four out of five teens source their supply from friends, and other typical sources include siblings, other family members, and acquaintances.[218] Interestingly, the recent wave of legalization has reduced the number of teens who are getting high, potentially because it's more difficult for young people to obtain marijuana when the informal marketplace is replaced by official, licensed dispensaries that require proof of age.[219]

Fortunately, most teens who experiment with cannabis don't go on to become problematic potheads later in life. Among adults without medical conditions, 8 percent report using marijuana regularly,[220] but only about 2.5 percent have a diagnosable cannabis use disorder.* [221] So if you find one of

* 3.5% for males and 1.5% for females

Houseplant's soft gel capsules hidden beneath your teen's mattress, all is not lost. But it would be worth having a conversation to understand if your teen really aspires to follow in Rogen's footsteps: "I'm honored to be associated with weed, honestly. Sometimes people expect me to try to wiggle out from under being a very famous stoner. But truthfully, that is a worthy thing to me. I'm as proud of it as anything."[222]

## *Amphetamines*

> Adderall has been, on and off, a part of my life since my sophomore year in high school. The decision to start plagues me every time I take a pill in the morning. At first, I used it in the same way as many other students, to crank up study sessions or to meet a strict deadline. By junior year, I started taking Adderall every morning just to wake up and to give me enough energy to last through the day. On those long, foggy days I'd forget to take it, my mind would be in sleep mode, dozing in class and drifting in thought… I know they do more harm than good; my moods can change on a dime and my memory is worse and worse. But getting a decent grade on a test that others seem to effortlessly ace seems worth it.[223]

Amphetamines (also commonly referred to as stimulants) are only supposed to be available via prescription, to address problems including depression and attention deficit hyperactivity disorder (ADHD).[224] However, because they make people feel more alert and can even produce a sense of euphoria, common forms such as Adderall and Ritalin are increasingly being diverted from legitimate sources, and manufactured or imported illegally, to feed a growing market for these so-called 'study drugs.'[225]

High school students are among the main offenders: between 5 and 12 percent of all high school seniors are misusing amphetamines,[226] although only 1 in 100 parents are aware of it.[227] The rate among college students is even worse: at two different large, public universities in the US, approximately a third of students reported misusing a prescription stimulant.[228] Students explain to researchers that stimulants have become part of the campus culture, and are openly discussed in public settings. According to one freshman, "Anybody can get it just about anytime they want it. It's easier than beer to get."[229] Ninety-five percent of users obtain the stimulants from friends and peers, who have often been prescribed the drugs legally.[230]

The problem is most acute at colleges in the US Northeast, and at those with more competitive admission standards. [231] Among the student body, those who are male, white, members of fraternities and sororities, or earning lower grade point averages are more likely to partake.[232] The emerging theme: Adderall and other stimulants are being misused most by those at top universities who are struggling academically.[233] Students abusing stimulants tend to skip classes more often, spend more time socializing, and spend less time studying than nonusers.[234] Then when the stress of finals week arrives, their anxiety and desperation make them vulnerable to the lure of a miracle 'study drug.'[235] But there's also a perceived arms race which is sucking additional students in. In the words of a computer science and economics major at Columbia, "the culture here actually encourages people to use stimulants." According to another fellow student, "the environment here is incredibly competitive. If you don't take them, you'll be at a disadvantage to everyone else."[236]

Students are convinced that amphetamines are effective; almost all users claim that ADHD medications increase their attention span, stave off fatigue, and even boost their cognitive abilities.[237] Many parents are similarly misinformed: around 20 percent think amphetamines can improve children's academic performance, even for those without ADHD.[238] These drugs certainly generate a sensation of concentration and focus, but their power to actually improve academic performance is an illusion (see box).

**The positives of amphetamines**

In the short term, people on stimulants appear to perform slightly better at tasks requiring pure rote memorization, particularly where the information must be retained for several days or more.[239] But these effects decline and reverse over time, and there is no improvement in complex memory of the type required for college exams.[240]

Another supposed benefit is the level of focus the drugs bring. According to one clinical psychiatrist, "taking a 'study drug' "won't increase your intelligence, it just increases your diligence. The drugs delay the onset of sleep so you can stay up all night and cram."[241] The strategy of staying up all night to study will be discussed in later chapters on achievement and sleep; for now, it suffices to say that the benefits of doing so are dubious at best.

Adolescents also simply assume amphetamines are safe: in one study, not a single one of the young users had even attempted to read up on amphetamines on the internet before popping a pill.[242] Media coverage doesn't help; 94 percent of articles that mention common amphetamines describe supposed cognitive benefits, but only 58 percent mention risks or side effects.[243] Here's an illustrative excerpt from *The New York Times*: "Designer stimulants like Adderall are far less dangerous than cocaine or methamphetamines... For many college students, the issue about Adderall is not so much health as it is fairness."[244]

It's worth delving into the reasons for these misperceptions. Any drug available via prescription has been thoroughly tested for safety and efficacy in those populations that need it, and the treatment benefits for managing the underlying conditions have been deemed to outweigh any potential side effects. Amphetamines have been in use for over 70 years, so are well-studied in the treatment of ADHD.[245] The calculus necessarily changes, however, when there is no underlying condition to treat.

Adderall and Ritalin are both classified in the US as Schedule II drugs, which are defined as drugs with "a high potential for abuse, with use potentially leading to severe psychological or physical dependence."[246] Approximately one in 20 nonmedical users of amphetamines meets the criteria for dependence or abuse,[247] and recovery from amphetamine dependence can be as difficult as recovering from a heroin or cocaine addiction,[248] with withdrawal typically precipitating 2-3 days of intense fatigue/sleepiness and depression.[249]

There are also a variety of insidious long-term effects. Common side-effects of chronic abuse can include mental illness, decreased growth, increased tics, headaches, and mood changes.* [250] There's also a risk of abusers developing auditory, visual and skin-crawling hallucinations, delusions, paranoia and psychosis, [251] which are similar to the symptoms of schizophrenia[252] and can be very frightening.[253] According to one review, this drug-induced psychosis has been reported in 8 to 46 percent of regular users; an unhelpfully wide range, but concerning nonetheless.[254] Finally, in a cruel twist of fate, there's anecdotal evidence that abusers of amphetamines can experience a potentially permanent decrease in mental activity and concentration.[255]

* In the rare cases where someone has the misfortune to have an undiagnosed heart defect, or suffers from high blood pressure, heart or blood vessel disease, stimulants can cause a heart attack or sudden death.

In summary, amphetamines are readily available and widely used, and the long-term downsides are both real and underreported. However, many important questions remain unresolved. No one yet knows what will happen to the current generation of stimulant users when they graduate from college – as they put the stress of final exams behind them, will they give up the study drugs, or be tempted to continue popping the pills for a leg up at work?[256] For some, it may not be a choice. Returning to the student from the beginning of this section:

> Adderall hasn't become a study drug to me, it's become a way of life. It's my morning cup of coffee, only nobody warned me about the insidious side effects. The standards of a top ranked school have that ability to cloud my judgement, and though I'm completely aware of it, I know there's not much I can do. Though I can feel my heart beating faster than normal when I take just half a pill, the thought that my habit could be ruining my body is only fleeting, and I return to my work, just like everyone else around me.[257]

## *Tranquilizers*

> Danny doesn't remember much about the first time he took a Xanax. "No one does ... you just blank the whole night," he says, playing with a pair of white headphones around his neck. Now, over a year later, sitting in his kitchen, he describes the drug as "the devil".* [258]

Tranquilizers, used by approximately seven percent of teens, are next on our list. Also known as benzodiazipines, these drugs are available by prescription to treat conditions like anxiety and insomnia,[259] the two most common being Valium and Xanax.[260] Like alcohol, they depress the central nervous system, so driving under the influence is akin to driving drunk, with a five times higher risk of crashing.[261]

Tranquilizers are responsible for very few overdose deaths,[262] but as Danny can attest, the habit can be hard to shake.[263] Even after only a month of taking them daily, users experience nasty withdrawal symptoms (see box),

* Name of protagonist has been changed for privacy purposes.

and those who have taken them for longer periods of time will find that the withdrawal process can last for months.[264]

**The delights of tranquilizer withdrawal**

For those hooked on tranquilizers, typical withdrawl symptoms include feelings of anxiety and panic, choking feelings, dry mouth, hot and cold, legs like jelly, etc.; irritableness; and significant sleep disturbance (e.g., sleeping only two to three hours a night during the first three or four days of drug withdrawal). Some users also experience hand tremors, profuse perspiration, severe headaches and generalized aches and pains. More than half lose their appetite and feel nauseous. Finally, a subset experience perceptual disturbances like intolerance to loud noises and bright lights, numbness, "pins and needles," unsteadiness, a feeling of motion, strange smells, and metallic tastes.[265] Symptoms can also persist longer term, with some patients showing reduced cognitive function even three months later.[266]

How do teens manage to source their tranquilizers? One study found that over half (64%) had gotten their supply free from a friend or relative.[267] Shockingly, it's parents themselves who sometimes offer these drugs to their children, presumably thinking they will help with their teen's anxiety.[268] The upshot? Don't.

## Opioids

> Lana McGovern was an honor student, athlete and "all-American girl," who one night was offered an OxyContin pill during a party at the home of a classmate. It made her feel "good" and "powerful." Soon enough, she was hooked. Her mother recalls feeling like she was stuck in the movie *The Exorcist* as the daughter she loved disappeared before her eyes. "That drug owned my daughter, wrapped its tentacles around her, squeezed the life out of her. It took over her brain." Lana died of a heroin overdose in 2011.* [269]

Opioids, also called narcotics, have swept across the nation over the last few decades.† Opioid usage among teens peaked in the early 2000s and has grad-

* Name of protagonist has been changed for privacy purposes.

† For a gripping chronicle of this epidemic, read *American Overdose: The Opioid Tragedy in Three Acts* (2018), by Chris McGreal.

ually been declining since then, but over 5 percent of teens are still misusing opioids today:[270]

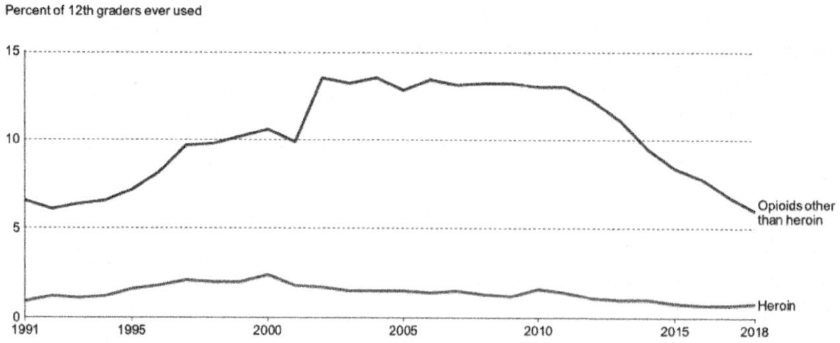


Most teens don't get sucked into a deathly spiral of addiction as Lana did, progressing from prescription opioids to stronger, cheaper, and more hazardous illegal formulations like street heroin. But enough do to warrant including opioids here. In the US, by age 18, 1.5 girls and 2 boys in every 1,000 have a diagnosed opioid use disorder.[271]

How do teens get their hands on dangerous quantities of these prescription medications in the first place? Here's what the teens themselves report:[272]

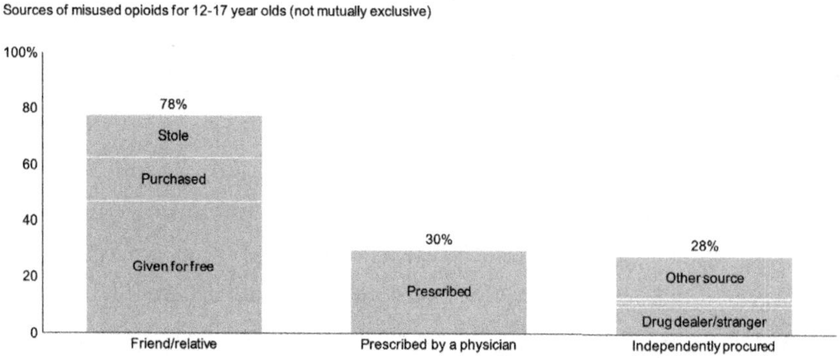


78 percent of teen opioid users are getting at least some of their supply from friends and relatives. Even if they don't actively offer the opioids up, it's not very difficult for teens to steal them: one in four homes with children between the ages of 12 and 24 have opioids in unlocked cabinets or otherwise accessible.[273]

More surprisingly, approximately 30 percent of teens get their opioids legitimately via a prescription.[274] (This is a common phenomenon; among teens prescribed any type of controlled medications, 22 percent report misusing them, including taking too much intentionally to get high, or using them to increase the effects of alcohol or other drugs.[275]) Primary care and ER physicians account for 13 and 12 percent of opioid prescriptions, respectively; but it's dentists who are the main prescribers for teens, accounting for almost a third of all prescriptions, primarily for wisdom tooth extractions (see box).[276]

**The wisdom tooth fallacy**

I suspect you wouldn't have predicted that a chapter on preventing drug abuse in teens would include a discussion about wisdom teeth. No dental procedure is pleasant, but the worst you would typically expect your teen to be dealing with in the aftermath of an extraction would be a swollen jaw and some nasty gauze to chew on. In fact, the prescription for painkillers your child comes home with can be the first step in a destructive chain. In a study of around 15,000 adolescents and young adults given opioids after an extraction, six percent subsequently developed an opioid abuse problem, versus only 0.4 percent of controls.[277]

There is very little publicly available information on how many people have their wisdom teeth removed; back in 1999, approximately 5 million people in the US were having the procedure each year, at an annual cost of over $3 billion.[278] Yet the case for removing them, even ignoring the opioid problem, is not clear cut. It's a major procedure, and around nine percent of patients need to come back for an emergency appointment due to complications.[279] Yet there are surprisingly few downsides to leaving the wisdom teeth alone: according to one study, only about twelve percent of kids with impacted molars will eventually have problems of any sort.[280]

The obvious conclusion would be to simply leave the wisdom teeth in. In fact, that's exactly what many professional, government and research bodies are now recommending, including The American Public Health Association (a professional organization of 25,000 public health professionals[281]) and various government, policy and research groups in Sweden,[282] Belgium[283], Australia,[284] and the UK.[285] A recent review from the highly respected Cochrane Policy Institute found "no evidence to support or refute routine prophylactic removal of asymptomatic impacted wisdom teeth."[286] Of course, a variety of dental bodies disagree with these conclusions, [287] although one has to question their motivation with billions in fees at risk.[288]

If your teen or anyone else in the family has an unavoidable need to use opioids for short-term pain relief for dental or any other unpleasant procedures, the best plan is to try to limit the course to at most a few days, given the risk of addiction escalates dramatically over time. Then dispose of any unused pills. One recent study found that the typical dental patient receives 28 opioid pills and has 15 pills left over.[289] No wonder friends and family have so many pills to gift or sell to eager adolescents.

If you want to increase the chance of your teen saying "no" to the OxyContin offered up at a party, you might suggest the show *16 and Recovering*, which gets rave reviews. [290] According to a professor of Psychiatry and Addiction Medicine at Stanford University, "This was probably among the most thoughtful, accurate, heart-wrenching depictions of addiction I've seen in film or print."[291] If your adolescent is already hooked, treatment with methadone is safe and doubles the chance of recovery from addiction.[292] [*]

We'll conclude with Katarina's story, the quintessential cautionary tale from the front lines of the opioid epidemic:

> My drug use started when I was in high school, with pain pills that I was prescribed after I injured my back at a track meet. It wasn't long before I became dependent on the pain medication. Once I couldn't get the same high from taking the pills, I was shown how to shoot up OxyContin. When the OxyContin became too expensive, I was introduced to heroin...I was given the opportunity to be in a Pilot Program which involved a monthly injection for 16 months. Today I'm 22 months clean and sober."[†] [293]

Fortunately this particular story, unlike many in this chapter, has a happy ending.

## Sedatives

Sedatives, also called barbiturates, are thoroughly nasty drugs. Marilyn Monroe died of "acute poisoning by overdose of barbiturates," and a mixture including these drugs is employed in some US states for executing prisoners.

There are some legitimate uses of sedatives; for example in the treatment of epilepsy, and for sedating patients during medical procedures.[294] Teens are tempted to use them, particularly short-acting formulations like pentobarbital and secobarbital, to counter the unpleasant effects of illicit stimulants, to reduce anxiety, and to get high.[295] Most teens are sensible and steer clear; only four percent of twelfth graders have tried them.[296] But there's a good

* The website https://findtreatment.samhsa.gov/ has a helpful map pinpointing treatment facilities

† Name of protagonist has been changed for privacy purposes

reason this topic hasn't been relegated to the appendix: those four percent probably have no idea that they're playing with fire.[297]

Tolerance develops rapidly; most users find that after only 1-2 weeks of regular use they need increasingly higher doses to get through the day,[298] and withdrawal can be nasty. For example, 100 percent of those taking more than 800 mg of pentobarbital or secobarbital daily will experience minor withdrawal symptoms, including tremors, weakness, insomnia, sweating and restlessness; 75 percent experience convulsions, and 60 percent confusion (delirium tremens). At the extremes, withdrawal can even be lethal if a patient who's been taking barbiturates in large doses or for a long time doesn't get appropriate treatment during the withdrawal process.[299]

However the real danger is the risk of overdose: like heroin, the difference between the usual dose and the dose that causes coma and death is narrow,[300] and taking even one extra pill can sometimes lead to an overdose.[301] Yet teens are clueless about the risks: less than half of twelfth graders are aware that barbiturates can cause serious harm.[302]

It's not entirely clear how teens get their hands on these destructive drugs specifically, as studies examining sources tend to bucket together all types of prescription medication, including opioids, stimulants, barbiturates, and sleeping medications. Such studies imply that the primary source is friends, which begs the question of how the friends themselves sourced them.[303] Although the internet could theoretically be an obvious channel, there's little evidence to date that young people are obtaining their sedatives this way.[304]

In the unlikely event that anyone in your family suffers from epilepsy or takes sedatives for other legitimate purposes, it's worth ensuring that no supply is going spare. Although it would seem unlikely, teens have a remarkable way of getting hold of things they shouldn't, and no one wants to have Marilyn's fate on their conscience.

## *If your child is using already*

Elizabeth Burton Phillips is a teacher, an ordinary middle-class mother who had always tried to do the best for her children; she never imagined that her identical twin sons, who had been doing so well at school, would become involved in drugs. She was shocked

> when they were suspended from school for smoking cannabis; but this was just the start of a terrible journey, culminating in a knock on the door in the early hours by the police, with the news that her son had killed himself in despair at his heroin addiction.[305]

Even if you've followed every bit of advice in this chapter, it's worth staying alert. Although 80 percent of parents feel sufficiently well-informed about alcohol and drugs, the average parent can name only two out of 38 warning signs of substance abuse. Worse, less than 20 percent of primary care physicians consider themselves "very prepared" to identify alcohol or drug dependence.[306] Here, then, is the list of the most important warning signs to look for (see box).[307]

**Warning signs of alcohol and drug use**

Physical indicators:

- Bloodshot eyes, widely dilated pupils, or pin-point pupils
- Unexplained and sudden weight loss, weight gain, or poor oral hygiene
- Needle tracks in the inner elbow region, or wearing long-sleeved clothes even in very warm weather
- Raw, dripping nostrils from snorting
- Constant urge to scratch or pick at skin and hair
- Neglected personal hygiene and appearance

Behavioral indicators:

- Frequently or abruptly changing friends
- Withdrawing from usual family bonding, routines, and activities
- Suddenly violating agreed upon hours of curfew, often inventing stories or behaviors
- Showing unusual and violent behavior following trivial arguments or simple requests; being unusually irritable and verbally abusive with siblings and parents
- Demonstrating unprecedented lack of self-control, aggressive behavior, or difficult temperament at school or within the community
- Suffering from poor morale, including crying spells and mood swings
- Slurring speech and showing other difficulties in verbal expression
- Showing unusual drowsiness or a tendency to become easily fatigued
- Suffering from apathy or low productivity
- Letting school grades deteriorate, skipping classes
- Asking for unusual amounts of money, pilfering money or stealing things
- Making and receiving frequent phone calls, mostly in hushed or whispered tones, and acting sneaky and suspicious
- Possessing items like tin foil, weight scales, smoking pipes, butane torches, bongs, Ziplock bags, square folded paper envelopes, cigarette lighters, small porcelain bowls, hypodermic needles, balloons, aluminum foil wrappers, mirrors or flat metal, short straws, glass pipes, capsules, and vials

If your teen is acting suspicious, the Drug Enforcement Agency (DEA) suggests checking for a hidden stash. The agency's website* lists some of the most common hiding places, including inside ordinary household items such as teddy bears, alarm clocks, calculators and even highlighters, although the website has come under fire for perhaps unintentionally providing teens with creative ideas for how to hide drugs.[308]

If you're concerned, the best approach is to enlist your teen in helping to assess the problem. The tool recommended by both the American Academy of Pediatrics and the National Institute on Alcohol Abuse and Alcoholism for screening adolescents for risky alcohol and drug use[309] is the CRAFFT instrument,† a mnemonic acronym for six screening questions.‡ [310]

**Don't Play Detective**

Testing your teen for drug use is a strategy that most experts don't recommend. Urine testing can't be done without the active participation of your teen, who may resent the request particularly if it proves to be unwarranted, and hair testing is impractical given it doesn't reflect use within the last week or detect occasional use. Dr. Sharon Levy, the director of the Adolescent Substance Use and Addiction Program at Boston Children's Hospital, says "Drug testing is a terrible tool for identifying use, since most teen and young adult drug use is sporadic, which is very unlikely to be picked up by a random test."[311] The American Academy of Pediatrics agrees.[312]

Similarly, dog-sniffing drug detection services are available across the US; for $200-$500, a highly-trained canine can sniff out the full range of popular street drugs, synthetic drugs, prescription drugs and alcohol.[313] However experts don't recommend going down this path either. According to the National Institute on Drug Abuse, such a step could create distrust between parents and teens, and wouldn't solve the underlying problem.[314]

If you ever do make the disturbing discovery that your adolescent has surreptitiously developed a drug problem, your first instinct after shouting obscenities might be to hunt down a rehab program, or for those with considerable means, to banish your wayward child to a detox facility. While many

* www.getsmartaboutdrugs.gov/content/hiding-places

† Available at www.ceasar-boston.org/CRAFFT/screenCRAFFT.php

‡

| | |
|---|---|
| C | Have you ever ridden in a CAR driven by someone (including yourself) who was "high" or had been using alcohol or drugs? |
| R | Do you ever use alcohol or drugs to RELAX, feel better about yourself, or fit in? |
| A | Do you ever use alcohol/drugs while you are by yourself, ALONE? |
| F | Do you ever FORGET things you did while using alcohol or drugs? |
| F | Do your family or FRIENDS ever tell you that you should cut down on your drinking or drug use? |
| T | Have you gotten into TROUBLE while you were using alcohol or drugs? |

Two or more "yes" answers indicates a problem.
Another alternative called the Alcohol, Smoking and Substance Involvement Screening Test (ASSIST) can be obtained from the WHO website: www.who.int/publications/i/item/978924159938-2

such programs undoubtably have excellent content and intentions, this strategy can backfire if it groups problem kids together. Teens will shift to benchmarking themselves against a group of adolescents for whom such behavior is the norm, and may even pick up ideas for new deviant behavior.[315] Individual treatment is therefore the better approach. "Brief Interventions," mentioned in the section on alcohol, show promise for helping addicts in general,[316] and teens specifically,[317] and involve a physician or facilitator interviewing the teen to figure out the scope of the problem and decide on a plan.[318]

Adolescents are drawn to alcohol and drugs in the same way they're drawn to all novel experiences that life has to offer. But the earlier teens start experimenting with any drug that has addictive potential, the more likely they are to become addicted.[*] [319] Teens may not even be the ones with the most to gain from expanding their consciousness. In the words of writer Michael Pollan, musing on the properties of psychedelics,

> I've begun to wonder if perhaps these remarkable molecules might be wasted on the young, that they may have more to offer us later in life, after the cement of our mental habits and everyday behaviors has set. Carl Jung once wrote that it is not the young but people in middle age who need to have an "experience of the numinous" to help them negotiate the second half of their lives.[320]

### KEY PARENTING TAKE-AWAYS:

Overall:

1. Empty or secure your liquor and medicine cabinets to remove the temptation of easy access to alcohol, opioids, stimulant and barbiturate prescriptions, and even cough syrup, and ask the parents of your teen's friends to do the same
2. Pay attention to the content your child is viewing, and restrict or comment on advertising and media that glamorize drinking, smoking or using drugs

Alcohol:

3. Clearly communicate that alcohol is off limits, acknowledging the positives (relaxed/pleasant mood, decreased self-consciousness, potential for enhanced social status) but conveying the downsides (higher risk of alcoholism, traffic accidents, assault, etc.)

* There's no way to definitively establish whether teens with the types of personalities that might make them prone to addiction are drawn to drugs earlier, or whether the early exposure itself causes the problem.[i] Animal studies suggest the latter, but since we can't ethically run experiments on young teens to test this question, we'll probably never know for certain.

4. If any close family members have a low response to alcohol or suffer from alcoholism, warn your adolescent about the genetic vulnerability
5. Discuss and agree what refusal/avoidance strategies your teen will use if offered alcohol by a friend, then document the plan in writing and have your teen sign it
6. Establish and enforce severe consequences for drinking
7. Model responsible drinking behavior yourself
8. Don't allow sipping or offer alcohol under your own roof
9. Ensure other parents who share your views on alcohol will be supervising any parties your child attends
10. If your adolescent already has experience with drinking, suggest taking the quiz to test for a low response to alcohol; a score of over 4.5 could mean a genetic vulnerability to future alcohol problems*

Tobacco:

11. Clearly communicate that tobacco is off limits, acknowledging the positives but conveying the downsides (shortened lifespan, wrinkly skin, etc.)
12. Maintain a "no smoking at home" rule even if you smoke yourself, and establish and enforce severe consequences for smoking
13. Inform your child that 85 percent of adolescents who begin smoking later regret it, and that "loss of autonomy" can begin with the very first cigarette, meaning the tobacco companies have hooked yet another customer for life
14. Discuss and agree in advance what refusal/avoidance strategies your teen will use if offered tobacco by a friend, then document the plan in writing and have your teen sign it
15. Keep your teen out of corner grocery, convenience, or liquor stores if at all possible
16. Enlist a cool, slightly older friend or relative to introduce your adolescent to the Truth campaign†
17. If your teen has already started lighting up, the American Lung Association's N-O-T (Not on Tobacco) program is the best option, available either in-person or online‡

E-cigarettes:

18. Warn your teen that JUUL and other vaping devices do indeed contain nicotine as well as various other harmful substances, and that as with regular cigarettes, "loss of autonomy" can begin with the first puff, meaning the e-cigarette companies have hooked yet another customer for life

---

* For the first 5 times you ever drank:

1. How many drinks did it take for you to begin to feel different (where you could feel an effect)?
2. How many drinks did it take for you to feel a bit dizzy or to begin to slur your speech?
3. How many drinks did it take for you to begin stumbling or walking in an uncoordinated manner?
4. How many drinks did it take for you to pass out or fall asleep when you did not want to?
5. Then divide the total number of drinks recorded in the four possible questions by the number of questions with a response. Those with a low responsiveness to alcohol will have an answer over 4.5.[1]

† www.thetruth.com

‡ https://notforme.org/

Marijuana:

19. Clearly communicate that marijuana is off limits, acknowledging the positives but conveying the downsides (higher risk of addiction, cognitive problems)
20. Discuss and agree in advance what refusal/avoidance strategies your teen will use if offered marijuana by a friend, then document the plan in writing and have your teen sign it
21. Establish and enforce severe consequences for getting high

Amphetamines:

22. Inform your teen that although amphetamines can feel like they improve concentration, they have virtually no beneficial effects on academic performance in the short term, and actually hinder performance in the longer term
23. Emphasize that for teens who don't have ADHD, these drugs have clear addictive potential, and over time can produce frightening hallucinations, delusions, paranoia and psychosis similar to the symptoms of schizophrenia
24. Consider reading the testimonial of the amphetamine user (at the beginning and end of the amphetamine section) to your teen

Tranquilizers:

25. Don't offer drugs like Valium and Xanax to your teen

Opioids:

26. Avoid prophylactic wisdom tooth extraction
27. If anyone in the household needs opioids for short-term pain relief, limit the course to a few days and immediately throw away the unused pills

Barbiturates:

28. If anyone in the household takes barbiturates for legitimate purposes, ensure no supply is accessible or going spare

Overall:

29. If your child has an alcohol or drug problem, seek individualized (not group) treatment, e.g. a "brief intervention"

# 2. SEXUAL ACTIVITY

## Dispense sex protection

> 2004: "A pregnant teenage mother today appealed against a sentence of death by stoning imposed on her in northern Nigeria, where Islamic law applies."[1]

> 2013: "More than 55,000 Tanzanian schoolgirls have been expelled from school over the last decade for being pregnant."[2]

Fortunately in most nations today, pregnant girls aren't stoned to death, or even expelled from school. Nevertheless, young pregnant women around the world face very real consequences. Even in the US, teenage pregnancy still attracts major social stigma: 83 percent of Republicans and 56 percent of Democrats say that single women having children without a partner is bad for society.[3] And adolescent girls can't assume they'll get much help from the father of their child: 30 percent of young single mothers don't receive child support at all, and another 40 percent only receive partial payment.[4]

**Off track?**
Getting knocked up as a teen is not actually the unmitigated disaster one might assume it to be. One clever study followed a group of pregnant adolescents and compared the life trajectories of those who had a spontaneous miscarriage with those who carried the baby to term. By their late twenties, the young mothers had achieved the same amount of education, were earning more, and were less likely to be on welfare than their childless counterparts.[5] These enterprising young women, forced early into adult responsibilities, rose to the occasion. Even so, most parents would probably prefer their children to follow a more traditional path.

We are making some progress lately. Adolescent pregnancy and birth rates in the US have gone down significantly over the last thirty years:[6]

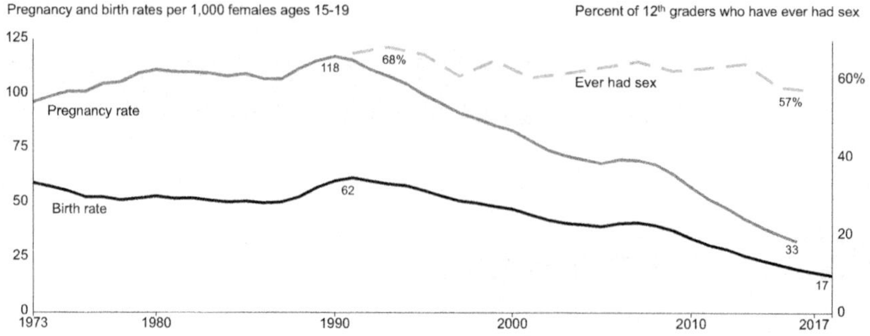


We haven't miraculously managed to curb teen libidos: the percentage of female twelfth graders who have had sex (the dotted line) has remained broadly the same over the last 30 years. An increase in abortion also isn't the cause; abortion rates have in fact declined over the same period. Instead, the decline reflects the heartening fact that modern teens are increasingly using contraception.[7]

The bad news is that teen pregnancy is still very common in the US compared to other countries:[8]

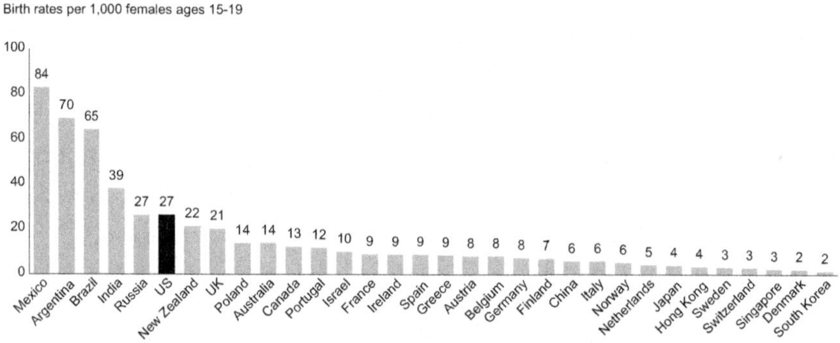


**How do they do it?**

The countries with the lowest birth rates in the tail of the chart fall into two very different categories. Liberal Nordic countries like Denmark have extensive sex education programs, and provide teens with confidential, non-judgemental access to low-cost or free sexual health services.[9] On the opposite end of the spectrum, industrialized but highly traditional societies like South Korea and Italy (where Catholicism holds sway) discourage sexual activity outside of marriage and attach enormous social stigma to teen pregnancy.[10]

Part of the problem may lie in the American approach to teaching kids about sex. Many US kids aren't getting sufficient or even any sex education in school: Maine is the only state requiring schools to teach "responsible decision-making regarding sexuality," and only 18 states require sex education classes to be medically accurate.[11]

As a nation, the US has a curious obsession with teaching abstinence, which categorically does not lower rates of teen pregnancy, as has been demonstrated by study after study.[12] Those who view teen abstinence as a moral imperative are generally not achieving their goal by preaching it. They are prioritizing adhering to a principle over taking practical actions which could improve their adolescents' sexual well-being.

The approach which does lower teen pregnancy rates is providing education and access to contraception.[13]

**A creative approach to teen abstinence**

Unusual approaches to warding off teen pregnancy have met with some success, including a counseling program delivered by older peers,[14] and a "Dollar a Day" program which paid disadvantaged teen mothers for each day they were not pregnant with an additional child.[15] No one has yet tested whether parents could achieve similar results by hiring a suave college student to talk sense into their teen, or by paying their adolescent a celibacy allowance.

**Virginity pledging**

Interestingly, the concept of virginity pledging can work to promote abstinence under very specific circumstances. The key to making this strategy effective is to create a minority group where the teens involved broadcast their participation visibly to others, e.g. by wearing special rings, and come to feel that membership in the group is an important part of their identity. The strategy is not without its risks, however, as those pledgers who do end up having sex are less likely to use contraception.[16] Similarly, teens from highly religious families do tend to have sex at a later age than their less religious counterparts, but are also less likely to use contraception when they do.[17]

Providing contraception does not increase sexual activity, despite the assumptions of many adults to the contrary.[18] To use an analogy, handing out a supply of free helmets is unlikely to cause teens to go searching for a motorcycle to ride. Kids see motorcycles around them all the time and may be yearning for an opportunity to go for a spin. If the opportunity arises and they're offered a ride, they'll be tempted to climb on, whether or not a helmet is handy. But the helmet is the annoyance; it's the motorcycle that's the draw.

It would be a rare teenager who had never considered riding a motorcycle, but after being offered a free helmet was suddenly itching to go for a ride. Teens simply aren't that rational.

Providing contraception has only one effect: it increases the likelihood that teens use the protection if and when they choose to become sexually active.[19] In spite of the incontrovertible evidence that has accumulated on this subject, and in spite of a 1977 US Supreme Court ruling which found that minors have a constitutional right to obtain contraceptives without the involvement of their parents as part of their right to privacy,[20] 50 percent of school-based health centers are currently prohibited by local and state laws from providing contraceptives to students.[21] The onus is therefore on parents and health care professionals to fill the gap.

Not all contraception is created equal. Below is a chart which shows which types are most effective, where the 'failure rate' is defined as the proportion of sexually-active women who will become pregnant within the first 12 months after starting to use that method:[*22]

Contraception failure rates

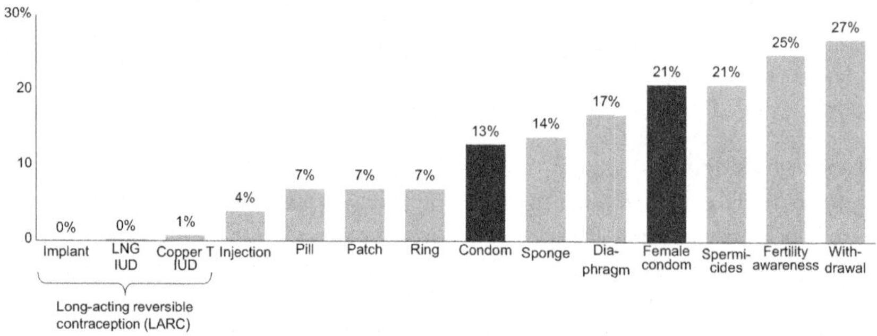


The three options on the left, each forms of "long-acting reversible contraception," are by far the most effective forms of birth control. Every major health organization, including the Centers for Disease Control and Prevention,[23] the American Academy of Pediatrics,[24] and the American College of Obstetricians and Gynecologists,[25] recommends that teens use

* The implant is a single, thin rod that is inserted under the skin of a women's upper arm, and contains a progestin that is released into the body over 3 years. The LNG intrauterine device (IUD) is a small T-shaped device which is placed inside the uterus by a doctor, releases a small amount of progestin each day, and can remain in the uterus for up to 3 to 6 years.
The Copper T intrauterine device (IUD) is similar to the LNG IUD, but is made of copper, and can stay in the uterus for up to 10 years. The injection or 'shot' involves an injection of the hormone progestin, which needs to be administered by a doctor in the buttocks or arm every three months.

one of these forms of long-acting reversible contraception (LARC) to prevent pregnancy, as well as condoms to prevent sexually-transmitted diseases.

Teens have gotten the memo about condoms: 97 percent of sexually active females say they've used one, which is fantastic. The various forms of long-acting reversible contraception, on the other hand, are languishing in obscurity. Only 2.8 percent of sexually active girls have an IUD and 3 percent an implant.* [26] Yes, it's a lot easier and more anonymous for a teen to surreptitiously slip a pack of condoms in with the shopping at a pharmacy or corner shop than to make an appointment with a doctor to have a birth control device installed. Yet that can't be the full explanation, because 56 percent of sexually active girls are on the pill, which is only available via prescription. It appears that either doctors or parents or both are providing teens poor council. A 7 percent failure rate for the pill isn't terrible, and it's positive news that over half of girls are on some form of long-term contraception; but 7 percent is orders of magnitude worse than the failure rate for the LARC options.[27] At the moment, a full 94 percent of sexually-active female teens are taking unnecessary risks.† [28]

**Condom failure**

It's worth understanding why condoms can occasionally be ineffectual. One study found that 4 percent of condoms broke and another 4 percent slipped off while being used. Some of these mishaps are due to poor technique, because couples who haven't used condoms before are more likely to have their condoms malfunction.[29] Bad ideas include opening the condom package with a sharp object, and unrolling the condom before putting it on.[30] If you can bear to have this conversation with your teen, a quick chat about those facts or even a banana demonstration would not be misplaced. Imaginary peers also rear their heads again when it comes to this subject. Teens are more likely to use a condom if they believe that their friends use condoms, whether or not this is actually true.[31]

When is the right moment to put a girl on long-acting reversible contraception? The chart below from the US would suggest before she enters tenth grade, or possibly sooner, e.g. as soon as she gets her period:[32]

* IUDs once had a reputation for complications, but these devices now have excellent safety profiles.[1]

† Absent from the chart above are forms of emergency contraception, which typically require a prescription for teens under 17[1] and which in theory should be useful for those not on a form of LARC, given that a common reason teens don't use contraception is that they didn't expect to have sex.[2] The American College of Obstetricians and Gynecologists recommends that teens keep emergency contraception on hand "just in case" to maximize its effectiveness.[3] However it's still not proven that access to emergency contraception actually reduces pregnancy rates.[4, 5, 6]

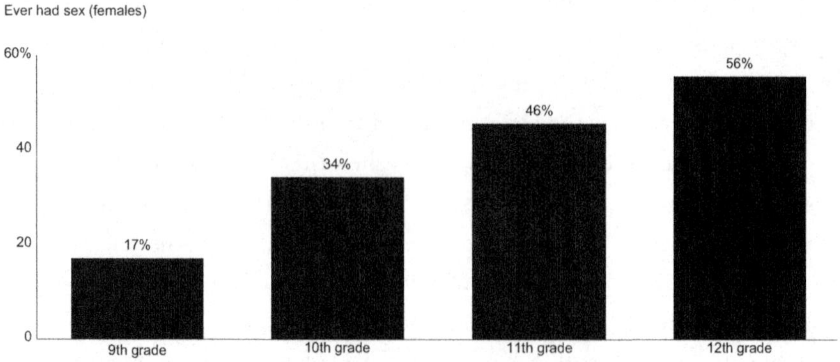


As we saw in the introduction, your assumptions about your teen's sexual behavior may be wrong. Based on a national survey of both parents and teens, if you think your tenth grader hasn't had sex, there's still around a 20 percent chance that your teen is no longer a virgin.[33]

Not only do parents underestimate the sexual activity of their teens; teens also underestimate their parents' level of disapproval of their engaging in sexual activity.[34] Here's yet another example of a missed opportunity to make your expectations clear. If handing out a virginity pledge ring isn't your thing, a simple conversation would do.

Of course, pregnancy isn't the only risk teens face when they become sexually active. In the 1800s, the prevailing wisdom held that sexually transmitted diseases (STDs) were a punishment for sin,[35] and even to this day, some religions preach that these diseases are demons lodged in genetic material.[36] Whether or not STDs are the work of the devil, they are devilishly difficult to contain.

Part of the difficulty is that young people frequently lie about their sexual history, causing their partners to underestimate the risks involved in a casual dalliance.[37] One survey of college students found that 47 percent of men and 42 percent women had understated their number of previous partners,[38] and another survey of adolescent couples found that 16 percent of boys and 37 percent of girls who thought they were in a monogamous relationship had partners who were actually sleeping with someone else at the same time.[39] When it comes to STDs, which are often a source of shame, people will dissemble even in the most extreme cases: one study of HIV-positive patients revealed that about 40 percent had failed to disclose their HIV status to their sexual partner.[40]

As a result, by the time they reach legal age, many adolescents have already contracted some sort of infection. The details on the various STDs can be found in Appendix III, but here's a chart which summarizes the take-aways:[41]

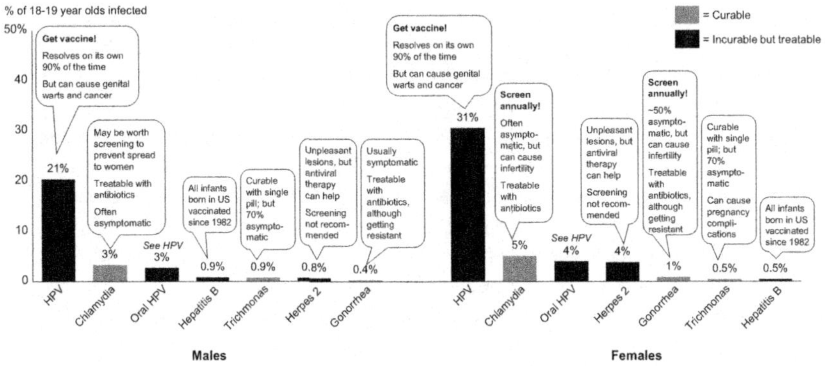


Simply showing your teen this chart is unlikely to have any effect; there's no evidence that communicating with adolescents helps reduce their risk of contracting an STD.[42] However, our chart does suggest several common-sense actions parents can take.

The first no-brainer is to ensure your teenager is up to date with the HPV vaccine, and with the hepatitis B vaccine if your child was born in a country without routine vaccination at birth. Secondly, if your child's school doesn't provide easy access, give your teen a large supply of condoms. Also provide a supply of testing kits and suggest your child use one in the event of symptoms, or a new sex partner (be sure to wait at least a week), or otherwise 1x per year.* [43] (A teen who tests positive and is too embarrassed to tell you can seek medical treatment without your involvement: in all 50 states and the District of Columbia, medical care for STDs can be provided to adolescents without parental consent or knowledge.[44]) And finally, inform your teen that condoms are important even for oral sex.

* The CDC recommends ensuring the test is FDA-approved and uses a lab which meets the standards of the Clinical Laboratory Improvement Amendments. MyLAB Box is an example of a company which meets these standards.

**The particular pitfalls of oral sex**

An article in *The New York Times* in 1997 first described an emerging trend among teens of engaging in oral sex in order to avoid the potential perils associated with intercourse, including not only pregnancy and common infections, but also HIV, the disease that at the time loomed large in the public consciousness.[45] The article referenced a 1994 study of American sexual practices, which showed that only a minority of women over 50 had ever performed oral sex, but three-quarters of women younger than 35 had done so.[46]

Even today, most young people incorrectly assume that oral sex is significantly less risky than vaginal sex when it comes to the health, social, and emotional consequences.[47] For example, a recent study found that a third of adolescents didn't know that oral sex can transmit HIV.[48] As a result, teens are more likely to start their journey of sexual exploration with a behavior that used to be marginalized: 20 percent of students in one recent study reported having had oral sex, while only 14 percent had had vaginal sex.[49] Unfortunately, oral sex is a poor substitute from an emotional perspective: teens are less likely to experience pleasure, feel good about themselves, or find their relationship has improved.[50]

Worse, very few adolescents use protection during oral sex,[51] despite the fact that STDs can be transmitted this way as well. It's difficult to say precisely how the risks of oral vs. vaginal sex compare with each other, because STDs tend to spread throughout the body, and many people who have had oral sex have also had vaginal sex, so the original source of the infection can be difficult to determine.[52] But both gonorrhea and chlamydia can infect the pharynx,[53] HPV can cause cancer of the mouth and pharynx,[54] and one study has estimated there's a 1 percent chance over time of contracting HIV from receptive oral intercourse with a partner who has HIV.[55] As a result, a CDC expert advisory group on AIDS recommends using a condom for oral sex.[56]

As today's teens reach young adulthood, they'll encounter a casual hook-up scene that has changed dramatically over the past two decades as a result of the internet, both for good and ill. According to the World Health Organization, "Dating apps are adding to more than a million new STD infections every day and driving a surge of untreatable superbug strains."[57] There's a cost to the ease of swiping right. On the positive side, there's now www.positivesingles.com, the "world's largest confidential STD dating and support community" for those living with Herpes, HPV, HIV/AIDS and other STDs. Nowadays there's an online community for everything.

# Dig deeper

In the Islamic tradition, betrothal could take place earlier than puberty, but the marriage was not supposed to be consummated until

> the girl was of age… In medieval Europe, the founder of Canon law in the twelfth century accepted the traditional age of puberty for marriage (between 12 and 14)… The fact that Shakespeare's Juliet was thirteen probably reflects the reality in England. Her mother, who was twenty-six, calls her almost an old maid.[58]

Marriage used to take place close to puberty, and even does today in some parts of the world (see box).

**Early marriage around the world**
In Colombia, boys over 14 and girls over 12 can marry with the consent of their parents; in Uruguay, the age with parental consent is 12 for girls and 14 for boys; in Iran, the legal minimum age of marriage for girls is 13, but girls as young as nine can be married with permission from the court and their father; and in Mexico, some states permit a minimum marital age of 14 for girls and 16 for boys with parental consent.[59]

But our modern obsession in the Western world with delaying adulthood extends to delaying our adolescents' initiation into the world of adult sexual behaviors, which most would agree is a positive development. Cultural norms are in fact more influential in determining the age at which teens begin to date and have intercourse than levels of sex hormones.[60] Nevertheless, the bounds of culture can only go so far to contain the natural adolescent exuberance to cross this barrier, and many teens are sexually active well before their parents would approve. Most parents have no idea: around 35 percent of mothers in one survey thought their teen was sexually active, whereas the true figure was 58 percent,[61] while another survey found a similar rate of sexual activity, but only 2 percent of parents suspected.[62]

Adolescents themselves fall into the opposite trap, and wrongly assume everyone around them is wantonly having sex. When asked what percentage of 18 and 19-year-olds in the US had had more than one sexual partner in the past year, most estimated in the range of 50 to 70 percent, when the real figure was 27 percent. In another survey, men on college campuses estimated that 80 percent of their fellow male students were having sex on any given weekend, when the true figure was 5 to 10 percent.[63] As in other domains, adolescents are influenced by these imaginary peers; if they believe their friends are sexually active, they are tempted to follow suit, even if their friends are abstaining in reality.[64]

For those teens who do follow their libidos, regrets are more common than you might expect, although how common depends on which survey you consult.[65] About 28 percent of teens in one survey described their first sexual event as not really wanted,[66] while another found that around 80 percent of girls ultimately wished they had waited, as did 60 percent of boys.[67]

**Causes of sexual regret**

Younger people are ultimately more likely to regret losing their virginity;[68] for example, 14 percent of adult men and 19 percent of women said they wished they'd waited longer, and this increased to 28 percent of men and 52 percent of women who had had sex before the age of 17.[69] Those of either sex who felt pressured at the time or who reported exerting pressure were also more likely to express regret about their decision to have sex, as were those for whom the act was a spontaneous decision rather than a planned one.[70] Having more sexual partners and having sex involving less intimacy (e.g. with a casual partner) is also related to regret.[71] And for girls at least, sexual activity is far more gratifying within the context of a relationship.[*] [72]

The decision to become sexually active is a momentous one for many teens, and it may be worth talking to them about this subject more than we do.

Many of us colloquially refer to "the birds and the bees" without considering what a bizarre euphemism this is for sex.[†] [73] Both birds and bees are egg-laying species, and bees in particular have a very peculiar mating ritual, in which the queen mates with several males while flying, all of whom leave behind part of their body and die shortly thereafter of a ripped abdomen.[74] Just as the metaphor itself is awkward, the "birds and the bees" talk is often uncomfortable for both adolescents and parents. Here are some examples:

> "I was 15 or 16 years old and not a virgin. My father and I were on an hour-long car trip. As soon as we got on our way, he introduced the topic in the form of a rap, then rambled vaguely. Awkwardest thing ever."

* According to a survey of approximately 13,500 undergraduate women, "Women reported orgasms in 11% of first hookups, 16% of second or third hookups, 34% of higher-order hookups, and 67% of relationship sexual events."

† It's likely the phrase was inspired by Samuel Coleridge Taylor, whose verses in "Work Without Hope" (1825) refer to birds and bees separately: "All nature seems at work . . . The bees are stirring--birds are on the wing . . . and I the while, the sole unbusy thing, not honey make, nor pair, nor build, nor sing."[1]

> "Anytime my mom brought it up I ran away. She could only manage to tell me 'you better come to me and ask for birth control, before you come to me and tell me you're pregnant.'"[75]

> "My dad was so uncomfortable he couldn't bring himself to say penis... for the longest time (at my suggestion apparently) we referred to it as the "Voldemort" because it "shall not be named.""

Is "the talk" helpful? It depends on who you ask. One survey of university students and their parents queried whether they had ever had a meaningful discussion about sex. More than half of the students answered, "No," yet in 60 percent of these cases, one or both of their parents said that there had been meaningful discussions.[76] And there's unfortunately not much conclusive evidence that parents can influence how their teens behave by talking with them.[77] Some studies find parent communication does change teen behavior, while others conclude the communication has no effect whatsoever.[78]

The Dutch, at least, seem to have the problem cracked. In the Netherlands, sex ed starts in kindergarten with age-appropriate conversations about friendship, family and love, and then progresses to cover all the details as kids mature.[*] Dutch girls tend to wait longer than their American counterparts to lose their virginity, have fewer partners, and are far more likely to feel happy with their first experiences. The numbers say it all: at a recent point in time, in Holland vs the US, the rate of gonorrhea amongst teens was 14 vs 459 in 100,000, and the rate of chlamydia was 150 vs 2,863 in 100,000.[79] (Of course, it's difficult to know whether the Dutch approach to sexual education causes adolescents to adopt sensible behavior, or whether both are simply manifestations of dramatically different cultural attitudes towards sex.)

The approach taken by the UK is also relatively progressive. The UK government has long encouraged sex education in schools, and even recently made a formal curriculum mandatory for schools to offer,[80] although parents are allowed to opt their children out.[81] Nevertheless, even British adolescents are still getting their information on sex from other less reliable sources in addition to school:[82]

---

* including anatomy, STDs, contraception, consent, relationships, masturbation, oral sex, orgasm, gender identity and same-sex encounters

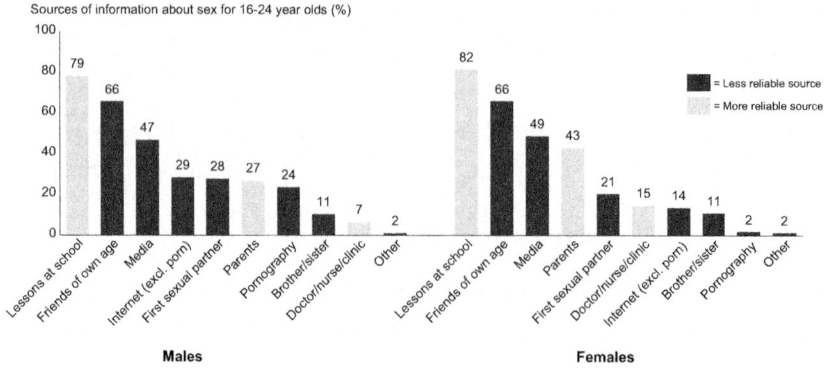


Ultimately, if you don't raise the subject, your child will be learning about sex primarily from friends, the media and porn. So no matter how cringeworthy the conversation becomes, it's worth an attempt at conversation when you stock your teen's room with contraception and STD test kits. To get you started: "Birds do it, bees do it, even educated fleas do it…"[83]

**KEY PARENTING TAKE-AWAYS:**

1. Share clear expectations with your child about when you believe it's appropriate to engage in sexual activity, acknowledging the positives but conveying the downsides, including pregnancy, STDs, and regret
2. If your child's school doesn't provide easy access, provide a large supply of condoms to stash somewhere, along with a quick tutorial (e.g. don't open the package with a sharp object or unroll the condom before putting it on)
3. Put girls on a form of long-acting reversible contraception (IUD or implant)
4. Ensure your teenager is up to date with the HPV vaccine
5. Seek out a hepatitis B vaccine if your child was born in a country without routine vaccination at birth
6. Provide a supply of testing kits and suggest your child use one in the event of symptoms, or a new sex partner (be sure to wait at least a week), or otherwise 1x per year.* Let your teen know that it's possible to seek medical treatment for a positive test without your involvement
7. Emphasize that condoms are necessary even with oral sex
8. Do all of the above well before you think any of it could possibly be necessary

* The CDC recommends ensuring the test is FDA-approved and uses a lab which meets the standards of the Clinical Laboratory Improvement Amendments. MyLAB Box is an example of a company which meets these standards.

# 3. DEATH & PHYSICAL HARM

## Install telematics

> "If you're going to have an early, untimely death, the most dangerous two years of your life are between 16 and 17, and the reason for that is driving." — Nichole Morris, researcher at the HumanFIRST* Laboratory[1]

Getting from one place to another is risky business for teens. When it comes to crashes, there are far too many cautionary tales from which to choose. Prefer tragic?

> After posing for prom pictures – a timeless tradition that made them late for dinner at a restaurant – four high school students climbed into a Tesla. They never made it to dinner. Or prom. Looking back, the fatal crash was the perfect storm: a 17-year-old driver behind the wheel of her father's luxury car, three teenage classmates in the car, and everyone in a rush to get to dinner. The driver reportedly was driving 112 mph in a 55 mph zone. The vehicle lost control, over-corrected, then struck a telephone pole. A back-seat passenger wasn't wearing her seat belt, reportedly because she didn't want to mess up her prom dress. She was thrown from the vehicle, and died three days later. The driver testified she will "never be forgiven for what happened" and will be "hated" by the families and everyone involved.[2]

How about gruesome/horrific?

---

* Human Factors Interdisciplinary Research in Safety and Transportation

> Reggie Stephey, 18 years old and intoxicated, was less than a mile from his driveway when he drifted across the road and struck a car head-on, killing the driver and one passenger. Jacqui Saburido Garcia remained inside the conflagration for nearly a minute before first responders managed to put out the flames. Saburido Garcia suffered devastating third-degree burns over 60 percent of her body, leaving her face unrecognizable. Her fingers had to be amputated. She lost her hair, ears, nose, lips, left eyelid, and much of her vision. Saburido subsequently underwent more than 120 reconstructive operations. Stephey was sentenced to seven years in prison, where he collaborated with Saburido Garcia on an anti-DWI [Driving While Intoxicated] campaign after she told him she forgave him.[3]

Search online for an image of Jacqui Saburido Garcia if you dare, then show it to your teen.

**Why are cars so bad?**
Excluding public transportation, cars are technically the safest way for kids to travel on a per mile basis (see 'Dig deeper' for more on this), but the average teen spends a lot of time in the car, so the risk adds up.

**Driver's ed is useless**
It would be easy to assume that the key to avoiding devastating teen crashes is to spend more time teaching them to drive safely. The British School of Motoring was founded in 1910,[4] and the first high school driver education course in the US launched in 1934.[5] Since then, taking 'driver's ed' has become a rite of passage for many teens.

Unfortunately, formal driver education is completely ineffectual. After decades of research on the topic, review after review concludes that forcing teens to take driver's ed does not reduce their risk of crashing a car.[6] Driver's ed perversely *increases* the number of teenagers involved in traffic crashes, by allowing them to get their licenses sooner than they would have otherwise.[7]

Educating teens about risks isn't a great strategy in general, so perhaps it's no surprise that the classroom element of driver's ed would be ineffectual. It's also possible that teens simply don't spend enough time behind the wheel with the driving instructor to make a noticeable difference in their driving skills. But even increasing the amount of parent-supervised practice doesn't help reduce teens' crash risk,[8] despite the fact that practicing with their parents does help them improve their driving skills.[9] Several European countries have experimented with lowering the age when teens could get their permit without changing the age when they were eligible for a license, to give them more time to practice. Crash rates failed to go down at all in France[10] or Norway,[11] and went down by only 15 percent in Sweden.[12] (Of course even a small potential reduction is better than nothing, so by all means take your responsibility to teach your child seriously. For tips, the National Safety Council has 52 lessons aimed at parents of novice drivers.[*] [13])

* Available at: www.nsc.org/driveithome/pointers-for-parents/pointers-for-parents-lessons

Educating our teens about the dangers of driving is frustratingly ineffectual (see box), so how can we protect them? Delaying the age they get their license by a year or two helps in the sense that it reduces the total number of miles they ultimately drive over the course of their lifetimes. But crash rates are almost as high for those who get their license at 17 or 18 as for those who are 16,[14] as is neatly illustrated in the chart below, based on a random sample of 1.7 million drivers in California:[15]

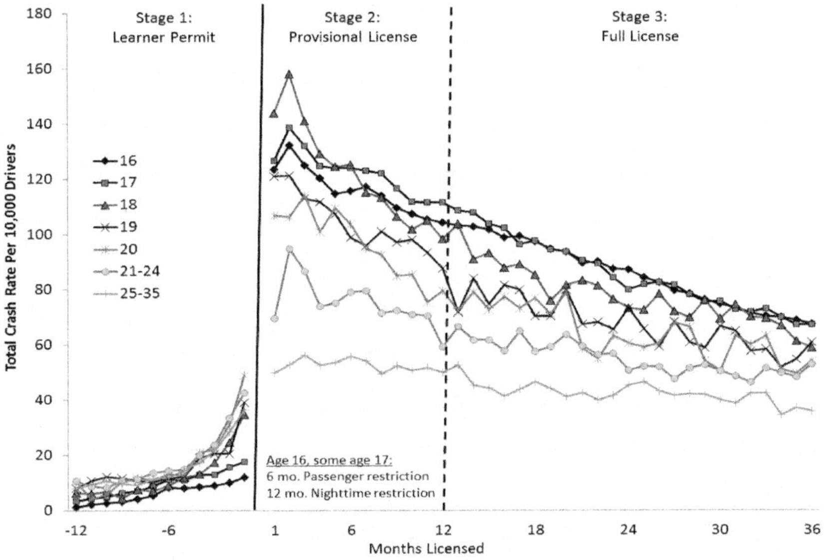


Teens are fully capable of driving safely during their lessons with their parents, as illustrated by their competent driving performance on the left-hand side of the chart. But the learnings don't carry over once they get their license.* Unfettered by adult supervision, teens start committing all sorts of driving sins, including speeding, rapidly accelerating, suddenly decelerating, swerving, and making hard turns.[16] This temporary intoxication with their newfound freedom can be fatal.

One option would be to discourage your child from getting a license at all until a few years down the road, at an age where crash rates no longer spike quite so dramatically (see the lowest two lines on the right of the chart).† [17] Of course, this option may be hard to swallow for parents and teens alike.

* Ideally this chart would show crash rates per mile driven, rather than per driver, since it's possible some of the spike could be attributed to teens spending more time on the road once they have the freedom to drive independently; but such data are not available and the different patterns by age are still revealing.

† For example, a study of 1 million drivers in New Jersey confirmed that while new drivers 21 or older do have a small increase in crashes in their first three months of having a license, the spike is much lower versus their younger counterparts.[i]

Are there other meaningful ways to increase the safety of teens behind the wheel? Fortunately, yes. Drafting a formal written contract for your teen to sign before handing over the keys can decrease risky driving behaviors.[18] There are many examples online,* but here are some ideas of what to include:

**No friends or driving after dark**: Teens drive differently in the presence of peers: no surprises there. In one classic study, researchers asked adolescents (13-16), youths (18-22), and adults (24+) to play a video game called "Chicken," which required decisions about whether to stop a car once a traffic light turned yellow. Adolescents and youths took far more risks when in peer groups than alone.[19] This phenomenon sadly plays out in the real world as well. The risk of death for a 17-year-old driver versus driving alone goes up by 48 percent with 1 passenger, 158 percent with 2 passengers, and 207 percent with 3 or more passengers.[20]

Teens are also more likely to drive badly after sunset. A third of fatal teen crashes happen at night, even though nighttime driving accounts for only 11 percent of total teen trips.[21] It therefore makes sense that 'graduated driver licensing' (GDL) laws, which restrict adolescents from driving at nighttime or carrying friends in their cars, categorically save lives. In the 1990s, a variety of US states began experimenting with these laws, and by now all states except Vermont restrict nighttime driving, and 46 states and DC restrict passengers during the risky teen years.[22] These laws reduce crash risk by 15 to 40 percent, depending on the study.[23]

Unfortunately, many parents don't enforce the GDL laws. Instead, they tend to constrain where teens can drive and what time they need to be back, neither of which are related to crash risk, assuming the return time is already after dark.[24] Similarly, many parents don't impose true consequences for breaking driving rules, relying on scolding and warnings rather than limiting driving privileges.[25] It's worth being more harsh.[26] Restrictions imposed by parents can help keep teens safe.[27]

**Mandatory seatbelts, even for short trips**: Many teenagers are badly misinformed about seatbelts. In a recent survey, 44 percent of 16 to 20-year-olds thought that seatbelts were as likely to harm as help, and 28 percent

---

* A few example sources of driving contracts:

- The US Centers for Disease Control and Prevention (www.cdc.gov/MotorVehicleSafety/pdf/Driving_Contract-a.pdf; www.cdc.gov/parentsarethekey/pdf/PATK_2014_TeenParent_Agreement_AAP-a.pdf)
- The Checkpoints program developed by National Institute of Child Health and Human Development (NICHD) (http://youngdriverparenting.org/)
- Students Against Drunk Driving (SADD) (www.saddonline.com)

believed that a crash close to home was usually not as serious. The most frequent excuses teens offer up for not wearing a belt include they forgot; they were only driving a short distance; they found the belt uncomfortable; or they were in a rush.[28] Yet wearing a seatbelt cuts the risk of serious injuries and deaths from crashes in half.[29]

**No texting, calling, eating or other distractions:** Some 40 to 45 percent of high school drivers admit to having texted while driving within the previous month.[30] When teens are texting, they spend around 40 percent of their time not looking at the road, and make 63 percent more excursions out of their lane,[31] so it's no surprise that their odds of crashing skyrocket by 3 to 4 times.[32] Similarly, dialing a phone, reaching for a phone or other object, and eating while driving all dramatically increase the odds of a crash.[33] Postmortems show teens were distracted in 58 percent of all crashes.[34]

**No music:** In a study of novice drivers, the majority (86 percent) reported listening to music all the time while driving. Yet when they were observed driving with their preferred choice of music, they were significantly more likely to drive poorly, including making miscalculations, committing traffic violations, and driving aggressively.[35] Banning music may not do wonders for your popularity, but it will help keep your teen safe.

**No driving under the influence**: Finally, teens far too frequently drive drunk or stoned. In a recent nationwide survey, 16.5 percent of students had ridden during the prior month in a vehicle driven by someone who had been drinking, and among drivers, 5.5 percent admitted to driving after drinking.[36] Driving under the influence massively increases the probability of a crash. Teens are 17 times more likely to die in a crash when they have a blood alcohol concentration of 0.08 percent than when they're sober.[37] The upshot? Approximately a quarter of fatal crashes for boys and 16 percent for girls involve alcohol, marijuana or both.*

Even if your teen has signed their written contract on the dotted line in blood, it's still worth being cynical about intoxication. In one large survey of teens, approximately 40 percent of those who had hosted a party reported that alcohol was served.[38] So regardless of what your teen tells you, it's better to assume parties will involve alcohol and plan your teen's transportation accordingly. In that same survey, 70 percent of the teens serving the alcohol claimed their parents were aware,[39] so you could contact the parents involved

* For calculations and sources, see Appendix VII.

to confirm.* [40] You could also proactively provide your adolescent with ideas for how to get out of dangerous situations; for example, claiming to be nauseous is a face-saving way to exit a car being driven recklessly.

Even teens who avoid a crash still risk a DUI ('driving under the influence') conviction. In 2018, 12,700 15- to 18-year-olds in the US were arrested on a DUI charge,[41] which works out to a 75.5 chance in 100,000.† [42] A DUI can have long-term implications, as it often has to be disclosed on college and job applications.[43]

Unfortunately teens are useless at judging of their own sobriety, and other people (including you) are equally useless at accurately assessing drunkenness without a proper testing device (see box).

**Impaired? Who, me?**

Adolescents who have imbibed are often tempted to drive because all humans, adolescents and adults alike, are terrible judges of their own impairment.[44] For example, college students who had reached a blood alcohol concentration (BAC) of 0.08% significantly underestimated their own intoxication, and those at higher BACs were even more deluded.[45]

In the US, the legal limit for driving is a BAC of 0.08%,* [46] which is in line with most European countries.† Yet there are nations that have adopted a stricter stance: Poland has set a limit of 0.03%, and Russia and Sweden 0.02%. Arguably, when it comes to teenagers, the limit should be closer to zero. Using driving simulators, researchers have demonstrated that teens start hitting the guardrails on a perfectly straight road with a BAC of 0.03%,[47] and collide with a surprise obstacle five times out of ten with a BAC below 0.05%, versus one time out of ten when perfectly sober.[48] According to the US Department of Transportation, a BAC of 0.02% already impairs performance.[49] And according to the National Highway Traffic Safety Administration, any level above zero BAC interferes with driving skills, and by a BAC of 0.05%, most studies report significant impairment.[50]

Observers are also terrible at judging sobriety. Adult observers in one study rated a target as sober, moderately intoxicated, or very intoxicated/legally drunk correctly only a quarter of the time, and typically underestimated the subject's level of intoxication.[51] And in a roadside survey, both law enforcement personnel and private citizens correctly identified only a fifth of drivers with BACs of 0.10% or higher.[52] As one review puts it, "There is little evidence that most existing sobriety tests are up to the task...Assessing sobriety in the low to moderate BAC ranges without resort to chemical tests remains a daunting task."[53]

---

* More than half of parents in another survey had intentions to contact the parents of the host of a party, yet not many actually followed through, presumably as the conversation can be awkward.[1]

† This calculation is based on a US population of 16,810,997 in 2018.

* The exception is Utah, where the limit is 0.05%.

† This includes Austria, Belgium, Bulgaria, Croatia, Denmark, Finland, France, Germany, Greece, Iceland, Italy, the Netherlands, Norway, Portugal, and Spain.

So if you suspect your teen might be tempted to drive drunk, consider purchasing a breathalyzer.* Other technologies which shine light through fingertips, measure involuntary eye movements, or react to saliva may also be coming to market in the near future.[54]

**Ignition interlock devices**

For serious cases of rebellion or non-compliance with drunk driving rules, consider an ignition interlock device, which attaches to the steering wheel and physically prevents anyone from operating the vehicle without submitting breath samples randomly while driving to prove sobriety.[55] While promising,[56] the jury is still out on the effectiveness of these devices,[57] and they don't seem to influence behavior once they're removed. Nevertheless, they could keep your teen safe in the meantime, and cost approximately $2–$3 a day.[58] In future, cars may even do the monitoring themselves, with built-in sensors in the dashboard monitoring alcohol in the breath, or controls monitoring alcohol levels via the skin.[59]

The most promising option of all for keeping your child safe behind the wheel is remote monitoring technology, also called telematics. If teens receive feedback from their vehicle or believe they're being monitored, they drive more safely.[60] Certain cars have monitoring systems built in,† [61] and there are also services that attach an accelerometer to any car and then provide reporting to both parents and teens.‡ [62] A variety of insurance companies will also attach these devices to your vehicle, and will then often reduce the premiums they charge for a teen driver. This implies the devices must be effective, and the lower cost makes the proposition a double win for you as a parent.[63] If you want a simpler solution, there are also apps which rely on the (less accurate) accelerometers and gyroscopes in smartphones: EverDrive, which is free, allows you to set up a safe driving competition between yourself and your teen,[64] and TrueMotion Family is a similar option.[65] In this case, there's only upside from playing Big Brother, or rather Big Parent.

The best case scenario would be to take the teen driver out of the equation entirely. Driverless cars exist today in limited applications, and safe-driving technologies such as automatic emerging braking, lane-keeping

* According to one recommendation website (www.carbibles.com/best-breathalyzer/), the best device is the BACtrack S80 Professional Breathalyzer for $150;[2] the best value option is the AlcoHAWK Slim Breathalyzer at $31.50, available at www.bactrack.com/products/bactrack-mobile-smartphone-breathalyzer.

† Examples include Chevrolet Teen Driver which provides reporting,[1] and Ford MyKey, which additionally allows parents to control car settings, e.g., limiting speed and music volume.[2]

‡ Examples include MOTOsafety[1], License+[2], Automatic Lite / Pro[3], and Optimus 2.0.[4]

and adaptive cruise control are available on current car models. Technology is no longer the limiting factor. Instead, it's our stubborn human resistance to change. In a recent survey, 56 percent of people said they had minimal interest in having a driverless car, and 61 percent said they wouldn't feel safe in such a vehicle.[66] Yet autonomous, technology-enhanced vehicles are the future, whether we like them or not.[67] Someday teen joyriding will be an anachronism. In the meantime, it's up to you to hold the keys.

## Veto motorcycles

> An acquaintance offered Elsa a ride on his new motorcycle. She hopped on in her miniskirt and stiletto heels. They were travelling at about 70 miles an hour when the bike hit a light reflector in the road. Elsa landed hard on her side and then skidded across the roadway on her back. Half of her body was covered in third degree burns and her skin had melted completely off in six locations, exposing the bones beneath. "When I saw myself in the mirror for the first time since the accident, it was the worst feeling in the world," Elsa said. "I remember thinking that I'll never have another boyfriend. I'll never look normal again in a bathing suit. I was devastated."[*] [68]

Elsa was one of the lucky ones. For teenagers, motorcycles are roughly 85 times more dangerous than cars.[†] They are more likely to crash in the first place, and when they do crash, the crashes are approximately 14 times more likely than car crashes to be fatal.[69]

Teens are liabilities on motorcycles because they tend to do bone-headed things like speeding, driving drunk, leaving behind their helmets, running yellow lights, and driving with too little space between them and the vehicle ahead.[‡] [70] As with cars, requiring additional training for teens doesn't seem to

* Name of protagonist has been changed for privacy purposes.

† See 'Dig deeper' at the end of this chapter for the calculation of the relative risks of motorcycles vs. cars.

‡ Based on similar findings from cars and ATVs, it's very likely that having a passenger along for the ride is a key risk factor for poor motorcycle driving behavior, but to date no studies have explicitly examined this topic.

help reduce their odds of crashing, although it does help lower their overall risk simply by delaying the moment when they get a license.[71]

What does help? Increasing the visibility of motorcycles shows promise: daytime lights have reduced deaths in several countries.[72] And wearing a helmet is the single most effective means of preventing devastating consequences from motorcycle crashes,[73] reducing the risk of death by 42 percent and the risk of head injury by around 70 percent.[74] Of course a helmet wouldn't have prevented the types of injuries suffered by Elizabeth. The simplest approach is to forbid motorcycles altogether.

If your teen is angling hard, here are some suggestions for how to say 'No' effectively, which can of course be applied in other situations as well (see box).[75]

**How to say 'No' effectively**

1. "Listen: By listening to your teen, you demonstrate respect for their point of view and you are more apt to convince them of the merit of your own point of view. If you don't listen, they may infer a lack of interest and will avoid future discussions.
2. Reflect: A quick no carries no weight with teens. They'll see you as intransigent, uninformed, and simply out to make them miserable. Even if you know you are right, take some time to consider the request and explain why you decided against it.
3. Keep cool: Your teen may try to bait you with unfair accusations or even insults. Don't respond. Agree to talk about it later and walk away if you have to.
4. Stick together: Parents who cannot put up a united front are in for a long and ugly battle. Reach a decision privately, and then stand firm and take the time to explain. If you remain consistent and united eventually your teens will figure out when they have no shot in the first place and spare you the grief of having to say no.
5. Offer evidence: You don't want to compare your teen with someone else. But if you ask your teen to observe the consequences of mistakes made by others, it just might sink in that you know a thing or two about life."

You're on your own for points 1-4, but for number 5, excerpts from this book should have you covered.

## Suicide-proof your house

Just weeks after a family ski vacation, Ginevra Falcone, 17-year-old high school junior, straight-A student, class officer and robotics whiz, made her bed, tidied her room, walked to a highway overpass,

> and jumped off the edge.[76] The more than 200 pages she left behind painted an anguished self-portrait of a perfectionist who became convinced she could never live up to her own standards. 'I put on a happy face so I could be alone with my thoughts and get more depressed... I'm never going to be the smartest, and if I'm not at the top then I'm nothing... Don't blame yourselves for not seeing the warning signs. I didn't want you to know how deep in my own mess I was.'[77]

Ginevra's anguish is not an anomaly. According to a large survey in the US, 17 percent of students had seriously considered and 7 percent of students had attempted suicide in the past year.* [78] The United States is not even the country with the highest rates of suicide. That dubious honor belongs to New Zealand, driven by high rates among indigenous populations:[79]

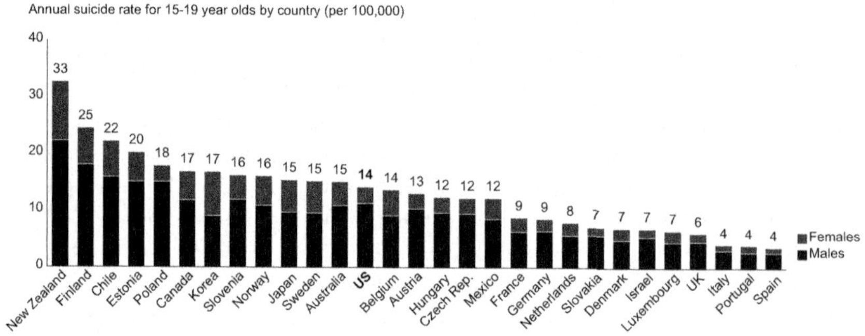


**Blame the screens?**
Some pundits have pointed out that the recent rise in suicides has corresponded with the widespread adoption of mobile phones and the dramatic increase in the amount of time teens spend interacting with devices. It's plausible there could be a connection, although it's tricky to prove; we'll return to this topic in the sections on depression and screen time.

Even more worrying, the rates of teen suicide have been steadily creeping up over recent years:[80]

* And as we saw in the introduction, some samples suggest the lifetime rate of attempting suicide for teens is even higher.[1]

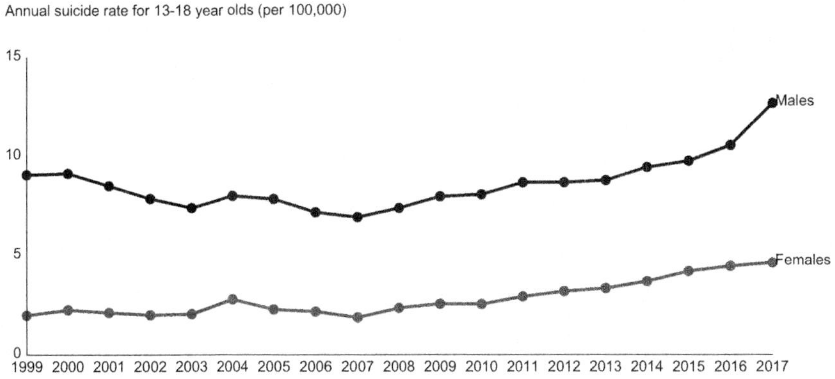


This rise in suicide rates is an urgent, critical problem. Many of our teens, on the brink of reaching their full potential as mature young adults, are feeling desperate enough to contemplate taking their own lives. Yet a lack of long-term, large-scale studies is hindering the ability of the scientific community to solve the conundrum of how to prevent these despairing adolescents from taking drastic action.[81] "We continue to rely almost entirely on people themselves to proactively tell us if they are suicidal," said Matthew Nock, a professor of psychology at Harvard University. "Yet research has shown that nearly 80 percent of people who die by suicide explicitly deny suicidal thoughts or intentions in their last communications."[82]

**A fiendishly difficult problem**

Back in 2002, a review despaired that no test could accurately assess suicide risk;[83] the only accurate predictors were previous suicide attempts and explicit statements about suicidal intentions.[84] Two years later the US Preventative Services Task Force concluded that things hadn't improved.[85] The UK National Institute for Health and Clinical Excellence (NICE) guidelines, written in 2011 and unchanged in 2016, acknowledge the hopelessness of the problem and advise medical professionals not to bother using risk assessment tools.[86] Most recently, Facebook even attempted to screen for suicide risk using artificial intelligence, and concluded that "this is not a simple problem."[87]

It's fiendishly difficult to diagnose suicidality (see box). Taking the approach that something is better than nothing, here are the warning signs of suicide according to the most recent report by the US Surgeon General. The more of these signs a person shows, the greater the risk:[88]

- Talking about wanting to die

- Looking for a way to kill oneself
- Talking about feeling hopeless or having no purpose
- Talking about feeling trapped or being in unbearable pain
- Talking about being a burden to others
- Increasing the use of alcohol or drugs
- Acting anxious, agitated, or reckless
- Sleeping too little or too much
- Withdrawing or feeling isolated
- Showing rage or talking about seeking revenge
- Displaying extreme mood swings

The first half of this list should be obvious; if your teen is showing these suicidal tendencies, take the situation seriously and seek professional help.

**Not a DIY situation**

Parents typically know when their child is depressed, but they unfortunately don't tend to enlist a professional unless their teen is causing the family inconvenience, for example, by being disobedient.[89] Don't fall into this trap.

With the second half of the list, it's not obvious at all how to distinguish suicidality from ordinary teen drama. One other option could be to ask your child to fill out the WHO-5 questionnaire, which the European Alliance Against Depression recommends physicians use as a first-level depression screen.[90] * [91]

* Please score the statements below as follows: All of the time (5); most of the time (4); more than half of the time (3); less than half of the time (2); some of the time (1); at no time (0). Over the last two weeks:

- I have felt cheerful and in good spirits
- I have felt relaxed and calm
- I have felt active and vigorous
- I woke up feeling refreshed and rested
- My daily life has been filled with things that interest me[1]

If the sum of the answers is below 13, or if your teen has answered 0 to 1 to any of the items, it's time to enlist professional help.[2]

**The "gender paradox"**

In the US, boys are close to four times more likely to die by suicide than girls, as shown on the left side of the chart below. However girls attempt suicide far more often than their male counterparts, as illustrated by the hospitalization rates on the right:[92]

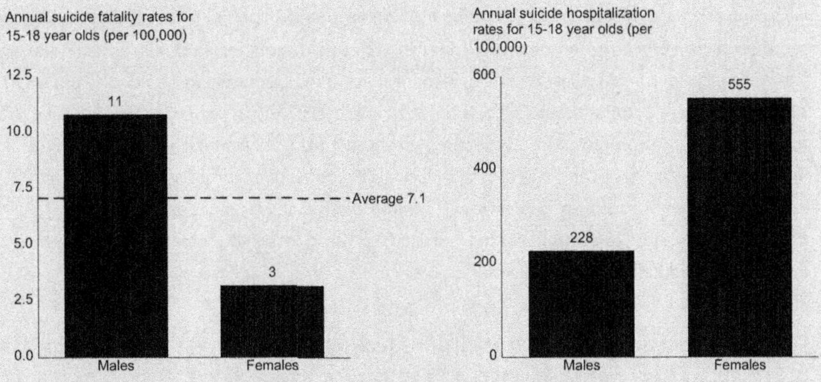


Although the drivers are not clear cut, one study from Sweden pointed out that three quarters of those who had sought professional help for suicidal thoughts were female, while three quarters of those who had committed suicide in the same year were male, suggesting that "women seek help, men die." Stigma surrounding male depression could be one root cause.[93] The gender difference in suicide rates is probably also driven by choices of method. 90 percent of suicide attempts by gun are lethal versus only 2 percent of suicide attempts using drugs and other poisons, a method more often chosen by females.[94]

The most tragic aspect of suicide is that it's very frequently a temporary crisis. Kevin Hines, who at age 19 miraculously survived a plunge off the Golden Gate Bridge in San Francisco, says the moment he jumped he knew he had made a terrible mistake. "The millisecond my hands left the rail, it was instant regret for my actions."[95] He is not alone. For many years, people opposed constructing anti-suicide barriers on the bridge, which holds the ignominious distinction of being the top suicide location in the world, as they assumed the suicide attempters would simply go elsewhere. Yet a study found that of the roughly 500 people who had attempted to jump off the bridge but had been restrained, approximately 90 percent did not ultimately die of suicide. The desire to die is often an acute crisis.[96] After a first unsuccessful attempt, the risk of dying by suicide is only 1.6 percent after one year, and around 4 percent after 10 years.[97] A temporarily suicidal individual will frequently go on to lead a long life.[98] We therefore need to erect more barriers, both literally and figuratively.

**Preventing suicide around the world**

In the 1950s, 40 percent of all suicides in the UK were by means of self-asphyxiation with domestic cooking gas. But when the carbon monoxide content of cooking gas was reduced drastically over the next decade, the total suicide rate in the country declined by 26 percent, with almost all of this decline attributed to the decrease in gas asphyxiation, since there was no increase in suicides by other methods.[99] A similar story played out in Japan after carbon monoxide was removed from coal gas. And high rates of suicide in rural China and Sri Lanka are hypothesized to be caused by the easy availability of lethal pesticides. According to a review, "The more difficult it is to access highly lethal methods of suicide, the more likely the person is to use a less lethal method and therefore the greater the likelihood of survival."[100]

So if you're concerned your child is feeling desperate, it's time to "suicide-proof" your house.[101] As the World Health Organization categorically states, "Restricting access to the means for suicide works."[102] Here are the methods adolescents currently use in the US:[103]

Suicide methods for 15-18 year olds (per 100,000)

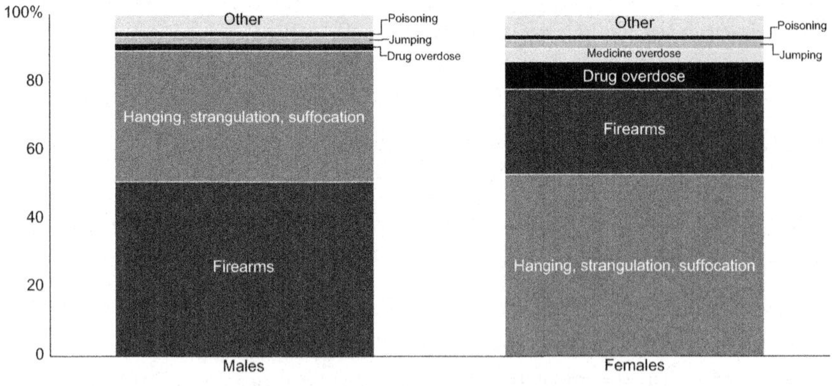


Unsurprisingly, firearms rear their ugly heads. Having a gun in the house, even unloaded, increases the risk for suicide in both adults and teens[104] by over three times,[105] and laws restricting firearm ownership have lowered suicide rates in many countries, including Australia, Canada, New Zealand, Norway and the UK.[106] For those who can't abide the thought of not having a gun in the house, basic safety measures like keeping guns unloaded under lock and key, and locking the ammunition in a separate location definitely help lower the risk.[107] Yet in a national survey of gun owners, around 20 percent kept a firearm both loaded and unlocked in their home.[108] Not a good plan if there's a sullen teenager in the vicinity.

The same caution applies to medicines, the fourth most common method of suicide among girls. Restricting access to large quantities of medications can prevent suicides.[109] For example, interviews with suicide survivors in the UK revealed that many who overdosed on paracetamol (Tylenol) had acted impulsively. Britain therefore passed legislation in 1988 to restrict paracetamol pack sizes to a maximum of 32 tablets, and saw a significant reduction nationwide in deaths due to paracetamol poisoning.[110] So if you're concerned your teen could be depressed, lock your medicine cabinet, don't hoard significant quantities of any single item, and throw unneeded medicines away.

Of course it's impossible to restrict access to items which could be used for "hanging, strangulation, and suffocation" without locking your child into an empty room, which is why seeking professional treatment for depressed adolescents is critical. The option that shows the most promise in reducing suicidality is cognitive behavioral therapy, or CBT, as we'll discuss further in the section on mental health.[111]

**To medicate or not to medicate?**
The case for anti-depressants is not clear cut. They seem to work for adults,* [112] but for children and teens, the benefits in controlling depression may not be sufficient to justify the potential for problematic side effects, which perversely can include an increase in suicidality.[113] A recent systematic review suggests that doctors who do choose to prescribe fluoxetine, the best choice, should monitor the risk of suicide closely.† [114]

---

* For example, a program to educate GPs about depression in the 1980s on the Swedish island of Gotland was associated with increased antidepressant prescriptions and a decrease in the annual suicide rate from 20 to 7 suicides per 100,000.[1 2]

† A variety of other treatment options show early promise but are probably too premature to recommend. Examples include Attachment-based Family Therapy (ABFT), which aims to "enhance the quality of attachment bonds via an interpersonal approach to individual and family therapy, as well as parent skills training;"[1 2] Dialectical Behavior Therapy (DBT), "a treatment focused on strengthening skills in interpersonal effectiveness, as well as mindfulness, distress tolerance, and emotion regulation;"[3] and Mentalization-Based Treatment for Adolescents (MBT-A), "a year-long, manualized, psychodynamic psychotherapy program which aims to enhance patients' capacity to represent their own and others' feelings accurately in emotionally challenging situations."[4] In cases where the suicidal behavior coincides with alcohol and drug use, Motivational Interviewing (MI) alongside cognitive behavioral therapy may help.[5 6] And the Youth-Nominated Support Team-Version II (YST) is a psychoeducational, social support program for adolescents hospitalized in a psychiatric unit due to suicidality, which appears effective in preliminary evalutions.[7] There is even a game-like app being designed to create aversion to suicidal behaviors.[8 9]

One easy preventative measure you can take at home is to simply talk openly with your children about suicide. According to the World Health Organization, many people don't know who to approach in moments of desperation and hesitate to reach out because of the stigma, yet talking to someone can often help a suicidal individual postpone dramatic action and consider other options.[115]

You could also program a helpline number into your child's phone; for example the National Suicide Prevention Lifeline in the US (800-273-8255, or 988).[116] Helplines have been shown to prevent suicide in adults in certain studies,[117] although the results are mixed, and the benefits haven't been sufficiently studied in adolescents.[118] On the other hand, it's important to avoid the so-called 'contagion effect.' Suicides among teenagers occasionally increase in clusters following widespread media coverage of a suicide.[119] So there's no need to describe Ginevra's story at the start of this section to your teen. And based on recent scare stories about suicide websites,[120] it might also be worth monitoring the web browsing history of any seriously depressed young person.

**When a Friend Succumbs**

The suicide of a close friend or family member can affect a teen seriously. [121] Young people will often struggle for a prolonged period of time with feelings of grief and guilt, with more than half of bereaved teens still feeling depressed nine months later, and many having difficulties being open with their family about their feelings.[122] This is another situation where professional help is warranted, and if your teen rejects the help initially, keep offering it periodically. It often takes time for an adolescent to absorb and process what has happened, and many teens who push away offers of help upfront welcome them later. If they do agree to see a psychologist, bereaved teens prefer when family members take responsibility for sharing the details of the event with the psychologist upfront, so they're spared having to do so themselves at the first session.[123]

To wrap up, this section has only discussed how to stave off the act of suicide itself. Ultimately, it's just as important to address the underlying problems that lead teens to become depressed in the first place; this will be covered in the later section on mental health.

Returning to the words of Kevin Hines, the suicide survivor who jumped from the Golden Gate Bridge: "I made a pact with myself that day that if one person intervened, I would tell them everything and beg them to save me," he says. No one did, so he leaped off the bridge.[124] When our children despair, the onus is on us to proactively intervene.

# Dig deeper

**Immortal**: adjective /ɪˈmɔr·t̬əl/. Living or lasting forever: Teenagers think they are immortal.[125]

Contrary to popular wisdom, adolescents don't necessarily think they will live forever. Sadly, an unlucky few will not even live into young adulthood. This section provides an overview of the key ways teens get themselves into serious trouble.

After an initially hazardous period in the first years of a child's life, the risk of death for kids is low throughout middle childhood, but begins to inexorably climb again like a tidal wave throughout the teen years:[126]

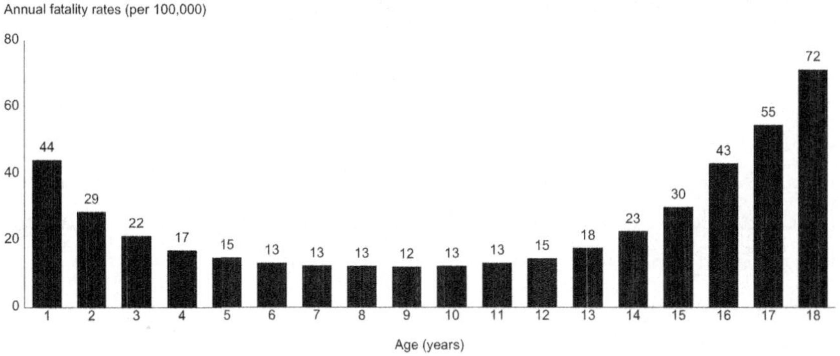


With every year that passes, life gets increasingly dangerous for teenagers. If only they could stay tweens forever.

The risk also depends on the gender of your child. Boys are way more likely to get themselves into life-threatening situations, and are more than twice as likely as girls to die during their teen years:[127]

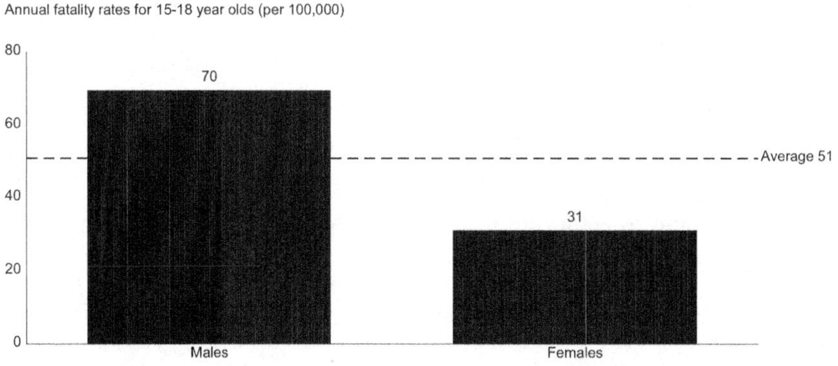

How do these unlucky few manage to end up in mortal peril? The top dangers are broken out in the chart below. Transportation accidents lead the way, followed by homicide and suicide, with diseases only representing about 20 percent of deaths amongst this age group:* [128]

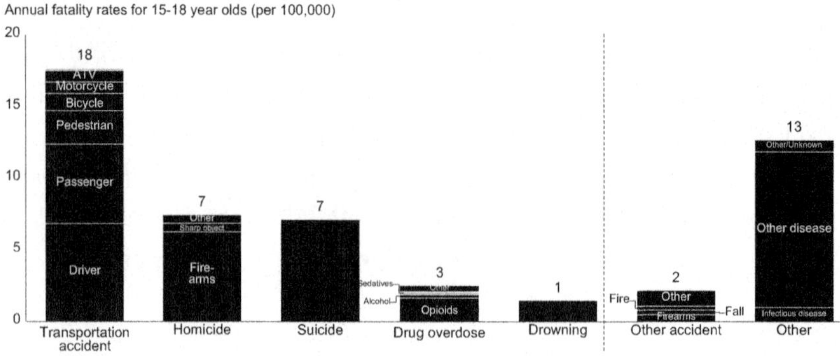


This chart is, of course, simply the extreme tip of the iceberg. For every child who tragically dies, there will be many more who experience a near miss. It's therefore also revealing to look at hospitalizations, added in gray to the chart below. The same three categories rank highest once again, although in a different order, and accidents feature significantly:[129]

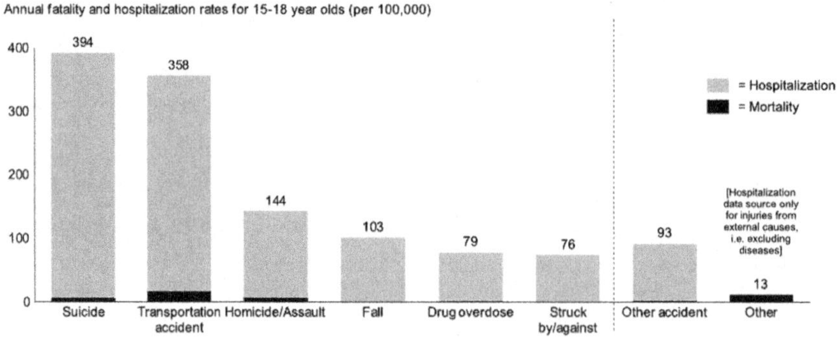


Both of these charts can be found in Appendix IV separated by gender for those who are interested.

One clear take-away is that getting from one place to another is a risky business for teens. Yet we can hardly insist they stay home. So what's the safest way for them to get around? The breakdown by mode of transportation

* Driver and passenger categories include cars, trucks and vans; 'unknown vehicle' allocated proportionally to other transportation fatalities; 'unknown drug' allocated proportionally to other drug fatalities

in the fatality chart is somewhat misleading. Teens travel far more miles by car (the 'driver' and 'passenger' categories) than they do by motorcycle, so we would expect more car crashes, even if cars were safer.

To make direct comparisons about the safety of various forms of conveyance, it's helpful to consider the risk per mile travelled. Inexplicably, this information is not readily available anywhere. The chart below, the first of its kind, combines the previous information on number of annual deaths (the numerator) with miles actually travelled by teens (the denominator), excluding public transportation:[130]

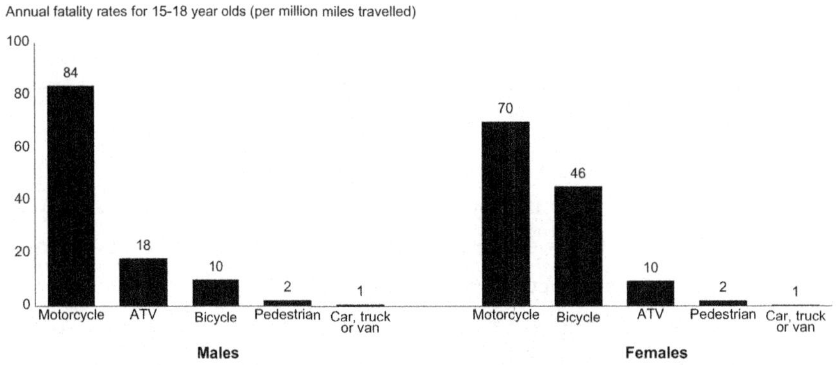


The chart reveals that per mile driven, motorcycles are roughly 70–85 times more dangerous for teens to drive than cars, as referenced previously. Cars cause an unacceptably large number of teen deaths, but they are still safer than any of the alternatives, even including walking.*

What can we do to keep our children safe from all the perils that face them in the wider world? Unfortunately, for certain types of danger we still have no idea. Shockingly, there are no good studies on preventing teen suffocation, drowning, burns, and falls,[131] although safely storing non-medicinal poisons may help prevent poisoning.[132] If you thought baby-proofing your house was a challenge, teen-proofing it is challenging on another level. Perhaps the scientific community will have better advice for us in time for the second edition of this book. In the meantime, we'll cover the additional categories where we do have insights, in decreasing order of threat (excluding drugs which have been covered previously).

* Newer forms of conveyance such as electric scooters and electric bikes aren't yet included as separate categories in these data sources, so although anecdotally they cause their fair share of accidents, they unfortunately cannot yet be added to this chart.

## *Pedestrian deaths*

> 15-year-old Christina Morris Ward was killed while crossing the street just two blocks from her high school in Maryland. She was dressed in dark clothes, wearing headphones and carrying a cell phone. In memory of Christina, her friends, family and community members distribute reflectors to wear when it's dark and encourage kids to remove their earphones and cross the street safely. "I'm not going to stop until we save as many lives as we can," Christina's mom, Gwendolyn Ward, told news reporters."[133]

Ms. Ward deserves our admiration for embracing a cause which otherwise attracts far too little public attention. No matter what the statistics tell us, it's difficult to internalize the possibility that walking could be dangerous, until someone in our community is tragically mowed down. Yet a survey of American teens found that 40 percent admitted to having been hit or nearly hit by a car, bike or motorcycle while walking.[134]

One could argue that Gwendolyn is misusing her time. Instead of focusing on the behaviors of the pedestrians themselves, she could be advocating for the driving safety measures discussed previously. About 70 percent of teen pedestrian deaths are caused by an error on the part of the driver, not the teen on foot.[135] But that's no reason to ignore the 30 percent of deaths involving poor pedestrian behavior, which can include darting into the road and crossing the road at a non-junction. It's not just toddlers with balls who are ignoring the basic rules of traffic safety.

A key problem is likely to be distraction.[136] If you want a moment of levity in the midst of reading about this otherwise gloomy topic, watch Conan O'Brien's "Guiding Hands" skit, poking fun at the phone zombies surrounding us.[137] There is apparently now a name for distracted walking while texting: 'twalking.'[138] Hawaii has even gone so far as to create a law against crossing the street while looking at a phone or other device, with a fine between $15 and $99.[139]

Teens are particularly frequent offenders. One study observed approximately 35,000 examples of teens crossing the street, and found 20 percent crossed while distracted by a mobile device, of which about 40 percent were also wearing headphones.[140] And distraction changes crossing behavior: in another study, texting pedestrians were approximately four times more likely to display at least one unsafe crossing behavior (e.g. disobeying the lights, crossing mid-intersection, or failing to look both ways).[141] Unsurprisingly, when it comes to teens, alcohol is also sometimes involved: of a sample of 16-20 year old pedestrians killed in traffic crashes, around a quarter had alcohol in their system.[142]

Unfortunately parents talk less to their kids about traffic safety as they grow up, even though teens are more likely than younger children to be walking out and about independently. Worse, parents themselves often model unsafe crossing behavior in front of their offspring.[143] Educating both children and adults about pedestrian traffic safety improves behavior, although this hasn't yet been definitively linked to fewer pedestrian deaths.[144] So telling your teen to pay attention when crossing the street could be worthwhile; it's at least easier than insisting on fluorescent or reflective clothing (which could help, although the jury is still out).[145]

These days there's an app for everything, including one designed to lower distracted walking if you happen to be a resident of New York City: "When users reach an intersection, a pair of graphic eyeballs pops up on the screen and the phone vibrates, imploring them to pay attention to their surroundings."[146] While some might question the value of such an app, at least it's an improvement on apps designed to distract while walking. Just ask the parents of the 15-year-old girl who wandered into a street and was struck by a car while playing 'Pokemon Go.'[147]

## Bicycle crashes

> A schoolboy filmed his own death when a jackass-style stunt went wrong. The teen had been sitting on a seat taped onto the handlebars of his friend's mountain bike and using his mobile phone to record the pair speeding down a steep hill at up to 40mph.[148]

When your 5-year-old tumbles off a bike, the collateral damage is rarely more serious than a scraped knee. When your teenager flies over the handlebars, on the other hand, the results will almost certainly be more than a band-aid can handle. As in many areas of life, consequences can escalate as your children age, and bicycles, the classic staple of innocence and childhood freedom, take on a new level of danger when operated by gangly youths housed in adult-sized bodies.

Helmets are the first and best line of defense if your child is travelling by two wheels. There is no question that they improve safety, reducing the risk of head and brain injuries by 60–90 percent.[149] But how in the world to convince your teen to wear one? Educational programs combined with free or subsidized helmets have had mixed success,[150] although public health campaigns in Seattle and in Victoria, Australia, did manage to reduce bicycle-related head injuries.[151] Popular culture isn't helping. An analysis of movie content showed that among the highest-grossing G- or PG-rated movies that featured bicycling, only 6 percent of the bicyclists wore helmets.[152]

One option to increase compliance with a seemingly trivial rule is to make the punishment disproportionate to the crime. (Singapore's ban on chewing gum is a classic example: as soon as a law was passed subjecting anyone selling or importing gum to a hefty fine and up to two years in prison, the telltale dirty splotches rapidly disappeared from the city's sidewalks.[153]) So although this strategy has never been tested, presumably establishing a severe consequence (e.g. permanently confiscating the bicycle) and hinting you'll find ways to spy could deter your adolescent from being tempted to whip off the helmet just after disappearing around the corner.

**Paltry options**

Unfortunately, there aren't many other possibilities for improving bicycle safety. There is some evidence that bicycle skills training can help,[154] but communities that offer bicycle classes are few and far between. Decking your teen out in fashionable fluorescent materials by day and flashing lights and reflectors by night will definitely make the bike more visible to drivers, but no one has studied whether this actually improves safety and is therefore a battle worth fighting.[155]

Maybe it's the bicycle helmets themselves that need to be improved. Collapsible helmets are a clever option to save your teen the inconvenience of carrying around an unwieldy encumbrance or leaving it behind to be stolen.[156] Of course, a collapsible option still doesn't solve the problem of aesthetics. Little did you know that there are helmets masquerading as hats: the Straw Hat Bike Helmet; the Tweed Bike Helmet; the Yakkay helmet system with 15 different covers, including the Paris style in Black Oilskin, and a fluffy fur cover that is "very Dr. Zhivago".[157] If that doesn't convince your teen, there's always "because I said so."

## All-terrain vehicle (ATV) crashes

> Eric Garcia, 14, was transported to a local hospital where he was pronounced dead. According to the local Sheriff, Garcia was the passenger on an ATV with two other teenagers, 15 and 17. The driver was traveling at a high rate of speed close to a ditch when he came up to a canal and lifted off the ground. The victims were thrown many feet into the air.* [158]

> Jessica Grant, 10, was killed Friday in an ATV accident. Jessica spent countless hours making much needed facial masks for her community and surrounding counties... Jessica was a remarkable child. She was bright, talented, wise beyond her years... She was always smiling."† [159]

For some readers who live in rural areas, ATVs are an everyday part of life. Other readers may have no idea what one even looks like. An ATV, sometimes known as a quad bike, is "a small open motor vehicle with one seat and three or more wheels fitted with large tires, designed for use on rough ground."[160]

**Joyride**

Many adolescents use ATVs for practical purposes, but that doesn't stop them from riding them for fun as well. According to a survey of teens at a Future Farmers of America convention, 93 percent used their ATV for recreational purposes, versus 75 percent for work.[161] And a similar survey of teens at Connecticut agricultural fairs found 94 percent rode primarily for recreation.[162]

ATVs driven by teens are hazardous, although their danger is closer to that of bicycles than motorcycles, presumably because they're less likely to reach high speeds.‡ [163] Nevertheless, according to the Consumer Federation of America, "ATVs are one of the most dangerous products the US Consumer Product Safety Commission (CPSC) regulates, causing more deaths and injuries than almost any other product under CPSC's jurisdiction."[164]

* Name of protagonist has been changed for privacy purposes

† Name of protagonist has been changed for privacy purposes.

‡ The data source used for fatalities in this book, CDC Wonder, has a single category for deaths from "all-terrain or other off-road motor vehicles," so this includes both ATVs and motocross. Motocross is an organized sport with national associations governing the competition of highly trained athletes, while ATVs are used both recreationally and commercially, typically for farming and ranching. We focus here on ATV use since it appears to have a higher mortality rate than motocross, although both sports have worrying rates of head, spinal cord, and extremity injury.[i]

**Myth: Smaller ATVs are safer**
One might assume that smaller models of ATVs would be safer, but they aren't: downgrading to a smaller engine size (<= 90cc) only reduces the risk of a crash by approximately 20 percent.[165]

The younger the teen, the greater the risk: [166] teens under 16 are the ones most likely to end up in the emergency room with an ATV-related injury.[167] Gender also matters: boys are roughly three times as likely as girls to hurt themselves, so there are more Erics than Jessicas.[168] And passengers also increase the odds of a crash, not only because they distract and probably egg on the driver, but also because they can affect the balance and control of the vehicle.[169] Finally, ATVs are more than twice as dangerous when taken on roads versus driven off-road.[170]

Many young riders don't follow basic safety guidelines.[171] In one survey, three quarters of teens admitted they didn't wear helmets consistently; 80 percent rode on paved roads, and the vast majority had taken a passenger.[172] In another survey, nearly half reported they had ridden after dark, and less than 5 percent had received any formal ATV riding/safety instruction.[173] Although there's no research on this topic specifically, presumably drafting a driving contract for your teen to sign forbidding these risky behaviors could equally be applied to ATVs.

Various government bodies have set guidelines encouraging parents to restrict their children's access to ATVs;[*] [174] for example, the president of the American Academy of Pediatrics has categorically stated that children under the age of 16 aren't developmentally capable of operating these machines safely.[175] When it comes to recreational use, ATVs are likely not worth the risk.

Here's a parting thought from Kaiden Ross, who at age 18 was drinking at a friend's house when he decided to take an ATV for a spin. The last thing Ross remembers is driving very fast with a friend down a rural road, before he was rushed to the hospital where he would spend the next 52 days:

---

* The Canadian Pediatric Society recommends the following:

- "Children younger than 16 years of age should not operate an ATV. The lack of evidence that youth models reduce the risk of injury means this recommendation must apply to all vehicle sizes, including youth models.
- ATV operators should wear a government-certified helmet, eye protection, and protective clothing and footwear at all times.
- Operators of ATVs designed for single riders should never take on passengers.
- ATV drivers should not operate a vehicle after drinking alcohol.
- ATV drivers should complete an approved training course."[1]

> I almost died. I had neurological tests at the very beginning and I was severely impaired. I was drooling… It's crazy how your life can change so quickly. I was thinking about wearing a helmet, but I was thinking if I get in a crash, nothing is going to happen to me.[176]

## Homicide

> Jason Johnson, 14, was stabbed to death in a frenzied attack after he was knocked off his moped by members of a rival gang driving a stolen car. They encountered Jason and "butchered" him in a residential street.[177] Jason's mother described her son's murder as barbaric, saying her son was a "loving and caring, family-oriented little boy,"who had ambitions to launch a clothing line, and had been moved to hand out gloves to the homeless in the winter.[*] [178]

Jason is the archetype of the American teen murder victim. You most likely had never heard of Jason until now. His death never made the national news. The disproportionate media attention on horrible tragedies like the shooting at Marjory Stoneman Douglas High School in Parkland, Florida, obscures the fact that murders of teens in the US are not primarily driven by school shootings: less than 3 percent of youth homicides take place at school.[179]

Inner city black children are those at highest risk of being killed. Firearms are the leading cause of death for black youth, who are between four[180] and 14 times more likely to be murdered than their white peers.[181] Kids in cities have twice the risk as those in rural areas,[182] and children from areas with predominantly low-income households are 4.5 times as likely to be killed.[183] In fact violence in the United States is highly concentrated: a quarter of all homicides occur in only 8 cities, and murders are concentrated in a small number of neighborhoods within those cities.[184] There's also not much risk of being killed randomly; only about 5 percent of victims are bystanders.[185]

The single most important source of risk for teens is involvement in a gang. 48 percent of teen gang members have had a knife or gun pulled on them, 21 percent have shot or stabbed someone, and 11 percent have been shot (the corresponding figures for non-gang members are 9, 1 and 1

* Name of protagonist has been changed for privacy purposes.

percent respectively).[186] However children often perversely join a gang for protection.[187] Teens in a gang feel less fear and anxiety, because the sources of risk are known (e.g., rival gangs and initiation rituals), the risks are viewed as controllable (because of the rules and expectations governing gang violence), and the gangs have taught and reinforced fearlessness in their members.[188] Thus the vicious cycle continues.

In an attempt to stem the violence, schools have tried to teach conflict de-escalation skills to students at risk, with the US Centers for Disease Control and Prevention (CDC) helping to fund many such programs. Thus far, there's little evidence they actually help.[189] A better strategy might involve restricting the means. The guns used in teen homicides are most frequently purchased illegally from "street" sources.[190] Such ready availability of firearms is a uniquely American problem, which contributes to the dramatic difference in homicide rates for teens and young adults in the US vs. other high income countries, as illustrated in the chart below:* [191]

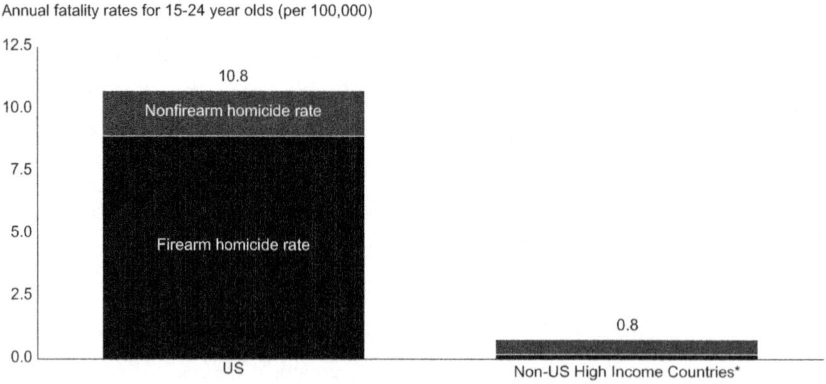


The best bet to protect a budding gang member would therefore be to move overseas. Closer to home, Rhode Island, Maine, or Vermont would also do.[192] Of course, the very families most affected by gang violence are precisely those without the means to move away from their violent neighborhoods to relocate to quaint, peaceful towns in New England or abroad. If you currently live in a neighborhood unaffected by gang violence, take a moment to appreciate your good fortune. Jason's mother wasn't as fortunate.

* Non-US High Income Countries: Australia, Austria, Belgium, Canada, Czech Republic, Denmark, Finland, France, Germany, Hungary, Ireland, Italy, Japan, Korea, Netherlands, New Zealand, Norway, Portugal, Slovak Republic, Spain, Sweden, United Kingdom (England and Wales, Northern Ireland, Scotland)

## *Drowning*

> A 14-year-old boy has become the second teen to drown on Lake Lanier this holiday weekend. Both drownings happened after the teens fell into drop-offs in otherwise shallow water.[193]

> Four boys between the ages of 13 and 15 years old snuck into a swim club pool just after midnight. One decided to jump from the high dive, but instead of landing on a raft, the boy plunged to the bottom. It turns out none of the boys could swim all that well -- if at all, police say.[194]

> A Memorial Day pool party turned tragic after partygoers found a teen dead from an apparent drowning. Cellphone videos show the pool area of an apartment complex filled with hundreds of people. Witnesses said the 19-year-old drowning victim was underwater for up to 20 minutes before someone noticed.[195]

These depressing and senseless deaths illustrate the three key sources of danger when it comes to water and teens: natural water, overconfidence, and partying/alcohol.

A full 80 percent of teen drowning deaths are boys who get themselves into trouble swimming, boating, or cavorting[196] in natural water (oceans, ponds, lakes, rivers, etc.):* [197]

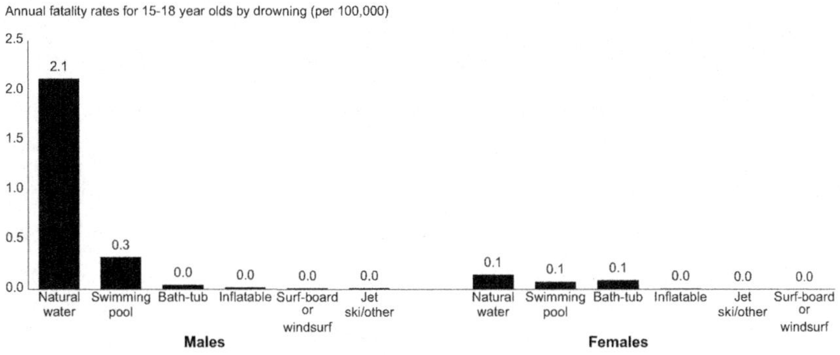


* Unknown cause of drowning allocated proportionally to other categories.

Presumably the vagaries of natural bodies of water, including uncertain depth, currents, waves, and invisible submerged rocks and other objects, cause adolescents who may not be confident swimmers to inadvertently end up literally 'in over their heads'.

Contributing to the risk posed by natural water is the problem of over-confidence, particularly with boys. Among teens who had never taken swimming lessons, a quarter of boys claimed to be 'excellent' or 'very good' swimmers, versus only 16 percent of girls, and young men seem to be particularly prone to taking risks in and around the water.[198]

Alcohol also plays a role in drowning deaths just as it does in transportation accidents. Drinking on or near the water increases the risk of drowning,[199] and alcohol has been detected in the blood of 30 to 70 percent of those who drown while involved in recreational activity.[200] Again, males are the risk-takers when it comes to drinking on the water.[*] [201]

Finally, teens (and adults) are cavalier about wearing life jackets. Of those who drowned in a boating accident, the vast majority weren't wearing a life jacket.[202] (This is no surprise, as it should be challenging to drown while wearing a device specifically designed to prevent drowning; presumably the approximately ten percent who drowned anyway had been knocked unconscious or had suffered other contributing injuries.) Here again alcohol plays a role: among men who were powerboating, those who drank were significantly less likely to wear life jackets.[†] [203]

**Poor behavior on the silver screen**

Popular culture doesn't help. In an analysis of popular G- and PG-rated movies, only 17 percent of characters depicted on boats wore Personal Flotation Devices (PFDs), and the gender differences in the real world were reflected: a third of females wore life jackets, compared with only 9 percent of males.[204]

Of course, the only real question we'd like answered as parents is how to prevent our teens from behaving stupidly near the water when we aren't there to yell at them. Unfortunately, there's been very little research about how to prevent adolescents from drowning.[205] Logically, swimming lessons should help, and the World Health Organization suggests this approach, but

* 33% of men vs. 23% of women said they drank on their last aquatic activity day during the previous month, and men reported an average of >8 drinks compared with >4 drinks for women.[1] These data points are not specific to adolescents, but it seems likely the conclusions would be equivalent in a younger population.

† Among women, there was virtually no difference in life jacket use by drinking: 30% vs 30%

specifies that lessons need to go beyond just basic strokes, and include instruction in how to identify and avoid rocks, currents, and dangerous weather, and how to escape from rip tides.[206]

If you've missed the boat on convincing junior to take swimming lessons, perhaps in the future swimwear innovation will come to the rescue: a buoyant swimsuit is supposedly in the works.[207] In the meantime, the Wingman, approved by the US Coastguard, is a slimmer life jacket which has a cord to pull which inflates, although it will set you back $199.[208] If you want to be really popular with your teenagers, buy them a pair of Dolfinus swim shorts (https://dolfinus.com/), guaranteed to make them both look and float like a walrus. Apologies, like a dolphin.

## Extreme sports

> The inaugural X Games, the new "Olympics" for extreme sports, were held during the summer of 1995. By 2019, the Games were attracting a crowd of 117,000, with more than 17 million video views.[209]
>
> Highs: August 2019: Mitchie Brusco becomes the first person to nail a 1260 in skateboarding history, making three and a half rotations before landing the move.[210]
>
> Lows: January 2015: Cameron Norton crashes during a freestyle event, landing face first in the snow with his 450-pound snowmobile on top of him.[*211]

Certain teens are inexorably drawn to the allure of extreme sports. While most adolescents are sensible and have no interest in risking their lives, a small subset can't seem to live without a constant adrenaline rush. Some people, like the extraordinary free climber Alex Honnold of *Free Solo* fame, have brains that don't even appear to register the risk.[212]

The explanation lies in their genes. 'Sensation seeking,' the scientific term for risk taking, is highly heritable,[213] and researchers have even isolated a gene associated with it.[214] So if you or your partner were adrenalin junkies

* Name of protagonist has been changed for privacy purposes.

in your youth, chances are your teen may be too. Those whose children prefer practicing the violin or curling up at home with a novel can skip this section. But if your son or daughter is constantly pestering you to go bungee jumping, read on.

There is no single credible source that compares the risks of various extreme sports, although many spurious sources with no citations can be found scattered across the internet. The chart below, again the first of its kind, has been compiled based on data from various national associations and academic publications.*

**An extreme sports primer**

Here's a quick primer for those who aren't familiar with some of the activities in the following chart:

- "Hang gliders have solid wing structures utilizing an aluminum frame to create a V-shaped wing that resembles a stealth bomber. Due to their heavier weight, hang gliders tend to have slightly faster flying speeds but need more winds to stay aloft."[215]
- "Paragliders have soft wing structures (no internal frame) that once inflated have an elliptical shape. Paragliders typically have slower flying speeds, but since the pilot is suspended from the wing, it's possible to use pendular momentum to perform some stunning air maneuvers (aerobatics)."[216]
- Base jumping is the practice of jumping off a fixed object such as a building, radio mast, bridge, or cliff, wearing a parachute.[217]

Here are the death rates for the most common extreme sports (drum roll please):† [218]

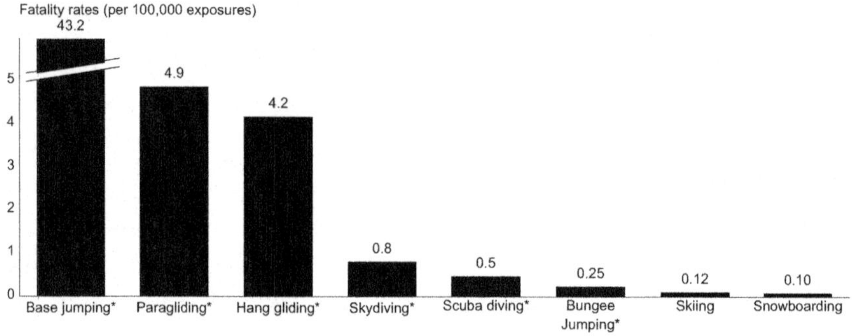


* For all the gory details on why certain sports have been included or excluded, and how the calculations have been made, please refer to Appendix V.

† Data for participants of all ages, not specific to adolescents; Exposure for base jumping, paragliding, hang gliding, skydiving and bungee jumping per jump; for scuba diving per dive; and for skiing and snowboarding per day

Base jumping is without question the most dangerous activity by far, to the point where the chart had to be truncated to avoid dwarfing most of the other bars into invisibility. When contrasted with base jumping, paragliding and hang gliding look positively harmless.

Yet even the comparatively innocuous scuba diving is considered by some to be too dangerous for teens. For example, a diving safety coordinator who has authored more than 100 scuba related articles[219] has a presentation entitled "Why I Do NOT Train Kids," with extensive reasoning for why he won't train anyone under age 18 due to the risks involved. His concluding rule of thumb: "Parents should wait until they trust their child to drive the family's most expensive automobile to the dive-training site."[220]

When it comes to skiing and snowboarding, not all teens are at equal risk; most tragedies on the slopes involve above-average skiers and snowboarders travelling at high speed on the edges of intermediate trails.[221] There are now various devices designed to protect skiers from injury, including helmets and back protectors, but their benefits unfortunately haven't been extensively researched,[222] although helmets likely do prevent head injuries on the slopes.[223]

One option for steering teens away from hazardous activities would be to find them less risky sources of adrenalin rush,[224] like indoor skydiving in a wind tunnel. Someday, when virtual reality versions of racecar driving or rock climbing are more ubiquitous, the problem may be partially solved.[225] In the meantime, there's always the vomit-inducing rides at the amusement park.

## *Sports and extracurricular pursuits*

> A correction officer has found former Patriots tight end Aaron Hernandez hanging from a bedsheet in his prison cell. The notorious football player had just been found not guilty of a double homicide, so his suicide was a shock... A postmortem brain scan revealed that Hernandez had been suffering from the degenerative brain disease chronic traumatic encephalopathy (CTE)...Following the diagnosis, Hernandez's family filed a $20 million lawsuit against the New England Patriots and the NFL."[226]

> "We [The National Federation of State High School Associations] are encouraged that the decline in high school football has slowed due, in part, to our efforts in reducing the risk of injury in the sport. We have attempted to assure student-athletes and their parents that thanks to the concussion protocols and rules in place in every state in the country, the sport of football is as safe as it ever has been."[227]

Should you let your child play football? It's not an easy decision. Well-publicized examples like the death of Aaron Hernandez would make any parent pause. Yet football is woven into the fabric of life across many American communities, and telling your son the star quarterback that he's not allowed back on the field would not make you very popular with the school at large, the coach, or the team, not to mention the athlete himself.

The media may have fixated on the dangers of football recently, but that doesn't necessarily mean it's the single sport worth worrying about. How do the risks of various sports and activities compare, and which are actually dangerous? Here, again, is a question which no one has ever answered satisfactorily (see box).

**Calculating risk**

Many websites and academic studies have cobbled together statistics on the risks of pursuing sports and other physical activities, but typically for a limited subset of sports, and on a single dimension like concussions. To answer the question properly, it's possible to combine information from two sources: government data on injuries associated with using different types of sports equipment, and a large survey that provides detailed information on how Americans, including teens, spend their time. We can then calculate a risk per hour for various activities.[*] [228]

Here are two charts illustrating the risks from various sports and physical activities. The first shows hospitalizations, the most serious category of injury:[†] [229]

---

* The two data sources don't match up perfectly, so some activities are ambiguous or fall through the cracks entirely. For example, the time-use survey has a single category for time spent playing "hockey," while injuries are more helpfully broken into ice, field, and street hockey; our combined "hockey" figure may therefore underestimate the risk of ice hockey. Similarly, we know the number of injuries from skateboards, but this activity is completely missing from the time-use survey. (There are sources which could tell us the approximate number of people participating in skateboarding,[1] but it's hard to estimate number of hours they spend, so this wouldn't be directly comparable.)

† In both charts, skiing, snowboarding, ice skating and skateboarding unfortunately not included, as the source for injuries buckets "fall involving ice skates, skis, roller skates or skateboards' into one category, and the time use survey buckets "skiing, ice skating, snowboarding" together and has no skateboarding category; time use survey doesn't have lacrosse, handball, or roller skating; Water sports includes swimming, surfing, diving, water skiing, and playing water polo; racquet sports include tennis, table tennis, badminton, squash; hockey includes ice, field and street hockey.

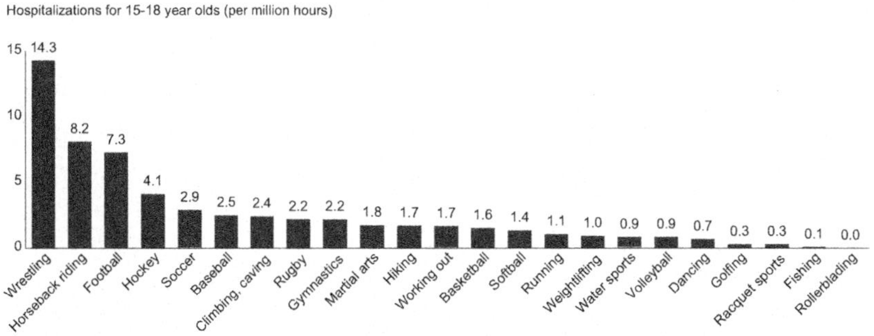


This second chart shows the more common cases of emergency room visits where the patient is treated and then sent home.* The lines indicate the number of concussions:† [230]

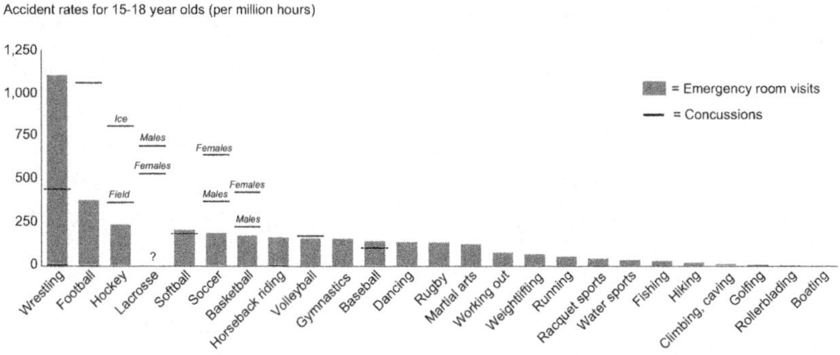


Surprisingly, it's wrestling that has the worst track record when it comes to both hospitalizations and ER visits. Horseback riding injuries also tend to be dramatic. But football is a close third when it comes to the risk of hospitalization, and second with regard to ER visits; it also has the highest rate of concussion. So when it comes to the most commonly played sports, football is indeed the one to worry about.‡ [231]

Concussions are common: 15 percent of American teens have had at least one concussion over the prior year from a physical activity.[232] These injuries are concerning as their impacts may be cumulative and lasting. Most

* The number of hospitalizations are so small by comparison, they wouldn't even show if they were also included on this chart.

† Where there is no line for concussion, it means no information was available. Other sports known to be associated with concussions include rugby, karate, horse riding, and parachuting.[1]

‡ Concussion, otherwise known as mild traumatic brain injury (MTBI), is not a well-defined term; for example, one review found that among approximately 100 studies on concussion, more than 50 different definitions of the term were used.[1] Some academics have even suggested that we scrap the term entirely, and instead acknowledge that there's a wide spectrum of traumatic brain injuries.[2] For better or worse, most sources of information still use the term, however undefined it may be.

teens with a brain injury recover within three months, but up to a third continue to have symptoms past 6 months,[233] and in 10 to 20 percent of cases, symptoms can persist for months or even years.[234] And even more minor head injuries can unfortunately have ramifications (see box).

**The risks of mild head injuries**

One study followed two groups of varsity-level college athletes: those playing contact sports (football, ice hockey) versus non-contact sports (track, crew, cross-country skiing). A higher percentage of contact sport athletes performed poorly on a test of verbal learning and memory, and their poor performance was correlated with head impact over the last week of the season and cumulatively over the course of the season.[235] There can be longer-term consequences as well: concussions are a risk factor for later dementia, Parkinson's disease, and amyotrophic lateral sclerosis (ALS), also known as Lou Gehrig's disease, a degenerative disease causing loss of muscle control.[236]

Chronic traumatic encephalopathy (CTE), the condition afflicting Aaron Hernandez, can only be diagnosed after death with an autopsy, so not enough is yet known about it. The largest study to date of 85 patients with repetitive concussions (64 athletes and 21 military veterans) found evidence of CTE in 80 percent of them.[237] CTE has been reported in professional boxers, football players, wrestlers and soccer players. Unfortunately, it's still unclear how severe the head injuries need to be or how often they need to occur to cause CTE,[238] or even whether a single particularly traumatic injury on its own can cause the disease.[239]

**In case of a concussion**

If you think your child might have a concussion, check this simple list of symptoms,* [240] or download this more detailed diagnostic sheet designed for nonphysicians on the sidelines of an athletic event.† [241]

---

* Observed:

- Can't recall events prior to or after a hit or fall
- Appears dazed or stunned
- Forgets an instruction, is confused about an assignment or position, or is unsure of the game, score, or opponent
- Moves clumsily
- Answers questions slowly
- Loses consciousness (even briefly)
- Shows mood, behavior, or personality changes

Reported:

- Headache or "pressure" in head
- Nausea or vomiting
- Balance problems or dizziness, or double or blurry vision
- Bothered by light or noise
- Feeling sluggish, hazy, foggy, or groggy
- Confusion, or concentration or memory problems
- Just not "feeling right," or "feeling down"

† Available at https://kuscholarworks.ku.edu/bitstream/handle/1808/15183/Ackley_1997.pdf?sequence=1 . Score is out of 30; average score for those who are healthy is 26; average score for those with a concussion is 21-22.

It's unclear if it's worth bringing your child in for a brain scan after a concussion,* [242] but you should definitely insist your child takes time off afterwards. A recent concussion can make any subsequent head injuries more severe,[243] and the risk of a repeat concussion is particularly high in the first 10 days after an initial concussion.[244] Although we still don't know how long it takes for the brain to recover,[245] experts suggest that kids shouldn't go back to sports until they are completely symptom-free.[246]

Just ask Kevin Pearce, who at 22 was a favorite to win a medal in snowboarding in the 2010 Winter Olympics in Vancouver, when a near-fatal injury derailed his life:

> About ten days before my accident, I sustained a bad concussion while trying to land a cab double cork. I didn't feel right after that, but I wasn't aware of the danger of potentially hitting my head again so soon after legitimately injuring my brain. I wouldn't have listened, anyway. I was that confident. I was that stupid. Looking back on it now, my brain was broken before I dropped into the pipe in Park City that morning. When I under-rotated and slammed my head on the bottom of the pipe just above my left eye, my brain suffered a massive trauma, and the swelling almost killed me. I don't remember the next 32 days. I had to relearn how to walk, I had to relearn how to talk. [Pearce was hospitalized for five months.] Had I paid attention to the warning signs, everything that happened to me might have been avoided."[247]

**The jury is out on helmets**

If your child is a fearless snowboarder like Kevin, is a helmet the solution? Helmets definitely reduce the risk of skull fractures and facial injuries in sports, but it's less clear whether they prevent concussions.[248] The answer is probably yes for rugby,[249] but it's more difficult to tell for soccer.[250] Headgear does decrease the force of the ball on impact, and one study in Canada found helmets lowered the risk for concussion. But it's also possible that wearing head protection could backfire by giving teenagers a false sense of security, causing them to pursue their sport more aggressively.[251]

---

* One review insists that even in cases of mild concussion, it's difficult to be sure the patient is fine without neuroimaging, and many patients may be falsely reassured and sent home when in fact they could have benefited from further treatment.[1] But a guideline from the American Academy of Neurology disagrees, saying it's not yet clear that interventions can actually enhance recovery or reduce the chances of long-term problems after a concussion.[2]

Other sport-related injuries can also have long-term repercussions. For example, if your teen ends up with a knee or ankle injury, this can cause osteoarthritis (painful joints) later in life.[252] More than 50 percent of those with a torn meniscus or anterior cruciate ligament (ACL) will eventually develop knee osteoarthritis, compared with 5 percent of those uninjured.[253] Fortunately, training routines designed to prevent injuries can protect kids from hurting themselves without banning them from the physical activities that are so beneficial for their overall health (see box).

**Injury prevention routines do work**

Strength training regimes have been shown to halve the number of injuries among male soccer players,[254] runners,[255] and handball players,[256] and reduce the risk of ACL injury in female basketball, football, volleyball, and team handball athletes.[257] One arthritis expert has suggested that a 10–20 minute injury prevention routine incorporated into training could substantially reduce the number of injuries and therefore future arthritis sufferers.[258] And there's robust evidence that training programs focused on muscle control, balance, coordination, flexibility, and leg strengthening can reduce the risk of overuse injuries.* [259] [260]

Training on ankle disks, also called wobble boards, could also be a beneficial addition to your teen's workout.[261] Female handball players who trained on one were less likely to injure themselves,[262] and such training can prevent ankle sprains in soccer players with previous ankle problems.[263] Prophylactic knee braces also reduce the risk of knee injuries for football players playing defensive positions,[264] and those who have already sprained their ankles can benefit from wearing ankle supports, which reduce the risk of future sprains.† [265] [266]

**Myth: stretching**

Most of us assume that stretching is an important part of any exercise routine to help prevent injuries, but in fact, there isn't much evidence that stretching provides any benefits beyond staying limber.[267] Two studies of stretching in runners[268] and army recruits[269] both failed to find any protective effects, and a systematic review found stretching didn't prevent stress fractures or other leg injuries.[270]

* If you want some inspiration – for example, workouts – soccer's international governing body, the Federation International Football Association (FIFA), has developed a strength training program for players 11+,[1] which has been estimated to reduce injuries by 35% when followed at least 1.5 times per week. (A manual, poster, and cards are available for free at www.yrsa.ca/fifa-11.html).[2] The International Olympic Committee has launched a free app called 'Get Set - Train Smarter,' which has exercises tailored for 30 different summer sports, with levels that become more difficult and challenging as you progress.[3] The American Academy of Pediatrics also sells a "Home Strength Training for Young Athletes" DVD and Flash Cards (https://shop.aap.org/home-strength-training-for-young-athletes-dvd-and-flash-cards/). And a Mayo Clinic physician recommends using padded gymnastics gyms for parkour, a pursuit which involves running, climbing and vaulting obstacles.[4]

† Shock-absorbing insoles have been shown to prevent stress fractures during military training, but there's insufficient evidence that they help in sports more generally, and it's not clear what's the best design to use.[1] [2]

Thus far we've focused on preventing acute injuries, but there's another important category: injuries caused over time by repetitive stress. There's lots of evidence that the more time adolescents spend each week playing a single sport, the more likely they are to injure themselves.[271] Here are the results from one large study in Canada, which shows that the risk of injury goes up relentlessly with the number of hours played: [272]

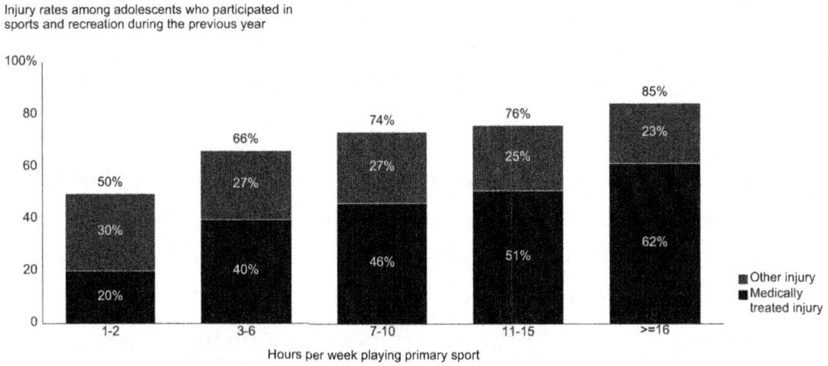


Similarly, an analysis of 28,000 tennis matches played across US super national tournaments found the medical withdrawal rate for adolescent players was twice as high in their fifth match or greater versus their first four matches.[273] Kids may be in peak heath, but even their bodies have a breaking point.

**More on overdoing it**

Many more studies have documented the downsides of too much play.[274] For example, young athletes participating in more hours of a single sport per week than their age in years, or who spend twice as many hours doing organized sports versus free time have almost double the odds of developing a serious overuse injury.[275] And girls who do more than 16 hours per week of moderate or vigorous activity have almost twice the risk of developing a stress fracture.[276]

**The particular hazards of baseball**

When it comes to repetitive stress injuries, baseball is particularly notorious,[277] to the point where the term 'Little League elbow' has entered the vernacular. One study found that young pitchers who played more than 100 innings per year were 3.5 times more likely to be injured than others with less intense schedules,[278] and another study found pitching often despite arm fatigue increased the risk of injury a whopping 36 times.[279] As a result, both the National Athletic Trainers' Association[280] and the American Journal of Sports Medicine[281] have laid out very specific limits for teen pitchers, which are worth checking out if you have a budding Pedro Martínez in your home.

As a result, the National Athletic Trainers' Association has gone on record with guidelines designed to rein in the hyper-competitive tendencies of certain parents, coaches, and adolescents (see box).

**National Athletic Trainers' Association guidelines**
"Pediatric athletes should be encouraged to participate in multiple sports and recreational activities throughout the year; should take time off between sport seasons and 2–3 nonconsecutive months away from a specific sport if they participate in that sport year round; should have at least one to two days off per week from competitive practices, competitions, and sport-specific training; and should avoid practices or games (or both) more than five days per week."[282]

We'll discuss the qualities that do make a difference in achieving sporting greatness in a later chapter on achievement; in the meantime, if your teen has an obsession with one particular sport, keep your eye out for insidious aches and pains that won't go away, and take them seriously.

If this discussion of the risks of sports persuades you to steer your adolescent away from physical activities in favor of needlepoint, a later chapter on health is there to change your mind. There will always be trade-offs inherent in any pursuit; but physical activity is a critical component of life, both for the passionate athletes and the wallflowers in school gym class. Here's a closing thought from a university student and keen football player who has wrestled with the trade-offs:

> This summer, I interned in a Brain Injury Research Lab, and worked extensively in the ER attempting to recruit patients for our ongoing studies. The number and nature of injuries I've seen from sports does not come anywhere near the injuries from car crashes, bike crashes or even people tripping and falling. This has reassured me that the benefits of sports do in fact outweigh the risks. I decided to attend college in hopes of becoming a physician, not an NFL athlete, so I understand the importance of maintaining a healthy brain. It is actually quite crucial for succeeding in school and doing well on the upcoming MCAT. But I have yet to consider quitting football simply because of a possible injury. I have experienced so many positive benefits from football that I could not imagine life without it.[283]

## *Take-aways*

All parents want to keep their children safe. But as the parents of the 'Bubble Boy' would attest,[284] perfect safety comes at too high a cost, and letting your child experience life to the fullest inevitably involves accepting some minimal level of risk. In the words of one teacher and author, "Making the decision to have a child is to decide forever to have your heart go walking around outside your body."[285] Of course, this doesn't absolve you of the responsibility for insisting your surly detached cardiac organ wears a helmet.

### KEY PARENTING TAKE-AWAYS:

Cars:

1. Draft a formal written contract for your teen to sign, with rules including no peers as passengers, no driving after dark, mandatory seatbelts even for short journeys, no texting, calling, eating or music while driving, and no driving under the influence of alcohol, marijuana or other drugs
2. Enforce severe consequences for breaking the contract (e.g. revoke driving privileges)
3. Assume parties will involve alcohol and plan transportation accordingly
4. Install telematics in the vehicle to remotely monitor your teen's driving behavior

Motorcycles:

5. Say no to motorcycles
6. If your teen attempts to negotiate, listen, reflect, keep cool, present a united front with your spouse, and offer the evidence from this book

Suicide:

7. Talk openly with your teen about suicide to reduce the stigma, although shield them from real-life examples where possible to avoid the 'contagion effect'
8. For depressed adolescents, seek professional treatment, ideally cognitive behavioral therapy (CBT)
9. If you're concerned, 'suicide-proof' your house (keep guns unloaded under lock and key and lock ammunition in a separate location; lock your medicine cabinet, don't hoard significant quantities of any single item, and throw unneeded medicines away). Program a helpline number, e.g., the National Suicide Prevention Lifeline (800-273-8255, or 988), into your teen's phone

Pedestrians:

10. Discuss basic pedestrian safety with your teen: obeying the lights, only crossing at designated locations, looking both ways, and never texting or listening to music when crossing the street

Bicycles:

11. Allow your teen to select a helmet
12. Enforce severe consequences for bicycling without it (e.g. revoke bicycling privileges)

All-terrain vehicles (ATVs):

13. Say no to ATVs for kids under 16
14. For kids 16 and older with a legitimate need to use an ATV, draft a formal written contract for your teen to sign, with rules including no peers as passengers, no driving after dark, no driving on roads, no driving under the influence, and mandatory helmets
15. Enforce severe consequences for breaking the contract (e.g. revoke driving privileges)

Homicide:

16. If your neighborhood suffers from gang violence and moving is not an option, ensure your teen is aware that members of gangs suffer more violence than non-members

Drowning:

17. It's never too late to sign your child up for swimming lessons
18. Ensure the lessons include instruction in natural water safety, e.g., how to identify and avoid rocks, currents, and dangerous weather, and escape from rip tides

Extreme sports:

19. Say no to base jumping
20. For teens who are drawn to extreme sports, find them less risky sources of adrenalin rush, like wind tunnel skydiving

Sports and extracurricular pursuits:

21. Kids with concussions shouldn't return to sports until completely symptom-free
22. Supplement your child's athletic training with a strength training program to reduce the risk of injury*
23. Encourage your teen to participate in multiple pursuits and avoid spending more than five days per week on a single sport to avoid overuse injury

---

* E.g., from FIFA (www.yrsa.ca/fifa-11.html) the International Olympic Committee ('Get Set - Train Smarter' app), or the American Academy of Pediatrics (https://shop.aap.org/home-strength-training-for-young-athletes-dvd-and-flash-cards/).

# 4. VICTIMIZATION

## Discuss dominant males

Two men follow a waitress home from work down deserted streets. They try to make small talk and put her at ease, but their intentions soon become clear. She runs, but they catch up, strike her in frustration and knock her unconscious. Fortunately, a shy restaurant busboy materializes just in time to ward off her attackers.

For many women who were coming of age in the 1990s, this scene from the movie *Untamed Heart* encapsulates their worst fears. Although many films feature similarly harrowing encounters, it's the portrayal of the aftermath of the assault that rings particularly true. It takes a long time for the waitress to recover from her ordeal, and she's still visibly shaken even when a friend lightly touches her a week later.[1] This is consistent with real life. Young women fear rape more than any other offense, including murder, assault and robbery.[2] Tragically, sexual assault is particularly rampant in the US, where the number of rape incidents reported to the police per 10,000 citizens is 27, versus 13 in Mexico and 1.7 in Canada.[3]

A discussion of sexual assault, as uncomfortable as it may be, needs to feature prominently in this book because the risk of rape is highest in high school. According to the FBI, 15 is the most common age of victims, and the risk for both sexes increases dramatically when kids reach puberty and declines dramatically in adulthood. (Once people reach middle age, their risk of sexual assault is miniscule.)[4] As a result, by twelfth grade, 14 percent of girls and 5 percent of boys have been physically forced to have sexual intercourse when they did not want to.[5]

**It's not just a girl thing**

It's worth pausing to clarify that while girls are more likely than boys to experience sexual assault, adolescents of both sexes are at risk; the experience of the 5 percent of males who have been assaulted is very real and deserves attention. The majority of the research in this field has focused on scenarios involving victimization of women and girls. Fortunately, the key take-aways can often be equally applied to protecting our sons.

On the flip side, the majority of perpetrators of sexual assault are male. Of all sexual assault incidents recorded in the National Crime Victimization Survey from 2008 to 2016 involving a single perpetrator, 96 percent were male. Similarly, almost all of the research on resisting assault is based on situations involving male perpetrators. Unforutunately, those findings might not apply to the 4 percent of situations with a female aggressor, about which very little is known.

As they begin to spend more time outside the house with friends, there are obviously more opportunities for teenagers to end up in compromising situations. But sex offenders of all ages also prefer young victims.[6] For example, one analysis of the behavior of robbers who had broken into a home found that these criminals were most likely to sexually assault women 15–29 years old.[7] The evidence is incontrovertible: rapists target young, fertile females.

Many girls and women intuitively grasp that they're at risk, and adopt cautious behaviors like checking in the back seat of their car; avoiding underground parking lots at night; walking with keys between their fingers; and carrying mace, bear spray, whistles, etc.[8] All of these are sensible precautions for preventing assault by a stranger. The problem is, strangers aren't typically the problem. Here's a chart, the first of its kind, showing a breakdown of who assaults adolescent girls:[*9]

* Dataset includes both attempts to attack and completed attacks; Only includes responses of "Severely" to the question "How distressing was being a victim of this crime to you?"; represents risk in a single year; analysis of incidents from 2009-2016, scaled up to represent population; missing data allocated proportionally

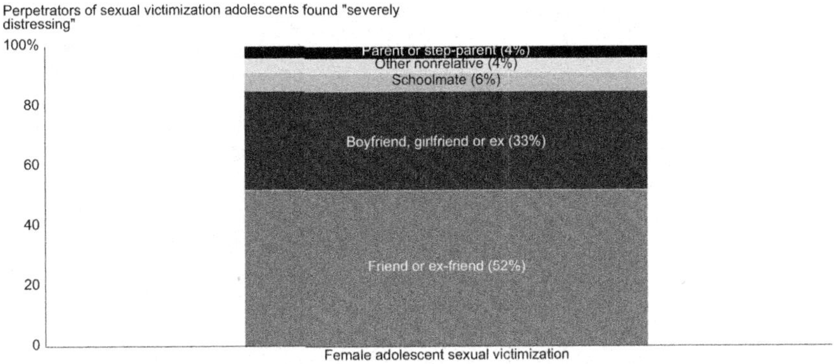


It's friends, significant others, classmates: people the girl knew well beforehand. And these findings have been confirmed by other studies.[10] For example, a survey of college women found that 9 in 10 knew their attacker, and the assault typically occurred when they were alone with the man at night in the privacy of a residence.[11]

This is not to imply that it's safe to wander around alone on dark streets at night. The reason the rate of assault by strangers is low is probably precisely because teens are on their guard when out and about, carrying their keys between their fingers. But conversely, it doesn't seem to occur to most teens to take precautions with males they know.[12]

**The dangers of crowds**

At venues like music concerts and festivals where teens are surrounded by drunken strangers, many rightly feel wary.[13] In one survey of music fans in the Chicago area, 92 percent of women said they'd experienced some type of harassment at a concert,[14] and another survey of UK music festival-goers found that 30 percent of females had experienced unwanted sexual behavior, and 17 percent had been sexually assaulted.[15] These could be useful stats to have on hand if your child is negotiating to attend a concert.

A shockingly high percentage of men are potential rapists. When college students from across North America were asked whether they personally would commit a rape if they could be assured of not being caught and punished, an average of 35 percent admitted they would.[16] This unacceptable result requires urgent societal intervention.

**What doesn't work**

Attempts to educate young people about the consequences of sexual assault, to change social norms, or to encourage bystander intervention haven't yet had an effect on the prevalence of rape.[17] Bystander intervention, while well-meaning, is particularly ineffective as a strategy, given that less than a fifth of assaults have a bystander present,[18] since very few rapes occur in public places:[*19]

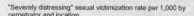

"Severely distressing" sexual victimization rate per 1,000 by perpetrator and location

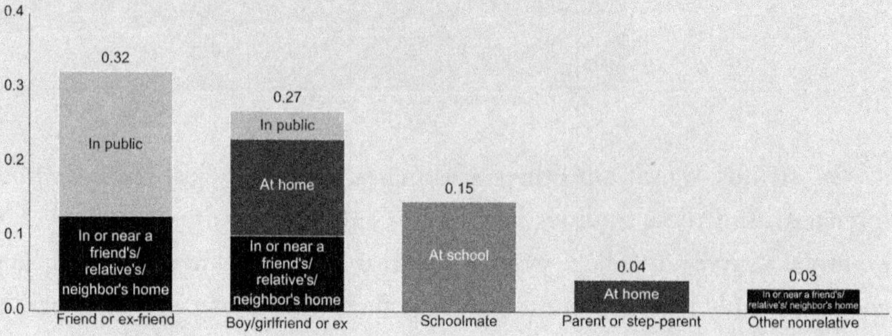


Educating our boys about the importance of respecting women's sexual integrity has never been more important, so although the definitive manual for how best to do so hasn't yet been written,[20] we should all be broaching this topic with our sons.

Thus far, the only approach that has been proven to reduce sexual violence is educating and training women themselves.[21] A variety of initiatives, many on college campuses, have taught women self-defense or assertiveness, and found these women were subsequently less likely than those without the training to be raped.[22]

**You go, girl!**

After taking a 30-hour self-defense course, only 12 percent of students reported sexual victimization over the following year, versus 31 percent of students who hadn't taken the course; and not a single self-defense student reported being raped, versus 2.8 percent of the students in comparison classes.[23] In another example, over half the girls who had received self-defense training reported having used the skills to avert sexual assault in the year after the training.[24]

* Dataset includes both attempts to attack and completed attacks; Only includes responses of "Severely" to the question "How distressing was being a victim of this crime to you?"; represents risk in a single year; analysis of incidents from 2009-2016, scaled up to represent population; missing data allocated proportionally

The 12 hour Enhanced Assess, Acknowledge, Act (EAAA)/Flip the Script™ Sexual Assault Resistance Program is the gold standard,[25] and has been shown to reduce both rape and attempted rape.[26] Unfortunately, it's not available self-serve, so one option would be to encourage your daughter's school to offer the program; the training materials are available online.[*] [27]

**Myth: Girls need to say no more clearly**

Many women and girls suffer under the misimpression that sexual aggression is their fault for having failed to say 'no' more clearly. It's common for women to report that they find it difficult to refuse unwanted sex, and victims of sexual assault often report feeling that they had 'failed to make their refusal sufficiently clear' or report that they 'lacked effective refusal skills'.[28] Yet this emphasis on the need for better communication is likely a red herring.

Saying no directly to anything is not normal conversational practice. Young women who don't explicitly use the word 'no', but who refuse in other more roundabout ways, are using well-recognized conversational patterns.[29] In fact, men can read such social cues perfectly well,[30] but troublingly, they sometimes choose to disregard them.[31]

Nevertheless, there is no harm in providing your daughter with a script to elegantly say no to a boyfriend without making him feel rejected. According to one study, saying, "I really care about you, but I want to wait until the relationship is stronger" can get an upstanding young man to stop his advances, while still having a positive effect on the relationship.[32]

One of the creators of the program has explained that the most important component of the training involves teaching women and girls how to avoid unwanted sexual behaviors from males they know.[33] With an acquaintance or potential date, the key is encouraging teens to look for danger cues. According to a study which interviewed women who had been attacked, those who ultimately avoided rape were able to perceive danger from ambiguous clues earlier, and so got themselves out of harm's way before it was too late.[34]

Danger cues fall into two categories: environmental and behavioral. Here is the list of the top environmental cues:[35]

- Isolation
- Indoor locations, including vehicles
- Alcohol

The first two should be self-explanatory. Yet the same teens who would hesitate to walk alone after dark often don't think twice about following a male friend into his house without checking if anyone else is home; visiting

* Available at: http://sarecentre.org/faqs.php

his dorm room without ascertaining if anyone else down the hall is in earshot; or getting into his car. When it comes to vehicles, current social norms suggest that men should chivalrously drive the car, but when a man is in control of the wheel, he has the power to take his passenger somewhere isolated without consent.

Alcohol can also be a dangerous addition to social scenarios, as it can warp the judgement of the potential victim, perpetrator, or both. As portrayed in the troubling movie *Promising Young Woman*, a potential victim will tend to feel more relaxed and will be less alert to danger signals when drinking. It's no surprise, then, that in one study of over 1,000 rape cases, more than a third of victims were found to have had alcohol circulating in their systems.[36]

**The roofie red herring**

Despite all the media scare headlines about 'roofies,'* only 0.5 percent of sexual assault victims in one study had been exposed to a low to moderate dose of this drug.† Although 'date rape drugs' sound scary, in reality, perpetrators have no need to resort to drugging their victims when they're surrounded by peers who are voluntarily drinking themselves silly.

In this case, the stereotypic advice given to teens about designating a non-drinker in the group makes good sense: teens who plans to drink at a party should probably consider enlisting a sober buddy to take responsibility for ensuring no one tries to isolate and control them, in addition to handling the drive home.

**Drunken aggression**

Men are far less likely to respect sexual boundaries when intoxicated. For example, male college students who consumed alcohol and then listened to a date rape scenario took significantly longer to determine that the male protagonist should refrain from attempting further sexual contact than their sober peers.[37] And in an anonymous survey of university men, a quarter of whom had actually committed a sexual assault, the more alcohol men drank, the more frequently they had misperceived women's sexual intentions, and the more frequently they had committed assault.[38]

Turning to the second category of danger cues, there are also behaviors which are warning signs, including:[39]

* otherwise known as Rohypnol or flunitrazepam

† It's also technically possible these individuals had been exposed via anesthesia for a recent medical procedure rather than as a result of a rape attempt, given the drug can linger in the body for up to a month.

- Insisting on paying
- Showing a need for power and control — interrupting people, acting competitive, using intimidating body language
- Having a quick temper; blaming others when things go wrong
- Using threats in displays of anger; using violence in borderline situations; justifying violence
- Showing feelings of sexual entitlement (e.g. inappropriate touching or comments)
- Persisting verbally and/or physically

If a male persists with unwanted advances and your teen hasn't been paralyzed by fear (a common reaction called 'tonic immobility,' discussed further in the 'Dig Deeper' section), the best strategy is to run away if possible and verbally and even physically resist. One study found the response most likely to have an effect was clearly informing the attacker that he was committing rape and threatening to call the police.[40] In another study, those who avoided acquaintance rape were most likely to have run away and screamed.[41] One informative study even surveyed violent men who had committed or attempted rape, who suggested the following strategies to potential victims: "label the situation as rape and threaten to call the police; cry, plead, and ask God to help; claim to have herpes; scream; yell 'No'; and use physical violence such as kneeing, biting, or kicking."[42] What these suggestions all have in common is active resistance.[*] [43]

Some victims hesitate to resist, for fear that fighting back could increase their risk of being hurt.[44] This is a missed opportunity.[45] For example, one analysis of approximately 700 rapes and 1,300 sexual assaults concluded that fighting back significantly reduced the chance of rape and didn't significantly increase the risk of serious injury.[46] However, not all forms of resistance are equal. Half the victims who resisted only wrestled ineffectively with their attacker, and none attempted to kick, gouge their attacker's eyes, or use an object as a weapon. But the small number of victims who hit their assailant all succeeded in warding him off.[47] There are only advantages from forcefully resisting (see box).[48]

---

* Voluntary or involuntary physiological responses (such as vomiting, urinating, or defecating), have not been proven to be effective in deterring an assault: "Although anecdotal cases of rape avoidance have been reported when women have such physiological responses, this type of resistance has not been examined systematically in rape avoidance studies."[i]

**Reasons to resist**

First are the physical implications: sexual assaults can cause injuries, increase the risk of chronic medical conditions, cause pregnancy, and spread sexually transmitted diseases:[49] the risk of acquiring an STD as a result of rape is estimated to be 5 to 10 percent.[50] The second rationale is emotional: women who are raped are more likely to suffer from depression, anxiety, suicidal thoughts and posttraumatic stress disorder (PTSD) than women who avoided the rape.[51] And finally, even if the assault takes place, physical evidence of resistance can increase the likelihood of successful prosecution if your teen wants to pursue charges.[52]

Consistent with this research, here is the advice offered by the EAAA training: "Yell, kick, bite, punch. The more you do, the less likely he is going to be able to complete the rape… If your attacker straddles your hips and holds down your arms with your hands by your ears, turn your head to the side, place your feet to buttocks and thrust your hip up while sweeping your arms down by your hips, all in one fluid motion. (The arms sweeping down look like a snow-angel motion.) The attacker will be thrown forward, off of you, possibly into a headboard."[53]

**Crazy gadgets**

In the future, it's possible that technological solutions could help ward off sexual assault. Many crazy gadgets have been designed to prevent rape, although we have no idea if they are effective. Undercover Colors is a nail polish that changes color upon contact with a drink that has Xanax, Rohypnol, or GHB in it. Go Guarded is a heavy-duty plastic serrated-edge weapon worn on a finger,[54] and the Invi bracelet can be activated to release a foul smell to deter aggressors.[55] Finally there are devices designed to block assault; examples include Safe Shorts,[56] the Anti-rape Bra,[57] the Killer tampon,[58] and the Rape-aXe, which features rows of jagged hooks designed to attach to a man's penis which can only be removed by a doctor.[59] These devices unsurprisingly suffer from various fundamental drawbacks, making them unlikely to be widely adopted anytime soon.[60]

It may also be worth proactively discussing the topic of assault, so your adolescent would feel more comfortable communicating with you if something happened. Here are two assault descriptions which were posted with the hashtag #WhyIDidntReport:

> "I reported it immediately. My vice-principal asked what I did to provoke it. I didn't tell my mom until 35 years later."

> "The man who raped me threatened to kill me if I went to the police. I believed him."[61]

Our kids may be taller than we are, but that doesn't preclude them from behaving like the children they are when faced with the very real threats posed by the wider world. We can harness their fright by convincing them that we, as adults, are capable of helping them handle the very worst if they are brave enough to confide in us.

**If your teen has been attacked**

We all hope we'll never have the conversation, but if your adolescent informs you about an assault, believe the report and encourage others to believe it, even if the details are fuzzy. It's very common for victims to be confused and seemingly irrational after an attack, which can cause doctors, nurses and police to discount their stories, when in fact they're exhibiting the classic emotional response to such trauma.[62]

If your teen has been attacked, there are urgent practical considerations. To preserve evidence, bring your child immediately to a medical facility and do nothing beyond sitting and waiting, to avoid destroying evidence.[*] [63] Many hospitals have staff who have been specifically trained to handle sexual assault cases; if yours doesn't, you can locate the nearest specialized examiner through the International Association of Forensic Nurses.[†] [64]

It's also critical to seek urgent professional psychological support. Approximately 50 percent of victims experience depression during the first year following an attack,[65] and 30 percent to 65 percent suffer from PTSD symptoms,[66] but appropriate support can help speed recovery.[67] Counselling, therapy and support groups have all been found to be helpful,[68] as has cognitive behavioral therapy.[69] There are also hotlines: 80 percent of users found the National Sexual Assault Telephone Hotline helpful,[‡] [70] and likewise over two thirds of users would recommend the online version, the National Sexual Assault Online Hotline.[§] [71]

If your teen is hesitant to seek help, it's totally understandable, but here are the encouraging words of a survivor:

> "You'd never believe it in the beginning, but talking about it more does help. I'd encourage people to also see a counsellor, because it's not your fault and you shouldn't suffer on your own."[72]

---

* This includes no bathing, changing clothes, douching, urinating, defecating, washing out the mouth, cleaning fingernails, smoking, eating, or drinking.

† www.forensicnurses.org/search/custom.asp?id=2093

‡ 800.656.HOPE (4673)

§ https://hotline.rainn.org/online

# Dig deeper

## *Assault*

"If you hang up on me, you'll die just like your mother!" threatens the figure with the white ghost mask who stalks Neve Campbell's character in the movie *Scream*. This cult classic is meant to be a satire, gleefully portraying various horror clichés. But one element of the film is more realistic than you might think, as we'll see by the end of this section.

When it comes to the threats posed by other humans, life gets more dangerous as kids get older, and not just in the movies. Here's a chart showing the chance a teen will end up in the emergency room as the result of any kind of assault, keeping in mind that ER visits will vastly under-represent the problem:* [73]

Annual emergency room visits for assault (per 1,000)

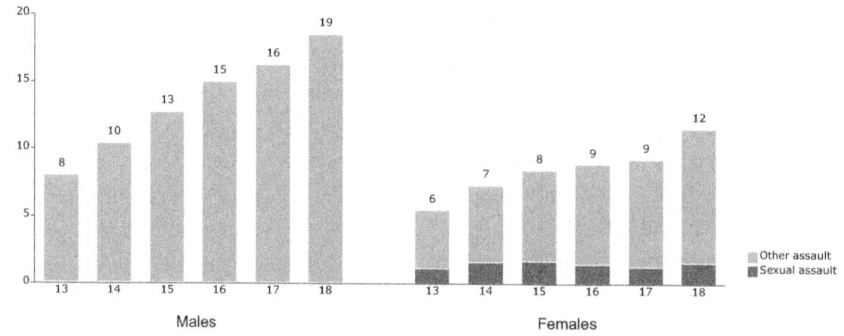


Boys are more likely than girls to be the victims of violence, or at least are more likely to seek medical attention, although sexual violence is disproportionately suffered by girls.

Yet emotional scars can be just as important as physical ones. Here is another chart,† which shows the rate of adolescents experiencing victimization they consider "severely distressing":‡ [74]

* Note: ER visits typically involve a patient being treated and released, so are distinct from and far more common than the hospitalizations shown in the chapter on death and physical harm.

† Data come from the National Crime Victimization Survey, a yearly survey of 160,000 nationally representative Americans run by the US Department of Justice

‡ Verbal includes threat of rape or other sexual assault, threat to kill, or threat of attack; dataset includes both attempts to attack and completed attacks; Only includes responses of "Severely" to the question "How distressing was being a victim of this crime to you?"; represents risk in a single year; analysis of incidents from 2009-2016, scaled up to represent population; missing data allocated proportionally

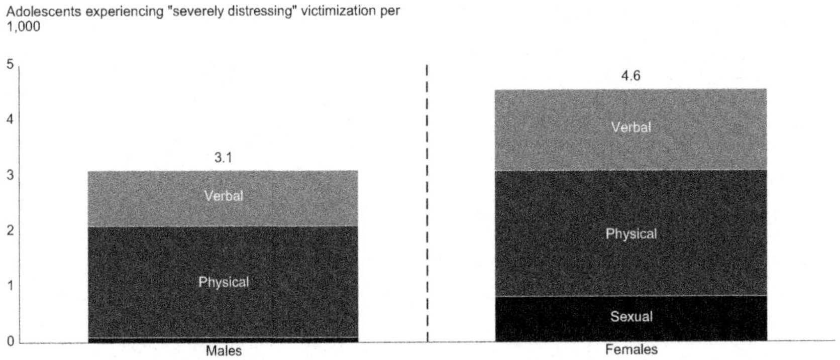


Using this metric, girls are the ones who are more likely to be victimized. (It might seem surprising that 'verbal' aggression could be severely distressing, but sometimes threats of violence can be almost as terrifying as violence itself, as any stalker movie illustrates.)

Who is responsible for victimizing teens? This is another curious information void. The only sources that report assaults by perpetrator bundle together victims from ages 0 to 18,[75] which inevitably shows that parents are the primary sources of violence against children: it's sadly parents who shake their screaming babies and hit their recalcitrant toddlers. Fortunately, combining many years of data allows us to have a large enough sample size to find out who exactly is causing adolescents severe distress:[76]

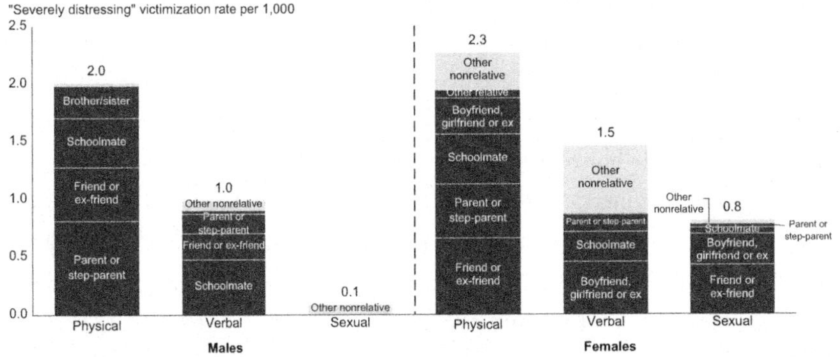


For teens, most aggressors are someone they know, often well. Instead of strangers lurking in bushes, it's the people they encounter in everyday life who are most likely to harm them.

How to protect our teens from these human threats that surround them? There are three broad types of protective strategies: 'avoid,' 'block,' and 'resist.' To bring these to life, let's take the example of a teen who finds herself alone with a friend who is becoming increasingly aggressive. 'Avoid' could involve running away; 'block' could involve retreating into the bathroom and locking the door; while 'resist' could involve physically fighting back to ward off her attacker.

Many common personal protection strategies focus on 'resisting.' It can be comforting to carry around a device like pepper spray in case of unwanted harassment. The problem with resisting is a phenomenon called 'tonic immobility,' a state of involuntary paralysis that can overcome someone facing an imminent threat of any kind. Some people are far more prone to this type of immobilizing reaction than others. For example, one study of victims of maritime and aircraft disasters concluded that in situations of extreme stress, only 10 to 15 percent of people are unimpaired, retaining the ability to stay calm and make rational decisions. 75 percent are overwhelmed by severe stress; their reasoning becomes sluggish and impaired, and they respond reflexively rather than strategically. Finally, 10 to 15 percent of the population react to stress in extreme and thoroughly counterproductive ways, becoming paralyzed with screaming, crying, overwhelming confusion, or anxiety.[77]

This spectrum of behavior is apparent when it comes to assault. For example, a significant proportion of survivors of sexual assault report having felt paralyzed and unable to react,[78] with many saying they completely froze like a deer in the headlights.[79] And a large study of rape victims found that the younger the age, the more submissive the victim.[80]

It therefore may be foolish to have your teen rely on carrying protective devices to keep safe. Fumbling around to find the pepper spray at the bottom of the bag or the panic button on the phone may be an impossibility by the time urgent action is required.[81] Resisting is a highly effective strategy for those who are capable, but for the majority of the population who panics in the face of an emergency, 'avoid' and 'block' strategies which can be implemented in advance are key. (The suggestion to be wary of dominant males sits firmly in the 'avoid' category, making it the most powerful strategy for avoiding sexual assault.)

Sexual assault may be particularly horrifying, but it's also worth considering how to protect our teens from other types of physical assault. For example:

> A UPS driver delivered much-needed help to the teenage victim of a beating and robbery on a New York street. Video of the incident

> shows two people in black chasing the victim down to the ground, punching and kicking him before taking off with his Nike Air Force 1s. The driver didn't hesitate to jump in when he saw the teen was in trouble, rushing to the victim's side as the suspects fled.[82]

Muggings like this one play out every day, and teens are typically powerless to protect themselves. Let's look at the paltry options available.

In the 'avoid' category, typical common-sense tips include turning around to face someone following; sitting or standing as close to the driver as possible on a bus; and walking on the far side in corridors. These strategies may help, but there's no evidence to support them. There may be benefit to walking confidently: one study asked volunteers to rate how easy it would be to attack a variety of walking figures, and those figures who walked faster, with higher energy, longer strides and more arm swinging, were judged harder to attack.[83] Running away would be another obvious 'avoid' strategy when faced with a mugger. Unfortunately, we still don't know whether it's better for your teen to run away from a mugger or not, because the studies that have looked at outcomes in crime situations have unhelpfully combined the act of running away with various forms of nonforceful resistance.[84]

In the 'resist' category, strategies like yelling, reasoning with potential assailants and attracting passersby are related to lower levels of loss, attack, and injury in a robbery.[85] Many people also carry self-defense devices like stun guns and irritant sprays. One survey of college students found around 20 percent carried Mace,[86] the self-defense spray[87] that includes pepper spray as a key component.[88] However there's no evidence that these devices deter assault, and they suffer from other drawbacks (see box).

**Self-defense sprays**

Self-defense sprays unfortunately have many drawbacks. They are only legal for minors in certain locations;[*] [89] they have a finite shelf life (an expiration date can be found on the canister); strong winds can drastically redirect the spray away from the assailant (and possibly toward bystanders);[90] and finally, any devices that aim to incapacitate an assailant could theoretically be used against the victim.[†]

* New Jersey, New York, Rhode Island, Wisconsin, the Annapolis/Baltimore area, Honolulu, Washington, D.C., and Illinois bar under eighteen-year-olds from carrying both stun guns and irritant sprays outside the home,[1] and pepper spray is illegal for anyone to use in the UK.[2]

† At present, there's no proof of this happening in practice.

**Personal alarms**

Whistles, horns, and loud alarms which are difficult to turn off are another potential option for protection, although they're less common, favored by only 3 percent of college students.[91] Alarms cannot be redeployed by an aggressor, but they've not yet been proven to be effective in stopping an attack.[92] They also have drawbacks, as they involve a dramatic, potentially public action, a challenging step for most people to take when it's not yet clear if an emerging threat is real or not. Users must make a single decision and may hesitate until it's too late, rather than having options to escalate their reactions gradually.[93]

As with sexual assault, it also makes sense for a victim to resist an assault physically if possible, without fearing this will escalate the level of violence. An analysis of incidents against victims of all ages concluded that those who resisted were both less likely to lose their property and less likely to be injured. Injuries only occurred in 10 percent of cases of self-protection, and in these cases the injuries were minor, suggesting physically resisting is a wise strategy.[94] The more your teen resists, the riskier the situation becomes for the perpetrator, who may decide to give up to avoid being arrested.[95]

**Self-defense classes**

If resisting can deter assault, a self-defense class would presumably be a good use of time for teens. Unfortunately, there aren't any studies that prove that such classes help, at least among civilians.[96] If you nevertheless would like to better equip your teen to handle potential threats, Krav Maga is the most promising option. Krav Maga is taught in over 70 countries to a variety of populations, and is an integral part of military and police training in countries like the US and France.[97] It was originally developed in the late 1930s by an internationally renowned Hungarian boxing champion, gymnast and wrestler, who had taken part in numerous street fights to prevent anti-Semitic mobs from terrorizing his Jewish community. It was later codified for use by the Israeli army before being redeveloped for civilian use in the 1960s.[98] As described by a guide, "Krav Maga not only teaches people to function under stress, in fact, the majority of techniques work better when the defender is under stress... [T]he system is built to reduce your options so that you do not hesitate under stress. Krav Maga emphasizes simple reactions without exposing the defender to additional dangers."[99] Of course, it's not realistic to expect most teens to dedicate their spare time to becoming Krav Maga experts. But for those who are keen on learning self-defense, it's likely the best option.

With so little in the arsenal to protect potential assault victims, entrepreneurs are finally working to innovate, primarily by creating safety apps.* [100] However these apps tend to be focused on helping potential victims resist; not enough thought has yet gone into inventing ways to block an attack with no effort required on the part of a victim who might be incapacitated by fear. Two clever new apps, One Scream and Chilla, are designed to detect a woman's screams and alert authorities on their behalf, but some victims might not even be able to muster a scream.

One innovation, the "No-Contact Jacket," had great promise. A neutral black shell coat, when 'armed' it would deliver an electric shock to anyone who touched it, without the risk of shocking the wearer. Like the jolt delivered by an electric fence, such a shock wouldn't harm an aggressor, but the momentary stunning effect would provide the victim time to escape.[101] Unfortunately, the developers never commercialized their idea for consumer use. So, for the moment, the options available for protecting your teen from assault are disappointing. If you or your teen has entrepreneurial tendencies, consider this discussion a call to arms: this is a market ripe for disruption.

## *Dating violence*

> Jack and I met at the age of 16. I was a happy, confident teenage girl, and for the first few months everything was great. Slowly little things were said that I initially thought came from a caring place: "I don't like when you wear those shorts, they are way too short. I just love you so much I hate it when other men look at you." Gradually

* For example, the Revolar app has a yellow alert level that allows people to reach out to family and friends, to say they're concerned about something but aren't yet prepared to call 911, while a red alert means please send professional help.[1] Companion is a free app that allows a student to alert a friend that they're leaving one location and traveling to another. Along the way, the app asks users to confirm they're okay and if they do not respond, alerts the companion or authorities.[2] And the UrSafe app allows users to set up their own code words representing different levels of threat, and the app also records what's going on.[3] Hotlines would also be a good idea for reducing assault, but haven't been widely adopted. A non-profit from Southeastern Louisiana offers cash rewards: "Crimestoppers, Inc., is an anonymous telephone hotline students can use to provide information on crime, including possession of guns or other dangerous weapons, possession of narcotics/alcohol, fights, extreme bullying, threats of terrorism, gang activity, robberies, sexual assaults, arson, battery, vandalism and bomb threats... The program offers $500 for tips leading to the apprehension of an individual in possession of a firearm on school campus, and up to $2,500 for administrative action taken by school administration and/or arrest. Callers are given a code number, with cash payouts made to that code number by a local bank."[4]

> his behavior changed. His obsession with controlling me got so strong I would have panic attacks simply deciding what to wear. If I wore something or did anything he did not like I was screamed at, and then he began to hit, choke, and slap me. It got to the point that I felt I could no longer figure out what I did to set him off, I just knew that when he reached a certain point of anger there was nothing I could do to stop it. Being choked became a regular occurrence. I cannot begin to count the number of times I attempted to break up with him. When I would try, he would threaten the safety of me and my family or threaten to commit suicide. It was worth dealing with the pain alone to prevent Jack from killing himself and anyone in my family being hurt.* [102]

This story is unpleasantly reminiscent of the fable of the frog stuck swimming in increasingly hot water. Yet it's the quintessential tale of dating violence. No one would knowingly enter into a relationship with someone abusive, so most of these dysfunctional relationships start well, and only over time does the partner's true character emerge. In fact, dating abuse can be surprisingly formulaic (see box).

**The typical phases of dating abuse**

- Phase 1 (Tension Building): The two people argue a lot; the abuser yells at the target for no reason or makes false accusations, and the target feels that she or he can't do anything right
- Phase 2 (Explosion): The tension is released in a burst of physical, sexual, and/or verbal/emotional abuse. The abuser may scream and yell in a way that is frightening and/or humiliating; hit, grab, shove, kick, slam the other person against the wall; throw objects; threaten to hurt the other person or a friend or relative, or rape or force sexual activity on the other person
- Phase 3 (Honeymoon): The abuser tries to make the target stay in the relationship by apologizing and/or trying to shift the blame for the abuse onto someone else, or something else such as alcohol, drug use or stress
- Repeat: Each of the above phases can last anywhere from a few minutes to a few years. After the honeymoon phase, the tension starts to build again, leading to another explosion. Over time, the honeymoon phase may get shorter and gradually disappear, and the explosions may become more violent and dangerous. Some targets of dating abuse never experience the honeymoon phase — just the tension building and explosion phases[103]

---

* Name of protagonist has been changed for privacy purposes.

Far too many teens are suffering in their relationships: 20 percent of girls and 10 percent of boys report having experienced some form of dating violence in the previous year.[*] [†] [104] It's actually possible to coach both potential perpetrators and potential victims, to help them avoid falling into destructive relationship patterns. Several school-based preventative programs have successfully reduced dating violence,[‡] [105] although it's unclear if the benefits last over the long term.[106] If you suspect your teen has fallen into a dysfunctional relationship and the local community doesn't offer such a program, you could familiarize them with the warning signs (see box), and share other adolescents' testimonials to kick-start a conversation.[§] [107]

**Warning signs of dating abuse**

An answer of 'Yes' to any of these questions may indicate an abusive relationship.[108]

Does the person I am with:

- Get extremely jealous or possessive?
- Accuse me of flirting or cheating?
- Constantly check up on me or make me check in?
- Tell me how to dress or how much makeup to wear?
- Try to control what I do and whom I see?
- Try to keep me from seeing or talking to my family and friends?
- Have big mood swings — angry/yelling one minute, sweet/apologetic the next?
- Make me feel nervous or as if I'm walking on eggshells?
- Put me down or criticize me?
- Make me feel that I can't do anything right?
- Make me feel that no one else would want me?

---

* Defined as a non-zero answer to either of the following two questions: "During the past 12 months, how many times did someone you were dating or going out with physically hurt you on purpose? (Count such things as being hit, slammed into something, or injured with an object or weapon)"; "During the past 12 months, how many times did someone you were dating or going out with force you to do sexual things that you did not want to do? (Count such things as kissing, touching, or being physically forced to have sexual intercourse.)"

† Many other studies have found different rates using different definitions;[1 2 3 4 5 6 7] for example, the rate goes up to 32% of all teens with a broader definition that includes violent verbal behavior such as swearing.[8]

‡ including Safe Dates,[1] the Youth Relationships Project,[2] The Forth R, and Coaching Boys into Men. There is also a program aimed at families, the Families for Safe Dates program, which has been shown to reduce dating violence;[3 4] unfortunately the full content isn't available online.

§ The "Love Doesn't Have to Hurt Teens" from the American Psychological Association features a number of brief anecdotes (www.apa.org/pi/families/resources/love-teens),[1] the "Love is Not Abuse" curriculum includes personal stories (www.uen.org/cte/facs_cabinet/downloads/AdultRoles/LINA_Curriculum%2010_07.pdf, see pages 29 and 41-42),[2] and various video testimonials from a "Choose Respect" campaign launched by the Centers for Disease Control are available (www.youtube.com/watch?v=9SOZ4Pji9OI). Finally, the short film *A Love that Kills* ($2.99 at www.nfb.ca/film/love_that_kills/#:~:text=A%20Love%20That%20Kills%20is,daughter's%20life%20and%20tragic%20death)[3] relates the true story of an adolescent who was killed by her abusive boyfriend. It's not a showcase for world-class acting talent, but it makes the point.

- Threaten to hurt me?
- Threaten to hurt my friends or family?
- Threaten to commit suicide?
- Threaten to hurt him- or herself because of me?
- Threaten to hurt my pet(s)?
- Threaten to destroy my things?
- Hurt me physically? (includes yelling, grabbing, pushing shoving, shaking, punching, slapping, holding me down, etc.)
- Break or throw things when we argue?
- Pressure or force me into having sex or going further sexually than I want to?

A male with parents whose marriage involves conflict and aggression is also more likely to be an aggressor himself in his own romantic relationships. Whether this is the effect of genetics or of witnessing and imitating the dysfunctional behavior is difficult to untangle, but it's a warning sign nonetheless.[109]

Detecting teen dating problems can require parents to be exquisitely attuned to subtle warning signs, rather than assuming a change in mood is simply normal adolescent angst. Returning to the teen from the beginning of the section:

> I knew I could always go to my parents for anything, but I never went to them for this, as I was simply too ashamed. I didn't want my parents to suffer because I had gotten myself into a dangerous situation. Little did I know that they had seen the huge change in me. I was no longer outgoing, confident, surrounded with friends, or doing well at school, so they were already suffering. They reached out and asked what was happening, but I never told them. They didn't know the warning signs, and I hid it all so well."[110]

## *Take-aways*

Countless websites, guides and handbooks have been written by well-meaning adults earnestly trying to root out the problems of assault and dating violence (as well as bullying and sexual harassment, which will be covered later). Yet none address the stubborn fact that most victims are unwilling to inform an adult. No matter how many concerned school counselors tell teens the best way to solve a problem with an aggressor is to confide in a trusted adult, teens simply don't. In an adolescent's mind, the potential negative consequences of telling a parent or teacher must loom even larger than the already intolerable status quo.

Teens may fear retribution from their aggressor, either implied or because of direct threats; they may be wary of a negative reaction from the adult (distress, disbelief, blame for having gotten themselves into the situation, reduced respect for their ability to handle problems, over-reaction); and/or they may fear losing control over the situation if the adult decides to take unilateral actions with which they disagree.

Although there is no research to support the following course of action, a way to lower the communication barrier could be to have frank, proactive conversations with our teens, laying out that many people their age find themselves victimized; that if they found themselves in such a situation, it would not be their fault; and that if they were to choose to confide in us, we would commit to believing their story, keeping their confidence confidential if they preferred, reacting calmly, brainstorming options together, and only pursuing a course of action if it was mutually agreed upon.

Returning to the movie *Scream* (with a spoiler alert): killers in Halloween masks are thankfully few and far between, but the boyfriend with the potential to turn menacing is one to watch.

## KEY PARENTING TAKE-AWAYS:

Sexual assault:

1. Encourage your local school to offer the Enhanced Assess, Acknowledge, Act (EAAA)/Flip the Script™ Sexual Assault Resistance Program
2. Discuss the importance of being careful even around people your teen thinks are trustworthy, by staying alert for examples of controlling behavior and by avoiding isolation
3. Recommend enlisting a sober buddy in drinking situations to take responsibility for ensuring no one tries to isolate your teen, in addition to handling the drive home
4. Advise your child to actively resist an attacker if at all possible, by yelling, kicking, biting, and punching
5. Proactively assure your child that you would provide wholehearted support in the case of an assault
6. If your teen describes being attacked, believe the account, even if the details are fuzzy

Other assault:

7. Encourage your child to walk confidently and with energy, particularly if alone at night
8. If targeted, advise your teen to resist in any possible way, including shouting, attracting passersby, reasoning with the assailant and even fighting back

Dating violence:

9. Familiarize yourself and your teen with the warning signs of dating violence
10. If you suspect your teen has fallen into a dysfunctional relationship and the local community doesn't offer a program, share other adolescents' testimonials with your child to kick-start a conversation

Overall:

11. Communicate that if your teen were victimized, you would believe the story, keep the confidence confidential, react calmly, brainstorm options together, and only pursue a course of action if it was mutually agreed-upon

# 5. MENTAL HEALTH

## Get struggling teens cognitive behavioral therapy

> "It's like drowning, except everyone around you is breathing."

> "When you're depressed you don't control your thoughts, your thoughts control you. I wish people understood that."

> "A human being can survive almost anything, as long as she sees the end in sight. But depression is so insidious — and it compounds daily — making it impossible to ever see the end. That fog is like a cage without a key." — Elizabeth Wurtzel[1]

> Wherever I sat — on the deck of a ship or at a street café in Paris or Bangkok — I would be sitting under the same glass bell jar, stewing in my own sour air. Menacing gods. I feel outcast on a cold star, unable to feel anything but an awful helpless numbness. Look at that ugly dead mask here and do not forget it. It is a chalk mask with dead dry poison behind it, like the death angel. The pouting disconsolate mouth, the flat, bored, numb, expressionless eyes: symptoms of the foul decay within. — Sylvia Plath[2]

If your adolescent hasn't experienced symptoms of depression, chances are that at least one of your child's close friends has. Not only do 16 percent of girls and 8 percent of boys suffer from full-blown depression in adolescence, about 40 percent of girls and 20 percent of boys have experienced feeling sad or hopeless every day for at least two weeks in a row within the previous year. That's a lot of misery for a young person to be shouldering.

Although the media is often quick to blame teens' obsessions with their devices, this is a problem that predates the internet and social media. Feelings of gloom have been haunting our teens for years, and the problem has only slightly increased for girls but not boys in recent times:* [3]

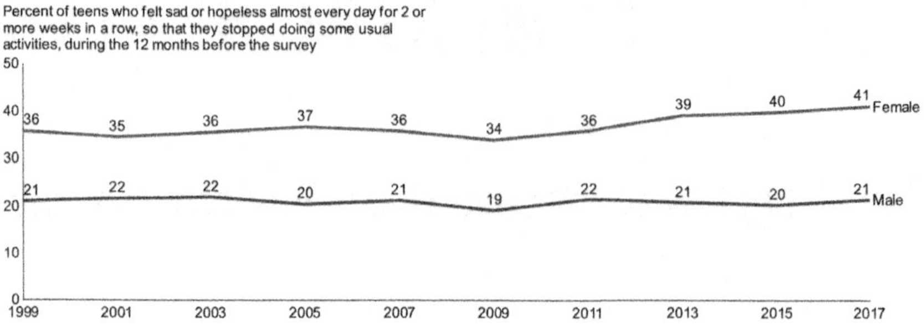


The good news is that our teens don't have to suffer in silence. Depression has been extensively studied, so by now we know exactly how to handle it.[4] †

**Preventing depression = parenting well?**
An expert panel recently convened to review the evidence and identify the top parenting strategies to reduce the risk of depression or anxiety disorders in adolescents. [5] Sounds promising, right? They summarized the results in a booklet, entitled, "How to prevent depression and clinical anxiety in your teenager: Strategies for parents."‡ § Here's a brief summary of the headlines, which read weirdly like suggestions from an overly generic parenting manual: "Establish and maintain a good relationship with your teenager; be involved and support increasing autonomy; establish family rules and consequences; minimize conflict in the home; encourage supportive relationships; help your teenager deal with problems; encourage good health habits; help your teenager to deal with anxiety; encourage professional help seeking when needed; and don't blame yourself." In other words, be a good parent. But don't blame yourself if you don't manage to be a good enough parent. Glad we've cleared that up.

The best treatment option is, without a doubt, a remarkably powerful technique called cognitive behavioral therapy (CBT), which can also be used to combat a wide variety of other mental ailments that can plague teens, from anxiety to

* Similar increases in mental health symptoms in girls have also been observed in other countries, including non-Western nations, and it remains unclear what the drivers could be.[1]

† Available at www.parentingstrategies.net/depression/media/pdf/Teen_Guidelines.pdf

‡ Available at www.parentingstrategies.net/depression/media/pdf/Teen_Guidelines.pdf

§ A caveat: it's difficult to ascertain to what extent the evidence upon which the experts drew involved interventions (e.g., teaching a strategy to a randomly selected group of parents and then determining whether their teens fared better, which would prove causation) versus studies that simply observed correlations (which might mix in the effects of genetics).

eating disorders. CBT treatment involves changing thinking patterns, for example learning to recognize distortions; facing fears instead of avoiding them; using role playing to prepare for tricky interactions with others; and learning to calm the mind and relax the body.[6] Most successful attempts to alleviate depression have incorporated CBT in some way,[7] and CBT is as effective as medication, with the added benefit of not causing side effects.[*][8] Between 50 and 85 percent of those treated with CBT will improve.[9] What's not to love?

**Can autonomy help?**
The lack of responsibility allocated to adolescents today could be one of the key root causes of teen angst.[†][10] Young people who in previous eras would have been taking on adult responsibilities and even launching their own families are now expected to stay at home and live as dependents for a much longer period. In the words of one teen, "I'm no good to anybody and I just cost my parents money."[11] Regrettably, no interventions have yet tested whether increasing teen autonomy does indeed help alleviate the symptoms of depression. The concept does work with other populations: for example, residents of nursing homes pep up when given small responsibilities like plants to tend.[12] So by all means look for ways to increase your teen's autonomy, even if it isn't a panacea.

Depression requires professional treatment, but there's a good chance that your child will ultimately reemerge from the bell jar and resume a more cheerful and productive life. Here's a thought to end this topic on a brighter note:

> "The broken will always be able to love harder than most because once you've been in the dark, you learn to appreciate everything that shines." — Anonymous[13]

# Dig deeper

> "Generation at risk: America's youngest facing mental health crisis...American children's mental health is worrying experts, with

---

* A variety of CBT-based interventions delivered via the internet and smartphones have recently been tested in adults (e.g., Beating the Blues™)[1] and college students,[2] and these delivery methods appear to be effective, but the research in this area is still somewhat nascent. Another promising area of current research involves treating depression with hallucinogens, but unfortunately, thus far the research has only been conducted on adult populations.[3]

† This argument is put forth in the book *Escaping the endless adolescence: How we can help our teenagers grow up before they grow old.*[1]

one in five kids suffering from a diagnosable mental, emotional or behavioral disorder." — CNN[14]

For once, a news headline was underplaying reality. In fact, about half of all adolescents will at some point face a mental health issue.* [15] Below is a chart showing how many teens are affected by various mental health disorders: † [16]

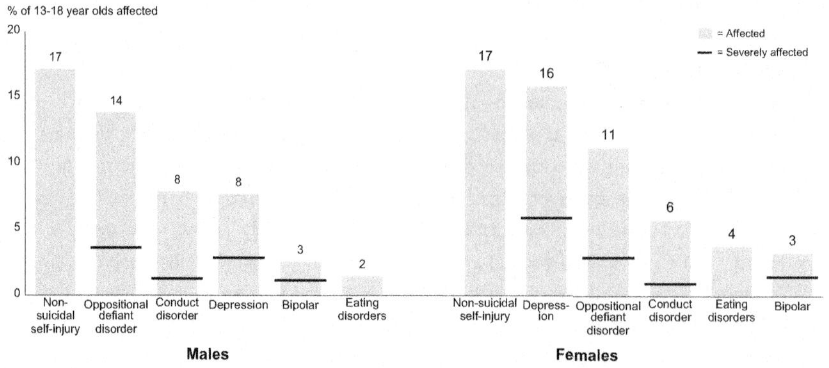


We've already discussed depression, so we'll cover the rest in turn.

## *Non-suicidal self-injury disorder (self-harm)*

Halfway through my freshman year, everything seemed to fall apart. The boy I was dating had just dumped me, and that's when I lost control. The first cuts were small and clean, using a staple or a pair of scissors. When that wasn't enough, I introduced myself to the razor. Cutting became a nightly ritual for me. I'd pull out my razor, slice myself open, and watch myself bleed as I listened to music and talked to my friends. It felt exhilarating to talk to them while participating in my own sick hobby.

When I was called to dinner, I would bandage up and throw on a pair of dark sweatpants so the blood wouldn't show through. The sting of the cut would push me into reality. It evaporated the numbness I

* These figures also include substance use disorders, covered previously.

† This chart excludes specific anxiety disorders which on average emerge by 6 years old,[1] and ADHD, where 95 percent of cases are diagnosed by age 11.[2] Posttraumatic stress disorder (PTSD) is also not included as it develops in response to specific traumas which are discussed elsewhere. A different data source has been used for Non-Suicidal Self-Injury (NSSI), as previously these behaviors were considered a form of attenuated suicide, although now NSSI has been recognized as a specific disorder.[3]

> felt inside and helped me feel real and alive. Cutting helped me sit at the dinner table and interact with others. It helped me smile and pretend that I was okay. It gave me hope. — Anonymous[17]

> It's not a secret that I went through a self-destructive period. I used to cut myself...I always felt caged, closed in, like I was punching at things that weren't there. — Angelina Jolie[18]

> When you see these marks on your child's beautiful skin, you're just filled with every emotion that you can possibly think of – fear, anxiety, disbelief, anger and just not knowing what to do. — Anonymous parent[19]

Non-suicidal self-injury is a shockingly common problem, affecting 17 percent of teens of both genders,[20] but because it's highly stigmatized, adolescents who self-harm often conceal their behavior from others. Girls are more likely to cut themselves, and because this is the most stereotypic self-injurious behavior, many people assume the problem is confined to girls. In fact, in boys the disorder is simply exhibited differently - males are more likely to hit themselves,[21] as well as pinch, scratch and bite.[22]

There is some concern that the number of kids harming themselves may be increasing,[23] although it could be that we're simply capturing better data on the subject.[24] Regardless, there has been an explosion of discussion of the topic online (see box). Although a virtual community could theoretically help a teen by providing emotional support, it's equally possible that interacting with other individuals who self-harm could normalize the behavior and cause it to spread.[25]

**#selfharm**

A community that initially formed on Instagram used the hashtag #selfharm. When that hashtag was subsequently blocked, users began to use #selfharmm and then ultimately #selfharmmm,[26] which had 1.7 million search results in 2014 and >2.4 million in 2015.[27] Since then, other secret terms have bubbled up, including some which are brief enough that they risk being found inadvertently by teens looking for very different content.[28] One large survey of children who had access to the internet found that 10 percent had seen self-harm websites, and 6 percent had seen sites that discussed forms of suicide.[29]

Not enough is yet known about what causes this troubling condition. Self-injury is a key risk factor for suicide,[30] so until recently, it was only considered a symptom of suicidal tendencies rather than a stand-alone diagnosis like depression. Self-harming behaviors seem to be highly complex, so far more basic research on the topic is urgently needed.[31]

Why do teens themselves say they self-injure? The most common justifications include 'to try to get a reaction from someone', 'to get control of a situation', and 'to stop bad feelings.'[32] The act of self-harm seems to help teens resolve feelings of anger, depression, loneliness, and frustration, and replace them with a sense of relief in the short term, although guilt, shame and disgust tend to follow. Boys tend to report self-harming in order to communicate with or influence others or out of boredom, whereas girls are more likely to report deep despair, self-hatred, self-punishment, and loneliness as reasons for self-harming.[33] Of course, it's difficult to know how accurately the boys in particular are describing their emotions, given the societal stigma associated with males showing weakness.

The topic of how to cope with self-harm hasn't been resolved yet; no treatments have been definitively proven to work.[34] Cognitive behavioral therapy may be helpful,[35] and various studies are underway to test specific types of CBT, including an approach called dialectical behavior therapy.[36] We're left to hope that a subsequent edition of this book will be able to provide more definitive advice.

In the meantime, the best source of wisdom is the cumulative experience of other parents who have coped firsthand with this problem. Common-sense suggestions include avoiding criticizing, overreacting, or making the child feel guilty (e.g., "you can't do this because I love you"); creating a hands-off communication mechanism (e.g., a blank text which means your teen feels upset but can't talk about it, or a notebook to write in and slip under your door); and finding a support group of other parents in the same situation.[37]

The only good news about self-harm is that it often simply resolves on its own. Around 80 percent of those who engage in self-harm as adolescents seem to give up the behavior by young adulthood.[38]

The artist Pink recently went on record to defend the music video for her song "Perfect," which includes scenes of a woman cutting her arm with a razor blade. The singer said she hoped that the video would encourage sufferers to seek help:

> I support the kids out there that feel so desperate/numb/powerless, that feel unseen and unheard, and can't see another way. I want them to know I'm aware. I have been there. I see them. Sometimes that's all it takes.[39]

Although Pink's intentions were noble, normalizing behaviors like playing with razor blades is a thoroughly risky business.

## *Disruptive behavior disorders*

> You can only subject people to anguish who have a conscience. You can only punish people who have hopes to frustrate or attachments to sever; who worry what you think of them. You can really only punish people who are already a little bit good. — *We Need to Talk about Kevin*[40]

*We Need to Talk About Kevin* is a work of fiction, but it addresses the very real difficulties facing the families of offspring who seem wired to behave in perverse, upsetting and occasionally shocking ways. All children, particularly during their teen years, will exhibit some level of defiance as they seek to test boundaries and assert their independence. Some, however, go further, and exhibit troubling behavior that parents are at a loss to control. How can we as parents distinguish between ordinary parenting challenges and a diagnosable disorder?

The American Psychiatric Association has a classification called "disruptive behavior disorders," which includes two specific conditions. Oppositional defiant disorder affects approximately 14 percent of teenage boys and 11 percent of girls, while conduct disorder affects 8 and 6 percent respectively. The criteria for these conditions read like a laundry-list of all the very worst behaviors you hope your child will never exhibit (see box); parenting kids with a disruptive behavior disorder is no picnic.

**How to diagnose disruptive behavior disorders**

Oppositional defiant disorder (ODD)[41] is defined as a pattern of negativistic, hostile and defiant behavior lasting at least 6 months, during which four (or more) of the following are present:

1. Often loses temper
2. Often argues with adults
3. Often actively defies or refuses to comply with adults' requests or rules
4. Often deliberately annoys people
5. Often blames others for any mistakes or misbehavior
6. Is often touchy or easily annoyed by others
7. Is often angry and resentful
8. Is often spiteful or vindictive

Conduct disorder (CD)[42] is a pattern of behavior in which an individual consistently violates the basic rights of others or violates major age-appropriate societal norms or rules. Specifically, the disorder is defined as the presence of at least three of the following 15 criteria in the past 12 months, with at least one in the past 6 months:

1. Often bullies, threatens or intimidates others
2. Often initiates physical fights
3. Has used a weapon that can cause serious physical harm to others (e.g., a bat, brick, broken bottle, knife, gun).
4. Has been physically cruel to people
5. Has been physically cruel to animals
6. Has stolen while confronting a victim (e.g., mugging, purse snatching, extortion, armed robbery).
7. Has forced someone into sexual activity
8. Has deliberately engaged in fire setting with the intention of causing serious damage
9. Has deliberately destroyed others' property (other than by fire setting)
10. Has broken into someone else's house, building or car
11. Often lies to obtain goods or favors or to avoid obligations (i.e., "cons" others)
12. Has stolen items of nontrivial value without confronting the victim (e.g., shoplifting, but without breaking and entering; forgery)
13. Often stays out at night despite parental prohibitions, beginning before age 13 years
14. Has run away from home overnight at least twice while living in the parental or parental surrogate home, or once without returning for a lengthy period
15. Often truant from school, starting before age 13

Approximately half of children affected are formally diagnosed before they reach their teen years, but the remaining half are only identified as adolescents,[43] which is problematic because the available treatments are most effective with younger children.[44] (Typical techniques involve highly structured and standardized consequences for problematic behavior, not dissimilar from those deployed on the popular television show *Super Nanny*.)[45]

Nevertheless, if your child has reached the teen years without a diagnosis, it's worth having the condition officially recognized. For a long time, both disorders were considered impossible to treat, but recently there have been incremental improvements in the techniques available (see box).

**Treatments for disruptive behavior disorders**

One treatment called parent management training can generate small improvements in children's behavior,[46] and four additional treatments, anger control/stress inoculation,[47] assertiveness training, multisystemic therapy[48] and rational-emotive therapy[49] also show promise.[50] Medications are typically used only as a last resort.[51]

Nevertheless, there are many heart-breaking testimonials from struggling parents which suggest our current mental health system doesn't always rise to the challenge in extreme cases. Here's a summary of one mother's experience:

> We turn to the mental health professionals, who we think have seen all of this before, but insurance pays only for short visits, and there's a shortage of professionals with expertise on the most "serious" kids. Parents like me are told, "I've done all I can for your child." The burden falls on us in a way that would be unthinkable with another kind of illness. I've read that the mother of Adam Lanza [perpetrator of the Sandy Hook Elementary School shooting in 2012] found that only she could defuse his crises. I'm sure that's what she did until she couldn't anymore.[52]

Our social work system doesn't always successfully fill the gaps either; here's another testimonial from a distraught parent:

> I live with a son who is mentally ill. I love my son. But he terrifies me. A few weeks ago, Michael pulled a knife and threatened to kill me and then himself after I asked him to return his overdue library books. When I asked my son's social worker about my options, he said that the only thing I could do was to get Michael charged with a crime. I don't believe my son belongs in jail. The chaotic environment exacerbates his sensitivity to sensory stimuli and doesn't deal with the underlying pathology. No one wants to send a 13-year old genius who loves Harry Potter and his snuggle animal collection to

> jail. But our society, with its stigma on mental illness and its broken healthcare system, does not provide us with other options.[53]

When children struggle with a disruptive behavior disorder, parents are left to cope as best they can, and often end up blaming themselves when disaster results. Returning to *We Need to Talk about Kevin*, one reader points out that "every incident of Kevin's upbringing is a chance for his mother to condemn herself: she was never loving enough to him; always too quick to anger; too focused on herself and not enough on him."[54] Of course this isn't fair or reasonable: these disorders most likely have a strong genetic component.[55]

The unsatisfying and inadequate take-away is that in addition to seeking professional help, parents should find a support group:

> If we're lucky, we find other parents like us. It's difficult to say my child is out of control or hurts himself or can't seem to succeed. But then the other person says, "Yes, I know. It's like that at my house, too." We share, we cry, we laugh. We applaud each other's successes and commiserate over the failures. Most of all we brainstorm, we point each other in the right direction and we slowly make progress. And we are not quiet. At least not until we leave the room.[56]

## *Eating disorders*

Almost a decade after she controversially made the statement that 'nothing tastes as good as skinny feels,' Kate Moss retracted her 'iconic' quote.[57] It would be unfair to blame Kate for popularizing the unhealthy look that was later termed "heroin chic." She was recruited to modelling at the age of 14, is estimated to have weighed only 98 pounds at her skinniest,[58] and describes having locked herself in a toilet and crying after being bullied into posing topless as a teen.[59] Kate was simply the most visible example of a wider trend in fashion glamourizing this particular body type. The blame lies squarely with the media executives who chose not only to exploit models like Kate, but to usher in an unattainable fashion aesthetic which warped the perspectives of an entire generation of girls and women.

The evidence is incontrovertible: exposure to fashion media makes girls less satisfied with their bodies. Study after study has shown that girls exposed to images of thin models in fashion magazines or commercials are subsequently far more preoccupied with their weight, and experience more stress, guilt, and insecurity than those shown average-sized models, news magazines, or other neutral images.[60] More recently, it's become clear that kids who use social networking sites are also more likely to be concerned about their body image and are more likely to suffer from disordered eating, which is unsurprising given the emphasis on uploading and often filtering pictures.[61]

**Trouble in paradise**

The best illustration of the effects of media on girls comes from the tiny South Pacific island of Fiji. The longstanding cultural aesthetic in Fiji had been supportive of large appetites and body sizes in both men and women (think Maui, caricatured in the Disney movie, *Moana*).[*] [62] Television only recently arrived in the rural areas of Fiji, so researchers were able to observe the impact of exposure to Western media. Lo and behold, after the introduction of television,[63] Fijian schoolgirls suddenly became preoccupied with their weight and started displaying symptoms of disordered eating.[64]

If media is often the source of the problem, it can also play a role in the solution. In 2006, Dove produced a short video showing a model with girl-next-door good looks being transformed first by hair and makeup artists and subsequently by digital photo editing into a glamorous billboard version which bears little resemblance to the original.[65] As the model's neck is digitally stretched and her eyes digitally enlarged to create the final image, it becomes clear that portrayals of female beauty in the media are impossible to emulate in real life. (The video is available for free on the internet; encourage your teen check it out.[†]) A research team found that simply watching this clip protected tween girls from the negative impact of exposure to images of ultra-thin models.[66] In a similar vein, other attempts to teach girls about media-literacy have also succeeded,[‡] [67] and viewing images of larger women seems to have a positive effect on women's body image.[68] We need more actresses like Rebel Wilson to pave the way.

---

* An intriguing explanation for the high rates of obesity found in the Pacific Islands is that the founding populations of these islands had survived long, perilous journeys by boat, and therefore were disproportionately composed of individuals whose genetics skewed towards higher body weights, allowing them to survive the journey while their slimmer companions died of starvation at sea.[1]

† Available at: www.youtube.com/watch?v=iYhCnOjf46U

‡ Available at: www.youtube.com/watch?v=C7143sc_HbU

Fortunately, full-blown eating disorders are not very common; 4 percent of adolescent girls and 2 percent of boys are affected in the US, and rates have been generally stable over the past several decades.[69] However elite student athletes in artistic pursuits like gymnastics, dancing, figure skating, aerobics, and diving, and those who participate in weight class sports and begin using extreme weight loss methods from a young age[70] can be particularly susceptible.

If your child is struggling with an eating disorder, the path to recovery can be long. After 10 years, about 70 percent of those diagnosed as teens still suffer from anorexia and 30 percent from bulimia, and even after 20 years, around 35 and 30 percent are still anorexic and bulimic, respectively.[71] But only about a quarter of individuals with eating disorders have ever gotten professional help, which may explain the poor recovery rates.[72] Recovery rates for bulimics treated with CBT are 40 to 45 percent, versus only 2 percent for those left alone.[73] Certain family-based approaches (where parents assume responsibility for feeding their child) can help, and even antidepressants and mood stabilizers can be effective.[74] The only approach to avoid is congregating teens with eating disorders in a group, unless the situation is so extreme that hospitalization is required. You don't want these kids to think their behavior is normal, and you definitely don't want them to start imitating and competing with each other.[75]

For those of us who derive great pleasure from our food, it's difficult to imagine waging a constant battle against our appetites. Yet the fact that these disorders revolve around food can distract from the reality that eating disorders are mental health conditions. The problems reside in the mind, and the distorted approach to food is the manifestation of these problems, which can't be resolved by simply urging a teen to eat. In the words of one sufferer,

> I had bulimia for years. It's a secret disease. You inflict it upon yourself because your self-esteem is at a low ebb, and you don't think you're worthy or valuable. You fill your stomach up and it gives you a feeling of comfort. It's like having a pair of arms around you, but it's temporary. Then you're disgusted at the bloatedness of your stomach, and you bring it all up again. It's a repetitive pattern which is very destructive." – Her Royal Highness Diana, The Princess of Wales[76]

## *Bipolar disorder*

> Hundreds of pages of rants penned in various journals, unrequited lust elevated to the level an existential condition, and of course, tortured anguish for a world so depraved and corrupt it could not recognize a truly special and unique literary talent walking among men: me, a high school sophomore. — Manic phase of a teenage bipolar sufferer[77]

Bipolar disorder emerges later in life than many of the other conditions discussed in this chapter: around 25 percent of cases are diagnosed in late adolescence, and the remainder in early adulthood. [78] Approximately 3 percent of teens of both sexes are affected, and the most common manifestation involves multiple, intense, prolonged mood swings each day, including short periods of euphoria and longer periods of irritability, although not all cases follow this formula.* [79]

If you think there's a chance your child might be suffering from bipolar disorder, the treatment guidelines from the Child and Adolescent Bipolar Foundation provide a full description of the symptoms.† [80] Bipolar disorder can be treated with medication and other therapies, so it's worth seeking a professional diagnosis.

The difficulty is that many parents are unaware of the condition, which can masquerade as other teen difficulties, as these parents can attest:

> We didn't have the facts or education to know that when our son seemed to derail from his goals because of "excessive partying," he was self-medicating at the onset of a mental illness. Our son was unknowingly using alcohol to battle severe depression, along with marijuana to counter his mania. We struggled to understand why he would jeopardize his scholarship and academic career after working so hard for them. We later found out about the biochemical imbalance that

* To be formally diagnosed, symptoms have to occur most days in a week; be severe enough to cause extreme disturbance in one domain or moderate disturbance in two or more domains; occur three or four times a day; and cumulatively last four or more hours a day. The full list of symptoms includes euphoric/expansive mood; irritable mood; grandiosity; decreased need for sleep; pressured speech (speaking quickly; loud, intrusive, difficult to interrupt); racing thoughts; distractibility; increase in goal-directed activity/agitation; excessive involvement in pleasurable or risky activities; psychosis; and suicidality.[1]

† Available at: www.dbsalliance.org/pdfs/BMPN/treatment_guidelines.pdf

> occurs with his illness. As parents, we have to walk that fine line of letting our kids leave the nest to grow on their own and keeping tabs on what could be warning signs of a much bigger problem.[81]

For teens riding an emotional roller-coaster, a diagnosis can be the key to stepping off the destructive amusement park ride and getting their feet back onto the ground.

## *Stress/Anxiety*

> Hye-Min Park is 16 and her day is typical of that of the majority of South Korean teenagers. She rises at 6:30am, is at school by 8am, finishes at 4pm, and pops back home to eat. She then takes a bus to her second school shift of the day at a private crammer or hagwon where she has lessons from 6 until 9pm. She spends another two hours in what she calls self-study back at school before arriving home after 11pm. She goes to bed at 2am and rises in the morning at 6.30am to do it all over again.
>
> There are just under 100,000 hagwons in South Korea and around three-quarters of children attend them. South Korea has been one of the highest achievers on international school tests in previous years. But the relentless pressure means Korea holds another much less enviable record: that of having the highest suicide rate of industrialized countries.[82]

> Among young South Koreans who confessed to feeling suicidal, an alarming 53 percent identified inadequate academic performance as the main reason for such thoughts.[83]

South Korea is not the only country coping with an epidemic of stress and anxiety among its youth, although it is certainly the most extreme. 35 percent of American teens say that stress has caused them to lie awake at night within the past month,[84] and stress levels of college students have been steadily creeping up over the past several years, particularly among girls:[85]

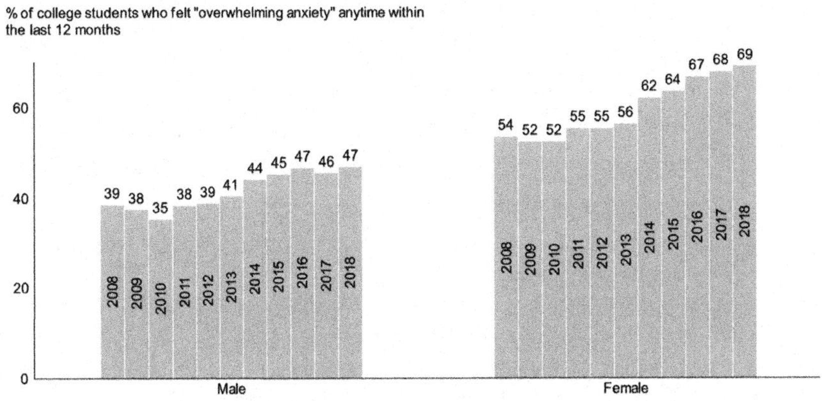


Full-blown anxiety disorders are typically diagnosed at a young age, and professional treatment by a skilled psychologist is the best solution.* [86] But we'd be remiss in closing a chapter about mental health without addressing stress, even if it doesn't amount to a diagnosable condition.† [87]

The best way to predict the anxiety of teens is to look at the affluence of their neighborhood, rather than the affluence of their family.[88] In the US, the problem is particularly acute in the suburbs;[89] 83 percent of teens say they're stressed about school, and 69 percent are stressed about getting into a good college or deciding what to do after high school.[90] These sources of stress reflect the reality of recent trends in college admissions. The average acceptance rate among the top 50 colleges in the US declined from 36 percent to 23 percent between 2006 and 2018, and among top 10 schools, it declined from 16 percent to 6.4 percent.[91]

**The tyranny of merit**

Michael Sandel, a professor at Harvard University, has written about the downsides of the merit-oriented sorting machine of higher education which has developed recently in the Western world, saying "among those who land on top, it induces anxiety, a debilitating perfectionism, and a meritocratic hubris," along with feelings of of worthlessness and shame amongst those who don't make the cut. His proposed solution? Encourage institutions like Harvard to scrap the whole admissions system in favor of a simple lottery for all those who meet an appropriately high threshold of academic capability.[92] Probably a pipe dream, but an appealing one nonetheless.

* For example, Anxiety Sensitivity Amelioration Training can help.[1]

† As with depression, there also appears to be a correlation between stress and screen time among teenagers, but it remains unclear which way the causal arrow points.

Stress is well known to have long-term health implications. Chronic stress can cause a cascade of problems within the body, including insulin resistance, plaque build-up in the arteries, and greater vulnerability to infections like the common cold. Stress can also lead to poor eating habits. In fact, a quarter of teens say they've overeaten or eaten unhealthy foods because of stress in the past month.[93]

**A telling example of chronic stress**

Among employees of the British Civil Service, death rates and serious diseases increase in lockstep from the lowest to the highest of the six grades of seniority,[94] which can't be coincidence. With greater responsibility comes greater stress.

Exercise is a great antidote to stress. More than half of adolescents say they feel good about themselves after exercising, and teens report that they find exercise better than playing video games, going online, or even watching TV or movies at busting stress. Two thirds of kids who exercise to manage stress rate it "highly effective."[95]

It's also worth considering whether you yourself could be one cause of your child's stress. 'Over-scheduling' per se is not the problem; as we'll discuss in a later chapter, being involved in lots of activities can have plenty of benefits, and kids can thrive on busy schedules.[96] Instead, it's specific pressure from parents to achieve academically and/or excel in extracurricular activities which can cause stress and anxiety.[97] Once again, it's difficult to tease out correlation versus causation. Parents who emphasize achievement over personal integrity or are highly critical of their offspring may have more maladjusted teens,[98] but this could be the effect of shared genetics. Until researchers launch a program to help parents dial down the levels of achievement angst and observe the results on their teens, we can't be sure.

Regardless, many affluent parents never question their assumption that helping their adolescent gain admission to a prestigious university is the ultimate metric of their success as a parent, as attending a good college will launch their child on the best path to success in life. In reality, the importance of getting into the right college can be a red herring. One analysis took a group of students who had similar admissions offers, and compared those who ultimately chose to attend a more selective school with those who chose a less selective one (often enticed by an attractive financial aid package). After graduation, both groups earned a similar amount. It was only students from disadvantaged family backgrounds who saw a benefit from attending an elite college.[99]

Why would this be the case? As Malcolm Gladwell has argued in his book *David & Goliath*, the psychological benefits of being a big fish in a little pond are very real. Those with high 'academic self-concept,' i.e. those who believe themselves to be good students, perform better in school.[100] Students invariably compare themselves to those around them, so attending a prestigious school and spending time surrounded by high-performing peers erodes self-confidence for those who don't fall at the upper end of the academic spectrum (see box). The big-fish–little-pond effect has been consistently demonstrated in a wide variety of student groups across many different settings and countries.[101]

**Small scientists in big ponds**

In demanding subjects like sciences, the demoralizing effect of being surrounded by high-caliber fellow students is particularly pronounced. By observing the behavior of college students in real life, one study estimates that the likelihood of persisting in a science major decreases by 2 percent for every 10-point increase in the college's selectivity,[102] and another has calculated that students are three or four times more likely to persist and achieve a science degree at an institution where they are competitive than at an institution where they are not.[103] Analyzing the number of publications by graduate students, a key measure of success in academia, shows that future academic success is far more related to a student's college class rank than to the quality of the institution itself.[104]

**The happy bottom quarter**

A former director of admissions at Harvard who was well aware of the small-fish-big-pond phenomenon explicitly crafted an admissions policy designed to ensure a "happy bottom quarter" by admitting students who had the innate self-confidence or the resilience drawn from outstanding achievement in an extra-curricular domain to weather the psychological effects of being surrounded by high-achieving peers.[105]

Even back in the 1960s, well before the current frenzy around college admissions, researchers were cautioning that sending a student to the "best possible school" wasn't in fact the best route to occupational mobility, advising:

> Counselors and parents should consider the drawbacks as well as the advantages of sending a boy to a 'fine' college, if, when doing so, it is fairly certain he will end up in the bottom ranks of his graduating class.[106]

Of course, college isn't just about getting a degree in science or earning a high salary after graduation. Alumni networks can be valuable professionally, and students make friends and acquaintances they'll often keep for life; approximately 30 percent of college grads will ultimately marry someone who went to the same school, even if the two didn't meet while there.[107]

Regardless of the benefits, pressuring a child to achieve has psychological drawbacks. Take the cautionary tale of Korean teenager Ha-eun Yang:

> She was the prodigy whose academic prowess, perfect SATs and otherworldly STEM skills led first to the equivalent of a bidding war between Harvard and Stanford, and then to an unprecedented proposal in which Yang would be allowed to attend each school for two years before choosing the one from which she'd graduate. Harvard enlisted billionaire Facebook founder Mark Zuckerberg to try to recruit her to its campus. For days, the Korean media gave Yang's unique achievement wall-to-wall coverage.
>
> Then, as suddenly as it erupted, the story imploded. Harvard and Stanford declared that in fact Yang had not been accepted to either school, and the congratulatory missives printed on official letterhead were found to be forgeries. Yang's father issued a public apology, taking responsibility for pressuring his daughter to the extent that she engineered the elaborate hoax: "I did not know until now how much my child was suffering."* [108]

## *Take-aways*

The mental health of many adolescents was already precarious before 2020. Then COVID closed the world down, and over the next several months a silent parallel epidemic spread. Since 2019, the number of mental health–related emergency department visits for adolescents increased by around 30 percent;[109] the number of teens calling the National Eating Disorders Association helpline increased by 65 percent;[110] 56 percent of students report that their stress about school has increased; and 32 percent of students report mental health as a major source of stress versus 26 percent pre-pandemic.[111]

* Name of protagonist has been changed for privacy purposes

As with many other difficulties, adolescents frequently try to cope with mental health issues alone. Teens aren't aware that treatment options are available; they assume their difficulties aren't serious enough to require help; they're concerned about the stigma; they're uncertain about confidentiality and whether they could truly trust an unknown person; and boys specifically worry that seeking help would be a sign of weakness.[112] Many of these barriers feel surmountable; perhaps simply discussing the topic of mental health with our teens could help them understand that mental illnesses are indeed illnesses, which can and should be treated.

Attempts to destigmatize mental illness through school-based education campaigns haven't yet worked.[113] What does seem to help is honesty on the part of celebrities.[114] Teens who were offered information about singer Demi Lovato's struggle with bipolar disorder subsequently overcame many of their negative stereotypes about the condition.[115] Increasingly, there's a long list of stars who have opened up about their own struggles (see box). For example, Dwayne "The Rock" Johnson has admitted to battling depression,[116] and Leonardo DiCaprio has revealed that he suffers from Obsessive Compulsive Disorder and has to force himself not to step on every chewing gum stain or walk through doorways several times.[117]

**Brave public testimonials**

Here are a few additional examples of stars openly discussing their mental health struggles, in case any might resonate with your teen:

"People don't know how to talk about being depressed – that it's totally okay to feel sad. I went through a time where I was really depressed. I locked myself in my room and my dad had to break my door down. It was a lot to do with, I had really bad skin, and I felt really bullied because of that." – Miley Cyrus[118]

"We don't talk enough about mental health and don't do enough to destigmatize talking about it." – Ryan Reynolds [who suffers from anxiety][119]

"Anxiety is nothing to be ashamed of; it affects millions of people every day. I know I have fans out there who have been through this kind of thing, too, and I wanted to be honest for their sake, if nothing else ... anxiety is so upsetting and difficult to explain. It's this thing that swells up and blocks out your rational thought processes. Even when you know you want to do something, know that it will be good for you, that you'll enjoy it when you're doing it, the anxiety is telling you a different story. It's a constant battle within yourself." – Zayn Malik (One Direction)[120]

"A mental illness is a thing that people cast in a different category [from other illnesses], but I don't think it is. It should be taken as seriously as anything else. You don't see the mental illness: It's not a mass; it's not a cyst. But it's there. Why do you need to prove it? If you can treat it, you treat it. I had pretty bad health anxiety that came from OCD and thought I had a tumor in my brain. I had an MRI, and the neurologist referred me to a psychiatrist. As I get older, the compulsive thoughts and fears have diminished a lot. Knowing that a lot of my fears are not reality-based really helps." — Amanda Seyfried[121]

"I've battled a lot of things, including anxiety and depression." — Kesha[122]

"I've suffered through depression and anxiety my whole life." — Lady Gaga[123]

Even Kevin Love and DeMar DeRozan — two NBA All-Stars — have been open about suffering from panic attacks and depression respectively.[124] Clearly a societal taboo is being torn down when male athletes admit to struggling with mental health. This particular taboo is not being torn down a moment too soon.

**KEY PARENTING TAKE-AWAYS:**

Depression:

1. If your child is depressed, seek professional treatment with cognitive behavioral therapy

Non-suicidal self-injury disorder:

2. If you discover your child is self-harming, avoid criticizing, overreacting, or making your teen feel guilty
3. Seek professional treatment, since cognitive behavioral therapy may be helpful
4. Establish a communication mechanism for your teen to use that's not face-to-face
5. Find a support group of other parents in the same situation

Oppositional defiant disorder and conduct disorder:

6. If you suspect your child suffers from one of these disorders, get an official diagnosis and seek professional treatment
7. Find a support group of other parents in the same situation

Eating disorders:

8. To the extent you can, limit your child's exposure to media portraying unrealistic body types, and comment on examples when you see them
9. Show your daughter the Dove commercial* and discuss the effects of unrealistic media on body image

* Available at: www.youtube.com/watch?v=iYhCn0jf46U

10. If you suspect or discover your child suffers from an eating disorder, seek professional treatment with cognitive behavioral therapy
11. Avoid any treatment that congregates affected teens in a group

Bipolar disorder:

12. If your child is struggling with severe mood swings or is otherwise behaving out of character in extreme ways, read the description of bipolar disorder in the guideline produced by the Child and Adolescent Bipolar Foundation*
13. If the symptoms match, seek professional treatment

Stress/anxiety

14. If your teen is feeling stressed or anxious, recomend exercise
15. Consider whether pressure from you to achieve academically and extracurricularly could be contributing, keeping in mind that ultimately 'big fish' tend to thrive in 'small ponds'

Overall:

1. Discuss the topic of mental health with your teen to clarify that mental illnesses are indeed illnesses, which can and should be treated
2. Consider sharing the celebrity testimonials from this conclusion section with your teen to destigmatize mental health issues

## *Sexual orientation and identity*

As both the mastermind behind a successful effort to crack the communication codes used by the Germans during World War II, and the father of the field of theoretical computer science which helped usher in the era of the modern computer, he should have been lauded two times over as a national hero. Instead, Alan Turing was sentenced to choose between jail and mandatory hormonal treatment. His crime? Being homosexual.

Even in the welcome new era of acceptance in some parts of the world, with National Coming Out Day and pride parades celebrated publicly, life is still very difficult for the majority of those who don't conform to standard gender norms. Teenagers in particular are far more likely to be bullied if they don't fit the gender mold.[125] Indeed, 70 percent of Lesbian, Gay, Bisexual, Transgender and Queer (LGBTQ+) students have been verbally harassed (e.g., called names or threatened); 60 percent feel unsafe at school

* Available at: www.dbsalliance.org/pdfs/BMPN/treatment_guidelines.pdf

because of their sexual orientation; 57 percent have been sexually harassed; 29 percent have been pushed or shoved; and 12 percent punched, kicked, or injured with a weapon in the past year at school.[126] Non-conforming teens are therefore unsurprisingly at high risk for depression, substance abuse and suicidal behavior,[127] which is why the topic of sexual orientation and identity is appearing here, in this chapter discussing mental health.

**How common?**

Being gay, lesbian or bisexual is a relatively common phenomenon. Somewhere between 2 and 5 percent of males and 7 to 12 percent of females age 18–19 say they are attracted to members of their own sex, often in addition to being attracted to members of the opposite sex.[128]

Another independent dimension beyond attraction is how individuals feel about their own gender. Some kids who are born female feel male and vice versa, as one former Olympic gold medal-winning male decathlete revealed before publicly transforming into Caitlyn. So-called gender incongruence[129] is not classified as a disorder, but if it leads to discomfort or distress, this is referred to as 'gender dysphoria.'[130] A recent large survey of adolescents which controlled for facetious responses (a common hazard in this type of research) found that around 0.6 percent of teens identified with the opposite sex, and 3.3 percent felt that they were non-binary.[131] * [132] The amount of politicized commentary on this topic tends to obscure the fact that this is an exceedingly rare phenomenon.

Experts categorically caution against attempting to change a child's sexual orientation. The American Academy of Pediatrics states that interventions have little or no potential for changing a child's orientation, and such 'therapy' typically only succeeds in provoking guilt and anxiety.[133] The American Psychiatric Association also concurs.[134]

The same holds for gender identity. Twin studies suggest that approximately 60 percent of the variance in gender identity is genetic,[135] which means gender identity is even more heritable than basic personality traits like extroversion, conscientiousness, etc.[136] Furthermore, kids who don't conform to traditional gender norms often face bullying and scorn at school and disapproval at home, reinforcing the likelihood that they haven't simply chosen this path voluntarily.[137]

Family support can dramatically improve quality of life for non-conforming teens.[138] Lesbian, gay, and bisexual young adults who report being

* Rates appear to be similar among adults,[1] although it's still unknown whether these feelings remain stable over time.[2]

rejected by their families during adolescence are eight times more likely to report having attempted suicide, six times more likely to report high levels of depression, and three times more likely to use illegal drugs.[139] Kids who are not allowed to express their preferred gender identity are also more likely to become homeless or incarcerated later in life.[140] On the flip side, gender-nonconforming youth whose families are strongly supportive have more positive mental health, fewer depressive symptoms, higher self-esteem and higher life satisfaction.[141] These studies don't prove causation; perhaps parents with the tendency to be supportive pass along positive genetics to their children, who are less likely to become depressed no matter what their circumstances. Nevertheless, there seems to be little downside to being supportive.[*] [142]

The problem is that many non-conforming teens are keeping their identity secret. One survey of approximately 10,000 LGBTQ–identified youth recruited online found that only just over half are 'out' to their immediate family. Of those 'in the closet,' 30 percent say their family is not accepting or is homo/bi/trans-phobic; 19 percent are scared of the reaction, or don't know how their family will react; 16 percent have religious reasons; 10 percent say they aren't ready, and 10 percent say they don't or can't talk with their family.[143] The struggles of Maria, a 15-year-old lesbian, illustrate the problem. Her parents had made various harsh comments about the LGBTQ+ community over time, so she worried that if she came out, her parents wouldn't love her anymore.[144]

Alan Turing is now lauded posthumously, too late for him to be aware of the public appreciation he has earned. In 2013, Turing was finally granted a royal pardon by the Queen; in 2019, the BBC television program voted Turing "The Greatest Person of the Twentieth Century;[145] and in 2021, a public nomination process culminated in his being chosen as the new face of Britain's £50 bank note.[146] In the words of one his nominators, "Turing deserves to be remembered and recognized for his fantastic contribution to the war effort and his legacy to science. A pardon from the Queen is a fitting tribute to an exceptional man."[147]

* For parents with a transgender child, there are many practical issues to consider in providing the right kind of support. A good resource is the World Professional Association for Transgender Health (WPATH) Standards of Care,[i] available at: www.wpath.org/publications/soc

**KEY PARENTING TAKE-AWAYS:**

1. If you suspect or find out that your teen's sexual orientation or identity is non-conforming, being supportive regardless of your own views will maximize the likelihood of a positive outcome for your child
2. Be alert for signs of bullying and/or depression in your non-conforming child, and see the relevant sections on bullying (brave bystander behavior) and depression (get struggling teens CBT) for key actions to take

# 6. DELINQUENCY

## Keep "tempteens" on a tight leash

> "If a man have a stubborn or rebellious son, of sufficient years and understanding (viz.) sixteen years of age, which will not obey the voice of his Father, or the voice of his Mother...such a son shall be put to death." — Capital Law of the General Court of Massachusetts Bay, November 6, 1646[1]

If your adolescent ever chafes against a consequence, you can point out that whatever punishment you are imposing pales in comparison to being put to death. But why have societies across history felt the need to resort to draconian laws to control their adolescents? Here's a selection of examples of misbehavior from our own time. A Florida teen posted footage on YouTube showing himself running his car through red lights and ramming into a trio of vehicles, before being cut out of his car and airlifted to the hospital;[2] a group of teens from Michigan killed a motorist with a game they dubbed 'Overpassing' in which they threw rocks off an overpass and shouted 'Dinger!' when a car was hit;[3] 60 New Jersey high school seniors were arrested after breaking into their school overnight, flipping desks and leaving petroleum jelly on doorknobs and urine in the hallways;[4] and another teenager filled the bathtub with fireworks, covered his body in protective clothing and set up a video camera to record the event, before launching a fireball that left him with burns covering 14 percent of his body.[5]

Most adolescents navigate their teen years without crashing their car, committing manslaughter, defiling their school or self-immolating; these are salacious outliers seized upon by the media for their newsworthiness. Nevertheless, even if they are not making headlines, teens are consistently misbehaving. According to a national survey, in the prior month 29 percent of high school students had drunk alcohol, 22 percent had used marijuana, and 39 percent of those who drove had texted or e-mailed while driving. A total of 38 percent had had sexual intercourse, of which only 54 percent had used a condom.[6] And only 13 percent of teens report that their parents are completely aware of the full extent of their online activities, with covert behavior including opening social media accounts, sending and receiving sexual messages online, cyberbullying, and meeting online contacts in person.[7]

Most parents are blissfully unaware of what is happening under their noses. In one revealing survey of parents and their adolescents, 2 percent of the parents believed their child had had sex; the actual figure was 58 percent. Five percent of parents suspected their child had drunk alcohol, when in fact 55 percent had imbibed. Carrying weapons to school, using LSD, cocaine, tobacco and marijuana were all significantly underestimated by parents. Perhaps most worrying of all: 22 percent of students in this particular sample admitted to a suicide attempt at some point in the past, with only 2 percent of their parents aware of it. In the words of the researchers, "When it came to recognizing significant risk behaviors in their adolescents, parents were clueless."[8]

When confronted with such sobering statistics, upper-middle class parents often fall back on the comforting delusion that the surveys are skewed by the misbehaviors of teens from disadvantaged inner-city neighborhoods. In fact there are countless examples of privileged kids behaving badly (see box).

**Pivileged misbehavior**

Wealthy Houston teenagers stole a plane and toilet-papered a high school stadium during a football game; youth from an affluent suburb in Virginia torched a car, setting fire to a nearby bungalow and burning it down;[9] and a group of young hooligans from a wealthy community in Georgia managed to rack up more than $100,000 worth of vandalism by setting fires and tossing homemade bombs before being caught.[10]

Adolescents from wealthier families and those with more educated parents tend to start their shenanigans at a later age, presumably because initially their parents are able to supervise them more. But when they're finally granted a longer leash, they rapidly catch up with their less affluent peers.[11] By twelfth grade there's little association between family wealth and drug use,[12] * property crime rates, or even violent crime rates.[13] And the naïveté

* This includes inhalants, LSD and other hallucinogens, ecstasy (MDMA), cocaine, amphetamines, and tranquilizers. Marijuana, synthetic marijuana, and heroin are the exceptions

gap can be even more pronounced in affluent families: children from wealthier homes are not only more likely to meet an online contact offline, but their parents are less likely to realize.[14]

Why are the teen years so fraught across the full spectrum of family backgrounds? The most likely explanation is that misbehavior is literally hardwired into their brains. Evolution rewarded adolescents who exhibited the risk-taking qualities that helped them break free of their parents, become independent, show off their prowess to future mates, and ultimately start their own families.[15] This explanation jibes with the natural shift in sleep cycles we observe in our increasingly nocturnal teenagers. The universal biological shift towards staying up late during adolescence is likely an adaptation nature provided to allow teens to spend time with others their own age, free from parental scrutiny.[16]

Our teens are physically gearing up to leave the nest, so the mismatch between their readiness and drive to break free and their continued status as subordinate family members is likely the root cause of most teen drama. For despite references in the bible about stoning disobedient adolescents,[17] teen misbehavior is predominantly a modern, Western phenomenon. A study of 186 present-day traditional societies worldwide ranging from the Yanamamo in Venezuela to the Samoa in Oceania found that in these cultures, there is no expectation that adolescents will misbehave, and the few individuals who do act in antisocial ways tend to be adults.[18] In preindustrial societies, teens were naturally forced by circumstance to play the role of an adult, in alignment with their burgeoning desire to do so. Now, many First-World teens are expected to spend much longer merely preparing for adult life. Adolescence is no longer a brief transition, but a long, drawn-out process, extending for many privileged teens through four years of high school and four more years of college, an unnaturally long time to continue to be dependent on parents.[19]

Further exacerbating the mismatch between teen desires to act as adults and societal pressures to prolong their childhood is the significant drop in the age of puberty over the past 200 years.[20] For example, the average age at which girls develop breasts has mysteriously decreased by almost a year since the 1970s.[21]

**Why are kids maturing sooner?**
No one is fully sure what is driving the worrying shift towards earlier puberty. Possible culprits include assisted reproductive technology, soy-based infant formula, obesity, and childhood exposure to environmental pollutants, hormones in food, plastics, preservatives, skin and hair care products.[22]

Puberty is the biological trigger for a huge spike in sensation-seeking and risk-taking; it's the timing of puberty rather than chronological age that predicts when teens begin to take risks.* [23] But puberty has no effect on the development of the brain's cognitive control network, which matures at its own separate pace up through the mid-twenties.[24] Since teens only gradually get better at controlling their impulses as they progress towards adulthood,[25] this shift to early puberty is causing a problematic misalignment.[26] Younger teens simply don't yet have the mature decision-making skills to handle the risky situations towards which they are inexorably drawn,[27] and can't properly absorb the lessons from negative outcomes in the way that older teens begin to do.[28]

Therefore the best strategy with "tempteens" is to restrict their opportunities to make bad choices, rather than attempting to educate them.[29] Once they hit puberty, the key is to shelter them from risky experiences as much as possible. Younger teens in particular ideally need their day filled up with positive, supervised activities, so they won't be tempted into behaving badly.[30] In other words, keep them on a very tight leash. Here's how.

### 1. Keep track of your teen

You may think you know what your children are up to when they're out of your sight, but there's a very real chance that you have no idea, and possibly wouldn't want to know. Case in point: two teenage boys were recently caught filming themselves lying on tracks as a train hurtled over them, risking being sucked up by their clothes.[31]

Adolescents are not known for their veracity. Around 75 percent of adolescents admit to lying, with an average of nearly three lies a day, and 60 percent telling up to five lies daily. (For comparison, younger children average 1.7 and adults 1.9 lies per day.)[32]

---

* On average, sensation-seeking peaks on average around age 19, and then declines as individuals move into their 20s.[i]

**Does monitoring work? The jury is out**

Because adolescents can't always be trusted to accurately report their doings, some parents require their teens to check in or independently verify their location. There are reams of observational studies which imply that this is a sensible approach, and that such monitoring can protect teens from drug use,[33] improve academic achievement,[34] limit risky sexual behavior, [35] reduce delinquent behavior,[36] and various combinations of all of the above.[37] Unfortunately, research in the field of parenting is constantly conflating correlation and causation, and we can't rule out the possibility that sensible parents who monitor their offspring have given birth to sensible children, who don't need much monitoring in the first place. (Similarly, children from single-parent households are more likely to drop out of school, as are children with many siblings, and while it's very possible that's because those children get less parental supervision, there could be many other explanations as well. [38])

It's therefore premature to conclude that monitoring works. Studies that have run randomized, controlled trials have typically only tested the effects of monitoring as a component of broader programs, making it difficult to untangle the effects. Furthermore, most studies of monitoring ask parents how much they know about their teens' activities and ask youth how much they disclose to their parents, rather than measuring true monitoring behavior.[39] A couple of outliers include the Family Check-Up intervention[40] and the ImPACT program; both encourage parents to know where their teens are, whom they are with, and what they are doing, and both have shown promise.[41]

An obvious twenty-first century solution to the conundrum of keeping tabs on a slippery teen's whereabouts would be to use tracking technology. For the moment, most parents don't seem to have seized this opportunity; a survey from 2015 found that only 16 percent were using monitoring tools on their teens' cellphones to track their location.[42] For those who are intrigued, the non-profit organization Common Sense Media has compiled a list of the best apps for different types of parental control and monitoring.* [43] There are even GPS tracking systems which can be installed in cars.† [44] These options sound promising, but there's no research yet on whether they can reduce misbehavior.

The difficulty is that most adolescents are more technologically savvy than their parents, and would be able to disguise their whereabouts if sufficiently motivated to do so. A tragic illustration of this point is the story of 19-year-old Leah Croucher, a missing person who changed the settings

* Available at: www.commonsensemedia.org/blog/parents-ultimate-guide-to-parental-controls

† e.g. the Teen Arrive Alive program for $19.99 a month

on her mobile phone to disable location services shortly before leaving the house one evening to "meet a friend" and never returning.[45]

There is also speculation that deploying such technologies could reduce the level of trust between parents and children,[46] although there's no research yet to back this theory up. On the other hand, in the case of an accident, it could be useful to have a means of tracking down your teen:

> "Lexi Draycott's family immediately knew something wasn't right when she was late coming home and calls or texts went unanswered. "The lack of response was out of character for her," her father said. Using the Find My Friends app, he pinpointed her daughter's whereabouts... Hidden from view, about 25 feet down the side of a tree-covered embankment, the teenager had been trapped in the wreckage of her car for almost seven hours — and she was alive. * [47]

**2. Keep your teen occupied**

> "Idle hands are the devil's workshop." — Proverb

In 1991, President George Bush praised a new program, Midnight Basketball, as one of his "thousand points of light." The concept of Midnight Basketball was to provide a league for young men ages 17–21 to play on summer nights between 10pm to 2am, with games supervised by police officers.[48] An initial study claimed the program had a achieved a 30 percent reduction in crime,[49] which sounded awfully promising. In fact, this result was too good to be true. The very small size of the initiative compared to the total number of young men on the streets made such a claim totally implausible.[50] Additional research now suggests that programs like these are often ineffectual, as the kids most in need of supervision tend to choose not to participate.[51]

---

* Name of protagonist has been changed for privacy purposes

**Cause or effect?**
There are endless academic studies showing extracurricular participation is associated with lower delinquency and better academic performance, but they don't technically prove anything useful, although many claim otherwise.[52] It's just as plausible that the types of kids who are naturally drawn to extracurriculars are precisely the types of kids who are achievement-oriented in other domains of their lives as well, and wouldn't have been drawn to delinquent behaviors in the first place. Similarly, programs designed to teach teens how to use their leisure time better[*] [53] get good reviews from participating students,[54] but there's no research so far proving they prevent delinquency. Fortunately, a handful of better studies have actually intervened with a randomized group of kids on a larger scale, and have shown that providing structured leisure activities for teens can help reduce delinquency and other problematic behaviors.[†] [55]

The most successful example of a concerted societal effort to reduce teen delinquency on a grand scale comes from the tiny country of Iceland, population roughly 330,000. In the 1980s, Harvey Milkman, an American psychology professor studying drug use, began experimenting with offering teenagers ways to achieve a 'natural high' without resorting to drugs or crime, by teaching them anything they wanted to learn: music, dance, art, martial arts. Then in 1991, he was invited to Iceland to give a lecture, and soon had been enlisted to consult on launching a large-scale social program.[56]

As Milkman explains, "In the late '90s, it was commonplace on Friday and Saturday nights to observe hordes of drunken teenagers sullying the streets of Reykjavik in mob-like revelry."[57] Determined to stem this problem, the government rolled out an ambitious and elaborate national plan. New laws banned kids aged 13 to 16 from being outside after 10pm in winter and midnight in summer, and raised the age to purchase tobacco and alcohol.

* TimeWise curriculum available for $135 at: www.etr.org/store/curricula/timewise/; descriptions of each lesson: www.personal.psu.edu/llc7/lesson_one.htm

† The Quantum Opportunities Program, considered a model program by the US Department of Justice Office of Juvenile Justice and Delinquency Prevention,[1] takes students from rough neighborhoods and provides them with a year-round set of activities throughout their four years of high school, including academic tutorials, computer skills training, community service, cultural activities (visits to museums, concerts), and life skills training (e.g. alcohol and drug abuse awareness family planning), along with financial incentives for participating. By the end of the program, 42% of students were enrolled in a postsecondary program vs. 16% of peers, and only 7% had arrest records vs. 13% of peers.[2 3]

Similarly, the Teen Outreach Program, which engages students in extensive volunteering, has reduced teenage pregnancy and school failure and dropout rates by 15-50%.[4] The Early College High School Initiative, funded in part by the Bill & Melinda Gates Foundation,[5] takes disadvantaged students and offers them an opportunity to earn an associate's degree or up to two years of college credits toward a bachelor's degree during high school at no cost, with instruction designed to engage students in understanding why they are learning a topic and make real-world connections; 22% of participating students go on to earn a college degree versus only 2% of comparison students.[6] And the successful and highly regarded Carrera Adolescent Pregnancy Prevention Program has taken a similar approach, engaging teen girls over several years with roughly 3 hours of after-school programming each weekday.[7 8]

Communities received funding to launch organized activities such as sports, music, art, dance, and other recreational activities. Schools were required to create parent organizations, tasked with offering talks for parents on spending time with their kids and monitoring their children's friends and whereabouts. These organizations were also encouraged to create agreements for parents to sign, pledging not to allow unsupervised parties or buy alcohol for minors, and to look out for the wellbeing of other children in addition to their own.[58]

The results speak for themselves:[59]

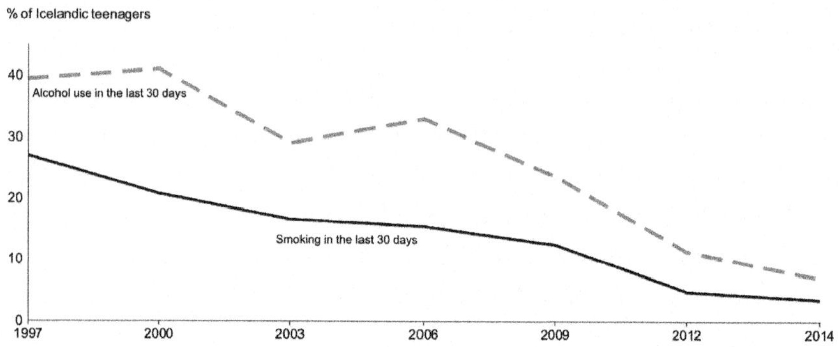


The "Icelandic model" is now is being rolled out in 14 countries across Europe.[60]

### 3. Collude with other parents

Neighborhood matters when it comes to delinquency. Crime is very concentrated; 3 percent of addresses produce 50 percent of reported crimes.[61] Irrespective of their family characteristics, teens who live in low-income neighborhoods have higher rates of delinquency,[62] while those who are fortunate enough to move to more affluent neighborhoods become correspondingly less likely to fall into the delinquency trap.[63]

At the other extreme, it's not excessive affluence that makes a better neighborhood either. The risk of juvenile delinquency is greatest at the two extreme ends of the spectrum of privilege; those from very poor neighborhoods, but also those from very wealthy neighborhoods.[64] One could speculate that the first group of teens feels hopeless, the second group purposeless. Although these are very different underlying problems, the result in both cases is apathy, manifesting as a complete disregard for the consequences of their behavior.

Zeroing in further, it's not even the wider neighborhood that seems to matter, but the demographics of the families whose children attend the same school, which is unsurprising since school is where kids spend their time, make their friends, and become integrated into a community.[65] Furthermore, certain communities stand out. For example, one study found that high school dropout rates averaged 14 percent for public schools and 12 percent for private schools, but only about 3.5 percent for Catholic and other religious schools. Families affiliated with religious schools who frequently attended religious services had teens with dropout rates that were lower still.[66]

Is this because adolescents who attend services are absorbing the teachings of their faith and adhering to them? That would be the explanation most religious leaders would offer, but it's unlikely to be the only explanation. The children in these communities are also benefiting from the interconnectedness of the parents, through a phenomenon known as "intergenerational closure." When parents work together to agree and enforce standards of behavior, they can not only monitor their own offspring but hold others' children accountable as well.[67]

Teens attending schools with a high density of parent ties tend to, for example, achieve better grades in math and drink less alcohol,[68] and the average competence of the parents of a teen's peers has been shown to matter more than the competence of the teen's own parents.[69] There's plenty of truth in the overused proverb "it takes a village to raise a child."[70]

The importance of interconnected parents may also help explain why moving in general is difficult for children, since it severs the ties of not only the children who have to start over socially, but also of the parents. All else being equal, 12 percent of teens drop out of high school if the family has not moved, 17 percent if the family has moved once, and 23 percent if it has moved twice.[71] So regardless of what kind of neighborhood you live in, get to know and collude with the other parents around you.

### 4. Involve competent adults

Scared Straight, a program invented in the 1970s and turned into a reality television show, organized field trips to prisons for delinquent teens, so they could observe the life that awaited them if they continued down their delinquent paths. This initiative and others like it backfired spectacularly, almost doubling the odds that students would get into later trouble.[72] Rather than deterring the budding delinquents, it effectively exposed them to terrible 'role models' to emulate. Similarly, programs such as summer camps that bring delinquent adolescents together can perversely cause peer contagion, where students come to view poor behavior as normal, exchange ideas for misbehavior, brag about deviant behavior, and compete to be the worst offenders.[73]

For the same reasons, creating locations without sufficient adult supervision where teens can congregate to pursue leisure activities can be counterproductive. For example, a series of leisure centers in Sweden offered pursuits such as pool, ping pong, video games, darts, TV, and music, and sponsored various special events such as outdoor field trips, movie night, and weekly basketball. An adult would be present, but typically didn't intervene in directing the activity.[74] Young people with antisocial tendencies were the most likely to become involved in the centers, and over time they began to influence the others who spent time there, to the point where the centers became training grounds for antisocial behavior.[75]

When it comes to occupying teens, the devil is in the details: the key element for success is adult interaction and supervision.[76] Sociologists have found that teens in preindustrial societies around the world spend the majority of their time either with their immediate family, or with other adults of the same sex being trained in productive work. Delinquent behavior is rare, and tends to arise only when boys are organized into groups, for example for military purposes. (This phenomenon is specific to boys; girls, in contrast, don't tend to behave badly when they congregate in groups.)[77]

For those of us who live in industrialized societies, work experience is the modern version of the apprenticeships of old, so you might want to consider encouraging your teen to get a job, particularly if the alternative is spending time home alone or unsupervised. Although clearly not all jobs are equal. [78] A job in a fast food outlet, performing rote tasks that require minimal initiative, surrounded by peers and overseen by a supervisor only a few years older, is not going to teach your child many useful life skills.[79] Neither will a glamorous job that provides a high salary or confers social status.[*] [80] The best types of jobs require responsibility and problem-solving and involve learning new skills directly from adults. So instead of lifeguard, think office clerk or museum usher.[81]

* Allowing teens to earn money without requiring them to pay for their share of the household costs could potentially backfire by giving them an artificial sense of the ease of adulthood, although no research yet proves this point. Insisting they contribute a percentage of their earnings towards a savings account could help prevent them becoming too flush with easy spending money.

**Too much of a good thing**
Too much work appears to be bad for teens, although the available research doesn't prove it's the work itself causing the problems.* Teens who work long work hours tend to get less sleep and exercise. They also underperform at school, perhaps because of insufficient time to do homework.[82]

**Big siblings? The jury is out**
Various non-profit organizations have attempted to harness the benefits of exposing adolescents to adult role models by pairing adolescents with adult mentors. Big Brothers/ Big Sisters of America (BB/BSA) is the largest such program with 235 agencies across the US,[83] and there are many others. Although mentoring makes sense conceptually, for the moment most programs haven't been rigorously evaluated,[84] and those that have been studied have demonstrated only small benefits.[85]

If you have the time yourself, by all means spend it with your teen. Adolescents who spend time with their families, particularly on weekends, are less likely to engage in delinquent behavior.[86] At least you can be sure they aren't behaving stupidly if they're with you.

### 4. Use positive reinforcement

A final way to cope with teens' tendency to misbehave is to utilize positive reinforcement. Because punishment only teaches children what not to do, it's not as effective at changing behaviour as reward-based strategies, which draw children towards what they should do. Punishment can fuel anger and alienation — boot camps for juvenile delinquents used to be popular in the US, but were found to be totally ineffective for this reason.[87] Reward does the opposite, and nonconfrontational programs for delinquents show far more promise.† [88] Think point systems for doing chores and increasing privileges (e.g. a later curfew) for good behavior — the teen version of the star chart from kindergarten.

* Studies often use an arbitrary cut-off of approximately 20 hours of work per week, but there's nothing magic about this number.

† For those who find it difficult to parent this way instinctively, there are several programs which teach "positive parenting." The top-ranked program according to the United Nations Office on Drugs and Crime is Triple P - Positive Parenting, which has achieved results in reducing delinquency,[1] [2] is available self-serve online and includes a module specifically for teens.[3] The program focuses generically on improving the skills, knowledge, and confidence of parents, as well as developing children's social, emotional, linguistic, intellectual, and behavioral competence.[4] Another example is Parenting Wisely, a self-administered online program that teaches parents and their children skills for enhancing relationships and decreasing conflict. (Available at: www.parentingwisely.com/)[5]

**Take-aways**

How do kids get drawn into deviant behavior in the first place? The root cause appears to be nature and nurture in equal measure. Initially teens are attracted to peers with similar tendencies. Spending time with those peers then reinforces the deviant tendencies.[89] It's easy to predict a student's behavior by looking at the behavior of the student's friends, so parents are right to be concerned if their kids have fallen in with the 'wrong crowd.'[90]

Over time, teens who frequently congregate begin to form a unique group identity. As described in *The Nurture Assumption: Why Children Turn Out the Way They Do*,

> Adolescents are not aspiring to adult status — they are contrasting themselves with adults. They adopt characteristic modes of clothing, hairstyles, speech, and behavior so that, even though they're now the same size as adults, no one will have any trouble telling them apart. If they truly aspired to adult status they would not be spraying graffiti on overpasses, going for joyrides in cars they do not own, or shoplifting nail polish from drug stores. They would be doing boring adult things, like figuring out their income tax or doing their laundry... When groupness is not salient, it is perfectly possible for teenagers to have warm relationships with adults. Some of their best friends are grownups.[91]

What approach should you take if your child is already a 'Rebel without a Cause'?

One drastic action, which is likely to be impossible for many families, would be to extract your teen from an unhelpful social milieu by moving to a different neighborhood and school. If that's not possible, we've seen that the best approaches are to keep track of your teen's activities and whereabouts; keep your teen productively occupied; collude with other parents; encourage your child to spend time with competent adults; and use positive reinforcement.

If none of these approaches work, don't despair. A study in Sweden that followed the lives of 1,000 children through to adulthood found that, among boys, modestly antisocial rule-breaking behavior as an adolescent was associated with being an entrepreneur as an adult.[*] [92] So if you have a mildly delinquent son, you can take solace in the thought that he may be ultimately destined for entrepreneurship.

Adolescents are both more optimistic and more resilient than their future cynical adult selves. In the words of Aristotle, "They look at the good side rather than the bad, not having yet witnessed many instances of wickedness. They trust others readily, because they have not yet often been cheated. They are sanguine... [because] they have as yet met with few disappointments... They have exalted notions, because they have not yet been humbled by life."[93] The types of major setbacks that might traumatize an adult are often taken in stride by resilient kids.[94] So if your teen has gotten into trouble running free without a leash, it's never too late to grab your child by the collar.

# Dig deeper

> Delinquent: a person, usually young, who behaves in a way that is illegal or not acceptable to most people.[95]

For most people, the term "juvenile delinquent" conjures up a vision of hoodlums lounging in a menacing group on an inner-city street corner. Fewer would picture this description: "Kids with rich parents are selling marijuana, and Ivy League-bound students are throwing eggs at houses and vandalizing cars."[96] Even if you're sure your child would never do such things, you could be wrong.

When it comes to committing crimes, boys are more troublesome than girls, although there are plenty of offenders of both sexes. Here are the reasons American teens get arrested:[†] [97]

* This relationship doesn't hold for more severe rule-breaking, e.g. crime.[1]

† Break-down of categories from FBI data applied to cumulative arrest % estimate from 'Demographic Patterns' study

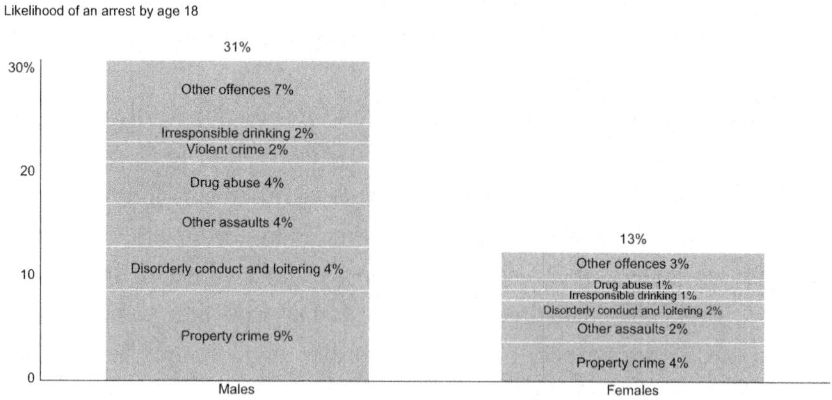


Since only 8 percent of boys and 6 percent of girls have a diagnosed conduct disorder, it's clear that plenty of mentally healthy teens are also getting themselves in trouble.

Although in the US adolescents under age 18 are handled within the juvenile justice system rather than tried as adults,* [98] even minor infractions of the law can have ramifications later in life. [99] Approximately two thirds of US college applications ask about criminal history,[100] 20 percent of colleges actually conduct criminal background checks,[101] and even a single arrest for disorderly conduct without a conviction can reduce future job offers.† [102]

* Except in 5 states, Texas, Missouri, Wisconsin, Michigan and Georgia, where a juvenile is defined as under age 17.

† For those who are concerned about a pattern of criminal behavior, the most successful attempts to divert adolescents from criminal trajectories have fallen into two broad categories. The first involves therapy aimed at families.[1] The best example in this category, lauded as a model program by the US Department of Justice Office of Juvenile Justice and Delinquency Prevention, is called Functional Family Therapy.[2] If you're concerned that your child is showing criminal tendencies, you can check to see if a version of the program is available in your area. (See www.fftllc.com/sites/)

The second category of intervention targets the adolescents themselves to help them develop "thinking skills,"[3] under the assumption that delinquents often don't think before they act, attribute their misfortunes to fate, misinterpret social cues, fail to consider alternative solutions to problems, and lack effective communication skills.[4] The best program for boys available in this category is called Becoming a Man,[5] which encourages participants to slow down in high-stakes settings and ask whether the situation could be construed differently. Here's an illustrative vignette from the training:

> Students are divided into pairs and one is given a ball, which the other student is told he has 30 seconds to get from his partner. Almost all youth use physical force to try to take the ball out of the other's fist. During the debrief, the group leader points out that no one simply asked for the ball. When prompted about why they did not simply ask, most respond with some version of "he wouldn't have given it," or "he would have thought I was a punk." The leader then asks the other youth, "How would you have reacted if asked nicely for the ball?" The answer typically is something like, "I would have given it; it's just a stupid ball."

The content from Becoming a Man isn't available for parents to access self-serve, so the only option would be to suggest that your child's school participate. (See www.youth-guidance.org/bam/)

Not all delinquent behaviors are necessarily illegal. Returning to the definition above, "behaving in a way that is not acceptable to most people" could also include many of the behaviors we've discussed previously, like taking drugs and having risky sex.

**Dropping out**

Dropping out of high school is also a common proxy for delinquency used in research, because a decision to leave school typically implies a short-sighted focus on less desirable priorities, notwithstanding the success of the handful of famous outliers like Richard Branson and Arnold Schwarznegger.[103] Like many of the other forms of misbehavior discussed previously, dropout rates have declined in the US, but remain a problem:[104]

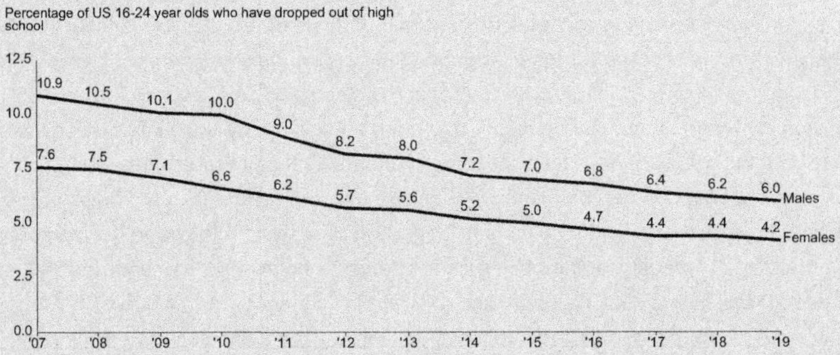


Why do kids fall into these traps so easily?

Older teens progressively develop the ability to assess risks just as accurately as adults (although as we'll soon see, this doesn't mean they act on this information as adults would).[105] For example, one study asked people of various ages to evaluate the possible consequences of risky behaviors such as drinking & driving, smoking marijuana, skipping school to go to a mall, taking their parent's car, having sex, and going to a party with beer being served. Adults and adolescents judged the risks similarly.[106] In the words of one review, teen risk-taking "doesn't stem from ignorance, irrationality, delusions of invulnerability, or faulty calculations."[107] In fact adolescents, like adults, even tend to overestimate the danger of risky behaviors,[108] and higher-risk adolescents often correctly believe that they're at greater risk than their peers.[109]

Nevertheless, the strategy of educating older adolescents about risks has repeatedly failed. Countless costly programs in schools and communities have warned teens about the potential perils of adolescence,[110] yet despite these programs, teens continue to play high-stakes games of roulette with their lives.[111] For example, a review of sex education programs found that simply providing information about risks had no effect whatsoever; the only programs that changed teen behavior were those that directly helped the students in practical ways, for example by offering easy access to more effective types of birth control.[112] Similarly, providing teens with facts about the risks of smoking, drinking or using drugs makes no difference at all.[113]

**Why doesn't teaching teens work?**

A key reason that education fails is that adolescents counterintuitively over-rely on reasoning. An entertaining study asked teens to rapidly press a button to evaluate whether a variety of scenarios were "a good idea" or not, including swimming with sharks, going for a walk, jumping off a roof, and eating salad. Adolescents took significantly longer than adults to respond to danger cues, but were the same as adults in reacting to "good" stimuli. The researchers hypothesize that when confronted with a dangerous scenario, adults automatically conjure up a mental image to which they have a visceral response. Lacking such mental images, adolescents are forced to rely primarily on reasoning.[114] In reality, adolescents take risks *despite* the possibility of undesirable consequences; they are taking calculated risks that in their minds are "worth it."[115]

Over-emphasizing risks and neglecting to mention "benefits" can sometimes even backfire. Many risks involve a small chance of a devastating outcome. If teens are given the misimpression that the devastating outcome is likely and then manage to avoid it, they could be left with a feeling of invincibility.[116] Lung cancer from smoking and infertility from sexually transmitted diseases often don't show up until much later in life, and many drunk teens do manage to arrive home without crashing, reinforcing their false belief that they were safe behind the wheel. Those adolescents whose risky shenanigans don't backfire immediately will often stop believing that the adult cautions about topics like unsafe sex and drug use are legitimate, particularly if adults have failed to mention that these activities can be fun, exciting and pleasurable, as previously discussed in the section on drugs.[117] As another study points out, "If the Partnership for a Drug Free America claims that smoking marijuana will transform your brain into a fried egg, and you nonetheless share a joint with friends on occasion and manage to maintain your grade point average, then why trust what they say about cocaine and heroin?"[118]

Adolescents also share similarities with compulsive gamblers. In gambling situations they seek out risks; for example they will favor a gamble with a small chance of winning a lot over one with a good chance of winning a moderate amount.[119] The excitement of the reward appears to have the capacity to short-circuit their rational deliberation processes.[120] And they rapidly learn from reward, but are less able to learn from punishment.[121]

Emotional content can also distract them, as has been cleverly revealed in studies asking teens to conduct an arbitrary task such as measuring nose width when viewing faces with varying emotional expressions. Adolescents, much more than either children or adults, are distracted by anything emotionally evocative or attention-grabbing.[122] They are drawn like flies towards honey, and have a remarkable capacity to overlook the flashing neon signs warning that the honey is poisonous.

Adolescents are also profoundly influenced by their peers, which can exacerbate their natural gambling propensities. They are far more likely to take risks playing a video game[123] or driving a simulated car if a peer is watching, because earning the admiration of their peers is worth the risk.[124] They're more likely to change their opinions about the riskiness of an everyday situation if told their peers think differently,[125] even though most will officially rank "what my peers are doing" dead last in a list of what would make them change their minds about a topic.[126] Even being told a peer is actively watching them is sufficient to induce self-conscious emotion which can be picked up on an MRI scan.[127] And older adolescents, when asked, describe the influence of their peer-group as affecting their appearance, illicit acts, attitudes, and values.[128]

These examples all come from research studies, but the effects of peers can also be observed 'in the wild.'* Teenagers are far more likely to drink, use drugs and have sex if their friends are doing so as well, and they're much more likely to smash their car when friends are along for the ride.[129] When teens are arrested for homicide, over half the time more than one adolescent gets rounded up. As one study wryly puts it, "When an adolescent robs, steals, breaks into a house, or shoots another youth in the company of co-offenders, one real motive for this act is responding to the explicit or implicit 'I dare you.' Fear of being called chicken is almost certainly the major cause of death and injury from youth violence in the United States."[130]

* These observational studies are useful to bolster the point that peer influence extends to real world situations beyond the laboratory, but they can't be relied upon exclusively, as causation is harder to establish – are teens actually being influenced by their peers, or are they simply drawn to like-minded souls?

**The plus side of rebelliousness**

Teens' defiant or rebellious tendencies can actually be harnessed for good. Suggest to eighth graders that healthy eating is a way to take a stand against the manipulative and unfair practices of the food industry, and many will forgo sugary snacks and drinks a day later in an unrelated context.[131] Show teens body bags being piled outside a tobacco company's headquarters to illustrate the daily death toll from tobacco use, and 20 percent fewer of those teens will start smoking.[132] Reframing rebellion as submission to the desires of scheming corporate adults swiftly squelches the allure of misbehavior.

As a result, educating adolescents about risky behaviors is typically fruitless.[133] But parents can prevent their children from ending up in situations where they'll make poor decisions to impress their friends. The key is to keep them away from temptation until they're developmentally prepared to make better decisions and handle the consequences.[134] Public policy experts also point out that 'evocative media' can make an impression on teens,[135] so scattered throughout this book are suggestions of movies, TV shows and other media which could help bring your teen around to more sensible points of view.

Lest you feel too anxious recalling your own perilous journey through adolescence, you can take solace in the fact that your teen is likely to be better behaved than you were at the same age. Over the last 30 years the proportion of teens who have ever tried cigarettes has gone down from 70 to 24 percent; ever drunk alcohol from 82 to 63 percent; and ever had sex from 54 to 38 percent.[136] Nowadays teens are less likely to get into a car driven by someone who has been drinking, and are even wearing seatbelts and bicycle helmets more reliably than their parents did at their age. [137] These numbers are trending in the right direction, but there is still plenty of room for improvement, hence the need for this book.

## KEY PARENTING TAKE-AWAYS:

1. Keep track of your teen — know your offspring's location, company and activities
2. Keep your teen occupied with recreational activities
3. Get to know the parents of your child's friends and collude with them to supervise behavior
4. Encourage or arrange for your older adolescent to spend time with competent adults, e.g. job supervisors, mentors, older relatives, etc.
5. Use positive reinforcement by rewarding your teen for good behavior rather than punishing bad

# 7. HEALTH

> American life expectancy fell by one-tenth of a year, from 78.9 to 78.8, according to a report released by the National Center for Health Statistics. Meanwhile, the number of years people are expected to live at 65 remained unchanged, suggesting people are falling ill and dying young.[1]

Having discussed ways to protect adolescents from immediate harm earlier in this book, we'll now turn to the salubrious habits that will ensure they live a full life. Here's the simple, pithy advice on adolescent health from the Centers for Disease Control and Prevention: "Encourage your teen to get enough sleep and physical activity, and to eat healthy, balanced meals."[2] These three pillars of health are so straightforward that it feels trite to mention them. Yet as we'll see, many adolescents are disregarding these basic tenets of well-being, to their long-term detriment.

## Maximize sleep

> After getting between 3 and 4 hours of sleep for several nights in a row while working on a term paper in his sophomore year of high school, Brandon O'Keefe went into his kitchen at 3am to get a snack. Instead of slicing through a wedge of cheese, he sliced through his thumb clear to the bone, severing a ligament.[*] [3]

---

* Name of protagonist has been changed for privacy purposes.

Sleep is critical for adolescents, and indeed for everyone of all ages. Exhausted teens are more likely to hurt themselves, not just in the kitchen, but in other spheres of life, such as on the playing fields.[4] On the flip side, getting sufficient sleep has huge benefits: for example, elite college basketball players who slept more improved their shooting accuracy,[5] and most Olympic athletes sleep for 8 hours and take a nap every day. Even in the field of music, the very best violinists sleep the most.[6]

When it comes to academic performance, the evidence is even more incontrovertible: teens who sleep more do better in school. This is apparent in the laboratory, where experimenters have manipulated the amount of sleep students get, and observed that sleep loss dramatically interferes with their ability to learn and perform in academic settings.[7] It's also apparent in the real world, where students who don't sleep enough or have erratic sleep schedules perform worse academically, [8] while those with better grades consistently report getting more sleep.[9] Students will do worse the following day if they stay up late one evening to study more than usual.[10] On the flip side, many important intellectual breakthroughs occur as the result of a good night of sleep, when the brain has had time to reorganize and tackle complex problems.[11]

What are the consequences of a teen (or anyone) being sleep-deprived? The first and most obvious is sleepiness. A sleep-deprived brain will seize any moment it can to catch up on the lost resting time, by surreptitiously snatching short stretches of micro-sleep during any periods of relative calm during the day. The sleep-deprived individual will often not even be aware of losing consciousness for 30 seconds to a minute at a time, which accounts for the bizarre head-bobbing behavior that can often be observed in classrooms during long lectures. This phenomenon is obviously less amusing when the adolescent head-bobber is behind the wheel on a monotonous stretch of highway.[12]

The second consequence of sleep deprivation is tiredness, which refers to a sapping of motivation or energy. Adolescents who are tired will be less able to force themselves to do anything tedious, or to undertake tasks requiring abstract processing, planning or complex thinking, as they become more easily distracted and impulsive. Sleep-deprived adolescents are also more likely to overreact to minor challenges they might have easily weathered if they'd had enough sleep, becoming quickly frustrated, angry, aggressive, irritable, impatient, or sad.[13] And over time, they're more vulnerable to depression.[14]

**A path to insanity?**
Prominent sleep researcher Matthew Walker even hypothesizes that sleep deprivation in adolescence could have long-term psychiatric consequences, since it's during adolescence that mental illnesses such as schizophrenia often manifest themselves for the first time, and a lack of REM sleep, which occurs in the final hours of rest, during this time of critical brain development could tip the balance between a stable and unstable mental state.[15]

Finally, sleep deprivation can contribute to weight problems. Insufficient sleep definitely causes adults to put on weight,[16] and one experiment with a group of children ages 8–11 found that kids too put on weight when they don't sleep enough.[17] These studies explain the fact that obese adolescents have been observed to sleep less than non-obese adolescents: it's likely the sleep deprivation that's contributing to the obesity, rather than the obesity that's causing sleep problems.[18] Unsurprisingly, sleep-deprived adolescents are less inclined to be physically active than their better-rested peers, which may be part of the explanation.[19]

How much sleep is enough for a growing teen? A panel of experts convened by the National Sleep Foundation concluded the magic range is 8–10 hours per night,[20] and other similar bodies concur.[21] The implication: the majority of adolescents today are seriously sleep-deprived.[22] 75 percent of all American teens are skimping on sleep according to this definition;[23] more than half get less than 7 hours per night,[24] and the quarter who get less than 6.5 hours are struggling through their days in a haze of tiredness,[25] reporting that they feel "really sleepy" particularly in the morning, and that they feel their grades have dropped because of sleepiness.[26] The problem is particularly acute for the those who are genetically wired to be night owls.[*] [27]

* According to sleep researcher Matthew Walker, "Although every human being displays an unyielding twenty-four-hour pattern, the respective peak and trough points are strikingly different from one individual to the next. For some people, their peak of wakefulness arrives early in the day, and their sleepiness trough arrives early at night. These are "morning types," and make up about 40 percent of the populace. They prefer to wake at or around dawn, are happy to do so, and function optimally at this time of day. Others are "evening types," and account for approximately 30 percent of the population. They naturally prefer going to bed late and subsequently wake up late the following morning, or even in the afternoon. The remaining 30 percent of people lie somewhere in between morning and evening types, with a slight leaning toward eveningness. You may colloquially know these two types of people as 'morning larks' and 'night owls,' respectively. Unlike morning larks, night owls are frequently incapable of falling asleep early at night, no matter how hard they try. It is only in the early-morning hours that owls can drift off. Having not fallen asleep until late, owls of course strongly dislike waking up early. They are unable to function well at this time, one cause of which is that, despite being 'awake,' their brain remains in a more sleep-like state throughout the early morning. An adult's owlness or larkness, also known as their chronotype, is strongly determined by genetics."[1]

Adolescents aren't merely being cavalier with their sleep by prioritizing other, more desirable activities like surfing the net or partying. They also face an immovable biological impediment to sleeping sufficiently. As mentioned previously, teens' circadian rhythms shift dramatically as they reach puberty; the melatonin wave which used to crest at a sensible bedtime in earlier childhood no longer builds momentum until much later in the evening, so they remain at peak wakefulness while both their younger siblings and their parents are feeling a strong urge to climb into bed.[28] This temporary shift during adolescence has been universally documented across countries and cultures, irrespective of local sleeping habits and patterns, and the implication is always the same: adolescents who continue to have to rise at the same time as the rest of society become increasingly sleep-deprived.[29]

Most parents are oblivious to this epidemic of sleep deprivation. One survey found that 90 percent of parents believed their adolescents were getting enough sleep on school nights, despite the fact that over half of the adolescents themselves reported feeling too tired or sleepy during the day, and more than a quarter reported recently falling asleep either at school or while doing homework.[30] Medical professionals are no better informed than parents. A survey of pediatricians found that only 38 percent regularly ask adolescents about their sleep habits.[31] The staff at colleges and universities are also uninformed and unintentionally shirking their pastoral responsibilities by catering to their students' desires for libraries that stay open 24 hours a day, even though sleep-deprived students are far less likely to succeed academically.[32]

There is no easy fix: for example, exposing adolescents to bright light in the morning doesn't help push their circadian rhythms back onto a more sensible cadence.[33] If the biology is immutable, there is only one conclusion. We must instead shift society's expectations of when adolescents should be awake, by delaying school start times.

The evidence that we should allow our teens to sleep later has been steadily accumulating.[34] In the US, 70 school districts containing nearly 1,000 schools have experimented with later high school start times.[35] The results? Improved attendance, less tardiness, less falling asleep in class, better grades, and fewer car crashes.[36] For example, one study of eight public high schools which delayed start times until 8:55am found that students' grades in core subjects like English, science and math all went up, while the incidence of car crashes among 16- to 18-year-olds went down dramatically.[37]

As a result of these experiments, every major body now agrees that secondary school start times should be pushed forwards (see box).[*] [38]

**Let them sleep!**

The American Sleep Association,[39] the American Academy of Sleep Medicine,[40] the American Academy of Pediatrics,[41] the US Centers for Disease Control and Prevention,[42] The American Medical Association,[43] the Education Commission of the States (a non-profit public policy think-tank),[44] the Society of Behavioral Medicine,[45] the American Psychological Association,[46] the National Association of School Nurses (NASN), the Society of Pediatric Nurses (SPN),[47] the National PTA,[48] the American Thoracic Society, [49] and the American Association of Sleep Technologists[50] all strongly recommend later school start times for adolescents.

As one journalist has provocatively expressed: "Starting schools before 8:30 a.m. shows a tragic disregard for both the mental health of children and for science." [51] Similarly, Judith Owens, Director of the Center for Pediatric Sleep Disorders, points out, "[I]f you knew that in your child's school there was a toxic substance that reduced the capacity to learn, increased the chances of a car crash and made it likely that 20 years from now he would be obese and suffer from hypertension, you'd do everything possible to get rid of that substance and not worry about cost. Early start times are toxic."[52]

---

* The following position statements could be useful fodder for any parents hoping to convince their local school district to take action. The American Sleep Association states "Middle school and high school should not start before 08:00. A time closer to 09:00 or later would be preferable."[1] The American Academy of Sleep Medicine "is calling on communities, school boards, and educational institutions to implement start times of 8:30 AM or later for middle schools and high schools to ensure that every student arrives at school healthy, awake, alert, and ready to learn."[2] The American Academy of Pediatrics "recognizes insufficient sleep in adolescents as an important public health issue that significantly affects the health and safety, as well as the academic success, of our nation's middle and high school students" and says "[t]he evidence strongly implicates earlier school start times (ie, before 8:30 am) as a key modifiable contributor to insufficient sleep."[3] The American Academy of Pediatrics and US Centers for Disease Control and Prevention "support delaying school start times for middle and high school students," saying "[c]hronic inadequate sleep is associated with poor academic performance including executive function impairments, mood, and behavioral issues, as well as adverse health outcomes such as an increased risk of obesity, hypertension, and cardiovascular disease."[4] The American Medical Association "calls on school districts across the United States to implement middle and high school start times no earlier than 8:30 a.m."[5] Finally, the Education Commission of the States, a non-profit public policy think-tank, says, "There is virtually unanimous agreement in the research community that later start times in adolescent education would produce a positive change in adolescent learning, health and safety. Few, if any, educational interventions are so strongly supported by research evidence from so many different disciplines and experts in the field."[6]

**No objections**

Typical objections about the practical challenges of shifting school schedules[53] have been shown to be spurious by the forward-thinking school districts that have trailblazed by adopting later start times, including many schools in the UK and New Zealand that now start at 10am or later.[54] For example, after-school athletics programs pushed later in the day aren't affected; schools have instead seen more students participate in sports and their teams perform better.[55] Furthermore, later finish times mean less of a gap between the end of school and the return of parents from work, reducing the amount of unsupervised after-school time which teens have historically used to get up to various mischief.[56]

Nevertheless, the average start time for public high schools in the US remains 8:00 am, which implies approximately half of schools are starting even earlier than 8:00am.[57] As a result, many American adolescents are being wrenched from their beds at what would feel like the equivalent of 4am for most adults, and asked to sit attentively and learn when their bodies are telling them they should be horizontal.

Not all of us have the ability or the bandwidth to agitate and convince our school district to wake up and smell the proverbial coffee. Fortunately, there are other ways to help children sleep more, irrespective of any dramatic changes to the school routine. The first step is to establish if your teen is currently sleep-deprived. (A good tool is the Epworth Sleepiness Scale for Children and Adolescents.[*] [58])

---

* Over the last month, how likely have you been to fall asleep while doing the things that are described below (activities)? Use the following scale to choose one number that best describes what has been happening to you during each activity over the last month. (If you haven't done some of these things in the last month, try to imagine how they would have affected you.) Write that number in the box below.

0 = would never fall asleep
1 = slight chance of falling asleep
2 = moderate chance of falling asleep
3 = high chance of falling asleep

Sitting and Reading ____________
Sitting and watching TV or a video ____________
Sitting in a classroom at school during the morning ____________
Sitting and riding in a car or bus for about half an hour ____________
Lying down to rest or nap in the afternoon ____________
Sitting and talking to someone ____________
Sitting quietly by yourself after lunch ____________
Sitting and eating a meal ____________

A normal score is between zero and 10.

**It's not just start times**

Although school start times have remained broadly constant, kids are getting less sleep than they did previously. One study in Australia found that adolescents in 2004 were getting half an hour less sleep than their equivalents did in 1985.[59] For reasons which are not fully clear, the pandemic has further exacerbated the problem, with close to half of teens reporting they now sleep less than they did pre-coronavirus.[60]

If the results aren't encouraging, one option is to **limit your child's consumption of caffeine.** Caffeine, particularly consumed in the afternoon or evening, can create a vicious cycle. Because it takes an extended period of time for the body to flush the drug away (the half-life of caffeine is five to seven hours, meaning 50 percent of the amount ingested is still left in the body after that time period),[61] many teens are heading off to sleep with caffeine still circulating in their veins, causing them to sleep badly, which in turn causes them to crave more caffeine the following day to counter the effects.[62] The net result is daytime sleepiness and worse performance in school (see box). Nevertheless, 85 percent of teens consume caffeine in some form.[63] It may be difficult to wean them off a coffee habit once they've started, but if your teen hasn't yet succumbed to the allure of the morning jolt, at least you can avoid offering them a sip of yours.

**Caffeine and performance**

No one has randomly dosed one group of students with caffeine and compared their alertness, academic performance and mood with a non-caffeinated control group, presumably since such a study wouldn't be considered ethical. We can therefore only observe how students who choose to caffeinate perform versus others, keeping in mind that the self-selection may have muddled the results (e.g., students who were struggling already might have been more likely to turn to caffeine in the first place). Regardless, it's clear that, whether through correlation or causation, caffeinated students fare worse than their non-caffeinated counterparts: they sleep less, feel sleepier during the day,[64] and don't perform as well in school.[65]

Even more worryingly, approximately 40 percent of adolescents drink caffeinated energy drinks like Red Bull and Monster Energy at least occasionally,[66] which is no surprise given these brands advertise heavily to teens, including sponsoring local sports and music events.[67] The American Academy of Pediatrics categorically says energy drinks have no place in the diet of children and adolescents,[68] in part because these drinks can send teens to the emergency room with caffeine overdoses.[69]

Another obvious means of influencing your adolescent's sleep is to **keep electronics, including phones, out of the bedroom at night**. Lately almost everyone has a device in bed with them, including around 90 percent of teens.[70] Unfortunately adolescents, like adults, are tempted by their devices to stay up later, [71] and about 30 percent of teens even say they've been woken up by incoming calls or notifications.[72] Furthermore, according to Harvard's Division of Sleep Medicine, doing anything else in the bedroom other than sleeping can weaken the mind's association between the bedroom and sleep.[73] The American Academy of Pediatrics therefore recommends a total ban on TVs, computers, smartphones and other devices in the bedroom at night, and even suggests avoiding devices for an hour before bedtime.[74]

This hour lag is designed to counter the wakeful effects of looking at a bright screen. Our circadian rhythms are tied to sunlight and evolved well before the invention of electricity, so even low levels of home lighting in the evening can suppress the production of melatonin in our bodies.[75] This is why staring at an iPad instead of a printed book can interfere with our ability to fall asleep.[76] Many devices do have a 'night-shift' mode which switches the screen to lower brightness levels at a pre-set time in the evening, so enabling this mode could be a quick win if you have difficulties wrestling the iPhone away from your teenager, although there's still debate about whether this really helps.[77] Ultimately, parents who make and enforce rules about sleep have teens who end up sleeping more, so these battles are worth fighting.[78]

No discussion about sleep would be complete without mentioning the **benefits of naps**. A behavior which you may have thought was exclusively the domain of babies, toddlers and great-grandparents is surprisingly also relevant for those in their primes. All humans naturally experience a lull in wakefulness in the early afternoon, and there's considerable evidence that for most of our evolutionary history, our species followed a schedule which included a long period of sleep at night plus a shorter afternoon nap.[79]

**Napping around the world**

In mainland China, naps are a culturally-accepted element of the daily routine for people of all ages, with schools enforcing naptime for students all the way through the end of high school.[80] Other cultures have historically prioritized napping as well; in Greece, the siesta was an important cultural phenomenon for those of all ages until recently, when the decline in napping has unfortunately corresponded with an increase in heart disease among adults.[81]

Even putting the long-term health benefits aside, there are practical benefits to teenagers from napping. Those who nap have a greater capacity for memorizing facts,[82] show more accuracy in nonverbal reasoning, and have faster reaction times on memory tasks.[83] Returning to the field of music, the very best violinists are those who are most likely to take a nap, as a brief bout of sleep during the day after a practice session appears to help solidify the learnings from the material they've practiced.[84]

If the nap is a tough sell, or if your teen is rebelling more generally against the sleep hygiene practices you're attempting to enforce, offer a (paper) copy of *Why We Sleep: The New Science of Sleep and Dreams*, which has been quoted throughout this book, and which makes a very thorough and convincing argument for why sleep is a critical pillar of health. There are lifelong benefits from establishing good sleep habits, so there's no time like the present to encourage your child to prioritize sleep. In the words of the author,

> "AMAZING BREAKTHROUGH! Scientists have discovered a revolutionary new treatment that makes you live longer. It enhances your memory and makes you more creative. It makes you look more attractive. It keeps you slim and lowers food cravings. It protects you from cancer and dementia. It wards off colds and the flu. It lowers your risk of heart attacks and stroke, not to mention diabetes. You'll even feel happier, less depressed, and less anxious. Are you interested?"[85]

## Engineer exercise

> As a teenager, Joe Decker was an overweight couch potato. He devoured beer, pizza and Twinkies, did no exercise and saw his weight balloon. When he joined the US Army, his inability to run two miles in 16 minutes meant he had to endure the humiliation of extra training in the 'fat boy program'.[86]

More and more of our teens are growing up like Joe. In the US, over 90 percent of adolescents fail to get the recommended 60+ minutes of exercise per day,[87] 75 percent don't manage to fit in the minimum of 150 minutes per week,[88] and 15 percent of adolescents aren't even accomplishing a single hour a week of moderate physical activity.[89] The problem isn't limited to the US; globally, over 80 percent of teens ages 11–17 aren't getting sufficient physical activity.[90]

It doesn't help that high schools are increasingly deprioritizing physical education. Over 15 years starting in the 1990s, the percentage of American high school students doing daily phys-ed at school dropped from 42 to 25 percent,[91] and even when they make it to a gym class, less than half of teens' time is actually spent engaging in moderate-to-vigorous physical activity, with the remainder of the time presumably wasted in listening to instructions, waiting for a turn, etc.[92] The focus on competitive sports also means that kids who are naturally talented or old for their grade are offered more and more opportunities to play and compete, while those students who aren't naturally sporty and therefore need the boost even more end up sidelined and demotivated as they get farther and farther behind from having less time on the field or less access to the ball.[93]

Since adolescents are entering the physical prime of their lives, does it really matter if they achieve the recommended daily allowance of exercise? In the short term, could their time be better spent pursuing their studies, with exercise a virtuous habit to take up later in life to stave off the eventual aging process? The answer is a resounding no: physical activity is critical for adolescents for multiple reasons.

First, the habits that adolescents and young adults adopt tend to be carried forward into later life. One study found that over 80 percent of college students who were inactive remained inactive indefinitely; while 85 percent of those who exercised in college continued to do so throughout their lives.[94] This phenomenon is likely driven by a vicious /virtuous circle embedded in our human biology. As described by professor Daniel Lieberman in his book, *Exercised*,

> "Dopamine receptors in the brain are less active in people who haven't been exercising than in fit people who are regularly active. Consequently, non-exercisers and obese individuals must struggle harder and for longer (sometimes months) to get their receptors normally active, at which point they can cause what is sometimes considered 'exercise addiction.'

> Endorphins aren't produced until after twenty or more minutes of intense, vigorous activity, making them more rewarding for people who are already fit enough to work out that hard... When we are sedentary, however, a vicious cycle ensues. As we become more out of shape, our brains become less able to reward us for exercising."[95]

An adolescent who starts down a path of inactivity may never again overcome the physical barriers to exercising, which become increasingly formidable as time passes.

Physical exercise is also essential to healthy physical development. Adolescence is the last window of opportunity when bones will bulk up and get stronger in response to physical activity,[96] so teens who are inactive are at greater risk of suffering from osteoporosis later in life.[97] Furthermore, we all know that sitting around is bad for your health as an adult, but even young people can be at risk of developing 'adult' conditions such as obesity, hypertension and early symptoms of heart disease with insufficient exercise.[98]

Finally, exercise is crucial for keeping teens in great mental shape. When researchers randomly assign a subset of students to a physical fitness regime, they find the students doing the workouts thrive in comparison to their sedentary peers:[99] they suffer from less anxiety,[100] are less likely to be depressed,[101] and report better self-esteem.[102] And counter to the reasoning of the well-meaning school boards who are slashing phys-ed programs in favor of more focus on academics, students who get enough exercise can even think and reason more clearly, and end up performing better academically.[103] So if your adolescent is among the third of boys or half of girls[104] who aren't getting exercise every day and a vigorous aerobic workout for 20 minutes at least three times a week, either nudge your school to reconsider its approach to athletics, or investigate opportunities outside of school to get your kid sweaty.[105] (Incidentally, make sure kids drink plenty of liquid to replenish all the water they're losing when they exercise, since staying hydrated is one of the best ways of improving physical performance.[106])

Although it might be efficient and therefore tempting to force your adolescent to run around the block a few times, the best way to encourage teens to sustain an exercise regimen is to make the activities enjoyable.[107] Teachers and coaches who are supportive and make involvement fun are far preferable to drill sergeants,[108] and kids respond well to activities which are engineered to build to peak moments or memorable milestones.[109] Friendship also plays a surprisingly important role in motivating kids to persist in physical pursuits. In one heartwarming study, researchers found that students who had a friend with them estimated that a hill in front of them was less steep than students who approached the same hill alone.[110] And adolescents frequently mention making new friends and maintaining friendships when discussing why they're motivated to participate in sports.[111]

We've known since the time of Plato and Hippocrates that exercise is important for both the body and the soul. [112] As another scholar once quipped, "those who think they have not time for bodily exercise will sooner or later have to find time for illness."[113] Fortunately, even teens in the worst possible physical shape can be pulled out of their vicious sedentary cycle with the right coaxing. For example, our couch potato Joe Decker is no longer sitting around gorging himself on pizza, demonstrating there is hope for everyone:

> "Scarred by the endless jibes about his weight, 30-year-old Decker is now enjoying the title bestowed on him by Guinness World Records of the world's fittest man, after completing the most grueling physical challenge on earth in a record time."[114]

## Serve old-fashioned food

> A 14-year-old boy goes to the doctor with complaints of tiredness. He's an extremely picky eater. (Think a daily diet of French fries, plus snacking on Pringles potato chips, white bread and some processed pork.) But overall, he appears OK. He's not overweight and takes no medications. Tests show he has anemia and low levels of vitamin B12, so he's given B12 injections and diet advice. But a year later, he has begun to lose his vision. Then, by age 17, he's legally blind. The boy's highly limited daily diet — lacking in healthy foods, vitamins and minerals — had led to optic neuropathy.[115]

> Elena Smith, 19 years old and weighing 880 pounds, is currently in stable condition after she was dramatically rescued from her home after her organs failed last week. Workmen had to demolish part of the house to get the teenager to an ambulance after she became too big to fit through the door.* [116]

Much of the decline in American life expectancy can be explained by our poor diets and burgeoning waistlines.[117] According to one estimate, diet and weight problems account for more than 10 percent of all American deaths, versus 3 percent in Japan.[118] We are gradually eating our way towards an early grave, and the cumulative effects of our problematic diets are already visible by the teen years:† [119]

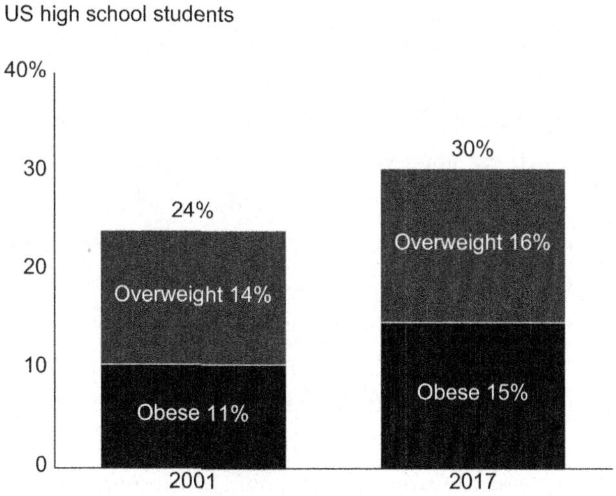


Once teens become overweight, their future health prospects aren't rosy. 80 percent of overweight adolescents go on to become obese as adults,[120] and the advances in medicine which have raised life expectancies across the wider populations of advanced nations haven't benefited those who start out overweight as teens.[121]

* Name of protagonist has been changed for privacy purposes.

† Students were classified as having obesity or being overweight based on their body mass index (kg/m2) (BMI), which was calculated from self-reported height and weight. BMI values were compared with sex- and age-specific reference data from the 2000 CDC growth chart. Obesity was defined as a BMI of ≥95th percentile for age and sex. Overweight was defined as a BMI of ≥85th percentile and <95th percentile for age and sex.

Even putting aside the question of longevity, overweight adolescents face many challenges. They are often teased by peers and even other family members about their size, which can be severely distressing.[122] Overweight girls also face blatant injustice: they are less likely to be accepted to college than their thinner peers, and once they join the workforce, they encounter job discrimination and hostile work environments.[123] And for both sexes, being overweight lowers wage levels,[124] particularly in occupations requiring interpersonal skills and social interactions.[125]

Why are so many adolescents struggling with their weight? In his intriguing book, *Why We Eat (too Much): The New Science of Appetite*,[126] bariatric surgeon Dr. Andrew Jenkinson convincingly argues that our previously held assumption that 'calories in minus calories expended = calories stored' is flawed, because this formula doesn't take into account the body's cunning ability to regulate weight by changing our metabolism. Eat too much cake at a birthday party? Your metabolism will rise and the excess calories will be burned off as heat. Going on a celery diet? The few calories you do eat will be carefully conserved as your body slows your metabolism down, making you sluggish and listless. In the same way that we maintain optimal hydration by producing more or less urine, we maintain whatever our body has determined is our perfect weight by flexing our metabolism. Our appetite is therefore only under our control to the extent that breathing is under our control — our body will overcome our resistance if we try to diverge from our 'optimal' weight.

Why, then, do so many of us, including our children, have bodies that seem to think the optimal weight is overweight or obese? Jenkinson discusses a variety of contributing factors, ranging from population-level selection pressures to epigenetic changes to sleep deprivation, but the two most important reasons are unsurprisingly diet-related. Firstly, we're eating too many foods derived from seeds and grains, particularly seed oils (sunflower, rapeseed, and soya), which are full of omega-6 fats. These particular fats interfere with our bodies' ability to monitor how much weight we have stored currently, perhaps as an evolutionary response to the implication that if we're eating grains and seeds, winter is coming and it's time to store up extra calories. And secondly, we're eating too much sugar and too many simple starches (white flour, corn) that rapidly break down into sugar, flooding our bodies with insulin, a hormone which in excess has also has been proven to cause weight gain.

If we could only switch to eating more fresh food, including vegetables, meat, and dairy from animals raised on (green) grass and fish raised on (green) plankton, our bodies would respond by gradually lowering our weight set point. But a recent survey revealed that nationwide, 7 percent of adolescents hadn't eaten a single vegetable in the previous week.[127] The most important root cause of the epidemic of adolescent obesity in developed nations is that we have replaced 'foods' with 'food-like substances' that have been designed and created by companies.

It's unsurprising that our teens are making poor food choices, given they are constantly bombarded with advertising. Back in the era when TV reigned supreme, the average teen saw 17 food ads per day (or 6,000 per year), of which 34 percent were for candy and snacks, 28 percent for cereal, 10 percent for fast food, and 0 percent for fruits or vegetables.[128] As viewing habits have shifted, the food advertisements have migrated to follow the eyeballs to the new forms of media. They have also shifted to more modern strategies; for example, the average adolescent now sees roughly 16 product placements per week, for example on reality shows (think soda on judges' desks).[129]

The processed food industry also designs the food itself to entice us to eat as much as possible, using salt, sugar, and fat in carefully crafted combinations to maximize the deliciousness of the products, with no regard for the health effects.[130] Acknowledging the unhelpful role that companies increasingly play in determining our eating habits, author and journalist Michael Pollan, who has spent much of his career investigating our modern difficulties with food, exhorts people to "Eat food. Not too much. Mostly plants," where he defines "food" as anything your great-grandmother would have recognized as such.* [131] This would rule out such modern delights as Twinkies, blue yoghurt tubes, BBQ-flavored potato chips, and microwave meals.

The thorny question we now face as a society is how to wean our children off of their well-established cravings for processed food, when temptation lurks not only in every corner store they pass, but even in the school cafeteria. Fortunately, a few intriguing studies suggest all is not lost, and it may still be possible to break the cycle of poor eating habits.

As we've seen previously in other domains, kids are susceptible to the suggestion that adults could be attempting to manipulate them, and their wariness

* It would be worth expanding his definition to incorporate anything a great-grandmother anywhere in the world would have recognized as food, to acknowledge the positive benefits of our modern access to diverse cuisines

and desire for autonomy can be harnessed and extended to food. When teens are explicitly educated about devious food marketing practices and offered the suggestion that eating healthfully can be one way to take a stand against corporate influence, they begin to make better choices,[132] and often will continue to avoid sweets, soda, and potato chips even several months later.[133] It's unlikely your school offers such a curriculum, but if your child is the bookish type, by all means suggest the book, *Salt, Sugar, Fat,*[134] to read to achieve a similar effect.

There is also hope for the picky eaters who scorn green vegetables. Even if your family diet has never featured greens previously, you shouldn't assume your child's (or even your own) food preferences are hopelessly immutable. In one amusing experiment, subjects were told, falsely, that they had loved to eat asparagus as children. These individuals were later more likely to say they enjoyed asparagus, were more likely to eat asparagus in a restaurant, and were even willing to pay more for asparagus in the grocery store.[135]

**What doesn't work**

Classic dieting, e.g. restricting food intake and feeling hungry, is considered by experts to be unhealthy,[136] and perversely backfires over the longer term, causing adolescents to gain even more weight over the longer term.[137] The body's logical response to what it perceives as a famine is to raise the optimal weight, to maximize the chance of surviving future famines. Fads like high protein diets are no better, having been shown to be ineffectual for children and teens.[138]

Intensive, school-based programs have been shown to reduce Body Mass Index (BMI),* [139] but most of us aren't lucky enough to have access to such programs, although we too can encourage our kids to eat better, watch less TV, and move around more.

Swapping out potato chips for crispy kale is unlikely to have any immediate effect, but moving to a better diet will definitely improve your teen's health over the long term.[140] If you're looking for a structured solution to cajole your teen into healthier habits, the Bright Bodies weight management program has been shown to help teens get into better shape,[141] and is partially available online.† Low glycemic index (GI) regimes, which involve sticking to low-GI foods such as non-starchy vegetables, fruits, legumes, nuts, and dairy, also appear to be promising.[142] Other tips and tricks that work: discourage your teen from having the largest meal in the evening or eating late at night [143] (which in addition to impacting metabolism can also interfere

* BMI = body mass index, a standard measure of weight status which takes into account weight in proportion to height

† Available at: www.brightbodies.org/education-media.html

with sleep quality),[144] and avoid insisting that children finish everything on their plate if they are no longer hungry.[145]

**Weight-loss drugs?**
In extreme cases, weight-control drugs like orlistat and sibutramine can also be prescribed by a doctor to complement changes in lifestyle, but they do have side effects, so are not a silver bullet.[146]

Supplements are also no substitute for a healthy diet. Although a third of children and adolescents take dietary supplements regularly,[147] there's no rationale for doing so:[148] the US Department of Agriculture currently advises that nutritional needs should be met primarily from foods. The only exceptions are vitamin D and iron.[149] Those with darker skin who live in Northern climes are at risk for being vitamin D deficient, so would benefit from a supplement, particularly during the winter months. When it comes to iron, adolescent girls are at higher risk of iron deficiency once they begin menstruating, with about 9 percent ending up deficient. Iron supplements may improve girls' academic performance,[150] and trials are underway to find out whether supplementation should be recommended for girls more routinely.[151] In the meantime, there's no harm in having your daughter's iron levels checked by her pediatrician.

**Myth: The family dinner**
While we're on the topic of food, we'd be remiss not to address the hoopla surrounding the concept of the 'family dinner.' The popular media, policy groups and researchers have all become nostalgic lately for the stereotypical 1950s evening scene in which family members all sit down for a home-cooked meal together.[152] There's no doubt that families that do manage to achieve this increasingly rare state of dinnertime nirvana have well-adjusted children who are happier,[153] less likely to drink, smoke and use drugs,[154] and show fewer behavioral problems,[155] among a host of other positive outcomes.[156]

Based on these exciting findings, there are now plenty of policy initiatives which aim to help families overcome the barriers to gathering for "these very important 20 minutes of the day."[157] There's even a book entitled, *The Family Dinner: Great Ways to Connect with Your Kids, One Meal at a Time*.[158] Yet hardly anyone swept up in this movement has stopped to consider that correlation doesn't prove causation.[159] Another equally plausible hypothesis is that those families lucky enough to have plenty of resources and naturally happy dispositions will have well-adjusted kids, and will also be inclined to gather for family meals.[160] The meal itself could simply be a marker rather than the underlying cause of the benefits. The only way to establish which way the causation flows would be to encourage a randomly-chosen group of families to have regular family meals, then follow up longer term to see if their children were better adjusted than a control group. Of course, no one has yet bothered doing this.[161]

Which is not to say that there's no point in eating together. Whether or not family dinners can change the life trajectory of your teenager, they are a cherished cultural tradition in many parts of the world. A shared meal can be a pleasurable opportunity to spend time together, pass along family values and teach kids the art of conversation. Or alternatively, a chore involving long hours standing in the kitchen rewarded by complaints about the food and kids kicking each other under the table, depending on the temperament of your family.

Whatever your family eating habits, you will have noticed that your teenager has a voracious appetite. Adolescents gain half their adult weight and half their bone mass during their teenage years.[162] So if ever the truism "you are what you eat" holds for your child, it's now.

# Take-aways

Researchers have dubbed sleep, exercise and healthy eating the "big three health behaviors."[163] This triumvirate helps people of all ages thrive, not just teenagers. If "Eat, Pray, Love"[164] is a mantra for spiritual health, here's a mantra for the physical health of our teens and ourselves too: "Eat, Sleep, Move."

**KEY PARENTING TAKE-AWAYS:**

Sleep:

1. If your adolescent isn't typically getting 8–10 hours of sleep per night, use the Epworth Sleepiness Scale to quickly assess sleep-deprivation
2. If your school system requires teens to start classes before 8:30am, consider agitating for change
3. Limit your child's consumption of caffeine, including coffee and energy drinks
4. Enable night-shift mode on devices, and keep all devices including phones out of your teen's bedroom at night
5. Encourage your adolescent to nap after lunch when feasible
6. For teens who enjoy reading non-fiction, recommend, *Why We Sleep: The New Science of Sleep and Dreams*

Exercise:

7. If your adolescent isn't getting exercise every day and a vigorous aerobic workout for 20 minutes at least three times a week, nudge your school or investigate opportunities outside of school to get your kid sweaty
8. Find teachers/coaches who are supportive and make exercise fun; activities which build to peak moments or memorable milestones; and pursuits which provide opportunities for your teen to interact with existing friends or make new ones

Food:

9. Educate your teen about food marketing practices, and suggest that eating healthfully is a way to take a stand against corporate influence; for keen readers, suggest the book *Salt, Sugar, Fat*
10. If your child is overweight, consider the Bright Bodies weight management program,* or a low glycemic index (GI) regime
11. Discourage your teen from having the largest meal in the evening or eating late at night
12. Avoid insisting that children finish everything on their plate if they are no longer hungry
13. Give a vitamin D supplement to your child in winter if your family has darker skin and you live in Northern climes
14. Have your daughter's iron levels checked periodically by her pediatrician

* Available at: www.brightbodies.org/education-media.html

# 8. ACHIEVEMENT

## Recommend flash cards

> Calvin: I should be doing my homework now. But the way I look at it, playing in the snow is a lot more important. Out here I'm learning real skills that I can apply throughout the rest of my life.
> Hobbes: Such as?
> Calvin: Procrastinating and rationalizing.[1]

Homework is a surprisingly controversial subject. Not everyone agrees that asking children to spend significant amounts of time toiling away at schoolwork outside of the regular school day actually enhances their learning in any meaningful way. For example, one study drawing on data from more than 200,000 students in 40 countries concluded that there's no clear-cut relationship between homework time and achievement.[2]

Nevertheless, homework is hardly optional for most of our offspring. So if they are going to put in time doing it, they might as well use that time wisely. Yet most schools give their students very little guidance on this front. As one educator remarked, "It's strange that we expect students to solve problems, yet seldom teach them about problem solving. And we require students to remember a considerable body of material, yet seldom teach them the art of memory."[3] It turns out that these skills can be taught, and the best time to begin teaching them is around seventh or eighth grade, when kids develop the cognitive capabilities to make use of them.[4]

Because students aren't explicitly taught how to learn currently, most resort to using study habits that don't work.[5] Two of the most common techniques used by teenagers, rereading material and highlighting,[6] are in fact useless,[7] and highlighting in particular might even be counterproductive.[8] The reason these practices don't help adolescents learn is because they don't require their brains to process the material in a new way. As one review explains, "The more a learning strategy involves manipulating or organizing material rather than just reviewing it, the more likely it is to result in deep understanding."[9] So what are the best techniques for getting the brain engaged?

**Use flashcards to create a practice test**: Hundreds of experiments with people of all ages learning all kinds of materials have shown that creating a practice test is a universally useful strategy for absorbing information,[10] and in the real world, college students who use practice tests achieve higher GPAs.[11] The best type of practice test forces the learner to recall the answer from memory, rather than simply recognizing the correct answer.[12] So rather than taking ordinary notes while reading, we should encourage teens to make flashcards as they go, with a question on one side and the answer on the back.[13]

**Shuffle the flashcards**: Another way to force the brain to work harder is to mix different types of problems together, a practice called 'interleaving.'[14] The most obvious application for interleaving is when practicing math — having a mix of problems requires the student to stop and think about which procedure to apply to solve each question, rather than simply following the same rote process over and over.[15] The concept also works in other domains, for example, when learning to differentiate the styles of different artists by flipping through images.[16] When asked, most adolescents don't realize that interleaving helps at all, and in fact tend to assume the opposite, namely that grouping similar items together is a better way to learn; but their performance on later tests shows differently.

**Spread the studying process out over multiple days:** As we saw in the chapter on sleep, staying up late to cram for an exam is a flawed strategy, as the study time would be better spent sleeping.[17] Our brains utilize the time overnight when we're unconscious to categorize and store away any information we learned during the day, so the corollary is that the more nights we have to process information, the better we retain it. Therefore reviewing a full stack of flashcards each day over several days is better than concentrating on learning only one chunk of the stack each day, even if this approach feels more challenging and less efficient.[18] Also, the more days between each study session, the longer your teen is likely to retain the information; so preparing for a cumulative exam at the end of a year would ideally involve spacing study sessions on any given topic as much as a month apart.[19]

**Plan the work and visualize the goal:** Researchers have observed that the highest-performing students tend to make a plan for completing their work, set subgoals, and then reward themselves for successfully reaching the milestones.[20] Teachers are aware of the benefits of this approach, and will often ask students to describe how they're planning to tackle a task, and pose questions to help clarify their thinking.[21] Similarly, when students are asked to visualize finishing their homework, they're more likely to subsequently finish it.[22]

**Planning for the long-haul**
Planning can be particularly valuable for long-term deadlines; for example, a randomly selected group of high school students who were preparing to take the PSAT in October were asked in May to spend 30 minutes writing about their intentions to study over the summer, including making 'if-then plans' of how they would respond to distractions, and visualizing completing their goals. These students ended up completing over 60 percent more practice questions than their peers.[23]

If you observe that your child is prone to procrastination, you could also suggest keeping a time log. When students are required to maintain a detailed account of how they've spent their time for a week, and then use that record to plan their future studying, they use their time more effectively.[24]

**Ask meta questions:** To encourage their students to intellectually engage with and manipulate new material in their minds, teachers frequently pose 'meta' questions like "what is this problem about?" and "what steps are you using to solve the problem?"[25] for problem-solving; "Can you summarize the text? What questions does this text raise? Can you predict what will happen next?" for reading;[26] and "Why would that be true?" when learning a fact.[27] Your adolescent could rhetorically pose these questions while trying to absorb new content.

**Mix up the study environment:** Bizarrely, when it comes to memorization, it helps to learn material in a range of different physical settings, for example, by sitting in a different room each evening.[28] A classic illustration from 1978 had college students memorize a list of words either in a cluttered room, or a room with large windows, or both on different occasions. Those who had studied in both locations recalled far more words than those who had stayed in one place both times.[29] So encourage your child to alternate between a desk, the dining room, the kitchen, or anywhere you can engineer a clear surface and not too many distractions.

**Minimize distractions**: Distractions, of course, are everywhere. The average adolescent now manages to spend less than six minutes on any given task before being distracted, typically by texts, social media alerts, and TV.[30] Teens are fully convinced that they're masterful multi-taskers, saying these distractions don't make any difference to the quality of their work.[31] They're wrong.[32] Experiments have shown that kids who attempt to learn material while using social media perform worse on a later test.[33] This fits with what we see in real life: top-performing students are more likely to say they avoid distractions,[34] and the more kids use electronic media, the worse they perform on exams[35] and the lower their grades.[36] In light of this overwhelming evidence, the American Academy of Pediatrics categorically recommends banning kids from using entertainment media while doing homework.[37] Background noise isn't helpful either. In one study, college students trying to memorize content fared worse at their task when exposed to background noise of people talking, but as with social media, they weren't aware that they had been distracted.[38]

**Music?**

The verdict on music while studying isn't black and white. Three quarters of teens habitually listen to music while doing their homework, and they're convinced it makes no difference.[39] In this case, the research generally backs them up.[40] However not all teens respond to music in the same way.[41] Extroverts tend to thrive with background music playing, while the performance of introverts is impaired by an accompanying soundtrack.[42] This is unsurprising, since one of the key ways to define the spectrum of introversion to extroversion is according to sensitivity to stimuli. Differences can even be observed in the first few weeks and months of life; those babies who are overwhelmed by stimuli grow up to become introverts who need to study in silence, while those who can handle plenty of stimulation grow up to be teenagers who both seek out stimulating social opportunities, and tend to study with the speakers cranked up to full volume. Fortunately, people seem to realize this naturally: introverts are far less likely to play music while studying in the first place.[43]

**Meditation?**

Meditation/mindfulness is another potential tool for enhancing learning; as societal interest in this topic has blossomed, researchers have begun exploring whether teaching young people meditation/mindfulness helps them learn more effectively and/or makes them more resilient in the face of academic stress. The preliminary research on this topic with younger children,[44] teenagers[45] and college students[46] is promising, but most of the studies have been small,[47] so it's premature to conclude that we should be encouraging all of our kids to start chanting 'Om' daily.[48]

What if your child simply refuses to do homework, and doesn't seem to care about the consequences? One approach, albeit not backed up by evidence, could be to insist your teen spends a fixed amount of time each evening in a setting with nothing to do except homework (even if your child claims not to have any). Out of sheer boredom, any homework might eventually get done. Or not. At least you will have done your duty by leading the proverbial horse to water.

In closing, here are the thoughts of a prominent foreign affairs journalist, which you could pass along to your kids if the homework battles get heated:

> When I was growing up, my parents used to say to me: "Finish your dinner — people in China are starving." I find myself wanting to say to my daughters: "Finish your homework — people in China and India are starving for your job." — Thomas Friedman[49]

## Dig deeper

> "Most of the prestigious schools start with 2-year-olds, and you have a 1-year-old in your house and have to describe your child's interests," explains one New York City preschool consultant. Parents apply in the hopes that they can get their kid into a preschool that could cost as much as a college. Many parents think that getting their kids into one of the "Baby Ivies" will help them get into one of the top private schools for kindergarten through senior year — then off to a top university.[50]

> On the highway below, the school bus rolls past without stopping. I am only seven, but I understand that it is this fact, more than any other, that makes my family different: we don't go to school... Dad said public school was a ploy by the Government to lead children away from God. "I may as well surrender my kids to the devil himself," he said, "as send them down the road to that school." — Excerpt from memoir of Tara Westover, Doctorate in Intellectual History, Cambridge; Visiting Fellow, Harvard University[51]

If you were to ask a selection of stressed-out parents living in Manhattan what they make of Tara Westover's life story, they would probably insist she's a fluke; a freakish, one-in-a-million example of someone who succeeded despite her parents hindering rather than helping her on her educational journey.

There is no doubt that Tara is an extraordinary person to have achieved such success despite the barriers she faced. An interesting question her life story raises, however, is whether parents really do play a critical role in the achievements of their children. Many modern parents have adopted the philosophical belief that their efforts are the key to their offspring's success, and are earnestly ploughing considerable time and energy into homework rituals and science projects. This belief is not limited to the wealthy and privileged; one public school district in the US was perplexed to observe that Asian immigrant families were frequently purchasing two copies of the required school textbooks for their child. The extra copy proved to be for the mother, who wanted to study herself so she could then help her child.[52]

When it comes to the raw material of intelligence, no matter what the efforts put in by Manhattanite or Asian immigrant parents, children's brains are not malleable lumps of clay. Studies of adoption have shown that children from low socio-economic status backgrounds who have the good fortune to be adopted into families of substantial means end up with slightly higher IQs, and in reverse, those from high socio-economic status families who are adopted into less fortunate circumstances pay a small price in lowered IQ.[53] But the difference rapidly fades as children reach adolescence, and ends up being small – about seven IQ points on average, according to behavioral geneticist Matt McGue, the leading expert on the topic.[54] And even these small differences may ultimately fade away to zero by the time children reach adulthood.[55] The same results hold for other types of cognitive abilities as well, including processing speed, memory, and spatial ability; children increasingly resemble their biological parents as they mature, irrespective of how they were raised.[56]

That's not to say that parents can't influence the future achievements of their children. Academic interests, career aspirations, hobbies and extra-curricular pursuits can all be cultivated at home.[57] You can support your child in establishing good study habits, as we saw in the previous section. If you're fortunate enough to have a choice of school, you hold the power to select the pool of peers from which your child's friends will be drawn. You can protect your child from stereotype threat, a phenomenon which can sap the confidence and academic performance of those who are made to feel part of a negatively stereotyped minority. And finally, you can convince your child that working hard at school is useful/important, and that he/she can succeed with sufficient effort. We'll discuss each of these in turn.

## *School choice*

> Encumbered by his status as heir to the throne, Charles was singled out as a victim from his first day [at boarding school Gordonstoun]. The housemaster at Charles's dorm was "a truly nasty piece of work. He was vicious, a classic bully, a weak man. He was wrong for Charles." Like other housemasters, he handed over the running of the houses to senior boys, who imposed a form of martial law, with ritualized psychological and physical abuse that included tying boys up in laundry baskets under a cold shower.[58]

Most children will never be tied up by their classmates and doused with frigid water. Nevertheless, choosing a school is arguably the most impactful decision you'll ever make for your child. It can be intimidating to hold the power to alter your child's life in your hands, without having any true idea of the ultimate impact of your choice.[59]

School choice isn't limited to those with the means to pay for private school. Over a third of all parents in the US have a choice of public school for their child.[60] The difficulty is that those parents who do have a choice often lack the information with which to choose. Ideally, parents would want to know how effectively each school increases the knowledge and skills of their students, a concept called 'value-added.'[61] In practice, there's no such measure available for secondary schools in the US.* [62]

* The Educational Opportunity Project at Stanford University has created an online database allowing parents to view several different measures of value-added for schools across the country, but for the moment it only covers schools up through eighth grade.[1]

**Privacy for public schools**
Systematic information about school performance is gathered by the National Assessment of Educational Progress,[63] but is only available to parents summarized at the level of the district, to "protect the confidentiality of schools."[64] Why exactly a public school should have a right to confidentiality about its performance is unclear.

Parents understandably use student achievement as the next best proxy. Unfortunately, this can drive perverse incentives for schools to focus on screening pupils rather than improving teaching. In certain communities, it can even create a zero-sum competition between schools for the best pupils, increasing inequality as schools shun disadvantaged students.[65]

In the absence of information on performance, parents could attempt to evaluate their options using the criteria developed by the National Research Council and Institute of Medicine.* [66] But a much simpler approach, arguably almost as informative, would be to simply ask current students who are the 'cool kids' at their school, or even conduct an informal poll, asking them to rate their answer to the question "To be popular in my school it is important that people think I am smart." (1: strongly disagree ... 5: strongly agree). This approach was taken by a team evaluating public high schools in Los Angeles, and they found dramatic differences between schools: in some being smart was considered cool, while in others, it was a total liability. More importantly, this school culture affected the behavior of the students (see box).

---

* School conditions that promote strong student engagement and positive academic mindsets:

- Presenting students with challenging but achievable tasks
- Communicating high expectations for student learning and providing supports that allow students to meet these expectations
- Making evaluation practices clear and fair and providing ample feedback
- Reinforcing and modeling a commitment to education and being explicit about the value of education to the quality of one's life
- Providing students with opportunities to exercise autonomy and choice in their academic work
- Requiring students to use higher-order thinking to compete academic tasks
- Structuring tasks to emphasize active participation in learning activities rather than passively 'receiving' information
- Emphasizing variety in how material is presented and in the tasks students are asked to do
- Requiring students to collaborate and interact with one another when learning new material
- Emphasizing the connection of schoolwork to students' lives and interests and to life outside of school
- Encouraging teachers to be fair, supportive, and dedicated to student learning while holding high expectations for student work

Classrooms that emphasize cooperation and a sense that everyone can achieve the learning goals are much more supportive of self-efficacy and a valuing of academic work than classrooms that emphasize competition and a zero-sum environment where only a limited number of students will earn good grades.[1]

**Uncool to do well in school**

In one example, when offered the chance to win a free SAT prep package, kids from a school where it wasn't viewed as socially acceptable to excel hesitated to enter the lottery unless they were told the odds of winning were high, presumably because they calculated that it wasn't worth risking the social stigma otherwise.[67] Similarly, in-depth studies of schools with anti-intellectual cultures have shown that the high-achieving students at these schools are forced to adopt strategies to avoid stigma, including 'clowning' and helping delinquents with their academic work in exchange for protection, strategies which divert energy that could otherwise be used for learning.[68]

The peer environment explains why students from more affluent neighborhoods are more likely to finish high school than similar students from poorer neighborhoods.[69] Along the same lines, when families are given vouchers to move from low-income neighborhoods to middle-income suburbs, their children struggle initially in school, but then adjust and do better academically than former peers who didn't make a move.[70] When students are part of a community that values academic work, they respond accordingly and up their game to fit in.[71]

**Magnificent Midwood**

Perhaps the best evidence that school culture matters comes from examples like the Midwood school in Brooklyn, New York in the 1990s. This 'magnet school' was an interesting hybrid; 55 percent of its student body was composed of students from all over New York City who had gone through a rigorous academic selection process, while the rest of the students were drawn from the local area, which was relatively poor. Not only did the selected students achieve academic distinction; the local students, too, performed unusually well. In the words of the principal, "The kids see it's O.K. to study, O.K. to do homework, to take part in academic discussions, do an extra report. That becomes the ethic of the school." A local student even commented, "Everybody in Midwood is smart."* [72] [73] These examples suggest the best approach to take is to send your child to the best school available, even if this involves a struggle to fit in initially.[74]

There is one caveat to this general rule. Some children are born with the intrinsic motivation to do well in school irrespective of their peer environment; they will put their hand up in class regardless of what other kids think of them, and will instinctively hang out with the "academic" crowd even if there are plenty of other, "cooler" crowds to choose from. If you happen to have a child like this, there may be other considerations at play in choosing a school,

* The Obamas understood the power of creating a culture of achievement; President Barack Obama said, "It's a privilege to discover new things. It's cool to be smart,"[1] and first Lady Michelle Obama said ,"I'm standing here ... because of education. I thought being smart was cooler than anything in the world."[2]

as long as each option on your list has enough like-minded peers. As discussed in the section on stress, kids who end up in the bottom quarter academically risk becoming unnecessarily disheartened. Hyper-competitive school environments can also be toxic; as one review wryly comments, "When neighbors set standards or create institutions that serve an entire neighborhood, affluent neighbors are likely to be an advantage. When neighbors compete with one another for scarce resources, such as high school grades or teenage jobs, affluent neighbors are a disadvantage."[75] It's also worth setting a high bar for moving to a different school if your child is not at a natural transition point, since for most kids, changing school is a fraught process.[76]

**Single-sex schools**

Some parents might be weighing the relative merits of single-sex versus coeducational schools. In the US, single-sex education is exceedingly rare, with only 0.4 percent of schools catering to one sex. In other parts of the English-speaking world, however, gender-segregated schooling is much more common; for example, 15 percent of schools in Australia and 18 percent in England are all-boys or all-girls.[77] Is the single-sex educational approach better? The results are equivocal, with no clear evidence of benefit or harm one way or another.* [78]

So far, we've focused exclusively on secondary education, but of course another momentous school choice looms for some in the not-so-distant future: college. There are endless parameters to evaluate colleges, from the sticker price to the facilities to the average wages of graduates, and many rankings combine various factors into a single score. However, below the top echelon of schools, the best metric to encourage your adolescent to focus on is graduation rates. Amongst American colleges, graduation rates vary from over 90 percent to under 10 percent, and are a good proxy for how much academic and social support an institution provides to its pupils.[79]

* According to a review by the US Department of Education, there is no evidence of either benefit or harm.[1] Similarly, a panel convened by the American Association of University Women Educational Foundation concluded there's no evidence that single-sex education works better, reduces sex stereotyping, or improves girls' math and science achievement.[2] Even in the UK, the Centre for Education and Employment Research has found that when it comes to academic achievement, "the jury is still out," with no consistent differences in the personal and social development of either girls or boys.[3] Several other reviews all agree that the evidence remains inconclusive.[4 5 6] However there is a remarkable lack of research on the long-term effects of gender segregation on social skills. One study suggests that kids from single-sex high schools tend to be more anxious in situations involving members of the opposite gender once they reach college, but it's not clear if this 'anxiety' has any practical implications.[7] Another study of men who went to all-male private schools in the UK revealed this group appeared to have more marital difficulties later in life than their co-educated counterparts,[8] but the British private schools of 40 years ago are probably not analogous to the single-sex schools of today.

Selecting a school for your child is a momentous life decision for those fortunate enough to have a choice; but as Tara Westover proves, children can succeed regardless of their school (or even lack thereof). Canarsie High School, a public school in Brooklyn, New York, was shuttered in 2011 after receiving an F on a city report card, with the Education Department opining that "Canarsie was in such disarray that the only way to fix it would be to shut it down."[80] One of the school's most notable alumni? Self-made billionaire Howard Schultz, longtime CEO of Starbucks.[81]

## *Stereotype threat*

> Women had to wield their intellects like a scythe, hacking away against the stubborn underbrush of low expectations. — Margot Lee Shetterly, *Hidden Figures*

In 1995, two social scientists, Claude Steele and Joshua Aronson, first described a syndrome they called "stereotype threat," which they defined as:

> A predicament that can arise from widely known negative stereotypes about one's group. Anything one does that conforms to it makes the stereotype more plausible in the eyes of others, and perhaps even in one's own eyes.[82]

Since they pointed out this phenomenon, reams of research have confirmed that stereotype threat is very real. People who feel part of a stereotyped group will worry the stereotype is true, causing them to under-perform in a self-fulfilling prophecy.

One vivid illustration arises from the misconception that girls can't perform as well as boys when it comes to math and other quantitative subjects. One study took a group of female college students who strongly agreed with the statements "I am good at math" and "It is important to me that I am good at math," and showed some of them commercials featuring females behaving stereotypically (e.g., a girl saying she's looking forward to college as a chance to meet cute guys). The students primed in this way were more likely to avoid math problems on an aptitude test, less likely to say they aspired to quantitative careers, and more likely to avoid leadership roles in a task soon after.[83] Another experiment used an elaborate cover story about purchasing behavior to convince people to try on and wear either a swimsuit or a V-neck sweater for 15 minutes. During this time they were given a math test, supposedly to use the time efficiently for a separate experiment. The women in the swimsuit performed much worse on the math test than the women wearing the V-neck sweater, whereas the men were unaffected.[84] It doesn't take ridiculous commercials or bathing suits to create stereotype threat. Strong female math students also did worse on an exam after being told the exam produced gender differences,[85] and even performed worse when the number of males in the room outnumbered the females, in direct proportion to how much they were outnumbered.[86]

Looking at other examples, African American students perform worse on a test when told that it diagnoses intellectual ability,[87] as do students of low socioeconomic status.[88] There's even speculation that consequential exams like the SATs may be underestimating the mathematical potential of both females and minorities,[89] simply because of the requirement to tick boxes at the beginning about gender and race, making those points salient in the minds of the test-takers at just the wrong moment.[90]

**A universal phenomenon**

Stereotype threat can in fact be made to apply to anyone.[91] One study took a group of white males with high mathematical ability and gave them articles describing amazing math achievements by Asian students, then told them that a test was designed to understand why Asians outperform others on tests of math ability. The white males proceeded to perform worse on the math test.[92]

Are there antidotes to this insidious phenomenon? The fortunate answer is yes. One approach is to reassure adolescents that adversity is normal and can be overcome, so they don't attribute any challenges they face to the effects of belonging to a group.[93] For example, a group of college freshmen were told that all students faced hardship and doubt in their first year, regardless of their race, and that these feelings were normal. This simple trick boosted the confidence of the black students in particular by 20 percentile points.[94]

Another option is to encourage kids to focus on other elements of their self-worth beyond their intellectual ability. When African American students were first asked to rank a list of 10 values and then write a brief essay about their most important value, giving an example of how they had demonstrated that value recently, they did far better on a subsequent GRE-like exam that ostensibly tested intellectual ability.[95] And writing about their values increased the grades of both underperforming and average students who were African American.[96]

The best way to counter stereotype threat is to address the issue head-on. When women were explicitly told about the concept and reassured that such stereotypes had nothing to do with their actual ability to succeed at the test in front of them, the performance deficit disappeared.[97] Even a simple paragraph at the beginning of a difficult calculus test saying that it hadn't shown gender differences helped to the point where the girls in fact outperformed the boys.[98]

Role models are also great — reading brief biographies about successful women generally,[99] hearing about a woman who had succeeded at math, or even learning about a man who achieved math success through working hard all improved girls' performance on a difficult math test.[100] So buy some biographies of inspirational figures who resemble your child. If you have a girl, you could suggest the movie, *Hidden Figures*, or the TV series, *Commander in Chief*, featuring Geena Davis earning the respect of everyone around her as a confident and assertive president of the United States.[*]

Even if your adolescent doesn't fall into a stereotyped group, you can still point out the phenomenon of unconscious bias. Psychologists have created a brief test which is designed to detect subconscious biases, and the results will surprise your adolescent. You yourself may think you have no biases, but if you take the test, you're likely to be surprised by the results too.[†] [101]

## Purpose

> Two out of three high-school students in a large survey say they are bored in class every single day. 75 percent report the material being taught is not interesting, and 60 percent said, "I didn't see the value in the work I was being asked to do.[‡] [102]

> School is boring and irrelevant, say teenagers: three-quarters think the current education system needs to undergo radical reform.[103]

---

* The show does feature a few scenes implying adolescent sexual behaviour, but contains nothing explicit

† Available at: https://implicit.harvard.edu/implicit/selectatest.html

‡ Findings from a survey of 81,000 high school students in the Midwest

School systems around the country should urgently be hiring video game designers to act as consultants. Kids learn best when the subject matter is presented in an engaging way, and when they get rapid or even instantaneous feedback on their performance. There's no reason why schools couldn't be doing more to liven things up.[104]

Since the video game version of education is probably a long way off, the best way to get our kids fired up about school in the meantime is to convince them that the work they're doing has value and serves a useful purpose.[105] Young people who think their schoolwork is useful perform better in school,[106] and experiments suggest that the positive mindset is the reason (see box).

**Considering why it's useful**

When high school students were asked to write a short essay about how the material they were learning in science class could be useful in their lives, they later reported having more interest in science.[107] Similar experiments worked on college students who wrote about how either math or psychology could be useful in their lives.[108] Parents can be influential too: when parents were mailed brochures discussing the usefulness of Science, Technology, Engineering and Math (STEM) courses, their children went on to take more science and math in their last two years of high school.[109]

What if you're stumped when your child asks you what possible use calculus could ever have? You could always recommend the book *Infinite powers: how calculus reveals the secrets of the universe.*[110] Or simply re-frame, as one software engineer has attempted to do:

> It's time to stop crying all about the math you've studied that's not useful in everyday life. Math is all about logic, thinking out of the box and creativity, and I bet you never question their relevance in life.[111]

## Growth mindset

> "Whether you think you can or you think you can't, you're right."
> — Quote attributed to Henry Ford[112]

> "No matter what your ability is, effort is what ignites that ability and turns it into accomplishment." — Carol Dweck[113]

Carol Dweck, a psychology professor at Stanford University, has become something of a celebrity. In 2006 she published a book, *Mindset*, in which she laid out her theory that an important key to success is adopting a "growth mindset," or a belief that intelligence and personality can change with effort. Her TED talk on the subject has now been viewed over 13 million times.[114]

The concept is catchy. If we can simply convince our children that they can accomplish anything with enough hard work, many will rise to the challenge, rather than assuming they don't have what it takes and giving up. Schools have embraced the idea of teaching a growth mindset to their students, and many parenting books have encouraged parents to avoid commenting on their children's ability, and instead praise their effort. Michelle Obama even delivered a speech as First Lady emphasizing the benefits of this approach. She explained that kids often wrongly assume that if they have to work hard at something, it must imply they aren't good at it, and many will stop trying to avoid the risk of failing and looking dumb in front of their peers and teachers.[*] [115]

Fortunately, instilling a belief in students that they have the capacity to succeed can be a positive self-fulfilling prophecy. Back in the 1980s, experiments suggested that when freshmen in college heard from upperclassmen that their GPAs[†] had improved since their first year, those freshmen were less likely to drop out of college, and achieved higher GPAs themselves.[116] More recently, African American college students who were told that intelligence could expand like a muscle with mental work went on to perform better academically,[117] and seventh graders performed better at math when told the same message.[118]

More recently, Dweck's original work on the benefits of the growth mindset has been criticized as being difficult to replicate,[119] and some mindset education interventions have failed to have much effect, suggesting that simply telling kids that intelligence is malleable isn't a panacea.[120] Dweck and colleagues have since refined their interventions,[121] and optimized them for a population of 14- to 15-year-olds.[122] In addition to educating kids about mindset, they now point out that hard work is not always enough when it comes to solving tricky problems, suggesting that when students get stuck, they need to try new strategies and approaches, or seek advice from adults.[123] For parents who want to apply the mindset approach at home with their teens, Dweck and team have created the Mindset Kit, which you can access online.[‡] [124]

* Available at: www.youtube.com/watch?v=_0bgwPR2Nzs&t=153, 2:32 onwards

† GPA = Grade Point Average

‡ Available at: www.mindsetkit.org

Here are words of advice from an MIT graduate who has fully embraced the growth mindset concept:

> The people who fail to graduate from MIT fail because they come in, encounter problems that are harder than anything they've had to do before, and not knowing how to look for help or how to go about tackling those problems, burn out.
>
> The students who are successful, by contrast, look at that challenge, wrestle with feelings of inadequacy and stupidity, and then begin to take steps hiking that mountain, knowing that bruised pride is a small price to pay for getting to see the view from the top. They ask for help, they acknowledge their inadequacies. They don't blame their lack of intelligence, they blame their lack of motivation.[125]

## *World-class achievement*

> "My hatred for tennis is focused on the dragon, a ball machine modified by my fire-belching father. When the dragon takes dead aim at me and fires a ball 110 miles an hour, the sound it makes is a bloodcurdling roar. I flinch every time. My father says that if I hit 2,500 balls each day, I'll hit 17,500 balls each week, and at the end of one year I'll have hit nearly one million balls. A child who hits one million balls each year will be unbeatable. I hate tennis, hate it with all my heart, and still I keep playing, keep hitting all morning, and all afternoon, because I have no choice." — Andre Agassi[126]

> "What Chinese parents understand is that nothing is fun until you're good at it...Tenacious practice, practice, practice is crucial for excellence; rote repetition is underrated in America. A child who starts to excel at something — whether it's math, piano, pitching or ballet — gets praise, admiration and satisfaction. This builds confidence and makes the once not-fun activity fun." — Amy Chua, author of *Battle Hymn of the Tiger Mother*[127]

What distinguishes the very best students from ordinary mortals? Why do a very small number of kids go on to become concert pianists, renowned mathematicians and Olympic athletes, while the majority are destined to lead perfectly satisfactory but more quotidian lives? Are the standouts simply born that way, or are their achievements the result of careful sculpting by the loving hands of their parents?

There is no doubt that becoming extraordinary in any domain requires tenacious practice. In his book, *Outliers*,[128] Malcolm Gladwell popularized the concept of 10,000 hours as the magic threshold of time investment required to master a complex skill. Although his theory is somewhat questionable,[129] many studies have indeed shown that elite performers typically have banked several thousand hours of practice by the time they leave their teen years behind.[130] In fact, it's likely that perseverance is just as important as innate talent in achieving excellence in most fields, although having some talent at the beginning makes it easier to get the virtuous cycle of practice kick-started, since it's more enjoyable for kids to spend time on an activity when they get some positive feedback.[131] But it's the rare child who has the temperament to excel by focusing single-mindedly on practicing a skill for days, weeks, years and even decades, at the expense of fun social and leisure activities.[132]

**Perserverance**
In settings as diverse as West Point military academy, the Scripps National Spelling Bee, the University of Pennsylvania undergraduate psychology department, and a private preparatory school, researchers have repeatedly concluded that perseverance is the key facet of personality that ultimately distinguishes the top performers from the rest.[133] * [134]

Sustained practice can sculpt the mind and body in astounding ways. With practice, humans can expand even supposedly rigid cognitive limits like working memory capacity.[135] In the domain of sports, it would be easy to assume that some people are gifted with the 'right' anatomy to excel. This is partially true; Michael Phelps' hyper-extended joints and unusually large hands certainly helped propel him to swimming glory.[136] And reports that marathoners have an unusual capacity to deliver and uptake oxygen in their muscles and that Olympic rowers have hearts twice the mass of a normal

* This holds true in the adult world as well – in myriad professional settings including investment banking, painting, journalism, academia, medicine, and law, it's not raw talent that matters as much as single-minded commitment to achieving a certain ambition.[i]

person's heart would seem to buttress this conclusion.[137] In reality, it's the sustained practice that causes most of these types of physical changes.[138] It's not that sprinters were born with vastly unnatural proportions of fast-twitch muscles; they took what would have been a small natural advantage initially and cultivated it to the extreme. From the perspective of sports performance, it appears that the only anatomical characteristic which isn't malleable at all is height.[139] That isn't to say that genetics don't play a role in sporting achievement; they undoubtedly do, but more significantly by influencing personality versus physical characteristics.

**The four-hour rule**

It's worth pointing out that there are limits to the amount of practice even the most determined teenager can sustain without incurring serious costs like physical injury and burnout. The body and brain need time to recuperate from intense practice, and even for adults operating at the highest level of their fields, the maximum amount of deliberate practice they can sustain long-term seems to be approximately four hours per day.[140]

Plenty of researchers over the past 50 years have attempted to shed light on the mystery of why certain children muster the determination to achieve great things. Of the five core personality traits referenced in the section on character, the trait most closely related to extraordinary achievement is conscientiousness, also called self-discipline; a person's conscientiousness is as important a factor in predicting academic achievement as intelligence.[141] This trait is part of a person's basic nature, rather than a quality that can be cultivated.[142] However conscientiousness doesn't fully capture the single-minded focus on a long-term goal.

A further refinement has been proposed by psychologist Angela Duckworth. If Carol Dweck is the celebrity proponent of growth mindset, Duckworth is the equivalent champion of 'grit,' with a TED talk on the subject that has been viewed 24 million times.[143] She defines grit as perseverance combined with a passion for long-term goals, and this combination appears even more closely linked with accomplishment than perseverance alone.[144] Although much of her research is focused on trying to intentionally cultivate grit, for the moment it appears that grit is an even more fundamental personality trait than conscientiousness, and is therefore difficult to change.[145]

People often point out the intensive investment by the parents of celebrities such as Tiger Woods, and assume that the parents cheering for their prodigies at gymnastics competitions and chess matches are the secret to their children's success. In fact, the primary credit they deserve is for providing the genes.[146] One psychologist who interviewed the parents of a variety of highly talented concert pianists, sculptors, Olympic swimmers, world-class tennis players, research mathematicians, and research neurologists, found that the parents hadn't coerced or pushed their children to success, but simply enabled them to pursue their passions by paying for the lessons, driving them to the practices, etc.[147] The parents also frequently commented that their stellar achiever wasn't necessarily the child in the family with the most natural ability, but rather the one who had consistently shown the most motivation and eagerness.[148]

In contrast, studies of young tennis players and swimmers who had suffered from burn-out found that these athletes who had shown great promise initially had often been forced to practice excessively by their parents.[149] Across a variety of pursuits, studies find that too much parental pressure can backfire, causing kids to enjoy an activity less and to feel stressed about potential failure.[150] Kids who specialize in a sport too early, for instance, often due to pressure from parents, often achieve early success, but then are much more likely to burn out and quit entirely before reaching the highest echelons.[151]

The most important way parents can kickstart a path to achievement for their children is to **help them enjoy and feel good at an activity**. Many high achievers mention a teacher or coach who they admired, respected, even loved, and most tennis stars specifically mention that their first coach made tennis enjoyable.[152] Parents and teachers who tell young people that they are talented or genetically gifted can help inspire the motivation and self-confidence required for a child to muster the considerable effort needed to fulfill the prophecy.[153] And emphasizing the intrinsic benefits (e.g., this activity is great for becoming and staying physically fit) is far superior to emphasizing extrinsic benefits (e.g., this activity will help you get into college).[154]

Perhaps the best way to make an activity fun is to **ensure that participating helps children make and maintain friends**, rather than preventing them from having a social life.[155] The Ford Sayre ski program, based in the community surrounding Dartmouth College, has turned out a disproportionately large number of Olympic skiers,[156] and core to their philosophy is encouraging even the most talented skiers to continue to train with peers of the same age, to ensure that skiing remains social and fun.[157] This phenomenon holds true in other sports as well: among junior tennis players, those who burned out were much more likely to have played up in age division.[158]

Thus far we've focused on extracurricular achievement, but can parents influence achievement in an academic setting? A wide range of well-meaning programs have attempted to encourage parents to be more involved in the education of their children, but none have had much effect, which isn't promising.[159] In academics, as with extracurriculars, decades of research have shown that intrinsic motivation is vastly more powerful in spurring kids to achieve than extrinsic motivators like financial rewards, academic awards, or praise or punishments from parents.[160]

Intrinsic motivation by definition comes from within, so isn't something that can be imposed upon a child. It arises when a young person is exposed to novel experiences that create curiosity and inspire a desire to learn.[161] The role of the parents is to avoid squelching this intrinsic motivation, because perversely, **providing extrinsic rewards backfires**.[162] Children who are offered a reward for academic success will often take away the message that the academic pursuit is simply a means to an end, rather than being pleasurable for its own sake.[163] This is analogous to offering dessert as a reward for finishing vegetables; we should instead be focused on emphasizing how delicious vegetables can be.

To conclude, here's another quote from Agassi:

> I'm playing in my last U.S. Open. In fact my last tournament ever. I play tennis for a living, even though I hate tennis, hate it with a dark and secret passion, and always have. As this last piece of identity falls into place, I slide to my knees and in a whisper I say: Please let this be over.[164]

As a parent it's possible you could create an Agassi, but only at a very high cost.

## Take-aways

> "I'm not holding myself out as a model, but I do believe that we in America can ask more of children than we typically do, and they will not only respond to the challenge, but thrive." — Amy Chua, author of *Battle Hymn of the Tiger Mother*[165]

On one level, Amy Chua is right about parental expectations. Parents who have high expectations for their children do have children who outperform.[166] Their kids have better attendance, are more likely to do well in school, and are more likely to attend college…[167] none of which proves that parents' expectations are the cause. Beyond her intensive parenting, Ms. Chua also gave her pianist prodigy child her genetic predisposition for persistence and discipline. She herself admits that her parenting style failed to produce the same results when applied to her second child, who had a different temperament. It's even technically possible that Chua's involvement in her child's piano playing was actually reducing the chance of her daughter succeeding, by making the piano practice more stressful and less fun than it might have been otherwise, and by replacing her daughter's intrinsic motivation to excel at the piano and make beautiful music with extrinsic motivation to make her mother proud.

Most children are born with an inherent desire to succeed. When kids don't work hard in school, teachers often assume it's because they lack grit, and write them off. In fact, many poor academic behaviors have other root causes. Kids will sometimes joke around in class because they fear they can't succeed at a task, and want to persuade both their peers and their teachers that they don't care, rather than risk trying hard and revealing they're not capable. Other students don't feel the work has any relevance to their life, or don't have a good strategy for approaching the problem at hand.[168] The best parents and teachers diagnose the root cause and then help a child discover intrinsic motivation, instead of resorting to carrots and sticks that extinguish this important commodity.[169] Helping your child to cultivate intrinsic motivation will be a life-long gift: adults from all walks of life consistently say their biggest regret looking back was not taking their education more seriously, particularly during their teen years.[170]

If you hope to encourage your child to succeed, there is one final behavior we should address that is categorically not helpful, confirmed by over 50 studies.[171] You can take your teen to museums or provide a lift to the library, but by all means, do not get overly involved in the content of your child's homework.

## KEY PARENTING TAKE-AWAYS:

Study habits:

1. Recommend your teen makes flashcards with a question on one side and the answer on the back, instead of taking notes
2. When studying for an exam, encourage your teen to spread the studying process over multiple days if possible; and if flashcards are involved, suggest reviewing the full stack each day over several days
3. If your child struggles with completing longer-term assignments, suggest visualizing the goal, and pose questions about the plan for tackling the task
4. If your child is prone to procrastination, suggest keeping a time log
5. Advise your teen against rereading material and highlighting as study strategies
6. If your teen comes to you for help, pose 'meta' questions like "what is this problem about?" and "what steps are you using to solve the problem?" for problem-solving; "Can you summarize the text? What questions does this text raise? Can you predict what will happen next?" for reading; and "Why would that be true?" when learning a fact
7. Suggest your teen mix different types of problems together (interleaving)
8. Help your adolescent mix up the study environment, for example by sitting in a different room each evening
9. Ban entertainment media while doing homework
10. Limit background noise to the extent feasible when your child is studying

School choice:

11. If you have a choice of school, evaluate the options using the National Research Council and Institute of Medicine's criteria; or choose a school where current students report that it's cool to do well in school
12. If your adolescent has the intrinsic motivation to work hard in any environment, avoid hyper-competitive schools, particularly if your child will end up in the bottom quarter academically

Stereotype threat:

13. If your child belongs to any type of stereotyped group, explicitly describe the concept of stereotype threat, and provide reassurance that those stereotypes have nothing to do with actual ability to succeed
14. Encourage your adolescent to regularly acknowledge other elements of self-worth beyond intellectual ability
15. Highlight inspirational figures who resemble your child in biographies or other media (good examples for girls include the movie *Hidden Figures* and the TV series *Commander in Chief*)

Purpose:

16. Help your child reflect on and brainstorm about why school work has value and serves a useful purpose

Growth mindset:

17. Explain to your teen that intelligence can expand like a muscle with mental work
18. Praise effort rather than attributing success to innate ability
19. Check out the Mindset Kit*

World-class achievement:

20. Don't provide rewards for academic or extracurricular success, as this extinguishes intrinsic motivation
21. If you have the means, help your child find activities to enjoy and feel good at, ideally with teachers or coaches your teen likes, admires, and respects
22. Emphasize the intrinsic benefits of a pursuit (e.g. this activity is great for becoming physically fit)
23. Ensure that participating in an activity helps your child make and maintain friends, rather than interferes with socializing
24. If your child develops a passion and your family is fortunate enough to have the capacity and resources, provide encouragement and logistical support, but avoid applying too much parental pressure to succeed

Overall:

25. If your child is struggling in school, don't resort to carrots and sticks; instead, work with a teacher to diagnose the root cause (e.g. fear of failure, lack of a good strategy for approaching a problem, or lack of understanding of the relevance or importance of the subject)
26. Don't get overly involved in the content of your child's homework

---

* Available at: www.mindsetkit.org

# 9. DISCRETIONARY TIME

## Delay social media

> "The thought process that went into building these applications, Facebook being the first of them, was all about: 'How do we consume as much of your time and conscious attention as possible?' That means that we need to give you a little dopamine hit every once in a while, because someone liked or commented on a photo or a post or whatever. And that's going to get you to contribute more content, and that's going to get you more likes and comments. It's exactly the kind of thing that a hacker like myself would come up with, because you're exploiting a vulnerability in human psychology. The creators — me, Mark [Zuckerberg], Kevin Systrom on Instagram — understood this consciously. And we did it anyway. God only knows what it's doing to our children's brains." — Sean Parker, founding president of Facebook[1]

Most children's brains are involved in our societal-wide experiment with social media.[*] [2] Even pre-Covid, 63 percent of American teens used social media every day, with boys spending an average of an hour and a half, and girls two and a quarter hours per day.[3] The older the teen, the greater the chance of an account, whether you like it or not:[4] 60 percent of adolescents have opened one without their parents' knowledge, while under 30 percent of parents suspect this.[5] Even if you're sure your little angel would never sneak around online without your permission, there's still a very good likelihood

* Thirteen years is the minimum age to register for most social media sites, because "13 years is the age set by Congress in the Children's Online Privacy Protection Act (COPPA), which prohibits Web sites from collecting information on children younger than 13 years without parental permission, and the official terms of service for many popular sites now mirror the COPPA regulations."[1]

your child is on TikTok, Snapchat, or whatever happens to be the latest incarnation of social media that's emerged since this book went to print.

Social media can undoubtedly be a tool for good in some cases. Adolescents who have difficulties relating to their local peers because they're different in some salient way can often find a community online.[6] If you have an obsession with collecting rare coins or can't get enough of Manga, there's a community online for you. Teenagers can also discover and connect with others equally passionate about any cause under the sun, from saving the whales to preventing gun violence.[7]

**The teen view**

Teens say they primarily use social media sites to connect with people they already know offline,[8] and they claim being online helps them stay informed about their friends' lives and understand their friends' feelings, as well as get support during difficult times. 18 percent feel that using social media makes them feel better about themselves, compared to only 4 percent who say worse, and 39 percent of more-vulnerable teens say social media makes them feel less lonely, versus only 13 percent who say it makes them feel more so.[9]

Teens themselves are convinced that social media helps them thrive (see box).[10] In contradiction with teens' claims, studies have found that in reality, the more time people of any age spend on social media, the worse their mood.[11] Connecting virtually is a poor substitute for interacting in person.

**More on mood**

One study messaged people multiple times throughout the day, and found that those who had been using Facebook at the previous time point felt worse the next time they were asked.[12] Various studies suggest the social media usage itself is causing the problem. One enlisted adult women to voluntarily take a break from Facebook, and found their life satisfaction and well-being improved,[13] while another analyzed a natural experiment caused by a company forbidding certain employees from using Facebook, and concluded that particularly the younger people (aged 18–23) were happier afterwards.* [14] A final more recent study took a group of undergraduates and limited their Facebook, Instagram and Snapchat, and found that after three weeks, they felt less lonely and depressed than a control group.[15] None of the studies above were with younger teens. However there is plenty of ongoing research on this topic, and the evidence increasingly suggests that social media can cause poor mental health.[16] It's not surprising that teens are getting hooked on the small burst of dopamine from someone 'liking' their posts.

* Given the speed with which young people migrate from one app/platform to another, research typically lags behind; Facebook is no longer the only social media app of choice among teenagers, so we have to assume the findings apply to other social media platforms as well.

Mood isn't the only potential casualty of too much time on social media. Teens often have terrible judgement about what to reveal about themselves online. One analysis of adolescent posts found that more than half of profiles referenced risky behavior, including substance use, sexual behaviors, and even violence.[17] It's worth some snooping to find out what persona your teen may be inadvertently displaying to the wider world.

Finally, there's the issue of distraction. Over half of teens agree that using social media often distracts them when they should be doing homework, or paying attention to the people around them.[18] Many admit that it takes away time that they could otherwise be spending with friends in person.[19] And kids are notorious for checking their messages during classes at school, which unsurprisingly distracts them from learning.[20] Many schools forbid phones, but simply having a device nearby, even turned off, can drain students' ability to concentrate.[21]

Teenagers aren't unique in this respect: it's difficult for anyone to resist these apps. When YouTube or TikTok suggest another video, the goal isn't to entertain. It's to capture the viewer's attention just a little while longer, to sell the eyeballs to advertisers. The massive algorithm powering the suggestions has been trained on billions of users to know exactly how to hook a user's attention.[22] It's no wonder kids find social media difficult to resist. As one headline proclaimed, "Your attention didn't collapse. It was stolen."[23]

Now even the US Surgeon General has gone on record cautioning that "social media can have a profound risk of harm to the mental health and well-being of children and adolescents."[24] Who would have thought back when Facebook's popularity was first exploding that this genre of technology would end up attracting an advisory warning akin to cigarette smoking.

If your children's entire social lives are already being conducted online, it's not a satisfying solution to rip the devices from their hands and render them social pariahs. But you can insist they watch the documentary-drama, *The Social Dilemma*.[25] If this doesn't convince teens of the drawbacks of social media, nothing will.

Parents aren't the only solution to this particular problem. One individual has the power to effect dramatic societal change: your school's principal. If a school makes the move to ban devices from the premises (or requires them to be locked up in special pouches during school hours), it can dramatically cut back on the percentage of the day kids spend glued to social media rather than interacting with each other.[26]

Here are the parting thoughts of one wise adolescent:

> We're taught to think that these platforms are for us; that they're a public service; that they make our lives easier and more efficient; that no one could properly communicate without them. But social media companies are profiting enormously off of everyone buying into that narrative, which is why these platforms are actually designed to be addictive. They're not benevolent.[27]

## Discuss misinformation

> "There's been this industrialization of the hoax news industry. A lot of news sites now exist that do nothing but publish fake news for the traffic and the ad revenue...Within very siloed communities, people tend to believe in a conspiracy or in misinformation more when it is debunked than they did before, so it's troubling."[28] — Caitlin Dewey, digital culture critic for the Washington Post, who has now given up writing her column called "What Was Fake on the Internet This Week?"

Online sources are slowly altering the base of widely agreed-upon societal truths by presenting 'alternative facts' as news.[29] They succeed because modern teens are not sufficiently discriminating about their sources of information, and have a tendency to believe that anything they encounter online is true. One recent survey found that 54 percent of American teenagers frequently read news on social media platforms, and 50 percent turn to YouTube for news. Over half of that news comes from celebrities and influencers rather than from legitimate news organizations, and the content has often been suggested by YouTube's recommendation algorithm.[30] More worrisome, over 80 percent of students in one large survey believed that an advertisement labelled 'sponsored content' was a real news article, and less than a third could identify that the agenda of an advocacy organization might have influenced the content of a tweet. [31] Teens are startlingly naïve and easily duped by information fed to them online.

Social media has accelerated the proliferation of fake news. Social media companies make money by maximizing the amount of time users spend on their platforms, and they use algorithms tested on billions of humans to draw people in with whatever content is most likely to resonate based on how they've behaved in the past. These algorithms have no embedded moral compass, so if they can succeed in making people feel part of a group, get them riled up by feeding them fake headlines, and pit them against others with opposing views, the anger they generate will serve their purpose of keeping their users online longer.[32]

Our teens lap up the information being served to them, true or false, because of a powerful and universal human foible called "confirmation bias."[33] No matter how rational we believe ourselves to be, all humans tend to be too accepting of information that supports a view we already hold, and too critical of information that might contradict it. A brief video called 'The Most Common Cognitive Bias' demonstrates this point handily.* [34] Unfortunately, the proliferation of news sources online, including those peddling blatant falsehoods, directly feeds this innate tendency — if you hold an opinion, it's simple and quick to find a source which 'proves' you are right. Worse, you can simply wait until a social media site serves you such news on your feed, trapping you inside a so-called 'filter bubble.'

The platforms gather as much information as possible about users of all ages, because they can then sell this information to anyone willing to pay for the opportunity to influence their user base. Most often the buyers are advertisers hoping to sell a product. But what happens when the buyer is a group hoping to subtlely change political views in order to swing an election? (For a disturbing read on this topic, see *Mindf*ck: Inside Cambridge Analytica's Plot to Break the World* by former Cambridge Analytica employee and whistleblower Christopher Wylie.) And these dynamics will only be exacerbated with the release of powerful AI tools like ChatGPT, which now enable anyone to churn out well-written misleading content on an industrial scale.

This hijacking of minds has chilling implications for the future of democracy if we don't take urgent steps to alert the next generation to the strange new world order they face. Fortunately, the country of Finland has proved that it's possible to inoculate teens against fake news. In the face of an onslaught of misinformation from their neighbor to the East, the Finns have risen to the challenge and incorporated media literacy into their school curricula. From elementary school onwards, pupils are taught in math that

* Available at: www.youtube.com/watch?v=vKA4w2O61Xo

statistics can mislead, in art that images can be manipulated, and in history that propaganda can shift public opinion in dramatic ways.[35] Finland now holds the top rank amongst 35 European countries in media literacy and resilience to fake news.[36]

**Filter bubbles and heroic pigs**

There is plenty of excellent and engaging content you can share with your adolescent on the topic of misinformation, including a TED talk about personalized news and filter bubbles,[*] [37] and a discussion with historian Yuval Noa Harari and ethicist Tristan Harris about the reality that we are being hacked by machines that have come to know us better than we know ourselves.[†] [38]

To prove the point that not all content is what it seems online, you could also introduce your adolescent to the story of the heroic swimming pig; through three brief, related videos, the viewer comes to realize that a video portraying an animal rescue is not what it seems.[‡] [39] Other intriguing material on this topic includes a segment from the BBC on the ability to doctor voices,[§] [40] and another demonstrating how such technology could be deployed to portray a person saying something they never said.[¶] [41]

Useful sources for fact-checking include www.Snopes.com, factcheck.org, The Washington Post fact checker, and Politifact.com, and for images, tineye.com, a search engine that can unearth similar pictures to help identify if an original image has been digitally altered.

So if the first step is to forewarn your teens about the morass of misinformation and the possibility of persuasion online, the next step is to equip them to proactively spot suspect content. Reality Check: The Game provides a brief online tutorial that covers the basics in identifying untrustworthy sources.[**] [42] It's also worth pointing out to adolescents that search engine algorithms don't necessarily put legitimate sites first, and that before getting incensed by any provocative article, they should do a brief search for the headline plus the word "hoax," "fake," "viral," or "scam," to see if any debunking counterpoints turn up.

In reality, it's not teens who should be causing us the most concern in the short term, although skepticism and fact-checking are critical life skills that will serve them well in future. Those over 65 share nearly seven times

* Available at: www.ted.com/talks/eli_pariser_beware_online_filter_bubbles/transcript?language=en.

† Available at: www.wired.com/story/artificial-intelligence-yuval-noah-harari-tristan-harris/.

‡ Available at: www.youtube.com/watch?v=g7WjrvG1GMk; www.youtube.com/watch?v=_2My_HOP-bw; www.youtube.com/watch?v=bvtJj6HoYHg.

§ Available at: www.youtube.com/watch?v=1aTApGWVGoI.

¶ Available at: www.youtube.com/watch?v=o2DDU4g0PRo.

** Available at: https://mediasmarts.ca/digital-media-literacy/educational-games/reality-check-game.

as many articles from fake news domains on Facebook as those who are 18–29.[43] So encourage your teen to share the heroic swimming pig story (see box) with grandma and grandpa, too.

# Dig deeper

"'Cause you're free
To do what you want to do."[44]

The lyrics to the 1990s dance anthem *Free* capture the spirit of our modern golden age. Many fortunate people in developed economies have been freed from a life of continuous drudgery, and have unprecedented levels of discretionary time.

American adolescents today have vastly more leisure time than adolescents of previous generations, where leisure is defined as time not consumed by school, homework, sleep, commuting, or working.[45] They even have far more leisure time than their counterparts in other parts of the world. Average American teens spend 40 to 50 percent of their time on discretionary activities; in Europe it's 35 to 45 percent, and in East Asia, only 25 to 35 percent. As one study dryly points out, "Whether this time is a liability or gives American youths an advantage depends largely on what they do with it."[46]

Here's what they're doing with it currently:[47]

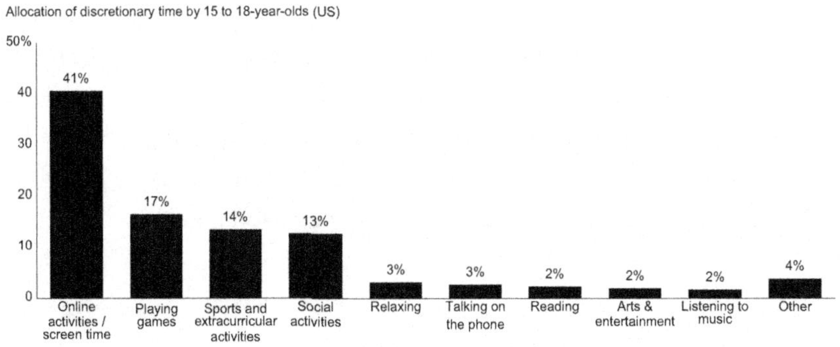

American teens spend almost half of their free time online, or probably more, given that the category 'playing games' lumps dining table board games like Scrabble® into the same category as massively multiplayer online role-playing (MMORPG) shooter games like Fortnite.

Fortunately, even today's screen-obsessed teens are still finding some time for more traditional pursuits, including socializing face-to-face with friends. Here's a tour of the considerations for parents.

## *Social activities*

"Should I let my 15-year-old go to a concert without an adult?"[48]

"Appropriate age for a teen to go to a concert? Am I being unreasonable?"[49]

The internet is rife with the queries of conflicted parents. The angst is palpable. How to balance the twin responsibilities of letting teens develop independence while keeping them safe from harm? The responses to these earnest posts are invariably divided down the middle, with some in the peanut gallery advocating caution, others suggesting various conditions, and a few firmly in the laissez-faire camp. In the back of the naysayers' minds are headlines of concert-goers being crushed to death or trampled in unruly crowds.[50]

No commentators in these discussions ever reference data on the dangers of concerts. That's partly because no one really knows for sure how dangerous concerts might be, beyond the risk of assault that we've already covered. One study did comb through news sources to collate a list of all deaths at concerts over a period of 16 years, and found about 45 per year of people of all ages (two thirds by trampling),[51] which for context is comparable to the number of people killed by lightning annually.[52] Of course not everyone goes to concerts, and we're unfortunately missing the denominator.*

* There's no group that collates attendance at concerts, and the only highly detailed national survey which captures how Americans of all ages use their time, the American Time Use Survey (ATUS), completely fails here: the category "Attending performing arts" would combine moshing at a thrash metal concert with suffering through a 6-year-old's first violin recital.

Similarly, there's no obvious way to calculate a risk from going to nightclubs, bars and other nightlife venues.* Ditto with parties. A single-sex slumber party with a parent supervising obviously isn't comparable with a free-for-all thrown by the cool kid whose parents are out of town for the weekend. (The key risks in the latter situation are substance use, intoxicated driving and assault, which have all been discussed previously.)

There is one source of risk from nightlife, however, which most parents and teens don't ever stop to consider. Dr. William Slattery, II, M.D., an unlikely film star, happens to be an expert on the subject:

> In a recent interview, the ever-effusive Bradley Cooper mentioned that he'd cast his own ear doctor to play his character's ear doctor in *A Star Is Born*. We reached out to Dr. Slattery, president of the House Ear Clinic in Los Angeles: "How did this come about? Was Bradley Cooper just like, hey, do you want to be in *A Star Is Born*?"
> "That's pretty much it, yep."[53]

Teens who haven't watched this particular romance featuring Cooper as a musician with escalating hearing problems would probably assume that hearing loss is an affliction suffered primarily by doddering grandfathers with bushy gray hair sprouting from their ear canals. When teens give any thought to the decibel levels of the sound coming their way, it's almost exclusively to pump the volume up, not dial it down.

As Dr. Slattery could attest, the tragedy of this disregard for their ears is that approximately 16 percent of American teens are already suffering from noise-induced hearing damage.† [54] The difficulty is that human ears aren't designed to warn us when noise levels pass the safety threshold. Hearing loss can begin at approximately 90 decibels, but many adolescents are regularly exposed to 100 decibels at discos, concerts and while listening to music on headphones. Noise only becomes irritating and painful at levels of 120–140 decibels, which means many teens are completely unaware that they are in the process of harming their ears.[55]

* There aren't any reports about incidents occurring in such venues, and the same time use survey's category of "Socializing and communicating with others" presumably could include both going to a bar or nightclub and chatting with neighbors after church.

† Populations as diverse as boys in vocational school classes in Scandinavia[1] and students at Wuhan University in China have also been found to be suffering from similar rates of hearing loss.[2]

It can be difficult to pinpoint the causes of hearing damage, since the effects of too much loud sound tend to be cumulative. However, loud events like rock concerts are obvious culprits. One study of patients with music-related hearing problems found that two thirds of these patients attributed their hearing issue to exposure at a single concert,[56] and another found that two thirds of young people who said they attended rock concerts at least twice a month were suffering from measurable hearing damage.[57] Listening to music with earbuds at high volume has also been shown to cause damage, although the effects are less extreme.[58] Nightclubs would be another obvious source of noise exposure for teenagers. As of yet there's no solid evidence of damage from this source,[59] but spending time in a nightclub can cause temporary tinnitus (the perception of hearing ringing or other persistent noise), which is not a good sign.[60]

Unfortunately, teens don't seem to care. Indeed, 75 percent of students in one survey said they were aware of the possibility of damaging their hearing through exposure to loud sound, and two thirds had even experienced tinnitus, but the vast majority were unconcerned and assumed that any hearing loss would only be noticeable when they were much older.[61] A campaign to convince high school students to wear ear plugs in a nightclub only managed to convince a paltry 4 percent of them to comply.[62] Even a panel of hearing experts convened to discuss the topic despaired of ever convincing adolescents to proactively protect their ears.[63]

It's possible your teen would be a sensible member of the 4 percent, so by all means buy some discrete wax earplugs for your child to take along to the next concert or rave. And many phones can also be set up to warn if the volume is set too high. The depressing reality is that your teen will care eventually: almost half of those who are 75 and older have disabling hearing loss.[64] It's easy for young people to discount the importance of their ears. In one survey of medical students, about 60 percent considered blindness worse than deafness, versus only 6 percent who considered deafness worse.[65] However that's not the perspective of the people who suffer from these afflictions. In the words of Helen Keller,

> Deafness is a much worse misfortune, for it means the loss of the most vital stimulus — the sound of the voice that brings language, sets thoughts astir and keeps us in the intellectual company of

> man… Blindness cuts us off from things; deafness cuts us off from people … to be cut off from hearing is to be isolated indeed.[66]

At Ministry of Sound, a nightclub in Southeast London known for its wall-vibrating house music, a 5ft tall black and yellow sign at the entrance proclaimed, "Caution: excessive sound levels." Every night hordes of young people would glance at the sign, grin, and proceed inside.[67]

**KEY PARENTING TAKE-AWAYS:**

Social activities:

1. Alert your teen to the higher risk of sexual harassment and assault in concert venues
2. Buy your teen some discrete earplugs to bring to concerts or raves

## *Online activities*

> When radio arrived, it was deemed a menace, blamed for distracting children from their homework. A 1936 article in Gramophone magazine reported that youngsters had "developed the habit of dividing attention between the humdrum preparation of their school assignments and the compelling excitement of the loudspeaker."[68]

We're not the first generation to fear that our teens are being sucked into a distracting virtual world. But the risks and temptations have relentlessly escalated in the century since the invention of the radio, and more than half of parents of adolescents are now worried about their teens overusing technology.[69]

Perhaps the most challenging aspect of parenting in the modern technological milieu is the opacity of our teens' behavior online. Most parents don't have the time to continuously watch over their child's shoulder, and teens often keep their online problems to themselves. A survey of 25,000 children ages 9 to 16 found that 55 percent of those bothered by an offline meeting with an online contact, 60 percent bothered by bullying online, 71 percent bothered by unwanted sexual messages, and 75 percent bothered by online sexual images never informed their parents.[70] Teens don't report for a variety of reasons: because they feel the incident wasn't a big deal; because they don't know how their parents will react or are concerned reporting would cause awkwardness; or because they worry they'll get in trouble or have their access taken away.[71] But as a parent, it's hard to protect our teens when we don't even know what issues they're facing.

Below is a grid which lays out all the various threats our teens could be encountering online.* [72] We'll discuss each of these risks in turn.

| | **Content (child as passive recipient)** | **Contact (child as participant)** | **Conduct (child as actor)** |
|---|---|---|---|
| **Overuse** | a) Screen time | Social Media | b) Video games |
| **Aggression** | c) Violent content | d) Cyberbullying | d) Cyberbullying |
| **Sexuality** | e) Sexual stereotypes<br>f) Pornography | d) Sexual harassment<br>g) Grooming | d) Sexual harassment<br>h) Sexting |
| **Commercialism** | i) Advertising<br>i) Embedded marketing | j) Identity theft | k) Gambling<br>l) Irresponsible spending<br>m) Plagiarism and copyright infringement |
| **Objectionable content** | Misinformation | n) Ideological persuasion | o) Sharing harmful or inappropriate content |

The letters in the table correspond to the sections below, with some in combination where the research spans multiple similar issues.

* Original sourced from "Risks and safety on the internet: the perspective of European children: full findings and policy implications from the EU Kids Online survey of 9–16 year olds and their parents in 25 countries," available at https://eprints.lse.ac.uk/33731/1/Risks%20and%20safety%20on%20the%20internet(lsero).pdf, but with further enhancements and additions made.

## a) Screen time

> Throughout the eight thousand years since civilization began, humankind has worked, played, invented, made love, fought, painted, written, read, gardened, raised children, sewed, sawed, solved problems, and resolved difficulties. [Now], instead of actually doing these things, we push a button and sit in our homes watching actors pretend to do them.[73]

> "Television has changed a child from an irresistible force to an immovable object."[74]

The amount of time our children spend in front of a screen, whether TV or smartphone, is high and increasing. A 2015 survey found that American teenagers averaged over 6 hours a day on screen media, excluding time spent at school or for homework.[75] By 2019 the figure had gone up to seven hours.[76] Some 45 percent of teens now admit to using the internet "almost constantly."[77] Here's what they're up to:* [78]

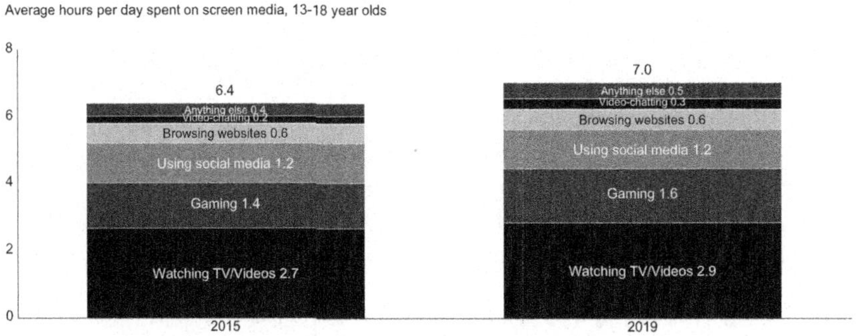


All of this time spent glued to a screen is displacing other things teens used to spend time doing. For example, the number of teens who get together with their friends nearly every day has dropped by more than 40 percent from 2000 to 2015.[79] Some pundits worry that this generation of children aren't developing strong social skills, and they may be right. One study took a group of preteens who had spent five days at a nature camp with no screens, and found that their recognition of nonverbal emotional cues was better than that of their peers who had stayed at school.† [80]

* Chart excludes time spent on these activities for school or homework.

† The study only measured the effects soon after, so we don't yet know if the improvement is lasting.

"School loneliness," one of the only measures of adolescent wellbeing captured in a world-wide survey of approximately 1 million adolescents over several years, appears to be on the rise, and is correlated with access to smartphones and the internet.[81] One can imagine that it must be harder to strike up conversations with classmates who are constantly buried in their phones. In the US, there has been a small decline in overall teen happiness and well-being since 2012 when internet usage and smartphones became ubiquitous, although it's not the dramatic drop that media scare stories tend to imply, and life satisfaction has actually gone up a tiny bit:[82]

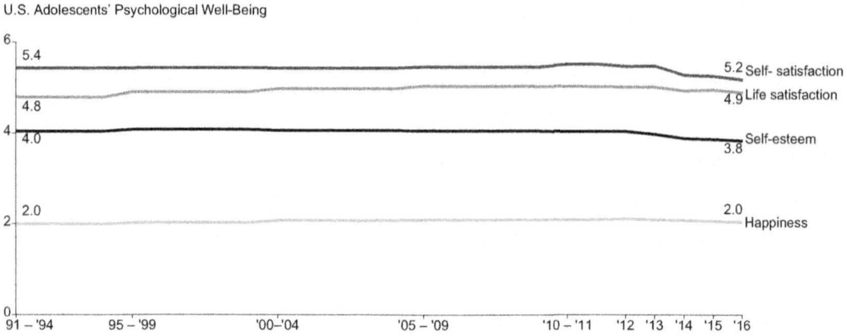


**Cause or effect?**

It's well documented that electronic media use correlates with unhappiness most at the two extremes.[83] Adolescents who spend very little time using the internet have slightly worse mental health than their more connected peers.[84] Perhaps those teens feel excluded from the extensive social interaction taking place online, or equally possible, perhaps their malaise derives from being deprived in additional ways beyond access to the internet. On the other end of the spectrum, teens who spend more than five hours a day online are twice as likely to be unhappy as those who spend less than an hour and instead spend their time seeing friends, playing sports, reading, doing homework, etc.[85] However, it's premature to conclude that the internet use causes the unhappiness — it could also be that unhappy teens seek solace in spending time online, and no research has yet teased out this distinction.[86] Furthermore, any negative effects of screen time on mood are likely to be small.[87]

Another difficulty with assessing the effects of screen time on our kids is that the generic concept of 'screen time' is somewhat meaningless: "It's like if someone asks you what you had for lunch, and you say, 'Food'; that doesn't provide any real information. Spending four hours creating a video for YouTube is different than spending four hours watching cat videos.

Lumping them both under screen time doesn't make much sense."[88] In fact, many teens are using online communication to reinforce their existing offline friendships,[89] and those who spend time messaging reap positive benefits that don't accrue to those who spend time in solitary pursuits such as playing Tetris.[90] Nevertheless, the authorities are negative about screen time (see box).

**The official take on screen time**
The American Academy of Pediatrics[91] and the UK Royal College of Pediatrics and Child Health[92] express concern about the correlation between screen time and mood. The National Institute for Health Research thinks the benefits of screen-based activities are largely outweighed by the possible detrimental effects on young people's wellbeing.[93] And the Canadian Society for Exercise Physiology, a body obviously focused on physical health, suggests no more than two hours per day of recreational screen time.[94]

Certain experts even assert that it's possible for children to suffer from a screen addiction (assessed via a questionnaire,[*] [95] although there's debate about the right cut-off to use[96]); they conclude that 4 to 5 percent of adolescents have a problem with compulsive internet use.[97] Researchers are now testing ways to wean kids off screens.[98] But for the moment, it's hard to say how all of this time staring at liquid crystal displays is affecting our children.

For many families, any attempts to limit screen time had to be abandoned during Covid, as devices became the sole portal for their children to access school, friends and the wider world. For other families, the debate has always been purely academic; those who are struggling to make ends meet

* Answer the following questions about your use of the internet for private purposes, according to the following scale: (0) Never, (1) Seldom, (2) Sometimes, (3) Often, (4) Very often:
1. How often do you find it difficult to stop using the internet when you are online?
2. How often do you continue to use the internet despite your intention to stop?
3. How often do others (e.g. partner, children, parents, friends) say you should use the internet less?
4. How often do you prefer to use the internet instead of spending time with others (e.g. partner, children, parents, friends)?
5. How often are you short of sleep because of the internet?
6. How often do you think about the internet, even when not online?
7. How often do you look forward to your next internet session?
8. How often do you think you should use the internet less often?
9. How often have you unsuccessfully tried to spend less time on the internet?
10. How often do you rush through your (home) work in order to go on the internet?
11. How often do you neglect your daily obligations (work, school or family life) because you prefer to go on the internet?
12. How often do you go on the internet when you are feeling down?
13. How often do you use the internet to escape from your sorrows or get relief from negative feelings?
14. How often do you feel restless, frustrated, or irritated when you cannot use the internet? [1]

A cumulative score of 21 or above may indicate problematic Internet use.[2]

are unlikely to have the bandwidth to police their children's screen time. In the words of one parenting expert:

> Before the pandemic, I lectured worried parents about the nine signs of tech overuse, like ditching sleep for screens. I advised them to write a 'family media contract' and trust, but verify, their tweens' doings online. An immediate consequence of the pandemic is that strict screen-time limits — which were always largely the province of more privileged families, like mine — went out the door, everywhere. I want to take this moment to apologize to anyone who felt judged or shamed by my implication that they weren't good parents because they weren't successfully enforcing a 'healthy balance' with screens, either for themselves or their children. That was a wad of privilege speaking.[99]

## *b) Video game addiction*

> A nine-year-old girl is in rehab after becoming so addicted to a computer game that she wet herself in order to keep playing. The parents only realized how bad things had become when they found their daughter sitting in a puddle of her own urine. She revealed she had been playing Fortnite for up to ten hours a day, sometimes until 5am.[100]

According to the (questionable)[101] rule of thumb that it takes 10,000 hours of deliberate practice to become world-class at a given pursuit,[102] many of the current generation of teens are on a path to successfully becoming masters — not of chess, creative writing, guitar, or baseball, but of video gaming.[103]

In the US, 83 percent of girls and 97 percent of boys play video games at least occasionally,[104] and a significant minority (mostly boys) play several hours a day.[105]

**Useful skills?**

There's no denying that habitual gamers are developing skills during all those hours of play. What skills they're acquiring, however, depends entirely on the type of game. Those who play shooter games improve their skills in special cognition (e.g. rotating objects) and top-down attention (e.g. tracking multiple objects),[106] and such gamers are less distracted by and need less attention to filter out irrelevant stimuli.[107] However, these skills don't appear to be generalizable: while they might be well-equipped to become air traffic controllers, their spatial navigation skills on screen don't extend to better spatial navigation skills in the physical world.[108]

Different types of games unsurprisingly have different effects on players. Young people who are assigned to play a prosocial game like Super Mario Sunshine or Chibi Robo are later more likely to behave kindly to another peer, while those assigned to play a violent game like Ty2 or Crash Twin Sanity tend to behave more aggressively.[109] Those who play casual, puzzle-type video games like Bejeweled II find gaming can increase their mood and decrease stress;[110] but adolescents who are allowed to keep playing games at night will often end up sleep-deprived, which can impact their mood.[111] So as with screen time more broadly, discussing the effects of video games is like discussing the effects of food — it depends a lot on what exactly is being consumed.[112]

Unsurprisingly, some types of games are also more addictive than others. One study had 18- to 20-year-olds play arcade, console, solo computer, or massively multiplayer online role-playing games (MMORPGs) for a month. Those who played MMORPGs[*] [113] reported more hours playing, worse health, worse sleep quality, and greater interference in 'real-life' socializing and academic work, as well as greater enjoyment in playing and greater interest in continuing to play.[114]

Many people have found themselves increasingly sucked into online worlds and unable to pull themselves away. As a result, in 2013, the American Psychiatric Association added 'internet gaming disorder (IGD)' to its list of officially-recognized diagnoses.[†] [115]

* For example, World of Warcraft, which appears to be particularly addictive.[i]

† Internet gaming disorder is defined as fulfilling five or more of the criteria below within a year:

1. Preoccupation with games: The individual thinks about previous gaming activity or anticipates playing the next game; gaming becomes the dominant activity in daily life;
2. Withdrawal symptoms when gaming is taken away: These symptoms are typically described as irritability, anxiety, or sadness;
3. Tolerance: The need to spend increasing amounts of time engaged in games;
4. Unsuccessful attempts to control or reduce participation in games;

**Addiction around the world**
Video game addiction levels vary by country, but the US is an outlier. Approximately 8.5 percent of teens in the US,[116] versus 5.5 percent in the Netherlands;[117] 5 percent in Tasmania, Australia;[118] and 1 to 2 percent in Germany show signs of having their lives significantly impacted by their obsession with playing.[119]

Those who are addicted to games are more likely to be depressed and to perform poorly in school,[120] although yet again it's difficult to know in which direction the causal arrow points — perhaps a life spent gaming is distracting and depressing, or perhaps those who are already depressed and struggling academically find solace in playing video games.*

Because internet gaming disorder has only been formally recognized for a decade, not enough is yet known about how to treat it,[121] although cognitive behavioral therapy shows some promise.[122] The best option is to prevent your teen from becoming addicted to gaming in the first place. The National Academy of Sciences recommends keeping game consoles out of children's bedrooms, and limiting the total amount of entertainment screen time to less than 1–2 hours per day.[123] Given the vast disparities between different types of games, it's also worth checking the ratings of games on a review site like Common Sense Media.

A group of parents recently attempted to sue the publisher of Fortnite for developing a product they alleged was as addictive and potentially harmful as cocaine.[124] The parents were conveniently ignoring the salient difference between Fortnite and illicit drugs; namely, that they themselves had allowed their children to play the game in the first place.

## c) Violent content

Virginia Tech Shooter Cho Seung-Hui was said to be an avid player of Counter-Strike, a popular team-based shooting game. Dylan

5. Loss of interest in real-life relationships, previous hobbies, and other entertainment as a result of, and with the exception of, games;
6. Continued excessive use of games despite knowledge of psychosocial problems;
7. Has deceived family members, therapists, or others regarding the amount of gaming;
8. Use of games to escape or relieve a negative mood (e.g., feelings of helplessness, guilt, or anxiety); and
9. Has jeopardized or lost a significant relationship, job, or educational or career opportunity because of participation in games.[1]

* There isn't yet sufficient research into the effects of immersive virtual reality environments, although it's a fair assumption that heightened realism will only exacerbate any effects that manifest currently with video games.

> Klebold and Eric Harris were fans of Doom and Wolfenstein 3D, referring to the games in the videos they left for police to find after the Columbine massacre.[125]

In our current media environment, children encounter violence everywhere they turn their eyeballs. Television was the original offender. An estimate from 1992 suggested that the average child had seen at least 8,000 murders and more than 100,000 other assorted acts of violence on television by the end of elementary school.[126] And as many as 8 percent of boys and 20 percent of girls report having nightmares at least monthly related to content they saw on TV.[127]

Movies are no better. PG-13-rated films now have as much or more gun violence on average as R-rated films.[128] Furthermore, many very young teens are watching R-rated movies. One study found that close to half of American 10- to 14-year-olds had seen *Scary Movie*, and 44 percent had seen *I Still Know What You Did Last Summer*, both of which contain horrific scenes of violence.* (If you haven't watch these flicks yourself, the first features many bloody stabbings, and the second involves various characters being killed in close-up with fish hooks and harpoons.)

**Think your child doesn't watch R-rated movies?**
Among teens whose parents forbade them from watching R-rated movies, 23 percent had still seen at least one movie from a list of the top 40 most violent popular R-rated films.[129]

The gore continues online. One survey of young people ages 10 to 15 years found that a third had been to a 'death' site (with pictures of dead bodies or people dying or being killed), a quarter had seen war, death or 'terrorism' online, and 2 percent had visited a violent X-rated site.[130]

Finally, we come to the most maligned category of media, violent video games. More than 85 percent of video games feature violence in some form,[131] and after a long parade of shooting sprees perpetrated by young, game-obsessed loners,[132] the general public has started to wonder whether the games themselves could be partially at fault. Entertainment industry executives point out that hordes of impressionable teens manage to play these games without deciding to enact them in real life, and the media coverage always allows both sides of the debate to have their say.[133]

* Both have been rated R for violence by the Motion Picture Association of America, UK 18 by the British Board of Film Classification, and coded for extreme violence by trained content coders.

In fact, the link between exposure to media violence and subsequent aggressive behavior is both extensively documented and incontrovertible. A report by the Surgeon General first reached this conclusion in 1972; since then, hundreds of studies have reinforced this finding, and every major review of the field concurs that exposure to violence on screen can spawn violence in the real world.[134] According to the American Academy of Pediatrics, "The evidence is clear and convincing: media violence is one of the causal factors of real-life violence and aggression. Pediatricians and parents need to take action."* [135]

One simple antidote is to comment on and express disapproval of violence if you see it on screen with your kids. When parents fail to say anything, children assume their parents are implicitly condoning the violence; in contrast, when parents proactively take a stance against violent content, their children are less likely to subsequently behave aggressively.[136] Options include pointing out that the aggressive feats are achieved via special effects; that the behaviors of the characters on-screen don't represent the behaviors of most people; and that in the real world, there are better ways to solve problems than resorting to violence.[137] If you're motivated to limit the amount of violence in your teen's daily screen diet, Common Sense Media also includes a rating and description of violence as one of the key components of its reviews.

In the words of a top American clinical psychologist, "If you came and you found a strange man teaching your kids to punch each other, you'd kick him right out of the house. But here you are; you come in and the TV is on, and you don't think twice about it."[138]

## d) Cyberbullying and harassment

> Ryan Halligan, 13 years old, committed suicide after years of bullying, both on and offline. "Ryan made friends with the bully for a while, and decided to tell him about something that happened during a medical examination, thinking it was a funny story to tell. The kid

* In case you need further convincing, the American Psychological Association states that "all existing quantitative reviews have found a direct association between violent video game use and aggressive outcomes."[1] And according to the American Academy of Family Physicians, "A body of literature that includes more than 2,000 scientific papers, studies, and reviews demonstrates the various effects that exposure to media violence can have on children and adolescents. These include increases in aggressive behavior, desensitization to violence, bullying, fear, depression, nightmares and sleep disturbances. Some studies found the strength of association to be nearly as strong as the association between cigarette smoking and lung cancer."[2]

> then spread a rumor around the school that Ryan said he liked it, and therefore Ryan must be gay... In the most chilling online conversation before the suicide, Ryan started off saying, "Tonight's the night I think I'm going to do it." And the kid fired back, "It's about blanking [sic] time." — John Halligan, father of Ryan[139]

Cyberbullying comes in many guises. Some examples of the many insidious ways teens torment each other online include exclusion (blocking an individual from buddy lists), impersonation, flaming (an online fight), trickery (soliciting personal information or nude pictures from someone and then sharing without consent), harassment (sending repetitive offensive messages), and cyber-stalking (sending repetitive threatening communications).[140] Both sexes are implicated in bullying, although the methods tend to vary somewhat by gender; for example, girls are more likely to threaten to harm friendships.[141]

It's unclear how common a phenomenon cyberbullying has become since there are many different ways to define it, but somewhere between 10 and 40 percent of teens claim to have been victims at some point.[142] Whatever the actual rate, cyberbullying is less common than ordinary bullying,[143] and as with Ryan, it's often an extension of bullying that's already taking place offline, [144] although there are examples of bullying taking place exclusively online.[145]

**Why bully online?**

There are many reasons why a bully might choose to target a victim electronically rather than in person. The most obvious advantage of cyberspace for an aspiring bully is anonymity. Although traditional bullies could already surreptitiously start a rumor, steal from the victim, or write a note in disguised handwriting, the internet provides the ultimate identity shield for those who wish to operate in the shadows.[146] Between 50 and 70 percent of cyberbullying victims don't know the identity of the perpetrator.[147]

Other purported advantages for bullies online are more speculative.[148] Operating online is the ultimate leveler in terms of physical differences, potentially allowing a physically smaller bully to intimidate someone of greater stature or strength in the physical world.[149] Theoretically, a bully has the potential to access a vast and practically limitless audience, and in certain very rare instances, public humiliation can go global.[150] Fortunately, this phenomenon is highly unusual, and most cases of bullying stay local.[151] Bullies online can potentially access their victims 24 hours a day rather than being limited to school hours, which is presumably even worse for the victim. Finally, most adults are unaware of much of what transpires in cyberspace and schools have less jurisdiction over happenings in an online environment, possibly making it less likely that bully will face any real consequences.[152]

Perhaps the most salient difference between online and traditional bullying is the lack of inhibition that cyberspace can encourage in the bully.[153] In the absence of any feedback about the emotional impact of their behavior, cyberbullies can dramatically underestimate the trauma caused by their bullying behavior, and are therefore less likely to feel sympathy and remorse.[154]

Victims of cyberbullying frequently have a tough time, although it's hard to distinguish between the pre-existing issues that may have attracted the attention of the bully in the first place from the effects of the bullying itself.[155] Irrespective of the root cause, victims of cyberbullying are at high risk for anxiety, insomnia and depression, headaches and abdominal pain, even poor performance in school and substance abuse.[156]

Parents are frequently oblivious.[157] Not only do they have no idea what platforms their children are using to communicate, most are not even aware that cyberbullying is an issue.[158] Kids are very unlikely to tell: only 10 to 15 percent of victims inform their parents,[159] typically because they're worried their parents will react counterproductively by restricting their internet access or taking their devices away entirely.[160]

If you believe your child could be vulnerable to bullying, advise your teen not to reveal personal information online, even to apparently trustworthy sources, and set rules about which types of websites are off limits (e.g. no chat rooms or social networking sites).[161]

**If your child is the victim**
In the unlikely scenario that you do discover your adolescent is being cyberbullied, volunteers at WiredSafety.org have expertise in working alongside law enforcement to preserve electronic evidence and trace perpetrators if you choose to pursue legal action. These experts also recommend informing the school, but in most cases schools, when left to their own devices, are ineffectual.[162] However, there are a number of school-based programs which have achieved success in reducing cyberbullying as well as traditional bullying. The best example available online is the KiVa antibullying program, which has materials aimed at schools, and also includes a guide for parents.[*] [†] [163]

Anecdotal evidence suggests that parents could also play a role in preventing at least more minor cases of cyberbullying by simply discussing

* Available at: www.kivaprogram.net/parents-guide/.

† Other effective programs which unfortunately aren't readily available include the ConRed Program,[1] [2] Cyberprogram 2.0,[3] [4] and the Cyber Friendly Schools Program.[5] [6]

the issue with their teens. One student commented, "I bully online and it doesn't mean anything."[164] This callous comment suggests that at least some online bullies are oblivious to the true ramifications of their behavior, and might reconsider their actions if they understood how traumatic online bullying can be for the victim. To prompt a conversation, you could watch *Cyber Bully* with your teen (age 14+).* [165] Made in 2011, the film features out of date technology (the protagonist accesses primitive-looking social media sites from a laptop rather than a phone), as well as an implausible confession and an even more implausible reconciliation between bully and victim. Nevertheless, it's a gripping portrayal of the effects of cyberbullying, and even features a bystander with high social status coming to the aid of the victim.

Some parents have become advocates for better protection from cyberbullying; for instance, Ryan Halligan's father:

> The year after Ryan's death, his father John Halligan directly influenced the creation of the Vermont Bullying Prevention Law. Now, Halligan spends his time traveling the country giving seminars to students, parents, and schools, and urging students to stand up for one another: "Don't be a bystander. Be an upstander."[166]

## e) Sexual stereotypes

> 2017: ABC's "Miss America" pageant attracts 5.4 million viewers.[167]
>
> 2020: The Ultimate Fighting Championship 251 generates roughly 1.3 million pay-per-view buys.[168]

Adolescents are impressionable creatures, constantly on the lookout for data points to calibrate their expectations about how the world works. While some of their impressions are formed by their own personal experiences, they are also constantly absorbing information from other sources subconsciously, including advertisements, magazines, TV shows, movies, and music

* Available at: www.youtube.com/watch?v=D_glF012QFs.

videos, without necessarily registering that these sources don't always reflect reality and often have other agendas.

Here are some examples of the messages reaching our teens:

- In a sample of magazine covers, more than three quarters of the women's magazines but none of the men's magazines contained a message regarding bodily appearance.[169]
- In a sample of music videos from Top 10 Billboard chart songs, female artists were significantly more likely to be provocatively dressed than male artists, and were far more likely to engage in sexually suggestive dance moves than male artists.[170]
- Among the top-grossing American films over 50 years, the average number of male main characters per movie has stayed constant over time at more than double the average number of female main characters; the proportion of female main characters engaging in sexual behavior is approximately two times greater than the proportion of male main characters; and male characters are the overwhelming perpetrators of violence.[171]
- Analyses of TV advertisements reveal that women are typically younger, are often suggestively dressed, and are less likely to provide a voice-over than men;[172] women are also 3.5 times more likely than men to be shown at home/in a domestic environment (versus at work), and 1.5 times more likely to give an opinion or a non-scientific argument (versus giving a factual/scientific argument) about a product.[173]

As with violence, so too with sexual stereotypes: young people observe and internalize.[174] It's very easy for researchers to test this effect, by priming subjects with media and then observing the consequences (see box). It's also easy to observe this phenomenon in real life. Young people who have been frequently exposed to genres like soap operas or music videos are more likely to agree with gender stereotypes and to express casual attitudes about sex.[175]

**Spawning chauvinists**

Women shown sexual stereotypes in popular sit-coms and dramas are more likely to agree with such stereotypes later,[176] and women exposed to rap videos featuring sexually subordinate women are more accepting when reading a vignette about a male assaulting his date.[177] Male undergraduates who had just watched clips from sexist movies (*9 ½ Weeks* and *Showgirls*) were two times as likely to say they themselves would act like the perpetrator in an acquaintance rape scene they were subsequently asked to read and evaluate.[178] And when educated, middle-class males are exposed to print advertisements featuring women as sex objects, they are later more likely to express acceptance of sexual aggression and violence against women (such as agreeing with awful statements like "Many women have an unconscious wish to be raped, and may then unconsciously set up a situation in which they are likely to be attacked.").[179]

Again as with violence, parents can influence their children's attitudes by actively commenting on examples where media doesn't accurately reflect the real world: children who hear this sort of commentary become more sophisticated consumers of media themselves.[180] So have the courage to be the annoying parent who insists on pausing the movie in the middle of the action to discuss (or fast-forwarding through inappropriate content). To get you fired up about the importance of this topic, *Miss Representation* and *The Mask You Live In* are two documentaries which are essential viewing for parents of teenagers who want to understand the societal gender dynamics their kids are facing,* although these films are less appropriate for adolescents themselves since they're littered with examples of the problematic media they've been designed to counter.

To wrap up, here's a quote from one spunky female who has had enough of media stereotypes:

> I regard romantic comedies as a subgenre of sci-fi, in which the world operates according to different rules than my regular human world. For me, there is no difference between Ripley from *Alien* and any Katherine Heigl character." – Mindy Kaling, American TV actress and producer[181]

* Available at: http://therepresentationproject.org/film/miss-representation-film/ ; https://therepproject.org/the-mask-you-live-in-watch-from-home/.

## f) Pornography

> Men who appear in sexually explicit material tend to have penises approximately 8–10 inches in length, relative to the average-sized penis ranging between 4.6 and 6 inches in length.[182]

The *Playboy* magazines which used to be displayed on top shelves and hidden under mattresses look thoroughly innocent in comparison to the material which can now be accessed instantly at the click of a button by anyone with unrestricted access to the internet. If the ancient Greeks opened Pandora's box, we've now opened Aphrodite's, and we're unlikely to ever succeed in stuffing the X-rated contents back in again.

Don't delude yourself that your teen is shielded; by age 18, 93 percent of boys and 62 percent of girls have seen pornography online,[183] and exposure can start early, particularly for boys:[184]

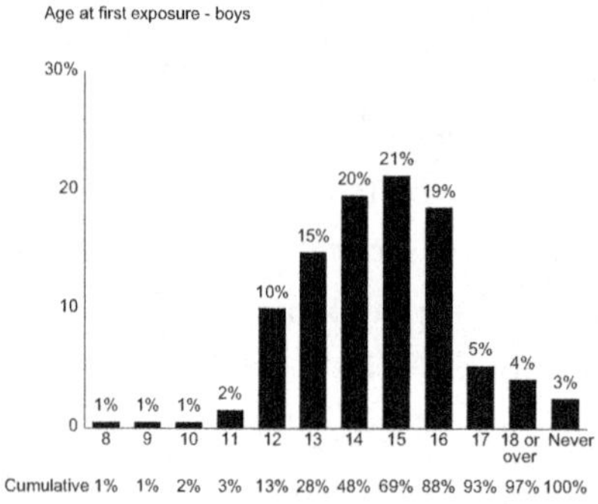


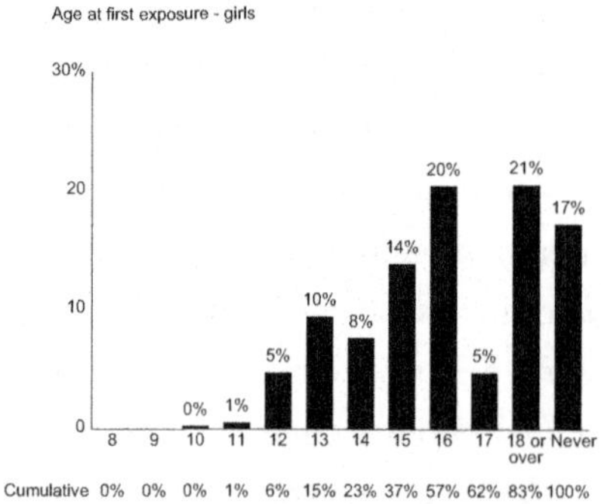


Many of these teens are intentionally hunting for sexually explicit material, but some are not;[185] 42 percent of girls and 7 percent of boys in one study reported they saw sexual images accidentally.[186]

Regardless, teens are viewing images that are increasingly extreme:[187]

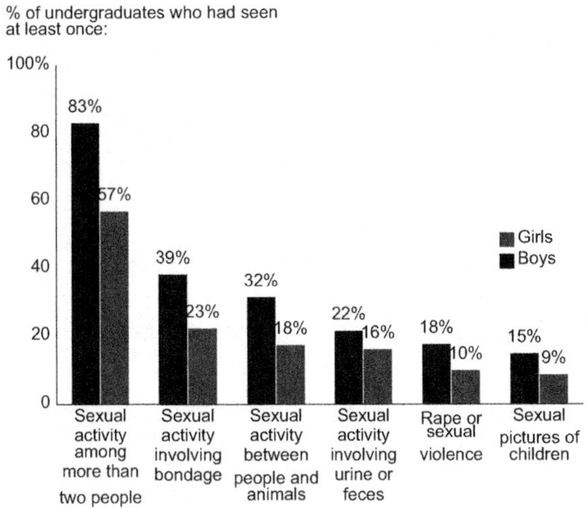


Further confirmation that *Playboy* is positively quaint.

Some teens are disturbed by what they're seeing online; somewhere between 4 and 10 percent of those who have seen porn say they were uncomfortable, repulsed or distressed,[188] with girls over five times more likely than boys to feel this way.[189] We should of course be endeavoring to shield these sensitive souls from unintentional exposure to such smut. On the flip side, it's even more disturbing to think that 90 to 96 percent of teens are <u>not</u> distressed or repulsed by all of this.

Parents, displaying their usual obliviousness, are simultaneously naïve and concerned about porn. One survey in the UK found that only 16 percent of parents thought their child had seen pornography on the internet.[190] On the other hand, a high percentage of parents worry that their children, if exposed, might believe that porn is realistic, become desensitized, or internalize the wrong messages from sexually explicit content.[191] Politicians have also woken up to the issue. In 2013, UK Prime Minister David Cameron warned that "many children are viewing online pornography and other damaging material at a very early age, and the nature of that pornography is so extreme it is distorting their view of sex and relationships."[192]

Cameron may be right in his assessment that pornography is changing the sexual views of an entire generation. Over half of boys and 39 percent of girls ages 11 to 16 say they think porn is realistic,[193] and children whose parents haven't discussed sexual health with them and who have been exposed to pornography are more likely to forgo using a condom.[194]

**Does porn affect real life?**
In one study of college students, males shown a scene of a beautiful woman in a sexual situation afterwards rated their own girlfriend as less attractive,[195] and in another, students of both sexes who were shown several hours of pornography over several weeks were later less satisfied with their own partners' physical appearance, sexual curiosity, and sexual performance.* [196]

When it comes to changes in behavior, there are very few long-term studies on 'unusual' sexual behaviors, mostly because it never occurred to anyone until very recently that this was a subject worth studying. But the few data points we have suggest that teens today may be more sexually adventurous than ever before.† [197]

How can we shield our children? So far, there's been very little useful research on this topic (see box). Installing a filter that restricts adult content should theoretically prevent kids from stumbling on porn accidentally, but the jury is still out on whether filters actually work in practice.[198]

**No useful research on porn**
School would be an obvious forum to address the issue of porn with teens, but we don't yet know whether school-based curriculums help teens think more critically about pornography or can ultimately change their views or behavior.[199] When it comes to the effects of parents, unenlightening studies do show relationships between the approaches parents take and their children's' behavior; for example, parents who restrict online social interactions have children who are less likely to view porn. However, as usual, it could be that sensible parents may simply have sensible children.[200] There have been no attempts to proactively encourage a group of parents to discuss porn with their children or restrict their access, to see what impact this might have.

If you're brave enough to attempt to broach the subject directly, you could print out either the tip sheet "What do young people need to know about porn?"‡ and/or one of the guides aimed at either 11- to 15-year-olds or adolescents age 15+ from the website "The Porn Conversation,"§ and offer to answer any questions your child might have.

* Fortunately, there's no evidence supporting the alarmist headlines proclaiming a staggering rise in cases of erectile dysfunction as a result of young men binging on increasingly exotic pornography and then finding real-life partners unexciting in comparison.[1 2] Between 1999 and 2013, the average percentage of young adult males who had such difficulties has remained constant at approximately 7-8%.[3 4]

† For example, from 1992 to 2010, the percentage of men age 20-24 who had ever participated in anal sex in their lifetime increased from 16% to 24%, and for women from 16% to 40%.[1 2] Similarly, back in 2005, college students describing playful and non-playful aggression during sex made no mention of choking,[3] but in 2020, more than a fifth of sexually-active women reported having been choked as part of sex.[4]

‡ Available at: https://itstimewetalked.com/wp-content/uploads/parent-tips-sheets/What_do_young_people_need_to_know_about_porn.pdf.

§ Available at: http://thepornconversation.org/.

In light of the incontrovertible reality that 93 percent of boys will explore watching porn as teens, the most pragmatic approach could be to proactively encourage them to pay for 'feminist' or 'ethical' porn. There are plenty of options available;* for example, a website called "Make Love Not Porn" describes itself as curating documentaries, in contrast with most porn sites which offer the X-rated equivalents of unrealistic Hollywood blockbuster movies.† [201] You could even gift your teen a subscription, which would probably be the most unexpected birthday present he (or she) would ever receive.

## g) Grooming

> Grooming (noun): The action by a pedophile of preparing a child for a meeting, especially via an internet chat room, with the intention of committing a sexual offense.[202]

"Video Games and Online Chats Are 'Hunting Grounds' for Sexual Predators" proclaimed *The New York Times* in 2020.[203] No matter that the article was filled with anecdotes rather than data; a further crop of parents doubtless came away feeling unnerved about the possibility of online predators. As a result of such headlines, three quarters of parents are concerned about the possibility of their child interacting with strangers online,[204] and 60 percent worry their child could become a victim of online grooming.[205]

In response to the blossoming panic, governments have stepped in. In 2007, Norway passed legislation making online grooming illegal. In 2017, Australia passed a law making it a crime for adults to engage in any planning or preparation to solicit a minor online, including by misrepresenting their age.[206] And most recently, Germany toughened an existing "cyber-grooming" law, making it illegal to attempt to communicate online with a child for sexual purposes.[207]

The widespread obsession with this issue dates back to a reality TV show called, *To Catch a Predator*, which aired in the US between 2004 and 2007. On this show, a confederate posing as a minor would arrange a sexual liaison with a stranger online, who would then be arrested upon showing up for the in-person

* Available at: www.dailydot.com/nsfw/guides/porn-ethical-premium/.

† Available at: https://makelovenotporn.tv/; charges $5 per video, or offers subscriptions of $10 per month for five videos per month, $30 per month for 30 videos per month, etc.

meeting. The concept of adults using the internet to prey upon children was then perpetuated by the popular press, with a huge spike in articles discussing what in reality was, and continues to be, an exceedingly rare phenomenon.[208]

There is no doubt that teens frequently interact with strangers online — close to half admit to doing so by age 16.[209] Why? Teens are driven by a powerful motivation to widen their horizons and meet new people as part of the primal drive to break free of the parental nest, an instinct which has existed since long before the invention of the internet.[210] Teens even occasionally arrange to meet online contacts in person: around 10 percent of children aged 9 to 16 have done so,[211] and over 70 percent of such encounters were conducted without their parents knowing anything about it.[212]

On the other hand, more than half were meeting a friend of a friend.[213] Over 99 percent of teens' close online relationships are with other teens, and age deception is surprisingly uncommon online, with those who do lie about their age shaving at most a few years off.[214] One study found that only 3 teens out of 1,560 had actually met someone over 21 face to face. In all three examples, the teen was 16 to 17, the oldest other person was 24, and only one case involved (consensual) sexual activity.[215]

Cyberspace, therefore, is hardly different than physical space. Teens who go to a party are likely to meet a similar assortment of people: some friends of friends, almost exclusively fellow teens; and on very rare occasions, perhaps someone's older sibling or another young adult. Encounters arranged online are also no more likely to lead to harm than any other in-person encounter. Of young people who met an internet contact offline, only around 2 to 5 percent left the meeting feeling upset.[216]

Perhaps the most convincing evidence that the panic about online grooming is unwarranted is the fact that the invention of the internet did not cause a spike in sexual victimization. The chart below reveals that teens living in the internet era are instead safer from sexual predation than they ever were before:[217]

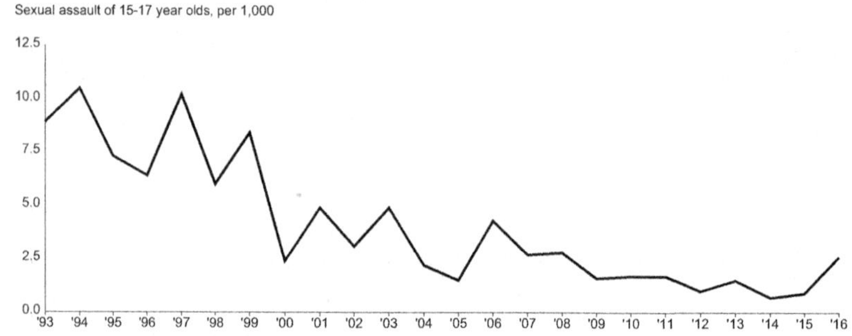

One study has even estimated that 93 percent of statutory rape victims today met their older partner offline versus only 7 percent online.[218]

Of course teens do attract unwanted sexual attention online, in the same way that they hear wolf whistles as they walk down the street. Between 10 and 15 percent of teens have been solicited online,[219] and between a quarter and a half of those were highly distressed by it.[220] Although the vast majority of these incidents take place while children are sitting within the safety of their own homes,[221] only approximately 20 percent of teens confide in their parents,[222] and more than half don't tell anyone at all.[223] Instead, they pragmatically deal with the problem themselves, by confronting their harassers and asking them to stop, ignoring them, blocking them, or leaving the site.[224]

**Who gets solicited?**

The risk factors for solicitation are straightforward and predictable: teens who use social networks and have online profiles,[225] and particularly those who post suggestive photographs[226] or converse online with unknown people,[227] particularly about sexual topics,[228] are at greater risk. Studies about the effects of parental monitoring are ambiguous,[229] and attempts to teach teens about online risks haven't yet proved to be very effective at reining in these behaviors.[230]

In summary, the threat posed by online predators is largely a red herring. Regardless of the headlines, no parents should feel irresponsible if their teen continues to think that the term 'grooming' refers to hairstyles or pet care.

## h) Sexting

> 13-year-old Stacy Jackson sent a topless photo of herself to a boy in hope of gaining his attention. Instead, she got the attention of her school, as well as the high school nearby. The incessant bullying by classmates that followed when the photo spread put an emotional weight upon her that she ultimately could not bear. Stacy hanged herself in her bedroom.* [231]

> A 16-year-old girl, a good student and popular in school, took a naked photo of herself while standing in front of a bathroom mirror. She sent

* Name of protagonist has been changed for privacy purposes.

> it via Snapchat, so that it would automatically disappear in seconds, to her 17-year-old boyfriend, with the words: "I love you. I trust you."
>
> The boyfriend took a screenshot before it disappeared and shared it with five of his friends. They in turn shared it with 47 of their friends. Within a few days, more than 200 people in the school had a copy. Someone uploaded it to a porn site, naming the girl and her school; over three months, with the help of online searches directing people to the site, the photo was downloaded 7,000 times.
>
> The family moved to a different city, but students there found the image as well, so the family fled to a different state. The girl refused to attend school. She self-medicated with drugs. And then, at the age of 21, she took her life.[232]

These tales of woe are emblematic of the heightened risks faced by the children of the internet era. In the vast majority of cases, sexting (sharing sexually explicit material digitally) doesn't cause any direct harm to the teens involved. Although there are undoubtedly examples of kids being coerced into sending images, the vast majority of adolescent sexting takes place in a romantic context with another teen, and senders typically describe the images they have sent as 'fun and flirtatious' or a 'sexy present'.[233] However once a digital image has been unleashed, it can be impossible to permanently eradicate it. Even if every online copy were taken down, anyone could have downloaded a copy in the meantime, and could choose to repost it later; there is simply no way to squeeze the genie back into the bottle.

The devastating implications of a single poor decision online can even extend to problems with the law. Sexting is technically illegal in most English-speaking countries and half of US states, even between consenting teens, as this behavior falls afoul of outdated and poorly-worded child pornography laws.[234] Here's another cautionary tale, this time affecting the perpetrator:

> After being confronted in school by a police officer and told that he was being investigated for child pornography and faced sex offender registration, honor roll student and hockey player Chase Mattison (16) left the school, walked to a five-story parking garage and jumped to his death. Mattison had recorded a video of himself and a female schoolmate engaged in sexual activity, and showed the video to his friends.* [235]

* Name of protagonist has been changed for privacy purposes

Sexting is increasingly normal among today's teens. In 2009 only 8 percent of teens had sent a sext,[236] but the numbers have climbed steadily;[237] now it's 15 to 30 percent[238] (and 30 to 45 percent of college students and young adults).[239] Yet once again, most parents are unaware. One revealing survey found that among adolescents who admitted to sexting, only 20 percent of their parents suspected.[240]

Most of these explicit images are seen only by the intended recipient, but a small handful of senders will inevitably find their confidence betrayed. On average, about 8 percent of sexts get forwarded without permission.* [241]

**Why do kids forward sexts?**
Although the concept of "revenge porn" has attracted attention recently, for teens the motivations for sharing images are typically far more mundane. Around 80 percent of those who forward sexts have no intention of causing any harm;[242] they simply have a careless attitude towards the privacy of their counterparty. Common reasons they give for spreading the explicit content include "showing off"/"bragging," "as a joke"/"to be funny," and "boredom."[243] Yet these thoughtless acts have the potential to cause significant and ongoing distress for the victims.[244]

The small amount of research on the effects of parents is inconclusive,[245] so yet again there is very little advice to provide, beyond talking to your teen about the potential consequences of both sending and thoughtlessly forwarding explicit messages. Whether your teen will listen and behave differently as a result is anyone's guess. Nevertheless, we should encourage empathy if we can. In the words of one high-profile celebrity whose nude photos were stolen and broadcast without her consent: "Anybody who looked at those pictures, you're perpetuating a sexual offense. You should cower with shame."[246]

## i) Advertising and embedded marketing

> "People have romantic notions about television. In the highest realms they think it's some sort of art medium. Others think it's an entertainment medium. It's not. It's a method to deliver advertising, like a cigarette is a method to deliver nicotine." — Bill Maher[247]

---

* although individual studies have found rates as high as 10 to 20 percent.

Bill may no longer be correct about the insidious nature of television in the new golden era of uninterrupted streaming. Yet his point still stands — if a product is being offered for free, the consumer is the product, being served up to advertisers hoping to peddle their wares. And there is no segment as attractive to advertisers as young people, whose tastes are still malleable and who have an entire lifetime of consumption ahead of them.

In the past, the average child was exposed to approximately 40,000 advertisements each year, typically for products such as sugary cereals, candy, fast food restaurants and toys.[248] Although the mediums have shifted, the relentless bombardment continues in today's online world: when using social media apps, teens see an average of 2.6 food marketing ads every 10 minutes, the vast majority for junk food.[249] Close to three quarters of modern teens engage with brands online, and almost two thirds click on social media ads.[250] Furthermore, over half of sites and apps collect and sell personal information about children to advertisers, without allowing them or their parents to opt out.[251]

Teens exposed to food advertising tend to eat more overall, and are more likely to choose the products they've seen advertised;[252] advertising exposure accounts for an estimated 2 percent of the variation in obesity.[253] This is unsurprising, since as discussed in the section on alcohol, advertisers wouldn't bother to pay for campaigns that didn't generate a good return. In fact, advertising on the internet has proven to be four times more effective for companies than advertising on television.[254]

**Sneaky marketing**

To demonstrate the cunning of the companies seeking to influence your children, here's an excerpt from a report entitled, "9 Strategies to Help Cater Your Digital Marketing to the Youth Under-24 Generation Z.": "Youth on social media want user-generated content and interactive content like polls, quizzes, chats, and conversation. Think of ways to include interactivity in your articles, images, and videos. You also want to encourage accumulating reviews, user-generated photos and videos... The average attention span of a millennial was 12 seconds long. For Generation Z, it's 8 seconds. They don't have time to waste and you don't have time to lose. Get to your marketing message fast."[255]

It's not only purveyors of junk food who are targeting your teens. Heineken and Google recently committed to a YouTube advertising partnership, which it was estimated would reach 103 million minors per month globally.[256]

Attempts to teach younger children to be more savvy about advertising typically fail. Even if they grasp the persuasive intent of advertising, kids continue to be influenced by the messages nevertheless.[257] Tweens start to develop the cognitive ability to differentiate between persuasive advertising and other content, and to muster the appropriate skepticism about commercially motivated messages to resist being fully persuaded.[258] There has been far less research on this topic focused on older teens, so it's difficult to know if teaching adolescents about "media literacy" actually has any effect on their behavior. If you want to encourage your teen to be more skeptical, one helpful video which describes three rhetorical strategies commonly used in advertising could be worth sharing.[*] [259]

Rather than passively absorbing advertising, some teens have turned the tables and become the advertisements themselves. "Posting Instagram Sponsored Content Is the New Summer Job," according to one headline:

> While some teens spent the summer babysitting, bagging groceries, or scooping ice cream, thousands of others made hundreds of dollars — and in some cases, much more — the new-fashioned way: by doing sponsored content on Instagram.
>
> According to one advertiser, "If you see an ad for clothing on TV or in a magazine, you know it's an ad, but on Instagram these profiles are just their personal profiles most of the time. When people post a picture of them doing something in the day and just tagging their outfits, it doesn't look like it's meant to be an ad, so it makes it seem more personal — even though they may be getting paid."
>
> Payment for services is always received via PayPal, where kids say it's easy to store money without scrutiny from their parents. PayPal sometimes requires a credit card to set up, but that's easy to spoof using a $5 prepaid Visa from a drugstore.[260]

It's difficult to elude corporate brainwashing when even your friends may have been enlisted as walking infomercials. At least teens have deep reserves of natural cynicism, which in this case could come in handy.

* Available at: www.readwritethink.org/video/art-rhetoric.

## j) Identity theft

> "The rate of identity theft for children is 51 times higher than that of adults." — 'Child Identity Theft' report, authored by Carnegie Mellon University's CyLab and Debix AllClear ID[261]

> "More than 1 million children were victims of ID theft last year." — 2018 Child Identity Fraud Study sponsored by Identity Guard[262]

If you set out in search of frightening headlines about identify theft, you'll find them. According to various articles, young people are uniquely vulnerable to exploitation online. However, the authors of such headlines are not neutral journalists; they're firms attempting to sell you their services by whipping you into an alarmist frenzy.

Adolescents do reveal more about themselves online than most adults. [263] According to a Pew Internet survey, over half of teens have profiles online; a quarter of these say it would be "pretty easy" for someone to identify them based on their online profile, and another 40 percent say it would be possible for someone to match them to their online identity with some effort.[264] Yet this lax approach surprisingly doesn't translate into serious difficulties in practice. Around 8 percent of teens say they've experienced someone using their password, and 2 percent have lost money in an online scam.[265] However, only 1.6 percent of 16 to 17-year-olds with a bank account and 2.5 percent of those with a credit card become victims of identity theft, which makes them far less susceptible to this problem than adults.* The consequences typically aren't dire either: over half of cases involving young people were resolved within one day, and only 2.5 percent took three months or more to resolve.[266]

One no-regrets action the Federal Trade Commission recommends is to check before age 18 if your child has a credit report. If anyone has been fraudulently using your teen's identity, it will be a much simpler matter to clear up while your offspring remains a minor and doesn't yet need to secure a loan or apply for a job.[267] The Consumer Financial Protection Bureau recommends requesting the credit reports from all three of the major credit

* Overall 7% of 18-24 year olds, 11% of 25-34 year olds, and 12% of 35-49 year olds become victims of dentity theft

agencies at the same time by using a dedicated government website which helps streamline the process.* [268]

**If someone's already masquerading as your teen**
The website IdentityTheft.gov, managed by the Federal Trade Commission, can guide you through the appropriate steps if you do uncover a case of identity theft. You should also file an online complaint with the Internet Crime Complaint Center (IC3),† which alerts the relevant authorities about the situation.[269]

Irrespective of the safeguards you put in place, there's also a possibility that your teen will at some point be involved in identity theft in the opposite direction: the market for fake IDs continues to thrive.[270]

## k) Gambling

> Bill Kaplan laughs, remembering his mother's reaction when he told her he was postponing his entrance to Harvard to make his fortune at gambling. "Oh my God, this is ridiculous! What am I going to tell my friends?" she said. Kaplan had read a book about card counting and believed he could use a mathematical model to make good money from blackjack. He took $1,000 and within nine months had turned it into about $35,000.
>
> His life took a dramatic turn when the leader of a small group of students from the Massachusetts Institute of Technology (MIT) who had dabbled with card counting overheard him discussing his Vegas exploits. They asked him to train and manage what would later become known as the infamous MIT Blackjack Team.[271]

The movie 21 glamorizes the story of the MIT Blackjack Team, portraying gambling as an audacious battle of wits between ambitious young students and large casino corporations.[272] In reality, most gamblers don't win against the house. Instead, they get sucked into playing games which are carefully designed to deliver perfectly-timed hits of dopamine from small wins in order to keep them hooked, while gradually draining them of their money.

* Available at: www.annualcreditreport.com/index.action

† Available at: www.ic3.gov

Although gambling is illegal for anyone under age 18 in most countries around the world,[273] it's laughably easy for kids to lie about their age online, and the internet is both convenient and anonymous.[274] It's therefore no surprise that many teens are now problematic gamblers. How many is difficult to say precisely since there are various ways to measure and define the problem, and no single source has tracked adolescent gambling rates over time. Studies suggest that 10 to 15 percent of adolescents have potentially problematic levels of gambling, while 2-8 percent likely suffer from a full-blown gambling disorder.[*] [275] [276] Boys are also approximately 50 percent more likely than girls to be drawn into compulsive gambling.[277]

Most parents view gambling as relatively harmless compared to other risks their adolescents face,[278] and only 20 percent of teens say their parents have set any rules about gambling.[279] Even professionals like child psychologists and social workers tend to be unconcerned, and are frequently unaware of how to help address the problem.[280] It's hardly their fault; there's very little information on how to treat adolescent problem gamblers.[281] The paltry research that is available suggests that an approach called personalized normative feedback (PNF) along with our old favorite cognitive behavioral therapy are the two most promising treatments.[282] There is also hope that a child with a gambling obsession might simply outgrow it. One study which tracked young gamblers for three years found that only a quarter maintained the habit.[283]

Nevertheless, it's a problem parents should be taking more seriously. In contrast to the portrayal in the movie *21*, here's what problematic gambling can look like in real life:

---

* These are the Diagnostic Criteria for Gambling Disorder according to the American Psychiatric Association: Persistent and recurrent problematic gambling behavior leading to clinically significant impairment or distress, as indicated by the individual exhibiting four (or more) of the following in a 12-month period (with the gambling behavior not better explained by a manic episode):

1. Needs to gamble with increasing amounts of money in order to achieve the desired excitement.
2. Is restless or irritable when attempting to cut down or stop gambling.
3. Has made repeated unsuccessful efforts to control, cut back, or stop gambling.
4. Is often preoccupied with gambling (e.g., having persistent thoughts of reliving past gambling experiences, handicapping or planning the next venture, thinking of ways to get money with which to gamble).
5. Often gambles when feeling distressed (e.g., helpless, guilty, anxious, depressed).
6. After losing money gambling, often returns another day to get even ("chasing" one's losses).
7. Lies to conceal the extent of involvement with gambling.
8. Has jeopardized or lost a significant relationship, job, or educational or career opportunity because of gambling.
9. Relies on others to provide money to relieve desperate financial situations caused by gambling.

Mild: 4–5 criteria met
Moderate: 6–7 criteria met
Severe: 8–9 criteria met[1]

> A teenager in the UK has lost £80,000 by gambling online. The boy, aged thirteen, claims he was influenced after seeing numerous advertisements for gambling sites on TV and at football matches. The youngster was able to bet online by stealing his dad's credit card, and within weeks he had gambled away around £20,000. The boy was forced by his parents to attend psychotherapy, but just a few months later he went straight back. This time, over a week he racked up losses of around £60,000. "I had no idea that gambling could be an addiction. It seemed like fun and I thought I would make money too. I just had to put in dad's name, address, date of birth and card details and checked a box saying I was 18 — it took literally seconds to start."[284]

## l) Irresponsible spending

> My little "habit" started out with shopping before and after my shifts at my mall job and spending close to $200 a week on clothes. A large part of the leisure time of my youth was spent shopping at the mall.[285]

> When I was a teenager, I'd beg my parents to buy me things and, eventually, they'd give in. They spoiled me rotten. I never really learned the value of money.
> When I went away to college, I opened several credit cards. I maxed out every single one in a matter of months. I couldn't even pay my minimums, and I panicked. Ashamed, I began throwing away the unopened bills. Then the debt companies started calling, sometimes up to 20 times a day. I changed my number."[286]

Only in the twenty-first century and only in the Western world could humans develop a mental affliction related to acquiring an overabundance of physical possessions.

**The origins of our consumerism**

If you or your teen happen to be curious about how our society has arrived at this nadir, *The Story of Stuff*, a brief, low-budget video, provides a remarkably insightful description of the political decisions which led to our destructive modern culture of consumerism, and the impact this culture is now having on the environment.* [287]

Oniomania, also known as compulsive buying disorder, is defined as "an irresistible–uncontrollable urge, resulting in excessive, expensive and time-consuming retail activity, resulting in gross social, personal and/or financial difficulties."[288] Those with compulsive buying disorder are unable to prevent themselves from purchasing items, even when they have no need for them, and even after they have spent well beyond their budget. And for teens, the internet is one of the easiest and fastest ways to purchase lots of stuff, although obviously this can be an off-line problem as well.

**An official affliction?**

This disorder has yet to be formally recognized in the American Psychological Association's official diagnostic manual of mental disorders,† because there isn't yet enough proof that it constitutes a full-blown addiction.[289] But it's an increasingly common problem,[290] affecting approximately 5 percent of the adult population and 8 percent of university students.[291]

If you fear your child may be in the grip of a spending obsession, the Compulsive Buying Scale is the tool most frequently used to diagnose this condition.‡ [292] [293] If your teen scores above the threshold, it's worth seeking professional help; as with many other disorders previously covered, cognitive behavioral therapy shows the most promise.[294] This is not a problem that should be left to fester, as the individual who changed her telephone number to escape her creditors will testify:

---

* Available at: www.youtube.com/watch?v=9GorqroigqM.

† The DSM-5.

‡ The Compulsive Buying Scale:
Rate the following on a scale of 1 = strongly disagree, up to 7 = strongly agree:
- "My closet has unopened shopping bags in it."
- "Others might consider me a 'shopaholic.'"
- "Much of my life centers around buying things."
- "I consider myself an impulse purchaser."

Rate the following on a scale of 1 = never, up to 7 = very often:
- "I buy things I don't need."
- "I buy things I did not plan to buy."

A cumulative score of 25 or more is classified as a compulsive buyer.[1]

> I'm still living with the repercussions. I've tried to get a single credit card so that I can begin to build back the credit I destroyed, but I can't get approved for any of them. I've also been denied bank loans for home improvements. My shopping addiction nearly destroyed my life.[295]

## m) Plagiarism and copyright infringement

> Harvard has rescinded an offer to Sarah Whitlow after reports surfaced that she had plagiarized material in articles for her local paper. [*] [296]

Plagiarism, defined as "presenting someone else's work or ideas as your own, with or without their consent, by incorporating it into your work without full acknowledgement,"[297] is a relatively modern concept. The first law establishing copyright was passed in 1710 in London, but it only protected publishers, and most writers at the time still thought it was acceptable to steal ideas from others: even the great original thinker Benjamin Franklin purportedly plagiarized another writer in his *Poor Richard's Almanac* in 1732.[298] Even today, the laws governing plagiarism in the US are unclear and typically unenforced by courts, allowing academic institutions to set their own standards and penalties for students.[299]

Despite the 'no tolerance' policies set by most universities, plagiarism is rampant.[†] [300] One survey of 80,000 undergraduates found that 38 percent admitted to having used material that wasn't their own without including an appropriate citation.[301] And this was before the release of ChatGPT.

Notwithstanding the occasional high-profile example like the case of Sarah above, it's unclear how many of these acts of plagiarism are caught. In one survey from Australia, only 7 percent of students reported being reprimanded for some form of academic misconduct,[302] although online tools like the Scribbr Plagiarism Checker[‡] [303] and Turnitin[§] do appear to have reduced the amount of blatant copy/pasting, presumably because students are savvy enough to realize they now run a greater risk of being caught.[304]

* Name of protagonist has been changed for privacy purposes.

† Like irresponsible spending, plagiarism isn't only an online issue, but nowadays it's much easier to copy and paste from a website than type up the contents of a book.

‡ Available at: www.scribbr.co.uk/plagiarism-checker/.

§ Available at: www.turnitin.com.

Another related pitfall facing our children online is copyright infringement. In 2008, a 16-year-old was taken to court for having downloaded and shared music using the peer-to-peer file sharing application KaZaA (which has now been discontinued). Although she successfully argued that she was too young to have understood the illegal nature of her actions, she was still ordered by the court to pay $200 per song, or a total of $7,400.[305] She was not alone in her ignorance: most teenagers answer "yes" when asked if they know the meaning of "copyright", but the vast majority get the definition wrong when pressed, which is unsurprising given the complexity of the laws regulating copyright and the disconnect with how people actually manipulate content online.[306] Young people also have difficulty understanding why violating copyright laws is morally wrong in the first place.[307]

Education can help; one program aimed at educating college students reduced rates of plagiarism by 37 percent.[308] The Electronic Frontier Foundation, a nonprofit, offers a copyright curriculum aimed at teachers but which is available for anyone to access for free online.[*] [309] You could also alert your teens to websites and search engines that return results that are acceptable to re-use; for example, "Photos for Class,"[†] [310] and the search engine provided by the non-profit, Creative Commons.[‡] [311]

Those teens who do stray into plagiarism will at least find themselves in famous company: in addition to Benjamin Franklin, they can count Mark Twain, George Orwell and Samuel Beckett as fellow plagiarists.[312] Sadly few academic institutions are likely to take this illustrious company as a legitimate excuse.

## n) Ideological persuasion

> Fatima Hasan, age 15, travelled to Syria in December, and is now believed to be living in Raqqa, the Islamic State stronghold. Fatima's father said he believed his daughter was targeted by Islamic State recruiters through the internet.[§] [313]

* Available at: www.eff.org/teachingcopyright/handouts#copyrightFAQ.

† Available at: www.photosforclass.com.

‡ Available at: https://search.creativecommons.org/.

§ Name of protagonist has been changed for privacy purposes.

In your youth, your neighborhood magazine shop and video rental store catered to the prevailing local tastes in news and entertainment, and your local library offered a curated set of volumes across genres. Radio and cable television channels offered more diversity, but still within bounds. In such a media environment, the likelihood of you stumbling upon and being converted to views drastically different than those held by your own community was small.

Now our children are no longer so shielded. Curiosity about any topic can be quickly gratified through Googling, and as they wander through the vast expanses of cyberspace, it's inevitable they'll chance upon content well beyond the bounds of their original search. Worse, as discussed previously, online companies greedy to capture and monetize their attention through advertising are motivated to serve them up increasingly provocative content if this shows any signs of keeping them engaged. This dynamic could theoretically set the stage for naïve teenagers to be pulled down a wormhole of ideological persuasion.

'Hate speech' is defined by the Oxford dictionary as "abusive or threatening speech or writing that expresses prejudice against a particular group, especially on the basis of race, religion, or sexual orientation."[314] Today's teens encounter hate speech frequently online:[315] 64 percent say they encounter such content "sometimes" or "often," according to one recent survey of teen social media users.[316]

Misinformation and hateful content can be well-disguised online. So-called 'cloaked sites' target young people searching for information for homework assignments, and are specifically designed to appear reasonable initially, in order to build trust with readers before gradually lead them down a path towards more extreme viewpoints.[317] For example, the domain name www.martinlutherking.org used to be owned by the Neo-Nazi website Stormfront, and was filled with misinformation about this important historical figure.[318] Before it was taken down, one analysis found that this cloaked site was receiving a similar amount of web traffic as the legitimate website for The King Center, run by Martin Luther King's family, with traffic peaking for both around MLK day and Black History Month.[319]

Are the gremlins lurking on the internet capable of capturing the attention of your teenager sufficiently to transform an empathetic kid researching a school project on Dr. King into a torch-wielding member of the KKK?

Hardly. Radicalization can't transpire solely on the internet; in-person recruitment is still key for extremist groups.[320] True radicalization happens in face-to-face social gatherings and is a years-long process, typically targeting youths who feel alienated and are seeking an outlet for their discontent; the internet is merely one initial form of outreach.[321] Digging deeper into the story of Fatima reveals a more complex picture:

> "Fatima's behavior changed after her mother died and she developed an intense interest in Islam," according to Fatima's father. "I thought this was normal because she lost the closest person to her, and she's an only child… She changed her dressing style and wore a scarf and started praying five times a day." He believes his daughter was groomed by two young women who took her to the airport and made sure she caught the flight to Turkey.[322]

## *o) Sharing of harmful or inappropriate content*

> After being announced as the host for the 2019 Academy Awards, comedian Kevin Hart publicly stepped down from the gig when a series of his old homophobic tweets resurfaced.[323]

> In the days leading up to the NFL draft, many noticed that Ohio State prospect Nick Bosa's Twitter page had been scrubbed of his controversial tweets. But in recent days, Bosa's Instagram history has been placed under the microscope, uncovering that he liked multiple Instagram posts that featured the N-word and a homophobic slur.[324]

In the pre-internet era, most people's teen escapades were captured only in the memories of their friends. Perhaps a compromising photo or two would end up stored away in a shoebox in a basement somewhere, but even the most egregious behavior would typically end up forgotten.

Now, our species has invented the internet, which functions as a single shared, global brain with near-infinite storage capacity, remembering anything and everything we choose to feed it. This functionality may be a boon to historians and those trying to track down their childhood friend who moved away. For teens who conduct the vast majority of their social lives online, however, this perpetual storage machine recording their every keystroke for posterity poses a very real risk.

Approximately 70 percent of college admissions officials believe that evaluating applicants' social media profiles is "fair game,"[325] and 9 percent admit to reversing an admissions offer as a result of what they've discovered about an applicant online.[326] The seductive allure of "private" chat rooms and purportedly ephemeral Snapchat posts can lull our teens into a false sense of security about the digital footprint they're trailing behind them. In one high-profile case, a group of students who had recently been admitted to Harvard College launched a private online chat dubbed "Harvard memes for horny bourgeois teens" in which they began to make increasingly offensive comments,[327] without having considered the possibility that even private chats could be captured and shared with a simple screenshot.[328] Harvard's admissions officials were not amused, and ultimately chose to rescind their offers.

Here's the advice to provide your teen, from a Google representative who delivers online safety training to teenagers: "Don't post anything you wouldn't want your grandmother to see."[329]

## *Take-aways*

A set of rules that describe our reactions to technologies:

1. Anything that is in the world when you're born is normal and ordinary and is just a natural part of the way the world works.
2. Anything that's invented between when you're fifteen and thirty-five is new and exciting and revolutionary and you can probably get a career in it.
3. Anything invented after you're thirty-five is against the natural order of things.[330]

Our offspring are coming of age in a digital world, and learning to navigate this world will be critical to their ability to participate in the modern information economy. This reality leaves parents with no option to simply forbid electronics and insist their teens switch off the grid completely. Nevertheless, there are downsides to the ubiquitous presence of the internet in our children's lives. For example, as the world becomes more global than local, we're no longer tied to our neighborhood. As one author bemoans,

> Back before television and the internet, we all had the chance to be the best at something. Small towns had adult baseball and hockey teams, bands, and community theater. Everyone had a shot at being the best mechanic, the best pie-maker, the choir soloist, the most well-read. Now, with media saturation, if we try to play sports we're comparing ourselves with people who are freaks of nature, perhaps enhanced by drugs, who get paid very well to do nothing but practice. Why should we try?[331]

With the pond expanding to the size of an ocean, very few of us can still enjoy the benefits and pleasures of being a big fish.

One way to insulate our teens could be to gate-keep how much time they spend and what they see. For example, Common Sense Media's "Parents' Ultimate Guide to Parental Controls" provides suggestions about monitoring online behavior.[*] [332] The problem with this approach is that teens categorically hate it.

**The teen view on monitoring**

If given the opportunity to rate online monitoring and safety apps, three quarters of teens give these apps the worst possible rating, and comment that in addition to precluding them from pursuing various useful tasks, the apps negatively impact their relationship with their parents, causing them to want to rebel, rather than negotiate or compromise.[333]

Moreover, many teens are more technically savvy than their parents, and the internet is rife with instruction manuals for side-stepping parental controls, so most apps promising online safety may only be providing illusory peace of mind.[334] As a result, the American Academy of Pediatrics doesn't recommend remote monitoring,[335] instead suggesting that parents draft a "family media plan" in conjunction with their children. (They provide a template that can be downloaded for free.[†] [336])

Perhaps it's not too late to emulate the Amish. It would be easy to dismiss them as a group of freakish luddites who categorically reject the modern world, but on closer inspection, they simply have vastly different priorities to the rest of us:

---

* Available at: www.commonsensemedia.org/blog/parents-ultimate-guide-to-parental-controls.

† Available at: www.healthychildren.org/English/media/Pages/default.aspx#home.

> Each church community of about 30 families has latitude in setting its technology boundaries. When a church member asks to use a new technology, the families discuss the idea and vote to accept or reject. The conversation centers on how a device will strengthen or weaken relationships within the community and within families. In one case, a family wanted to run propane gas pipes for lights to every room of their home instead of running them only to the kitchen and living room. (The Amish choose not to tap the electrical grid.) Church members discussed how the change would affect the family. If the family members could separate into bedrooms to read at night, instead of gathering in the living room, would their ties fray? Of course they would.[337]

No one is suggesting we should all return to an era without electricity. On the other hand, our cavalier attitude towards immediately buying the latest device and downloading the newest app, without pausing to think about the impact it could have on ourselves, our children and our communities, may be short-sighted. We've reached an inflection point which will require a new level of sophistication in embracing technology openly but thoughtfully.

**KEY PARENTING TAKE-AWAYS:**

1. Discuss the potential for addiction, distraction, cyberbullying and misinformation on social media, and encourage your teen to watch the movie *The Social Dilemma*
2. Share any or all of 'The Most Common Cognitive Bias',[*] the TED talk about personalized news and filter bubbles,[†] the discussion about being hacked by machines,[‡] the story of the heroic swimming pig,[§] the segments on doctoring voices[¶] and videos,[**] and "Reality Check: The Game"[††]
3. Point out that search engine algorithms don't put legitimate sites first
4. Suggest searching for any surprising headline plus the word "hoax," "fake," "viral," or "scam"; and recommend fact-checking on Snopes.com, factcheck.org, the Washington

* Available at: www.youtube.com/watch?v=vKA4w2O61Xo

† Available at: www.ted.com/talks/eli_pariser_beware_online_filter_bubbles/transcript?language=en

‡ Available at: www.wired.com/story/artificial-intelligence-yuval-noah-harari-tristan-harris/

§ Available at: www.youtube.com/watch?v=g7WjrvG1GMk; www.youtube.com/watch?v=_2My_HOP-bw; www.youtube.com/watch?v=bvtJj6HoYHg

¶ Available at: www.youtube.com/watch?v=1aTApGWVGoI

** Available at: www.youtube.com/watch?v=o2DDU4gOPRo

†† Available at: https://mediasmarts.ca/digital-media-literacy/educational-games/reality-check-game

Post fact checker, Politifact.com, or tineye.com for images
5. Check your teen's online presence for unwise disclosures or content
6. Insist your teen switches off devices / logs out of social media accounts while doing homework
7. Read reviews of video games and movies to minimize your teen's exposure to violence, sexual stereotypes and other negative messages, and limit entertainment screen time to less than 1–2 hours per day
8. Comment on any violence, sexual stereotypes and advertising/embedded marketing you see with your teen on screen
9. Recommend and discuss the movie *Cyber Bully*
10. Consider buying your child access to 'feminist' or 'ethical' porn
11. Warn your teen about the potential consequences of both sending and thoughtlessly forwarding explicit messages
12. When your child is 16 or so, check with the three US credit agencies for fraudulent credit reports[*]
13. Take gambling and excessive spending seriously and get professional help
14. Have your teen read the FAQs about copyright, fair use, and public domain,[†] and suggest "Photos for Class"[‡] and the Creative Commons search engine[§] for school projects
15. Recommend against doing anything online that your teen wouldn't want a grandparent to see, no matter how supposedly private the forum might be

* Available at: www.annualcreditreport.com/index.action.

† Available at: www.eff.org/teachingcopyright/handouts#copyrightFAQ.

‡ Available at: www.photosforclass.com.

§ Available at: https://search.creativecommons.org/.

# 10. CHARACTER

## Encourage brave bystander behavior

> "Sticks and stones may break my bones, but words can also hurt me. Stones and sticks break only skin, while words are ghosts that haunt me."[1]

Although we've all heard the old adage, this modern adaptation is probably closer to the truth. Here are some testimonials from victims of bullying:

> "I got teased my entire school life." "Her experience was so traumatic that she directed her wedding guests to donate to the charity BeatBullying." "He was relentlessly bullied as a child." "I was beat up in the bathrooms, in the hallways, shoved in the lockers." "He was tormented by bullies who mocked him for his hyperactive personality and big ears." "I was teased for being ugly, having a big nose, being annoying." "One bully in particular preyed on the fact that I was so scared and would avoid her. It was torture." "People kicked my a--, spit in my face, and kicked me down the stairs."[2]

These quotes describe the experiences of a group, not of social outcasts, but of household names: Rihanna, Kate Middleton, Elon Musk, Eminem, Michael Phelps, Lady Gaga, Eva Mendes, and Chris Rock, respectively.[3]

Bullying is shockingly common.[4] It usually peaks around age 13,[5] but remains an ongoing fact of life for many high schoolers:[*] [6]

* Sixth to eighth graders answered the question "were ever bullied"; ninth to twelfth graders answered "were bullied in the last 12 months"; national averages unavailable for sixth to eighth grades, so weighted average of results from 22 states with reported figures.

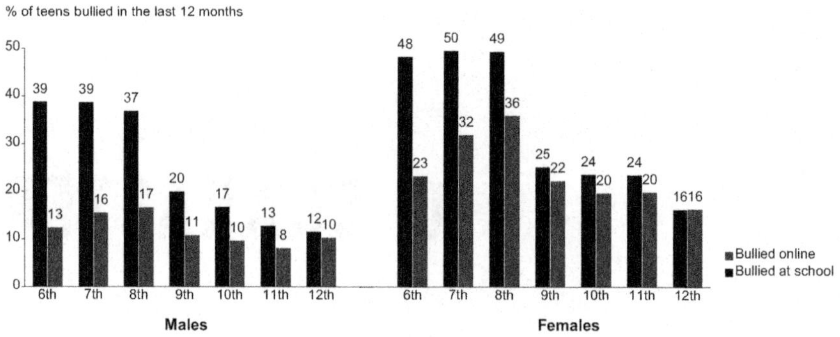


Bullying can be deeply traumatic for victims, although some of the issues they face may have pre-dated the bullying, and may even have inadvertently drawn the bully in the first place. Victims often suffer from depression, low self-esteem, loneliness, and social anxiety, and may contemplate suicide.* [7] Children who are bullied have even been found to suffer from higher levels of inflammation, a physical manifestation of the constant wash of stress hormones.[8]

By the time they reach adolescence, the bullies have become more mature and strategic than they were in elementary school, and are consciously using their cruelty and clout to gain social status. [9] Bullies are often perceived as cool, powerful, and popular by their peers, and the act of bullying helps them gain social prestige,[10] although classmates tend to avoid their company. [11] Displaying dominance can even help male bullies improve their standing with the other sex.[12] Bullying, unfortunately, pays.

Bullies tend to select their victims carefully. As we all recall from our own childhoods, they gravitate towards the students who are the least able to protect themselves and fight back: those who are physically weak, insecure, or belong to a marginalized group (by LGBTQ status, race, religion, disability, etc.).[13] Bullies also select their moments carefully: 85 to 88 percent of bullying episodes take place in front of an audience of peers.[14]

Adults with good intentions have compiled various lists of coping strategies to help kids being bullied, but victims don't tend to find any of these adult-condoned tactics useful.[15] Certain strategies imply the victim simply needs to undergo a personality transplant and all will be well ('stick up for

* These are correlations, and it's difficult to prove causality; technically, it could be that children with such tendencies are more likely to be bullied.

oneself').[16] Others suggest involving an adult ('talk to the school counselor', 'talk to a professional person', 'use the school's anti-harassment/bullying procedures', 'ask a teacher for help with bullying', 'talk to parents about the bullying'). These strategies not only don't address the root cause of the dysfunctional dynamic between the bully and victim; they also risk exacerbating the situation, since appealing to an adult ('tattling') can cause the victim to lose even more social status.

In practice, adolescent victims, especially boys, rarely tell an adult.[17] Similarly, adolescent bystanders rarely inform teachers, as they too aren't willing to take the hit to their own status that could result from 'tattling.' [18] It's therefore incumbent upon parents to stay alert for warning signs (see box), particularly if a teen is less socially confident.

**Warning signs of bullying** [19]

- Comes home with damaged clothing, books, or other belongings, or frequently "loses" or "forgets" belongings
- Has unexplained bruises, cuts, or scratches
- Has fewer friends
- Seems afraid to go to school, ride the school bus, walk to school, or take part in community activities with peers
- Loses interest in school or suddenly does poorly in school
- Seems sad, moody, teary, or depressed when coming home from school
- Complains of a variety of physical ailments (headaches, stomachaches), particularly on school days
- Can't sleep or complains of bad dreams
- Avoids using the telephone or the internet
- Seems anxious and has low self-esteem
- Talks about suicide

The vast majority of efforts to stop bullying are completely ineffectual because the focus on helping victims and reforming bullies misses the point entirely. The key to breaking the vicious circle of bullying lies not with either of the principal actors in the performance, the bully or the victim, but with the audience. It's the bystanders who are key. If classmates subtly indicate by their reactions that they support the actions of the bully, the bullying will escalate, while if classmates challenge the behavior, the bully will back down.[20]

Most students inherently disapprove of bullying.[21] But in the same way that many are hesitant to inform adults when they observe a bullying situation transpiring, they're also often hesitant to follow their consciences by showing disapproval when surrounded by peers. It's easier to appear to go along with a bully than to risk looking foolish, or worse, to risk becoming a target of the bully as well.[22] Research suggests that in a typical classroom setting, only around 20 percent of students will proactively come to the defense of a victim.[23] The bystanders who do take action aren't typical students: they disproportionately tend to be popular,[24] suggesting they can afford to spend some of their social capital on helping others and still have plenty to 'spare.'

As with other problematic behaviors, adolescents fall prey to incorrectly assuming that others who remain silent condone bullying.[25] Furthermore, bystanders are acutely sensitive to the prevailing attitudes of other bystanders. When students change to a different class, their behavior in bullying situations is more related to that of the new class than to how they themselves had behaved previously.[26] Kids who believe that others expect them to come to the support of victims are more likely to do so.[27] In about 60 percent of cases where peers intervene, they succeed in stopping the bullying.[28] So it should be possible to influence the bystander culture in a school or classroom and thereby defang the bullies.

Indeed, school-based programs that take this approach can succeed in reducing bullying.[29] For example, one enlisted highly connected students to become the public faces of an anti-bullying campaign.[30] * [31] But parents can also be important influencers: the school progams that are most successful frequently include training for parents.[32] If your teen is confident and popular, encourage your child to sympathize with bullying victims and intervene.

**A Girl Like Her**

One way to develop sympathy in your teen could be to watch a movie that addresses bullying and discuss the topic. *A Girl Like Her* (age 12+)† is a gripping documentary-style but fictional portrayal of psychological bullying among girls which also unflinchingly addresses suicide.[33] However it's worth pointing out to your teen that this movie falls into the typical trap of focusing on the bully and the victim, and misses the importance of the bystanders, who repeatedly fail to intervene until it's too late.

---

* Many other programs have been inspired by the work of the pioneer of the field, Norwegian psychology professor Dan Olweus,[1 2] and the "Olweus Bullying Prevention Program" has been named a model program by the US Department of Justice Office of Juvenile Justice and Delinquency Prevention,[3] although some concerns have been raised that the program hasn't been as effective in the US as it originally was in Norway, for reasons no one has yet understood.[4]

† Available on Netflix.

**If your child is the victim**

If you suspect your child is being bullied, you could encourage your school to adopt an anti-bullying program. Failing that, a high-risk but possibly high-reward strategy could be to find out from your teen which students at school are both popular and kind. You could then approach the parents in confidence and ask if they could encourage their child in a generic way to intervene in any bullying situations they might see at school (without referencing the specific situation which could cause embarrassment). A helpful teacher could also be enlisted to make the approaches.

A more drastic course of action, if you're lucky enough to have the option, would be to help your child change schools. Sometimes kids get off on the wrong foot with their peers for totally arbitrary reasons early on, but once they get assigned a nasty nickname or develop a reputation for being an easy victim, it can be nearly impossible to shed that persona. Peer groups are unforgiving, so kids stuck at the bottom of the totem pole can often benefit from a fresh start.[34]

Bullying can be traumatic for the victims, but many bullied kids go on to live fulfilling and highly successful lives. Michael Phelps, recalling being bullied as a child, says, "I kind of laugh at it now. I think it made me stronger going through that." And, according to Chris Rock, being bullied made him determined to succeed: the experience was "the defining moment of my life."[35]

## Emphasize that harassment isn't funny

Their school was a competitive, pressure-cooker environment where everyone was competing for grades to get into Ivy League schools, and the girls all said they wanted to be doctors. Rachael was giving a presentation when some guy in the front of the class said, "I have a question," and he raised his phone and it was a porn video. According to her friends, "she couldn't concentrate. The teacher didn't even know, she was at the back." Why did no one tell the teacher? "If you tell on them, they'll never let you forget it."* [36]

Danielle was 15 when graffiti about her appeared in a boy's bathroom stall. For more than a year, statements like "Danielle does it with farm animals" littered the walls, despite repeated requests

* Name of protagonist has been changed for privacy purposes.

> from Danielle and her parents to have them removed. The principal responded with "No one reads it, anyhow," and "It'll make you a strong person." In the hall, boys yelled, "Hey, Danielle, I took a leak in your stall today," and girls wondered aloud what she'd done to 'deserve' the harassment. Finally, her older brother, home from college, took matters into his own hands and easily removed the graffiti by himself.* [37]

Harassment at school is an everyday fact of life for many students. Over half of girls and 40 percent of boys have been sexually harassed at least once,[38] and 30 percent of girls and a quarter of boys are harassed often.[39] In one survey, 12 percent of students reported they had stayed home from school because of sexual harassment, 9 percent had changed the way they went to or from school, 8 percent had quit an activity or sport, and 4 percent had changed schools completely.[40] Kids from high- and low-income households are equally likely to report they've been harassed,[41] but for girls, surprise surprise, those who are more physically developed and who are considered more attractive are at highest risk.[42]

**No escape**

The problem also follows girls outside of school. Girls encounter harassment virtually everywhere they go, including at parties, on buses and in cars.[43] One survey in the UK found that 35 percent of girls had received unwanted sexual attention or contact while out in public in their school uniforms.[44] And 87 percent of 18 to 25-year-old females in another survey said they had experienced at least one of the following: having a stranger tell them they were "hot" (61 percent); being catcalled (55 percent); having a stranger say something sexual to them (52 percent); being insulted with sexualized words (e.g., "slut," "bitch," "ho") by a man (47 percent); and being touched without permission by a stranger (41 percent).[45]

All of this unwanted attention is difficult to ignore, particularly for girls, the vast majority of whom report it has a negative effect on them. Many say they don't want to go to school as a result, and some admit the harassment causes them to have trouble sleeping.† [46] Yet most victims don't report what's happening to adults. They worry about being seen to be making a big deal out of nothing, and assume no one would care.[47] As a result, only a third of

* Name of protagonist has been changed for privacy purposes.

† The comparable figures for boys were 14% and 25%, but boys were less likely than girls in all cases to say they had felt that way for "quite a while."

girls and 20 percent of boys tell a parent or other family member, and even fewer confide in a teacher.[48] Victims instead try to cope with the problem themselves, for example, by changing their seat assignment, avoiding their harassers in the halls, and talking less in class to avoid calling attention to themselves.[49]

**The failings of schools**
Schools are supposed to be taking the issue of harassment within their walls seriously. Title IX in the US is a federal law which asserts that no one shall be subjected to discrimination or denied the benefits of an education on the basis of sex, and courts have ruled that sexual harassment is a form of sex discrimination. As a result, the US Department of Education has mandated that schools must publish and disseminate a policy opposing sex discrimination (including sexual harassment), as well as establishing a prompt grievance procedure for addressing complaints.[50] Yet most schools are falling woefully short of their obligations. One investigation found that less than 15 percent of schools had sexual harassment policies available online, although all had other school policies available.[51] Worse, around 80 percent of public schools reported zero incidents of sexual harassment. The vast majority of the iceberg is still lurking beneath the surface.[52]

American adults are oblivious to the toxic climate that's brewing in classrooms around the country. Less than a quarter of parents have ever broached the topic of harassment with their teen.[53] But the comments of teen harassers reveal a shocking disconnect between how they assume their comments are landing and how they're being received in reality. **44 percent of those who admitted to harassment thought it wasn't a big deal, and 39 percent said they were trying to be funny.**[54] Here are a few typical comments: "Girls love it; they just don't want to admit it!" "If a girl starts to hit on a guy, he doesn't get upset — it makes his day!"[55] In fact, close to two thirds of young women admit to feeling offended, scared or angry in response to being catcalled.[56] So it's worth emphasizing to teens who might be inadvertent perpetrators that sexual comments are not funny or wanted.

If you're concerned your child could be a victim, you could download the "Not Your Baby" app on your teen's phone, which allows users to input information about where they are and who is harassing them, and generates a suggested response to help them safely navigate the situation.* [57] You could also suggest that your teen's school establish an anonymous harassment reporting channel, which was the top suggestion made by students asked for their opinions on how to combat harassment.[58]

* Unfortunately, no research has yet established if the app indeed helps improves outcomes for the victim.

**If your child is the victim**

If you do find out about any harassment, encourage your child to keep a journal and retain or photograph any evidence (notes, etc.), to provide firepower in case it ever makes sense to pursue a complaint officially.[59] If your school is among the majority that don't have a pre-existing harassment policy, you can direct an administrator to "Harassment-Free Hallways: How to Stop Sexual Harassment in School,"* which has examples of a user-friendly policy, a formal policy, a complaint form, and a teen safety plan.[60]

You can even consider escalating if, as in the case of Danielle and the graffiti, the response by the school is underwhelming.† [61] Supreme Court cases have established school liability for sexual harassment, and if the school district showed deliberate indifference to known acts of sexual harassment, plaintiffs have been awarded from $15,000 up to more than $400,000.[62]

When Austin Powers continually propositions Vanessa Kensington, the character played by Elizabeth Hurley in the movie, *Austin Powers: International Man of Mystery*, she recoils, looks slightly disconcerted, and gently admonishes him to keep his libido in check; but behind her tortoise-shell glasses, her eyes harbor a glint of amusement and interest. Most women in the real world, trapped alone in an airplane or hotel room with such an aggressive character would be on the brink of a panic attack. Of course the movie is a parody.‡ Nevertheless, such subtleties are being lost on our adolescents, and letting them run around emulating Austin Powers is doing their peers a disservice.

# Take-aways

The answer to both increasing the supportiveness of bystanders and curbing the aggression of potential perpetrators lies in cultivating their compassion. Steven Pinker, in *The Better Angels of our Nature: Why Violence has Declined*, suggests that one of the key historical forces which precipitated the remarkable decline of human violence worldwide over the past centuries was the invention of the printing press and the widespread rise of literacy.[63] Books, and more recently movies, have the remarkable ability to help us walk for a short time in the shoes of others, and any media that helps our adolescents

* Available at https://files.eric.ed.gov/fulltext/ED534504.pdf.

† The US Department of Education Office for Civil Rights is a logical port of call.

‡ In a sequel, Vanessa is ultimately revealed to be a Fembot rather than a human, which finally makes their "romance" more plausible

sympathize with the victimized is likely to be a worthwhile use of their time. Let's help the better angels of our teens' natures prevail.

**KEY PARENTING TAKE-AWAYS:**

Bullying:

1. Encourage teens with high social status to sympathize with any victims of bullying and intervene
2. If your child is being bullied, ask your school to adopt the Olweus Bullying Prevention Program
3. Failing that, find out from your teen which students at school are both kind and have high social status. Approach the parents in confidence and ask if they could encourage their children in a generic way to intervene in any bullying situations they might see at school (without referencing the specific situation which could cause embarrassment)
4. As a last resort, consider changing schools if possible

Sexual harassment:

5. Proactively emphasize to teens who might be inadvertent perpetrators that sexual comments are not funny or wanted
6. Communicate to those who might be victims that they should inform you if they witness or experience harassment
7. Download the "Not Your Baby" app on your teen's phone
8. Suggest to your teen's school that they establish an anonymous harassment reporting channel
9. If the case of harassment, encourage your teen to keep a journal, and retain or photograph any evidence
10. If your school doesn't have a harassment policy, direct them to the materials at "Harassment-Free Hallways: How to Stop Sexual Harassment in School"*
11. Consider legal escalation if the response by the school is underwhelming

# Dig deeper

## *Self-sufficiency*

> "We are men who still live at home. We're not here to apologize about who we are. I'm looking around this table, hombres, and I see three winners, huh? And to every one of those out there who sees

* Available at https://files.eric.ed.gov/fulltext/ED534504.pdf

> something different, I say bring it on, 'cause it's gonna take a stick of dynamite to get me out of my parents' house." — 2006 Rom-com, *Failure to Launch*[64]

As the twenty-first century progresses, more and more teens are 'failing to launch,' or to reach the classic milestones of independence that we used to take for granted (see box). In the words of one expert, "18-year-olds now act like 15-year-olds used to, and 13-year-olds like 10-year-olds. Teens are physically safer than ever, yet they are more mentally vulnerable."[65]

**Independence on the wane**

In 1998, 44 percent of American 16-year-olds had a driver's license; by 2018, it was only 26 percent.* [66] In 2006, the average college student communicated with a parent around 10 times per week; by 2013, this had climbed to 22 times, with students often initiating the contact.[67] In 1985, 45 percent of 20 to 22-year-olds were living with their parents; by 2003, it was 57 percent.† [68] And in 1982, 47 percent of young adults aged 23 to 24 were receiving financial assistance from their parents; by 2011, this figure had climbed to 68 percent.[69]

One theory offered up by pundits for why teens and young adults are less mature than they used to be is that parents are simply enabling their offspring to remain immature by failing to allocate them real-world responsibilities sooner.[70] There's no doubt that chores are in decline. In agrarian settings, the typical teen used to undertake 8 or more hours of household labor per day; the contemporary average in the US is 20 to 40 minutes.[71] There has also been a shift within modern times: a study in Germany has found that teens now spend far fewer hours on housework than they did twenty years ago,[72] and a survey of adults in the US found that 82 percent did chores themselves growing up, but only 28 percent have assigned chores to their kids.[73]

From the perspective of developing skills, this modern freedom from chores should be a boon, as household work is typically repetitive and unchallenging for kids once they've mastered the tasks.[74] However, it could be that by depriving them of responsibility, we're doing our adolescents a disservice. There's clearly little downside in encouraging our offspring to help

* This could be attributed in part to the increased available of services like Uber/Lyft, electric scooter rentals, etc.

† This increase was seen across almost all subgroups (by education, gender, etc.), and is unexplained by changes in job opportunities.

in basic ways, like making the occasional dinner or insisting they do their own laundry if they want to have clean clothes; at the very least, they'll know how to cook for themselves and operate the washing machine if and when they leave the nest.

**Chores and success?**

Some studies have suggested a relationship between chores as a child and effectiveness as an adult.[75] For example, one study followed ~450 underprivileged boys from age 14 through to middle age and found that the best predictor of success as an adult was their capacity to work in childhood.[76] Unfortunately no one has yet tested whether increasing chores for a group of teens actually makes them more self-sufficient later in life.

It's worth stepping back to reflect that this is a problem of privilege. According to Unicef, in the least developed countries, more than a quarter of children ages 5 to 17 are doing work that negatively affects their health and development.[77] You can remind your teen of this fact if there is any muttering about taking out the trash.

**KEY PARENTING TAKE-AWAYS:**

1. Consider assigning teens basic practical chores so they will be prepared for living independently (for example, co-create a chore chart that 'de-personalizes' which child attends to which specific task, or use a wheel style to rotate chores between children)

## *Personality*

> "Parents can only give good advice or put them on the right paths, but the final forming of a person's character lies in their own hands."[78] — Anne Frank

Anne Frank was a child wise beyond her years. Based on a narrow slice of life and without the benefit of higher education, she intuitively grasped a truth which the academic establishment has now come to view as counter-intuitive but nevertheless correct: children's characters are not formed by their parents.

Psychologists have settled on a definition of personality based on five core traits: openness to experience, conscientiousness, extraversion, agreeableness and neuroticism.[79] Where we fall on each of these five spectrums is in large part determined by our genes.[80] What accounts for the remaining variation? Whatever it is, it's not parenting. The evidence overwhelmingly suggests that parents have very little influence on their children's long-term personalities, beyond the critical initial contribution of their own genetic material. As Judith Rich Harris describes in *The Nurture Assumption: Why Children Turn Out the Way They Do*, her seminal work on the topic, "Parents have no long-term effects on their children's personalities or on the way that they behave when they're outside the home."[81]

This is a bold statement which both laypeople and researchers initially disbelieve. Harris's book seemingly contradicts reams of research showing, for example, that parents who adopt an "authoritative" style of parenting (not too lenient, not too strict) have children who turn out better. Harris was one of the first to point out that such research suffers from a fundamental flaw which is obvious in retrospect — such studies don't control for genetics. So if reasonable parents have children who ultimately behave reasonably, they may attribute the positive behavior to their stellar parenting skills, when in fact it could be that the kids are simply a chip off the ol' block. To support her argument that the correct explanation is the latter, Harris draws on a variety of studies of adopted children to demonstrate that kids brought up in the same home don't turn out to be similar unless they share genes.

Which is not to imply that parents don't matter. Children absolutely depend upon their parents to care for them emotionally and practically, and to protect them from harm. Parents can provide their kids with resources to help them learn and thrive if the family is sufficiently affluent (as per the discussion on achievement), and can teach them important and useful skills.

Most importantly, parents play a critical role by determining the society/ neighborhood/school and therefore the peer culture in which their children grow up. Kids are desperate to fit in with the society of their peers, and during adolescence, will permanently mold their personality to conform with the norms of their peer group.[82] Parents can still influence their children's views on topics that don't tend to come up with peers, like religion and politics. But that's the extent of it. If the concept of parents being irrelevant to the formation of their children's personalities still feels deeply implausible, which it does to most people, pick up a copy of *The Nurture Assumption* and see if Harris can convince you.

Even if personality characteristics are less mutable, surely parents can at least teach their children to be upstanding moral citizens? Well, yes and no. When it comes to views on what is moral in the first place, children absorb the underlying philosophies of the culture and community in which they're raised. Collectivist cultures, such as those in many East Asian countries, emphasize conformity and duty, and moral transgressions tend to evoke shame ("What will other people think of me?"). In contrast, in individualist cultures like the United States and much of Western Europe, morality is based on individual needs and rights, and moral transgressions bring guilt ("How can I live with myself?"). So a trade-off that involved harming an innocent person to prevent greater harm to a group might be morally acceptable in one culture but thoroughly unacceptable in another.* [83]

However, parents can't take credit for being the only vector for transmitting these cultural values and morals to their children, or even the most important. For example, when families from collectivist cultures immigrate to Western countries, their children do tend to retain certain elements of the mores of their native culture, such as respect for the importance of family, but they rapidly pick up the tenets of individualism from their friends along with the local language and accent.[84]

Whatever our children profess to believe is moral or not on paper, a more interesting question is how they behave in the real world. When it comes to extreme acts of bravery and selflessness like jumping into a burning building to save someone inside, the people who have behaved heroically report afterwards that they didn't stop to think, they just acted.[85] They risked their lives, not because of what their parents or even their Sunday-school teachers had taught them, but because of what felt right instinctively in the moment.

How about a more quotidian situation like resisting the temptation to cheat? Here again, people who behave honestly tend to do so automatically, rather than stopping to think about it. When you put adults in brain scanners and give them the opportunity to earn money by self-reporting whether they predicted computerized coin tosses, they tend to fall into two distinct

* Humans are also surprisingly plastic in our moral views. We respond differently to the identical moral dilemma depending on seemingly unrelated factors such as whether the subject is someone from our own group, or whether there is psychological distance (e.g. diverting a trolley to a different track that will kill one person instead of five is easier than pushing someone onto a track to stop a trolley from killing the same five). Even thoroughly unrelated variables such as whether we're hungry, stressed, or exposed to a bad smell can change our moral judgments.

categories. Some people simply never cheat, and show virtually no activity in control-related regions of the brain. The honesty is taking no effort, presumably since they would never consider cheating in the first place. In contrast, those who tend to cheat have far more brain activity in control-related regions on the specific occasions when they don't cheat — the difficulty for them is in resisting temptation, while the cheating itself seems to come naturally.[86]

No studies have intervened in childhood or the teenage years to test whether it's possible to flip the default switch, or whether the factory settings for cheating versus not cheating are fixed at birth. Equally, we have no idea whether lectures on morality, punishments for transgressions or kudos for honesty can help our kids strengthen their brains to resist temptation if cheating comes naturally. However in practice, peers are once again the most powerful influence. If kids have the impression that others around them are cheating, they will unsurprisingly be far more tempted to cheat too.[87]

What about a premeditated act of kindness, like giving to charity? There's no doubt that parents who give generously are more likely to have kids who do so, and kids who volunteer as teenagers also tend to give more when they grow up.[88] But is that because the parents are teaching their kids about the importance of giving, because the parents are role-modelling positive behavior, because both generations are members of a community that emphasizes charity and volunteering, because the family members all share common genes for altruism? Who knows.

If we had a recipe for churning out future saints like Mother Teresa or philanthropists like Bill Gates, the world would undoubtedly be a better place. Unfortunately, for the moment we don't. In the meantime, your local soup kitchen would undoubtably benefit from an extra pair of teenage hands now, even if there's no guarantee your child's future adult self will follow suit.

# 11. APPEARANCE

## Help your ugly duckling become a swan

Examples of appearance-related collective insanity are scattered throughout history. Chinese foot binding would now be considered akin to medieval torture.[1] Eye drops made from deadly nightshade (a plant also known as belladonna, Italian for 'beautiful woman') were used by women in sixteenth-century Italy to dilate their pupils, which could result in short-term memory loss, coma and death.[2] Corsets would permanently deform the ribs and misalign the spines of the ladies who wore them.[3] And women in Myanmar traditionally wore permanent brass coils to lengthen their necks.[4] Not only women have fallen prey to nonsensical fashion trends over the ages; certain Nihang Sikhs in India wear outsize turbans, the largest of which incorporated 1,312 feet of material wound round one man's head.[5] For anyone who would argue that modern teens are unhealthily obsessed with their looks and spend inordinate amounts of time making duck faces for social media posts, this is only the latest manifestation of the fundamental human obsession with appearance.

There is good reason for all of this peacocking. Attractiveness does matter. Women who are obese and members of both sexes who are unattractive are less likely to get married.[6] At the other end of the spectrum, people who have won the genetic lottery and are considered attractive are more popular, date more, and have more marriage options;[7] they also achieve greater professional success, earn higher wages,[8] and tend to marry people who earn higher wages as well.[9]

Beauty discrimination starts early. Teachers will interpret a report card more favorably if the accompanying picture shows an attractive child, and assume the child has a higher IQ and is more likely to succeed.[10] Similarly, teachers reading an account of misbehavior will assign less blame and rate the personality of the student as more desirable if the accompanying picture of the child is attractive.[11] (Incidentally, this beauty discrimination works both ways — students will rate an attractive teacher as more competent than an unattractive one.[12]) Universally across cultures, being attractive confers all sorts of advantages upon both children and adults.[13]

The multi-billion-dollar fashion, makeup and personal grooming industries would like to convince us that attractiveness is not an immutable quality, but rather a nirvana we can achieve with the investment of sufficient time, energy and expenditure. The average adult woman invests 55 minutes a day on improving her appearance.[14] This may help when it comes to attracting a romantic partner, but any potential increase in wages is at least somewhat offset by the absurd amounts of money spent on chasing beauty.[15] So we certainly shouldn't be encouraging our adolescents to become vain fashionistas. The intent here is to contextualize the teenage obsession with appearance, and to acknowledge that there are valid reasons why they care so deeply about their looks.

When it comes to altering children's appearance, one of the most common practices in Western society today is straightening teeth. Sporting uncomfortable dental wear has become almost a rite of passage for teens in many wealthy communities. There is no question that straightening and fixing other obvious problems like underbites can make kids more attractive,[16] and can even affect how much others perceive them as agreeable, intelligent and extroverted.[17] Although braces aren't cheap, consider the following: kids who have orthodontic treatment earn 6 to 7 percent more as adults than those who don't.[*] [18]

Teens can achieve a similar boost in attractiveness by replacing their glasses with contact lenses.[19] Adults wearing glasses may project authority and honesty,[20] but for kids, the stereotypes are far more negative — think nerdy librarian.[21] So it's no surprise that teens say switching to contact lenses massively improves their quality of life.[22]

Next we come to the most common aesthetic scourge of teens everywhere: acne. Here are some testimonials:

> Acne sufferer Trina was bullied at school and started to cut herself to cope with the trauma: "My acne started young, at about 11 to 12 years

* This fact should be taken with a grain of salt since the source was an observational study rather than a randomized trial, but it did control for education level and parent income, and it puts the sticker-shock of orthodontic treatment into perspective for those who can afford it.

old. My back, neck and face were covered in spots. I blamed my skin for causing the problems, so I took it out on my skin. I felt it didn't matter, as who would ever look at me anyway, except to mock me?"* [23]

Acne sufferer Michael's 15-year battle with the condition left him on the brink of suicide: "It first came on when I was 15. I was using over-the-counter products and covering my face with make up to hide it… It got really severe — I was begging my mum and dad not to make me go to school." Michael was so embarrassed by his spots that he spent two years refusing to see anyone.† [24]

**Acne 101**

For those who may not remember the sordid details from their own adolescence, here's a quick primer on acne. Changes in hormones during adolescence cause the inner linings of the skin's hair follicles to thicken, which results in the pores becoming blocked by sebum, an oily, waxy substance produced by the body to keep the skin lubricated and protected. A "whitehead" is a white bump beneath the skin that arises from one of these plugged up hair follicles, while a "blackhead" is also a plugged hair follicle, but which is open to the surface. (Sebum naturally becomes dark colored when in contact with the air, so a blackhead is not dirty.[25]) These blocked pores can then become infected with a usually harmless bacteria that resides on the skin called *P. acnes*.[26]

Acne is a global affliction; it affects 80-90 percent of modern-day teenagers worldwide, from Hong Kong to Nigeria to Scotland to New Zealand,[27] with nearly all humans between ages 15 and 17 experiencing the problem to some degree.[28]

**A modern scourge**

Acne is mysteriously a disease of the modern world; studies of rural, non-Westernized populations in Ghana, Papua New Guinea, Paraguay,[29] Brazil, and Peru, as well as the Innuits, the natives of Okinawa, and the Bantu, Zulu, and Aché tribes, all reveal that these populations suffer from very little acne, although as they Westernize their lifestyles, they too fall prey to this affliction.[30]

As Trina and Michael would attest, severe acne can be traumatic,[31] rivalling even chronic diseases like asthma, epilepsy, diabetes, arthritis, and back pain.[32] Students with severe acne tend to avoid social activities out of embarrassment,[33] and are more likely to suffer from depression[34] and even contemplate suicide.[35]

* Name of protagonist has been changed for privacy purposes.

† Name of protagonist has been changed for privacy purposes.

Although it's tempting for adolescents to pick at, pop or squeeze their unsightly blemishes since releasing the infected contents appears to make the pimple shrink, this approach typically backfires; kids who fiddle with their zits end up with worse inflammation a few days later.[36] Rupturing the little sack that had tightly contained the acne bacteria can cause the bacteria to spill into adjacent pores, and/or drive the bacteria deeper into the skin where it can cause worse damage.[37]

Most teens also incorrectly assume that washing is the best solution for improving their skin. 30 percent end up washing five times a day.[38] Unbeknownst to these earnest scrubbers, washing doesn't help and probably even exacerbates the problem.[39] Cleaning removes sebum from the surface of the skin, which dries the skin out and prompts it to call for more sebum, [40] causing even further clogging in the pores beneath.[41] Most other folk remedies are equally useless. Despite the reams of advice online with headlines like "The 7-Day Meal Plan to Banish Acne,"[42] there's no evidence at the moment that diet has any impact on pimples.[43] And sunlight doesn't help, although tanning may make the red marks slightly less visible.[44]

**Beware beauticians**

Beauticians prey on the desperation of acne sufferers by offering a variety of quack remedies like chemical peels and comedo (whitehead/blackhead) removal. Complexion looking splotchy? For a small fee, we'll use a harsh chemical to remove an entire layer of skin from your face, guaranteed to leave you looking redder than before! Got an unsightly volcanic eruption on your forehead? We're happy to attack it with a scalpel or squeeze it with professional flair, spreading or driving the infection deeper so you'll return for more! These services may help their customers psychologically by providing them the satisfaction of taking action, but since they do nothing about the sebum accumulating beneath the skin, in the very best case they can provide at most temporary cosmetic improvement.[45]

Not only is the general public misinformed; doctors are often equally unaware, so your teen's GP may give flawed advice.[46] If your son or daughter's face is beginning to resemble a pepperoni pizza, it's time to seek out a specialist. Dermatologists do have treatments they can prescribe,* [47] although shockingly for such a common affliction, professionals still don't agree on the optimal treatment.[48] (The Institute of Medicine is finally on the case; one of

* These include topical retinoids, topical antimicrobial agents, oral antibiotics, benzoyl peroxide and azaleic acid, or oral isotretinoin for severe acne, although side effects are common. Patience is also required: "Because acne treatments work by preventing new lesions rather than treating existing ones, an initial response might not appear for some weeks. Most effective treatments can require months to work."[i]

their 100 priority topics for future research is evaluating treatments for skin disorders including acne.[49] So perhaps by the time your teen has a teen, this modern scourge will be history.)

For miserable adolescents covered in spots, it might be some consolation to know that 60-80 percent of cases of acne resolve before age 25.[50] To end on a hopeful note, here are the thoughts of an acne sufferer who managed to find meaning in his condition:

> Every afternoon when school ended, I went straight to the boarding school's shower block so I could remove my undershirt – and with it, half the skin off my back.
>
> If there were any positives to emerge from this experience, it was my attitude towards superficial appearance and vanity. My trauma had shown me that real beauty lies far beneath the skin. The Japanese art and philosophy of kintsugi — translated as "gold scars" — tells us that repairing broken ceramics gives a new lease of life to pottery that in turn becomes even more refined and unique. That was my choice: to become whole again and stronger at the broken places."[51]

Most adolescents go through an awkward phase, and most are preoccupied with how they look, which doesn't mean they're either superficial or vain. Appearance matters for teens just as it does for adults. Their personalities are being shaped by their peers throughout the crucible of the teen years,[52] and those kids who develop social confidence during this critical phase seem to carry that confidence with them for life (see box). So help your ugly duckling become a swan.

**Confidence for life**

Kids with higher popularity in high school go on to earn higher wages as adults, irrespective of their other personality traits.[53] Similarly, those who are taller during adolescence earn higher salaries later, irrespective of their final adult height.[54] One potential explanation is that teens with such advantages are more likely to participate in activities like athletics and school clubs and spend more time socializing informally,[55] so they get extra opportunities to practice the social skills that will serve them well later in life.[56]

# Dig deeper

## *Sun protection*

> A teenager has shared photos of her agonizing giant balloon-shaped blisters after getting sunburned while on holiday. Tanya Sutton, 16, suffered severe burns to her entire back while snorkeling with her family in Cuba. Her blisters were so bad that they visibly stuck out underneath her T-shirt.* [57]

A mother chasing after her toddler clutching a floppy hat and a spray bottle of sunscreen is a familiar beach scene. That same parent will be far less likely to go chasing after her teenager someday: while 91 percent of kids ages one to 12 wear sunscreen, only two thirds of adolescents do,[58] and only a quarter of teens "often or always" use sunscreen when outside for at least six hours in the summer.[59]

No surprise, then, that many teens end up getting crispy: about 70 percent get at least one sunburn over the course of a given summer, and 30 percent get burned three or more times. (Sometimes the adolescent had applied sunscreen insufficiently, but over half of cases involved no sunscreen at all.[60]) All of these sunburns matter because it's the cumulative number of burns, not sun exposure in general, that's related to the risk of skin cancer (melanoma).[61] But less than half of adolescents are aware of this fact.[62]

**Tanning beds**

Showing further disregard for the health of their skin, around 5 percent of American adolescents use tanning beds, although at least this trend appears to be on the wane, down from 16 percent a decade ago.[63] Their peers in Sweden are worse offenders, with over half reporting using a sunbed 4 times a year, although it's hard to blame them for seeking an antidote to the Swedish climate.[64]

Harping on about the risk of skin cancer decades ahead is unlikely to dampen your teen's desire to cultivate a glowing tan in the present. The better tack is to appeal to that same vanity, by pointing out that tanning damages skin and causes premature wrinkles. This approach has convinced both college students and young adults to slather on more sunscreen.[65] One

* Name of protagonist has been changed for privacy purposes

clever persuasion technique involves allowing teens to look at their own skin using ultraviolet light, and observe the pigment changes which indicate skin damage first-hand. (American Cancer Society offices have Dermascan™ units available to loan out,[66] or UV skin analyzers can also be purchased for approximately $50 online.)

Apply the scan to your own skin if you dare. It's never too late to halt the aging process.

## *Clothing / fashion*

> A debate in the UK: "Should girls ever be sent home from school because their skirts are too short? 'Yes,' says Alison Colwell, head teacher of Ebbsfleet Academy in Kent, who appeared in national newspapers after sending 20 teenage girls home for 'showing too much thigh'. 'No,' says Jessica Eaton, researcher, speaker and writer in the psychology of victim blaming in sexual violence and the Founder of VictimFocus."[67]

> A debate in Rwanda: "Recently, there was a debate on social media involving two ministers, about a photo of students who appeared to be wearing short skirts popularly known as 'mini skirts'... While some people argued that girls and women should not wear short skirts, many others dismissed the claims saying that women should be allowed to wear whatever is comfortable for them."[68]

How short is too short? Are we sexualizing our daughters by allowing them to cavort about in skimpy clothing, or are we hampering the development of their self-expression by forcing them to cover up? And why do these conversations invariably center around the attire of girls and women, rather than also including a critique of the fashion choices of boys and men? These are perennial questions.

The best way for a community to short-circuit these controversies is to roll out a school uniform. Uniforms are becoming increasingly common: back in 2000 only 12 percent of US public schools required one, whereas now it's climbed to 20 percent.[69] There isn't much research on the benefits of uniforms, but when schools make a switch, the students themselves do report that they observe less bullying and gang involvement, and that they feel more confident and waste less time getting ready for school in the morning.[70] These are all positive arguments you could make to your local school board if you felt like agitating for change after a particularly heated clothing debate with your teen.

The topic of fashion sense may appear to be a trivial subject, but humans are quick to make assumptions about other people based on appearance, including clothing.[71] People judge both adults and teens who are wearing nice but conservative clothing as more competent,[72] while those dressed in a sexually provocative way are frequently deemed both less competent and less intelligent.[73] Teachers are humans, not automatons, and are therefore not immune from making these same subconscious snap assumptions about their students based on how they dress.[74] Teachers shown photographs of students dressed in four different styles, 'Hood,' 'Artsy,' 'Dressy,' and 'Casual,' thought those wearing the 'dressy' attire were more likely to be intelligent and had greater academic potential than those sporting the 'hood' style.[75]

Why should first impressions matter, when students have the entire school year to demonstrate their intelligence and academic potential? Studies with younger children suggest that teacher expectations can become self-fulfilling prophecies. One devious study in an elementary school planted a false belief in the minds of teachers that certain children had shown great intellectual potential in an aptitude test, when in fact those children had been chosen at random. At the end of a year, the selected children had indeed shown greater IQ gains than their peers, presumably because the teachers invested more in those students.[76] The effects were less pronounced with older children, so we can at least hope that by high school this phenomenon is less relevant.

Of course, it's not only teachers who judge your child based on appearance. Peers are the ultimate arbiters of style, and can be very quick to make judgements. Girls in one study given a profile and photograph of a 'new girl' immediately expressed strong opinions about whether they would make friends with her and allow her into their group, and these opinions were very different based on the clothing style of the fictional girl.[77] When asked, girls explicitly admit that clothing and popularity are often related, and that the popular girls are frequently also the 'best dressed.'[78] It's difficult to unpick whether it's the clothes that boost the popularity, or the popularity that makes others aspire to wear the clothes; probably a little of both.* Regardless, clothing is an essential form of self-expression for teenagers.[79] So next time you're tempted to opine on the suitability of an outfit, keep in mind that children understand their own social milieu better than an outsider ever could. You would hardly take your teen's advice on what to wear to work, nor take kindly to being forced to wear something socially inappropriate like fuzzy-footed pajamas to the office.

**Goth**

There is one style of clothing which should raise alarm bells. The goth culture has a well-established uniform (head-to-toe black, combat boots, piercings, etc.), and tends to attract adolescents who are feeling angry, depressed, or rejected by society. Goth teens are three times more likely to suffer from depression than their non-goth peers,[80] and are also more likely to turn to self-harm and to attempt suicide.[81] The clothing in this case is not the cause but rather the outward expression of their angst, which needs to be taken seriously.

Teens are also notorious for using their clothes (or lack thereof) to look sexy. Male clothing simply isn't up to the task — women don't interpret even an open shirt, tight pants, or jewelry as provocative on a man.[82] Girls' attire, however, is much more closely scrutinized by members of both sexes, as per the debates about skirt lengths. Some girls may wear revealing clothing because they view it as fashionable, or want to imitate and fit in with their peers, versus explicitly trying to be provocative.[83] Regardless, both genders assume girls wearing sexy clothing must be more flirtatious and more interested in sex.[84]

**The allure of red**

A high skin-to-clothing ratio isn't the only tool girls can use to signal sexual intent; they can also do so with posture (strike a pose!),[85] and with their choice of clothing color. It's no coincidence that red is the siren's color of choice for nails, lips and even clothing. Non-human primates often use red to signal sexual intent, and experiments show that human men will sit closer to a woman wearing a red shirt than a green one.[86]

The unfortunate corollary, which may not be palatable but remains true nonetheless, is that members of both sexes perceive women wearing sexy clothes to be at higher risk of being attacked and raped.[87] There is no information available about whether provocatively dressed women are more likely

* Clothing presumably has some relevance for boys' social standing as well, but less research has been done on this topic.

to actually experience rape, presumably because of the potential sensitivities. The last thing a victim of assault needs is to be blamed for what she had chosen to wear, although such victim-blaming is rampant. For this reason, the so-called 'Rape Shield Rule' in the US specifically prevents clothing or other lifestyle choices from being considered in rape cases.[88]

Ultimately, the acceptability and interpretation of clothing is highly culturally dependent. In Saudi Arabia, a girl can be arrested for failing to cover her head, while in other countries, she can be arrested for covering it.[89] Next time your child is making an outrageous fashion decision, take comfort from the fact that it's only the fashion police who will care.

## *Tattoos and piercings*

Rick Genest, a self-professed outcast and goth as a youth, was diagnosed with brain cancer during his teens, at which point he became increasingly obsessed with the morbid and macabre. His coping response involved gradually tattooing his entire body, earning him the nickname 'Zombie Boy,' as well as a place in the Guinness Book of World Records and a role in a Lady Gaga video. He tragically died at the age of 32, but is forever immortalized in a disturbing makeup commercial.[90] If your teen is angling for a tattoo, or indeed is already sporting one, it's helpful to put this behavior in perspective.

Tattoos are increasingly common. Six percent of today's grandparents sport one, but this rises to 15 percent of Baby Boomers, 32 percent of Gen X, and 38 percent of Millennials.[91] How those Millennials' tattoos will look when they reach their 70s is anyone's guess.

As with clothing, tattoos project an image, and people without tattoos themselves can be judgmental; half think tattooed people are less attractive and assume they are more rebellious, and about a third are inclined to believe they are less intelligent.[92] (Piercings generate similar negative perceptions, although at least a piercing can be removed.[93]) When it comes to job applications, an applicant with a visible tattoo in a photo is less likely to be called for an interview with a bank than the identical applicant whose photo has been altered to have no tattoo.[94] Yes, someone has bothered to officially confirm this.

It could well be that the type of person who is attracted to tattooing has no interest in applying for a job at a bank anyway, so a better line of investigation would be to find out whether those who permanently decorate themselves later feel any regrets about their actions. Estimates of regret vary widely depending on whom you ask; 14 percent of Dutch adults with a tattoo regret their decision,[95] as do 23 percent of US adults;[96] and 33 percent of a smaller sample of Colorado adolescents later wished they hadn't proceeded with the body art.[97]

**Why the change of heart?**
Among American adults, the top contenders for later regret are: "Too young when they got the tattoo;" "Personality changes/Doesn't fit my present lifestyle;" "Got someone's name that I'm no longer with;" "Poorly done/Doesn't look professional," and "Isn't meaningful."[98]

Unfortunately, tattoos live up to their promise of being permanent; removal doesn't work very well, is expensive, and can leave unsightly scars. Of those who've attempted removal, a third weren't satisfied with the results, and only 38 percent managed to remove the tattoo pigment completely.[99]

Another point which most people don't consider is that the process of applying a tattoo involves health risks. Teens who go to a professional tattoo parlor are unlikely to contract hepatitis C.[100] But in many states it's not legal to get a tattoo before age 18,[101] so a teen may resort to a less reputable option. Furthermore, in the US the FDA doesn't regulate tattoos so there's no centralized reporting of tattoo reactions,[102] although many people react badly to the ink. According to one large survey in Germany, 9 percent of those with a tattoo were still having a tattoo-related health problem four weeks later, and 6 percent suffered persistent health problems.[103]

The longer-term risk of injecting pigments beneath the skin is also unknown. Tattoo ink chemicals are typically developed by companies for purposes such as coloring cars and plastics, and then enlisted for secondary use in tattoos. These inks are not regulated or tested for human safety, and can contain a wide range of hazardous chemicals including Polycyclic Aromatic Hydrocarbons (found in 43 percent of samples) and heavy metals (found in 9 percent).[104]

Why do adolescents have the urge to disfigure their beautiful young skin in the first place? For most teens who aren't grappling with a life-threatening brain tumor, a tattoo is simply a way of proving to peers they don't care about adult rules: a visual badge of belonging to a tribe of like-minded teens.[105] The best way to avoid this instinct for disfigurement is therefore to prevent the tribe of adolescents from coalescing in the first place: keep your teen busy and engineer quality time with adults instead of peers, as per the chapter on delinquency.

If the tattoo is non-negotiable, you can at least regale your child with the cautionary tale of Johnny Depp's tattoo evolution from 'Winona Forever' to 'Wino Forever.'[106]

## Makeup, cosmetics and personal care products

> How young is too young to start wearing makeup? That's the question being asked in the beauty world after John Lewis and Mac cosmetics cancelled a "back-to-school mini masterclass" on makeup for children as young as 12 after attracting criticism.[107]

John Lewis and Mac cosmetics are hardly the most egregious offenders when it comes to makeup for children; clearly their critics haven't watched the Toddlers & Tiaras video, "Airbrush Makeup for a 1-year-old."[108] On average kids start requesting makeup at age six, but most parents aren't comfortable with them wearing any until around age 10.[109] By early adolescence, many girls have established a makeup routine: over half of 12- to 14-year-olds wear eye makeup, 45 percent use foundation/concealer, and 10 percent color their hair, saying it makes them feel more confident.[110]

Makeup has practical implications for adult women. Women wearing makeup are deemed to be more attractive.[111] (Eye makeup and foundation appear to make the greatest difference; lipstick, surprisingly, is not particularly impactful in comparison.)[112] Intriguingly, women wearing makeup also come across as healthier and more confident and sociable,[113] more likeable and trustworthy,[114] and are assumed to have higher earning potential/come from higher-status professions.[115] Men even tip a waitress more if she's wearing makeup.[116]

If all of these benefits flow to adults, surely it would help our girls to look their best? The counter-argument for allowing makeup in childhood and adolescence is that only 5 percent of teens will meet their spouse before graduating from high school, as we will see in the section on significant others, and in the meantime, we're exposing their young, growing bodies to a concoction of untested chemicals.

This concern applies to more than just makeup. Teens of both sexes start slathering on lots of products, often establishing routines they'll follow for life (see box).

**Teen routines**
American kids are regularly smothering themselves in chemicals. 85 percent of adolescent boys use shampoo/conditioner, 85 percent hygiene products, 62 percent body products, and 43 percent hairstyling gel/spray on a daily basis. Girls are even more liberal with their personal care products: 94 percent use hygiene products, 90 percent shampoo/conditioner, 85 percent body products, 74 percent facial products, 66 percent perfume, and 62 percent cosmetics daily. On a more occasional basis, 71 percent of girls use nail products, 51 percent use hairstyling gel/spray, and 42 percent use hair dye.[117]

The cumulative impact of all of these products is unknown, but accumulate they do. When a group of teenage girls was tested for a range of problematic chemicals, including several known hormone disruptors, each had between 10 and 15 present in her body.[118] Although the girls may have been exposed to these chemicals from other sources,* it's telling that when teens are encouraged to stop using personal care products, the concentration of chemicals in their urine goes down within a few days.[119]

The US doesn't currently require safety testing for any personal care products, in stark contrast with the EU, which requires companies to develop safety assessments and has banned the use of over 1,300 chemicals in cosmetic products.[120] There's not even a mechanism in the US to track consumer complaints systematically, since manufacturers are not required to report such complaints to the FDA.[121]

In the absence of action from the government, parents can at least help minimize their children's exposure. If your teen is already wedded to a beauty routine, encourage products free from items such as synthetic fragrances, preservatives, parabens, petrochemicals and sodium lauryl sulfate.[122] The Environmental Working Group's Skin Deep® Cosmetics Database is a great resource, which has evaluated the safety of the ingredients in thousands of personal care products.†

* including air fresheners, cleaning products, detergents, fabric softeners, and food additives

† Available at: www.ewg.org/skindeep/

Perhaps someday in the not-too-distant future, parents will look back on the beauty regimes of today with incredulity and derision. In the sixteenth century, members of the aristocracy, including Queen Elizabeth I, would whiten their faces with lead makeup, which would temporarily improve their complexion; unfortunately, over time it would also cause their skin to become discolored, their hair to fall out, and their teeth to rot.[123] Little do we know now what will prove to be the twenty-first century equivalents.

## *Take-aways*

> Three teenagers were killed while taking selfies on a railway track in India, the country which researchers say has the worst record for selfie-related deaths. When the victims saw a train approaching, they jumped to a second track without realizing another train was coming on that.[124]

In 2013, "Selfie" was named word of the year by Oxford Dictionaries.[125] Close to 100 percent of teens across cultures admit to having taken one, often daily.[126]

Alarmist media articles claim that kids are sometimes going to extremes to improve their appearance, and 55 percent of plastic surgeons even report patients requesting surgery to improve their appearance in selfies.[127] Fortunately, the articles have it wrong. In actual fact, the number of American teenagers undergoing plastic surgery has declined in recent years:[128]

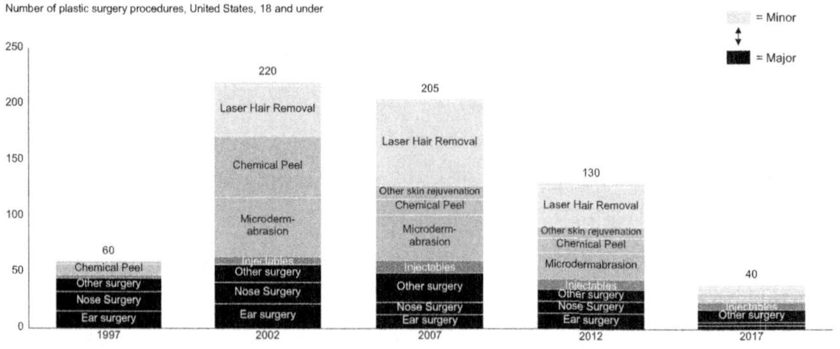

For the small number of adolescents who do have cosmetic surgery, mostly for correcting highly visible and upsetting defects such as scars, facial deformities and benign tumors, the surgery tends to greatly improve their well-being.[129]

So no matter how ridiculous your teen's aesthetic concerns may appear to you, take them seriously. They are the ones who have to cope with the consequences of their appearance every day.

**KEY PARENTING TAKE-AWAYS:**

Skincare:

1. Advise your teen not to pick at, pop or squeeze blemishes and avoid frequent washing, as both will typically exacerbate acne
2. Inform your teen that changes in diet, sunlight and beautician treatments are all useless at improving skin condition
3. In cases of severe acne, seek professional help from a dermatologist

Sun protection:

4. Ensure your teen is aware that tanning damages skin and causes premature wrinkles
5. If your child isn't convinced, consider finding an opportunity for your teen observe any skin damage first-hand under ultraviolet light by visiting an American Cancer Society office or purchasing a UV skin analyzer

Clothing/fashion:

6. Communicate that adults, including teachers, may be making subconscious judgments based on your teen's attire
7. However when it comes to dubious fashion choices, keep in mind that kids understand their own social milieu better than you
8. If your child is drawn towards a goth look, treat this as a warning sign for depression
9. If your daughter wishes to dress provocatively, alert her to the fact that members of both sexes perceive women wearing sexy clothes to be at higher risk of being attacked

Tattoos and piercings:

10. Forewarn teens angling for permanent body art that people will often judge an individual with a tattoo as less attractive, more rebellious, and less intelligent; approximately 10 percent of people have an adverse physical reaction to the tattoo ink; about 25 percent of people ultimately regret getting a tattoo; and those who attempt to remove one are frequently unsatisfied with the results

Makeup, cosmetics and personal care products:

11. Minimize your child's exposure to the myriad chemicals in personal care products to the extent possible
12. For essentials, guide your teen towards products free from items such as synthetic fragrances, preservatives, parabens, petrochemicals and sodium lauryl sulfate; and check the safety of a product's ingredients using the Skin Deep® Cosmetics Database*

Overall:

13. Orthodontics and even contact lenses are also a good investment for those whose are able to afford them
14. If your teen has a highly visible and upsetting defect such as a scar, facial deformity or benign tumor, and you're fortunate enough to have the means to afford it, consider plastic surgery

* Available at: www.ewg.org/skindeep/

# 12. RELATIONSHIPS

## Keep calm and carry on

> "There are no rules in this house; I'm not like a regular mom, I'm a cool mom." — Amy Poehler as Mrs. George in *Mean Girls*[1]

> *The World's Strictest Parents*: Unruly British teenagers are sent abroad to live with strict families in an experiment to find out the right way to bring up a child.[2]

It may seem odd that it's only now that we're finally turning to the topic that makes up close to 100 percent of the content of many adolescent parenting books. However, if you want to talk so your teenager will listen, there are many popular guides that will purportedly help you do just that, so there's no need to belabor the point here.

**Teen communication SOS**

If you do feel that your communication dynamics with your teenager are becoming dysfunctional, the best book on this topic, *Negotiating Parent-Adolescent conflict: A Behavioral-Family Systems Approach*, isn't found on the parenting shelves since it's aimed at therapists, but it contains lots of example scripts outlining ways to improve common dysfunctional interactions.[3]

Parenting a teenager requires both handling conflicts and finding ways to engage in positive interactions. We'll start with navigating the negative before turning to cultivating the positive.

**Drama**

The chart below shows the most common sources of conflict with younger teenagers ordered from left to right, with the height of the bar, where available, representing the typical intensity of the conflict.[4] This has no practical significance; it's just included here to reassure you that most other parents are struggling with similar sources of drama:[5]

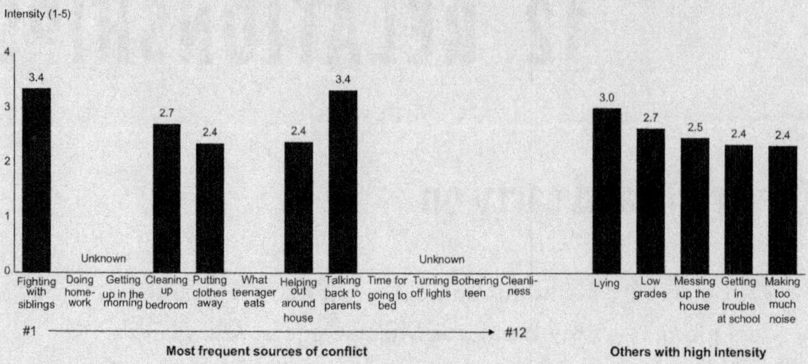


And here are some examples of egregious teen behaviors from other households: "One woman's son texts her abusive messages from his bedroom while she's cooking in the kitchen below; another's children have defected to live with their father because he allows them unrestricted access to their phones and laptops; another's daughter won't invite friends home or allow her parents to pick her up from school because she is ashamed of the family's modest house and car."[6] Whatever your teen is doing, another parent somewhere is grappling with similar craziness.

When it comes to handling conflict, the American Academy of Pediatrics is a great source of evidence-based, common-sense advice (see box).

**Parenting tips**

Here's a quick summary of the American Academy of Pediatrics' top parenting tips:

- Respond consistently each time to similar behavioral situations
- Be clear about what the problem behavior is and what immediate consequence the child can expect when this behavior occurs (usually removing privileges or denying participation in activities, e.g., grounding for an evening with no TV or loss of driving privileges)
- Provide a reason for the consequence for a specific behavior
- Deliver the consequence calmly and with empathy
- Be flexible through listening and negotiation
- In the case of an intense emotional exchange, take a break from the situation and discuss it later when emotions have subsided[7]

The Canadian equivalent also provides some helpful tips to add to this list:

- Set rules in a noncritical way and avoid lectures or predicting catastrophes
- Ensure that the child knows the correction is directed against the behavior and not the person
- Avoid shouting and name-calling as these behaviors reduce respect and trust
- Guard against humiliating the child
- Model forgiveness and avoid bringing up past mistakes[8]

Much of successfully parenting a teen boils down to consistently enforcing logical consequences. Typical consequences to get your imagination flowing could include assigning additional household tasks, or limiting your teen's access to friends, media, or freedom to come and go.

When explaining the reason for a consequence, your child is more likely to accept your logic if you emphasize the effects of the behavior on you, as opposed to focusing on the impact for your teen (e.g. "when you stay out late I worry about where you are," instead of "when you stay out late you're more likely to get into trouble"). Involving your offspring in determining an appropriate consequence can also help you to come across as reasonable.[9] Finally, it's less effective to grant a privilege with a pre-negotiated agreement about future good behavior than to set up a future reward that a child can work towards earning. The former requires a punishment if the child doesn't comply (revoking the privilege), whereas the latter is more positive, and more accurately reflects the way the adult world actually functions.[10]

Even if you feel that you're constantly warring with your adolescent, your child may not feel this way. Parents (and mothers in particular) tend to be far more bothered by conflict[11] and also tend to ruminate more after conflicts than the teens themselves, who typically view conflicts as relatively benign events with no long-term relationship consequences.[12] Mothers who have a richer life outside the home (career, social life, etc.) also tend to have more harmonious relationships with their teens, an intriguing finding which needs to be investigated further.[13]

**What if a teen is abusive?**

At the most extreme end of the spectrum, some parents can find themselves coping with a difficult teenager who is physically larger and stronger than they are, and in the worst cases, teens can even become abusive towards their parents. Such situations are likely to be under-reported, making it difficult to know how widespread this problem might be. These cases also tend to be mishandled by authorities when they do arise, since the blame is often laid on the parents for mishandling the discipline of their child, rather than acknowledging that discipline can become impossible to enforce in these situations,[14] particularly in the case of a single mother and her adult-sized son.[15] The Canadian Health Service has compiled a useful resource for any parent in such difficult circumstances, which can be downloaded for free.* [16]

Turning to a more pleasant subject, how can parents engineer constructive interactions with their teens? As will be obvious to anyone who already

* Available at: http://publications.gc.ca/collections/Collection/H72-21-180-2000E.pdf.

has a teen in the house, adolescents naturally progress towards spending less time at home and with their families. In early adolescence, this means spending more time alone in their bedrooms; then as they age, it means spending more time out and about with peers.[17] Throughout this shift, however, the amount of time teens spend alone with their parents typically remains fairly constant, and girls in particular will often want to discuss interpersonal issues at length with an adult they trust, confirming the saying that your teen may want to fire you as a parent, but re-hire you as an advisor.[18]

In early adolescence, teens perceive their family members and parents in particular as less friendly, and tend to enjoy their company less; fortunately this is only temporary, and by the later high school years, they usually return to appreciating their families more.[19] Throughout adolescence, they may give the impression of not needing adult connection because they don't want to seem dependent (even to themselves) by making the first move, so the onus needs to fall more on parents to stay connected, even if regularly rebuffed.[20] Surveys of teens show that they really do appreciate spending time with their parents, and 20 percent even say that not having enough time with their parents is their top concern.[21]

**Engage!**

If you're struggling to find ways to engage, the American Psychological Association has some suggestions for initiating conversations, even if your teen spends most of the time wearing headphones and a sullen look.[*] [22]

---

* Here are some suggestions for initiating conversations with teens:

- Engage adolescents with nonthreatening questions. Choosing only one or two questions at a given time, ask adolescents questions that help them to define their identities. For example, whom do you admire? What is it about that person that makes them admirable? What do you like to do in your free time? What do you consider to be your strengths? What are your hopes for the future? What have you done in your life that you feel proud of (even if just a little)?
- Listen nonjudgmentally (and listen more than you speak)
- Ask open-ended questions that require more than a yes or no response; this helps the adolescent think through ideas and options
- Avoid "why" questions. "Why?" questions tend to put people on the defensive
- Match the adolescent's emotional state, unless it is hostile. If the adolescent seems enthusiastic or sad, let your responses reflect this mood. Reflecting someone's mood helps the individual feel understood
- Casually model rational decision-making strategies. Discuss how you once arrived at a decision. Explain, for example, how you (or someone you know well) defined the problem, generated options, anticipated positive and negative consequences, made the decision, and evaluated the outcome. Keep in mind that the adolescent has a relatively short attention span, so be brief. Choose a topic that is relevant to adolescents (e.g., deciding how to deal with an interpersonal conflict, identifying strategies for earning money for college)
- Discuss ethical and moral problems that are in the news. Encourage the adolescent to think through the issues out loud. Without challenging your child's point of view, wonder aloud about how others might differ in their perspective on the issue and what might influence these differences

To conclude, here's a pithy description of your job as the parent of an adolescent:

> "Give the ones you love wings to fly, roots to come back and reasons to stay." - The fourteenth Dalai Lama[23]

## Dig deeper

> "There is no happiness like that of being loved by your fellow creatures, and feeling that your presence is an addition to their comfort." — Jane Eyre[24]

> "Happiness is only real when shared." — Jon Krakauer[25]

> "Let us be grateful to people who make us happy; they are the charming gardeners who make our souls blossom." — Marcel Proust[26]

Relationships are central to the well-being of all humans at any age, but the time when we perceive the truth of this tenet most acutely is during adolescence, when relationships not only undergo long-term structural changes, but can also be subject to abrupt, often painful fluctuations.

One study surveyed young people ages 11 to 19 about the emotional benefits they derived from the most important people in their lives: parents, siblings, friends and teachers. As they matured, both boys and girls gradually relied less and less on their parents, while the relative importance of siblings and, particularly, friends steadily grew, to the point where friends eventually eclipsed all others as sources of emotional support.[27] The downside of this increasing reliance on people outside the family circle is that friends have no obligations to remain emotionally close forever. Losing a best friend, which will undoubtedly happen to your child at some point, can feel cataclysmic. For this reason, we'll start our discussion of relationships with friends.

## *Friends*

> "Your high school popularity is irrelevant the day you graduate."
> — Anonymous[28]

This truism sounds comforting, but is it really true? Many fortunate college-bound kids will have the opportunity to cast away the baggage of their high school friendships and start afresh. On the face of it, their high school popularity will indeed have become irrelevant. But teens may carry emotional scars from previous social situations with them, long after the perpetrators are gone from their lives. Researchers now believe that in adolescence, the peer group is the crucible in which our personalities are molded and hardened, and how we navigate these memorable and formative years helps determine the person we will become.[29]

Teens are completely obsessed with their social standing, as we can all vividly recall from our own teen years. Fortunately, this period of insanity is short-lived, but it can drive plenty of drama and poor choices in the interim. For example, when posed a variety of dilemmas pitting popularity against other priorities such as friendship, achievement, rule following, altruism, and romance, young teens tend to prioritize popularity above all else.[30] Girls in particular can become highly self-conscious, vulnerable to criticism, and overly concerned with popularity at the expense of achievement.[31]

Although most teens are unaware of the fact, social standing can actually be measured on two different scales: pecking order popularity and genuine popularity.* Pecking order popularity corresponds to the visible hierarchy that's the source of all the angst, with those at the top held in awe and even feared, and typically considered dominant, aggressive, and stuck-up by their peers. In contrast, genuine popularity is measured by how much a child is actually liked or disliked by others. Kids who have high genuine popularity may not occupy a particularly lofty position on the official pecking order in early adolescence, but they are viewed by those around them as kind and trustworthy.[32]

In early adolescence, the pecking order reigns supreme. Particularly among girls, groups or cliques form, with the leader insisting that others conform to the group's social norms or face expulsion.[33] Many popular

* These two categories are officially called perceived and sociometric popularity in academia.

parenting books describe the dynamics that emerge within these cliques, and the various roles teens will play to maintain their position and status.

For those children who reach a social pinnacle, maintaining their precarious position at the top of the ladder requires aggression, since challengers who want to climb past them must be forcefully pushed back down.[34] These kids with high popularity must also shun those of lower social status in order to retain their exalted position. As a result, they are increasingly disliked by virtually everyone in the school,[35] and their eventual fall from grace becomes inevitable.[36] By later adolescence, the rigid hierarchy collapses as teens abandon their collective mania for the pecking order and begin choosing their friends as they should have done in the first place, i.e., on the basis of genuine popularity and underlying shared interests.[37]

**Precarious popularity**

During early adolescence, the popular kids seem to know that their status is fragile. In one study, public middle and high school students were asked to sort themselves and their peers into various categories. Of the group of students rated as popular by their peers, only approximately a quarter rated themselves as popular.[38]

Friendships are also very unstable in general during early adolescence. Two thirds of all students and 84 percent of girls report losing a best friend during this time, which can cause overwhelming sadness.[39] At age 12–13, only 50 percent of best friends in the fall remain best friends by the spring;[40] a quarter of these relationships survive a year, 9 percent two years, and only 1 percent last five years.[41] Girls in particular tend to churn through friends throughout early adolescence, perhaps because they aren't yet emotionally mature enough to fulfill each other's high expectations for friendship.[42] It's only by around age 15–16 that friendships tend to stabilize.[43]

No matter how emotionally painful these friendship upheavals may be, we can't shield our children from them. Difficult interactions teach teens valuable social skills. Cautionary tales of children who are raised without a peer group demonstrate the critical importance of this learning process. Child prodigies are perhaps the most tragic examples: children who are highly intellectually advanced naturally gravitate towards older children and adults, and are often permitted to skip several grades. The unfortunate consequence is that they are never properly integrated into their natural peer group, and frequently end up as awkward, even peculiar, adults who are unable to reach their full potential.[44]

For those who naturally play the social game with ease, high school can be a breeze, but those who are ostracized by their peers unsurprisingly suffer (see box).

**The ostracism game**

We know definitively that ostracism itself is the key cause of misery, rather than depression coming first and causing social isolation. Researchers have artificially created brief episodes of social exclusion using a computer game supposedly played with peers, and observed the effects on people of various ages. After only five minutes of 'rejection,' virtually everyone ends up in a worse mood, but teenagers in particular become increasingly distressed and anxious,[45] and teens who are overweight will proceed to consume far more calories immediately afterwards if offered food, suggesting ostracism and obesity may be linked in a vicious cycle.[46]

Although the effects of ostracism become less acute as we age, even adults will behave in absurd ways to fit in and avoid exclusion and ostracism, including buying things they don't need, giving to charities they don't care about, even changing their mind about the length of a piece of string if everyone else in the group seems to agree.[47]

Those kids who find themselves at the bottom of the social hierarchy face a daunting challenge going to school each day, but there is hardly any research about how to support them. The most promising strategy, called 'positive reappraisal,' involves helping them reframe a negative experience as an opportunity for personal growth, for example by asking them what they learned from a stressful experience, and how it made them stronger.

**Other ideas for struggling teens**

Various coping strategies have been shown to help improve the mental health of ostracized adults, including practicing mindfulness, reminding oneself of one's values and the lack of such values in the perpetrators of any unkindness, and finding other sources of control and power.[48] These haven't yet been tested with teens, but it seems likely the same techniques could also help adolescents who are struggling.

By the later part of high school, most teens have an established social niche and a chosen persona. Anyone familiar with the movie *The Breakfast Club* may be amused to hear that one study asked teens at age 16 which character from the movie they thought they most resembled, and then followed their levels of self-esteem from then until age 24. The good news is that virtually everyone's self-esteem improved by young adulthood. The even better news is that for both sexes, the 'brains' caught up in self-esteem with the 'jocks,' and for girls, the 'jocks' and 'brains' both ended up surpassing the 'princesses.'[49] Your high school popularity isn't irrelevant the day you graduate; it's just more fleeting than you think.

## *Boyfriends / girlfriends*

> "Anything happens to my daughter, I got a .45 and a shovel, I doubt anybody would miss you." — Mel Horowitz, Cher's father, *Clueless*[50]

Your adolescent is very likely to date at some point during the teen years, whether you approve or not. A third of 13-year-olds, more than half of 15-year-olds, and 70 percent of 17-year-olds say they've been in a relationship recently.[51] If you're not aware of a romantic partner, your teen may be keeping a secret from you, since adolescents, particularly girls, often fear recrimination from their parents.[52]

**It's nothing serious (yet)**
If your child's current choice of partner doesn't fill you with delight, take comfort from the fact that teenagers are unlikely to meet their future spouse in high school. One large recent survey found only about five percent of couples had met in adolescence (down from ten percent twenty years previously).[53] According to research by Match.com, the average woman meets her life partner at age 25, and the average man at 28, with half of all people ending up paired up in their twenties.[54] Teenage dating is just a prelude, an opportunity to practice and prepare for the serious impending task of choosing a life partner.

**Female tempteen + older man = trouble**
Girls who physically mature early are at risk of getting drawn into relationships with older men who are already working and therefore able to offer material benefits beyond what the boys their own age could offer. Unfortunately these relationships can derail girls' life trajectories;[55] for example, a study in Sweden found that girls who had matured early were less likely to pursue higher education and more likely to end up in lower status jobs, as result of their early relationships with working class older men.[56] If your daughter is being courted by an older guy, it would indeed be tempting to adopt Cher's father's approach to scaring him off.

Not much is known yet about teen dating — no one has studied what makes adolescent relationships successful, or how many relationships are optimal.[57] But one common mistake teens make is to attempt to use sex to create intimacy and strengthen their relationship. In one survey of sexually active teens, the most common reason given by both boys and girls for having sex was "so that my partner would love me more."[58] This strategy clearly isn't working, as the majority of teens have sex only a handful of times with their partner before the relationship ends.[59]

**For bragging rights?**
Peer pressure is less influential in teens' decision-making about sex than stories of boys accumulating notches on their belts might suggest, perhaps because it's easy enough for teens to simply lie about their sexual exploits.[60] In one in-depth survey, only about 14 percent of boys suggested they had first had intercourse because they wanted to lose their virginity; 80 percent said their reason for pursuing sex was "I really liked the person."[61]

Even if their early relationships were always going to be doomed for failure, teens take romantic break-ups seriously, and a break-up can even occasionally trigger depression in a vulnerable adolescent.[62] The recovery process can be long and drawn-out, although a teen's self-esteem will typically rebound within a year.[63] Parents may feel helpless in the face of a morose and rejected adolescent, but there are ways to shake them out of their funk. Teens who are encouraged to dwell on any bad qualities of their former romantic partners will start to feel less enamored with the object of their affection, buth this won't help improve their mood, and could backfire later if they choose to get back together with their ex. So to cheer them up, distraction is by far the best remedy.[64]

Although it may seem that your child has no interest in your opinion on any topic, let alone romantic entanglements, you may be wrong. Teens rightly perceive that adults are their most credible source of information regarding dating, more reliable than friends or siblings.[65] They may resist your involvement initially, but it's worth gently persisting, since 70 percent of 18- to 25-year-olds ultimately say they wish they had received more information from their parents on topics including "how to have a more mature relationship," "how to avoid getting hurt in a relationship," and "how to deal with breakups."[66]

A hypothetical question is whether the drama of teen romance is even necessary. In India, an estimated 90 percent of marriages are arranged by the family.[67] This practice will always run deeply contrary to our Western philosophies, but it certainly has the potential to short-circuit lots of drama and heartbreak.

## *Siblings*

Siblings have been squabbling for millenia. Beyond the original feud between Cain and Abel, consider Cleopatra's systematic killing of her siblings to retain her hold on power,[68] or the war between the two Incan brothers Huascar and Atahualpa, which dramatically weakened the Incan state and paved the way for the Spanish conquest.[69] Much more recently, Liam Gallagher reportedly precipitated the break-up of the band Oasis by flinging insults as well as a tambourine at his brother Noah, and Julia Roberts helped her brother's ex-wife gain custody of their children.[70] Examples like these should put whatever drama is going on within your household into context.

**What is there to fight about?**
If you ask adolescents why they fight with their siblings, they say the drama centers around personal property (26 percent); abusive behavior (21 percent — two thirds psychological, one third physical); controlling behavior (21 percent); sharing/turn taking (17 percent); and relationship betrayal, including untrustworthiness and neglect (14 percent).[71]

Sibling conflict is a nearly universal problem, and most parents want help managing it.[72] Many parents attempt to stop the feuding directly; about 80 percent will intervene in property disputes and conflicts over shared resources, although fewer will get involved in quarrels about power issues, chores, or abuse.[73] When they do intervene, parents tend to use a mix of providing solutions and threatening punishment.[74]

For a while, the prevailing theory of non-intervention assumed that if left to their own devices, siblings would eventually realize that fighting wasn't the best way to resolve their problems and would stop feuding.[75] The difficulty with this theory is that with the rare exception of certain twins, siblings aren't equals either physically or mentally; one will always be dominant over the other. In practice, siblings left to resolve their conflicts on their own will indeed stop fighting eventually, but the resulting equilibrium will be tilted in the favor of the dominant child, with the lesser sibling having reached a point of despair and learned helplessness in the way of an abused spouse.[76]

There is a very little research about how to manage sibling conflicts during adolescence,[77] and the only intervention which was developed specifically for this age group failed to have any effect.[78] However, teaching mediation to parents definitely increases harmony between younger siblings,[79] by focusing on the general principles of perspective taking, identifying the feelings of both parties, regulating emotions and dealing with angry feelings, and problem solving.* [80] There is also a theory that rather than focusing on reducing conflict, parents should instead focus on engineering more positive interactions between siblings, to build a scaffolding of enjoyment and trust on which the relationship can grow.[81]

A curriculum has also been designed to help adolescents resolve conflicts more generally, which could equally be applied to the challenges of communicating and negotiating with siblings.† [82] Fortunately no matter how much your children feud, they are likely to fight less and less as they age. This decline comes about not only because each party becomes more mature, but also because the salience of their age difference shrinks, and their relationship naturally becomes more egalitarian.[83] They may spend less time together, but they'll be emotionally closer and feel more warmth towards each other by the time they reach young adulthood.[84]

In the end, the number of Americans who are completely estranged from a sibling is small — probably less than 5 percent.[85] No matter how much they feud currently, most siblings ultimately don't end up hurling insults and objects at each other like the Gallaghers.

## Take-aways

There's a reason that one of the most severe punishments we impose on criminals is solitary confinement. *Homo Sapiens* is an inherently collaborative and social species, and people who have strong interpersonal connections not

---

* A free online program for parents with younger children is available at: https://funwithsistersandbrothers.org/.

† Here are the six key premises of conflict resolution which you could share with each sibling:

1. Describe what you want. "I want to use the book now." This includes using good communication skills and defining the conflict as a small and specific mutual problem.
2. Describe how you feel. "I'm frustrated." Disputants must understand how they feel and communicate it accurately and unambiguously.
3. Describe the reasons for your wants and feelings. "You have been using the book for the past hour. If I don't get to use the book soon my report will not be done on time. It's frustrating to have to wait so long."
4. Take the other's perspective and summarize your understanding of what the other person wants, how the other person feels, and the reasons underlying both. "My understanding of you is..." This includes understanding the perspective of the opposing disputant and being able to see the problem from both perspectives simultaneously.
5. Invent three optional plans to resolve the conflict that maximize joint benefits. "Plan A is..., Plan B is..., Plan C is..."
6. Choose the wisest course of action to implement and formalize the agreement with a handshake. "Let's agree on Plan B!"

only feel happier, but also enjoy better health and have lower levels of stress hormones.[86] With adolescents, as with all human beings, being ostracized can cause them terrible unhappiness, while relationships can be their sources of greatest joy. A consideration to weigh next time your adolescent is begging to postpone homework and spend time with friends.

### KEY PARENTING TAKE-AWAYS:

Parents:

1. Set rules in a noncritical way and avoid lectures or predicting catastrophes
2. Be clear about what the problem behavior is and what immediate consequence the child can expect when this behavior occurs (usually removing privileges or denying participation in activities, e.g., grounding for an evening with no TV or loss of driving privileges)
3. Respond consistently each time to similar behavioral situations
4. Ensure that the child knows the correction is directed against the behavior and not the person
5. Provide a reason for the consequence for a specific behavior, and deliver the consequence calmly and with empathy
6. Be flexible through listening and negotiation
7. In the case of an intense emotional exchange, take a break from the situation and discuss it later when emotions have subsided; avoid shouting and name-calling as these behaviors reduce respect and trust
8. Guard against humiliating the child; model forgiveness and avoid bringing up past mistakes
9. If you are coping with an abusive adolescent, download the advice from the Canadian Health Service*
10. When your teen withdraws (as all teens do), continue to make the first move to reach out and stay connected, even if regularly rebuffed

Friends:

11. Reassure your younger teen that any rigid popularity hierarchy will eventually fall apart, and most people will go back to choosing their friends based on underlying shared interests
12. Encourage even a shy teen to participate in activities like athletics and school clubs and spend time socializing informally with peers to develop social skills
13. If your child is struggling at the bottom of the totem pole, help reframe stressful social situations as learning experiences, and discuss how they have made your adolescent stronger
14. Also consider suggesting mindfulness exercises, emphasize your adolescent's values and the lack of such values in the perpetrators of any unkindnesses, and find your child other sources of control and power
15. Let your teen know that virtually everyone's self-esteem improves by young adulthood

---

* Available at: http://publications.gc.ca/collections/Collection/H72-21-180-2000E.pdf

Significant others:

16. Alert your teen to the fact that using sex to create intimacy and strengthen a relationship is an ineffective strategy
17. If your teen is suffering through a break-up, distraction is the best remedy
18. Talk openly with your adolescent about how to have a more mature relationship, how to avoid getting hurt in a relationship, and how to deal with breakups

Siblings:

19. Help resolve sibling feuding by focusing on perspective taking, identifying the feelings of both parties, regulating emotions and dealing with angry feelings, and problem solving
20. Engineer positive interactions between siblings to build a scaffolding of enjoyment and trust

## *Divorce*

> Deciding to split with her first husband Chris Martin was painful enough, but nothing could have prepared Gwyneth Paltrow for the public mockery that greeted the announcement of their 'conscious uncoupling.' "The public's surprise gave way quickly to ire and derision, a strange combination of mockery and anger that I had never seen," Paltrow wrote.[87] "The phrase was introduced by the couple's therapist as they were working out how to avoid acrimony and stay close despite their split. "Frankly, the term sounded a bit full of itself, painfully progressive and hard to swallow....I was intrigued, less by the phrase, but by the sentiment."[88]

No one imagines on their wedding day that their union might be destined for failure. We enter into matrimony with joy and high hopes. Nevertheless, approximately 40 to 50 percent of marriages in the US will end in divorce.[89] If your marriage is on the rocks or has blown up spectacularly, at least you're in good company.

Mediation is the best bet for achieving a harmonious separation.[90] In one study, couples randomly assigned to mediation were more satisfied with their post-divorce outcome, communicated more constructively with each other, and managed to maintain more contact between the children and the non-resident parent, with the positive effects still noticeable when the researchers followed up 12 years later.[91] Divorce education classes can also be helpful:[92] the couples who attend them say they find the classes useful,[93] and subsequently tend to view the divorce more positively, experience less conflict with their former spouse, and avoid further litigation.[94]

Divorce is never easy for children; both the process of separation and the often-complex living arrangements that emerge can be difficult to navigate. How difficult is hard to say, since studies of children with divorced parents can't separate whether some children struggle because of inherited genes from their parents, or because they lived through a difficult time, or some combination of both. Fortunately, the effects on children are modest at most,[95] and the majority end up just as well-adjusted as their peers.[96]

To minimize the impact of divorce on your kids, various programs have been developed to help children manage during a divorce. A number of these show promise,[97] including Focus on Kids (FOK)[98] and the Children of Divorce Intervention Program (CODIP),[99] although these programs aren't widely available, so may not be an option in your area. Developing a parenting plan in conjunction with your legal representation can be a useful step; it's as easy as downloading a template.*

Experts also offer the following common-sense principles for navigating a divorce while parenting effectively:

- "Parents shouldn't involve their children in disputes over children's living arrangements, visitation, and child support
- Children thrive on stability, and tend to adjust better if they are able to remain in the same neighborhood and school
- Parents need to be careful not to introduce their new romantic partners into children's lives too soon. Children can form close bonds with parents' partners and stepparents, but only when they've had sufficient time to establish new norms, boundaries, and relationships with these individuals."[100]

A final important and less obvious point: avoid denigrating your former spouse at all costs. It could be highly tempting to cast your partner as

* Examples of parenting plans can be found at: www.state.ak.us/courts/forms/dr-475.pdf; www.supreme.state.az.us/dr/Pdf/Parenting_Time_Plan_Final.pdf; and www.afccnet.org (follow "Resource Center" from menu; then follow "Resources for Parents").

the villain and attempt to win the kids over to your side, but this strategy backfires: children perversely feel less close to and are more likely to blame the parent who does the denigrating.[101] When asked, children of divorce generally say they would prefer to be able to spend as much time as they like with both parents, and 70 percent say the best living arrangement would be equal time with each parent.[102]

Divorce is inherently fraught, but some couples do manage to navigate the process with minimal acrimony. If you ignore the cringeworthy name, the concept of "conscious uncoupling" isn't as laughable as it first sounds. It focuses on helping couples maintain mutual respect during the process of parting ways, and reframing arguments as opportunities for internal reflection and spiritual healing.[103] Despite the public backlash against her approach, Gwyneth's divorce story even has a happy ending:

> Paltrow married for a second time in 2018 to television producer Brad Falchuk. Martin attended the wedding and joined the newlyweds on their honeymoon. She said times have changed in the way people treat their breakups. "Instead of people approaching me with, 'Why did you say that?', they now approach me with, 'How do you do that?'[104]

**KEY PARENTING TAKE-AWAYS:**

1. Consider mediation and divorce education classes, and seek out a program for kids of divorce if one is available in your area
2. Develop a parenting plan in conjunction with your legal representation, which ideally allows the children to remain in the same neighborhood and school
3. Don't involve children in disputes over living arrangements, visitation, and child support
4. Don't introduce new romantic partners into children's lives too soon
5. Avoid denigrating your former spouse

# FINAL THOUGHTS

> "Action is character, our English teacher says. I think it means that if we never did anything, we wouldn't be anybody." — Jenny, young female protagonist of *An Education*[1]

*An Education* is a sweet film about the naïveté of an adolescent girl and her equally clueless parents.[*] [2] These are parents you don't want to be emulating when raising your own child. If there is a single take-away from this book, it's to watch out for your own naïveté. We all love our children, so it's easy to fall prey to seeing the world through rose-tinted glasses, and to assume that the types of misbehaviors rampant among teens would never apply to our own precious offspring. This is wishful thinking.

Here's a quick refresher on the most important ways parents can protect their teens from getting into serious trouble:[†]

**Alcohol**: When it comes to alcohol, a zero-tolerance policy is the best bet. Don't condone sipping, or allow teens to drink in the "safety" of your own home under your supervision; lock up the alcohol cabinet; and collude with other parents to prevent access to alcohol at friends' homes. Finally, assume that parties may involve alcohol, so discuss ways to say no to drinking while saving face, and plan transportation assuming that all involved will be unreliable drivers.

**Tobacco**: It's pointless to lecture your child about the dangers of smoking. In the words of young smokers reflecting on their unhealthy habit, "It's kind of sophisticated. Grunge sophisticated." "It almost feels like rejection of wellness culture." "We all have this flamboyant death wish, if you will. We see fires, and the ground shakes beneath us, and they tell us the waters are rising. So we ask, 'What the hell is the difference?'"[3] Teens with this type

* appropriate for teens age 15+

† For the rationale behind these recommendations, see Appendix VII.

of mindset will see the "smoking kills" message on the side of the pack and light up anyway.

To protect your teens from tobacco, communicate your strong disapproval of smoking and enforce a firm no-smoking policy in your home; try to keep teens out of corner shops full of advertising; limit their access to R-rated movies and other content depicting glamorous people smoking (and drinking); and perhaps enlist an older friend or relative they respect to forward them "The Truth"* campaign about helping to defeat the influence of big tobacco companies. It's also worth warning them that vaping devices contain nicotine, one of the most addictive substances known to man, and a single casual puff of a flavored vapor could enable the vaping company to successfully snag them as a customer for life.

**Sex**: Regardless of your views on the merits of abstinence during the teen years and how often you preach, you can't assume you've successfully converted your teen. Both boys and girls are at risk of contracting HPV, an STD that not only can cause embarrassing warts, but also cancer later in life. So if you haven't yet, get your teen vaccinated as soon as possible. Then provide lots of condoms with instructions to use for both oral and regular sex, and a few STD test kits to use at a minimum once a year, one week after an encounter with a new partner, or anytime in case of worrying symptoms. Also put girls on long-acting reversible contraception. None of these actions will encourage teens to become sexually active sooner, particularly if you reinforce the message that you hope they wait. These steps will simply help keep them safe if they decide the time is right to take this major step towards adulthood.

**Transportation**: When it comes to cars, buying a vehicle with a monitoring system or installing a telematics device provided by an insurance company is the best way to ensure your novice driver is behaving sensibly on the road once you're no longer sitting in the passenger seat. Draft a written contract which includes the Graduated Drivers License rules (no driving after dark, and no driving with friends in the car), plus insist on mandatory seatbelts, no distractions while driving like eating, texting, or listening to music, and categorically no alcohol or marijuana before taking the wheel. Then follow through and revoke driving privileges for any infractions. Beyond cars, say no to motorcycles and ATVs, and impose serious consequences for bicycling without a helmet.

---

* www.thetruth.com.

**Suicide**: If your child is showing signs of being depressed, take the warning signs seriously and get professional help, ideally cognitive behavioral therapy. In addition, empty the medicine cabinet of non-essentials, only keep small quantities of medicines or lock them away, and keep guns and bullets out of the house or each locked securely in separate locations.

**Assault**: The vast majority of perpetrators of assault are friends or acquaintances. Encourage your teen to think carefully before agreeing to go somewhere alone with any dominant male, no matter how seemingly trustworthy, and suggest looking out for warning signs of controlling behavior.

Implementing all of these recommendations will require some uncomfortable conversations with your teen, who may not understand why you're being so strict in comparison to other parents. That's why collusion is the best approach. Just as the Icelanders succeeded in taming their terrible teens, we too can band together and help our children avoid the most common pitfalls of adolescence. So proactively meet the parents of your child's friends, and if they're sufficiently like-minded and can stomach a read filled with references and charts, lend them your copy of this book.

Your adolescent is living through both the most fraught but also the most memorable phase of life. If you ask older people to recall 100 or even 1,000 significant events from their lives, they remember by far the most detail about the period when they were between 10 and 25 years old.[4] This phenomenon, dubbed the "reminiscence bump," is universal across cultures.[5]

Many people sifting back through the vivid memories of their youth will recall the angst of their teen years, and wish they could tell their younger selves not to care as much or as deeply, as the following (anonymous) quotations illustrate:

> "I would tell my teenage self that it's okay to be different."[6]

> "Not everyone is going to like you; not everyone is going to want to be your friend and not everyone is going to be your friend, and that's Okay!"[7]

> "I regret caring as much as I did. Always caring about how others viewed me, my friends, teachers, family, etc. I spent so much time worrying about how people perceived things that I said or did,

whether they might take offense if I say I didn't want to do something etc., that I forgot to ever really consider how I felt in all of it."[8]

The problem with these reflections is that their teenage selves wouldn't have listened. There's a reason teens care so much about what other people think: the way that others perceive them is highly consequential at a time when they're on the brink of choosing their friends, their partners, and their career paths. Once these windows of opportunity begin to close and the major decisions of life are already taken, it's easy to feel more self-assured and care less about the opinions of others.

For parents, having an adolescent at home is challenging.[9] This is partly because teens are less appealing than they used to be; they get pimply, grow big noses, exude stinky sweat, and no longer trigger our nurturing instincts in the same way as they did when they were small and helpless and cute.[10] It's also partly because of their behavior, which can put a strain on their relationships with their parents.

Fortunately there's an end in sight: when young adults leave home, both parents and children typically note a significant improvement in the amount of respect, understanding, enjoyment, and affection in their relationship.[11] For the parents, life tends to get easier, happiness and life satisfaction go up, and the parents' marriage improves when their adolescent leaves the nest,[12] particularly if their child stays in touch.[*] [13]

At least the monumental effort of raising children is worth it.[14] A global survey of well-being across 97 countries has concluded that parents with adult children living outside the home are happier and more satisfied with life than their childless counterparts in the same life phase.[15] Very few people ultimately regret having children, no matter how exhausting or heart-rending the process proved to be in the interim. So whether you have a budding tween or a full-blown young adult living under the same roof with you, take comfort: the best is yet to come.

---

* Italy seems the exception to this rule; in Italy often young adults only leave home when they marry, and Italian mothers show a decline in happiness when their children leave, especially when the child is the last one to depart.[I]

# APPENDIX I: PROMISING DRUG PROGRAMS

As discussed in the chapter on drugs, several promising programs designed to steer kids away from drugs have made their content available self-serve to parents. Life Skills Training (LST) is one that has been held up as a model.[1] The program consists of 16 sessions aimed at seventh grade students, with eight booster sessions in each of the following two grades. The program teaches students how to resist media influences, manage stress and anxiety, communicate effectively, develop healthy personal relationships, use anger management and conflict resolution skills, and assert themselves in situations involving peer pressure, using frequent role-playing.[2] In several large, randomized trials, LST reduced drug use across various student populations including both suburban white youth and inner-city minority students,[3] in addition to reducing physical fighting and delinquent behavior.[4] (The program costs $95 for one teacher's manual and one student guide, or $265 for a manual plus 30 student guides.[5])

Unplugged, another highly commended program developed in Europe,[6] teaches social influence and life skills across 12 hours of lessons, and has been shown to reduce teen substance use.[7] And Keepin'it REAL,[*] aimed at Mexican American youth, uses student-developed videos and narratives to portray four strategies for successfully resisting offers of substance use (refuse, explain, avoid, and leave) and has shown positive effects on substance use.[8] Other school-based programs have also achieved positive results, including the Midwestern Prevention Project,[9] and two programs focused specifically on alcohol, including the School Health and Alcohol Harm Reduction

---

* Available at https://sirc.asu.edu/kir, with a basic set priced at $99.95.

Project (SHAHRP),[10] the Alcohol Misuse Prevention Study (AMPS),[11] and the Adventure trial.[12]

Another category of interventions are those aimed at families, delivered by a facilitator, which don't always specifically focus on drugs, but rather attempt to indirectly influence drug use by increasing teen supervision and monitoring, improving communication of expectations and family values, and promoting positive family time together to reduce the negative influence of peers.[13] These aren't necessarily effective at reducing alcohol consumption,[14] but can selectively reduce other drug use.

One highly regarded intervention,[15] the Iowa Strengthening Families Program (ISFP),[*] was initially developed for 10- to 14-year-olds and their families.[16] There are now multiple formats available, including a web and DVD-based version which parents can access self-serve. The style feels very dated, but it does offer various practical tips.[17] Several trials have shown the program can reduce adolescent drug use up to several years later. [18]

Other examples of effective programs include:

- The Family Check-up (FCU)[†] is a three-session intervention which has been effective in reducing substance abuse.[19]
- Staying Connected with your Teen, typically led by a facilitator over seven two-hour sessions, is also available online in a self-serve format.[‡] One study found that African American teenagers who participated in the self-administered version were 70% less likely to initiate substance abuse.[20]
- Family Matters[§] is delivered through four booklets plus follow-up telephone calls by health educators.[21] Participating adolescents were 16% less likely to begin smoking and 11% less likely to drink.[22]

---

* DVD available online for $5: https://strengtheningfamiliesfoundation.org/purchase-dvd/. Full program available at: www.extension.iastate.edu/sfp10-14/content/ordering-information: $195 for facilitator manual; $298 for DVD set. In addition, a new Web- and DVD-based 10-session version for children ages 10–16 has been developed but not yet evaluated for effectiveness; available free of charge at www.strengtheningfamiliesprogram.org.

† Book for $28.05 available for purchase at: www.guilford.com/books/Intervening-in-Adolescent-Problem-Behavior/Dishion-Kavanagh/9781593851729.

‡ Family Guide & DVD Set $71.00, available at: www.channing-bete.com/prevention-programs/staying-connected-w-your-teen/staying-connected-w-your-teen.html.

§ Available for free online: https://familymatters.sph.unc.edu/Program_materials.htm.

There are also a number of programs that have some proof of effectiveness, but are not readily available to parents self-serve, so would only be relevant if they happen to be offered near you; these include Brief Strategic Family Therapy (BSFT),[23] Familias Unidas,[24] [25] Generation PTMO,[26] Preparing for the Drug Free Years (PDFY)[27] now re-named Guiding Good Choices,[28] Parent-Based Intervention,[29] I Hear What You're Saying,[30] Urban Youth,[31] Mothers and Daughters,[32] and Project Chill.[33]

Various other popular and well-researched programs haven't proven to be effective, so don't bother pursuing them; these include the school-based Project Toward No Drug Abuse,[34] Adolescent Learning Experiences Resistance Training (ALERT),[35] and the well-known but sadly ineffectual Drug Abuse Resistance Education program (DARE).[36]

# APPENDIX II: OTHER DRUGS

The following substances, which weren't discussed in detail in the chapter on drugs, are covered here in order of declining popularity (the percentage of twelfth graders who have tried the drug is listed in parentheses).

**Creatine (9%)**

What is creatine?

Creatine is a popular and well-researched supplement. Supplementing with creatine enables adults who do heavy resistance training to achieve greater increases in their strength and muscle mass.[1] However it appears that creatine may be less effective in adolescents, whose tissues don't uptake this supplement as effectively.[2]

Where do adolescents get creatine from?

Creatine is readily available for sale anywhere that sells supplements, and can be purchased on Amazon. According to teens who use creatine, three quarters got their information primarily from friends, and most (86%) purchased the supplement from health food stores.[3] Health food stores seem to be highly motivated to sell this particular supplement; when researchers posing as 15-year-old high school athletes seeking to increase muscle strength contacted health food stores in the US by phone, 39% of sales staff recommended creatine unprompted, and an additional 29% recommended creatine after being asked specifically about it.[4]

What are the risks associated with creatine use?

Creatine is generally considered safe for use by adults; however there's still only minimal evidence of its effects in adolescents.[5] As a result, the American Academy of Pediatrics "strongly condemns the use of performance-enhancing substances and vigorously endorses efforts to eliminate their use among children and adolescents."[6] The American College of Sports Medicine similarly states that "the data on potential and real side effects in the pediatric (<18 yr) population is grossly inadequate" and therefore creatine supplementation is "not advised for the pediatric population (i.e., <18 yr of age)."[7]

There are no restrictions limiting the sale of creatine directly to adolescents, and the market is not regulated by the Food and Drug Administration in the US.[8] As a result, one survey found that three quarters of teens taking creatine didn't realize how much they were taking, and many were taking more than the recommended dose.[9] Furthermore, steroids and other banned substances can also be hidden in supposedly innocuous sports supplements.[10] An analysis of 634 sports supplement samples from 13 countries found that 14.8% of the samples overall and 18.8% of those from the US contained steroids that were not declared on the label.[11] Moreover, a company which conducted an analysis of supplements in Australia found 20% contained banned substances which were not on the ingredients list.[12]

**Diet pills (6%)**

What are diet pills?

There are three different types of diet pills. Stimulants stimulate the central nervous system to increase energy and can also minimize appetite. Appetite suppressants target receptors in the brain so people feel full. And finally, fat inhibitors block fat absorption in the stomach and intestines.[13] Phentermine, an appetite suppressant available over the counter, is the most common diet pill, used by roughly 2.5 million people in the US (of all ages). Orlistat and sibutramine are only available via prescription, so are less common,[14] although there is also an over-the-counter (OTC) version of orlistat (Alli).[15] In adolescents, the effectiveness of these pills is unclear; some studies have reported an effect,[16] while others haven't.[17]

Where do adolescents get diet pills from?

Most adolescents get diet pills over the counter.[18]

What are the risks associated with diet pill use?

Most appetite suppressants (e.g. Contrave®) are FDA-approved and have a low risk for addiction. Other diet pills are Schedule IV substances (including Belviq® and Qsymia®), meaning they also have a low potential for abuse.[19] Abuse is mainly a problem with stimulants.[20] These include Benzphetamine (Didrex®), Diethylpropion (Tenuate®, Tepanil®), Methamphetamine (Desoxyn®), Phendimetrazine (Bontril®, Prelu-2®, Plegine®), and Phentermine (Adipex®, Ionamin®, Suprenza®).[21] There have been very few studies of the effects of diet pills on adolescents,[22] although there is some evidence that some who take them experience significant side effects,[23] and orlistat has been shown to reduce vitamin D levels in adolescents.[24] Another concern with diet pills is that adolescents often don't disclose the fact that they are taking them to their health care provider,[25] which could cause risks if they interacted badly with other medications.

Ultimately, the American Academy of Pediatrics discourages the use of diet pills, saying "instead, encourage and support the implementation of healthy eating and physical activity behaviors that can be maintained on an ongoing basis. The focus should be on healthy living and healthy habits rather than on weight."[26]

**Opioids other than Heroin (6%)**

Covered previously

**LSD (5%)**

What is LSD?

LSD was created in a laboratory in 1938, and its hallucinogenic properties were only discovered when it was ingested several years later by mistake. Since then, it has been marketed as a drug for therapeutic purposes under the name Delysid®, in addition to being used illegally for recreational purposes.[27]

Where do adolescents get LSD from?

Producing LSD is a complex process, requiring an experienced chemist.[28] There's very little information about how LSD moves from laboratories to the hands of consumers, given the drug is illegal.[29] Surveys of drug users in various countries consistently find that a certain percentage source their supplies from the dark web, so presumably these purchasers then sell on part of their supply locally to others.[30]

What are the risks associated with LSD use?

There have been no documented deaths from LSD overdose,[31] and there is no evidence that LSD increases the risk of suicide[32] or sustained long-term brain damage.[33] The most common problem, experienced by 56% of young people who had tried LSD in one study,[34] is a "bad trip," in which users find their hallucinations terrifying, bringing on feelings of loss of control and panic.[35] It's difficult to predict who is at risk of having a negative experience, although there is some evidence that people who are high in self-control, who are naturally cautious and who like to plan are more likely to fare poorly on LSD.[36] Fortunately, bad trips can be easily managed if someone is there to calm down and reassure the user that the experience will only last a limited amount of time and won't do any permanent harm,[37] since LSD users are very suggestible.[38]

Another common problem is 'flashbacks' or later recurrences of hallucination. Various studies have reported wildly differing rates of this phenomenon ranging between 15% and 77%, with reporting complicated by the fact that some subjects actually welcome these experiences as a "free trip."[39] Only approximately 4% of users find these flashbacks serious enough to seek treatment,[40] with such cases on very rare occasions diagnosed as "Hallucinogen Persisting Perception Disorder" (HPPD).[41]

**Solvents/Inhalants (4%)**

What are solvents/inhalants?

Solvents/inhalants are liquids that easily vaporize. Lots of common household products fall into this category, including paint thinners and removers, dry-cleaning fluids, degreasers, gasoline, glues, correction fluids, and felt-tip markers.* [42] [43]

Where do adolescents get solvents/inhalants from?

These products can be found in most households.[44]

What are the risks associated with solvent/inhalant use?

Individuals who consistently use inhalants often report they feel a strong need to continue using them, and experience mild withdrawal symptoms when they quit, suggesting these substances can be addictive.[45]

Inhalants are highly toxic to many organs in the body, including the brain, heart, lungs, liver, and kidneys, and the damage done by inhalants can be irreversible. Long-time users often show difficulties with movement, vision and hearing, and cognitive problems including early-onset dementia.[46]

**MDMA (ecstasy) (4%)**

What is MDMA?

MDMA, also called "ecstasy" or "molly," was developed by accident in 1912 by chemists who were trying to find a compound to synthesize medications that controlled bleeding. In the 1970s psychiatrists began using the drug during patient sessions to help improve communication, but in 1985 the United States banned MDMA based on its potential for abuse.[47] MDMA is a stimulant that enhances enjoyment from sensory experiences, increases self-awareness and empathy, and can cause hallucinations.[48]

Where do adolescents get MDMA from?

As with LSD, MDMA can only be produced in a lab,[49] and is typically imported into the US in mass quantities by criminal enterprises. Middle- to upper-class white men ages 18–30 who sell only MDMA (not other drugs) are the most common retail distributors, and the drug is often for sale at beach resorts, on college campuses, and at raves, dance clubs, and bars, although it can also be found in some high schools.[50]

* Prescription nitrite inhalants used to be a more common drug of abuse, but this category was dropped by the Monitoring the Future survey in 2010 as the percent of users was so small.[1] This is fortunate as isobutyl nitrite has a very low safety ratio, only slightly better than heroin.[2]

What are the risks associated with MDMA use?

More than half of regular users of MDMA develop tolerance to the drug, and approximately a third report they have trouble concentrating and/or feel depressed, although 30% also suggest they 'feel more open towards people.'[51] Recreational use also appears to cause memory problems,[52] and to impair complex problem-solving abilities,[53] and there is some evidence that MDMA can cause long-term disruptions in sleep cycles.[54] The problem with all of these studies is that users of MDMA may be different from non-users in other ways; for example, they may have taken other drugs as well. However one study recruited adult volunteers who had never tried MDMA before and randomly assigned half of the participants to start using the drug; the users were found to have worse verbal recall after taking MDMA.[55]

There is also risk that MDMA is adulterated with other substances. Samples seized by police have frequently been found to contain additives including cocaine, ketamine, methamphetamine, synthetic cathinones ("bath salts"),[56] and even in rare cases N-ethylpentylone (a riskier stimulant linked to psychosis and deaths).[57] One study found that the MDMA being sold at a festival was twice as likely to be adulterated than MDMA bought off-site, presumably because festival-goers don't have an established relationship with the dealer, so are easier to cheat.[58]

**Stay awake pills (4%)**

What are stay awake pills?

Stay awake pills provide caffeine in pill form, with common brands including NoDoz®, Vivarin®, Wake®, Dexatrim®, and Caffedrine®.[59] The maximum strength formulations typically contain 200mg of caffeine, more than the 110mg found in a standard cup of coffee, but considerably less than the 550mg found in a "grande" Starbucks® Coffee.[60]

Where do adolescents get stay awake pills from?

These pills are readily available over the counter.

What are the risks associated with stay awake pill use?

It's worth acknowledging that there can be certain benefits associated with consuming caffeine. For example, caffeine appears to slightly enhance performance in endurance or high-intensity sports,[61] with a report by the American College of Sports Medicine estimating an impact on performance in the range of 2–4%.[62] As a result, caffeine is banned by the US National College Athletic Association (NCAA).[63]

The downsides of exposure to caffeine may include effects on the cardiovascular and neurological systems, and it's hypothesized that children and adolescents are at higher risk of negative effects because of their size and lack of tolerance to the drug,[64] although there are not enough good studies yet.[65] As discussed in the chapter on sleep, the American Academy of Pediatrics therefore categorically states that "caffeine and other stimulant substances contained in energy drinks have no place in the diet of children and adolescents."[66]

**Synthetic marijuana (4%)**

What is synthetic marijuana?

Synthetic marijuana is also called K2, Spice, and many other names. This category is a recent addition to the menu of mind-altering substances available to most teenagers. The production of these drugs involves spraying any chemical with psychoactive properties onto shredded plant material in order to create a substance that resembles marijuana and is smoked the same way.[67] Of course, the drugs sprayed on can vary wildly, and more than 150 new substances have been identified in versions on the street in the last decade, including but not limited to synthetic, and far more potent, versions of THC, the psychoactive ingredient in marijuana. Most of these new drugs come and go within several months, as drug innovators continue to experiment with new formulations.[68]

Where do adolescents get synthetic marijuana from?

Because these drugs can masquerade as cannabis or even as potpourri or incense with a label saying "not for human consumption," they are often sold openly in gas stations and convenience stores.[69] They can also be purchased over the internet.[70]

What are the risks associated with synthetic marijuana use?

It's difficult to say definitively what the risks of these drugs might be, given the chemical formulations involved are constantly changing. Thus far, there's little evidence that these substances tend to be addictive.[71] In terms of other side effects, a somewhat outdated report based on 2010 data from the US National Poison Data Center suggests the most common side effects include an elevated heart rate (40%), agitation/irritability (23%), drowsiness/lethargy (14%), confusion (12%), hallucinations or delusions (9%) and dizziness (7%).[72]

**OTC cough/cold medicines (3%)**

What are OTC cough/cold medicines?

Among the over 100 different cough/cold medicines found in pharmacies, the most common being Robitussin® and NyQuil®, the common active ingredient is called Dextromethorphan (DXM). Although safe in small doses, DXM in large doses, e.g., from 'extra-strength' products, can cause all sorts of effects including euphoria, distortions of color and sound, poor judgement, blurred vision, vomiting, seizures, and hallucinations lasting up to six hours.[73]

Where do adolescents get OTC cough/cold medicines from?

These medicines are inexpensive and readily available in pharmacies and grocery stores, as well as found in many medicine cabinets at home.[74]

What are the risks associated with OTC cough/cold medicine use?

For unknown reasons, some 5% of people from a European background are genetically unable to process DXM, meaning that taking too much can rapidly become toxic.[75] There have also been reports of individuals becoming addicted to DXM and experiencing withdrawal, although this is quite rare.[76] In addition, acetaminophen, another ingredient found in many OTC cough and cold medications, can cause liver damage and failure if taken in large quantities.[77]

**Cocaine (3%)**

What is cocaine?

Coco leaves were first used by the Incas, who chewed them during religious ceremonies. In 1859, a pure version of the drug was extracted from the leaves by a German chemist, and in the 1880s cocaine began to be used for medical purposes. By 1903, Coca-Cola was forced to remove the drug from its soft drink, as the dangers of cocaine started becoming more apparent. However, it was only in the 1970s that use of the drug became widespread, and a network was set up to smuggle cocaine from Columbia into the US in large quantities.[78]

There are a variety of ways to use the drug. In powder form it can be snorted through the nose, rubbed into the gums, or dissolved and injected into the blood; in rock crystal form (called Crack), it can be heated and inhaled,[79] which is the most potent and addictive form since the effects are experienced within seconds.[80]

Where do adolescents get cocaine from?

Like most other illicit drugs, cocaine flows from a concentrated number of cocaine wholesalers to a network of mid-level cocaine dealers, who then sell to countless street-level dealers, who are often users themselves.[81] Teens tend to source their cocaine from older friends, although some also interact with dealers directly.[82] There are now apps that will supply cocaine as well, and although most teens are still wary, this source is likely to grow rapidly.[83] Evidently, 48% of teens use the drug at a friend's house; night clubs are the next most popular location, and a third use the drug outside on a street.[84]

What are the risks associated with cocaine use?

Cocaine can cause a variety of "irreversible structural changes of the brain, heart, lungs, liver and kidneys." Chest pain is the most common problem, and 6%–26% of crack users report coughing up blood. One study of young subjects who were frequent users of cocaine found that 75% had advanced thickening/hardening of the arteries.[85]

Cocaine purchased on the street is also adulterated with other substances; the average street sample contains only 40% cocaine, while the very purest contains 75%, so some of the harmful effects could stem from the other random, unknown substances being absorbed.[86]

Cocaine can be highly addictive for a subset of people.[87] One study of users of all ages found 5–6% became dependent,[88] but this likely under-estimates the addiction potential for teens specifically. Intriguingly, researchers are investigating a vaccine which could help addicts by training the immune system to target the drug, and prevent it from reaching the brain.[89]

**Anabolic-androgenic steroids (1.5%)**

What are anabolic-androgenic steroids?

Anabolic-androgenic steroids, often simply called steroids, are synthetic versions of the male sex hormone, testosterone. (Steroids are technically a broader class of signaling molecules within the body; 'anabolic' means building muscle, and 'androgenic' means having male sex characteristics.)[90] The most common reason teenagers take steroids is to gain muscle strength, which can provide an advantage in strength-dependent sports like weightlifting and football.[91] For this reason, the International Olympic Committee banned steroids in 1975, and using them without a prescription is illegal in the US and Canada.[92] However, non-athletes have been found to occasionally abuse steroids too.[93]

Where do adolescents get anabolic steroids from?

Back in 1995, a survey found that teens' main sources of anabolic steroids were friends (55%), trainers (26%), doctors (12%), and parents (7%).[94] (Doctors occasionally prescribe steroids to teens with stunted growth or who are late to go through puberty.[95]) In 2005, investigators found that hundreds of websites were offering anabolic steroids, and shipping the orders from foreign countries to the US.[96] Nowadays, many international pharmacy websites accept all common forms of payment, and will deliver to addresses around the world.[97]

What are the risks associated with anabolic steroid use?

As discussed in the chapter on drugs, it's important to acknowledge to teens that there are benefits to using steroids; they do work to increase muscle mass and strength.[98] Unfortunately, they also come with "a host of severe, long-term, and in some cases, irreversible health consequences," in the words of one review.[99]

Effects can include acute health problems like heart attacks, strokes, kidney failure, liver tumors, and stunted growth, as well as unpleasant physical side effects like infertility, baldness, severe acne, breast development and atrophy of the testicles in boys, and growth of facial hair, male-pattern baldness, and deeper voices among girls.[100]

Steroids can also cause behavioral and psychological effects, such as aggression and violent conduct.[101] One study found that 23% of steroid users experienced mood swings ranging from mania to depression,[102] and other effects include paranoia, jealousy, extreme irritability, delusions, and poor judgment/feelings of invincibility.[103]

Some 30% of users become dependent, and can experience depression upon quitting,[104] although there is not yet enough known about who is most susceptible.[105] Animal studies also suggest that adolescence is a time of particular susceptibility to long-lasting changes in various brain regions due to steroid exposure.[106]

Finally, steroids are often injected, so users risk contracting diseases such as HIV and hepatitis B and C from unclean needles. [107]

As a result, the American Academy of Pediatrics "condemns the use of anabolic steroids for body building or enhancement of sports performance;"[108] the National Federation of State High School Associations (NFHS) Sports Medicine Advisory Committee "strongly opposes the use of anabolic, androgenic steroids," saying usage "imposes unacceptable long-term health risks."[109] And the American College of Sports Medicine "deplores the use of anabolic-androgenic steroids by athletes."[110]

# APPENDIX III: SEXUALLY TRANSMITTED DISEASES

For those who would like to understand the risks their child faces when it comes to sexually transmitted diseases, we'll review each of the common STDs in order of prevalence, starting with Human papillomavirus (HPV).

**HPV** is a virus which can cause genital warts and cancer,[1] and which can't be cured with treatment.[2] Not only can transmission be prevented by using condoms;[3] in fact, HPV is fully preventable with a highly effective vaccine.[4] (Fortunately, even without the vaccine, the human immune system often emerges victorious: a year after contracting the virus, 30% of women are no longer infected, and by 24 months approximately 90% are virus-free.[5])

The risk for teens of contracting warts from HPV is not a figure that anyone appears to have calculated previously, although there are plenty of estimates of how many cases of genital warts are caused by HPV.[6] Here's an estimate for teens ages 14–19 calculated from a variety of sources:[*] [7]

| | Females | Males |
|---|---|---|
| Vaccinated: | 0.3% | 0% |
| Unvaccinated: | 2.4% | 2.9% |

Genital warts can be uncomfortable,[8] but the warts themselves can be treated with some combination of topical prescription medication and cryotherapy (freezing).[9] When it comes to this particular symptom, the physical

* Calculated based on the incidence from the National Health and Nutrition Examination Survey (NHANES) of the wart-causing strains of HPV among teens for females[1] and males[2] and the ratio of infection rates for vaccinated versus unvaccinated females[3] and males.[4, 5]

implications are less problematic than the psychological ones:[10] a diagnosis of this STD can understandably trigger depression, as well as anger and anxiety.[11]

Worse, HPV can cause various types of cancer in both women and men, which typically appear many years after the initial infection.[12] Although there are lots of studies which report what percent of cervical and other cancers are caused by HPV,[13] again apparently no one has ever bothered to calculate the one useful statistic from the perspective of a parent or teen aiming to understand the risk; namely, the percentage of those with HPV who end up contracting cancer. The following table shows the lifetime risk of cancer from HPV contracted during adolescence, again calculated based on combining data points from a variety of sources:* [14]

| | Females | | Males | |
|---|---|---|---|---|
| | Developing | Dying from | Developing | Dying from |
| Vaccinated | 0.3% | 0.1% | 0 | 0 |
| Unvaccinated | 2.6% | 1.0% | 0.7% | 0.3% |

The Advisory Committee on Immunization Practices (ACIP) recommends that all 11- to 12-year-olds of both sexes get vaccinated against HPV.[15] The timing of the vaccine before they become full blown teenagers is not accidental, since most parents fail to predict when their children will lose their virginity, and a high proportion of girls contract HPV soon after becoming sexually active.[16] But in 2016, only 60% of teens had begun the vaccination process, and only 43% were fully up to date with the 3-dose series.[17] This is an obvious missed opportunity.

Next we come to **chlamydia**, a relatively common STD with 5% of females and 3% of males infected by the time they reach age 18–19. Chlamydia can cause long-term problems primarily for women, including pelvic inflammatory disease (PID), ectopic pregnancies and infertility.[18] Again, there are

* Calculating these figures required combining several data points:

1. The lifetime risk of developing and of dying from HPV-related cancers (used the number of cases and the number of deaths for every type of cancer related to HPV from the National Cancer Institute,[1] and combined with data on lifetime risk from the American Cancer Society using cancer of the cervix as an example data point since lifetime risk figures only given for a limited number of types of cancer[2]).
2. The percentage of these cancers caused by HPV from the CDC.[3, 4]
3. The probability of contracting HPV in adolescence versus later for females[5] and males.[6]
4. The ratio of infection rates for vaccinated versus unvaccinated females[7] and males.[8, 9]

plenty of estimates of the percent of infertility cases that are caused by chlamydia,[19] but far fewer that flip the information more usefully and tell us the likelihood of becoming infertile or suffering other consequences due to catching chlamydia. It's difficult to estimate the risks because of ethical constraints: if an infection is discovered, it's treated immediately, rather than left to fester and cause future problems, which could then be tracked.[20] Our best estimate is that after a known infection, the risk of infertility is between 1 and 5%.[21]

Sometimes chlamydia causes noticeable symptoms, such as discomfort,[22] but a full 77% of all cases of chlamydia infection are asymptomatic,[23] and it's not fully known how frequently asymptomatic cases lead to complications.[24] One study has estimated a 9% chance of pelvic inflammatory disease,[25] and another a 0.07% chance of ectopic pregnancy and a 0.02% chance of infertility after an asymptomatic infection.[26] Adolescent girls also appear to have cervixes that are particularly susceptible to infection,[27] because their cervical development is incomplete.[28]

Fortunately, the treatment for chlamydia is straightforward: a single dose of antibiotics or a 7-day course clears it up,[29] and dramatically reduces the likelihood of future problems, if the infection has been caught in time.[30] As a result, the Centers for Disease Control and Prevention recommends yearly screening of all sexually active women under 25;[31] the US Preventive Services Task Force concurs and also suggests testing sexually active men under 25 to avoid them spreading the infection to their female partners,[32] while Public Health England goes the farthest and suggests screening both sexes not only every year but also after every change of sexual partner.[33]

**Herpes simplex virus 2 (HSV-2)** is otherwise known as genital herpes. The first outbreak is typically the worst and can include flu-like symptoms, although the virus can continue to cause recurrent outbreaks.[34] But somewhere between 50 and 85% of cases are completely asymptomatic,[35] and the virus can still be transmitted to a partner even in the absence of noticeable symptoms.[36]

HSV-2 can cause two difficulties beyond the unpleasant lesions. The first is meningitis, an inflammation of the linings of the brain.[37] Approximately 7.8 adults in a million will contract meningitis caused by HSV in their lifetime,[38] although the problem does sometimes resolve on its own without treatment.[39] The other problematic outcome is neonatal herpes, which can cause a baby to become seriously ill or die.[40] An existing HSV-2 infection reactivates during pregnancy only approximately 3% of the time, so the likelihood of having a problem in pregnancy as a result of an HSV-2 infection contracted in adolescence can be calculated as roughly 0.07%.[*] [41]

Nevertheless, routine screening for HSV-2 is not recommended. Although antiviral therapy can help those with symptoms, there isn't any evidence that it helps prevent long-term problems in those who are asymptomatic, or can reduce the likelihood of neonatal herpes. The US Preventive Services Task Force has therefore concluded that the potential harms of screening, include false-positive test results, labeling, and anxiety, outweigh the potential benefits.[42]

It is also worth referencing **herpes simplex virus type 1 (HSV-1)**. This is a lifelong infection with no cure which is fortunately benign: by age 70, 90% of people have contracted HSV-1,[43] and most people were infected as children or young adults from ordinary contact with saliva.[44] Many people have no symptoms at all, while others can get cold sores or blisters on or around the mouth.[45] The reasons to cover the topic at all here are twofold. Firstly, being infected with HSV-1 provides moderate protection against getting HSV-2, and reduces its severity.[46] Secondly, HSV-1 can be spread from the mouth to the genitals through oral sex, so some cases of genital herpes are caused by HSV-1.[47]

The next STD on our list, **gonorrhea**, is similar to both chlamydia and HSV-2 in that it's often asymptomatic: between 45% and 65% of all cases of gonorrhea infection never cause any symptoms.[48] Like chlamydia, it can cause pelvic pain, ectopic pregnancy, and infertility in women,[49] and in men, a painful condition in the tubes attached to the testicles and, in rare cases, sterility.[50] However, gonorrhea is particularly insidious because it's well-established that women can suffer permanent consequences without any symptoms.[51]

Gonorrhea is somewhat treatable with antibiotics, although by now the bacteria has developed resistance to nearly every drug used for treatment, so two drugs need to be used simultaneously.[52] As a result, all major bodies, including the American College of Obstetricians and Gynecologists,[53] the American Academy of Family Physicians,[54] and the US Preventive Services Task Force (USPSTF),[55] recommend annual screening for girls and possibly also boys who are sexually active.

---

* According to one study, disseminated disease and central nervous system disease were reported in 17.5% and 22.8% of cases, respectively, and nine of 58 cases were fatal.[1] So 4% (likelihood of having HSV-2 from NHANES) x 3% (probability of reactivation during pregnancy) x (17.5%+22.8%+9/58) = 0.067%.[1]

Moving down the list, we come next to **trichomonas**, which is caused by infection with a protozoan parasite. Yet again, only about 30% of those infected develop symptoms, but trichomoniasis can increase the risk of contracting other sexually transmitted infections like HIV, and pregnant women with trichomoniasis are more likely to have their babies born prematurely and with low birth weight. Trichomoniasis can be treated with oral medications,[56] which cure 90–100% of infections.[57]

**Hepatitis B**, a sexually-transmitted virus which infects the liver and can cause cirrhosis and cancer,[58] is included in the routine vaccinations all infants receive in the US.[59] As a result, approximately 70% of infections in the United States are among those who were born elsewhere,[60] since Hep B remains a significant problem in other parts of the world.[61]

Finally, a discussion of STDs would not be complete without a reference to **HIV**. By now, this scourge of the '80s and '90s is so rare it doesn't even show on the chart in Chapter 2: the rate for 15- to 19-year-olds is roughly 8 in 100,000.[62] In one study from back in 2003, 49% of teen males who tested positive had contracted it through male-to-male sex, and only 11% through hetero-sexual contact; in contrast, 56% of teen females had contracted it through heterosexual contact.[63] These days, the prospect of contracting an incurable and potentially deadly disease may serve as a deterrent for many teens, but in practical terms, it's unlikely to affect them. Similarly, **syphilis**, one of the largest health problems of the sixteenth through nineteenth centuries, is now far more rare, and also doesn't even show on the chart: in 2018, rates among teens were 10.9 for males and 4.3 females per 100,000,[64] and the majority of all syphilis cases occur among men who have sex with men, many of whom are also infected with HIV.[65]

# APPENDIX IV: DEATH AND HOSPITALIZATIONS BY GENDER

In the 'Dig deeper' section of the chapter on death and physical harm, two charts showed annual fatality rates and hospitalization rates for teens across a variety of categories. However those charts presented a combined view for both sexes, and boys and girls face somewhat different hazards as they navigate their teen years. Here are the charts showing fatality and hospitalization rates for adolescent boys:

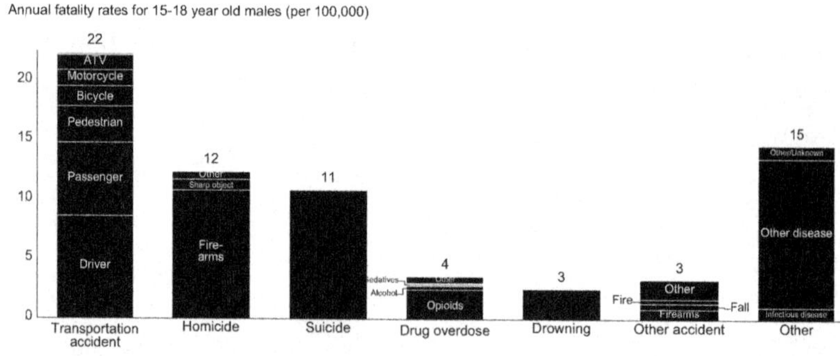


Note: Driver and passenger categories include cars, trucks and vans; 'unknow n vehicle' allocated proportionally to transportation accidents; 'unknow n drug' allocated proportionally to other drug fatalities
Source: Centers for Disease Control and Prevention, National Center for Health Statistics. Underlying Cause of Death 1999-2016 on CDC WONDER Online Database, released in 2020. Data are fromthe Multiple Cause of Death Files, 1999-2016, as compiled fromdata provided by the 57 vital statistics jurisdictions through the Vital Statistics Cooperative Program. Accessed at http://w onder.cdc.gov/ucd-icd10.html

Annual fatality and hospitalization rates for 15-18 year old males (per 100,000)

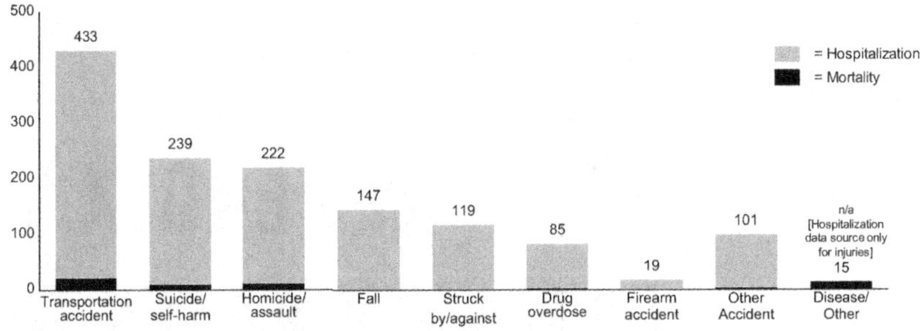


Note: Driver and passenger categories include cars, trucks and vans; 'unknown vehicle' allocated proportionally to transportation accidents; 'unknown drug' allocated proportionally to other drug fatalities; drug overdose includes all poisonings for hospitalization figure
Sources: Fatality rates: Centers for Disease Control and Prevention, National Center for Health Statistics, Underlying Cause of Death 1999-2016 on CDC WONDER Online Database, released in 2020. Data are from the Multiple Cause of Death Files, 1999-2016, as compiled from data provided by the 57 vital statistics jurisdictions through the Vital Statistics Cooperative Program. Accessed at http://wonder.cdc.gov/ucd-icd10.html; Hospitalization rates: Centers for Disease Control and Prevention National Electronic Injury Surveillance System-All Injury Program (NEISS-AIP) Nonfatal Injury Reports, 2001 - 2014, downloaded from Web-based Injury Statistics Query and Reporting System (WISQARS)

# And for adolescent girls:

**Annual fatality rates for 15-18 year old females (per 100,000)**

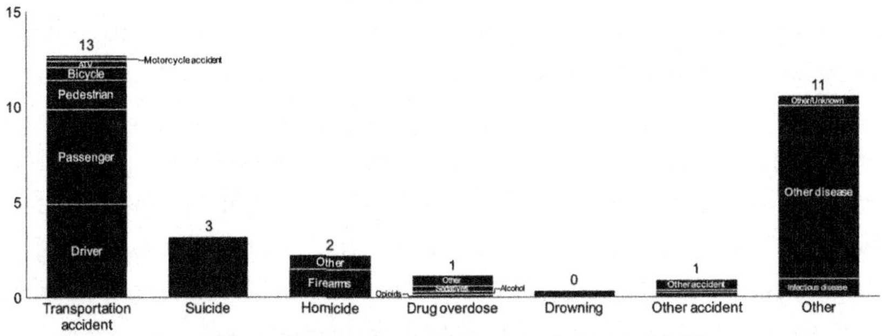


Note: Driver and passenger categories include cars, trucks and vans; 'unknown vehicle' allocated proportionally to transportation accidents; 'unknown drug' allocated proportionally to other drug fatalities
Source: Centers for Disease Control and Prevention, National Center for Health Statistics. Underlying Cause of Death 1999-2016 on CDC WONDER Online Database, released in 2020. Data are from the Multiple Cause of Death Files, 1999-2016, as compiled from data provided by the 57 vital statistics jurisdictions through the Vital Statistics Cooperative Program. Accessed at http://wonder.cdc.gov/ucd-icd10.html

Annual fatality and hospitalization rates for 15-18 year old females (per 100,000)

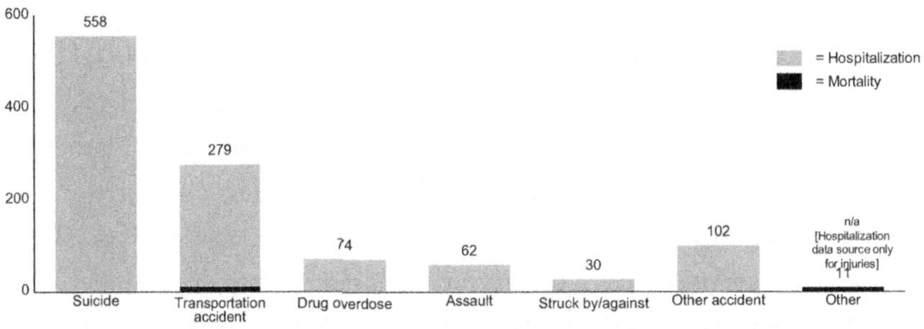


Note: Driver and passenger categories include cars, trucks and vans; 'unknown vehicle' allocated proportionally to transportation accidents; 'unknown drug' allocated proportionally to other drug fatalities; drug overdose includes all poisonings for hospitalization figure
Sources: Fatality rates: Centers for Disease Control and Prevention, National Center for Health Statistics, Underlying Cause of Death 1999-2016 on CDC WONDER Online Database, released in 2020. Data are from the Multiple Cause of Death Files, 1999-2016, as compiled from data provided by the 57 vital statistics jurisdictions through the Vital Statistics Cooperative Program. Accessed at http://wonder.cdc.gov/ucd-icd10.html; Hospitalization rates: Centers for Disease Control and Prevention National Electronic Injury Surveillance System-All Injury Program (NEISS-AIP) Nonfatal Injury Reports, 2001 - 2014, downloaded from Web-based Injury Statistics Query and Reporting System (WISQARS)

# APPENDIX V: FATALITY RATES OF EXTREME SPORTS

When comparing the risks of various extreme sports, it's difficult to compare injury rates, as different sports bodies and academic studies use different definitions. What's considered a 'catastrophic' injury, for example, is not well defined, although most of us would know it when we see it.

There are national sources of data on injuries which use consistent definitions, but these have various shortcomings. The National Electronic Injury Surveillance System (NEISS),[1] a program run by the US Consumer Product Safety Commission (CPSC) which collects detailed data on injuries related to consumer products from a random representative sample of hospitals across the country, would capture injuries from sports that use gear like skiing and skateboarding, but wouldn't capture injuries from an activity like base jumping that doesn't have a product involved. A broader program run by NEISS in conjunction with the CDC, called the National Electronic Injury Surveillance System-All Injury Program (NEISS-AIP), collects nationwide data on serious injuries beyond just those related to products; but that data set doesn't describe the cause with enough specificity to be useful (one category is "Unintentional Struck By/Against"). It therefore makes sense to compare deaths rather than injuries, since death is well defined, and a decent proxy for the chance of a terrible injury as well.

Certain sports regrettably cannot be included in our comparison of death rates. One example is motocross. The Centers for Disease Control and Prevention maintains an online database of all recorded deaths in the United

States (CDC Wonder), but the description of the cause of death in a vehicle doesn't distinguish what the vehicle was used for, so there is no way to separate out two-wheeled vehicles used for racing as opposed to transportation.

Similarly, the category of deaths as a result of a "fall involving ice-skates, skis, roller-skates or skateboards" makes it impossible to separate the risk of these disparate activities from each other. Fortunately there are national organizations which track fatalities for skiing and snowboarding, so we can still include them in our comparison. But ice-skating, roller-skating and skateboarding are unknowns. Skateboarding in particular is an unfortunate omission, as it features in the X-games, and is undoubtedly perilous when pursued to a high level of skill. Back in 1977, an editorial in the *British Medical Journal* opined, "It is highly regrettable that the BBC television program *Nationwide* should encourage and publicize the dangerous sport of skateboarding with a national skateboard competition. The evidence of serious injury in those attempting this hobby is at present impression only, but I predict that it will soon amass and label the skateboard as highly dangerous. The skateboard can achieve speeds of up to 40 mph (64 kph) and the skill and fun in its use lies in its inherent instability."[2] We at least cover the topic of skateboarding elsewhere when discussing injuries from concussions.

What follows is a description of how fatality rates were calculated for the various pursuits which appear in the chart in the section on extreme sports.

### Skiing and Snowboarding

For skiing and snowboarding, the US National Ski Areas Association (NSAA) collects data on fatalities, for some years broken down for skiing versus snowboarding, and also provides information on the number of visitor days. This allows us to calculate fatalities per visitor day, which for the years 2009–2020 works out to 0.76 and 0.62 fatalities per million visitor days for skiing and snowboarding, respectively.[3] This is very similar to the rate reported in Switzerland of 0.7 deaths per one million skier days (0.7 for skiers and 0.9 for snowboarders).[4]

These figures are for everyone, adults and youths combined; but given what we know about adolescent behavior, we would expect that teens would be at higher risk. This appears to be true according to various statements by the NSAA ("the majority of 2019/20 fatalities were male skiers between the ages of 21-30 on intermediate or advanced terrain;"[5] "the majority of 2018/19 fatalities were male skiers under the age of 30 on intermediate terrain;"[6] and "[t]he highest injury rate was among children (age 7–12) and teens (age 13–17)"[7]). Similarly, according to Dr. Jasper Shealy, a professor emeritus at the Rochester Institute of Technology who has studied ski related injuries for more than 30 years, "most fatalities occur in the same population that engages in high-risk behavior. Victims are predominantly male (85 percent) from their late teens to late 30s (70 percent)."[8]

So assuming that under 35s represent 70 percent of fatalities, and using data from the NSAA that suggests this age bracket has represented an average of 45 percent of ski visits over the last decade,[9] we can calculate an adjusted rate of 0.12 fatalities for skiers and 0.10 fatalities for snowboarders under the age of 35 per 100,000 visitor days.[10] This may still be an under-estimate, as teens are likely to be riskier skiers than 34-year-olds, but it's as close as we can get.

**Bungee jumping**

The academic literature on the risks of bungee jumping is sparse; according to one report from 2012, "Risk with bungee jumping is only sporadically reported in the literature, most often in connection with eye injuries, but also rare events of serious, life-threatening injuries and even death."[11] The only published source which offers an estimate states that "[s]ince 1987, when the first jumps are reported to have occurred in the US, over 2 million people have participated in the sport. Of these, 5 have died from trauma and approximately 80 (as reported by one insurance company) have suffered injury."[12] This equates to a risk of death of 0.25 per 100,000 jumps.

**Scuba diving**

One source of data on the risks of scuba diving is a 2018 report from the UK British Sub-Aqua Club (BSCA), which provides the total number of members and the number of member deaths over several decades, giving a fatality rate of 17.9 per 100,000 members.[13] Unfortunately, it's hard to say how many of the members are actively diving each year versus just paying their dues, and of those who dive, how much time they are spending under the water.

An article published by the BBC, also drawing on BSCA information, although less recent, is more helpful since it provides the number of dives: "The British Sub-Aqua Club keeps a careful tally of diving fatalities and recorded 197 deaths over the 12 years from 1998 to 2009, an average of around 16 a year.

They estimated around 30 million dives over this time, so the average lethal risk was around 8 micromorts per dive."[14] A micromort is a one-in-a-million chance of death, so that's the equivalent of 0.8 fatalities per 100,000 dives.

Similarly, a study on the risks of scuba diving in the US and Canada has concluded there were roughly 306 million dives from 2006–2015 resulting in 563 recreational diving deaths, a fatality rate of 0.18 per 100,000 dives.[15]

Taking an average of these two sources, we come to a calculation of 0.5 fatalities per 100,000 dives, which applies to all divers, as there is, unfortunately, no way to separate out rates for adolescents versus adults.

**Skydiving**

According to data from the United States Parachute Association, "[F]rom 2000 to 2018, there were 450 fatalities and an estimated 55.1 million jumps, for a fatality rate of 8.2 per million jumps."[16] Putting it into the same units as our other activities, this is equivalent to a rate of 0.8 fatalities per 100,000 jumps.

**Paragliding**

Three data points on the risks of paragliding are available; one from Turkey, one from Norway, and the last from the UK. According to an analysis of 242,355 paragliding flights from Fethiye Baba Mountain, one of the favorite paragliding regions in Turkey: "[T]he mortality rate of paragliding jumps in this study was found as 7 per 100,000 jumps."[17] A Norwegian analysis of civilian sport parachuting from 1963 to 2008 found a total of 32 deaths among 1,435,884 jumps, or a fatality rate of 2.2 per 100,000 jumps.[18] And finally, in the UK, a total of 110,000 parachute jumps resulted in six fatalities, or 5.5 fatalities per 100,000 jumps.[19] Taking the average of these three estimates (7, 2.2, 5.5) yields a rate of 4.9 fatalities per 100,00 jumps.

**Hang gliding**

It's difficult to estimate the risk of hang gliding, since no one knows how many flights are taken each year: "The problem with estimating participation is that hang gliders are easy to transport and can be used in a variety of environments — from backyard hills to beachside cliffs to mountain ridges. There are even portable power winches that will pull hang gliders airborne for those without an elevated launch site. Association/club membership is only a rough index. Some members fly, some don't. Some pilots are joiners, some anti-organization. Some fly — and die — all by themselves in remote areas."[20] So while we know approximate fatalities from the United States Hang Gliding and Paragliding Association (USHPA), [21] this information isn't very useful without a denominator.

Fortunately, the British Hang Gliding and Paragliding Association (BHPA) has data on fatality rates for both hang gliding and paragliding, as it is a legal requirement in the UK to report accidents: "The calculated yearly fatality rate (fatalities/100,000 participants) was 40.4 in hang gliding, and 47.1 in paragliding."[22]

These figures are per participant rather than per flight, so they're not directly comparable to the calculations for the other sports. But if we assume that the number of jumps for paragliding and hang gliding is approximately similar (to be clear, a big assumption which could be incorrect), we can take the paragliding rate of 4.9 fatalities per 100,00 jumps, and calculate 4.9 x 40.4/47.1 = 4.2 fatalities per 100,000 jumps for hang gliding.

**Base jumping**

The best information on base jumping comes from the Kjerag Massif, a 3,280-foot high cliff in Norway near the tiny village of Lysebotn (population: 6), which has become one of the most popular base jumping locations in the world.[23]

During an 11-year period, a total of 20,850 jumps resulted in 9 fatal accidents, which equates to a fatality rate of 43.2 per 100,000 jumps.[24]

# APPENDIX VI: RECOMMENDED MEDIA

For reference, here is a summary of all the resources recommended throughout the book, organized by chapter.

**1. Drugs**

Tobacco

- The UK National Health Service recently launched a series of "shockvertisements" with the tagline "Get Unhooked" (search for images online if you aren't put off by graphic photos)
- The Truth campaign,* funded in Florida by a settlement with the tobacco industry and positioned as a hip, rebellious, youth-led movement, cut rates of teen smoking dramatically[1] [2]
- The same group launched a subsequent campaign, dubbed "Truth FinishIt," at the MTV Video Music Awards, urging teens to use their social influence to become the generation that ends the tobacco epidemic[3]
- The FDA's nationwide campaign, The Real Cost,† has reached many US adolescents, and successfully fostered negative attitudes toward tobacco products[4] ‡ [5]

---

* www.thetruth.com.

† https://therealcost.betobaccofree.hhs.gov.

‡ There are also sub-campaigns currently being assessed which are aimed at specific demographics: "Fresh Empire" (https://freshempire.betobaccofree.hhs.gov) targets teens who identify with hip-hop culture,[1] [2] and "This Free Life" is designed to appeal to those who are lesbian, gay, bisexual, and transgender (LGBTQ+).[3] [4]Such campaigns are part of a wider set of strategies focused on helping teens building the skills to resist negative influences, including recognising advertising tactics and peer influences, improving communication and decision-making skills, and cultivating assertiveness, collectively called "social influence resistance."[5] [6]

### 3. Death & serious physical harm

Car crashes

- EverDrive (free) allows you to set up a safe driving competition between yourself and your teen,[6] and TrueMotion Family[7] is similar

Suicide

- If you're concerned, program a helpline number into your teen's phone; for example the National Suicide Prevention Lifeline (800-273-8255, or 988)[8]

Pedestrian fatalities

- "Look Up" is an app designed to lower distracted walking if you happen to be a resident of New York City[9]

Opioid overdose

- If you want to increase the chance of your teen saying "no" to the OxyContin offered up at a party, suggest the show, *16 and Recovering*, which gets rave reviews[10]

### 4. Victimization

Sexual assault

- 80% of users found the National Sexual Assault Telephone Hotline helpful,[*][11] and likewise over two thirds of users would recommend the online version, the National Sexual Assault Online Hotline, to others[†] [12]

Dating violence:

- The "Love Doesn't Have to Hurt Teens" from the American Psychological Association features a number of brief anecdotes[‡] [13]
- The "Love is Not Abuse" curriculum includes personal stories[§] [14]
- Various video testimonials from a "Choose Respect" campaign launched by the Centers for Disease Control are available[¶]
- The short film, *A Love that Kills,*[**] [15] relates the true story of an adolescent who was killed by her abusive boyfriend (not a showcase for world-class acting talent, but it makes the point)

---

* 800.656.HOPE (extension 4673)

† https://hotline.rainn.org/online .

‡ Available at www.apa.org/pi/families/resources/love-teens.

§ Available at www.uen.org/cte/facs_cabinet/downloads/AdultRoles/LINA_Curriculum%2010_07.pdf, see pages 29 and 41–42.

¶ Available at www.youtube.com/watch?v=9SOZ4Pji9OI.

** $2.99 at www.nfb.ca/film/love_that_kills/#:~:text=A%20Love%20That%20Kills%20is,daughter's%20life%20and%20tragic%20death.

**5. Mental health**

Eating disorders:

- In 2006, Dove produced a short video showing a model with girl-next-door good looks being transformed first by hair and makeup artists and subsequently by digital photo editing into a glamorous billboard version of herself which bears little resemblance to the original.[16] The video is available for free on the internet*

Take-aways:

- See chapter take-aways for a long list of celebrities who have been opening up about their own struggles with mental health

**7. Health**

Sleep

- If the nap is a tough sell, or if your teen is rebelling more generally against the sleep hygiene practices you're attempting to enforce, provide a (hard) copy of *Why We Sleep: The New Science of Sleep and Dreams*, which has been quoted throughout this book, and which makes a very thorough and convincing argument for why sleep is a critical pillar of health

Food

- If your child is the bookish type, suggest the book, *Salt, Sugar, Fat*
- The Bright Bodies weight management program, which combines nutritional education and high-intensity exercise, has been shown to help teens get into better shape,[17] and is partially available online†

**8. Achievement**

Stereotype threat

- Buy some biographies of inspirational figures who resemble your child. If you have a girl, you could suggest the movie, *Hidden Figures*, or the TV series, *Commander in Chief*, featuring Geena Davis, who earns the respect of everyone around her as a confident and assertive president of the United States.‡

---

* Available at: www.youtube.com/watch?v=iYhCnOjf46U.

† Available at: www.brightbodies.org/education-media.html.

‡ The show does feature a few scenes implying adolescent sexual behaviour, but contains nothing explicit.

- Psychologists at Harvard University, the University of Virginia, and the University of Washington have created a brief test which is designed to detect subconscious biases, and the results will surprise your adolescent. You yourself may think you have no biases, but if you take the test, you're likely to be surprised by the results too[*] [18]

**9. Discretionary time**

Cyberbullying and harassment:

- The movie, *Cyber Bully*,[†] (age 14+)[19] was made in 2011 so the technology is slightly out of date (e.g. the protagonist accesses primitive-looking social media sites from a laptop rather than a phone), and it features an implausible confession and even more implausible reconciliation between the bully and the victim. Nevertheless, it's a gripping portrayal of the effects of cyberbullying, and even features a bystander with high social status coming to the aid of the victim

Sexual stereotypes:

- *Miss Representation* and *The Mask You Live In* are two documentaries, which are essential viewing for parents of teenagers who want to understand the societal gender dynamics their kids are facing.[‡] However, these films are less appropriate for adolescents themselves since they're littered with examples of the problematic media they've been designed to counter

Pornography:

- Print out either the tip sheet, "What do young people need to know about porn?"[§] and/or one of the guides aimed at either 11- to 15-year-olds or adolescents age 15+ from the website, "The Porn Conversation,"[¶] and offer to answer any questions they might have
- Pay for 'feminist' or 'ethical' porn: there are plenty of options available;[**] for example, a website called "Make Love Not Porn" describes itself as

* Available at: https://implicit.harvard.edu/implicit/selectatest.html.

† Available at: www.youtube.com/watch?v=D_gIF012QFs.

‡ Available at: http://therepresentationproject.org/film/miss-representation-film/ ; https://therepproject.org/the-mask-you-live-in-watch-from-home/.

§ Available at: https://itstimewetalked.com/wp-content/uploads/parent-tips-sheets/What_do_young_people_need_to_know_about_porn.pdf.

¶ Available at: http://thepornconversation.org/.

** Available at: www.dailydot.com/nsfw/guides/porn-ethical-premium/.

curating documentaries, in contrast with most porn sites which offer the X-rated equivalents of unrealistic Hollywood blockbuster movies* [20]

Plagiarism and copyright infringement

- Have your teen read the FAQs about copyright, fair use, and public domain,† and suggest "Photos for Class"‡ and the Creative Commons search engine§ for school projects

Misinformation and ideological persuasion

- Share the TED talk about personalized news and filter bubbles,¶ [21] a discussion with historian Yuval Noa Harari and ethicist Tristan Harris about the reality that we are being hacked by machines that have come to know us better than we know ourselves,** [22] and the compelling and accessible documentary, *The Social Dilemma*[23]
- To prove the point that not all content is what it seems online, you could also introduce your adolescent to the story of the heroic swimming pig; through three brief, related videos, the viewer comes to realize that a video portraying an animal rescue is not what it seems.†† [24]
- Other intriguing material on this topic includes a segment from the BBC on the ability to doctor voices,‡‡ [25] and another demonstrating how such technology could be deployed to portray a person saying something they never said§§ [26]
- "Reality Check: The Game" provides a brief online tutorial that covers the basics in identifying untrustworthy sources.¶¶ [27]
- Other useful sources for fact-checking include www.Snopes.com, factcheck.org, The Washington Post fact checker, and Politifact.com, and for images, tineye.com, a search engine that can unearth similar pictures to help identify if an original image has been digitally altered

* Available at: https://makelovenotporn.tv/; charges $5 per video, or offers subscriptions of $10 per month for five videos per month, $30 per month for 30 videos per month, etc.

† Available at: www.eff.org/teachingcopyright/handouts#copyrightFAQ.

‡ Available at: www.photosforclass.com.

§ Available at: https://search.creativecommons.org/.

¶ Available at: www.ted.com/talks/eli_pariser_beware_online_filter_bubbles/transcript?language=en.

** Available at: www.wired.com/story/artificial-intelligence-yuval-noah-harari-tristan-harris/.

†† Available at: www.youtube.com/watch?v=g7WjrvG1GMk; www.youtube.com/watch?v=_2My_HOP-bw; www.youtube.com/watch?v=bvtJj6HoYHg.

‡‡ Available at: www.youtube.com/watch?v=1aTApGWVGoI.

§§ Available at: www.youtube.com/watch?v=o2DDU4g0PRo.

¶¶ Available at: https://mediasmarts.ca/digital-media-literacy/educational-games/reality-check-game.

**10. Character**

Bullying

- *A Girl Like Her* (age 12+)* is a gripping documentary-style but fictional portrayal of psychological bullying among girls, which also unflinchingly addresses suicide.[28] (It's worth pointing out to your teen that this movie misses the importance of the bystanders, who repeatedly fail to intervene until it's too late)

Sexual harassment

- Consider downloading the "Not Your Baby" app on your teen's phone, which allows users to input information about where they are and who is harassing them, and generates a suggested response to help them safely navigate the situation† [29]

Personality

- *The Nurture Assumption* makes the case for genes and peers determining character, rather than parents

* Available on Netflix.

† although no research has yet established if the app indeed helps improves outcomes for the victim

# APPENDIX VII: THREAT SCORE CALCULATIONS

What are the top threats facing teenagers today? It's an important question, but not one that's easy to answer, since it requires comparing apples not only with oranges but also with brussels sprouts and rutabagas.

**Comparing fruits and vegetables**

Let's take some examples of the hazards of adolescence. A depressed teen who has swallowed an entire container of painkillers will be in obvious short-term danger, but may live to tell the tale if her family gets her to the emergency room in time. Her brother may be simultaneously coping with his feelings of angst by stealthily siphoning off the alcohol from the dusty bottles in the back of his parents' cabinet, and could end up dying prematurely of liver cirrhosis many years down the line after a lifetime of alcoholism. Another teenager may terminate an unwanted pregnancy or put up her baby for adoption at age 16, and spend the rest of her life regretting her decision. How can we say which of these potential pitfalls is most "dangerous," and which warrants the most active intervention on the part of parents?

Any attempt at ranking dangers will by definition be subjective. On the other hand, we do have access to many good data points on how likely teenagers are to die, end up in the emergency room, or suffer long-term health effects from a variety of causes, so we should be able to calculate a 'threat score' that somehow captures these differing levels of risk. The most difficult conundrum is how to weigh the risk of threats that vary in seriousness, i.e. how to compare a small chance of something horrible happening in the short term with a larger chance of something less serious happening in the future.

The chart below lays out an arbitrary scale which has been used to overcome this problem and calculate a 'threat score' for the most serious dangers adolescents face.

| Impact | Magnitude |
|---|---|
| Death | 1 |
| Serious injury | 0.1 |
| Long-term consequences | 0.01 |

Using this scale, all potential risks can be converted into odds in 100,000, and then weighted by the magnitude of the risk. So ending up in the hospital with an overdose would be categorized as a 'serious injury,' as would dying prematurely of liver damage, while the unwanted pregnancy would fall under 'long-term consequences.'

To illustrate this approach further, let's take the risk posed by opioids as an example. For males, the annual death rate from opioids is 2.4 out of 100,000,[1] the annual hospitalization rate is 55 in 100,000,[2] and the prevalence of opioid use disorder (addiction) is two in 1,000, or 200 in 100,000, for males by age 18.[3] The threat score for opioids can then be calculated as Death [2.4] x 1 + Serious injury [55] x 0.1 + Long-term consequences [200] x .01 = 10. So for males, the threat posed by opioids would receive a score of 10.

Nevertheless, something is better than nothing, so below are two charts which compile 'threat scores' for the most serious risks facing teens. The methodology for how these scores have been calculated can be found in the box, and the details of the calculations below.

As we've seen throughout this book, some threats affect either boys or girls disproportionately; for example, boys are more likely to end up in the ER from assault, while only girls can fall pregnant. We therefore need a separate chart for each gender. We'll start with boys:

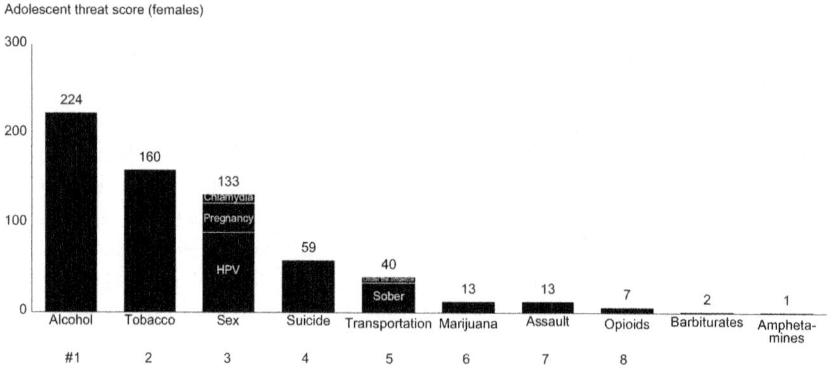


If you have a son, the top threats to your child by far are tobacco and alcohol. This shouldn't come as a surprise. The chart at the beginning of the section on drugs depicting "Disability Adjusted Life Years" showed that these twin grim reapers account for vast numbers of premature deaths around the world. Given that teen brains are uniquely vulnerable to being re-wired by addictive substances, and ultimately about 4 percent and 8 percent of the adult population is destined to die prematurely from tobacco and alcohol-related causes respectively, these two easily emerge as the most serious risks facing teens today.

For girls, the picture looks somewhat different, although alcohol and tobacco still occupy the top two places. Girls incur greater risks when having sex, and are also more likely to attempt suicide:

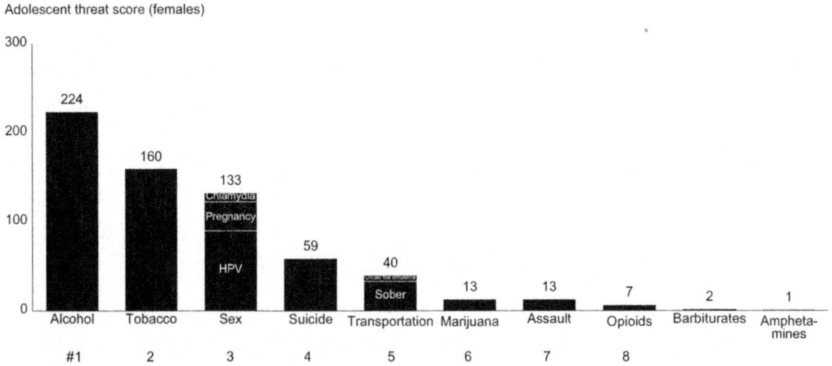


These charts are the source of the content and ordering of the top 10 list used to organise the threats section of this book.

The following sections detail the calculations used to arrive at the numbers in the chart above. These calculations were made based on the latest data points available at a single point in time. Undoubtedly the inputs will fluctuate slightly year to year; however the figures are unlikely to shift sufficiently to change the conclusions we would draw about which are the most important threats facing our teens.

## 1. Death & serious accidents

**Transportation and driving under the influence**

It's helpful to break out the dangers from transportation into general transportation risk and risk specific to driving under the influence.

For alcohol, the National Highway Traffic Safety Administration estimates that in fatal crashes in which the driver was 15 to 20 years old, 15%

of these drivers had a blood alcohol content (BAC) >0.8%.[4] Unfortunately, the figures for this age group are not available split by gender, but for fatal crashes across drivers of all ages, 21% of male drivers and 14% of female drivers had a blood alcohol content (BAC) >0.8%.[5] Applying that ratio to the 15-20 year old figure, we can estimate that for male drivers, 15% x 21%/ average (21%, 14%) = 18% of fatal crashes involved a BAC > 0.8%, and for female drivers, 15% x 14% / average (21%, 14%) = 12%.

Cannabis is also implicated in fatal crashes, although reporting on cannabis-related crash risk is less extensive. According to one study of crashes from 2000 to 2018 for drivers of all ages and genders, alcohol was consistently involved in ~40% of crash fatalities. The percentage of crashes involving cannabis was 21.5% in 2018, and the percentage of fatalities involving both cannabis and alcohol was 10.3%.[6]

Using these ratios implies that for teenage males, the percentage of fatal crashes due to:

- Alcohol alone is 18% x (40% - 10.3%)/40% = 13%
- Both is 18% x 10.3%/40% = 4.6%
- Cannabis alone is 18% x (21.5%-10.3%)/40% = 4.9%
- The total percentage of fatal crashes from driving under the influence of alcohol/cannabis is 13% + 4.6% + 4.9% = 23%

Similarly for teenage females, the percentage of fatal crashes due to:

- Alcohol alone is 12% x (40% - 10.3%)/40% = 9%
- Both is 12% x 10.3%/40% = 3.2%
- Cannabis alone is 12% x (21.5%-10.3%)/40% = 3.5%
- The total percentage of fatal crashes from driving under the influence of alcohol/cannabis is 9% + 3.2% + 3.5% = 16%

**Transportation (excluding driving under the influence)**

Males:

- Death: For males, the annual death rate from transportation accidents is 22.4 out of 100,000,[7] minus the 23% attributable to driving under the influence as calculated above
- Serious injury: For males the annual hospitalization rate from transportation accidents is 410 out of 100,000,[8] again minus the 23% attributable to driving under the influence as calculated above

- Long-term consequences: not applicable
- Threat score calculation: Death [22.4 x (1 – 23%)] x 1 + Serious Injury [410 x (1 – 23%)] x 0.1 + Long-term consequences [0] x 0.01 = 49

Females:

- Death: For females the annual death rate from transportation accidents is 12.7 out of 100,000,[9] minus the 16% attributable to driving under the influence as calculated above.
- Serious injury: For females the annual hospitalization rate from transportation accidents is 266 out of 100,000,[10] again minus the 16% attributable to driving under the influence as calculated above.
- Long-term consequences: not applicable
- Threat score calculation: Death [12.7 x (1 – 16%)] x 1 + Serious injury [266 x (1 – 16%)] x 0.1 + Long-term consequences [0] x 0.01 = 33

**Driving under the influence of alcohol or drugs**

Long-term consequences are defined as the risk of a conviction for driving under the influence (DUI). In a single year, 12,700 15- to 18-year-olds in the US were arrested for 'Driving under the influence'[11]; divided by the total estimated population of 15- to 18-year-olds at the time of 16,810,997,[12] that works out to a 75.5 chance in 100,000. Since DUI figures aren't available split by sex, the ratio of males to females for DUIs is assumed to be equivalent to that of deaths from driving under the influence.

Males:

- Threat score calculation: Death [22.4 x 23%] x 1 + Serious injury [410 x 23%] x 0.1 + Long-term consequences [75.5 x 23%/average(23%, 16%)] x .01 = 15

Females:

- Threat score calculation: Death [12.7 x 16%] x 1 + Serious injury [266 x 16%] x 0.1 + Long-term consequences [75.5 x 16%/average(23%, 16%)] x .01 = 6.8

**Suicide**

Males:

- Death: For males the annual death rate from suicide is 10.8 out of 100,000.[13]
- Serious injury: For males the annual hospitalization rate from suicide is 228 out of 100,000.[14]
- Long-term consequences: not applicable
- Threat score calculation: Death [10.8] x 1 + Serious injury [228] x 0.1 + Long-term consequences [0] x .01 = 34

Females:

- Death: For females the annual death rate from suicide is 3.2 out of 100,000.[15]
- Serious injury: For males the annual hospitalization rate from suicide is 555 out of 100,000.[16]
- Long-term consequences: not applicable
- Threat score calculation: Death [3.2] x 1 + Serious injury [555] x 0.1 + Long-term consequences [0] x .01 = 59

**Drowning**

Males:

- Death: For males the annual death rate from drowning is 2.5 out of 100,000.[17]
- Serious Injury: For males the annual hospitalization rate from drowning is 2 out of 100,000.[18]
- Long-term consequences: not applicable
- Threat score calculation: Death [2.5] x 1 + Serious injury [2] x 0.1 + Long-term consequences [0] x .01 = 2.7

Females:

- Death: For females the annual death rate from drowning is 0.3 out of 100,000.[19]
- Serious Injury: For females the annual hospitalization rate from drowning is negligible
- Long-term consequences: not applicable

- Threat score calculation: Death [0.3] x 1 + Serious injury [0] x 0.1 + Long-term consequences [0] x .01 = 0.3

**Firearms**

Males:

- Death: For males the annual death rate from firearms is 0.9 out of 100,000.[20]
- Serious Injury: For males the annual hospitalization rate from firearms is 18 out of 100,000.[21]
- Long-term consequences: not applicable
- Threat score calculation: Death [0.9] x 1 + Serious injury [18] x 0.1 + Long-term consequences [0] x .01 = 2.7

Females:

- Death: For females the annual death rate from firearms is 0.1 out of 100,000.[22]
- Serious Injury: For females the annual hospitalization rate from firearms is 3 out of 100,000.[23]
- Long-term consequences: not applicable
- Threat score calculation: Death [0.1] x 1 + Serious injury [3] x 0.1 + Long-term consequences [0] x .01 = 0.4

**Opioids**

Males:

- Death: For males the annual death rate from opioids is estimated to be 2.4 out of 100,000 (note: unknown drug deaths allocated proportionally to the known drugs, including opioids).[24]
- Serious Injury: For males the annual hospitalization rate from opioids is estimated to be 55 in 100,000.[25] This estimate is based on an annual hospitalization rate of 81 in 100,000 for all cases of poisoning (including drug overdoses), allocated based on the proportion of deaths from opioids versus other drugs.
- Long-term consequences: A study which has estimated the prevalence of opioid use disorder (addiction) by gender and age suggests that 2 in 1,000 males (or 200 in 100,000) suffer from this condition by age 18.[26]

- Threat score calculation: Death [2.4] x 1 + Serious injury [55] x 0.1 + Long-term consequences [200] x .01 = 10

Females:

- Death: For females the annual death rate from opioids is estimated to be 0.8 out of 100,000 (note: unknown drug deaths allocated proportionally to the known drugs, including opioids).[27]
- Serious Injury: For females the annual hospitalization rate from opioids is estimated to be 42 in 100,000.[28] This estimate is based on an annual hospitalization rate of 72 in 100,000 for all cases of poisoning (including drug overdoses), allocated based on the proportion of deaths from opioids versus other drugs.
- Long-term consequences: The same study referenced above for males suggests that 1.5 in 1,000 females (or 150 in 100,000) suffer from opioid use disorder by age 18.[29]
- Threat score calculation: Death [0.8] x 1 + Serious injury [42] x 0.1 + Long-term consequences [150] x .01 = 6.5

## 2. Assault

Males:

- Death: For males the annual death rate from assault is 12.4 out of 100,000.[30]
- Serious Injury: For males the annual hospitalization rate from assault is 210 out of 100,000.[31]
- Long-term consequences: For males, the annual rate of "severely distressing" victimization is estimated to be 3.1 in 1,000 (or 310 in 100,000), based on a compilation of eight years of data from the National Crime Victimization Survey.[32]
- Threat score calculation: Death [12.4] x 1 + Serious injury [210] x 0.1 + Long-term consequences [310] x .01 = 37

Females:

- Death: For females the annual death rate from assault is 2.2 out of 100,000.[33]

- Serious Injury: For females the annual hospitalization rate from assault is 60 out of 100,000.[34]
- Long-term consequences: For males, the annual rate of "severely distressing" victimization is estimated to be 4.6 in 1,000 (or 460 in 100,000), based on a compilation of 8 years of data from the National Crime Victimization Survey.[35]
- Threat score calculation: Death [2.2] x 1 + Serious injury [60] x 0.1 + Long-term consequences [460] x .01 = 13

## 3. Drugs

**Alcohol (excluding driving under the influence)**

Males:

- Death: For males the annual death rate from alcohol poisoning is estimated to be 0.3 out of 100,000 (note: unknown drug deaths allocated proportionally to the known drugs, including alcohol).[36]
- Serious Injury: For males the annual hospitalization rate from alcohol poisoning is estimated to be 7 in 100,000.[37] This estimate is based on an annual hospitalization rate of 81 in 100,000 for all cases of poisoning (including drug overdoses), allocated based on the proportion of deaths from alcohol vs. other drugs.
- Long-term consequences: Those who start drinking at an earlier age have a higher likelihood of becoming alcoholics later in life. A large survey assessing rates of alcohol dependence among a random sample of 43,000 adults breaks down the age at which they started drinking (if at all), and the prevalence of alcohol dependence by age cohort. The probability of alcohol dependence overall was 12.7%, but among the 22.1% of teens who began drinking under 18 it was 35.3%, vs. 6.3% among those who started drinking at age 18 or later.[38] This would suggest that the likelihood of drinking before age 18 and developing dependence as a result would be 22.1% x (35.3%-6.3%) = 6.4%. Since this data source didn't provide a split by gender, another source was then used to calculate the relative risk weighting for males versus females based on the lifetime prevalence of alcoholism by gender.[39] The resulting estimate is 7.0%, or 7,015

in 100,000 males become alcoholics because of starting drinking young.

- Serious injury part 2: Alcoholism can also cause individuals to die prematurely. A study has estimated that 3.6% of all deaths in the US result from excessive alcohol consumption.[40] As discussed above, 12.7% of the adult population suffers from alcohol dependence, so this implies that 3.6% / 12.7% or 28.3% of those with alcohol dependence will die prematurely. So given the odds are 7,015 in 100,000 of a male becoming an alcoholic, 28.3% would be odds of 1,988 in 100,000 of a male dying prematurely because of starting to drink young.
- Threat score calculation: Death [0.3] x 1 + Serious injury [7+1,988] x 0.1 + Long-term consequences [7,015] x .01 = 270

Females:

- Death: For females the annual death rate from alcohol poisoning is estimated to be 0.1 out of 100,000 (note: unknown drug deaths allocated proportionally to the known drugs, including alcohol).[41]
- Serious Injury: For females the annual hospitalization rate from alcohol poisoning is estimated to be 7 in 100,000.[42] This estimate is based on an annual hospitalization rate of 72 in 100,000 for all cases of poisoning (including drug overdoses), allocated based on the proportion of deaths from alcohol versus other drugs.
- Long-term consequences: As calculated for males above, the resulting estimate for females is 5.8%, or 5,813 in 100,000, females become alcoholics because of starting to drink before age 18.
- Serious injury part 2: As above, 28.3% of alcoholics die prematurely, so 5,813 x 28.3% = 1,647 in 100,000 odds of a female dying prematurely because of starting to drink young.
- Threat score calculation: Death [0.1] x 1 + Serious injury [7+1,647] x 0.1 + Long-term consequences [5,813] x .01 = 224

**Marijuana (excluding driving under the influence)**

Males:

- Death: Deaths among teenagers from marijuana overdoses are negligibly small (for males, approximately 3 in 234 million)

- Serious injury: Serious injuries are also assumed to be negligibly small given small death rates (data source for hospitalizations doesn't split out poisoning / drug overdose category into sub-categories). Unlike alcohol and tobacco, there is no compelling evidence that cannabis use results in premature death.[43]
- Long-term consequences: One study has concluded that cannabis use disorder affects approximately 3.5% of male adults.[44] Another study estimates that those who start using cannabis between ages 12–17 have a 20.6% chance of suffering from a cannabis use disorder 4 years later, vs. a 10.5% chance for those who first start between ages 18-25.[45] According to the most recent national Monitoring the Future survey, 44% of twelfth graders have tried marijuana, with little difference in usage rates by gender.[46] So the chance of an increase in risk of cannabis use disorder as a result of starting before age 18 versus from age 18 onwards is 44% x 3.5% x 20.6%/10.5% = 3,001 in 100,000.
- Threat score calculation: Death [0] x 1 + Serious injury [0] x 0.1 + Long-term consequences [3,001] x .01 = 30

Females:

- Death: As referenced above, deaths among teenagers from marijuana overdoses are negligibly small (for females, 0 in 221 million)
- Serious injury: As referenced above, serious injuries are also assumed to be negligibly small
- Long-term consequences: In the same study referenced above, the rate of cannabis use disorder among female adults is 1.5%,[47] so as with males, the chance of an increase in risk of cannabis use disorder as a result of starting before age 18 versus from age 18 onwards is 44% x 1.5% x 20.6%/10.5% = 1,286 in 100,000
- Threat score calculation: Death [0] x 1 + Serious injury [0] x 0.1 + Long-term consequences [1,286] x .01 = 13

**Tobacco**

According to the Monitoring the Future survey, the rate of frequent smoking among male twelfth graders is 7%, while among females it's 4%.[48]

Males:

- Death: Deaths among teenagers from tobacco use are negligibly small during the teen years themselves (for males approximately 2 in 234 million)
- Serious injury: According to the Monitoring the Future survey, 22.3% of twelfth graders in 2019 had tried smoking versus 23.8% in 2014.[49] According to a report by the Surgeon General in 2014, 86.9% of adults who had ever smoked daily had tried their first cigarette by age 18, and the proportion of those under 18 years old who were projected to become smokers and die prematurely as adults because of a smoking-related illness was estimated to be 7.5%.[50] Weighted for the slight decrease in smoking rates and the male higher likelihood of smoking, that would be 22.3% / 23.8% x 86.9% x 7.5% x 7%/average (7%, 4%) = 1.85%, or 1,850 in 100,000
- Long-term consequences: As above, 22.3% of twelfth graders have tried smoking, although this needs to be weighted for the male higher likelihood of smoking. And one study estimates that approximately one third of people who try smoking who go on to become dependent.[51] So that would be 22.3% x 7%/average(7%,4%) x 1/3 = 9.461%, or 9,461 in 100,000
- Threat score calculation: Death [0] x 1 + Serious injury [1,850] x 0.1 + Long-term consequences [9,461] x .01 = 280

Females:

- Death: Deaths among teenagers from tobacco use are negligibly small during the teen years themselves (for females approximately 1 in 222 million)
- Serious injury: As above, 22.3% of twelfth graders have tried smoking,[52] 86.9% of adults who had ever smoked daily had tried their first cigarette by age 18, and the proportion of those under 18 years old who are projected to become smokers and die prematurely as adults because of a smoking-related illness is estimated to be 7.5%.[53] Weighted for the female lower likelihood of smoking, that would be 22.3% x 86.9% x 7.5% x 4%/average (7%, 4%) = 1.057%, or 1,057 in 100,000

- Long-term consequences: 22.3% of twelfth graders have tried smoking, although this needs to be weighted for the female lower likelihood of smoking. As above, approximately one third of people who try smoking who go on to become dependent,[54] so that would be 22.3% x 4%/average(7%,4%) x 1/3 = 5.406%, or 5,406 in 100,000
- Threat score calculation: Death [0] x 1 + Serious injury [1,057] x 0.1 + Long-term consequences [5,406] x .01 = 160

**E-cigarettes**

E-cigarettes do not pose a significant risk of death or serious injury to teens during their teen years. (In the second half of 2019 there was an outbreak of lung injury associated with e-cigarette use, hypothesized to be caused by the presence of vitamin E acetate in certain vaping products; but at the peak there were only 68 deaths and 2,807 hospitalizations[55] in a US population of roughly 271 million in the 15 and older age group;[56] and there has been a "gradual but persistent decline" in such cases since then.)

It is unfortunately too premature to calculate the risk of serious injury from long-term use of e-cigarettes.

In 2019, 35.5% of twelfth graders in the Monitoring the Future survey reported vaping nicotine.[57] No split by gender has been available since 2016, when 16.7% of males vs. 8.3% of females reported using E-cigarettes.[58] Applying the same ratio to the 2019 figure would imply in 2019, an estimated 47.4% of males and 23.6% of females had tried vaping.

In the US, among teens who had tried e-cigarettes, 42.5% had vaped in the past 30 days, and of those, 53.1% reported they felt addicted to vaping.[59]

<u>Males</u>:

- Long-term consequences: 47.4% ever vaped x 42.5% vaped in past 30 days x 53.1% feel addicted to vaping = 10.7%, or 10,697 odds in 100,000
- Threat score calculation: Death [0] x 1 + Serious injury [0] x 0.1 + Long-term consequences [10,697] x .01 = 107

<u>Females</u>:

- Long-term consequences: 23.6% ever vaped x 42.5% vaped in past 30 days x 53.1% feel addicted to vaping = 5.3%, or 5,326 odds in 100,000

- Threat score calculation: Death [0] x 1 + Serious injury [0] x 0.1 + Long-term consequences [5,326] x .01 = 53

**Amphetamines**

Males:

- Death: Deaths among teenagers from amphetamine use are negligibly small (for males approximately 10 in 234 million)
- Serious injury: Serious injuries are also assumed to be negligibly small given small death rates (data source for hospitalizations doesn't split out poisoning / drug overdose category into sub-categories)
- Long-term consequences: According to the Monitoring the Future survey, 10.5% of males have used prescribed ADHD drugs (the most common type of amphetamine) by twelfth grade.[60] Approximately 1.8% of male users develop dependence,[61] so 10.5% x 1.8% = 189 in 100,000.
- Threat score calculation: Death [0] x 1 + Serious injury [0] x 0.1 + Long-term consequences [189] x .01 = 1.9

Females:

- Death: Deaths among teenagers from amphetamine use are negligibly small (for females approximately 4 in 222 million)
- Serious injury: As above, serious injuries are assumed to be negligibly small given small death rates (data source for hospitalizations does not split out poisoning / drug overdose category into sub-categories).
- Long-term consequences: According to the Monitoring the Future survey, 7.4% of females have used prescribed ADHD drugs (the most common type of amphetamine) by twelfth grade.[62] Approximately 1.6% of female users develop dependence,[63] so 7.4% x 1.6% = 118 in 100,000.
- Threat score calculation: Death [0] x 1 + Serious injury [0] x 0.1 + Long-term consequences [118] x .01 = 1.2

**Barbiturates**

Males:

- Death: For males the annual death rate from sedatives (barbiturates) is estimated to be 0.2 out of 100,000 (note: unknown drug deaths allocated proportionally to the known drugs, including sedatives).* [64]

* Note: This figure may be an overestimate of deaths / hospitalizations, as data source groups all deaths from "antiepileptic, sedative-hypnotic, antiparkinsonism and psychotropic drugs."

- Serious Injury: For males, the annual hospitalization rate from sedatives is estimated to be 5.2 in 100,000.[65] As described previously, this estimate is based on an annual hospitalization rate of 72 in 100,000 for all cases of poisoning (including drug overdoses), allocated based on the proportion of deaths from sedatives versus other drugs.
- Long-term consequences: According to the Monitoring the Future survey, 4.2% of twelfth graders have used sedatives (barbiturates), with rates of usage similar for both genders.[66] Among males ages 15–54 who have tried anxiolytic (anti-anxiety), sedative, and hypnotic drugs, 1% develop dependence.[*] [67] The risk of addiction can therefore be calculated as 4.2% x 1% = 42 in 100,000
- Threat score calculation: Death [0.2] x 1 + Serious injury [5.2] x 0.1 + Long-term consequences [42] x .01 = 1.2

<u>Females</u>:

- Death: For females, the annual death rate from sedatives (barbiturates) is similarly estimated to be 0.2 out of 100,000 (note: unknown drug deaths allocated proportionally to the known drugs, including sedatives). [†] [68]
- Serious Injury: For females the annual hospitalization rate from sedatives is estimated to be 9.1 in 100,000.[69] As described previously, this estimate is based on an annual hospitalization rate of 72 in 100,000 for all cases of poisoning (including drug overdoses), allocated based on the proportion of deaths from sedatives versus other drugs.
- Long-term consequences: As referenced above, 4.2% of twelfth graders have used sedatives (barbiturates), with rates of usage similar for both genders.[70] Among females ages 15–54 who have tried anxiolytic (anti-anxiety), sedative, and hypnotic drugs, 1.4% develop dependence.[‡] [71] The risk of addiction can therefore be calculated as 4.2% x 1.4% = 59 in 100,000

---

* This figure may be an underestimate given both that younger people can be more prone to addiction, and that barbiturates are likely to be more addictive than anti-anxiety and hypnotic drugs, but no better estimates are available

† Note: This figure may be an overestimate of deaths / hospitalizations, as data source groups all deaths from "antiepileptic, sedative-hypnotic, antiparkinsonism and psychotropic drugs".

‡ This figure may be an underestimate given both that younger people can be more prone to addiction, and that barbiturates are likely to be more addictive than anti-anxiety and hypnotic drugs, but no better estimates are available.

- Threat score calculation: Death [0.2] x 1 + Serious injury [9.1] x 0.1 + Long-term consequences [59] x .01 = 1.7s

## 4. Sexual activity

### HPV

HPV can cause cancer in a variety of sites around the body, as well as genital warts. Serious injury for HPV is therefore defined as dying prematurely as a result of contracting cancer, while long-term consequences for HPV are defined as contracting cancer or contracting genital warts.

The American Cancer Society provides estimates of the lifetime risk of developing or dying of various cancers,[72] but unfortunately only for a certain subset of cancer types, which don't include all of the cancer types associated with HPV. However the National Cancer Institute provides a detailed breakdown of the number of cases and the number of deaths from cancer by gender for all of the types of cancer associated with HPV,[*] [73] so combining these two data sources yields an estimate of the total lifetime risk for males of developing a cancer of a type associated with HPV of 2.85%, and of dying from such a cancer of 1.23%; while for women, the equivalent estimates are 2.96% and 1.06% respectively. Of course not all cancers in these particular locations are caused by HPV, so drawing on estimates of the proportion of such cancers caused by HPV from the CDC,[74] we can calculate a lifetime risk for males of developing cancer specifically caused by HPV as 2.25% and dying from it 1.02%, and for women 2.42% and 0.90%.[†]

We then need to calculate the likelihood the HPV was contracted in adolescence as opposed to later in life. For males, one study estimated that the odds of contracting HPV infection before age 21 are 30 out of 100,000 versus 132 out of 100,000 over a full lifetime, which implies 23% of cases of HPV infection are contracted before age 21.[75] For females, another study provides estimates of the prevalence of different strains of HPV among females ages 14–19 and 20–24;[76] taking the average of these to figures to

* For women this includes cancer of the cervix, vagina, vulva, anus, rectum and oropharynx, while for men this includes cancer of the penis, anus, rectum and oropharynx; the National Cancer Institute's figures combine deaths for colon and rectum cancers, so the number of deaths from rectal cancer alone was estimated based on the proportion of cases of rectum versus colon cancers.

† Detailed calculations broken down by cancer type available upon request.

approximate the rates of infection at the end of adolescence compared to the rate of infection later in life, weighted by the proportional contribution of the four specific strains of HPV that cause cancer,[77] yields an estimate of 68% for the probability that a cancer was caused by an infection a female contracted in adolescence as opposed to later.

Therefore for males, the lifetime risk of developing cancer caused by HPV contracted in adolescence is 2.25% x 23% = 0.51%, and for dying of cancer is 1.02% x 23% = 0.23%, and for females, the equivalent figures are 2.42% x 68% = 1.63%, and 0.9% x 68% = 0.61%.

HPV can also cause genital warts.[78] In the post-vaccine era, approximately 1.55% of females contract the strains of HPV that cause warts by the end of adolescence.[79] For males, the equivalent figure is approximately 2.9%.[80] Vaccinated males are virtually immune from infection.[81] For females, one study[82] found 10.8% of women overall were infected with the wart-causing strains of HPV, but the rates of infection were 2.1% for vaccinated versus 16.9% for unvaccinated individuals. Applying this ratio to the 1.55% of females currently infected suggests the rates of infection with wart-causing strains would be 2.1/10.8 x 1.55% = 0.3% of vaccinated females, and 16.9/10.8 x 1.55% = 2.4% of unvaccinated females infected. At the moment, 51.8% of adolescent males and 56.8% of adolescent females are vaccinated,[83] so we can estimate the current risk of contracting genital warts in adolescence to be 2.9% x (1 – 51.8%) = 1.4% for males, and 0.3% x 56.8% + 2.4% x (1 – 56.8%) = 1.2%.

<u>Males</u>:

- Serious Injury: Likelihood of dying of cancer from HPV later in life: 0.23%, or 233 in 100,000
- Long-term consequences: Likelihood of contracting cancer from HPV later in life (0.51% or 511 in 100,000) + Likelihood of contracting warts (1.4% or 1,398 in 100,000) = 1,909 in 100,000
- Threat score calculation: Death [0] x 1 + Serious injury [233] x 0.1 + Long-term consequences [1,909] x .01 = 42

<u>Females</u>:

- Serious Injury: Likelihood of dying of cancer from HPV later in life: 0.61%, or 611 in 100,000

- Long-term consequences: Likelihood of contracting cancer from HPV later in life (1.63% or 1,635 in 100,000) + Likelihood of contracting warts (1.2% or 1,219 in 100,000) = 2,854 in 100,000
- Threat score calculation: Death [0] x 1 + Serious injury [611] x 0.1 + Long-term consequences [2,584] x .01 = 90

**Chlamydia**

Males can be infected and spread chlamydia to their female partners, but suffer no ill effects themselves, so there is no threat score for males.

For females, the risk of contracting chlamydia is suffering the long-term consequence of infertility. As covered in the chapter on STDs, our best estimate is that after a known infection, the risk of infertility is between 1 and 5%.[84] 77% of all cases of chlamydia infection are asymptomatic, [85] and one study has estimated a 0.02% chance of infertility after an asymptomatic infection.[86] Therefore the risk of long-term consequences would be 33% x average (1%,5%) + 77% x 0.02% = 1.0%, or 1,005 in 100,000.

Females:

- Threat score calculation: Death [0] x 1 + Serious injury [0] x 0.1 + Long-term consequences [1,005] x .01 = 10.1

**Pregnancy**

The pregnancy rate among teen females is currently 33 in 1,000, or 3,300 in 100,000.[87]

Females:

- Threat score calculation: Death [0] x 1 + Serious injury [0] x 0.1 + Long-term consequences [3,300] x .01 = 33

# INDEX

## N



## O



## P



## R



## S

**T**



**U**



**V**

**W**

# ENDNOTES

## Prologue


1 Gates, B. (2021). *How to avoid a climate disaster: the solutions we have and the breakthroughs we need.* Knopf.


## 1. Drugs


1 Alcohol can make a monkey out of us. (2011). *The Guardian.* www.theguardian.com/science/punctuated-equilibrium/2011/apr/26/1;
Young, R. J. (2015). *Drunken monkeys? Only humans really don't know when they've had enough.* The Conversation. https://theconversation.com/drunken-monkeys-only-humans-really-dont-know-when-theyve-had-enough-43093

2 Ervin, F. R., Palmour, R. M., Young, S. N., Guzman-Flores, C., & Juarez, J. (1990). Voluntary consumption of beverage alcohol by vervet monkeys: population screening, descriptive behavior and biochemical measures. *Pharmacology Biochemistry and Behavior, 36*(2), 367-373. www.researchgate.net/profile/Simon_Young3/publication/20800298_Voluntary_consumption_of_beverage_alcohol_by_Vervet_monkeys_Population_screening_descriptive_behavior_and_biochemical_measures/links/5a92dc60aca272140565c00b/Voluntary-consumption-of-beverage-alcohol-by-Vervet-monkeys-Population-screening-descriptive-behavior-and-biochemical-measures.pdf;
Vivian, J. A., Higley, J. D., Linnoila, M., & Woods, J. H. (1999). Oral ethanol self-administration in rhesus monkeys: Behavioral and neurochemical correlates. *Alcoholism: Clinical and Experimental Research, 23*(8), 1352-1361. https://deepblue.lib.umich.edu/bitstream/handle/2027.42/66306/j.1530-0277.1999.tb04357.x.pdf;sequence=1

3 Grant, K. A., Stafford, J., Thiede, A., Kiley, C., Odagiri, M., & Ferguson, B. (2008). Who Is at Risk?: Population Characterization of Alcohol Self-Administration in Nonhuman Primates Helps Identify Pathways to Dependence. *Alcohol Research & Health, 31*(4), 289. https://pubs.niaaa.nih.gov/publications/arh314/289-297.htm

4 Kraemer, G. W., & McKinney, W. T. (1985). Social separation increases alcohol consumption in rhesus monkeys. *Psychopharmacology, 86*(1-2), 182-189. https://link.springer.com/article/10.1007/BF00431706#page-1

5 Juarez, J., Guzman-Flores, C., Ervin, F. R., & Palmour, R. M. (1993). Voluntary alcohol consumption in vervet monkeys: individual, sex, and age differences. *Pharmacology Biochemistry and Behavior, 46*(4), 985-988. www.sciencedirect.com/science/article/pii/009130579390232I

6 Curry, A. (2017). Our 9,000-Year Love Affair With Booze. *National Geographic.* www.nationalgeographic.com/magazine/2017/02/alcohol-discovery-addiction-booze-human-culture/

7 World Health Organization. (2019). *Global status report on alcohol and health 2018.* World Health Organization. https://apps.who.int/iris/rest/bitstreams/1151838/retrieve

8 Stahre, M., Roeber, J., Kanny, D., Brewer, R. D., & Zhang, X. (2014). Peer reviewed: contribution of excessive alcohol consumption to deaths and years of potential life lost in the United States. *Preventing chronic disease, 11.* www.ncbi.nlm.nih.gov/pmc/articles/PMC4075492/

9 Heath, A. C., Bucholz, K. K., Madden, P. A. F., Dinwiddie, S. H., Slutske, W. S., Bierut, L. J., ... & Martin, N. G. (1997). Genetic and environmental contributions to alcohol dependence risk in a national twin sample: consistency of findings in women and men. *Psychological medicine, 27*(6), 1381-1396. https://genepi.qimr.edu.au/contents/p/staff/CV191Heath_UQ_Copy.pdf;
Schuckit, M. A. (2009). An overview of genetic influences in alcoholism. *Journal of substance abuse treatment.* http://psycnet.apa.org/record/2008-17411-014;

Footnote reference: [1] Edition, F. (2013). *Diagnostic and statistical manual of mental disorders.* Am Psychiatric Assoc, 21, 591-643. http://repository.poltekkes-kaltim.ac.id/657/1/Diagnostic%20and%20statistical%20manual%20of%20mental%20disorders%20_%20DSM-5%20(%20PDFDrive.com%20).pdf

10 *A person's high or low response to alcohol says much about their risk for alcoholism.* (2009). Science Daily. www.sciencedaily.com/releases/2009/05/090522172457.htm

11 Schuckit, M. A. (2009). An overview of genetic influences in alcoholism. *Journal of substance abuse treatment.* http://psycnet.apa.org/record/2008-17411-014

12 King, A. C., Cao, D., deWit, H., O'Connor, S. J., & Hasin, D. S. (2019). The role of alcohol response phenotypes in the risk for alcohol use disorder. *BJPsych open, 5*(3). www.cambridge.org/core/journals/bjpsych-open/article/role-of-alcohol-response-phenotypes-in-the-risk-for-alcohol-use-disorder/98BC9AB3AA3CDF5869B6D17FB2DAF600

13 Schuckit, M. A. (1994). Low level of response to alcohol as a predictor of future alcoholism. *The American journal of psychiatry.* www.semanticscholar.org/paper/Low-level-of-response-to-alcohol-as-a-predictor-of-Schuckit/4b6b6170ed53efcb891d5141363d558012025af2;
Schuckit, M. A., Smith, T. L., Trim, R. S., Allen, R. C., Fukukura, T., Knight, E. E., ... & Kreikebaum, S. A. (2011). A prospective evaluation of how a low level of response to alcohol predicts later heavy drinking and alcohol problems. *The American journal of drug and alcohol abuse, 37*(6), 479-486. www.tandfonline.com/doi/abs/10.3109/00952990.2011.598590

14 Schuckit, M. A., Smith, T. L., Heron, J., Hickman, M., Macleod, J., Lewis, G., ... & Davey-Smith, G. (2011). Testing a level of response to alcohol-based model of heavy drinking and alcohol problems in 1,905 17-year-olds. *Alcoholism: clinical and experimental research, 35*(10), 1897-1904. www.ncbi.nlm.nih.gov/pmc/articles/PMC3183150/;
*A Person's High Or Low Response To Alcohol Says Much About Their Risk For Alcoholism.* (2009). Science Daily. www.sciencedaily.com/releases/2009/05/090522172457.htm

15 Footnote reference: [1] Bernard, M., Halfon, O., & Daeppen, J. B. (2007). Identification of adolescents with a low level of response to alcohol using the" self rating of the effects of alcohol" questionnaire. *Schweizer Archiv für Neurologie und Psychiatrie Archives suisses de neurologie et de psychiatrie, 158*(1), 19-24. https://serval.unil.ch/resource/serval:BIB_50A8A5D803AE.P001/REF.pdf

16 Schuckit, M. A., Smith, T. L., Clausen, P., Fromme, K., Skidmore, J., Shafir, A., & Kalmijn, J. (2016). The low level of response to alcohol-based heavy drinking prevention program: one-year follow-up. *Journal of studies on alcohol and drugs, 77*(1), 25-37. www.ncbi.nlm.nih.gov/pmc/articles/PMC4711317/

17 Zucker, R. A., Donovan, J. E., Masten, A. S., Mattson, M. E., & Moss, H. B. (2008). Early developmental processes and the continuity of risk for underage drinking and problem drinking. *Pediatrics, 121(Supplement 4)*, S252-S272. www.ncbi.nlm.nih.gov/pmc/articles/PMC2581879/;
Silveri, M. M. (2012). Adolescent brain development and underage drinking in the United States: identifying risks of alcohol use in college populations. *Harvard review of psychiatry, 20*(4), 189-200. www.ncbi.nlm.nih.gov/pmc/articles/PMC4669962/;
Zeigler, D. W., Wang, C. C., Yoast, R. A., Dickinson, B. D., McCaffree, M. A., Robinowitz, C. B., & Sterling, M. L. (2005). The neurocognitive effects of alcohol on adolescents and college students. Preventive medicine, 40(1), 23-32. www.sciencedirect.com/science/article/pii/S0091743504002658;
Gruber, E., DiClemente, R. J., Anderson, M. M., & Lodico, M. (1996). Early drinking onset and its association with alcohol use and problem behavior in late adolescence. *Preventive medicine, 25*(3), 293-300. https://d1wqtxts1xzle7.cloudfront.net/49762286/pmed.1996.005920161021-7700-1mpsp5d.pdf?1477048772=&response-content-disposition=inline%3B+filename%3DEarly_Drinking_Onset_and_Its_Association.pdf&Expires=1619032524&Signature=EATZumiR2n0TNVECnCqeSJ4Viw3G8XU9JY5tgmZ~NvCkcT9M3uWj7Q-4pI4Y6FCuVtXERFUSwsRcink3kPk0KQ97tF-Og2ZTCjAxv65mHZ97QehPhVjTiOBq1WT7lfBznochn-31LSDTN2~ACx~Khv3i6Go0IhRCPaSMCaYq5eslO5Vf9GH2lTxdQWdhucOgf~~7DHK1vDafarl~vlvh38W3tU1ESWg1uQhq-OzNYpxs8x9y1BnSoswLfbuEN-gO0-zfhrvZDscjr5zY7wsCg~yrzREL1ZKAYsgvARpIRGGMmsoZrGSyyAf0BxD6akS1lLybWWyiE9WT6BhXtAcfcg__&Key-Pair-Id=APKAJLOHF5GGSLRBV4ZA;
Hawkins, J. D., Graham, J. W., Maguin, E., Abbott, R., Hill, K. G., & Catalano, R. F. (1997). Exploring the effects of age of alcohol use initiation and psychosocial risk factors on subsequent alcohol misuse. *Journal of studies on alcohol, 58*(3), 280-290. www.ncbi.nlm.nih.gov/pmc/articles/PMC1894758/;
Hingson, R. W., Heeren, T., & Winter, M. R. (2006). Age at drinking onset and alcohol dependence: age at onset, duration, and severity. *Archives of pediatrics & adolescent medicine, 160*(7), 739-746. https://jamanetwork.com/journals/jamapediatrics/articlepdf/205204/poa60009_739_746.pdf;
Guttmannova, K., Bailey, J. A., Hill, K. G., Lee, J. O., Hawkins, J. D., Woods, M. L., & Catalano, R. F. (2011). Sensitive periods for adolescent alcohol use initiation: Predicting the lifetime occurrence and chronicity of alcohol problems in adulthood. *Journal of studies on alcohol and drugs, 72*(2), 221-231. www.ncbi.nlm.nih.gov/pmc/articles/PMC3052892/;

Pitkänen, T., Lyyra, A. L., & Pulkkinen, L. (2005). Age of onset of drinking and the use of alcohol in adulthood: a follow-up study from age 8–42 for females and males. *Addiction, 100*(5), 652-661. https://ssl.rima.org/web/medline_pdf/Addiction_652-61.pdf

18 Grant, B. F., & Dawson, D. A. (1997). Age at onset of alcohol use and its association with DSM-IV alcohol abuse and dependence: results from the National Longitudinal Alcohol Epidemiologic Survey. *Journal of substance abuse, 9,* 103-110. https://citeseerx.ist.psu.edu/viewdoc/download?doi=10.1.1.473.9819&rep=rep1&type=pdf

19 Hingson, R., & White, A. (2014). New research findings since the 2007 Surgeon General's Call to Action to Prevent and Reduce Underage Drinking: A review. *Journal of studies on alcohol and drugs, 75*(1), 158-169. www.ncbi.nlm.nih.gov/pmc/articles/PMC3893630/

20 Grant, J. D., Scherrer, J. F., Lynskey, M. T., Lyons, M. J., Eisen, S. A., Tsuang, M. T., ... & Bucholz, K. K. (2006). Adolescent alcohol use is a risk factor for adult alcohol and drug dependence: evidence from a twin design. *Psychological medicine, 36*(1), 109-118. https://digitalcommons.wustl.edu/cgi/viewcontent.cgi?article=4873&context=open_access_pubs

21 Agrawal, A., Sartor, C. E., Lynskey, M. T., Grant, J. D., Pergadia, M. L., Grucza, R., ... & Heath, A. C. (2009). Evidence for an interaction between age at first drink and genetic influences on DSM-IV alcohol dependence symptoms. *Alcoholism: Clinical and Experimental Research, 33*(12), 2047-2056. www.ncbi.nlm.nih.gov/pmc/articles/PMC2883563/

22 Zeigler, D. W., Wang, C. C., Yoast, R. A., Dickinson, B. D., McCaffree, M. A., Robinowitz, C. B., & Sterling, M. L. (2005). The neurocognitive effects of alcohol on adolescents and college students. *Preventive medicine, 40*(1), 23-32. www.academia.edu/15191797/The_neurocognitive_effects_of_alcohol_on_adolescents_and_college_students

23 Silveri, M. M. (2012). Adolescent brain development and underage drinking in the United States: identifying risks of alcohol use in college populations. *Harvard review of psychiatry, 20*(4), 189-200. www.ncbi.nlm.nih.gov/pmc/articles/PMC4669962/

24 Silveri, M. M. (2012). Adolescent brain development and underage drinking in the United States: identifying risks of alcohol use in college populations. *Harvard review of psychiatry, 20*(4), 189-200. www.ncbi.nlm.nih.gov/pmc/articles/PMC4669962/; McNeely, C., & Blanchard, J. (2010). *The teen years explained: A guide to healthy adolescent development.* Jayne Blanchard. www.jhsph.edu/research/centers-and-institutes/center-for-adolescent-health/_includes/_pre-redesign/Interactive%20Guide.pdf

25 Pascual, M., Boix, J., Felipo, V., & Guerri, C. (2009). Repeated alcohol administration during adolescence causes changes in the mesolimbic dopaminergic and glutamatergic systems and promotes alcohol intake in the adult rat. *Journal of neurochemistry, 108*(4), 920-931. http://onlinelibrary.wiley.com/doi/10.1111/j.1471-4159.2008.05835.x/full

26 Nasrallah, N. A., Yang, T. W., & Bernstein, I. L. (2009). Long-term risk preference and suboptimal decision making following adolescent alcohol use. *Proceedings of the National Academy of Sciences, 106*(41), 17600-17604. www.pnas.org/content/pnas/106/41/17600.full.pdf

27 Zeigler, D. W., Wang, C. C., Yoast, R. A., Dickinson, B. D., McCaffree, M. A., Robinowitz, C. B., & Sterling, M. L. (2005). The neurocognitive effects of alcohol on adolescents and college students. *Preventive medicine, 40*(1), 23-32. www.academia.edu/15191797/The_neurocognitive_effects_of_alcohol_on_adolescents_and_college_students

28 Silveri, M. M. (2012). Adolescent brain development and underage drinking in the United States: identifying risks of alcohol use in college populations. *Harvard review of psychiatry, 20*(4), 189-200. www.ncbi.nlm.nih.gov/pmc/articles/PMC4669962/;
Acheson, S. K., Stein, R. M., & Swartzwelder, H. S. (1998). Impairment of semantic and figural memory by acute ethanol: age-dependent effects. *Alcoholism: Clinical and Experimental Research, 22*(7), 1437-1442. https://onlinelibrary.wiley.com/doi/abs/10.1111/j.1530-0277.1998.tb03932.x

29 Rehm, J., Shield, K. D., Joharchi, N., & Shuper, P. A. (2012). Alcohol consumption and the intention to engage in unprotected sex: Systematic review and meta-analysis of experimental studies. *Addiction, 107*(1), 51-59. https://onlinelibrary.wiley.com/doi/abs/10.1111/j.1360-0443.2011.03621.x;
Fromme, K., Katz, E., & D'amico, E. (1997). Effects of alcohol intoxication on the perceived consequences of risk taking. *Experimental and Clinical Psychopharmacology, 5*(1), 14. https://psycnet.apa.org/record/1997-02874-002;
Scott-Sheldon, L. A., Carey, K. B., Cunningham, K., Johnson, B. T., Carey, M. P., & MASH Research Team. (2016). Alcohol use predicts sexual decision-making: a systematic review and meta-analysis of the experimental literature. *AIDS and Behavior, 20*(1), 19-39. www.ncbi.nlm.nih.gov/pmc/articles/PMC4683116/;

Stoner, S. A., George, W. H., Peters, L. M., & Norris, J. (2007). Liquid courage: Alcohol fosters risky sexual decision-making in individuals with sexual fears. *AIDS and Behavior, 11*(2), 227-237. www.researchgate.net/profile/William_George3/publication/6982850_Liquid_Courage_Alcohol_Fosters_Risky_Sexual_Decision-Making_in_Individuals_with_Sexual_Fears/links/0fcfd508183783011a000000/Liquid-Courage-Alcohol-Fosters-Risky-Sexual-Decision-Making-in-Individuals-with-Sexual-Fears.pdf;
Weafer, J., & Fillmore, M. T. (2016). Low-dose alcohol effects on measures of inhibitory control, delay discounting, and risk-taking. *Current Addiction Reports, 3*(1), 75-84. www.infona.pl/resource/bwmeta1.element.springer-doi-10_1007-S40429-016-0086-Y

30 Hingson, R., & White, A. (2014). New research findings since the 2007 Surgeon General's Call to Action to Prevent and Reduce Underage Drinking: A review. *Journal of studies on alcohol and drugs, 75*(1), 158-169. www.ncbi.nlm.nih.gov/pmc/articles/PMC3893630/

31 World Health Organisation. (2004). *Interactive charts: Alcohol prevalence.* http://gamapserver.who.int/gho/interactive_charts/substance_abuse/bod_alcohol_prevalence/atlas.html

32 Rolando, S., Beccaria, F., Tigerstedt, C., & Törrönen, J. (2012). First drink: What does it mean? The alcohol socialization process in different drinking cultures. *Drugs: education, prevention and policy, 19*(3), 201-212. https://s3.amazonaws.com/academia.edu.documents/37191554/First_drink_what_does_it_mean.pdf?response-content-disposition=inline%3B%20filename%3DFirst_drink_What_does_it_mean_The_alcoho.pdf&X-Amz-Algorithm=AWS4-HMAC-SHA256&X-Amz-Credential=AKIAIWOWYYGZ2Y53UL3A%2F20191112%2Fus-east-1%2Fs3%2Faws4_request&X-Amz-Date=20191112T093847Z&X-Amz-Expires=3600&X-Amz-SignedHeaders=host&X-Amz-Signature=f36f8dcbc745a00966c03527f329ba1aab3cc19aee6f1fff16133299346c6b7e

33 Rolando, S., Beccaria, F., Tigerstedt, C., & Törrönen, J. (2012). First drink: What does it mean? The alcohol socialization process in different drinking cultures. *Drugs: education, prevention and policy, 19*(3), 201-212. https://s3.amazonaws.com/academia.edu.documents/37191554/First_drink_what_does_it_mean.pdf?response-content-disposition=inline%3B%20filename%3DFirst_drink_What_does_it_mean_The_alcoho.pdf&X-Amz-Algorithm=AWS4-HMAC-SHA256&X-Amz-Credential=AKIAIWOWYYGZ2Y53UL3A%2F20191112%2Fus-east-1%2Fs3%2Faws4_request&X-Amz-Date=20191112T093847Z&X-Amz-Expires=3600&X-Amz-SignedHeaders=host&X-Amz-Signature=f36f8dcbc745a00966c03527f329ba1aab3cc19aee6f1fff16133299346c6b7e

34 Rolando, S., Beccaria, F., Tigerstedt, C., & Törrönen, J. (2012). First drink: What does it mean? The alcohol socialization process in different drinking cultures. *Drugs: education, prevention and policy, 19*(3), 201-212. https://s3.amazonaws.com/academia.edu.documents/37191554/First_drink_what_does_it_mean.pdf?response-content-disposition=inline%3B%20filename%3DFirst_drink_What_does_it_mean_The_alcoho.pdf&X-Amz-Algorithm=AWS4-HMAC-SHA256&X-Amz-Credential=AKIAIWOWYYGZ2Y53UL3A%2F20191112%2Fus-east-1%2Fs3%2Faws4_request&X-Amz-Date=20191112T093847Z&X-Amz-Expires=3600&X-Amz-SignedHeaders=host&X-Amz-Signature=f36f8dcbc745a00966c03527f329ba1aab3cc19aee6f1fff16133299346c6b7e

35 Rolando, S., Beccaria, F., Tigerstedt, C., & Törrönen, J. (2012). First drink: What does it mean? The alcohol socialization process in different drinking cultures. *Drugs: education, prevention and policy, 19*(3), 201-212. https://s3.amazonaws.com/academia.edu.documents/37191554/First_drink_what_does_it_mean.pdf?response-content-disposition=inline%3B%20filename%3DFirst_drink_What_does_it_mean_The_alcoho.pdf&X-Amz-Algorithm=AWS4-HMAC-SHA256&X-Amz-Credential=AKIAIWOWYYGZ2Y53UL3A%2F20191112%2Fus-east-1%2Fs3%2Faws4_request&X-Amz-Date=20191112T093847Z&X-Amz-Expires=3600&X-Amz-SignedHeaders=host&X-Amz-Signature=f36f8dcbc745a00966c03527f329ba1aab3cc19aee6f1fff16133299346c6b7e

36 Jackson, C., Ennett, S. T., Dickinson, D. M., & Bowling, J. M. (2012). Letting children sip: Understanding why parents allow alcohol use by elementary school–aged children. *Archives of pediatrics & adolescent medicine, 166*(11), 1053-1057. https://jamanetwork.com/journals/jamapediatrics/fullarticle/1360891?post=-6579638_1799

37 Donovan, J. E., & Molina, B. S. (2011). Childhood risk factors for early-onset drinking. *Journal of studies on alcohol and drugs, 72*(5), 741-751. www.ncbi.nlm.nih.gov/pmc/articles/PMC3174021/;
Hingson, R., & White, A. (2014). New research findings since the 2007 Surgeon General's Call to Action to Prevent and Reduce Underage Drinking: A review. *Journal of studies on alcohol and drugs, 75*(1), 158-169. www.ncbi.nlm.nih.gov/pmc/articles/PMC3893630/;
Fergusson, D. M., Lynskey, M. T., & Horwood, L. J. (1994). Childhood exposure to alcohol and adolescent drinking patterns. *Addiction, 89*(8), 1007-1016. https://onlinelibrary.wiley.com/doi/abs/10.1111/j.1360-0443.1994.tb03360.x

38 Jackson, K. M., Barnett, N. P., Colby, S. M., & Rogers, M. L. (2015). The prospective association between sipping alcohol by the sixth grade and later substance use. *Journal of studies on alcohol and drugs, 76*(2), 212-221. www.ncbi.nlm.nih.gov/pmc/articles/PMC5374474/

39 McMorris, B. J., Catalano, R. F., Kim, M. J., Toumbourou, J. W., & Hemphill, S. A. (2011). Influence of family factors and supervised alcohol use on adolescent alcohol use and harms: similarities between youth in different alcohol policy contexts. *Journal of studies on alcohol and drugs, 72*(3), 418-428. www.ncbi.nlm.nih.gov/pmc/articles/PMC3084357/

40 Ennett, S. T., Jackson, C., Choi, S., Hayes, K. A., Dickinson, D. M., & Bowling, J. M. (2016). A Parenting Program to Promote an Alcohol-Free Childhood: Influence on Parents' Readiness to Prevent Child Sipping. *Journal of studies on alcohol and drugs, 77*(2), 327-336. www.ncbi.nlm.nih.gov/pmc/articles/PMC4803665/

41 LaBrie, J. W., Hummer, J. F., Lac, A., Ehret, P. J., & Kenney, S. R. (2011). Parents know best, but are they accurate? Parental normative misperceptions and their relationship to students' alcohol-related outcomes. *Journal of Studies on Alcohol and Drugs, 72*(4), 521-529. www.ncbi.nlm.nih.gov/pmc/articles/PMC3125876/;
Napper, L. E., Hummer. J. F., Lac, A., & LaBrie, J. W. (2014). What are other parents saying? Perceived parental communication norms and the relationship between alcohol-specific parental communication and college student drinking. *Psychology of Addictive Behaviors, 28*(1), 31. www.ncbi.nlm.nih.gov/pmc/articles/PMC3986266/

42 '80 to '16: National Center for Health Statistics. (2017). *Health, United States: Table 051*. Centers for Disease Control and Prevention. www.cdc.gov/nchs/hus/contents2017.htm#051;
'17 onwards: Johnston, L. D., Miech, R. A., O'Malley, P. M., Bachman, J. G., Schulenberg, J. E., & Patrick, M. E. (2019). *Monitoring the Future National Survey Results on Drug Use, 1975-2018: Overview, Key Findings on Adolescent Drug Use*. Institute for Social Research. https://files.eric.ed.gov/fulltext/ED594190.pdf

43 McCance-Katz, E. F. (2019). *The national survey on drug use and health: 2019*. Substance Abuse and Mental Health Services Administration. Table 5.4B. www.samhsa.gov/data/sites/default/files/reports/rpt29394/NSDUH-DetailedTabs2019/NSDUHDetTabsSect5pe2019.htm#tab5-4a

44 McDuffie, T. E., & Bernt, F. M. (1993). Contrasts between the perceptions of parents and their adolescent children regarding drug and alcohol use and prevention. *Journal of Alcohol and Drug Education*. https://psycnet.apa.org/record/1994-13042-001;
Bogenschneider, K., Wu, M. Y., Raffaelli, M., & Tsay, J. C. (1998). Other teens drink, but not my kid": Does parental awareness of adolescent alcohol use protect adolescents from risky consequences?. Journal of Marriage and the Family, 356-373. https://digitalcommons.unl.edu/cgi/viewcontent.cgi?article=1115&context=psychfacpub;
Bylund, C. L., Imes, R. S., & Baxter, L. A. (2005). Accuracy of parents' perceptions of their college student children's health and health risk behaviors. *Journal of American College Health, 54*(1), 31-37. www.naspa.org/images/uploads/main/BylundC-Et_al_2005_Accuracy_of_Parents_Perceptions_of_College_Students_Health_and_Health_Risk_Behavior.pdf

45 Guilamo-Ramos, V., Jaccard, J., Turrisi, R., Johansson, M., & Bouris, A. (2006). Maternal perceptions of alcohol use by adolescents who drink alcohol. *Journal of studies on alcohol, 67*(5), 730-737. www.ncbi.nlm.nih.gov/pmc/articles/PMC2928568/

46 Resnick, M. D., Bearman, P. S., Blum, R. W., Bauman, K. E., Harris, K. M., Jones, J., ... & Ireland, M. (1997). Protecting adolescents from harm: findings from the National Longitudinal Study on Adolescent Health. *Jama, 278*(10), 823-832. https://academiccommons.columbia.edu/doi/10.7916/d8-78f6-mt67/download;
Ryan, S. M., Jorm, A. F., & Lubman, D. I. (2010). Parenting factors associated with reduced adolescent alcohol use: a systematic review of longitudinal studies. *Australian & New Zealand Journal of Psychiatry, 44*(9), 774-783. https://pdfs.semanticscholar.org/0dfa/840cae27332f2e7a6ff96b178262b0905104.pdf

47 Wagenaar, A. C., Toomey, T. L., Murray, D. M., Short, B. J., Wolfson, M., & Jones-Webb, R. (1996). Sources of alcohol for underage drinkers. *Journal of studies on alcohol, 57*(3), 325-333. www.researchgate.net/profile/Alexander_Wagenaar/publication/14491943_Sources_of_alcohol_for_underage_drinkers/links/555257db08ae6fd2d81d46b0.pdf;
US Department of Health and Human Services. (2016). *Results from the 2016 National Survey on Drug Use and Health: Detailed Tables*. www.samhsa.gov/data/sites/default/files/NSDUH-DetTabs-2016/NSDUH-DetTabs-2016.pdf

48 Resnick, M. D., Bearman, P. S., Blum, R. W., Bauman, K. E., Harris, K. M., Jones, J., ... & Ireland, M. (1997). Protecting adolescents from harm: findings from the National Longitudinal Study on Adolescent Health. *Jama, 278*(10), 823-832. https://academiccommons.columbia.edu/doi/10.7916/d8-78f6-mt67/download;
*Parents in the Dark*. (2014). Hazelden's Adolescent and Young Adult Services. www.hazelden.org/web/public/document/parents-in-dark.pdf

49 Friese, B., Grube, J. W., & Moore, R. S. (2012). How parents of adolescents store and monitor alcohol in the home. *The journal of primary prevention, 33*(2-3), 79-83. www.ncbi.nlm.nih.gov/pmc/articles/PMC3407279/

50 Ryan, S. M., Jorm, A. F., & Lubman, D. I. (2010). Parenting factors associated with reduced adolescent alcohol use: a systematic review of longitudinal studies. *Australian & New Zealand Journal of Psychiatry, 44*(9), 774-783. https://www.teappoyo.com/bibliografia/Ryan,%20S.%20M.,%20Jorm,%20A.%20F.,%20&%20Lubman,%20D.%20I.%20(2010).%20Parenting%20factors%20associated%20with%20reduced%20adolescent%20alcohol%20use%20a%20systematic%20review%20of%20longitudinal%20studies.pdf;
Ryan, S. M., Jorm, A. F., & Lubman, D. I. (2010). Parenting factors associated with reduced adolescent alcohol use: a systematic review of longitudinal studies. *Australian & New Zealand Journal of Psychiatry, 44*(9), 774-783. https://pdfs.semanticscholar.org/0dfa/840cae27332f2e7a6ff96b178262b0905104.pdf

51 Turrisi, R., Jaccard, J., Taki, R., Dunnam, H., & Grimes, J. (2001). Examination of the short-term efficacy of a parent intervention to reduce college student drinking tendencies. *Psychology of Addictive Behaviors, 15*(4), 366. https://psycnet.apa.org/record/2001-05427-013

52 Beck, K. H., Shattuck, T., Haynie, D., Crump, A. D., & Simons-Morton, B. (1999). Associations between parent awareness, monitoring, enforcement and adolescent involvement with alcohol. *Health Education Research, 14*(6), 765-775. www.researchgate.net/profile/Denise_Haynie/publication/12716698_Associations_between_parent_awareness_monitoring_enforcement_and_adolescent_involvement_with_alcohol/links/02e7e53b449da443a4000000/Associations-between-parent-awareness-monitoring-enforcement-and-adolescent-involvement-with-alcohol.pdf

53 McAlaney, J., & McMahon, J. (2007). Normative beliefs, misperceptions, and heavy episodic drinking in a British student sample. *Journal of studies on alcohol and drugs, 68*(3), 385-392. https://bradscholars.brad.ac.uk/bitstream/handle/10454/2798/McAlaney%20and%20McMahon%20Normative%202007.pdf?sequence=3

54 Perkins, H. W., & Berkowitz, A. D. (1986). Perceiving the community norms of alcohol use among students: Some research implications for campus alcohol education programming. *International journal of the Addictions, 21*(9-10), 961-976. www.researchgate.net/profile/Alan-Berkowitz/publication/19369252_Perceiving_the_Community_Norms_of_Alcohol_Use_Among_Students_Some_Research_Implications_for_Campus_Alcohol_Education_Programming/links/56907bae08aecd716aedfe7e/Perceiving-the-Community-Norms-of-Alcohol-Use-Among-Students-Some-Research-Implications-for-Campus-Alcohol-Education-Programming.pdf;
Borsari, B., & Carey, K. B. (2003). Descriptive and injunctive norms in college drinking: a meta-analytic integration. *Journal of studies on alcohol, 64*(3), 331-341. www.ncbi.nlm.nih.gov/pmc/articles/PMC2431131/;
Prentice, D. A., & Miller, D. T. (1993). Pluralistic ignorance and alcohol use on campus: some consequences of misperceiving the social norm. *Journal of personality and social psychology, 64*(2), 243. http://citeseerx.ist.psu.edu/viewdoc/download?doi=10.1.1.470.522&rep=rep1&type=pdf;
Perkins, H. W., & Wechsler, H. (1996). Variation in perceived college drinking norms and its impact on alcohol abuse: A nationwide study. *Journal of Drug Issues, 26*(4), 961-974. https://journals.sagepub.com/doi/abs/10.1177/002204269602600413;
Matjasko, J. L., Cawley, J. H., Baker-Goering, M. M., & Yokum, D. V. (2016). Applying behavioral economics to public health policy: illustrative examples and promising directions. *American journal of preventive medicine, 50*(5), S13-S19.

55 Neighbors, C., Foster, D. W., & Fossos, N. (2013). *Peer influences on addiction.* Principles of addiction: Comprehensive addictive behaviours and disorders, 1, 323-331. https://books.google.com/books?hl=en&lr=&id=5gRNl3oIwWEC&oi=fnd&pg=PA323&dq=Peer+Influences+on+Addiction&ots=j7Nqa3-doz&sig=iGyUlMF8hnKaEMeXirBZGm-uJKs#v=onepage&q=Peer%20Influences%20on%20Addiction&f=false

56 Frauenfelder, M. (2001). The Year In Ideas: A To Z.; Social-Norms Marketing. *The New York Times.* www.nytimes.com/2001/12/09/magazine/the-year-in-ideas-a-to-z-social-norms-marketing.html

57 Frauenfelder, M. (2001). The Year In Ideas: A To Z.; Social-Norms Marketing. *The New York Times.* www.nytimes.com/2001/12/09/magazine/the-year-in-ideas-a-to-z-social-norms-marketing.html

58 Haines, M. P. (1996). *A Social Norms Approach to Preventing Binge Drinking at Colleges and Universities.* www.researchgate.net/profile/Michael_Haines/publication/237503478_A_Social_Norms_Approach_to_Preventing_Binge_Drinking_at_Colleges_and_Universities/links/004635345415bcd2a3000000/A-Social-Norms-Approach-to-Preventing-Binge-Drinking-at-Colleges-and-Universities.pdf;

59 Hansen, W. B., & Graham, J. W. (1991). Preventing alcohol, marijuana, and cigarette use among adolescents: Peer pressure resistance training versus establishing conservative norms. *Preventive medicine, 20*(3), 414-430. www.sciencedirect.com/science/article/abs/pii/0091743591900397

60 Wechsler, H., Seibring, M., Liu, I. C., & Ahl, M. (2004). Colleges respond to student binge drinking: Reducing student demand or limiting access. *Journal of American College Health, 52*(4), 159-168. http://archive.sph.harvard.edu/cas/Documents/respond/respondingg.pdf

61 Haines, M. P., Barker, G. P., & Rice, R. (2003). Using social norms to reduce alcohol and tobacco use in two midwestern high schools. *The social norms approach to preventing school and college age substance abuse: A handbook for educators, counselors, and clinicians*, 235-244. www.researchgate.net/publication/262673122_Using_social_norms_to_reduce_alcohol_and_tobacco_use_in_two_Midwestern_high_schools

62 Foxcroft, D. R., Moreira, M. T., Santimano, N. M. A., & Smith, L. A. (2015). Social norms information for alcohol misuse in university and college students. *Cochrane database of systematic reviews*, (12). www.cochranelibrary.com/cdsr/doi/10.1002/14651858.CD006748.pub4/full

63 Council on Communications and Media. (2010). Children, Adolescents, Substance Abuse, and the Media. *Pediatrics, 126*(4), 791-799. https://pediatrics.aappublications.org/content/126/4/791
Citing: Leiber, L. (1996). *Commercial and character slogan recall by children aged 9 to 11 years: Budweiser frogs versus Bugs Bunny*. Berkeley, CA: Center on Alcohol Advertising.

64 Collins, R. L., Ellickson, P. L., McCaffrey, D. F., & Hambarsoomians, K. (2005). Saturated in beer: Awareness of beer advertising in late childhood and adolescence. *Journal of Adolescent Health, 37*(1), 29-36. www.sciencedirect.com/science/article/abs/pii/S1054139X04004598

65 Council on Communications and Media. (2010). Children, Adolescents, Substance Abuse, and the Media. *Pediatrics, 126*(4), 791-799. https://pediatrics.aappublications.org/content/126/4/791

66 Anderson, P., De Bruijn, A., Angus, K., Gordon, R., & Hastings, G. (2009). Impact of alcohol advertising and media exposure on adolescent alcohol use: a systematic review of longitudinal studies. *Alcohol and alcoholism, 44*(3), 229-243. https://academic.oup.com/alcalc/article/44/3/229/178279

67 Rideout, V. J., Foehr, U. G., & Roberts, D. F. (2010). *Generation M 2: Media in the Lives of 8-to 18-Year-Olds*. Henry J. Kaiser Family Foundation. https://files.eric.ed.gov/fulltext/ED527859.pdf

68 Tansil, K. A., Esser, M. B., Sandhu, P., Reynolds, J. A., Elder, R. W., Williamson, R. S., ... & Hungerford, D. W. (2016). Alcohol electronic screening and brief intervention: a Community Guide systematic review. *American journal of preventive medicine, 51*(5), 801-811. https://pubmed.ncbi.nlm.nih.gov/27745678/;
Wallace, P., & Bendtsen, P. (2014). Internet applications for screening and brief interventions for alcohol in primary care settings–implementation and sustainability. *Frontiers in psychiatry*, 5, 151. www.frontiersin.org/articles/10.3389/fpsyt.2014.00151/full

69 *Alcohol – Excessive Consumption: Electronic Screening and Brief Interventions (e-SBI)*. (2012). The Community Guide. www.thecommunityguide.org/findings/alcohol-excessive-consumption-electronic-screening-and-brief-interventions-e-sbi

70 Cunningham, J. A., Wild, T. C., Cordingley, J., Van Mierlo, T., & Humphreys, K. (2009). A randomized controlled trial of an internet-based intervention for alcohol abusers. *Addiction, 104*(12), 2023-2032. https://onlinelibrary.wiley.com/doi/full/10.1111/j.1360-0443.2009.02726.x

71 Doumas, D. M., & Hannah, E. (2008). Preventing high-risk drinking in youth in the workplace: a web-based normative feedback program. *Journal of substance abuse treatment, 34*(3), 263-271. https://scholarworks.boisestate.edu/cgi/viewcontent.cgi?article=1000&context=counsel_facpubs

72 Doumas, D. M., & Haustveit, T. (2008). Reducing heavy drinking in intercollegiate athletes: Evaluation of a web-based personalized feedback program. *The Sport Psychologist, 22*(2), 212-228. https://scholarworks.boisestate.edu/cgi/viewcontent.cgi?article=1004&context=counsel_facpubs;
Footnote reference:
[1]*Program Reviews: Electronic Screening and Brief Intervention (e-SBI)*. (n.d.) Center for Technology and Behavioral Health. www.c4tbh.org/program-review/electronic-screening-and-brief-intervention-e-sbi/

73 Dimeff, L. A. (Ed.). (1999). *Brief alcohol screening and intervention for college students (BASICS): A harm reduction approach*. Guilford Press. http://lib.adai.washington.edu/dbtw-wpd/exec/dbtwpub.dll?BU=http%3A//lib.adai.washington.edu/ebpsearch.htm&TN=EBP&QY=Find+AccessNo=47&RF=Full+Display&DF=Full+Display&NP=3&RL=1&DL=0&XC=/dbtw-wpd/exec/dbtwpub.dll&AC=QBE_QUERY&CS=0

74 Gable, R. S. (2006). Macroscope: The Toxicity of Recreational Drugs. *American scientist, 94*(3), 206-208. https://web.cgu.edu/faculty/gabler/Amer%20Scientist.pdf

75 *Drunk Driving Impacts Every American. Every Day.* (n.d.). Mothers Against Drunk Driving. www.madd.org/the-problem/

76 Mackay, J. & Eriksen, M. (2002). *The Tobacco Atlas*. World Health Organization. https://apps.who.int/iris/bitstream/handle/10665/42580/9241562099.pdf?sequence=1&isAllowed=y

77 Van Amsterdam, J., Opperhuizen, A., Koeter, M., & van den Brink, W. (2010). Ranking the harm of alcohol, tobacco and illicit drugs for the individual and the population. *European addiction research, 16*(4), 202-207. https://karger.com/ear/article-abstract/16/4/202/119853/Ranking-the-Harm-of-Alcohol-Tobacco-and-Illicit?redirectedFrom=fulltext

78 DiFranza, J. R., Savageau, J. A., Fletcher, K., O'Loughlin, J., Pbert, L., Ockene, J. K., ... & Wellman, R. J. (2007). Symptoms of tobacco dependence after brief intermittent use: the Development and Assessment of Nicotine Dependence in Youth–2 study. *Archives of pediatrics & adolescent medicine, 161*(7), 704-710. https://jamanetwork.com/journals/jamapediatrics/articlepdf/570706/poa70005_704_710.pdf

79 DiFranza, J. R., Rigotti, N. A., McNeill, A. D., Ockene, J. K., Savageau, J. A., St Cyr, D., & Coleman, M. (2000). Initial symptoms of nicotine dependence in adolescents. *Tobacco control, 9*(3), 313-319. https://tobaccocontrol.bmj.com/content/tobaccocontrol/9/3/313.full.pdf

80 Anthony, J. C., Warner, L. A., & Kessler, R. C. (1997). *Comparative epidemiology of dependence on tobacco, alcohol, controlled substances, and inhalants: basic findings from the National Comorbidity Survey.* www.researchgate.net/profile/Lynn_Warner2/publication/232545123_Comparative_Epidemiology_of_Dependence_on_Tobacco_Alcohol_Controlled_Substances_and_Inhalants_Basic_Findings_From_the_National_Comorbidity_Survey/links/0fcfd5124debe9ee41000000.pdf

81 United States Public Health Service Office of the Surgeon General, National Center for Chronic Disease Prevention, & Health Promotion (US) Office on Smoking. (2012). *Preventing tobacco use among youth and young adults: a report of the surgeon general.* US Government Printing Office. www.surgeongeneral.gov/library/reports/preventing-youth-tobacco-use/full-report.pdf

82 Johnston, L. D., O'Malley, P. M., Bachman, J. G., & Schulenberg, J. E. (2007). *Monitoring the future national survey results on drug use, 1975-2006. Volume II: College students and adults ages 19-45.* https://deepblue.lib.umich.edu/bitstream/handle/2027.42/137787/vol2_2006.pdf?sequence=1&isAllowed=y

83 *Most regret ever starting smoking.* (2012). Cancer Research UK. www.cancerresearchuk.org/about-us/cancer-news/press-release/2012-07-21-most-regret-ever-starting-smoking

84 *Most regret ever starting smoking.* (2012). Cancer Research UK. www.cancerresearchuk.org/about-us/cancer-news/press-release/2012-07-21-most-regret-ever-starting-smoking

85 Kann, L., McManus, T., Harris, W. A., Shanklin, S. L., Flint, K. H., Hawkins, J., ... & Zaza, S. (2016). Youth risk behavior surveillance—United States, 2015. *Morbidity and Mortality Weekly Report: Surveillance Summaries, 65*(6), 1-174. www.cdc.gov/mmwr/volumes/65/ss/ss6506a1.htm

86 US Department of Health and Human Services. (2014). *The health consequences of smoking—50 years of progress: a report of the Surgeon General.* (Table 12.2.2, p.790) www.ncbi.nlm.nih.gov/books/NBK179276/pdf/Bookshelf_NBK179276.pdf

87 Sullivan, P. F., & Kendler, K. S. (1999). The genetic epidemiology of smoking. *Nicotine & Tobacco Research, 1(Suppl_2),* S51-S57. https://academic.oup.com/ntr/article-abstract/1/Suppl_2/S51/1097866;
Lessov-Schlaggar, C. N., Pergadia, M. L., Khroyan, T. V., & Swan, G. E. (2008). Genetics of nicotine dependence and pharmacotherapy. *Biochemical pharmacology, 75*(1), 178-195. www.ncbi.nlm.nih.gov/pmc/articles/PMC2238639/

88 Carmelli, D., Swan, G. E., Robinette, D., & Fabsitz, R. (1992). Genetic influence on smoking—a study of male twins. *New England Journal of Medicine, 327*(12), 829-833. www.nejm.org/doi/full/10.1056/NEJM199209173271201;
Heath, A. C., & Martin, N. G. (1993). Genetic models for the natural history of smoking: evidence for a genetic influence on smoking persistence. *Addictive Behaviors, 18*(1), 19-34. https://keppel.qimr.edu.au/contents/publications/staff/CV125.pdf;
True, W. R., Xian, H., Scherrer, J. F., Madden, P. A., Bucholz, K. K., Heath, A. C., ... & Tsuang, M. (1999). Common genetic vulnerability for nicotine and alcohol dependence in men. *Archives of general psychiatry, 56*(7), 655-661. https://jamanetwork.com/journals/jamapsychiatry/fullarticle/205093;
Xian, H., Scherrer, J. F., Madden, P. A., Lyons, M. J., Tsuang, M., True, W. R., & Eisen, S. A. (2005). Latent class typology of nicotine withdrawal: genetic contributions and association with failed smoking cessation and psychiatric disorders. *Psychological medicine, 35*(3), 409-419. http://digitalcommons.wustl.edu/cgi/viewcontent.cgi?article=4955&context=open_access_pubs;
Madden, P. A., Heath, A. C., Pedersen, N. L., Kaprio, J., Koskenvuo, M. J., & Martin, N. G. (1999). The genetics of smoking persistence in men and women: a multicultural study. *Behavior genetics, 29*(6), 423-431. https://genepi.qimr.edu.au/contents/publications/staff/CV254Madden_UQ_Copy.pdf;
Lessov, C. N., Martin, N. G., Statham, D. J., Todorov, A. A., Slutske, W. S., Bucholz, K. K., ... & Madden, P. A. (2004). Defining nicotine dependence for genetic research: evidence from Australian twins. *Psychological*

*medicine, 34*(5), 865-879. http://digitalcommons.wustl.edu/cgi/viewcontent.cgi?article=4908&context=open_access_pubs;
McGue, M., Elkins, I., & Iacono, W. G. (2000). Genetic and environmental influences on adolescent substance use and abuse. *American journal of medical genetics, 96*(5), 671-677. www.researchgate.net/profile/Irene_Elkins/publication/12271486_Genetic_and_environmental_influences_on_adolescent_substance_use_and_abuse/links/59e6518f4585151e545cd9f4/Genetic-and-environmental-influences-on-adolescent-substance-use-and-abuse.pdf

89 Pomerleau, O. F., Pomerleau, C. S., & Namenek, R. J. (1998). Early experiences with tobacco among women smokers, ex-smokers, and never-smokers. *Addiction, 93*(4), 595-599. https://onlinelibrary.wiley.com/doi/abs/10.1046/j.1360-0443.1998.93459515.x;
Chen, X., Stacy, A., Zheng, H., Shan, J., Spruijt-Metz, D., Unger, J. B., ... & Shakib, S. (2003). Sensations from initial exposure to nicotine predicting adolescent smoking in China: a potential measure of vulnerability to nicotine. *Nicotine & Tobacco Research, 5*(4), 455-463. www.researchgate.net/profile/Jennifer_Unger/publication/10578798_Sensations_from_initial_exposure_to_nicotine_predicting_adolescent_smoking_in_China_a_potential_measure_of_vulnerability_to_nicotine_Nicotine_Tob_Res_5_455-463/links/0912f507d993e55026000000.pdf;
Wang, M. Q., Fitzhugh, E. C., Trucks, J., Cowdery, J., & Perko, M. (1995). Physiological sensations of initial smoking in the development of regular smoking behavior. *Perceptual and motor skills, 80*(3_suppl), 1131-1134. www.researchgate.net/profile/Eugene_Fitzhugh/publication/15719970_Physiological_sensations_of_initial_smoking_in_the_development_of_regular_smoking_behavior/links/582d915708aef19cb813930a.pdf

90 Adriani, W., Spijker, S., Deroche-Gamonet, V., Laviola, G., Le Moal, M., Smit, A. B., & Piazza, P. V. (2003). Evidence for enhanced neurobehavioral vulnerability to nicotine during periadolescence in rats. *Journal of Neuroscience, 23*(11), 4712-4716. www.jneurosci.org/content/jneuro/23/11/4712.full.pdf;
Slotkin, T. A. (2002). Nicotine and the adolescent brain: insights from an animal model. *Neurotoxicology and teratology, 24*(3), 369-384. www.sciencedirect.com/science/article/abs/pii/S089203620200199X

91 Yuan, M., Cross, S. J., Loughlin, S. E., & Leslie, F. M. (2015). Nicotine and the adolescent brain. *The Journal of physiology, 593*(16), 3397-3412. https://physoc.onlinelibrary.wiley.com/doi/pdf/10.1113/JP270492

92 US Department of Health and Human Services. (2016). *E-cigarette use among youth and young adults: A report of the Surgeon General.* Atlanta, GA. https://e-cigarettes.surgeongeneral.gov/documents/2016_sgr_full_report_non-508.pdf

93 Kendler, K. S., Myers, J., Damaj, M. I., & Chen, X. (2013). Early smoking onset and risk for subsequent nicotine dependence: a monozygotic co-twin control study. *American Journal of Psychiatry, 170*(4), 408-413. https://ajp.psychiatryonline.org/doi/full/10.1176/appi.ajp.2012.12030321

94 Treur, J. L., Willemsen, G., Bartels, M., Geels, L. M., van Beek, J. H., Huppertz, C., ... & Vink, J. M. (2015). Smoking during adolescence as a risk factor for attention problems. *Biological psychiatry, 78*(9), 656-663. https://d1wqtxts1xzle7.cloudfront.net/43311067/Smoking_during_adolescence_as_a_risk_fac20160303-17510-1qmkzh3.pdf?1457013703=&response-content-disposition=inline%3B+filename%3DSmoking_During_Adolescence_as_a_Risk_Fac.pdf&Expires=1617158601&Signature=PUunFZX927i-0j69MybFw-f3WUcCYcSNdfEBe-NWyQpqmoq94jHdyhyIytLBD3cc4Tpr67LLHCW5alzFABG0jjAX-Q7Xb-oA3Bx87d1Zp6tGODCd7M8hc-v4z-uCjLSrmj4My-DvomoA1m-TR0R0TBhkzKzFf4bIgEoNjAFf-gjpiWLjCn8W1wp75BNgitxAgD6QekEeHo9iLwxL-8xw-Ivmh3Fw97M8bBd02lkBClLd9BFFUjiFghY-6wDMNWqdWCoDF9UeNCXH-kTU99cHmOal-11cJTeiXMZdDATDn1m48MQxQ5gFOz9sKCMN7mE-Z9hg6bsCBcdxaze4Sq5KQFWaxxQ__&Key-Pair-Id=APKAJLOHF5GGSLRBV4ZA

95 E-*Cigarette Use Among Youth and Young Adults*. (2016). U.S. Department of Health and Human Services, Public Health Service, Office of the Surgeon General. https://e-cigarettes.surgeongeneral.gov/documents/2016_sgr_full_report_non-508.pdf

Citing: Jacobsen, L. K., Krystal, J. H., Mencl, W. E., Westerveld, M., Frost, S. J., & Pugh, K. R. (2005). Effects of smoking and smoking abstinence on cognition in adolescent tobacco smokers. *Biological psychiatry, 57*(1), 56-66. https://d1wqtxts1xzle7.cloudfront.net/45705128/j.biopsych.2004.10.02220160517-11662-6rhglr.pdf?1463486093=&response-content-disposition=inline%3B+filename%3DEffects_of_smoking_and_smoking_abstinenc.pdf&Expires=1617158820&Signature=dIIQOF0LstTyFF2Ub0B--5PVJxhoc34y5cue2nhwmp8O-9DOD-d59vbYgNT2-U0nE7yksvNjZWBg0-8khhmLDW39SrSVNK3rYHf6DXsTkHgMNcVyEtpabqgkPe-JGtdRpRk5RXc-qCJ6Z41Jni3hKNr25jxndgwMv-Lr8-25WSZL3UGsW2E-wVaDn4y6vkiEqYmntM0eRSB-gNQwjpU7USMimDQpMmZesesKg-oqpO6ieQscHpnh18o4UIA2JhsJt6p9MrMW0aiJkp8UWc-J1k3w4E-BOMxcpItBsC5tF2-XeMZoLDZuN7WSw5pK7jiJA7HbcY8M5-G8HJVoQA-UBzIFhQ__&Key-Pair-Id=APKAJLOHF5GGSLRBV4ZA

96 *Hooked smoking ads 'broke rules'.* (2007). BBC News. http://news.bbc.co.uk/1/hi/uk/6658335.stm

97 Johnston, L. D., Miech, R. A., O'Malley, P. M., Bachman, J. G., Schulenberg, J. E., & Patrick, M. E. (2018). *Monitoring the Future national survey results on drug use, 1975-2018: Overview, key findings on adolescent drug use.* www.monitoringthefuture.org/pubs/monographs/mtf-overview2018.pdf

98 Eissenberg, T., & Balster, R. L. (2000). Initial tobacco use episodes in children and adolescents: current knowledge, future directions. *Drug and alcohol dependence*, 59, 41-60. www.sciencedirect.com/science/article/abs/pii/S0376871699001647;
United States. Public Health Service. Office of the Surgeon General, National Center for Chronic Disease Prevention, & Health Promotion (US). Office on Smoking. (2012). *Preventing tobacco use among youth and young adults: a report of the surgeon general.* US Government Printing Office. www.ncbi.nlm.nih.gov/books/NBK99237/

99 Miech, R. A., Johnston, L. D., O'Malley, P. M., Bachman, J. G., & Schulenberg, J. E. (2016). *Monitoring the Future national survey results on drug use, 1975-2015: Volume I, Secondary school students.* The National Institute on Drug Abuse. www.monitoringthefuture.org/pubs/monographs/mtf-vol1_2015.pdf

100 Brock, B., Schillo, B. A., & Moilanen, M. (2015). Tobacco industry marketing: an analysis of direct mail coupons and giveaways. *Tobacco control, 24*(5), 505-508. https://ijbe-research.com/wp-content/uploads/2017/02/out_29.pdf

101 Anderson, S., Hastings, G., & MacFadyen, L. (2002). Strategic marketing in the UK tobacco industry. *The lancet oncology, 3*(8), 481-486. www.sciencedirect.com/science/article/pii/S1470204502008173

102 United States. Public Health Service. Office of the Surgeon General, National Center for Chronic Disease Prevention, & Health Promotion (US) Office on Smoking. (2012). *Preventing tobacco use among youth and young adults: a report of the surgeon general.* US Government Printing Office. www.ncbi.nlm.nih.gov/books/NBK99237/

103 Pollay, R. W. (2000). Targeting youth and concerned smokers: evidence from Canadian tobacco industry documents. *Tobacco control, 9*(2), 136-147. https://tobaccocontrol.bmj.com/content/tobaccocontrol/9/2/136.full.pdf

104 Hastings, G., & MacFadyen, L. (2000). A day in the life of an advertising man: review of internal documents from the UK tobacco industry's principal advertising agencies. *Bmj, 321*(7257), 366-371. www.ncbi.nlm.nih.gov/pmc/articles/PMC1118336/

105 Brock, B., Schillo, B. A., & Moilanen, M. (2015). Tobacco industry marketing: an analysis of direct mail coupons and giveaways. *Tobacco control, 24*(5), 505-508. https://ijbe-research.com/wp-content/uploads/2017/02/out_29.pdf

106 Rooke, C., Cheeseman, H., Dockrell, M., Millward, D., & Sandford, A. (2010). Tobacco point-of-sale displays in England: a snapshot survey of current practices. *Tobacco Control, 19*(4), 279-284. www.research.ed.ac.uk/portal/files/2805743/RookeEtAl_TobaccoPointOfSaleDisplays.pdf

107 Rooke, C., Cheeseman, H., Dockrell, M., Millward, D., & Sandford, A. (2010). Tobacco point-of-sale displays in England: a snapshot survey of current practices. *Tobacco Control, 19*(4), 279-284. www.research.ed.ac.uk/portal/files/2805743/RookeEtAl_TobaccoPointOfSaleDisplays.pdf

108 Henriksen, L., Feighery, E. C., Wang, Y., & Fortmann, S. P. (2004). Association of retail tobacco marketing with adolescent smoking. *American Journal of Public Health, 94*(12), 2081-2083. https://ajph.aphapublications.org/doi/pdfplus/10.2105/AJPH.94.12.2081

109 Brock, B., Schillo, B. A., & Moilanen, M. (2015). Tobacco industry marketing: an analysis of direct mail coupons and giveaways. *Tobacco control, 24*(5), 505-508. https://ijbe-research.com/wp-content/uploads/2017/02/out_29.pdf

110 Dalton, M. A., Adachi-Mejia, A. M., Longacre, M. R., Titus-Ernstoff, L. T., Gibson, J. J., Martin, S. K., ... & Beach, M. L. (2006). Parental rules and monitoring of children's movie viewing associated with children's risk for smoking and drinking. *Pediatrics, 118*(5), 1932-1942. https://pediatrics.aappublications.org/content/118/5/1932.short

111 Strasburger, V. C. (2010). Policy statement--children, adolescents, substance abuse, and the media. *Pediatrics, 126*(4), 791-799. https://pediatrics.aappublications.org/content/126/4/791

112 Sargent, J. D., Beach, M. L., Adachi-Mejia, A. M., Gibson, J. J., Titus-Ernstoff, L. T., Carusi, C. P., ... & Dalton, M. A. (2005). Exposure to movie smoking: its relation to smoking initiation among US adolescents. *Pediatrics, 116*(5), 1183-1191. www.researchgate.net/profile/James-Sargent-2/publication/7503339_Exposure_to_Movie_Smoking_Its_Relation_to_Smoking_Initiation_Among_US_Adolescents/links/54c0ec1d0cf28a6324a42f1a/Exposure-to-Movie-Smoking-Its-Relation-to-Smoking-Initiation-Among-US-Adolescents.pdf

113 Flay, B. R., Hu, F. B., Siddiqui, O., Day, L. E., Hedeker, D., Petraitis, J., ... & Sussman, S. (1994). Differential influence of parental smoking and friends' smoking on adolescent initiation and escalation and smoking. *Journal of Health and Social behavior*, 248-265. https://pdfs.semanticscholar.org/39db/1b8b9cbfccb36ba4c68aaffd635d-7be7dffa.pdf

114 Dishion, T. J., & McMahon, R. J. (1998). Parental monitoring and the prevention of child and adolescent problem behavior: A conceptual and empirical formulation. *Clinical child and family psychology review, 1*(1), 61-75. www.researchgate.net/profile/Thomas_Dishion/publication/12012274_Parental_Monitoring_and_the_Prevention_of_Child_and_Adolescent_Problem_Behavior_A_Conceptual_and_Empirical_Formulation/links/5763220808ae192f513e3f9d/Parental-Monitoring-and-the-Prevention-of-Child-and-Adolescent-Problem-Behavior-A-Conceptual-and-Empirical-Formulation.pdf
Citing: Friedman, L. S., Lichtenstein, E., & Biglan, A. (1985). Smoking onset among teens: An empirical analysis of initial situations. *Addictive Behaviors, 10*(1), 1-13. www.sciencedirect.com/science/article/abs/pii/0306460385900486

115 US Department of Health and Human Services. (2012). *Preventing tobacco use among youth and young adults: a report of the Surgeon General.* Atlanta, GA: US Department of Health and Human Services, Centers for Disease Control and Prevention, National Center for Chronic Disease Prevention and Health Promotion, Office on Smoking and Health, 3. www.cdc.gov/tobacco/data_statistics/sgr/2012/index.htm

116 Lantz, P. M., Jacobson, P. D., Warner, K. E., Wasserman, J., Pollack, H. A., Berson, J., & Ahlstrom, A. (2000). Investing in youth tobacco control: a review of smoking prevention and control strategies. *Tobacco control, 9*(1), 47-63. http://tobaccocontrol.bmj.com/content/9/1/47.full

117 US Department of Health and Human Services. (2012). *Preventing tobacco use among youth and young adults: a report of the Surgeon General.* www.hhs.gov/sites/default/files/preventing-youth-tobacco-use-exec-summary.pdf

118 Lantz, P. M., Jacobson, P. D., Warner, K. E., Wasserman, J., Pollack, H. A., Berson, J., & Ahlstrom, A. (2000). Investing in youth tobacco control: a review of smoking prevention and control strategies. *Tobacco control, 9*(1), 47-63. http://tobaccocontrol.bmj.com/content/9/1/47.full

119 Niederdeppe, J., Farrelly, M. C., & Haviland, M. L. (2004). Confirming "truth": more evidence of a successful tobacco countermarketing campaign in Florida. *American journal of public health, 94*(2), 255-257. https://ajph.aphapublications.org/doi/pdfplus/10.2105/AJPH.94.2.255;
Holtgrave, D. R., Wunderink, K. A., Vallone, D. M., & Healton, C. G. (2009). Cost–utility analysis of the national truth® campaign to prevent youth smoking. *American journal of preventive medicine, 36*(5), 385-388. www.ajpmonline.org/article/S0749-3797%2809%2900075-0/pdf

120 Evans, W. D., Rath, J. M., Hair, E. C., Snider, J. W., Pitzer, L., Greenberg, M., ... & Vallone, D. (2018). Effects of the truth FinishIt brand on tobacco outcomes. *Preventive medicine reports*, 9, 6-11. www.ncbi.nlm.nih.gov/pmc/articles/PMC5724797/

121 Huang, L. L., Lazard, A. J., Pepper, J. K., Noar, S. M., Ranney, L. M., & Goldstein, A. O. (2017). Impact of The Real Cost campaign on adolescents' recall, attitudes, and risk perceptions about tobacco use: a national study. *International journal of environmental research and public health, 14*(1), 42. www.mdpi.com/1660-4601/14/1/42/pdf;
Footnote references:
[1] Fresh Empire Campaign. (2021). U.S. Food & Drug Administration. www.fda.gov/tobacco-products/fresh-empire-campaign
[2] Fresh Empire Research & Evaluation. (n.d.). U.S. Food and Drug Administration. www.fda.gov/media/94558/download
[3] Uncited Guillory, J., Crankshaw, E., Farrelly, M. C., Alam, I., Fiacco, L., Curry, L., ... & Delahanty, J. (2020). LGBT young adults' awareness of and receptivity to the This Free Life tobacco public education campaign. *Tobacco Control.* https://tobaccocontrol.bmj.com/content/tobaccocontrol/early/2020/01/14/tobaccocontrol-2019-055239.full.pdf
[4] This Free Life Campaign. (2021). U.S. Food and Drug Administration. www.fda.gov/tobacco-products/free-life-campaign
[5] Lantz, P. M., Jacobson, P. D., Warner, K. E., Wasserman, J., Pollack, H. A., Berson, J., & Ahlstrom, A. (2000). Investing in youth tobacco control: a review of smoking prevention and control strategies. *Tobacco control, 9*(1), 47-63. http://tobaccocontrol.bmj.com/content/9/1/47.full
[6] Thomas, R. E., McLellan, J., & Perera, R. (2013). School-based programmes for preventing smoking. *Evidence-Based Child Health: A Cochrane Review Journal, 8*(5), 1616-2040. www.prevencionbasadaenlaevidencia.com/uploads/PDF/RP_Cochrane_School_SmokingPrev_2013.pdf

122 De Vries, H., Backbier, E., Dijkstra, M., Van Breukelen, G., Parcel, G., & Kok, G. (1994). A Dutch social influence smoking prevention approach for vocational school students. *Health Education Research, 9*(3), 365-374. www.researchgate.net/profile/Gerjo_Kok/publication/31407916_A_Dutch_social_influence_smoking_pre-

vention_approach_for_vocational_school_students/links/579dfca108ae6a2882f538fa/A-Dutch-social-influence-smoking-prevention-approach-for-vocational-school-students.pdf;
Dijkstra, M., Mesters, I., De Vries, H., Van Breukelen, G., & Parcel, G. S. (1999). Effectiveness of a social influence approach and boosters to smoking prevention. *Health Education Research, 14*(6), 791-802. https://academic.oup.com/her/article/14/6/791/745892;
Lotrean, L., Dijk, F., Mesters, I., Ionut, C., & De Vries, H. (2010). Evaluation of a peer-led smoking prevention programme for Romanian adolescents. *Health Education Research, 25*(5), 803-814. https://academic.oup.com/her/article/25/5/803/567387

123 Lantz, P. M., Jacobson, P. D., Warner, K. E., Wasserman, J., Pollack, H. A., Berson, J., & Ahlstrom, A. (2000). Investing in youth tobacco control: a review of smoking prevention and control strategies. *Tobacco control, 9*(1), 47-63. http://tobaccocontrol.bmj.com/content/9/1/47.full

124 US Department of Health and Human Services. (2012). *Preventing tobacco use among youth and young adults: a report of the Surgeon General.* Atlanta, GA: US Department of Health and Human Services, Centers for Disease Control and Prevention, National Center for Chronic Disease Prevention and Health Promotion, Office on Smoking and Health, 3. www.cdc.gov/tobacco/data_statistics/sgr/2012/index.htm

125 Distefan, J. M., Gilpin, E. A., Choi, W. S., & Pierce, J. P. (1998). Parental influences predict adolescent smoking in the United States, 1989–1993. *Journal of adolescent health, 22*(6), 466-474. www.sciencedirect.com/science/article/pii/S1054139X98000135;
Kristjansson, A. L., Sigfusdottir, I. D., Allegrante, J. P., & Helgason, A. R. (2008). Social correlates of cigarette smoking among Icelandic adolescents: a population-based cross-sectional study. *BMC Public Health, 8*(1), 1-8. https://bmcpublichealth.biomedcentral.com/articles/10.1186/1471-2458-8-86

126 Bernat, D. H., Erickson, D. J., Widome, R., Perry, C. L., & Forster, J. L. (2008). Adolescent smoking trajectories: results from a population-based cohort study. *Journal of Adolescent Health, 43*(4), 334-340. www.ncbi.nlm.nih.gov/pmc/articles/PMC2743902/

127 Wakefield, M. A., Chaloupka, F. J., Kaufman, N. J., Orleans, C. T., Barker, D. C., & Ruel, E. E. (2000). Effect of restrictions on smoking at home, at school, and in public places on teenage smoking: cross sectional study. *Bmj, 321*(7257), 333-337. www.ncbi.nlm.nih.gov/pmc/articles/PMC27448/;
Farkas, A. J., Gilpin, E. A., White, M. M., & Pierce, J. P. (2000). Association between household and workplace smoking restrictions and adolescent smoking. *Jama, 284*(6), 717-722. https://jamanetwork.com/journals/jama/fullarticle/192966

128 Petrie, J., Bunn, F., & Byrne, G. (2006). Parenting programmes for preventing tobacco, alcohol or drugs misuse in children <18: a systematic review. *Health education research, 22*(2), 177-191. https://academic.oup.com/her/article/22/2/177/622709;
US Department of Health and Human Services. (2012). *Preventing tobacco use among youth and young adults: a report of the Surgeon General.* Atlanta, GA: US Department of Health and Human Services, Centers for Disease Control and Prevention, National Center for Chronic Disease Prevention and Health Promotion, Office on Smoking and Health, 3. www.surgeongeneral.gov/library/reports/preventing-youth-tobacco-use/full-report.pdf;
Jackson, C., & Dickinson, D. (2006). Enabling parents who smoke to prevent their children from initiating smoking: results from a 3-year intervention evaluation. *Archives of pediatrics & adolescent medicine, 160*(1), 56-62. https://pubmed.ncbi.nlm.nih.gov/16389212/

129 *Not On Tobacco (NOT)—Smoking Cessation Program for 14–19 Year Olds Selected as a Model Program.* (n.d.) Prevention Research Centers, Centers for Disease Control and Prevention. www.cdc.gov/prc/pdf/not-on-tobacco-smoking-cessation.pdf

Citing: Horn, K., Dino, G., Kalsekar, I., & Mody, R. (2005). The impact of Not On Tobacco on teen smoking cessation: End-of-program evaluation results, 1998 to 2003. *Journal of Adolescent Research, 20*(6), 640-661. http://journals.sagepub.com/doi/abs/10.1177/0743558405274891

130 *N-O-T: Not On Tobacco—Proven Teen Smoking and Vaping Cessation Program.* (2020). American Lung Association. www.lung.org/stop-smoking/helping-teens-quit/not-on-tobacco.html

131 Foxcroft, D. R., Moreira, M. T., Santimano, N. M. A., & Smith, L. A. (2015). Social norms information for alcohol misuse in university and college students. *Cochrane database of systematic reviews,* (12). www.cochranelibrary.com/cdsr/doi/10.1002/14651858.CD006748.pub4/full

132 Zernike, K. (2018). 'I Can't Stop': Schools Struggle With Vaping Explosion. *The New York Times.* www.nytimes.com/2018/04/02/health/vaping-ecigarettes-addiction-teen.html

133 Zernike, K. (2018). 'I Can't Stop': Schools Struggle With Vaping Explosion. *The New York Times.* www.nytimes.com/2018/04/02/health/vaping-ecigarettes-addiction-teen.html

134 Kirkham, C. (2018). *Special Report: Juul copycats flood e-cig market, despite FDA rule.* Reuters. www.reuters.com/article/us-vaping-regulation-juul-specialreport/special-report-juul-copycats-flood-e-cig-market-despite-fda-rule-idUSKCN1M418W

135 Johnston, L. D., Miech, R. A., O'Malley, P. M., Bachman, J. G., Schulenberg, J. E., & Patrick, M. E. (2018). *Monitoring the Future national survey results on drug use, 1975-2018: Overview, key findings on adolescent drug use.* www.monitoringthefuture.org/pubs/monographs/mtf-overview2018.pdf

136 Interlandi, J. (2019). Vaping Is Big Tobacco's Bait and Switch. *The New York Times.* www.nytimes.com/2019/03/08/opinion/editorials/vaping-ecigarettes-nicotine-safe.html?action=click&module=Opinion&pgtype=Homepage

137 Kirkham, C. (2018). *Special Report: Juul copycats flood e-cig market, despite FDA rule.* Reuters. www.reuters.com/article/us-vaping-regulation-juul-specialreport/special-report-juul-copycats-flood-e-cig-market-despite-fda-rule-idUSKCN1M418W

138 Johnston, L. D., Miech, R. A., O'Malley, P. M., Bachman, J. G., Schulenberg, J. E., & Patrick, M. E. (2018). *Monitoring the Future national survey results on drug use, 1975-2018: Overview, key findings on adolescent drug use.* www.monitoringthefuture.org/pubs/monographs/mtf-overview2018.pdf

139 Willett, J. G., Bennett, M., Hair, E. C., Xiao, H., Greenberg, M. S., Harvey, E., ... & Vallone, D. (2019). Recognition, use and perceptions of JUUL among youth and young adults. *Tobacco control, 28*(1), 115-116. https://tobaccocontrol.bmj.com/content/28/1/115.full?int_source=trendmd&int_medium=trendmd&int_campaign=trendmd

140 Kaplan, S. (2018). Vaping Can Be Addictive and May Lure Teenagers to Smoking, Science Panel Concludes. *The New York Times.* www.nytimes.com/2018/01/23/health/e-cigarettes-smoking-fda-tobacco.html?hpw&rref=health&action=click&pgtype=Homepage&module=well-region&region=bottom-well&WT.nav=bottom-well;
*New Report One of Most Comprehensive Studies on Health Effects of E-Cigarettes; Finds That Using E-Cigarettes May Lead Youth to Start Smoking, Adults to Stop Smoking.* (2018). The National Academies of Sciences, Engineering and Medicine. www8.nationalacademies.org/onpinews/newsitem.aspx?RecordID=24952

141 National Academies of Sciences, Engineering, and Medicine. 2018. *Public Health Consequences of E-Cigarettes.* The National Academies Press. http://nationalacademies.org/hmd/Reports/2018/public-health-consequences-of-e-cigarettes.aspx

142 National Academies of Sciences, Engineering, and Medicine. 2018. *Public Health Consequences of E-Cigarettes.* The National Academies Press. http://nationalacademies.org/hmd/Reports/2018/public-health-consequences-of-e-cigarettes.aspx

143 National Academies of Sciences, Engineering, and Medicine. 2018. *Public Health Consequences of E-Cigarettes.* The National Academies Press. http://nationalacademies.org/hmd/Reports/2018/public-health-consequences-of-e-cigarettes.aspx

144 Sassano, M. F., Davis, E. S., Keating, J. E., Zorn, B. T., Kochar, T. K., Wolfgang, M. C., ... & Tarran, R. (2018). Evaluation of e-liquid toxicity using an open-source high-throughput screening assay. *PLoS biology, 16*(3), e2003904. https://journals.plos.org/plosbiology/article?id=10.1371/journal.pbio.2003904

145 Rubinstein, M. L., Delucchi, K., Benowitz, N. L., & Ramo, D. E. (2018). Adolescent exposure to toxic volatile organic chemicals from e-cigarettes. *Pediatrics, 141*(4), e20173557. https://us.vocuspr.com/Newsroom/ViewAttachment.aspx?SiteName=AAP&Entity=PRAsset&AttachmentType=F&EntityID=121686&AttachmentID=3b026982-97a7-4e43-8713-fef7106071c7;
Ogunwale, M. A., Li, M., Ramakrishnam Raju, M. V., Chen, Y., Nantz, M. H., Conklin, D. J., & Fu, X. A. (2017). Aldehyde detection in electronic cigarette aerosols. *ACS omega, 2*(3), 1207-1214. https://pubs.acs.org/doi/abs/10.1021/acsomega.6b00489;
Khlystov, A., & Samburova, V. (2016). Flavoring compounds dominate toxic aldehyde production during e-cigarette vaping. *Environmental science & technology, 50*(23), 13080-13085. https://pubs.acs.org/doi/abs/10.1021/acs.est.6b05145

146 US Department of Health and Human Services. (2016). *E-cigarette use among youth and young adults: A report of the Surgeon General.* Atlanta, GA. https://e-cigarettes.surgeongeneral.gov/documents/2016_sgr_full_report_non-508.pdf

147 Allen, J. G. (2018). The Formaldehyde in Your E-Cigs. *The New York Times.* www.nytimes.com/2018/04/04/opinion/formaldehyde-diacetyl-e-cigs.html;

Allen, J. G., Flanigan, S. S., LeBlanc, M., Vallarino, J., MacNaughton, P., Stewart, J. H., & Christiani, D. C. (2016). Flavoring chemicals in e-cigarettes: diacetyl, 2, 3-pentanedione, and acetoin in a sample of 51 products, including fruit-, candy-, and cocktail-flavored e-cigarettes. *Environmental health perspectives, 124*(6), 733. https://ehp.niehs.nih.gov/15-10185/

148 National Academies of Sciences, Engineering, and Medicine. 2018. *Public Health Consequences of E-Cigarettes.* The National Academies Press. http://nationalacademies.org/hmd/Reports/2018/public-health-consequences-of-e-cigarettes.aspx

149 National Academies of Sciences, Engineering, and Medicine. 2018. *Public Health Consequences of E-Cigarettes.* The National Academies Press. http://nationalacademies.org/hmd/Reports/2018/public-health-consequences-of-e-cigarettes.aspx

150 Miech, R., Patrick, M. E., O'malley, P. M., & Johnston, L. D. (2017). E-cigarette use as a predictor of cigarette smoking: results from a 1-year follow-up of a national sample of 12th grade students. *Tobacco control, 26*(e2), e106-e111. https://tobaccocontrol.bmj.com/content/26/e2/e106

151 National Academies of Sciences, Engineering, and Medicine. 2018. *Public Health Consequences of E-Cigarettes.* The National Academies Press. http://nationalacademies.org/hmd/Reports/2018/public-health-consequences-of-e-cigarettes.aspx

152 Marynak, K., Gentzke, A., Wang, T. W., Neff, L., & King, B. A. (2018). Exposure to electronic cigarette advertising among middle and high school students—United States, 2014–2016. *Morbidity and Mortality Weekly Report, 67*(10), 294. www.cdc.gov/mmwr/preview/mmwrhtml/mm6452a3.htm?s_cid=mm6452a3_w

153 Patrick, M. E., Miech, R. A., Carlier, C., O'Malley, P. M., Johnston, L. D., & Schulenberg, J. E. (2016). Self-reported reasons for vaping among 8th, 10th, and 12th graders in the US: nationally-representative results. *Drug and alcohol dependence,* 165, 275-278. www.ncbi.nlm.nih.gov/pmc/articles/PMC4939118/

154 Pepper, J. K., Coats, E. M., Nonnemaker, J. M., & Loomis, B. R. (2019). How do adolescents get their e-cigarettes and other electronic vaping devices?. *American Journal of Health Promotion, 33*(3), 420-429. https://journals.sagepub.com/doi/abs/10.1177/0890117118790366

155 O'Connor, S., Pelletier, H., Bayoumy, D., & Schwartz, R. (2019). *Interventions to Prevent Harms from Vaping.* www.otru.org/wp-content/uploads/2019/05/special_vape_interventions.pdf

156 Kalamut, A. (2010). *This Is Your Brain...This Is Your Brain On Drugs - 80s Partnership For A Drug Free America* [Video]. YouTube. www.youtube.com/watch?v=GOnENVylxPI

157 Footnote references:
[1] U.S. Department of Health and Human Services (HHS), Office of the Surgeon General. (2016). *Facing Addiction in America: The Surgeon General's Report on Alcohol, Drugs, and Health.* https://addiction.surgeongeneral.gov/sites/default/files/chapter-3-prevention.pdf
[2] Toumbourou, J. W., Stockwell, T., Neighbors, C., Marlatt, G. A., Sturge, J., & Rehm, J. (2007). Interventions to reduce harm associated with adolescent substance use. *The Lancet, 369*(9570), 1391-1401. www.aracy.org.au/publications-resources/command/download_file/id/106/filename/Interventions_to_reduce_harm_associated_with_adolescent_substance_use.pdf
[3] United Nations Office on Drugs and Crime. (2010). *Compilation of evidence-based family skills training programmes.* www.unodc.org/documents/prevention/family-compilation.pdf
[4] Kumpfer, K. L., & Alvarado, R. (1998). *Effective family strengthening interventions.* US Department of Justice, Office of Justice Programs, Office of Juvenile Justice and Delinquency Prevention. https://pdfs.semanticscholar.org/2a2e/4c1628d55289fbc94e45718c7582d7bb50a7.pdf

158 Ferri, M., Allara, E., Bo, A., Gasparrini, A., & Faggiano, F. (2013). Media campaigns for the prevention of illicit drug use in young people. *Cochrane Database of Systematic Reviews,* (6). www.cochranelibrary.com/cdsr/doi/10.1002/14651858.CD009287.pub2/full

159 Gottfredson, D. C., Wilson, D. B., & Najaka, S. S. (2002). School-based crime prevention. *Evidence-based crime prevention*, 56, 164. www.ncjrs.gov/works/chapter5.htm;
Botvin, G. J. (1990). *Substance abuse prevention: Theory, practice, and effectiveness.* In M. Tonry and J. Q. Wilson (eds.), *Drugs and Crime.* Chicago: The University of Chicago Press.;
Tobler, N. S., Roona, M. R., Ochshorn, P., Marshall, D. G., Streke, A. V., & Stackpole, K. M. (2000). School-based adolescent drug prevention programs: 1998 meta-analysis. *Journal of primary Prevention, 20*(4), 275-336. https://link.springer.com/article/10.1023/A:1021314704811

160 Lipp, A. (2011). Universal school-based prevention programmes for alcohol misuse in young people. *International Journal of Evidence-Based Healthcare, 9*(4), 452-453. www.cochranelibrary.com/cdsr/doi/10.1002/14651858.CD009113/full

161 Reyna, V. F., & Farley, F. (2006). Risk and rationality in adolescent decision making: Implications for theory, practice, and public policy. *Psychological science in the public interest, 7*(1), 1-44. https://pdfs.semanticscholar.org/1de4/966482722d1f7da8bbef16d108639d9a1c38.pdf

162 Goldberg, L., Bents, R., Bosworth, E., Trevisan, L., & Elliot, D. L. (1991). Anabolic steroid education and adolescents: do scare tactics work?. *Pediatrics, 87*(3), 283-286. https://pediatrics.aappublications.org/content/87/3/283

163 Hecht, M., Trost, M. R., Bator, R. J., & MacKinnon, D. (1997). *Ethnicity and sex similarities and differences in drug resistance.* https://d1wqtxts1xzle7.cloudfront.net/40612596/Hecht_et_al._1997.pdf?1449169112=&response-content-disposition=inline%3B+filename%3DEthnicity_and_sex_similarities_and_diffe.pdf&Expires=1617222282&Signature=hST1Qlm5cvsRc0dXDNZzx9z-uzzbKEqPMIvzxLWNoMDhjedy5k2EoPUDQQDtR-AMcbrr0H0Ks0kWo1rQULYZ7KLjZLH25UVvrhyt4OGumsP78IC2rAojJSjypig92vGPkYJH0ubN2KRViPO8aGJ-pzkci6zKSjBWXa5O1z-zCoyHBfS25dsV6Ocf0B3cU9GcO4-nNVvYl0gRh8pOfqh0-OQ2BTsvi9VqXR0ukI7XK4Uszh1K63zri1fb4yb5fcsaQKTvy8dSUcptf8T4nlW08fC7oN9nS0LrZOhnFY5AuJlML72gt91cgVFeyjuV6JhnbQUI-vGLS3PtuYxne59zVw__&Key-Pair-Id=APKAJLOHF5GGSLRBV4ZA

164 Hecht, M., Trost, M. R., Bator, R. J., & MacKinnon, D. (1997). *Ethnicity and sex similarities and differences in drug resistance.* https://d1wqtxts1xzle7.cloudfront.net/40612596/Hecht_et_al._1997.pdf?1449169112=&response-content-disposition=inline%3B+filename%3DEthnicity_and_sex_similarities_and_diffe.pdf&Expires=1617222282&Signature=hST1Qlm5cvsRc0dXDNZzx9z-uzzbKEqPMIvzxLWNoMDhjedy5k2EoPUDQQDtR-AMcbrr0H0Ks0kWo1rQULYZ7KLjZLH25UVvrhyt4OGumsP78IC2rAojJSjypig92vGPkYJH0ubN2KRViPO8aGJ-pzkci6zKSjBWXa5O1z-zCoyHBfS25dsV6Ocf0B3cU9GcO4-nNVvYl0gRh8pOfqh0-OQ2BTsvi9VqXR0ukI7XK4Uszh1K63zri1fb4yb5fcsaQKTvy8dSUcptf8T4nlW08fC7oN9nS0LrZOhnFY5AuJlML72gt91cgVFeyjuV6JhnbQUI-vGLS3PtuYxne59zVw__&Key-Pair-Id=APKAJLOHF5GGSLRBV4ZA

165 Alberts, J. K., Hecht, M. L., Miller-Rassulo, M., & Krizek, R. L. (1992). The communicative process of drug resistance among high school students. *Adolescence, 27*(105), 203-226. https://d1wqtxts1xzle7.cloudfront.net/33563601/Alberts_hecht_MillerRassulo_1992_communicative_process.pdf?1398517688=&response-content-disposition=inline%3B+filename%3DThe_Communicative_Process_of_Drug_Resist.pdf&Expires=1617221793&Signature=eU7wBFK07XCko3tmvuYCh-JgTD6kdWk7yezAGOvlrr1PMhlqoN-8Al6hIEKD6S9S08oHALOvta8JNdztx0f4CfW69zUfnV345ZpkoU6LB2o6fjf5RxVzrV2ie0EL0y6TboLND3n-sRaTM8SStfegolh67cKRpvsNgzTyW7KTRLKnEqWZ3Ddo5AwqVDBXRSPlYFtM54Dt9pM5eNb4aZT-VpomIC7nHuo7DYAZwWjz3ED-C4WnGiVlhiaJ4dy9WIPrmR2IqNkuFgjVERkGWZjM1HAf7szZQ2wI-Y-cVckQMb911-ek2BvQ5xMMxHxWeeuAjO7MC3X0tYDKdgGcanW0V-UkLg__&Key-Pair-Id=APKAJLOHF5GGSLRBV4ZA

166 Coomber, R., & Moyle, L. (2014). Beyond drug dealing: Developing and extending the concept of 'social supply' of illicit drugs to 'minimally commercial supply'. *Drugs: education, prevention and policy, 21*(2), 157-164. www.tandfonline.com/doi/abs/10.3109/09687637.2013.798265

167 Levine, J. M., Alexander, K. M., & Hansen, T. (2010). *Self-control in groups.* https://academic.oup.com/book/32883/chapter-abstract/276400382?redirectedFrom=fulltext

168 Lenton, S. (2016). Why do our friends pressure us into drinking? *The Sydney Morning Herald.* www.smh.com.au/lifestyle/life-and-relationships/why-do-our-friends-pressure-us-into-drinking-20161230-gtjppk.html

169 Gilchrist, L. D., Snow, W. H., Lodish, D., & Schinke, S. P. (1985). The relationship of cognitive and behavioral skills to adolescent tobacco smoking. *Journal of School Health, 55*(4), 132-134. www.researchgate.net/profile/William_Snow2/publication/227747137_The_Relationship_of_Cognitive_and_Behavioral_Skills_to_Adolescent_Tobacco_Smoking/links/5a579d0445851529a2edb8bf/The-Relationship-of-Cognitive-and-Behavioral-Skills-to-Adolescent-Tobacco-Smoking.pdf

170 Miller-Day, M. A., Alberts, J., Hecht, M. L., Trost, M. R., & Krizek, R. L. (2014). *Adolescent relationships and drug use.* Psychology Press. https://books.google.co.uk/books?hl=en&lr=&id=VSt6AgAAQBAJ&oi=fnd&pg=P-P1&ots=FRPzbL9vEa&sig=u7BxcqZbleUWBDmsRY9-uFd4-WA#v=snippet&q=The%20social%20process%20of%20drug%20resistance%20in%20a%20relational%20context&f=false;
Kern, J. M. (1982). Predicting the impact of assertive, empathic-assertive, and nonassertive behavior: The assertiveness of the assertee. *Behavior Therapy, 13*(4), 486-498. www.sciencedirect.com/science/article/abs/pii/S0005789482800117

171 Wildman, B. G. (1986). Perception of refusal assertion: The effects of conversational comments and compliments. *Behavior modification, 10*(4), 472-486. https://journals.sagepub.com/doi/abs/10.1177/01454455860104006

172 Gilchrist, L. D., Snow, W. H., Lodish, D., & Schinke, S. P. (1985). The relationship of cognitive and behavioral skills to adolescent tobacco smoking. *Journal of School Health, 55*(4), 132-134. www.researchgate.net/profile/William_Snow2/publication/227747137_The_Relationship_of_Cognitive_and_Behavioral_Skills_to_Adolescent_Tobacco_Smoking/links/5a579d0445851529a2edb8bf/The-Relationship-of-Cognitive-and-Behavioral-Skills-to-Adolescent-Tobacco-Smoking.pdf

173 *Teens need communication, negotiation skills to resist drugs.* (2000). EurekAlert! www.eurekalert.org/pub_releases/2000-07/PS-Tncn-2007100.php

174 Conner, M., & Higgins, A. R. (2010). Long-term effects of implementation intentions on prevention of smoking uptake among adolescents: a cluster randomized controlled trial. *Health Psychology, 29*(5), 529. https://s3.amazonaws.com/academia.edu.documents/35590800/pub_2010_11.pdf?response-content-disposition=inline%3B%20filename%3DLong-term_effects_of_implementation_inte.pdf&X-Amz-Algorithm=AWS4-HMAC-SHA256&X-Amz-Credential=AKIAIWOWYYGZ2Y53UL3A%2F20190610%2Fus-east-1%2Fs3%2Faws4_request&X-Amz-Date=20190610T151925Z&X-Amz-Expires=3600&X-Amz-SignedHeaders=host&X-Amz-Signature=43917957d39d3cb50fd8d7021e6cb6c0efed9ff031f8952889689b1895957dab

175 Pollan, Michael. *How to Change Your Mind* (p. 83). Penguin Publishing Group. Kindle Edition.
176 Marijuana. (n.d.). Britannica. www.britannica.com/science/marijuana

177 Curry, A. (2017). Our 9,000-Year Love Affair With Booze. *National Geographic.* www.nationalgeographic.com/magazine/2017/02/alcohol-discovery-addiction-booze-human-culture/

178 Crocq, M. A. (2007). Historical and cultural aspects of man's relationship with addictive drugs. *Dialogues in clinical neuroscience, 9*(4), 355. www.ncbi.nlm.nih.gov/pmc/articles/PMC3202501/

179 *Parents in the Dark.* (2014). Hazelden's Adolescent and Young Adult Services. www.hazelden.org/web/public/document/parents-in-dark.pdf

180 Johnston, L. D., Miech, R. A., O'Malley, P. M., Bachman, J. G., Schulenberg, J. E., & Patrick, M. E. (2018). *Monitoring the Future national survey results on drug use, 1975-2018: Overview, key findings on adolescent drug use.* The National Institute on Drug Abuse. www.monitoringthefuture.org/pubs/monographs/mtf-overview2018.pdf

181 Johnston, L. D., Miech, R. A., O'Malley, P. M., Bachman, J. G., Schulenberg, J. E., & Patrick, M. E. (2018). *Monitoring the Future national survey results on drug use, 1975-2018: Overview, key findings on adolescent drug use.* The National Institute on Drug Abuse. www.monitoringthefuture.org/pubs/monographs/mtf-overview2018.pdf

182 Johnston, L., Miech, R., O'Malley, P., Bachman, J., Schulenberg, J., & Patrick, M. (2020). *Monitoring the Future national survey results on drug use, 1975-2019: Overview, key findings on adolescent drug use.* https://deepblue.lib.umich.edu/bitstream/handle/2027.42/162579/FINAL.pdf?sequence=1

183 Swendsen, J., Burstein, M., Case, B., Conway, K. P., Dierker, L., He, J., & Merikangas, K. R. (2012). Use and abuse of alcohol and illicit drugs in US adolescents: Results of the National Comorbidity Survey–Adolescent Supplement. *Archives of general psychiatry, 69*(4), 390-398. http://jamanetwork.com/journals/jamapsychiatry/fullarticle/1151056

184 Bogenschneider, K., Wu, M. Y., Raffaelli, M., & Tsay, J. C. (1998). Other teens drink, but not my kid": Does parental awareness of adolescent alcohol use protect adolescents from risky consequences?. *Journal of Marriage and the Family,* 356-373. https://digitalcommons.unl.edu/cgi/viewcontent.cgi?referer=http://scholar.google.co.uk/&httpsredir=1&article=1115&context=psychfacpub;
Williams, R. J., McDermitt, D. R., Bertrand, L. D., & Davis, R. M. (2003). Parental awareness of adolescent substance use. *Addictive Behaviors, 28*(4), 803-809. www.uleth.ca/dspace/bitstream/handle/10133/413/Parental?sequence=1

185 Fisher, S. L., Bucholz, K. K., Reich, W., Fox, L., Kuperman, S., Kramer, J., ... & Bierut, L. J. (2006). Teenagers are right—Parents do not know much: An analysis of adolescent–parent agreement on reports of adolescent substance use, abuse, and dependence. *Alcoholism: Clinical and experimental research, 30*(10), 1699-1710. http://citeseerx.ist.psu.edu/viewdoc/download?doi=10.1.1.375.7190&rep=rep1&type=pdf

186 Merikangas, K. R., He, J. P., Burstein, M., Swanson, S. A., Avenevoli, S., Cui, L., ... & Swendsen, J. (2010). Lifetime prevalence of mental disorders in US adolescents: results from the National Comorbidity Survey Replication–Adolescent Supplement (NCS-A). *Journal of the American Academy of Child & Adolescent Psychiatry, 49*(10), 980-989. www.ncbi.nlm.nih.gov/pmc/articles/PMC2946114/?_escaped_fragment_=po=2.63158

187 Lund, T. J., Dearing, E., & Zachrisson, H. D. (2017). Is affluence a risk for adolescents in Norway?. *Journal of Research on Adolescence, 27*(3), 628-643. https://fhi.brage.unit.no/fhi-xmlui/bitstream/handle/11250/2562366/Lund_et_al-2017-Journal_of_Research_on_Adolescence.pdf?sequence=2

188 Luthar, S. S., & D'Avanzo, Karen (1999). Contextual factors in substance use: A study of suburban and inner-city adolescents. *Development and psychopathology, 11*(4), 845-867. www.ncbi.nlm.nih.gov/pmc/articles/PMC3535189/

189 Lyman, E. L., & Luthar, S. S. (2014). Further evidence on the "costs of privilege": Perfectionism in high-achieving youth at socioeconomic extremes. *Psychology in the Schools, 51*(9), 913-930. www.ncbi.nlm.nih.gov/pmc/articles/PMC4559285/

190 Luthar, S. S., & Latendresse, S. J. (2005). Children of the affluent: Challenges to well-being. *Current directions in psychological science, 14*(1), 49-53. www.ncbi.nlm.nih.gov/pmc/articles/PMC1948879/?_escaped_fragment_=po=32.3529

191 Luthar, S. S., & Latendresse, S. J. (2005). Children of the affluent: Challenges to well-being. *Current directions in psychological science, 14*(1), 49-53. www.ncbi.nlm.nih.gov/pmc/articles/PMC1948879/?_escaped_fragment_=po=32.3529

192 Degenhardt, L., Whiteford, H. A., Ferrari, A. J., Baxter, A. J., Charlson, F. J., Hall, W. D., ... & Flaxman, A. (2013). Global burden of disease attributable to illicit drug use and dependence: findings from the Global Burden of Disease Study 2010. *The Lancet, 382*(9904), 1564-1574. www.thelancet.com/journals/lancet/article/PIIS0140-6736(13)61530-5/fulltext;
Lim, S. S., Vos, T., Flaxman, A. D., Danaei, G., Shibuya, K., Adair-Rohani, H., ... & Aryee, M. (2012). A comparative risk assessment of burden of disease and injury attributable to 67 risk factors and risk factor clusters in 21 regions, 1990–2010: a systematic analysis for the Global Burden of Disease Study 2010. *The lancet, 380*(9859), 2224-2260. www.ncbi.nlm.nih.gov/pmc/articles/PMC4156511/

193 Gable, R. S. (2006). Macroscope: The Toxicity of Recreational Drugs. *American scientist, 94*(3), 206-208. https://web.cgu.edu/faculty/gabler/Amer%20Scientist.pdf

194 Lachenmeier, D. W., & Rehm, J. (2015). Comparative risk assessment of alcohol, tobacco, cannabis and other illicit drugs using the margin of exposure approach. *Scientific reports*, 5, 8126. www.ncbi.nlm.nih.gov/pmc/articles/PMC4311234/#b3

195 Gable, R. S. (2004). Comparison of acute lethal toxicity of commonly abused psychoactive substances. *Addiction, 99*(6), 686-696. http://chemistry.mdma.ch/hiveboard/rhodium/pdf/psychoactives.acute.lethal.toxicity.pdf

196 Gable, R. S. (2006). The Toxicity of Recreational Drugs. *American Scientist*. www.americanscientist.org/libraries/documents/200645104835_307.pdf
Gable, R. S. (n.d.) Drug Toxicity. Robert Gable. https://rgable.wordpress.com/drug-toxicity/

197 Footnote references:
[1] Gable, R. S. (2006). *Acute toxicity of drugs versus regulatory status*. Drugs and society: US public policy, 149-62. https://books.google.co.uk/books?hl=en&lr=&id=xpZhjBuDkuwC&oi=fnd&pg=PA149&dq=Acute+Toxicity+of+Drugs+versus+Regulatory+Status&ots=YJNgvQXs88&sig=T-w8cw-FL3ojIOelvrMI4Us39DQ#v=onepage&q=Acute%20Toxicity%20of%20Drugs%20versus%20Regulatory%20Status&f=false
[2] Anthony, J. C., Warner, L. A., & Kessler, R. C. (1994). Comparative epidemiology of dependence on tobacco, alcohol, controlled substances, and inhalants: basic findings from the National Comorbidity Survey. *Experimental and clinical psychopharmacology, 2*(3), 244. www.biblioteca.cij.gob.mx/articulos/PatronDeUsoYDependencia/1994AnthonyComparativeEpidemiologyOfDependenceOnTobacco,Alcohol,ControlledSubstances,AndInhalants.pdf
[3] Lopez-Quintero, C., de los Cobos, J. P., Hasin, D. S., Okuda, M., Wang, S., Grant, B. F., & Blanco, C. (2011). Probability and predictors of transition from first use to dependence on nicotine, alcohol, cannabis, and cocaine: Results of the National Epidemiologic Survey on Alcohol and Related Conditions (NESARC). *Drug and alcohol dependence, 115*(1), 120-130. www.ncbi.nlm.nih.gov/pmc/articles/PMC3069146/?utm_source=tech.mazavr.tk&utm_medium=link&utm_compaign=article

198 Demers, C. H., Bogdan, R., & Agrawal, A. (2014). The genetics, neurogenetics and pharmacogenetics of addiction. *Current behavioral neuroscience reports, 1*(1), 33-44. https://link.springer.com/article/10.1007/s40473-013-0004-8;
Agrawal, A., Verweij, K. J. H., Gillespie, N. A., Heath, A. C., Lessov-Schlaggar, C. N., Martin, N. G., ... & Lynskey, M. T. (2012). The genetics of addiction—a translational perspective. *Translational psychiatry, 2*(7), e140. www.nature.com/articles/tp201254

199 Nutt, D., King, L. A., Saulsbury, W., & Blakemore, C. (2007). Development of a rational scale to assess the harm of drugs of potential misuse. *The Lancet, 369*(9566), 1047-1053. http://dobrochan.ru/src/pdf/1109/lancet-norway.pdf;
Nutt, D. J., King, L. A., & Phillips, L. D. (2010). Drug harms in the UK: a multicriteria decision analysis. *The Lancet, 376*(9752), 1558-1565. www.thelancet.com/journals/lancet/article/PIIS0140-6736(10)61462-6/fulltext

200 Van Amsterdam, J., Opperhuizen, A., Koeter, M., & van den Brink, W. (2010). Ranking the harm of alcohol, tobacco and illicit drugs for the individual and the population. *European addiction research, 16*(4), 202-207. www.karger.com/Article/Abstract/317249

201 van Amsterdam, J., Nutt, D., Phillips, L., & van den Brink, W. (2015). European rating of drug harms. *Journal of Psychopharmacology, 29*(6), 655-660. www.samuel-widmer.ch/wp-content/uploads/2016/06/Van-Amsterdam-European-Rating-of-drugs-J.-Psychopharmacology-2015.pdf

202 Caulkins, J. P., Reuter, P., & Coulson, C. (2011). Basing drug scheduling decisions on scientific ranking of harmfulness: false promise from false premises. *Addiction, 106*(11), 1886-1890. https://europepmc.org/abstract/MED/21895823;
Nutt, D. (2011). Let not the best be the enemy of the good. *Addiction, 106*(11), 1892-1893. https://onlinelibrary.wiley.com/doi/full/10.1111/j.1360-0443.2011.03527.x

203 Nutt, D. J., King, L. A., & Phillips, L. D. (2010). Drug harms in the UK: a multicriteria decision analysis. *The Lancet, 376*(9752), 1558-1565. www.thelancet.com/journals/lancet/article/PIIS0140-6736(10)61462-6/fulltext

204 Nutt, D., King, L. A., Saulsbury, W., & Blakemore, C. (2007). Development of a rational scale to assess the harm of drugs of potential misuse. *The Lancet, 369*(9566), 1047-1053. http://dobrochan.ru/src/pdf/1109/lancet-norway.pdf

205 Johnston, L. D., Miech, R. A., O'Malley, P. M., Bachman, J. G., Schulenberg, J. E., & Patrick, M. E. (2018). *Monitoring the Future national survey results on drug use, 1975-2018: Overview, key findings on adolescent drug use.* www.monitoringthefuture.org/pubs/monographs/mtf-overview2018.pdf

206 Usage: Johnston, L. D., Miech, R. A., O'Malley, P. M., Bachman, J. G., Schulenberg, J. E., & Patrick, M. E. (2018). *Monitoring the Future national survey results on drug use, 1975-2018: Overview, key findings on adolescent drug use.* The National Institute on Drug Abuse. www.monitoringthefuture.org/pubs/monographs/mtf-overview2018.pdf;
Harm score: Nutt, D. J., King, L. A., & Phillips, L. D. (2010). Drug harms in the UK: a multicriteria decision analysis. *The Lancet, 376*(9752), 1558-1565. Available at: www.thelancet.com/journals/lancet/article/PIIS0140-6736(10)61462-6/fulltext

207 Hasse, J. (2019). Seth Rogen On His New Weed Products: 'We Want Consumers To Understand Cannabis On A Deeper Level'. *Forbes.* www.forbes.com/sites/javierhasse/2019/10/16/houseplant-seth-rogen-weed/#62024b18208d

208 Russo, E. B. (2007). History of cannabis and its preparations in saga, science, and sobriquet. *Chemistry & biodiversity, 4*(8), 1614-1648. http://letfreedomgrow.org/cmu/Russo2007.pdf

209 United Nations Office on Drugs, & Crime. (2019). *World drug report 2019.* United Nations Publications. https://wdr.unodc.org/wdr2019/prelaunch/WDR19_Booklet_1_EXECUTIVE_SUMMARY.pdf

210 Sevigny, E. L. (2013). Is today's marijuana more potent simply because it's fresher?. *Drug testing and analysis, 5*(1), 62-67. https://s3.amazonaws.com/academia.edu.documents/41687027/Is_todays_marijuana_more_potent_simply_20160128-25003-xv2za.pdf?AWSAccessKeyId=AKIAIWOWYYGZ2Y53UL3A&Expires=1517579597&Signature=FpXevNo1mdT4hfxuuT1tMM3Webw%3D&response-content-disposition=inline%3B%20filename%3DIs_todays_marijuana_more_potent_simply_b.pdf

211 Davis, K. L. & Kreek, M. J. (2019). Marijuana Damages Young Brains. *The New York Times.* www.nytimes.com/2019/06/16/opinion/marijuana-brain-effects.html?action=click&module=Opinion&pgtype=Homepage

212 Joy, J. E., Watson, S. J., & Benson, J. A. (1999). *Marijuana and medicine: Assessing the science base.* Washington DC: National Academy. https://nurturingnature.com/files/1999-Institute-of-Medicine-Report.pdf

213 Jacobus, J., Bava, S., Cohen-Zion, M., Mahmood, O., & Tapert, S. F. (2009). Functional consequences of marijuana use in adolescents. Pharmacology *Biochemistry and Behavior, 92*(4), 559-565. www.ncbi.nlm.nih.gov/pmc/articles/PMC2697065/

214 Meier, M. H., Caspi, A., Ambler, A., Harrington, H., Houts, R., Keefe, R. S., ... & Moffitt, T. E. (2012). Persistent cannabis users show neuropsychological decline from childhood to midlife. *Proceedings of the National*

*Academy of Sciences, 109*(40), E2657-E2664. www.pnas.org/content/pnas/early/2012/08/22/1206820109.full.pdf

215 Davis, K. L. & Kreek, M. J. (2019). Marijuana Damages Young Brains. *The New York Times*. www.nytimes.com/2019/06/16/opinion/marijuana-brain-effects.html?action=click&module=Opinion&pgtype=Homepage

216 Committee on Substance Abuse. (2015). The impact of marijuana policies on youth: clinical, research, and legal update. *Pediatrics, 135*(3), 584-587. https://pediatrics.aappublications.org/content/135/3/584

217 Calabria, B., Degenhardt, L., Hall, W., & Lynskey, M. (2010). Does cannabis use increase the risk of death? Systematic review of epidemiological evidence on adverse effects of cannabis use. *Drug and alcohol review, 29*(3), 318-330. http://citeseerx.ist.psu.edu/viewdoc/download?doi=10.1.1.660.1986&rep=rep1&type=pdf;
Hall, W., & Solowij, N. (1998). Adverse effects of cannabis. *The Lancet, 352*(9140), 1611-1616. https://dickkesslerphd.com/wp-content/uploads/2019/01/Adverse-Effects-of-Cannabis-pot-1.pdf

218 Harrison, P. A., Fulkerson, J. A., & Park, E. (2000). The relative importance of social versus commercial sources in youth access to tobacco, alcohol, and other drugs. *Preventive medicine, 31*(1), 39-48. www.researchgate.net/profile/Paul_Turnbull2/publication/238093328_Arenas_of_drug_transactions_Adolescent_cannabis_transactions_in_ENGLAND_-_Social_supply/links/551a7e870cf2f51a6fea5387.pdf

219 Anderson, D. M., Hansen, B., Rees, D. I., & Sabia, J. J. (2019). Association of marijuana laws with teen marijuana use: new estimates from the youth risk behavior surveys. *JAMA pediatrics, 173*(9), 879-881. https://jamanetwork.com/journals/jamapediatrics/fullarticle/2737637?guestAccessKey=5e4e41eb-ec96-4641-86f9-b5c-89cc7cc48&utm_source=For_The_Media&utm_medium=referral&utm_campaign=ftm_links&utm_content=tfl&utm_term=070819

220 Dai, H., & Richter, K. P. (2019). A national survey of marijuana use among US adults with medical conditions, 2016-2017. *JAMA network open, 2*(9), e1911936-e1911936. https://jamanetwork.com/journals/jamanetworkopen/fullarticle/2751558

221 Hasin, D. S., Kerridge, B. T., Saha, T. D., Huang, B., Pickering, R., Smith, S. M., ... & Grant, B. F. (2016). Prevalence and correlates of DSM-5 cannabis use disorder, 2012-2013: findings from the National Epidemiologic Survey on Alcohol and Related Conditions–III. *American Journal of Psychiatry, 173*(6), 588-599. https://pubmed.ncbi.nlm.nih.gov/26940807/

222 Williams, A. (2021). Seth Rogen Is All Fired Up. *The New York Times*. www.nytimes.com/2021/03/06/style/seth-rogen-pot.html

223 In Their Own Words: 'Study Drugs'. (n.d.). *The New York Times*. http://archive.nytimes.com/www.nytimes.com/interactive/2012/06/10/education/stimulants-student-voices.html?_r=1

224 Kirkham, C. (2018). *Special Report: Juul copycats flood e-cig market, despite FDA rule*. Reuters. www.reuters.com/article/us-vaping-regulation-juul-specialreport/special-report-juul-copycats-flood-e-cig-market-despite-fda-rule-idUSKCN1M418W

225 Johnston, L. D., Miech, R. A., O'Malley, P. M., Bachman, J. G., Schulenberg, J. E., & Patrick, M. E. (2018). *Monitoring the Future national survey results on drug use, 1975-2018: Overview, key findings on adolescent drug use*. www.monitoringthefuture.org/pubs/monographs/mtf-overview2018.pdf

226 Johnston, L. D., Miech, R. A., O'Malley, P. M., Bachman, J. G., Schulenberg, J. E., & Patrick, M. E. (2019). *Monitoring the Future National Survey Results on Drug Use, 1975-2018: Overview, Key Findings on Adolescent Drug Use*. Institute for Social Research. www.monitoringthefuture.org/pubs/monographs/mtf-overview2018.pdf;
Teter, C. J., DiRaimo, C. G., West, B. T., Schepis, T. S., & McCabe, S. E. (2020). Nonmedical use of prescription stimulants among US high school students to help study: results from a national survey. *Journal of pharmacy practice, 33*(1), 38-47. https://digital.library.txstate.edu/bitstream/handle/10877/8539/nihms980214.pdf?sequence=1;
Partnership Attitude Tracking Study. (2013). Parents and teens in grades 9 through 12, 2013. https://drugfree.org/wp-content/uploads/2014/07/PATS-2013-FULL-REPORT.pdf;
Palamar, J. J., & Le, A. (2017). Discordant reporting of nonmedical amphetamine use among Adderall-using high school seniors in the US. *Drug and alcohol dependence*, 181, 208-212. https://europepmc.org/articles/pmc5689455

227 Mott, C.S. (2013). *Children's Hospital National Poll on Children's Health One in ten teens using "study drugs," but are parents paying attention?* 18(3):1–2. https://mottpoll.org/sites/default/files/documents/052013_StudyDrugs.pdf

228 Garnier-Dykstra, L. M., Caldeira, K. M., Vincent, K. B., O'Grady, K. E., & Arria, A. M. (2012). Nonmedical use of prescription stimulants during college: Four-year trends in exposure opportunity, use, motives, and sources. *Journal of American College Health, 60*(3), 226-234. www.ncbi.nlm.nih.gov/pmc/articles/PMC3313072/; DeSantis, A. D., Webb, E. M., & Noar, S. M. (2008). Illicit use of prescription ADHD medications on a college campus: a multimethodological approach. *Journal of American college health, 57*(3), 315-324. www.researchgate.net/profile/Seth_Noar/publication/23448261_Illicit_Use_of_Prescription_ADHD_Medications_on_a_College_Campus_A_Multimethodological_Approach/links/02e7e52ae673804d5a000000/Illicit-Use-of-Prescription-ADHD-Medications-on-a-College-Campus-A-Multimethodological-Approach.pdf

229 DeSantis, A. D., Webb, E. M., & Noar, S. M. (2008). Illicit use of prescription ADHD medications on a college campus: a multimethodological approach. *Journal of American college health, 57*(3), 315-324. www.researchgate.net/profile/Seth_Noar/publication/23448261_Illicit_Use_of_Prescription_ADHD_Medications_on_a_College_Campus_A_Multimethodological_Approach/links/02e7e52ae673804d5a000000/Illicit-Use-of-Prescription-ADHD-Medications-on-a-College-Campus-A-Multimethodological-Approach.pdf

230 McCabe, S. E., Teter, C. J., & Boyd, C. J. (2006). Medical use, illicit use and diversion of prescription stimulant medication. *Journal of psychoactive drugs, 38*(1), 43-56. www.ncbi.nlm.nih.gov/pmc/articles/PMC1761861/?_escaped_fragment_=po=10.8696

231 Pierson, E. (2015). *College Students Aren't The Only Ones Abusing Adderall.* FiveThirtyEight. https://fivethirtyeight.com/features/college-students-arent-the-only-ones-abusing-adderall/

232 McCabe, S. E., Knight, J. R., Teter, C. J., & Wechsler, H. (2005). Non-medical use of prescription stimulants among US college students: Prevalence and correlates from a national survey. *Addiction, 100*(1), 96-106. https://deepblue.lib.umich.edu/bitstream/handle/2027.42/74786/j.1360-0443.2005.00944.x.pdf?sequence=1&isAllowed=y

233 Arria, A. M., Wilcox, H. C., Caldeira, K. M., Vincent, K. B., Garnier-Dykstra, L. M., & O'Grady, K. E. (2013). Dispelling the myth of "smart drugs": Cannabis and alcohol use problems predict nonmedical use of prescription stimulants for studying. *Addictive behaviors, 38*(3), 1643-1650. www.ncbi.nlm.nih.gov/pmc/articles/PMC3558594/

234 Arria, A. M., O'Grady, K. E., Caldeira, K. M., Vincent, K. B., & Wish, E. D. (2008). Nonmedical use of prescription stimulants and analgesics: Associations with social and academic behaviors among college students. *Journal of drug issues, 38*(4), 1045-1060. www.ncbi.nlm.nih.gov/pmc/articles/PMC2857807/

235 DeSantis, A. D., Webb, E. M., & Noar, S. M. (2008). Illicit use of prescription ADHD medications on a college campus: a multimethodological approach. *Journal of American college health, 57*(3), 315-324. www.researchgate.net/profile/Seth_Noar/publication/23448261_Illicit_Use_of_Prescription_ADHD_Medications_on_a_College_Campus_A_Multimethodological_Approach/links/02e7e52ae673804d5a000000/Illicit-Use-of-Prescription-ADHD-Medications-on-a-College-Campus-A-Multimethodological-Approach.pdf

236 Jacobs, A. (2005). The Adderall Advantage. *The New York Times.* www.nytimes.com/2005/07/31/education/edlife/the-adderall-advantage.html

237 DeSantis, A. D., Webb, E. M., & Noar, S. M. (2008). Illicit use of prescription ADHD medications on a college campus: a multimethodological approach. *Journal of American college health, 57*(3), 315-324. www.researchgate.net/profile/Seth_Noar/publication/23448261_Illicit_Use_of_Prescription_ADHD_Medications_on_a_College_Campus_A_Multimethodological_Approach/links/02e7e52ae673804d5a000000/Illicit-Use-of-Prescription-ADHD-Medications-on-a-College-Campus-A-Multimethodological-Approach.pdf

238 Partnership for a Drug-Free America. (2013). *Key findings: The 2013 partnership attitude tracking study, sponsored by MetLife foundation.* https://drugfree.org/wp-content/uploads/2014/07/PATS-2013-FULL-REPORT.pdf

239 Smith, M. E., & Farah, M. J. (2011). Are prescription stimulants "smart pills"? The epidemiology and cognitive neuroscience of prescription stimulant use by normal healthy individuals. *Psychological bulletin, 137*(5), 717. www.ncbi.nlm.nih.gov/pmc/articles/PMC3591814/

240 Lakhan, S. E., & Kirchgessner, A. (2012). Prescription stimulants in individuals with and without attention deficit hyperactivity disorder: misuse, cognitive impact, and adverse effects. *Brain and behavior, 2*(5), 661-677. https://onlinelibrary.wiley.com/doi/pdf/10.1002/brb3.78

241 Jacobs, A. (2005). The Adderall Advantage. *The New York Times.* www.nytimes.com/2005/07/31/education/edlife/the-adderall-advantage.html

242 DeSantis, A. D., Webb, E. M., & Noar, S. M. (2008). Illicit use of prescription ADHD medications on a college campus: a multimethodological approach. *Journal of American college health, 57*(3), 315-324. www.researchgate.

net/profile/Seth_Noar/publication/23448261_Illicit_Use_of_Prescription_ADHD_Medications_on_a_College_Campus_A_Multimethodological_Approach/links/02e7e52ae673804d5a000000/Illicit-Use-of-Prescription-ADHD-Medications-on-a-College-Campus-A-Multimethodological-Approach.pdf

243 Partridge, B. J., Bell, S. K., Lucke, J. C., Yeates, S., & Hall, W. D. (2011). Smart drugs "as common as coffee": media hype about neuroenhancement. *PloS one, 6*(11), e28416. https://journals.plos.org/plosone/article?id=10.1371/journal.pone.0028416

244 Jacobs, A. (2005). The Adderall Advantage. *The New York Times*. www.nytimes.com/2005/07/31/education/edlife/the-adderall-advantage.html#:~:text=%22It%20won't%20increase%20your,dangerous%20than%20cocaine%20or%20methamphetamines
.

245 Jacobs, A. (2005). The Adderall Advantage. *The New York Times*. www.nytimes.com/2005/07/31/education/edlife/the-adderall-advantage.html#:~:text=%22It%20won't%20increase%20your,dangerous%20than%20cocaine%20or%20methamphetamines
.

246 *Drug Scheduling*. (n.d.). United States Drug Enforcement Administration. www.dea.gov/drug-scheduling

247 Smith, M. E., & Farah, M. J. (2011). Are prescription stimulants "smart pills"? The epidemiology and cognitive neuroscience of prescription stimulant use by normal healthy individuals. *Psychological bulletin, 137*(5), 717. www.ncbi.nlm.nih.gov/pmc/articles/PMC3591814/

248 Shoptaw, S. J., Kao, U., Heinzerling, K., & Ling, W. (2009). Treatment for amphetamine withdrawal. *Cochrane Database of Systematic Reviews*, (2). www.cochranelibrary.com/cdsr/doi/10.1002/14651858.CD003021.pub2/abstract

249 O'Malley GF, O'Malley R. (2003). *Merck Manual: Professional Version - Amphetamines*. www.merckmanuals.com/professional/special-subjects/recreational-drugs-and-intoxicants/amphetamines

250 DeSantis, A. D., & Hane, A. C. (2010). "Adderall is definitely not a drug": justifications for the illegal use of ADHD stimulants. *Substance use & misuse, 45*(1-2), 31-46. https://pdfs.semanticscholar.org/9090/f3b6e1dd446386ca2ae6d946ec186569d331.pdf

251 O'Malley GF, O'Malley R. (2003). *Merck Manual: Professional Version - Amphetamines*. www.merckmanuals.com/professional/special-subjects/recreational-drugs-and-intoxicants/amphetamines;
Lakhan, S. E., & Kirchgessner, A. (2012). Prescription stimulants in individuals with and without attention deficit hyperactivity disorder: misuse, cognitive impact, and adverse effects. *Brain and behavior, 2*(5), 661-677. https://onlinelibrary.wiley.com/doi/pdf/10.1002/brb3.78;
Angrist, B. M., & Gershon, S. (1970). *The phenomenology of experimentally induced amphetamine psychosis: preliminary observations*. Biological psychiatry. https://psycnet.apa.org/record/1972-08355-001
Bell, D. S. (1973). The experimental reproduction of amphetamine psychosis. *Archives of General Psychiatry, 29*(1), 35-40. https://jamanetwork.com/journals/jamapsychiatry/article-abstract/490932

252 Bramness, J. G., Gundersen, Ø. H., Guterstam, J., Rognli, E. B., Konstenius, M., Løberg, E. M., ... & Franck, J. (2012). Amphetamine-induced psychosis-a separate diagnostic entity or primary psychosis triggered in the vulnerable?. *BMC psychiatry, 12*(1), 221. www.ncbi.nlm.nih.gov/pmc/articles/PMC3554477/

253 Shuckit, M. A. (2013). *Drug and alcohol abuse: a clinical guide to diagnosis and treatment*. Springer Science & Business Media. https://books.google.ch/books?hl=en&lr=&id=d-RVBgAAQBAJ&oi=fnd&pg=PA1&dq=Drug+and+Alcohol+Abuse:+A+Clinical+Guide+to+Diagnosis+and+Treatment&ots=_5dqle7zAz&sig=Ff0yR80OOE7XROmBljHW4IXrDHE#v=onepage&q=amphetamine&f=false

254 Bramness, J. G., Gundersen, Ø. H., Guterstam, J., Rognli, E. B., Konstenius, M., Løberg, E. M., ... & Franck, J. (2012). Amphetamine-induced psychosis-a separate diagnostic entity or primary psychosis triggered in the vulnerable?. *BMC psychiatry, 12*(1), 221. www.ncbi.nlm.nih.gov/pmc/articles/PMC3554477/

255 Shuckit, M. A. (2013). *Drug and alcohol abuse: a clinical guide to diagnosis and treatment*. Springer Science & Business Media. https://books.google.ch/books?hl=en&lr=&id=d-RVBgAAQBAJ&oi=fnd&pg=PA1&dq=Drug+and+Alcohol+Abuse:+A+Clinical+Guide+to+Diagnosis+and+Treatment&ots=_5dqle7zAz&sig=Ff0yR80OOE7XROmBljHW4IXrDHE#v=onepage&q=amphetamine&f=false

256 Smith, M. E., & Farah, M. J. (2011). Are prescription stimulants "smart pills"? The epidemiology and cognitive neuroscience of prescription stimulant use by normal healthy individuals. *Psychological bulletin, 137*(5), 717. www.ncbi.nlm.nih.gov/pmc/articles/PMC3591814/

257 In Their Own Words: 'Study Drugs'. (n.d.). *The New York Times*. http://archive.nytimes.com/www.nytimes.com/interactive/2012/06/10/education/stimulants-student-voices.html?_r=1

258 Marsh, S. (2018). 'My personality changed': Johnny, 16, on Xanax addiction. *The Guardian*. www.theguardian.com/society/2018/feb/05/my-personality-changed-johnny-xanax-addiction

259 Johnston, L. D., O'Malley, P. M., Miech, R. A., Bachman, J. G., & Schulenberg, J. E. (2017). *Key findings on adolescent drug use*. www.monitoringthefuture.org/pubs/monographs/mtf-overview2017.pdf

260 Johnston, L. D., Miech, R. A., O'Malley, P. M., Bachman, J. G., Schulenberg, J. E., & Patrick, M. E. (2018). *Monitoring the Future national survey results on drug use, 1975-2018: Overview, key findings on adolescent drug use*. www.monitoringthefuture.org/pubs/monographs/mtf-overview2018.pdf

261 Movig, K. L., Mathijssen, M. P. M., Nagel, P. H. A., Van Egmond, T., De Gier, J. J., Leufkens, H. G. M., & Egberts, A. C. (2004). Psychoactive substance use and the risk of motor vehicle accidents. *Accident Analysis & Prevention, 36*(4), 631-636. https://dspace.library.uu.nl/bitstream/handle/1874/11680/movig_04_psychoactive-substanceuseandtheriskof.pdf?sequence=2

262 Longo, L. P., & Johnson, B. (2000). Addiction: Part I. Benzodiazepines-side effects, abuse risk and alternatives. *American family physician, 61*(7), 2121-2128. https://pdfs.semanticscholar.org/725c/bab0f1060a771d1d5c5d-6cf2594e1d8c91be.pdf

263 Longo, L. P., & Johnson, B. (2000). Addiction: Part I. Benzodiazepines-side effects, abuse risk and alternatives. *American family physician, 61*(7), 2121-2128. www.aafp.org/afp/2000/0401/p2121.html?wvsessionid=wv21521b9127b84069909a72a7623d7c60

264 Johnson, B., & Streltzer, J. (2013). Risks associated with long-term benzodiazepine use. *American family physician, 88*(4), 224-226. www.aafp.org/afp/2013/0815/p224.html

265 Petursson, H., & Lader, M. H. (1981). Withdrawal from long-term benzodiazepine treatment. *Br Med J (Clin Res Ed), 283*(6292), 643-645. www.ncbi.nlm.nih.gov/pmc/articles/PMC1506756/pdf/bmjcred00675-0021.pdf

266 Stewart, S. A. (2005). The effects of benzodiazepines on cognition. *The Journal of clinical psychiatry, 66*(suppl 2), 9-13. www.psychiatrist.com/JCP/article/Pages/effects-benzodiazepines-cognition.aspx

267 McCabe, S. E., & West, B. T. (2014). Medical and nonmedical use of prescription benzodiazepine anxiolytics among US high school seniors. *Addictive behaviors, 39*(5), 959-964. www.ncbi.nlm.nih.gov/pmc/articles/PMC4312492/

268 Pedersen, W., & Lavik, N. J. (1991). Adolescents and benzodiazepines: prescribed use, self-medication and intoxication. *Acta Psychiatrica Scandinavica, 84*(1), 94-98. https://onlinelibrary.wiley.com/doi/abs/10.1111/j.1600-0447.1991.tb01427.x

269 *Grieving mother testifies to the terrible cost of opioid abuse: That drug owned my daughter*. (2018). Women in the World.com. https://womenintheworld.com/2018/04/14/grieving-mother-testifies-to-the-terrible-cost-of-opioid-abuse-that-drug-owned-my-daughter/

270 Johnston, L. D., Miech, R. A., O'Malley, P. M., Bachman, J. G., Schulenberg, J. E., & Patrick, M. E. (2018). *Monitoring the Future national survey results on drug use, 1975-2018: Overview, key findings on adolescent drug use*. The National Institute on Drug Abuse. www.monitoringthefuture.org/pubs/monographs/mtf-overview2018.pdf

271 Davenport, S & Matthews, K. (2018). *Opioid use disorder in the United States: Diagnosed prevalence by payer, age, sex, and state*. Milliman. www.milliman.com/en/insight/opioid-use-disorder-in-the-united-states-diagnosed-prevalence-by-payer-age-sex-and-sta

272 Schepis, T. S., Wilens, T. E., & McCabe, S. E. (2019). Prescription drug misuse: sources of controlled medications in adolescents. *Journal of the American Academy of Child & Adolescent Psychiatry, 58*(7), 670-680. www.sciencedirect.com/science/article/abs/pii/S0890856718319129

273 Salsberg, B. (2015). *Task force: Massachusetts Is in Midst of Opioid Abuse Epidemic*. www.hazelden.org/web/public/document/parents-in-dark.pdf

274 McCabe, S. E., West, B. T., & Boyd, C. J. (2013). Leftover prescription opioids and nonmedical use among high school seniors: a multi-cohort national study. *Journal of Adolescent Health, 52*(4), 480-485. www.jahonline.org/article/S1054-139X(12)00350-3/fulltext

275 McCabe, S. E., West, B. T., Cranford, J. A., Ross-Durow, P., Young, A., Teter, C. J., & Boyd, C. J. (2011). Medical misuse of controlled medications among adolescents. *Archives of pediatrics & adolescent medicine, 165*(8), 729-735. https://jamanetwork.com/journals/jamapediatrics/articlepdf/1107576/poa15027_729_735.pdf

276 Volkow, N. D., McLellan, T. A., Cotto, J. H., Karithanom, M., & Weiss, S. R. (2011). Characteristics of opioid prescriptions in 2009. *Jama, 305*(13), 1299-1301. https://jamanetwork.com/journals/jama/fullarticle/896134

277 Schroeder, A. R., Dehghan, M., Newman, T. B., Bentley, J. P., & Park, K. T. (2019). Association of opioid prescriptions from dental clinicians for US adolescents and young adults with subsequent opioid use and abuse. *JAMA internal medicine, 179*(2), 145-152. https://jamanetwork.com/journals/jamainternalmedicine/fullarticle/2717503

278 Friedman, J. W. (2007). The prophylactic extraction of third molars: a public health hazard. *American journal of public health, 97*(9), 1554-1559. www.ncbi.nlm.nih.gov/pmc/articles/PMC1963310/

279 Lee, C. T., Zhang, S., Leung, Y. Y., Li, S. K., Tsang, C. C., & Chu, C. H. (2015). Patients' satisfaction and prevalence of complications on surgical extraction of third molar. *Patient preference and adherence*, 9, 257. www.researchgate.net/publication/272842981_Patients'_satisfaction_and_prevalence_of_complications_on_surgical_extraction_of_third_molar

280 Stanley, H. R., Alattar, M., Collett, W. K., Stringfellow Jr, H. R., & Spiegel, E. H. (1988). Pathological sequelae of "neglected" impacted third molars. *Journal of Oral Pathology & Medicine, 17*(3), 113-117. https://onlinelibrary.wiley.com/doi/abs/10.1111/j.1600-0714.1988.tb01896.x

281 American Public Health Association. (2021). *Wikipedia*. https://en.wikipedia.org/wiki/American_Public_Health_Association;
American Public Health Association. (2008). *Opposition to prophylactic removal of third molars (wisdom teeth)*. Policy Statement Database. Policy, (20085). www.apha.org/policies-and-advocacy/public-health-policy-statements/policy-database/2014/07/24/14/29/opposition-to-prophylactic-removal-of-third-molars-wisdom-teeth

282 Suska, F., Kjeller, G., Molander, A., Samuelsson, O., Svanberg, T., & Liljegren, A. (2010). *Health Technology Assessment: Removal of impacted wisdom teeth*. Göteborg: Regional HTA Centre, Västra Götaland, 51. http://epipublic.vgregion.se/upload/SU/HTA-centrum/HTA-rapporter/HTA-rapport%20Wisdom%20teeth%202010-10-05%20till%20publicering.pdf

283 Stordeur, S., & Eyssen, M. (2012). *Prophylactic removal of pathology-free wisdom teeth: rapid assessment. Good Clinical Practice (GCP)*. Brussels: Belgian Health Care Knowledge Centre KCE Report. C, 182. https://kce.fgov.be/sites/default/files/atoms/files/KCE_182C_wisdom_teeth.pdf

284 Kandasamy, S., Rinchuse, D. J., & Rinchuse, D. J. (2009). The wisdom behind third molar extractions. *Australian dental journal, 54*(4), 284-292. https://onlinelibrary.wiley.com/doi/pdf/10.1111/j.1834-7819.2009.01152.x

285 National Institute for Clinical Excellence. (2000). *Guidance on the Extraction of Wisdom Teeth (Technology Appraisal Guidance-No. 1)*. www.nice.org.uk/guidance/ta1/resources/guidance-on-the-extraction-of-wisdom-teeth-pdf-63732983749

286 Mettes, T. D. G., Ghaeminia, H., Nienhuijs, M. E., Perry, J., van der Sanden, W. J., & Plasschaert, A. (2012). Surgical removal versus retention for the management of asymptomatic impacted wisdom teeth. *Cochrane Database of Systematic Reviews*, (6). www.dentistrytoday.info/sites/default/files/CD003879.pdf

287 *Opposition to Prophylactic Removal of Third Molars (Wisdom Teeth)*. (2008). American Public Health Association. www.apha.org/policies-and-advocacy/public-health-policy-statements/policy-database/2014/07/24/14/29/opposition-to-prophylactic-removal-of-third-molars-wisdom-teeth;
*Review of TA1; Guidance on the extraction of wisdom teeth*. (2000). National Institute for Health and Care Excellence Guidance Executive (GE). www.nice.org.uk/guidance/ta1/resources/wisdom-teeth-removal-appendix-a-rpp-decision-paper-march-20152

288 Friedman, J. W. (2007). The prophylactic extraction of third molars: a public health hazard. *American journal of public health, 97*(9), 1554-1559. https://ajph.aphapublications.org/doi/pdfplus/10.2105/AJPH.2006.100271

289 Maughan, B. C., Hersh, E. V., Shofer, F. S., Wanner, K. J., Archer, E., Carrasco, L. R., & Rhodes, K. V. (2016). Unused opioid analgesics and drug disposal following outpatient dental surgery: a randomized controlled trial. *Drug and alcohol dependence*, 168, 328-334. www.sciencedirect.com/science/article/abs/pii/S0376871616302563

290 Dehnart, A. (2020). *16 and Recovering: a powerful look at addiction that's MTV's best reality show in years*. Reality Blurred. www.realityblurred.com/realitytv/2020/09/16-recovering-mtv-review/

291 Gold, J. (2020). MTV Showcases The Realities Of Teen Opioid Addiction In 16 And Recovering. *Forbes*. www.forbes.com/sites/jessicagold/2020/09/22/mtv-shifts-the-narrative-of-teen-addiction-with-16-and-recovering/?sh=73270e985be2

292 Connery, H. S. (2015). Medication-assisted treatment of opioid use disorder: review of the evidence and future directions. *Harvard review of psychiatry, 23*(2), 63-75. https://journals.lww.com/hrpjournal/FullText/2015/03000/Medication_Assisted_Treatment_of_Opioid_Use.2.aspx

293 Kristina. (2019). *True Story: Kristina. Get Smart About Drugs.* www.getsmartaboutdrugs.gov/consequences/true-stories/true-story-kristina

294 López-Muñoz, F., Ucha-Udabe, R., & Alamo, C. (2005). The history of barbiturates a century after their clinical introduction. *Neuropsychiatric disease and treatment, 1*(4), 329. www.ncbi.nlm.nih.gov/pmc/articles/PMC2424120/

295 Coupey, S. M. (1997). Barbiturates. *Pediatrics in review, 18*(8), 260-4. https://europepmc.org/abstract/med/9255991

296 Johnston, L. D., Miech, R. A., O'Malley, P. M., Bachman, J. G., Schulenberg, J. E., & Patrick, M. E. (2018). *Monitoring the Future national survey results on drug use, 1975-2018: Overview, key findings on adolescent drug use.* www.monitoringthefuture.org/pubs/monographs/mtf-overview2018.pdf

297 Nutt, D., King, L. A., Saulsbury, W., & Blakemore, C. (2007). Development of a rational scale to assess the harm of drugs of potential misuse. The Lancet, 369(9566), 1047-1053. http://dobrochan.ru/src/pdf/1109/lancetnorway.pdf

298 Henn, D., & DeEugenio, D. (2007). *Barbiturates.* Infobase Publishing. https://books.google.ch/books?hl=en&lr=&id=ZWJKERVlRhoC&oi=fnd&pg=PA5&dq=barbiturates+teenagers&ots=edFf1IRPM2&sig=8L0ZrClyHW5hheU2GdpJPSKy_1A#v=onepage&q=illegal&f=false

299 Hodding, G. C., Jann, M., & Ackerman, I. P. (1980). Drug withdrawal syndromes: a literature review. *Western Journal of Medicine, 133*(5), 383. www.ncbi.nlm.nih.gov/pmc/articles/PMC1272349/pdf/westjmed00231-0013.pdf; Coupey, S. M. (1997). Barbiturates. *Pediatrics in review, 18*(8), 260-4. https://europepmc.org/abstract/med/9255991

300 Henn, D., & DeEugenio, D. (2007). *Barbiturates.* Infobase Publishing. https://books.google.ch/books?hl=en&lr=&id=ZWJKERVlRhoC&oi=fnd&pg=PA5&dq=barbiturates+teenagers&ots=edFf1IRPM2&sig=8L0ZrClyHW5hheU2GdpJPSKy_1A#v=onepage&q=illegal&f=false

301 Henn, D., & DeEugenio, D. (2007). *Barbiturates.* Infobase Publishing. https://books.google.ch/books?hl=en&lr=&id=ZWJKERVlRhoC&oi=fnd&pg=PA5&dq=barbiturates+teenagers&ots=edFf1IRPM2&sig=8L0ZrClyHW5hheU2GdpJPSKy_1A#v=onepage&q=illegal&f=false

302 Miech, R., Johnston, L., O'Malley, P., Bachman, J., Schulenberg, J., & Patrick, M. (2019). *Monitoring the future national survey results on drug use, 1975-2018: volume I, secondary school students.* https://deepblue.lib.umich.edu/bitstream/handle/2027.42/150622/Vol%201%202018%20FINAL3.pdf?sequence=1

303 McCabe, S. E., Veliz, P., Wilens, T. E., West, B. T., Schepis, T. S., Ford, J. A., ... & Boyd, C. J. (2019). Sources of nonmedical prescription drug misuse among US high school seniors: differences in motives and substance use behaviors. *Journal of the American Academy of Child & Adolescent Psychiatry, 58*(7), 681-691. www.sciencedirect.com/science/article/abs/pii/S0890856719302114

304 McCabe, S. E., & Boyd, C. J. (2005). Sources of prescription drugs for illicit use. *Addictive behaviors, 30*(7), 1342-1350. www.ncbi.nlm.nih.gov/pmc/articles/PMC1706073/

305 Phillips, E. B. (2008). *Mum Can You Lend Me Twenty Quid?: What drugs did to my family.* Piatkus Books. www.amazon.co.uk/Mum-Can-Lend-Twenty-Quid/dp/0749951729

306 *Parents in the Dark.* (2014). Hazelden's Adolescent and Young Adult Services. www.hazelden.org/web/public/document/parents-in-dark.pdf

307 Ali, S., Mouton, C. P., Jabeen, S., Ofoemezie, E. K., Bailey, R. K., Shahid, M., & Zeng, Q. (2011). Early detection of illicit drug use in teenagers. *Innovations in clinical neuroscience, 8*(12), 24. www.ncbi.nlm.nih.gov/pmc/articles/PMC3257983/

308 Pile, T. (2017). DEA might have inadvertently told teens where to hide drugs. *New York Post.* https://nypost.com/2017/05/11/the-dea-might-have-accidentally-told-teens-where-to-hide-drugs/

309 *Planning and Implementing Screening and Brief Intervention for Risky Alcohol Use: A Step-by-Step Guide for Primary Care Practices.* (2014). Centers for Disease Control and Prevention, National Center on Birth Defects and Developmental Disabilities. www.cdc.gov/ncbddd/fasd/documents/AlcoholSBIImplementationGuide.pdf

310 Knight, J. R., Sherritt, L., Shrier, L. A., Harris, S. K., & Chang, G. (2002). Validity of the CRAFFT substance abuse screening test among adolescent clinic patients. *Archives of pediatrics & adolescent medicine, 156*(6), 607-614. https://jamanetwork.com/journals/jamapediatrics/articlepdf/203511/poa10425.pdf

311 *Should You Drug Test Your Child?* (2020). Partnership to End Addiction. https://drugfree.org/parent-blog/should-you-drug-test-your-child/

312 Levy, S., Siqueira, L. M., & Committee on Substance Abuse. (2014). Testing for drugs of abuse in children and adolescents. *Pediatrics, 133*(6), e1798-e1807. https://pediatrics.aappublications.org/content/133/6/e1798.long?utm_source=TrendMD&utm_medium=TrendMD&utm_campaign=Pediatrics_TrendMD_0

313 Seay, N. (2019). *Should Parents Hire Drug-Sniffing Dogs for Private Use?* American Addiction Centers, National Rehab Directory. www.rehabs.com/blog/parents-can-hire-drug-sniffing-dogs-but-should-they/

314 Netter, S. (2010). *Could Your Kids be On Drugs? New Biz Sends Search Dogs to Sniff Out Their Rooms.* ABC News. https://abcnews.go.com/US/kids-drugs-rent-search-dog-sniff-rooms/story?id=11947385

315 Dishion, T. J., & Andrews, D. W. (1995). Preventing escalation in problem behaviors with high-risk young adolescents: immediate and 1-year outcomes. *Journal of consulting and clinical psychology, 63*(4), 538. https://psycnet.apa.org/record/1995-44489-001

316 Bien, T. H., Miller, W. R., & Tonigan, J. S. (1993). Brief interventions for alcohol problems: a review. *Addiction, 88*(3), 315-336. www.semanticscholar.org/paper/Brief-interventions-for-alcohol-problems%3A-a-review.-Bien-Miller/5191ea3bcc523d74fe592f282dd5a94c2446c8ee;
Tevyaw, T. O. L., & Monti, P. M. (2004). Motivational enhancement and other brief interventions for adolescent substance abuse: foundations, applications and evaluations. *Addiction*, 99, 63-75. http://citeseerx.ist.psu.edu/viewdoc/download?doi=10.1.1.1020.6037&rep=rep1&type=pdf;
Gates, S., McCambridge, J., Smith, L. A., & Foxcroft, D. (2006). Interventions for prevention of drug use by young people delivered in non-school settings. *Cochrane Database of Systematic Reviews*, (1). www.cochranelibrary.com/cdsr/doi/10.1002/14651858.CD005030.pub2/full

317 Tait, R. J., & Hulse, G. K. (2003). A systematic review of the effectiveness of brief interventions with substance using adolescents by type of drug. *Drug and Alcohol review, 22*(3), 337-346. www.biblioteca.cij.gob.mx/Archivos/Materiales_de_consulta/Drogas_de_abuso/Articulos/systematicreviwefectivensesbriefinterventionssubstancedrug.pdf;
McCambridge, J., & Strang, J. (2004). The efficacy of single-session motivational interviewing in reducing drug consumption and perceptions of drug-related risk and harm among young people: results from a multi-site cluster randomized trial. *Addiction, 99*(1), 39-52. www.biblioteca.cij.gob.mx/Archivos/Materiales_de_consulta/Drogas_de_Abuso/Articulos/efficacysinglesessionmotivationalinterviewingreducingdrugconsumtionperception-drugrelated.pdf;
Marlatt, G. A., Baer, J. S., Kivlahan, D. R., Dimeff, L. A., Larimer, M. E., Quigley, L. A., ... & Williams, E. (1998). Screening and brief intervention for high-risk college student drinkers: results from a 2-year follow-up assessment. *Journal of consulting and clinical psychology, 66*(4), 604. https://bobcat.militaryfamilies.psu.edu/sites/default/files/placed-programs/Marlatt,%20Baer,%20Kivlahan,%20Dimeff,%20Larimer,%20Quigley,%20Somers,%20%26%20Williams%20(1998)%20Screening%20and%20brief%20intervention%20for%20high-risk%20college%20student%20drinkers.pdf

318 Dunn, C., Deroo, L., & Rivara, F. P. (2001). The use of brief interventions adapted from motivational interviewing across behavioral domains: a systematic review. *Addiction, 96*(12), 1725-1742. https://onlinelibrary.wiley.com/doi/abs/10.1046/j.1360-0443.2001.961217253.x;
Center for Substance Abuse Treatment. (1999). *Brief interventions and brief therapies for substance abuse.* www.ncbi.nlm.nih.gov/books/NBK64950/

319 Chen, C. Y., Storr, C. L., & Anthony, J. C. (2009). Early-onset drug use and risk for drug dependence problems. *Addictive behaviors, 34*(3), 319-322. www.ncbi.nlm.nih.gov/pmc/articles/PMC2677076/;
Anthony, J. C., & Petronis, K. R. (1995). Early-onset drug use and risk of later drug problems. *Drug and alcohol dependence, 40*(1), 9-15. www.sciencedirect.com/science/article/abs/pii/037687169501194 3;
Reboussin, B. A., & Anthony, J. C. (2006). Is there epidemiological evidence to support the idea that a cocaine dependence syndrome emerges soon after onset of cocaine use?. *Neuropsychopharmacology, 31*(9), 2055-2064. www.nature.com/articles/1301037;
Footnote reference: 1 Lynskey, M. T., & Agrawal, A. (2018). Denise Kandel's classic work on the gateway sequence of drug acquisition. *Addiction, 113*(10), 1927-1932. https://onlinelibrary.wiley.com/doi/10.1111/add.14190

320 Pollan, Michael. *How to Change Your Mind* (p. 7). Penguin Publishing Group. Kindle Edition.

# 2. Sexual activity


1 *Pregnant teenager appeals against death by stoning sentence.* (2004). Irish Examiner. www.irishexaminer.com/breakingnews/world/pregnant-teenager-appeals-against-death-by-stoning-sentence-173102.html

2 *Tanzanian leader reaffirms ban on pregnant girls attending state schools.* (2017). Reuters. www.reuters.com/article/uk-tanzania-education-idUKKBN19E19F

3 Livingston, G. (2018). *The Changing Profile of Unmarried Parents.* Pew Research Center. www.pewsocialtrends.org/2018/04/25/the-changing-profile-of-unmarried-parents/

4 Grall, T. (2016). *Custodial Mothers and Fathers and Their Child Support: 2013.* United States Census Bureau, U.S. Department of Commerce. www.census.gov/content/dam/Census/library/publications/2016/demo/P60-255.pdf

5 Hotz, V. J., McElroy, S. W., & Sanders, S. G. (2005). Teenage childbearing and its life cycle consequences exploiting a natural experiment. *Journal of Human Resources, 40*(3), 683-715. www.nber.org/papers/w7397.pdf

6 Pregnancy rate:
*1973 to 2013: Kost, K., Maddow-Zimet, I., & Arpaia, A. (2017). Pregnancies, Births and Abortions Among Adolescents and Young Women in the United States, 2013: National and State Trends by Age, Race and Ethnicity.* Guttmacher Institute. www.guttmacher.org/report/us-adolescent-pregnancy-trends-2013;
2014 to 2016: Maddow-Zimet I., Kost, K. & Finn, S. (2020). *Pregnancies, Births and Abortions in the United States, 1973–2016: National and State Trends by Age.* Guttmacher Institute. www.guttmacher.org/report/pregnancies-births-abortions-in-united-states-1973-2016; https://data.guttmacher.org/states/trend?state=US&topics=170&dataset=data;
Birth rate: 1970 to 2013: Martin, J. A., Hamilton, B. E., Osterman, M. J., Curtin, S. C., & Mathews, T. J. (2015). *National Vital Statistics Reports Volume 64, Number 1 Births: Final Data for 2013.* Centers for Disease Control and Prevention. www.cdc.gov/nchs/data/nvsr/nvsr64/nvsr64_01.pdf;
2014 to 2018: Martin, J. A., Hamilton, B. E., Osterman, M. J., & Driscoll, A. K. (2019). *Births: final data for 2018. Table 2.* Centers for Disease Control and Prevention. https://stacks.cdc.gov/view/cdc/82909/cdc_82909_DS1.pdf;
Ever had sex: Centers for Disease Control and Prevention. (n.d.) *High School Youth Risk Behavior Survey, 1991-2019 Results.* https://nccd.cdc.gov/youthonline/App/Results.aspx?TT=K&OUT=0&SID=HS&QID=H59&LID=LL&YID=YY&LID2=&YID2=&COL=T&ROW1=N&ROW2=N&HT=QQ&LCT=LL&FS=S1&FR=R1&FG=G1&FA=A1&FI=I1&FP=P1&FSL=S1&FRL=R1&FGL=G1&FAL=A1&FIL=I1&FPL=P1&PV=&TST=&C1=&C2=&QP=G&DP=1&VA=CI&CS=Y&SYID=&EYID=&SC=DEFAULT&SO=ASC

7 Brody, J. E. (2018). Contraception for Teenagers. *The New York Times.* www.nytimes.com/2018/02/19/well/live/contraception-for-teenagers.html

8 United Nations Statistics Division, Department of Economic and Social Affairs, United Nations. (n.d.) *Millenium Development Goals Indicators.* United Nations. https://millenniumindicators.un.org/unsd/mdg/SeriesDetail.aspx?srid=761

9 Honig, A. S. (2012). Teen pregnancy. *International Journal of Adolescence and Youth, 17*(4), 181-187. www.tandfonline.com/doi/full/10.1080/02673843.2012.655912

10 Jones, R. K., & Singh, S. (2010). *Difference and Disparity in Adolescent Pregnancy in Developed Countries.* Santé de la reproduction au Nord et au Sud: Actes de la Chaire Quetelet 2004, 169. https://books.google.ch/books?hl=en&lr=&id=QFktjmEBCvoC&oi=fnd&pg=PA169&dq=low+teen+pregnancy+rates+industrialized+asian+nations&ots=Gi1t2gUihm&sig=yV_aW8EtRg80S-0u422mBH4gJPk&redir_esc=y#v=snippet&q=korea&f=false

11 Orenstein, P. & Park, I. (2021). What Will Happen When Americans Start Having Sex Again? *The New York Times.* www.nytimes.com/2021/04/17/opinion/sunday/sex-stds-stis-covid.html?referringSource=articleShare

12 Kirby, D. (2007). *Emerging Answers: Research findings on programs to reduce teen pregnancy and sexually transmitted diseases.* The National Campaign to Prevent Teen and Unplanned Pregnancy. https://powertodecide.org/what-we-do/information/resource-library/emerging-answers-2007-new-research-findings-programs-reduce;
Blake, S. M., Simkin, L., Ledsky, R., Perkins, C., & Calabrese, J. M. (2001). Effects of a parent-child communications intervention on young adolescents' risk for early onset of sexual intercourse. *Family planning perspectives,* 52-61. https://s3.amazonaws.com/academia.edu.documents/34745982/Effects_of_a_Parent-Child_Communications.pdf?AWSAccessKeyId=AKIAIWOWYYGZ2Y53UL3A&Expires=1517250491&Signature=e9gNgdh-

stGiHHT3%2B%2B%2Fb0hTkI2C0%3D&response-content-disposition=inline%3B%20filename%3DEffects_of_a_Parent-Child_Communications.pdf

13 Oringanje, C., Meremikwu, M. M., Eko, H., Esu, E., Meremikwu, A., & Ehiri, J. E. (2009). Interventions for preventing unintended pregnancies among adolescents. *Cochrane Database Syst Rev, 4*(4). www.researchgate.net/profile/Ekpereonne_Esu/publication/26887084_Interventions_for_preventing_unintended_pregnancies_among_adolescents/links/0912f50805539d66fb000000/Interventions-for-preventing-unintended-pregnancies-among-adolescents.pdf

14 Howard, M., & McCabe, J. B. (1990). Helping teenagers postpone sexual involvement. *Family planning perspectives*, 21-26. www.jstor.org/stable/2135434?seq=1#page_scan_tab_contents

15 Curtis, J. (2019). *How Placing a Fly in a Urinal Might Be Just What Your Business Needs: 7 Awesome Nudging Examples.* US Imprints. www.usimprints.com/blog/7-nudging-examples/

16 Bearman, P. S., & Brückner, H. (2015). Promising the future: Virginity pledges and first intercourse. *American journal of Sociology.* https://academiccommons.columbia.edu/doi/10.7916/D8ZG73VN/download

17 Manlove, J. S., Terry-Humen, E., Ikramullah, E. N., & Moore, K. A. (2006). The role of parent religiosity in teens' transitions to sex and contraception. *Journal of Adolescent Health, 39*(4), 578-587. www.jahonline.org/article/S1054-139X(06)00102-9/abstract

18 Kirby, D. (2007). *Emerging Answers: Research findings on programs to reduce teen pregnancy and sexually transmitted diseases.* The National Campaign to Prevent Teen and Unplanned Pregnancy. https://powertodecide.org/what-we-do/information/resource-library/emerging-answers-2007-new-research-findings-programs-reduce;
Wang, T., Lurie, M., Govindasamy, D., & Mathews, C. (2018). The effects of school-based condom availability programs (CAPs) on condom acquisition, use and sexual behavior: a systematic review. *AIDS and Behavior, 22*(1), 308-320. www.ncbi.nlm.nih.gov/pmc/articles/PMC5758683/

19 Kirby, D. (2007). *Emerging Answers: Research findings on programs to reduce teen pregnancy and sexually transmitted diseases.* The National Campaign to Prevent Teen and Unplanned Pregnancy. https://powertodecide.org/what-we-do/information/resource-library/emerging-answers-2007-new-research-findings-programs-reduce;
Wang, T., Lurie, M., Govindasamy, D., & Mathews, C. (2018). The effects of school-based condom availability programs (CAPs) on condom acquisition, use and sexual behavior: a systematic review. *AIDS and Behavior, 22*(1), 308-320. www.ncbi.nlm.nih.gov/pmc/articles/PMC5758683/

20 *Minors' Access to Contraceptive Services.* (2021). Guttmacher Institute. www.guttmacher.org/state-policy/explore/minors-access-contraceptive-services

21 Lofink, H., Kuebler, J., Juszczak, L., Schlitt, J., Even, M., Rosenberg, J., & White, I. (2013). *2010-2011 Census Report of School-Based Health Centers.* School-Based Health Alliance. https://files.eric.ed.gov/fulltext/ED586060.pdf

22 Fertility awareness, withdrawal: Hatcher, R. A. (2007). *Contraceptive technology.* Ardent Media. https://books.google.co.uk/books?hl=en&lr=&id=txh0LpjjhkoC&oi=fnd&pg=PA1&dq=Hatcher+RA,+Trussell+-J,+Nelson+AL,+Cates+W+Jr,+Kowal+D,+Policar+MS.+Contraceptive+Technology.+20th+rev+ed.+Valley+Stream,+NY:+Ardent+Media%3B+2011&ots=pZeOzX4ACD&sig=2lOlBYj--KppKj65HrYnNANMH-c8&redir_esc=y#v=onepage&q=27-1&f=false; Other methods: Division of Reproductive Health, National Center for Chronic Disease Prevention and Health Promotion. (2020). *Reproductive Health: Contraception.* Centers for Disease Control and Prevention. www.cdc.gov/reproductivehealth/contraception/index.htm

23 *Few teens use the most effective types of birth control.* (2015). CDC Newsroom, Centers for Disease Control and Prevention, U.S. Department of Health and Human Services. www.cdc.gov/media/releases/2015/p0407-teen-pregnancy.html

24 Ott, M. A., & Sucato, G. S. (2014). Committee on Adolescence: Contraception for adolescents. *Pediatr, 134*(4): 1257-81. https://pediatrics.aappublications.org/content/pediatrics/early/2014/09/24/peds.2014-2299.full.pdf

25 American College of Obstetricians and Gynecologists. (2012). Adolescents and long-acting reversible contraception: implants and intrauterine devices. Committee Opinion No. 539. *Obstet Gynecol, 120*(983), 8. www.acog.org/clinical/clinical-guidance/committee-opinion/articles/2018/05/adolescents-and-long-acting-reversible-contraception-implants-and-intrauterine-devices

26 Footnote reference: [1] Yoost, J. (2014). Understanding benefits and addressing misperceptions and barriers to intrauterine device access among populations in the United States. *Patient preference and adherence*, 8, 947. www.ncbi.nlm.nih.gov/pmc/articles/PMC4090129/

27 Abma, J. C., & Martinez, G. M. (2017). Sexual activity and contraceptive use among teenagers in the United States, 2011-2015. *National health statistics reports*, (104), 1-23. www.cdc.gov/nchs/data/nhsr/nhsr104.pdf

28 Footnote references:
[1] U.S. Department of Health and Human Services (HHS), Office of the Surgeon General. (2016). *Facing Addiction in America: The Surgeon General's Report on Alcohol, Drugs, and Health.* HHS. https://addiction.surgeongeneral.gov/sites/default/files/chapter-3-prevention.pdf
[2] Toumbourou, J. W., Stockwell, T., Neighbors, C., Marlatt, G. A., Sturge, J., & Rehm, J. (2007). Interventions to reduce harm associated with adolescent substance use. *The Lancet, 369*(9570), 1391-1401. www.aracy.org.au/publications-resources/command/download_file/id/106/filename/Interventions_to_reduce_harm_associated_with_adolescent_substance_use.pdf
[3] United Nations Office on Drugs and Crime. (2010). *Compilation of evidence-based family skills training programmes.* www.unodc.org/documents/prevention/family-compilation.pdf
[4] Kumpfer, K. L., & Alvarado, R. (1998). *Effective family strengthening interventions.* US Department of Justice, Office of Justice Programs, Office of Juvenile Justice and Delinquency Prevention. https://pdfs.semanticscholar.org/2a2e/4c1628d55289fbc94e45718c7582d7bb50a7.pdf

29 Steiner, M., Piedrahita, C., Glover, L., & Joanis, C. (1993). Can condom users likely to experience condom failure be identified?. *Family Planning Perspectives*, 220-226. www.researchgate.net/profile/Carla_Piedrahita/publication/14937464_Can_Condom_Users_Likely_to_Experience_Condom_Failure_Be_Identified/links/00b7d528cc02f3895f000000/Can-Condom-Users-Likely-to-Experience-Condom-Failure-Be-Identified.pdf

30 Spruyt, A., Steiner, M. J., Joanis, C., Glover, L. H., Piedrahita, C., Alvarado, G., ... & Cordero, M. (1998). Identifying condom users at risk for breakage and slippage: findings from three international sites. *American Journal of Public Health, 88*(2), 239-244. https://ajph.aphapublications.org/doi/pdfplus/10.2105/AJPH.88.2.239

31 Kirby, D. (2007). *Emerging Answers: Research findings on programs to reduce teen pregnancy and sexually transmitted diseases.* The National Campaign to Prevent Teen and Unplanned Pregnancy. https://powertodecide.org/what-we-do/information/resource-library/emerging-answers-2007-new-research-findings-programs-reduce

32 Centers for Disease Control and Prevention. (n.d.) *High School Youth Risk Behavior Survey, 1991-2017 Results.* https://nccd.cdc.gov/youthonline/App/Results.aspx?TT=K&OUT=0&SID=HS&QID=H59&LID=LL&YID=YY&LID2=&YID2=&COL=T&ROW1=N&ROW2=N&HT=QQ&LCT=LL&FS=S1&FR=R1&FG=G1&FA=A1&FI=I1&FP=P1&FSL=S1&FRL=R1&FGL=G1&FAL=A1&FIL=I1&FPL=P1&PV=&TST=&C1=&C2=&QP=G&DP=1&VA=CI&CS=Y&SYID=&EYID=&SC=DEFAULT&SO=ASC

33 Mollborn, S., & Everett, B. (2010). Correlates and consequences of parent–teen incongruence in reports of teens' sexual experience. *Journal of sex research, 47*(4), 314-329. www.ncbi.nlm.nih.gov/pmc/articles/PMC3172317/

34 Jaccard, J., Dittus, P. J., & Gordon, V. V. (1998). Parent-adolescent congruency in reports of adolescent sexual behavior and in communications about sexual behavior. *Child development, 69*(1), 247-261. https://srcd.onlinelibrary.wiley.com/doi/abs/10.1111/j.1467-8624.1998.tb06146.x

35 du Boulay, H. H. (2011). 'The bad disorder': syphilis before 1944. *Sexually transmitted infections, 87*(7), 570-570. https://sti.bmj.com/content/87/7/570

36 DeRogatis, A. (2009). "Born Again Is a Sexual Term": Demons, STDs, and God's Healing Sperm. *Journal of the American Academy of Religion, 77*(2), 275-302. http://citeseerx.ist.psu.edu/viewdoc/download?doi=10.1.1.986.6206&rep=rep1&type=pdf

37 Desiderato, L. L., & Crawford, H. J. (1995). Risky sexual behavior in college students: Relationships between number of sexual partners, disclosure of previous risky behavior, and alcohol use. *Journal of Youth and Adolescence, 24*(1), 55-68. https://link.springer.com/article/10.1007/BF01537560

38 Cochran, S. D., & Mays, V. M. (1990). Sex, lies, and HIV. *The New England journal of medicine, 322*(11), 774. https://s3.amazonaws.com/academia.edu.documents/35397105/44.pdf?response-content-disposition=inline%3B%20filename%3DSex_lies_and_HIV.pdf&X-Amz-Algorithm=AWS4-HMAC-SHA256&X-Amz-Credential=AKIAIWOWYYGZ2Y53UL3A%2F20190820%2Fus-east-1%2Fs3%2Faws4_request&X-Amz-Date=20190820T171218Z&X-Amz-Expires=3600&X-Amz-SignedHeaders=host&X-Amz-Signature=228a6eba28cda064b10630993aede49b856d96297ec727db694b2241b6ef34e2

39 Lenoir, C. D., Adler, N. E., Borzekowski, D. L., Tschann, J. M., & Ellen, J. M. (2006). What you don't know can hurt you: Perceptions of sex-partner concurrency and partner-reported behavior. *Journal of Adolescent Health, 38*(3), 179-185. www.jahonline.org/article/S1054-139X(05)00054-6/fulltext

40 Stein, M. D., Freedberg, K. A., Sullivan, L. M., Savetsky, J., Levenson, S. M., Hingson, R., & Samet, J. H. (1998). Sexual ethics: disclosure of HIV-positive status to partners. *Archives of Internal Medicine, 158*(3), 253-257. https://jamanetwork.com/journals/jamainternalmedicine/fullarticle/191291

41 National Center for Health Statistics. (2016). *National Health and Nutrition Examination Survey Data*. Centers for Disease Control and Prevention (CDC). www.cdc.gov/nchs/nhanes/

42 Diiorio, C., Pluhar, E., & Belcher, L. (2003). Parent-child communication about sexuality: A review of the literature from 1980–2002. *Journal of HIV/AIDS Prevention & Education for Adolescents & Children, 5*(3-4), 7-32. www.academia.edu/32873818/Parent-Child_Communication_About_Sexuality

43 Haelle, T. (2017). *You Can Order a Dozen STD Tests Online — But Should You?* NPR. www.npr.org/sections/health-shots/2017/08/13/536905120/you-can-order-a-dozen-std-tests-online-but-should-you

44 Workowski, K. A., & Berman, S. M. (2006). *Sexually transmitted diseases treatment guidelines, 2006*. www.cdc.gov/mmwr/PDF/rr/rr5511.pdf

45 Remez, L. (2000). Oral sex among adolescents: is it sex or is it abstinence?. *Family planning perspectives, 32*(6), 298-304. www.guttmacher.org/sites/default/files/article_files/3229800.pdf

46 Lewin, T. (1997). Teen-Agers Alter Sexual Practices, Thinking Risks Will Be Avoided. *The New York Times*. www.nytimes.com/1997/04/05/us/teen-agers-alter-sexual-practices-thinking-risks-will-be-avoided.html

47 Halpern-Felsher, B. L., Cornell, J. L., Kropp, R. Y., & Tschann, J. M. (2005). Oral versus vaginal sex among adolescents: *Perceptions, attitudes, and behavior. Pediatrics, 115*(4), 845-851. http://citeseerx.ist.psu.edu/viewdoc/download?doi=10.1.1.323.97&rep=rep1&type=pdf

48 Boekeloo, B. O., & Howard, D. E. (2002). Oral sexual experience among young adolescents receiving general health examinations. *American Journal of Health Behavior, 26*(4), 306-314. www.ingentaconnect.com/content/png/ajhb/2002/00000026/00000004/art00007

49 Halpern-Felsher, B. L., Cornell, J. L., Kropp, R. Y., & Tschann, J. M. (2005). Oral versus vaginal sex among adolescents: Perceptions, attitudes, and behavior. *Pediatrics, 115*(4), 845-851. http://citeseerx.ist.psu.edu/viewdoc/download?doi=10.1.1.323.97&rep=rep1&type=pdf

50 Brady, S. S., & Halpern-Felsher, B. L. (2007). Adolescents' reported consequences of having oral sex versus vaginal sex. *Pediatrics, 119*(2), 229-236. http://pediatrics.aappublications.org/content/119/2/229.short

51 Boekeloo, B. O., & Howard, D. E. (2002). Oral sexual experience among young adolescents receiving general health examinations. *American Journal of Health Behavior, 26*(4), 306-314. www.ingentaconnect.com/content/png/ajhb/2002/00000026/00000004/art00007

52 *STD Risk and Oral Sex - CDC Fact Sheet*. (2020). Division of STD Prevention, National Center for HIV/AIDS, Viral Hepatitis, STD, and TB Prevention, Centers for Disease Control and Prevention. www.cdc.gov/std/healthcomm/stdfact-stdriskandoralsex.htm

53 Edwards, S., & Carne, C. (1998). Oral sex and transmission of non-viral STIs. *Sexually transmitted infections, 74*(2), 95-100. https://sti.bmj.com/content/sextrans/74/2/95.full.pdf

54 Stanley, M. (2014). HPV vaccination in boys and men. *Human vaccines & immunotherapeutics, 10*(7), 2106-2108. www.tandfonline.com/doi/pdf/10.4161/hv.29138

55 Hawkins, D. A. (2001). Oral sex and HIV transmission. https://sti.bmj.com/content/sextrans/77/5/307.full.pdf

Citing: Samuel, M. C., Hessol, N., Shiboski, S., Engel, R. R., Speed, T. P., & Winkelstein, J. W. (1993). Factors associated with human immunodeficiency virus seroconversion in homosexual men in three San Francisco cohort studies, 1984-1989. *Journal of acquired immune deficiency syndromes, 6*(3), 303-312.

56 Hawkins, D. A. (2001). *Oral sex and HIV transmission*. https://sti.bmj.com/content/sextrans/77/5/307.full.pdf; *STD Risk and Oral Sex - CDC Fact Sheet*. (2020). Division of STD Prevention, National Center for HIV/AIDS, Viral Hepatitis, STD, and TB Prevention, Centers for Disease Control and Prevention. www.cdc.gov/std/healthcomm/stdfact-stdriskandoralsex.htm

57 Matthews-King, A. (2019). *Dating apps blamed as a million new STD cases diagnosed every day amid warnings infections are becoming untreatable*. Independent. www.independent.co.uk/news/health/std-superbug-gonorrhoea-treatment-sex-disease-sti-infection-sexually-transmitted-disease-who-chlamydia-syphilis-a8947111.html

58 Bullough, V. L. (n.d.). *Age of Consent*. Encyclopedia of Children and Childhood in History and Society. www.faqs.org/childhood/A-Ar/Age-of-Consent.html

59 Kerry, J. F. (2015). *Country Reports on Human Rights Practices for 2015*. Bureau of Democracy, Human Rights and Labor. Section 6: Children: Early and Forced Marriage. https://2009-2017.state.gov/j/drl/rls/hrrpt/humanrightsreport//index.htm#fndtn-panel1-1

60 Allen, Joseph. *Escaping the Endless Adolescence: How we can help our teenagers grow up before they grow old*. Random House Publishing Group. Kindle Edition. https://books.google.co.uk/books?hl=en&lr=&id=myEH-FTWAmjwC&oi=fnd&pg=PR9&dq=Escaping+the+Endless+Adolescence&ots=8yCPQ5RSm7&sig=Zg52iG-B3ugS5gz0mW19DUdLsUiA&redir_esc=y#v=onepage&q=Escaping%20the%20Endless%20Adolescence&f=-false

61 Jaccard, J., Dittus, P. J., & Gordon, V. V. (1998). Parent-adolescent congruency in reports of adolescent sexual behavior and in communications about sexual behavior. *Child development, 69*(1), 247-261.

62 Young, T. L., & Zimmerman, R. (1998). Clueless: parental knowledge of risk behaviors of middle school students. *Archives of pediatrics & adolescent medicine, 152*(11), 1137-1139. https://jamanetwork.com/journals/jamapediatrics/fullarticle/190069

63 Weissbourd, R., Anderson, T. R., Cashin, A., & McIntyre, J. (2017). The talk: How adults can promote young people's healthy relationships and prevent misogyny and sexual harassment. *Harvard Graduate School of Education, 16*(8), 1-46. https://static1.squarespace.com/static/5b7c56e255b02c683659fe43/t/5bd51a0324a69425bd079b59/1540692500558/mcc_the_talk_final.pdf

64 Babalola, S. (2004). Perceived peer behavior and the timing of sexual debut in Rwanda: A survival analysis of youth data. *Journal of youth and adolescence, 33*(4), 353-363. https://search.proquest.com/docview/204652639?pq-origsite=gscholar&fromopenview=true;
DiIorio, C., Dudley, W. N., Kelly, M., Soet, J. E., Mbwara, J., & Potter, J. S. (2001). Social cognitive correlates of sexual experience and condom use among 13-through 15-year-old adolescents. *Journal of Adolescent Health, 29*(3), 208-216. https://core.ac.uk/download/pdf/149230116.pdf;
Prinstein, M. J., Meade, C. S., & Cohen, G. L. (2003). Adolescent oral sex, peer popularity, and perceptions of best friends' sexual behavior. *Journal of pediatric psychology, 28*(4), 243-249. https://academic.oup.com/jpepsy/article/28/4/243/942606

65 Wight, D., Parkes, A., Strange, V., Allen, E., Bonell, C., & Henderson, M. (2008). The quality of young people's heterosexual relationships: A longitudinal analysis of characteristics shaping subjective experience. *Perspectives on sexual and reproductive health, 40*(4), 226-237. www.guttmacher.org/sites/default/files/article_files/4022608.pdf

66 Houts, L. A. (2005). But was it wanted? Young women's first voluntary sexual intercourse. *Journal of Family Issues, 26*(8), 1082-1102. https://journals.sagepub.com/doi/abs/10.1177/0192513X04273582

67 EDK Associates for Seventeen magazine and the Ms. Foundation for Women. (1996). *Teenagers Under Pressure*. www.city-journal.org/html/regrets-teen-sex-12294.html

68 Wight, D., Parkes, A., Strange, V., Allen, E., Bonell, C., & Henderson, M. (2008). The quality of young people's heterosexual relationships: A longitudinal analysis of characteristics shaping subjective experience. *Perspectives on sexual and reproductive health, 40*(4), 226-237. www.guttmacher.org/sites/default/files/article_files/4022608.pdf

69 Layte, R., & McGee, H. (2007). *Regret about the timing of first sexual intercourse: The role of age and context* (No. 217). ESRI Working Paper. www.econstor.eu/bitstream/10419/68012/1/550862250.pdf

70 Wight, D., Henderson, M., Raab, G., Abraham, C., Buston, K., Scott, S., & Hart, G. (2000). Extent of regretted sexual intercourse among young teenagers in Scotland: a cross sectional survey. *Bmj, 320*(7244), 1243-1244. www.ncbi.nlm.nih.gov/pmc/articles/PMC27366/;
Wight, D., Henderson, M., Raab, G., Abraham, C., Buston, K., Scott, S., & Hart, G. (2000). Extent of regretted sexual intercourse among young teenagers in Scotland: a cross sectional survey. *Bmj, 320*(7244), 1243-1244. www.ncbi.nlm.nih.gov/pmc/articles/PMC27366/;
Wight, D., Parkes, A., Strange, V., Allen, E., Bonell, C., & Henderson, M. (2008). The quality of young people's heterosexual relationships: A longitudinal analysis of characteristics shaping subjective experience. *Perspectives on sexual and reproductive health, 40*(4), 226-237. www.guttmacher.org/sites/default/files/article_files/4022608.pdf

71 Oswalt, S. B., Cameron, K. A., & Koob, J. J. (2005). Sexual regret in college students. *Archives of sexual behavior, 34*(6), 663-669. http://citeseerx.ist.psu.edu/viewdoc/download?doi=10.1.1.553.1736&rep=rep1&type=pdf;
Wight, D., Parkes, A., Strange, V., Allen, E., Bonell, C., & Henderson, M. (2008). The quality of young people's heterosexual relationships: A longitudinal analysis of characteristics shaping subjective experience. *Perspectives on sexual and reproductive health, 40*(4), 226-237. www.guttmacher.org/sites/default/files/article_files/4022608.pdf

72 Armstrong, E. A., England, P., & Fogarty, A. C. (2012). Accounting for women's orgasm and sexual enjoyment in college hookups and relationships. *American Sociological Review, 77*(3), 435-462. https://journals.sagepub.com/doi/pdf/10.1177/0003122412445802

73 Footnote reference: [1]Kelleher, K. (2000). Birds Do It, Bees Do It, but Why'd We Say That? *Los Angeles Times.* www.latimes.com/archives/la-xpm-2000-sep-04-cl-15141-story.html#:~:text=It%20appears%20likely%20that%20the,%E2%80%9D%20(HarperCollins%2C%201988)

74 Honey Bee Eggs. (n.d.). Orkin. www.orkin.com/stinging-pests/bees/honey-bee-eggs#:~:text=The%20life%20cycle%20of%20all,drones%20or%20honey%20bee%20males

75 Torremoro, I. (n.d.). *23 Parents Gave Awful Advice about "The Birds and the Bees".* Texts from Last Night. https://tfln.co/23-parents-gave-awful-advice-birds-bees/

76 King, B. M., & Lorusso, J. (1997). Discussions in the home about sex: Different recollections by parents and children. *Journal of Sex & Marital Therapy, 23*(1), 52-60. www.tandfonline.com/doi/abs/10.1080/00926239708404417

77 Wight, D., & Fullerton, D. (2013). A review of interventions with parents to promote the sexual health of their children. *Journal of Adolescent Health, 52*(1), 4-27. www.ncbi.nlm.nih.gov/books/NBK99397/;
Gavin, L. E., Williams, J. R., Rivera, M. I., & Lachance, C. R. (2015). Programs to strengthen parent–adolescent communication about reproductive health: a systematic review. American Journal of Preventive Medicine, 49(2), S65-S72. www.sciencedirect.com/science/article/abs/pii/S0749379715001440;
Wight, D., & Fullerton, D. (2013). A review of interventions with parents to promote the sexual health of their children. *Journal of Adolescent Health, 52*(1), 4-27. www.ncbi.nlm.nih.gov/books/NBK99397/;
Meschke, L. L., Bartholomae, S., & Zentall, S. R. (2000). Adolescent sexuality and parent-adolescent processes: Promoting healthy teen choices. *Family Relations, 49*(2), 143-154. http://engl020detroit.pbworks.com/f/Adolescent%20Sexuality%20and%20Parent-Adolescent%20Processes.pdf;
Kirby, D. (2007). *Emerging Answers: Research findings on programs to reduce teen pregnancy and sexually transmitted diseases.* The National Campaign to Prevent Teen and Unplanned Pregnancy. https://powertodecide.org/what-we-do/information/resource-library/emerging-answers-2007-new-research-findings-programs-reduce

78 Diiorio, C., Pluhar, E., & Belcher, L. (2003). Parent-child communication about sexuality: A review of the literature from 1980–2002. *Journal of HIV/AIDS Prevention & Education for Adolescents & Children, 5*(3-4), 7-32. www.academia.edu/32873818/Parent-Child_Communication_About_Sexuality

79 Orenstein, P. & Park, I. (2021). What Will Happen When Americans Start Having Sex Again? *The New York times.* www.nytimes.com/2021/04/17/opinion/sunday/sex-stds-stis-covid.html?referringSource=articleShare

80 Relationships and sex education (RSE) and health education. (2019). Gov.UK. www.gov.uk/government/publications/relationships-education-relationships-and-sex-education-rse-and-health-education

81 *Relationships Education, Relationships and Sex Education (RSE) and Health Education.* (2000). UK Department for Education. https://assets.publishing.service.gov.uk/government/uploads/system/uploads/attachment_data/file/908013/Relationships_Education__Relationships_and_Sex_Education__RSE__and_Health_Education.pdf

82 Tanton, C., Jones, K. G., Macdowall, W., Clifton, S., Mitchell, K. R., Datta, J., ... & Wellings, K. (2015). Patterns and trends in sources of information about sex among young people in Britain: evidence from three National Surveys of Sexual Attitudes and Lifestyles. *BMJ open, 5*(3). https://bmjopen.bmj.com/content/5/3/e007834.full

83 Porter, C. (1928). Let's Do It (Let's Fall in Love) [song]. Harms, Inc.

## 3. Death and physical harm

1 Feiler, B. (2016). Teenage Drivers? Be Very Afraid. *The New York Times.* www.nytimes.com/2016/03/20/fashion/teenagers-driving-parents.html

2 *Monroe prom night crash shows teen driving dangers.* (2018). Dayton Daily News. www.daytondailynews.com/news/why-the-fatal-monroe-prom-night-crash-posted-child-for-teen-driving-dangers/YypMbNM6RCZpzGQiwrBrBL/

3 Allen, K. (2019). *Jacqui Saburido, who became the face of an anti-drunk driving campaign, has died.* CNN. https://edition.cnn.com/2019/04/23/us/jacqui-saburido-drunk-driving-dead-trnd/index.html
Steinbuch, Y. (2019). Jacqui Saburido, face of anti-DWI campaigns, dies at 40. *New York Post.* https://nypost.com/2019/04/23/jacqui-saburido-face-of-anti-dwi-campaigns-dies-at-40/

4 Russell, P. (2002). *A Brief History of Driver Education in the UK.* Driver Education Research Foundation. http://derf.org.uk/history.htm

5 Driving Instruction Pioneer: Amos Earl Neyhart. (n.d.). *The Intensive Driving Crash Course Experts.* www.road-and-track.co.uk/driver-instruction-pioneer-neyhart/

6 Mayhew, D. R., Simpson, H. M., Williams, A. F., & Ferguson, S. A. (1998). Effectiveness and role of driver education and training in a graduated licensing system. *Journal of public health policy, 19*(1), 51-67. www.researchgate.net/profile/Susan_Ferguson3/publication/13703494_Effectiveness_and_Role_of_Driver_Education_and_Training_in_a_Graduated_Licensing_System/links/09e4151012c8686176000000.pdf;
Williams, A. F. (2006). Young driver risk factors: successful and unsuccessful approaches for dealing with them and an agenda for the future. *Injury Prevention, 12*(suppl 1), i4-i8. www.ncbi.nlm.nih.gov/pmc/articles/PMC2563437/

7 Vernick, J. S., Li, G., Ogaitis, S., MacKenzie, E. J., Baker, S. P., & Gielen, A. C. (1999). Effects of high school driver education on motor vehicle crashes, violations, and licensure. *American journal of preventive medicine, 16*(1), 40-46. www.sciencedirect.com/science/article/pii/S0749379798001159;
Roberts, I., & Kwan, I. (2006). Cochrane Injuries Group Driver Education Reviewers 2002: School based driver education for the prevention of traffic crashes. https://researchonline.lshtm.ac.uk/17513/1/Roberts_et_al-2001-The_Cochrane_library.pdf ;
Motevalian, A. (2015). *Evidence-based safety education and training for traffic injury prevention.* Journal of Local and Global Health Science, 2015 (Proceedings of the 24th World International Traffic Medicine Association Congress, Qatar 2015), 89. www.qscience.com/doi/abs/10.5339/jlghs.2015.itma.89

8 Simons-Morton, B., & Ouimet, M. C. (2006). Parent involvement in novice teen driving: a review of the literature. *Injury Prevention, 12*(suppl 1), i30-i37. www.ncbi.nlm.nih.gov/pmc/articles/PMC2563441/;
Gershon, P., Ehsani, J. P., Zhu, C., Sita, K. R., Klauer, S., Dingus, T., & Simons-Morton, B. (2018). Crash risk and risky driving behavior among adolescents during learner and independent driving periods. *Journal of Adolescent Health, 63*(5), 568-574. www.jahonline.org/article/S1054-139X(18)30189-7/fulltext

9 Curry, A. E., Peek-Asa, C., Hamann, C. J., & Mirman, J. H. (2015). Effectiveness of parent-focused interventions to increase teen driver safety: A critical review. *Journal of Adolescent Health, 57*(1), S6-S14. www.ncbi.nlm.nih.gov/pmc/articles/PMC4483193/

10 Page, Y., Ouimet, M. C., & Cuny, S. (2004). An evaluation of the effectiveness of the supervised driver-training system in France. In *Annual proceedings/association for the advancement of automotive medicine* (Vol. 48, p. 131). Association for the Advancement of Automotive Medicine. www.ncbi.nlm.nih.gov/pmc/articles/PMC3217433/

11 Sagberg, F., & Gregersen, N. P. (2005). *Effects of lowering the age limit for driver training. Traffic and transport psychology: theory and application.* Amsterdam: Elsevier Science, 171-8. https://books.google.co.uk/books?hl=en&lr=&id=jrEKoWfO-Jc0C&oi=fnd&pg=PA171&dq=Effects+of+lowering+the+age+limit+for+driver+training&ots=qENWKaXeMt&sig=gaL-vRStBwEe5xxsazdTV-KOKXW0#v=onepage&q=Effects%20of%20lowering%20the%20age%20limit%20for%20driver%20training&f=false

12 Gregersen, N. P., Berg, H. Y., Engström, I., Nolén, S., Nyberg, A., & Rimmö, P. A. (2000). Sixteen years age limit for learner drivers in Sweden—an evaluation of safety effects. *Accident Analysis & Prevention, 32*(1), 25-35. www.sciencedirect.com/science/article/abs/pii/S0001457599000457

13 *Pointers for Parents: Roadmap to Teen Driver Safety.* (n.d.). National Safety Council. www.nsc.org/driveithome/pointers-for-parents/pointers-for-parents-lessons

14 Simons-Morton, B. G., Ouimet, M. C., & Catalano, R. F. (2008). Parenting and the young driver problem. *American journal of preventive medicine, 35*(3), S294-S303. www.ncbi.nlm.nih.gov/pmc/articles/PMC2562681/

15 Chapman, E. A., Masten, S. V., & Browning, K. K. (2014). Crash and traffic violation rates before and after licensure for novice California drivers subject to different driver licensing requirements. *Journal of safety research,* 50, 125-138. http://scholar.google.com/scholar_url?url=https%3A%2F%2Fwww.researchgate.net%2Fprofile%2FScott_Masten%2Fpublication%2F263574311_Crash_and_traffic_violation_rates_before_and_after_licensure_for_novice_California_drivers_subject_to_different_driver_licensing_requirements%2Flinks%2F0c96053b436cb2891b000000%2FCrash-and-traffic-violation-rates-before-and-after-licensure-for-novice-California-drivers-subject-to-different-driver-licensing-requirements&hl=en&sa=T&oi=gga&ct=gga&cd=0&d=11998363284016816949&ei=OkZEXburGpGdmQHX0oT4DA&scisig=AAGBfm0ngYAsZkuBavvJm4fuJtLV2gUt-

4w&nossl=1&ws=1920x929&at=Crash%20and%20traffic%20violation%20rates%20before%20and%20after%20licensure%20for%20novice%20California%20drivers%20subject%20to%20different%20driver%20licensing%20requirements

16 Gershon, P., Ehsani, J. P., Zhu, C., Sita, K. R., Klauer, S., Dingus, T., & Simons-Morton, B. (2018). Crash risk and risky driving behavior among adolescents during learner and independent driving periods. *Journal of Adolescent Health, 63*(5), 568-574. www.jahonline.org/article/S1054-139X(18)30189-7/fulltext

17 Footnote reference: [1] Curry, A. E., Metzger, K. B., Williams, A. F., & Tefft, B. C. (2017). Comparison of older and younger novice driver crash rates: Informing the need for extended Graduated Driver Licensing restrictions. *Accident Analysis & Prevention*, 108, 66-73. www.researchgate.net/profile/Allison_Curry/publication/319423569_Comparison_of_older_and_younger_novice_driver_crash_rates_Informing_the_need_for_extended_Graduated_Driver_Licensing_restrictions/links/59e78873aca272bc423cfa82/Comparison-of-older-and-younger-novice-driver-crash-rates-Informing-the-need-for-extended-Graduated-Driver-Licensing-restrictions

18 Haggerty, K. P., Fleming, C. B., Catalano, R. F., Harachi, T. W., & Abbott, R. D. (2006). Raising healthy children: examining the impact of promoting healthy driving behavior within a social development intervention. *Prevention Science, 7*(3), 257. http://citeseerx.ist.psu.edu/viewdoc/download?doi=10.1.1.724.2245&rep=rep1&type=pdf

19 Gardner, M., & Steinberg, L. (2005). Peer influence on risk taking, risk preference, and risky decision making in adolescence and adulthood: an experimental study. *Developmental psychology, 41*(4), 625. http://citeseerx.ist.psu.edu/viewdoc/download?doi=10.1.1.1047.6482&rep=rep1&type=pdf

20 Chen, L. H., Baker, S. P., Braver, E. R., & Li, G. (2000). Carrying passengers as a risk factor for crashes fatal to 16-and 17-year-old drivers. *Jama, 283*(12), 1578-1582. https://jamanetwork.com/journals/jama/fullarticle/192524

21 Shults, R. A., & Williams, A. F. (2016). Graduated driver licensing night driving restrictions and drivers aged 16 or 17 years involved in fatal night crashes—United States, 2009–2014. *Morbidity and Mortality Weekly Report, 65*(29), 725-730. www.cdc.gov/mmwr/volumes/65/wr/mm6529a1.htm?s_cid=mm6529a1_w

22 *Teen and Novice Drivers*. (n.d.). Governors Highway Safety Association. www.ghsa.org/state-laws/issues/teen%20and%20novice%20drivers

23 Shope, J. T. (2007). Graduated driver licensing: review of evaluation results since 2002. *Journal of safety research, 38*(2), 165-175. www.researchgate.net/profile/Jean_Shope/publication/281266128_Graduated_driver_licensing_in_the_United_States_Evaluation_results_since_2002/links/55e5e0f608aecb1a7ccd5ee4.pdf;
Margolis, L. H., Masten, S. V., & Foss, R. D. (2007). The effects of graduated driver licensing on hospitalization rates and charges for 16-and 17-year-olds in North Carolina. Traffic injury prevention, 8(1), 35-38. www.researchgate.net/profile/Scott_Masten/publication/6441679_The_Effects_of_Graduated_Driver_Licensing_on_Hospitalization_Rates_and_Charges_for_16-and_17-Year-Olds_in_North_Carolina/links/00b7d52f9dad1c30ae000000/The-Effects-of-Graduated-Driver-Licensing-on-Hospitalization-Rates-and-Charges-for-16-and-17-Year-Olds-in-North-Carolina.pdf;
Hartling, L., Wiebe, N., Russell, K. F., Petruk, J., Spinola, C., & Klassen, T. P. (2004). Graduated driver licensing for reducing motor vehicle crashes among young drivers. Cochrane database of systematic reviews, (2). http://scholar.google.co.uk/scholar_url?url=https%3A%2F%2Fera.library.ualberta.ca%2Fitems%2F246bac6e-ff28-412e-b8e7-7cf1862c7c10%2Fview%2F6e486daa-fc9b-485f-b1cd-b669ac347f04%2FRussell-20Vandermeer-20Hartling-20Graduated-20driver-20licensing.pdf&hl=en&sa=T&oi=gga&ct=gga&cd=0&d=11894166139480542630&ei=nTIbXfehBcGomQGcmKm4Dw&scisig=AAGBfm2_WyU8PQhRt1R3oqdv_9UrAF9YZA&nossl=1&ws=1920x934&at=Graduated%20driver%20licensing%20for%20reducing%20motor%20vehicle%20crashes%20among%20young%20drivers;
O'connor, R. E., Lin, L., Tinkoff, G. H., & Ellis, H. (2007). Effect of a graduated licensing system on Motor Vehicle Crashes and Associated Injuries Involving Drivers Less Than 18 Years-of-Age. *Prehospital emergency care, 11*(4), 389-393. www.tandfonline.com/doi/abs/10.1080/10903120701536727;
Chen, L. H., Baker, S. P., & Li, G. (2006). Graduated driver licensing programs and fatal crashes of 16-year-old drivers: a national evaluation. *Pediatrics, 118*(1), 56-62. https://pediatrics.aappublications.org/content/118/1/56.short

24 Simons-Morton, B., & Ouimet, M. C. (2006). Parent involvement in novice teen driving: a review of the literature. *Injury Prevention*, 12(suppl 1), i30-i37. https://pdfs.semanticscholar.org/d2a1/5038894a1e3aa77af546e80cf69eb295ec5e.pdf;
Hartos, J. L., Eitel, P., Haynie, D. L., & Simons-Morton, B. G. (2000). Can I take the car? Relations among parenting practices and adolescent problem-driving practices. *Journal of Adolescent Research, 15*(3), 352-367. http://journals.sagepub.com/doi/abs/10.1177/0743558400153003

25 Simons-Morton, B., & Ouimet, M. C. (2006). Parent involvement in novice teen driving: a review of the literature. *Injury Prevention*, 12(suppl 1), i30-i37. https://pdfs.semanticscholar.org/d2a1/5038894a1e3aa77af546e80cf69eb295ec5e.pdf;
Hartos, J. L., Shattuck, T., Simons-Morton, B. G., & Beck, K. H. (2004). An in-depth look at parent-imposed driving rules: Their strengths and weaknesses. *Journal of Safety Research, 35*(5), 547-555.

26 Hartos, J., Eitel, P., & Simons-Morton, B. (2002). Parenting practices and adolescent risky driving: A three-month prospective study. *Health education & behavior, 29*(2), 194-206. http://citeseerx.ist.psu.edu/viewdoc/download?doi=10.1.1.922.7111&rep=rep1&type=pdf;
Hartos, J. L., Eitel, P., Haynie, D. L., & Simons-Morton, B. G. (2000). Can I take the car? Relations among parenting practices and adolescent problem-driving practices. *Journal of Adolescent Research, 15*(3), 352-367. http://journals.sagepub.com/doi/abs/10.1177/0743558400153003

27 Simons-Morton, B., & Ouimet, M. C. (2006). Parent involvement in novice teen driving: a review of the literature. *Injury Prevention*, 12(suppl 1), i30-i37. https://pdfs.semanticscholar.org/d2a1/5038894a1e3aa77af546e80cf69eb295ec5e.pdf;

28 Boyle, J. M., Lampkin, C., & Schulman, R. (2008). *2007 motor vehicle occupant safety survey. Volume 2, Seat belt report* (No. DOT-HS-810-975). United States. National Highway Traffic Safety Administration. www.nhtsa.gov/sites/nhtsa.dot.gov/files/documents/810975.pdf

29 *Seat Belts: Get the Facts.* (2020). Centers for Disease Control and Prevention, National Center for Injury Prevention and Control. www.cdc.gov/motorvehiclesafety/seatbelts/facts.html;
Kahane, C. J. (2000). *Fatality reduction by safety belts for front-seat occupants of cars and light trucks: Updated and expanded estimates based on 1986-99 FARS Data* (No. DOT-HS-809 199). United States. National Highway Traffic Safety Administration. https://rosap.ntl.bts.gov/view/dot/5157

30 Olsen, E. O., Shults, R. A., & Eaton, D. K. (2013). Texting while driving and other risky motor vehicle behaviors among US high school students. *Pediatrics, 131*(6), e1708-e1715. https://pdfs.semanticscholar.org/7466/84db7f585643f06b4d442fceb7e2a78f6784.pdf;
Kann, L., McManus, T., Harris, W. A., Shanklin, S. L., Flint, K. H., Queen, B., ... & Lim, C. (2018). Youth risk behavior surveillance—United States, 2017. *MMWR Surveillance Summaries, 67*(8), 1. www.ncbi.nlm.nih.gov/pmc/articles/PMC6002027/

31 Hosking, S. (2007). *The effects of text messaging on young novice driver performance.* Distracted driving, 155-187. www.researchgate.net/profile/Michael_Regan3/publication/251346060_The_Effects_of_Text_Messaging_on_Young_Novice_Driver_Performance/links/542a9ba40cf29bbc1267b809.pdf

32 Delgado, M. K., Wanner, K. J., & McDonald, C. (2016). Adolescent cellphone use while driving: An overview of the literature and promising future directions for prevention. *Media and communication, 4*(3), 79. www.ncbi.nlm.nih.gov/pmc/articles/PMC5041591/

33 Klauer, S. G., Guo, F., Simons-Morton, B. G., Ouimet, M. C., Lee, S. E., & Dingus, T. A. (2014). Distracted driving and risk of road crashes among novice and experienced drivers. *New England journal of medicine, 370*(1), 54-59. www.nejm.org/doi/full/10.1056/NEJMsa1204142

34 Gross, A. (2015). *Distraction and Teen Crashes: Even Worse than We Thought.* Newsroom. https://newsroom.aaa.com/2015/03/distraction-teen-crashes-even-worse-thought/

35 Brodsky, W., & Slor, Z. (2013). Background music as a risk factor for distraction among young-novice drivers. *Accident Analysis & Prevention*, 59, 382-393. www.gwern.net/docs/music-distraction/2013-brodsky.pdf

36 Kann, L., McManus, T., Harris, W. A., Shanklin, S. L., Flint, K. H., Queen, B., ... & Lim, C. (2018). Youth risk behavior surveillance—United States, 2017. *MMWR Surveillance Summaries, 67*(8), 1. www.ncbi.nlm.nih.gov/pmc/articles/PMC6002027/

37 National Center for Injury Prevention and Control, Centers for Disease Control and Prevention. *Teen Drinking and Driving A Dangerous Mix,* October 2012 CDC Vital Signs. www.cdc.gov/vitalsigns/teendrinkinganddriving/index.html

38 Friese, B., & Grube, J. W. (2014). Teen parties: who has parties, what predicts whether there is alcohol and who supplies the alcohol?. *The journal of primary prevention, 35*(6), 391-396. www.ncbi.nlm.nih.gov/pmc/articles/PMC4512649/

39 Friese, B., & Grube, J. W. (2014). Teen parties: who has parties, what predicts whether there is alcohol and who supplies the alcohol?. *The journal of primary prevention, 35*(6), 391-396. www.ncbi.nlm.nih.gov/pmc/articles/PMC4512649/

40 Footnote reference: [1]Ward, B., & Snow, P. (2009). *Parents, parties, and adolescent alcohol use.* Report for DEECD, 1-47. www.education.vic.gov.au/documents/school/teachers/health/parentres09.pdf

41 U.S. Department of Justice, Criminal Justice Information Services Division. *2018 Crime in the United States.* Table 38, Arrests by Age, 2018. https://ucr.fbi.gov/crime-in-the-u.s/2018/crime-in-the-u.s.-2018/topic-pages/tables/table-38

42 United States Census Bureau. *National Population by Characteristics: 2010-2019.* www.census.gov/data/tables/time-series/demo/popest/2010s-national-detail.html

43 Nolo. (n.d.). *Teen Drunk Driving: The Consequences of an Underage DUI.* http://dui.drivinglaws.org/resources/dui-and-dwi/dui-basics/the-sobering-facts-underage-duis.htm

44 Wicki, J., Gache, P., & Rutschmann, O. T. (2000). Self-estimates of blood-alcohol concentration and ability to drive in a population of soldiers. *Alcohol and alcoholism, 35*(1), 104-105. https://pdfs.semanticscholar.org/39a9/c786b59e6cb1acb4fb0ec51336075fe10896.pdf;
Montgomery, C., Ashmore, K. V., & Jansari, A. (2011). The effects of a modest dose of alcohol on executive functioning and prospective memory. *Human Psychopharmacology: Clinical and Experimental, 26*(3), 208-215. http://research.gold.ac.uk/11167/1/Montgomery_Effects_2011.pdf

45 Grant, S., LaBrie, J. W., Hummer, J. F., & Lac, A. (2012). How drunk am I? Misperceiving one's level of intoxication in the college drinking environment. *Psychology of addictive behaviors, 26*(1), 51.

46 *Alcohol Impaired Driving.* (n.d.). Governors Highway Safety Assocation. www.ghsa.org/state-laws/issues/alcohol%20impaired%20driving

47 Zhao, X., Zhang, X., & Rong, J. (2014). Study of the effects of alcohol on drivers and driving performance on straight road. *Mathematical Problems in Engineering,* 2014. www.hindawi.com/journals/mpe/2014/607652/

48 Laurell, H. (1977). Effects of small doses of alcohol on driver performance in emergency traffic situations. *Accident Analysis & Prevention, 9*(3), 191-201. www.diva-portal.org/smash/get/diva2:675034/FULLTEXT01.pdf

49 Moskowitz, H., Burns, M., Fiorentino, D., Smiley, A., & Zador, P. (2000). *Driver characteristics and impairment at various BACs* (No. DOT-HS-809-075). United States. National Highway Traffic Safety Administration. https://rosap.ntl.bts.gov/view/dot/1635

50 Moskowitz, H., & Florentino, D. (2000). *A review of the literature on the effects of low doses of alcohol on driving-related skills* (No. DOT-HS-809-028). United States. National Highway Traffic Safety Administration. https://rosap.ntl.bts.gov/view/dot/1677

51 Langenbucher, J. W., & Nathan, P. E. (1983). Psychology, public policy, and the evidence for alcohol intoxication. *American Psychologist, 38*(10), 1070. www.researchgate.net/profile/Jim_Langenbucher/publication/16839299_Psychology_public_policy_and_the_evidence_for_alcohol_intoxication/links/00b495331ffbb71095000000/Psychology-public-policy-and-the-evidence-for-alcohol-intoxication.pdf

52 McGuire, F. L. (1986). The accuracy of estimating the sobriety of drinking drivers. *Journal of Safety Research, 17*(2), 81-85. www.sciencedirect.com/science/article/pii/0022437586900976

53 Rubenzer, S. (2011). Judging intoxication. *Behavioral sciences & the law, 29*(1), 116-137. https://heinonline.org/HOL/Page?collection=journals&handle=hein.journals/bsclw29&id=131&men_tab=srchresults

54 Mariakakis, A., Parsi, S., Patel, S. N., & Wobbrock, J. O. (2018, April). Drunk User Interfaces: Determining Blood Alcohol Level through Everyday Smartphone Tasks. In *Proceedings of the 2018 CHI Conference on Human Factors in Computing Systems* (p. 234). ACM. https://faculty.washington.edu/wobbrock/pubs/chi-18.01.pdf;
Jung, Y., Kim, J., Awofeso, O., Kim, H., Regnier, F., & Bae, E. (2015). Smartphone-based colorimetric analysis for detection of saliva alcohol concentration. *Applied optics, 54*(31), 9183-9189. www.osapublishing.org/ao/abstract.cfm?uri=ao-54-31-9183

54. *Car breathalyzer devices to prevent drunk driving.* (n.d.). Intoxalock. www.intoxalock.com/drunk-driving-prevention/teens

55 *Car breathalyzer devices to prevent drunk driving.* (n.d.). Intoxalock. www.intoxalock.com/drunk-driving-prevention/teens

56 Babor, T., Caetano, R., Casswell, S., Edwards, G., Giesbrecht, N., Graham, K., ... & Homel, R. (2003). Alcohol: no ordinary commodity: research and public policy. *Rev Bras Psiquiatr,* 26(4), 280-3. www.scielo.br/pdf/%0D/rbp/v26n4/a15v26n4.pdf

57 Willis, C., Lybrand, S., & Bellamy, N. (2004). Alcohol ignition interlock programmes for reducing drink driving recidivism. Cochrane Database of Systematic Reviews, (3). www.cochranelibrary.com/cdsr/doi/10.1002/14651858.CD004168.pub2/full

58 How Much Does it Cost to Have an Ignition Interlock Device Installed in my Car? (n.d.). Alcolock. https://alcolockusa.com/faqs/how-much-does-it-cost-to-have-an-ignition-interlock-device-installed-in-my-car

59 Smouse, B. 2015. New car tech could stop drunken drivers. USA Today. www.usatoday.com/story/money/cars/2015/07/06/new-technology-to-prevent-drunk-driving/29125417/

60 Farmer, C. M., Kirley, B. B., & McCartt, A. T. (2010). Effects of in-vehicle monitoring on the driving behavior of teenagers. *Journal of safety research, 41*(1), 39-45. www.sciencedirect.com/science/article/pii/S0022437510000058;
Tee*n Driver Monitoring Technology.* (2018). U.S. Department of Transportation, National Highway Safety Administration. www.nhtsa.gov/sites/nhtsa.dot.gov/files/documents/812578_teen-driver-monitoring-technology-traffic-tech.pdf;
Simons-Morton, B. G., Ouimet, M. C., & Catalano, R. F. (2008). Parenting and the young driver problem. *American journal of preventive medicine, 35*(3), S294-S303. www.ncbi.nlm.nih.gov/pmc/articles/PMC2562681/

61 Footnote references:
[1]Murdock, J. (n.d.). *Top Six Latest Automotive Tech that will Keep Your Teen Drivers Safe.* Car Buying Strategies. www.car-buying-strategies.com/automotive-tech-teens.html
[2] *3 Technologies To Help Prevent Teen Crashes.* (2015). Guardian Interlock. https://guardianinterlock.com/blog/3-technologies-help-prevent-teen-crashes/

62 Footnote references:
[1] Murdock, J. (n.d.). *Top Six Latest Automotive Tech that will Keep Your Teen Drivers Safe.* Car Buying Strategies. www.car-buying-strategies.com/automotive-tech-teens.html
[2] Murdock, J. (n.d.). *Top Six Latest Automotive Tech that will Keep Your Teen Drivers Safe.* Car Buying Strategies. www.car-buying-strategies.com/automotive-tech-teens.html
[3] Jolly, J. (2017). *Got a teen driver? Here is tech to help keep them safe.* USA Today. https://eu.usatoday.com/story/tech/columnist/2017/06/25/got-teen-driver-here-tech-help-keep-them-safe/103076252/
[4] Jones, T. (2021). *10 Best Car Tracking Devices for Parents in 2021.* Wondershare FamiSafe. www.famisafe.com/trackers/car-tracking-device-for-parents.html

63 *Teen Safe Driver.* (n.d.). American Family Insurance. www.amfam.com/insurance/car/teensafedriver;
*Driver Behavior Monitoring: Vehicle Telematics Insurance.* (n.d.). Insurance & Mobility Solutions. https://ims.tech/opinion/driver-behavior-monitoring/;
*BIBA Research Reveals Telematics-based Policies Almost Reaches One Million Mark.* (2018). British Insurance Brokers' Association. www.biba.org.uk/press-releases/biba-research-reveals-telematics-almost-reach-one-million-mark/

64 Birnbaum, S.(2017). *6 Types of Technology to Track Your Teen Driver.* Tech.Co. https://tech.co/news/technology-track-teen-driver-2017-02

65 *TrueMotion App Moves to Make Driving Safer.* (2017). Cars.com. www.cars.com/articles/truemotion-app-moves-to-make-driving-safer-1420693277580/

66 *Leefeldt, E. (2018). Self-driving cars are a nonstarter for many teens.* CBS News. www.cbsnews.com/news/self-driving-cars-are-a-nonstarter-for-many-teens/

67 *Automated Vehicles for Safety.* (n.d.). National Highway Traffic Safety Administration, U.S. Department of Transportation. www.nhtsa.gov/technology-innovation/automated-vehicles-safety#topic-road-self-driving

68 Hayes, K. (n.d.). *From Horror to Hope, Surviving a Traumatic Motorcycle Accident.* Enjuris. www.enjuris.com/blog/my-accident/surviving-motorcycle-accident/

69 *NCSA Tools, Publications, and Data.* (n.d.). United States Department of Transportation, National Highway Traffic Safety Administration. https://cdan.nhtsa.gov/SASStoredProcess/guest

70 Lin, M. R., & Kraus, J. F. (2009). A review of risk factors and patterns of motorcycle injuries. *Accident Analysis & Prevention, 41*(4), 710-722. http://smarter-usa.org/wp-content/uploads/2018/02/2009-A-Review-of-Risk-Factors-and-Patterns-of-Motorcycle-Injuries.pdf

71 Motevalian, A. (2015). Evidence-based safety education and training for traffic injury prevention. *Journal of Local and Global Heath Science*, (2), 89. www.qscience.com/doi/abs/10.5339/jlghs.2015.itma.89

72 Branche, C., Ozanne-Smith, J., Oyebite, K., & Hyder, A. A. (2008). *World report on child injury prevention.* World Health Organization. https://books.google.co.uk/books?hl=en&lr=&id=UeXwoNh8sbwC&oi=fnd&pg=PR7&dq=World+report+on+child+injury+prevention&ots=hH6uXQfz0M&sig=vmVyuC8mg1osvJd8Pwnv3oJ_BZY&redir_esc=y#v=onepage&q=World%20report%20on%20child%20injury%20prevention&f=false

73 Branche, C., Ozanne-Smith, J., Oyebite, K., & Hyder, A. A. (2008). *World report on child injury prevention.* World Health Organization. https://books.google.co.uk/books?hl=en&lr=&id=UeXwoNh8sbwC&oi=fnd&pg=PR7&dq=World+report+on+child+injury+prevention&ots=hH6uXQfz0M&sig=vmVyuC8mg1osvJd8Pwnv3oJ_BZY&redir_esc=y#v=onepage&q=World%20report%20on%20child%20injury%20prevention&f=false

74 Liu, B. C., Ivers, R., Norton, R., Boufous, S., Blows, S., & Lo, S. K. (2008). Helmets for preventing injury in motorcycle riders. *Cochrane database of systematic reviews,* (1). www.cochranelibrary.com/cdsr/doi/10.1002/14651858.CD004333.pub3/full

75 Kadlec, D. (2010). *Five Ways to Say No to Your Teen.* CBS News. www.cbsnews.com/news/five-ways-to-say-no-to-your-teen/

76 Axelrod, J. (2018). *Parents blindsided by daughter's tragic suicide hope her story helps save others.* CBS News. www.cbsnews.com/news/alexandra-valoras-parents-blindsided-by-daughters-tragic-suicide-hope-her-story-helps-save-others/

77 Arsenault, M. (2018). Secrets of a Lost Girl. *The Boston Globe.* www.bostonglobe.com/metro/2018/06/23/diary/ep6tAOTtMVVLYCBYx0o9GJ/story.html

78 Footnote reference: [1] Young, T. L., & Zimmerman, R. (1998). Clueless: parental knowledge of risk behaviors of middle school students. *Archives of pediatrics & adolescent medicine, 152*(11), 1137-1139. https://jamanetwork.com/journals/jamapediatrics/fullarticle/190069;
Kann, L., McManus, T., Harris, W. A., Shanklin, S. L., Flint, K. H., Queen, B., ... & Lim, C. (2018). Youth risk behavior surveillance—United States, 2017. *MMWR Surveillance Summaries, 67*(8), 1. www.ncbi.nlm.nih.gov/pmc/articles/PMC6002027/

79 Roh, B. R., Jung, E. H., & Hong, H. J. (2018). A Comparative Study of Suicide Rates among 10–19-Year-Olds in 29 OECD Countries. *Psychiatry investigation, 15*(4), 376. www.ncbi.nlm.nih.gov/pmc/articles/PMC5912485/

80 NCHS Vital Statistics System for numbers of deaths. (n.d.). *Bureau of Census population estimates.* Centers for Disease Control and Prevention. https://webappa.cdc.gov/sasweb/ncipc/mortrate.html

81 Bunney, W. E., Kleinman, A. M., Pellmar, T. C., & Goldsmith, S. K. (Eds.). (2002). *Reducing suicide: A national imperative.* National Academies Press. http://books.google.co.uk/books?hl=en&lr=&id=9xGdAgAAQBAJ&oi=fnd&pg=PT17&dq=Reducing+Suicide:+A+National+Imperative&ots=mRIG9kqLlH&sig=vIY1_OdrfbYjX3g8tv9gZXgvg7k

82 Carey, B. (2018). Defying Prevention Efforts, Suicide Rates Are Climbing Across the Nation. *The New York Times.* www.nytimes.com/2018/06/07/health/suicide-rates-kate-spade.html?hpw&rref=health&action=click&pgtype=Homepage&module=well-region&region=bottom-well&WT.nav=bottom-well

83 Bunney, W. E., Kleinman, A. M., Pellmar, T. C., & Goldsmith, S. K. (Eds.). (2002). *Reducing suicide: A national imperative.* National Academies Press. http://books.google.co.uk/books?hl=en&lr=&id=9xGdAgAAQBAJ&oi=fnd&pg=PT17&dq=Reducing+Suicide:+A+National+Imperative&ots=mRIG9kqLlH&sig=vIY1_OdrfbYjX3g8tv9gZXgvg7k

84 Mann, J. J. (2002). A current perspective of suicide and attempted suicide. *Annals of internal medicine, 136*(4), 302-311. https://pdfs.semanticscholar.org/1cb2/f91c1c0c427e16fc03236a7dcd1e2ab5e753.pdf

85 Gaynes, B. N., West, S. L., Ford, C. A., Frame, P., Klein, J., & Lohr, K. N. (2004). Screening for suicide risk in adults: a summary of the evidence for the US Preventive Services Task Force. *Annals of internal medicine, 140*(10), 822-835. www.researchgate.net/profile/Bradley_Gaynes/publication/8558228_Screening_for_Suicide_Risk_in_Adults_A_Summary_of_the_Evidence_for_the_U.S._Preventive_Services_Task_Force/links/00b7d52e8099a7b028000000.pdf

86 *Draft self-harm guidelines from the National Institute for Health and Clinical Excellence (NICE).* (2011). National Institute for Health and Clinical Excellence (NICE). www.nice.org.uk/guidance/cg133/resources/selfharm-in-over-8s-longterm-management-pdf-35109508689349

87 Odgers, C. (2018). *Smartphones are bad for some teens, not all.* Nature. www.nature.com/articles/d41586-018-02109-8

88 Office of the Surgeon General (US, & National Action Alliance for Suicide Prevention US). (2012). *2012 national strategy for suicide prevention: goals and objectives for action: a report of the US Surgeon General and of the National Action Alliance for Suicide Prevention.* www.ncbi.nlm.nih.gov/books/NBK109906/

89 Luthar, S. S., & Latendresse, S. J. (2005). Children of the affluent: Challenges to well-being. *Current directions in psychological science, 14*(1), 49-53. www.ncbi.nlm.nih.gov/pmc/articles/PMC1948879/?_escaped_fragment_=-po=32.3529

90 Hegerl, U., & Wittenburg, L. (2009). Focus on mental health care reforms in Europe: the European alliance against depression: a multilevel approach to the prevention of suicidal behavior. *Psychiatric Services, 60*(5), 596-599. https://ps.psychiatryonline.org/doi/full/10.1176/ps.2009.60.5.596

91 Footnote references:
[1] Topp, C. W., Østergaard, S. D., Søndergaard, S., & Bech, P. (2015). The WHO-5 Well-Being Index: a systematic review of the literature. *Psychotherapy and psychosomatics, 84*(3), 167-176. www.karger.com/Article/Fulltext/376585
[2] *WHO (Five) Well-Being Index.* (1998). Psychiatric Research Unit WHO Collaborating Centre in Mental Health.
www.psykiatri-regionh.dk/who-5/Documents/WHO-5%20questionaire%20-%20English.pdf

92 Elnour, A. A., & Harrison, J. (2008). Lethality of suicide methods. *Injury prevention, 14*(1), 39-45. http://citeseerx.ist.psu.edu/viewdoc/download?doi=10.1.1.584.4724&rep=rep1&type=pdf;
Fatality rates: National Center for Health Statistics. (2020). *CDC WONDER: Underlying Cause of Death 1999-2016.* Centers for Disease Control and Prevention. http://wonder.cdc.gov/ucd-icd10.html
Hospitalization rates: National Center for Injury Prevention and Control. (n.d.). *Web-based Injury Statistics Query and Reporting System (WISQARS), 2001-2014.* Centers for Disease Control and Prevention.

93 Möller-Leimkühler, A. M. (2003). The gender gap in suicide and premature death or: why are men so vulnerable?. *European archives of psychiatry and clinical neuroscience, 253*(1), 1-8. www.researchgate.net/profile/Anne-Moeller-Leimkuehler/publication/10832400_The_Gender_Gap_in_Suicide_and_Premature_Death_or_Why_Are_Men_So_Vulnerable/links/55c8a63c08aebc967df8fc13/The-Gender-Gap-in-Suicide-and-Premature-Death-or-Why-Are-Men-So-Vulnerable.pdf

94 Elnour, A. A., & Harrison, J. (2008). Lethality of suicide methods. *Injury prevention, 14*(1), 39-45. http://citeseerx.ist.psu.edu/viewdoc/download?doi=10.1.1.584.4724&rep=rep1&type=pdf

95 Weller, F. (2020). *'It was instant regret': Golden Gate Bridge suicide survivor to share story in virtual event in Wilmington.* WECT News 6. www.wect.com/2020/11/17/it-was-instant-regret-golden-gate-bridge-suicide-survivor-share-story-virtual-event-wilmington/

96 Seiden, R. H. (1978). Where are they now? A follow-up study of suicide attempters from the Golden Gate Bridge. *Suicide and Life-Threatening Behavior, 8*(4), 203-216. https://pubmed.ncbi.nlm.nih.gov/217131/

97 Carroll, R., Metcalfe, C., & Gunnell, D. (2014). Hospital presenting self-harm and risk of fatal and non-fatal repetition: systematic review and meta-analysis. *PLoS One, 9*(2), e89944. https://journals.plos.org/plosone/article?id=10.1371/journal.pone.0089944

98 World Health Organization. (2014). *Preventing suicide: a global imperative.* World Health Organization. http://apps.who.int/iris/bitstream/handle/10665/131056/9789241564779_eng.pdf;jsessionid=B5B6BCA774CF-2B456EF7DBACC0A1C192?sequence=1

99 Shaffer, D., Garland, A., Gould, M., Fisher, P., & Trautman, P. (1988). Preventing teenage suicide: A critical review. *Journal of the American Academy of Child & Adolescent Psychiatry, 27*(6), 675-687. www.jaacap.org/article/S0890-8567(09)65844-5/pdf

100 Mann, J. J. (2002). A current perspective of suicide and attempted suicide. *Annals of internal medicine, 136*(4), 302-311. https://pdfs.semanticscholar.org/1cb2/f91c1c0c427e16fc03236a7dcd1e2ab5e753.pdf

101 *Draft self-harm guidelines from the National Institute for Health and Clinical Excellence (NICE).* (2011). National Institute for Health and Clinical Excellence (NICE). www.nice.org.uk/guidance/cg133/resources/selfharm-in-over-8s-longterm-management-pdf-35109508689349;
Mann, J. J., Apter, A., Bertolote, J., Beautrais, A., Currier, D., Haas, A., ... & Mehlum, L. (2005). Suicide prevention strategies: a systematic review. *Jama, 294*(16), 2064-2074. http://dhmh.maryland.gov/suicideprevention/Documents/Suicide%20prevention%20strategies-systematic%20review.pdf;
Gould, M. S., Greenberg, T. E. D., Velting, D. M., & Shaffer, D. (2003). Youth suicide risk and preventive interventions: a review of the past 10 years. *Journal of the American Academy of Child & Adolescent Psychiatry, 42*(4), 386-405. www.ohiospf.org/files/Suicide%2010%20Year%20Review.pdf;

Beautrais, A., Fergusson, D., Coggan, C., Collings, C., Doughty, C., Ellis, P., ... & Poulton, R. (2007). Effective strategies for suicide prevention in New Zealand: a review of the evidence. *NZ Med J,* 120(1251). www.researchgate.net/profile/Dee_Mangin/publication/6422234_Prevalence_of_complementary_medicine_use_in_Christchurch_New_Zealand_children_attending_general_practice_versus_paediatric_outpatients/links/53fa97c60cf2e3cbf565c47a.pdf#page=67

102 World Health Organization. (2014). *Preventing suicide: a global imperative.* World Health Organization. http://apps.who.int/iris/bitstream/handle/10665/131056/9789241564779_eng.pdf;jsessionid=B5B6BCA774CF-2B456EF7DBACC0A1C192?sequence=1

103 National Center for Health Statistics. (2020). *CDC WONDER: Underlying Cause of Death 1999-2016.* Centers for Disease Control and Prevention. http://wonder.cdc.gov/ucd-icd10.html

104 Mann, J. J. (2002). A current perspective of suicide and attempted suicide. *Annals of internal medicine, 136*(4), 302-311. https://pdfs.semanticscholar.org/1cb2/f91c1c0c427e16fc03236a7dcd1e2ab5e753.pdf

105 Anglemyer, A., Horvath, T., & Rutherford, G. (2014). The accessibility of firearms and risk for suicide and homicide victimization among household members: a systematic review and meta-analysis. *Annals of internal medicine, 160*(2), 101-110. http://annals.org/aim/fullarticle/1814426

106 World Health Organization. (2014). *Preventing suicide: a global imperative.* World Health Organization. http://apps.who.int/iris/bitstream/handle/10665/131056/9789241564779_eng.pdf;jsessionid=B5B6BCA774CF-2B456EF7DBACC0A1C192?sequence=1

107 Grossman, D. C., Mueller, B. A., Riedy, C., Dowd, M. D., Villaveces, A., Prodzinski, J., ... & Harruff, R. (2005). Gun storage practices and risk of youth suicide and unintentional firearm injuries. *Jama, 293*(6), 707-714.

108 Hemenway, D., Solnick, S. J., & Azrael, D. R. (1995). Firearm training and storage. *Jama, 273*(1), 46-50. https://jamanetwork.com/journals/jama/article-abstract/385426

109 World Health Organization. (2014). *Preventing suicide: a global imperative.* World Health Organization. http://apps.who.int/iris/bitstream/handle/10665/131056/9789241564779_eng.pdf;jsessionid=B5B6BCA774CF-2B456EF7DBACC0A1C192?sequence=1

110 Hawton, K., Bergen, H., Simkin, S., Dodd, S., Pocock, P., Bernal, W., ... & Kapur, N. (2013). Long term effect of reduced pack sizes of paracetamol on poisoning deaths and liver transplant activity in England and Wales: interrupted time series analyses. *Bmj,* 346, f403. www.bmj.com/CONTENT/346/BMJ.F403

111 Bunney, W. E., Kleinman, A. M., Pellmar, T. C., & Goldsmith, S. K. (Eds.). (2002). *Reducing suicide: A national imperative.* National Academies Press. http://books.google.co.uk/books?hl=en&lr=&id=9xGdAgAAQBAJ&oi=fnd&pg=PT17&dq=Reducing+Suicide:+A+National+Imperative&ots=mRIG9kqLIH&sig=vIY1_OdrfbYjX3g8t-v9gZXgvg7k;
Rudd, M. D., Bryan, C. J., Wertenberger, E. G., Peterson, A. L., Young-McCaughan, S., Mintz, J., ... & Wilkinson, E. (2015). Brief cognitive-behavioral therapy effects on post-treatment suicide attempts in a military sample: results of a randomized clinical trial with 2-year follow-up. *American Journal of Psychiatry, 172*(5), 441-449. https://ajp.psychiatryonline.org/doi/full/10.1176/appi.ajp.2014.14070843;
Cha, C. B., Franz, P. J., M. Guzmán, E., Glenn, C. R., Kleiman, E. M., & Nock, M. K. (2018). Annual Research Review: Suicide among youth–epidemiology,(potential) etiology, and treatment. *Journal of child psychology and psychiatry, 59*(4), 460-482. https://onlinelibrary.wiley.com/doi/pdf/10.1111/jcpp.12831;
Robinson, J., Hetrick, S. E., & Martin, C. (2011). Preventing suicide in young people: systematic review. *Australian and New Zealand journal of psychiatry, 45*(1), 3-26. www.researchgate.net/publication/49698854_Preventing_Suicide_in_Young_People_Systematic_Review

112 Footnote references:
[1] Mann, J. J. (2002). A current perspective of suicide and attempted suicide. *Annals of internal medicine, 136*(4), 302-311. https://pdfs.semanticscholar.org/1cb2/f91c1c0c427e16fc03236a7dcd1e2ab5e753.pdf
[2] Rutz, W., Knorring, V. L., & Wålinder, J. (1989). Frequency of suicide on Gotland after systematic postgraduate education of general practitioners. Acta Psychiatrica Scandinavica, 80(2), 151-154. https://onlinelibrary.wiley.com/doi/abs/10.1111/j.1600-0447.1989.tb01318.x

113 Jureidini, J. N., Doecke, C. J., Mansfield, P. R., Haby, M. M., Menkes, D. B., & Tonkin, A. L. (2004). Efficacy and safety of antidepressants for children and adolescents. *Bmj, 328*(7444), 879-883. www.ncbi.nlm.nih.gov/pmc/articles/PMC387483/

114 Hetrick, S. E., McKenzie, J. E., Cox, G. R., Simmons, M. B., & Merry, S. N. (2012). Newer generation antidepressants for depressive disorders in children and adolescents. *Cochrane Database of Systematic Reviews*, (11). www.cochranelibrary.com/es/cdsr/doi/10.1002/14651858.CD004851.pub3/full/es;
Footnote references:
[1] Cha, C. B., Franz, P. J., M. Guzmán, E., Glenn, C. R., Kleiman, E. M., & Nock, M. K. (2018). Annual Research Review: Suicide among youth–epidemiology,(potential) etiology, and treatment. *Journal of child psychology and psychiatry, 59*(4), 460-482. https://onlinelibrary.wiley.com/doi/pdf/10.1111/jcpp.12831
[2] Diamond, G. S., Wintersteen, M. B., Brown, G. K., Diamond, G. M., Gallop, R., Shelef, K., & Levy, S. (2010). Attachment-based family therapy for adolescents with suicidal ideation: a randomized controlled trial. *Journal of the American Academy of Child & Adolescent Psychiatry, 49*(2), 122-131. https://jdc.jefferson.edu/cgi/viewcontent.cgi?referer=https://scholar.google.com/&httpsredir=1&article=1007&context=phbfp
[3] Cha, C. B., Franz, P. J., M. Guzmán, E., Glenn, C. R., Kleiman, E. M., & Nock, M. K. (2018). Annual Research Review: Suicide among youth–epidemiology,(potential) etiology, and treatment. *Journal of child psychology and psychiatry, 59*(4), 460-482. https://onlinelibrary.wiley.com/doi/pdf/10.1111/jcpp.12831
[4] Rossouw, T. I., & Fonagy, P. (2012). Mentalization-based treatment for self-harm in adolescents: a randomized controlled trial. *Journal of the American Academy of Child & Adolescent Psychiatry, 51*(12), 1304-1313. www.unige.ch/formcont/files/9014/4223/8601/Rossouw2012.pdf
[5] Brent, D. A., McMakin, D. L., Kennard, B. D., Goldstein, T. R., Mayes, T. L., & Douaihy, A. B. (2013). Protecting adolescents from self-harm: a critical review of intervention studies. *Journal of the American Academy of Child & Adolescent Psychiatry, 52*(12), 1260-1271. www.ncbi.nlm.nih.gov/pmc/articles/PMC3873716/
[6] Esposito-Smythers, C., Spirito, A., Kahler, C. W., Hunt, J., & Monti, P. (2011). Treatment of co-occurring substance abuse and suicidality among adolescents: a randomized trial. *Journal of consulting and clinical psychology, 79*(6), 728. www.ncbi.nlm.nih.gov/pmc/articles/PMC3226923/
[7] Crime / Violence Prevention. (n.d.). Social Programs that Work. https://evidencebasedprograms.org/policy_area/crime-violence-prevention/
[8] Franklin, J. C., Fox, K. R., Franklin, C. R., Kleiman, E. M., Ribeiro, J. D., Jaroszewski, A. C., ... & Nock, M. K. (2016). A brief mobile app reduces nonsuicidal and suicidal self-injury: Evidence from three randomized controlled trials. *Journal of consulting and clinical psychology, 84*(6), 544. https://static1.squarespace.com/static/54de6056e4b0409b0654ceb4/t/57dd85318419c2abeeb7450d/1474135346803/Franklin+et+al.%2C+2016+%28TEC+for+SITBs%29.pdf
[9] Youth-Nominated Support Team-Version II. (2019). *Social Programs that Work.* https://evidencebasedprograms.org/programs/youth-nominated-support-team-version-ii-program-to-prevent-adolescent-suicide/

115 World Health Organization. (2014). *Preventing suicide: a global imperative.* World Health Organization. http://apps.who.int/iris/bitstream/handle/10665/131056/9789241564779_eng.pdf;jsessionid=B5B6BCA774CF2B456EF7DBACC0A1C192?sequence=1

116 *Self-Directed Violence and Other Forms of Self-Injury.* (2019). Centers for Disease Control and Prevention, Safety and Children with Disabilities. www.cdc.gov/ncbddd/disabilityandsafety/self-injury.html;
Morris, P. (2021). I Don't Want Another Family to Lose a Child the Way We Did. *The New York Times.* www.nytimes.com/2021/03/25/opinion/suicide-prevention.html?action=click&module=Opinion&pgtype=Homepage

117 Gould, M. S., Kalafat, J., HarrisMunfakh, J. L., & Kleinman, M. (2007). An evaluation of crisis hotline outcomes part 2: suicidal callers. *Suicide and life-threatening behavior, 37*(3), 338-352. https://pdfs.semanticscholar.org/34b1/ecdbf2ca16e91a6c53e75f20eae4f874756e.pdf

118 Cha, C. B., Franz, P. J., M. Guzmán, E., Glenn, C. R., Kleiman, E. M., & Nock, M. K. (2018). Annual Research Review: Suicide among youth–epidemiology,(potential) etiology, and treatment. *Journal of child psychology and psychiatry, 59*(4), 460-482. https://onlinelibrary.wiley.com/doi/pdf/10.1111/jcpp.12831

119 Gould, M. S., & Kramer, R. A. (2001). Youth suicide prevention. *Suicide and life-threatening behavior, 31*(s1), 6-31. https://guilfordjournals.com/doi/pdfplus/10.1521/suli.31.1.5.6.24219

120 Twohey, M. & Dance, G. J. X. (2021). Where the Despairing Log On, and Learn Ways to Die. *The New York Times.* www.nytimes.com/interactive/2021/12/09/us/where-the-despairing-log-on.html

121 Bartik, W., Maple, M., Edwards, H., & Kiernan, M. (2013). The psychological impact of losing a friend to suicide. *Australasian Psychiatry, 21*(6), 545-549. www.researchgate.net/profile/Warren-Bartik/publication/253339831_The_psychological_impact_of_losing_a_friend_to_suicide/links/541cf0f00cf203f155bd6b14/The-psychological-impact-of-losing-a-friend-to-suicide.pdf

122 Dyregrov, K. (2009). How do the young suicide survivors wish to be met by psychologists? A user study. *OMEGA-Journal of death and dying, 59*(3), 221-238. www.researchgate.net/profile/Kari-Dyregrov/publication/26858263_How_Do_the_Young_Suicide_Survivors_Wish_to_Be_Met_by_Psychologists_A_User_Study/links/0deec51a2547f9cc15000000/How-Do-the-Young-Suicide-Survivors-Wish-to-Be-Met-by-Psychologists-A-User-Study.pdf

123 Dyregrov, K. (2009). How do the young suicide survivors wish to be met by psychologists? A user study. *OMEGA-Journal of death and dying, 59*(3), 221-238. www.researchgate.net/profile/Kari-Dyregrov/publication/26858263_How_Do_the_Young_Suicide_Survivors_Wish_to_Be_Met_by_Psychologists_A_User_Study/links/0deec51a2547f9cc15000000/How-Do-the-Young-Suicide-Survivors-Wish-to-Be-Met-by-Psychologists-A-User-Study.pdf

124 Weller, F. (2020). *'It was instant regret': Golden Gate Bridge suicide survivor to share story in virtual event in Wilmington.* WECT News 6. www.wect.com/2020/11/17/it-was-instant-regret-golden-gate-bridge-suicide-survivor-share-story-virtual-event-wilmington/

125 *Immortal.* (n.d.). Cambridge Dictionary. https://dictionary.cambridge.org/dictionary/english/immortal

126 National Center for Health Statistics. (n.d.). *CDC WONDER: Underlying Cause of Death 1999-2019.* Centers for Disease Control and Prevention, http://wonder.cdc.gov/ucd-icd10.html

127 National Center for Health Statistics. (2020). *CDC WONDER: Underlying Cause of Death 1999-2016.* Centers for Disease Control and Prevention. http://wonder.cdc.gov/ucd-icd10.html

128 National Center for Health Statistics. (2020). *CDC WONDER: Underlying Cause of Death 1999-2016.* Centers for Disease Control and Prevention. http://wonder.cdc.gov/ucd-icd10.html

129 Fatality rates: National Center for Health Statistics. *CDC WONDER: Underlying Cause of Death 1999-2016.* Centers for Disease Control and Prevention. http://wonder.cdc.gov/ucd-icd10.html;
Hospitalization rates: National Electronic Injury Surveillance System-All Injury Program (NEISS-AIP). (n.d.). *Web-based Injury Statistics Query and Reporting System (WISQARS): Nonfatal Injury Reports, 2001 - 2014.* Centers for Disease Control and Prevention.

130 Fatalities: National Center for Health Statistics. *CDC WONDER: Underlying Cause of Death 1999-2016.* Centers for Disease Control and Prevention. http://wonder.cdc.gov/ucd-icd10.html;
Miles travelled: Federal Highway Administration. (2017). *2017 National Household Travel Survey.* US Department for Transportation.

131 Salam, R. A., Arshad, A., Das, J. K., Khan, M. N., Mahmood, W., Freedman, S. B., & Bhutta, Z. A. (2016). Interventions to prevent unintentional injuries among adolescents: A systematic review and meta-analysis. *Journal of Adolescent Health, 59*(4), S76-S87. www.sciencedirect.com/science/article/pii/S1054139X16302397

132 Towner, E., Dowswell, T., Mackereth, C., & Jarvis, S. (2001). What works in preventing unintentional injuries in children and young adolescents: an updated systematic review. In *Database of Abstracts of Reviews of Effects (DARE): Quality-assessed Reviews* [Internet]. Centre for Reviews and Dissemination (UK). www.ncbi.nlm.nih.gov/books/NBK68509/

133 Ferguson, R. W., Xu, Z., Green, A., & Rosenthal, K. M. (2013). *Teens and Distraction: An In-Depth Look at Teens' Walking Behaviors.* www.safekids.org/sites/default/files/documents/ResearchReports/skw_pedestrian_study_2013.pdf

134 Ferguson, R. W., Green, A., & Rosenthal, K. (2014). *Teens on the Move.* Safe Kids Worldwide. www.safekids.org/sites/default/files/documents/ResearchReports/skw_pedestrian_study_2014_final.pdf

135 DaSilva, M. P., Smith, J. D., & Najm, W. G. (2003). *Analysis of pedestrian crashes* (No. DOT-VNTSC-NHTSA-02-02,). www.google.com/url?sa=t&rct=j&q=&esrc=s&source=web&cd=1&cad=rja&uact=8&ved=2ahUKEwiF7rSZ5I_eAhXmKsAKHdRLCoUQFjAAegQICRAC&url=https%3A%2F%2Fwww.nhtsa.gov%2FDOT%2FNHTSA%2FNRD%2FMultimedia%2FPDFs%2FCrash%2520Avoidance%2F2003%2FDOTHS809585.pdf&usg=AOvVaw0aMx2w6N6JFLZRGVCXwR5R

136 Mwakalonge, J., Siuhi, S., & White, J. (2015). Distracted walking: Examining the extent to pedestrian safety problems. *Journal of traffic and transportation engineering (English edition), 2*(5), 327-337. www.sciencedirect.com/science/article/pii/S2095756415000689

137 Team Coco. (2016). *Introducing Guiding Hands - CONAN on TBS* [Video]. YouTube. www.youtube.com/watch?v=v6Wpc9s35ZY

138 Chen, B. X. (2019). Texting While Walking Is Dangerous. Here's How to Stop. *The New York Times.* www.nytimes.com/2019/11/13/technology/personaltech/distracted-walking-twalking.html

139 Chappell, B. (2017). *Honolulu's 'Distracted Walking' Law Takes Effect, Targeting Phone Users.* NPR. www.npr.org/sections/thetwo-way/2017/10/25/559980080/honolulus-distracted-walking-law-takes-effect-targeting-phone-users?t=1581961004193

140 Ferguson, R. W., Xu, Z., Green, A., & Rosenthal, K. M. (2013). *Teens and Distraction: An In-Depth Look at Teens' Walking Behaviors.* SafeKids.org. www.safekids.org/sites/default/files/documents/ResearchReports/skw_pedestrian_study_2013.pdf

141 Thompson, L. L., Rivara, F. P., Ayyagari, R. C., & Ebel, B. E. (2013). Impact of social and technological distraction on pedestrian crossing behaviour: an observational study. *Injury prevention, 19*(4), 232-237. https://injuryprevention.bmj.com/content/19/4/232

142 National Center for Statistics and Analysis. (2018). *Pedestrians: 2016 data.* (Traffic Safety Facts. Report No. DOT HS 812 493). National Highway Traffic Safety Administration. https://crashstats.nhtsa.dot.gov/Api/Public/Publication/812493

143 Ferguson, R. W., Xu, Z., Green, A., & Rosenthal, K. M. (2013). *Teens and Distraction: An In-Depth Look at Teens' Walking Behaviors.* SafeKids.org. www.safekids.org/sites/default/files/documents/ResearchReports/skw_pedestrian_study_2013.pdf

144 Towner, E., Dowswell, T., Mackereth, C., & Jarvis, S. (2001). What works in preventing unintentional injuries in children and young adolescents: an updated systematic review. In *Database of Abstracts of Reviews of Effects (DARE): Quality-assessed Reviews* [Internet]. Centre for Reviews and Dissemination (UK). www.ncbi.nlm.nih.gov/books/NBK68509/;
Duperrex, O., Roberts, I., & Bunn, F. (2002). Safety education of pedestrians for injury prevention. *Cochrane Database of Systematic Reviews,* (2). www.ncbi.nlm.nih.gov/pmc/articles/PMC107905/;
Motevalian, A. (2015). Evidence-based safety education and training for traffic injury prevention. *Journal of Local and Global Heath Science,* (2), 89. www.qscience.com/doi/abs/10.5339/jlghs.2015.itma.89

145 Branche, C., Ozanne-Smith, J., Oyebite, K., & Hyder, A. A. (2008). *World report on child injury prevention.* World Health Organization. https://books.google.co.uk/books?hl=en&lr=&id=UeXwoNh8sbwC&oi=fnd&pg=PR7&dq=World+report+on+child+injury+prevention&ots=hH6uXQfz0M&sig=vmVyuC8mg1osvJd8Pwnv3oJ_BZY&redir_esc=y#v=onepage&q=World%20report%20on%20child%20injury%20prevention&f=false;
Kwan, I., & Mapstone, J. (2006). Interventions for increasing pedestrian and cyclist visibility for the prevention of death and injuries. *Cochrane Database of Systematic Reviews,* (4). https://core.ac.uk/download/pdf/13110528.pdf

146 Cohen, J. (2016). *New App Eyeballs Distracted Pedestrians.* Next City. https://nextcity.org/daily/entry/look-up-app-walking-city-sights-distracted-walking

147 Ingram, S. (2016). *Teenager hit by car blames 'Pokemon Go'.* Pittsburgh's Action News. www.wtae.com/article/teenager-hit-by-car-blames-pokemon-go/7481057#

148 Boy filmed own death in 'Jackass' bicycle stunt. (2006). *Daily Mail.* www.dailymail.co.uk/news/article-422947/Boy-filmed-death-Jackass-bicycle-stunt.html

149 Thompson, D. C., Rivara, F., & Thompson, R. (1999). Helmets for preventing head and facial injuries in bicyclists. *Cochrane database of systematic reviews,* (4). www.cochranelibrary.com/cdsr/doi/10.1002/14651858.CD001855/full

150 Towner, E., Dowswell, T., Mackereth, C., & Jarvis, S. (2001). What works in preventing unintentional injuries in children and young adolescents: an updated systematic review. In *Database of Abstracts of Reviews of Effects (DARE): Quality-assessed Reviews* [Internet]. Centre for Reviews and Dissemination (UK). www.ncbi.nlm.nih.gov/books/NBK68509/;
Salam, R. A., Arshad, A., Das, J. K., Khan, M. N., Mahmood, W., Freedman, S. B., & Bhutta, Z. A. (2016). Interventions to prevent unintentional injuries among adolescents: A systematic review and meta-analysis. *Journal of Adolescent Health, 59*(4), S76-S87. www.sciencedirect.com/science/article/pii/S1054139X16302397;
Royal, S., Kendrick, D., & Coleman, T. (2005). Non-legislative interventions for the promotion of cycle helmet wearing by children. *Cochrane Database of Systematic Reviews,* (2). www.cochranelibrary.com/cdsr/doi/10.1002/14651858.CD003985.pub2/full

151 Rivara, F. P., Thompson, D. C., Thompson, R. S., Rogers, L. W., Alexander, B., Felix, D., & Bergman, A. B. (1994). The Seattle children's bicycle helmet campaign: changes in helmet use and head injury admissions. *Pediatrics, 93*(4), 567-569. https://pediatrics.aappublications.org/content/93/4/567.short;
Wood, T., & Milne, P. (1988). Head injuries to pedal cyclists and the promotion of helmet use in Victoria, Australia. *Accident Analysis & Prevention, 20*(3), 177-185. https://trid.trb.org/view/348559

152 Pelletier, A. R., Quinlan, K. P., Sacks, J. J., Van Gilder, T. J., Gilchrist, J., & Ahluwalia, H. K. (2000). Injury prevention practices as depicted in G-rated and PG-rated movies. *Archives of pediatrics & adolescent medicine, 154*(3), 283-286. https://jamanetwork.com/journals/jamapediatrics/fullarticle/348875

153 Benedictus, L. (2015). Gum control: how Lee Kuan Yew kept chewing gum off Singapore's streets. *The Guardian*. www.theguardian.com/lifeandstyle/shortcuts/2015/mar/23/gum-control-how-lee-kuan-yew-kept-chewing-gum-off-singapores-streets

154 Towner, E., Dowswell, T., Mackereth, C., & Jarvis, S. (2001). What works in preventing unintentional injuries in children and young adolescents: an updated systematic review. In *Database of Abstracts of Reviews of Effects (DARE): Quality-assessed Reviews* [Internet]. Centre for Reviews and Dissemination (UK). www.ncbi.nlm.nih.gov/books/NBK68509/

155 Kwan, I., & Mapstone, J. (2006). Interventions for increasing pedestrian and cyclist visibility for the prevention of death and injuries. *Cochrane Database of Systematic Reviews*, (4). https://core.ac.uk/download/pdf/13110528.pdf

156 *The Best Foldable Bike Helmets*. (2021). BostonBikes. www.bostonbikes.org/advice/buyers-guides/best-foldable-bike-helmets-for-commuters/

157 Davies, M. (2013). *10 Shockingly Chic Bicycle Helmets*. Bike Pretty. https://bikepretty.com/blogs/blog/10-shockingly-chic-bicycle-helmets

158 *Authorities release new details on ATV crash that killed one teenager*. (2019). CBS Austin. https://cbsaustin.com/news/local/three-people-injured-following-atv-rollover-south-of-la-feria

159 Burch, J. (2020). *Knox County girl, 10, who made hand sewn masks for hospitals killed in ATV accident*. KTXS12, ABC News. https://ktxs.com/news/local/knox-county-girl-10-who-made-hand-sewn-masks-for-hospitals-killed-in-atv-accident

160 *All-terrain Vehicle*. (n.d.) Oxford Languages & Google.

161 Burgus, S. K., Madsen, M. D., Sanderson, W. T., & Rautiainen, R. H. (2009). Youths operating all-terrain vehicles—implications for safety education. *Journal of agromedicine, 14*(2), 97-104. www.tandfonline.com/doi/abs/10.1080/10599240902751047

162 Campbell, B. T., Kelliher, K. M., Borrup, K., Corsi, J., Saleheen, H., Bourque, M. D., & Lapidus, G. (2010). All-terrain vehicle riding among youth: how do they fair?. *Journal of pediatric surgery, 45*(5), 925-929. https://d1wqtxts1xzle7.cloudfront.net/52081118/j.jpedsurg.2010.02.02120170308-9949-i9934h.pdf?1489020439=&response-content-disposition=inline%3B+filename%3DAll_terrain_vehicle_riding_among_youth_h.pdf&Expires=1615644915&Signature=S4QKkTfe7te7MvS51FoUGhvuR4bSYAaD1jz9dARIr-meN78dl81jdNH1F8utEVx4mmKhn2kljCgyhuptIX06cIs6cinUpmaziCM~MxTElF7yoOyA6bqkYAv1FemsF-dzLmwJoLxIHKuk7bwAETto01Ycz-2Xc2rs6~ZLF~oWI6bjdFNiQ45lB1vc1Q7y~9iPTHw~A6-ajxQ8LIg-TIqrgY0p2BIOvB7sec7qveurWY~929HwZVRe6YdDVll6xOQKVYUdElDw9d2oWnd1vdeYmSak9rS-fOk4hyLfC4NxAeuEgYpoqp1sUHc-SyQQbZy8NKTPaDVKzpLU24qkYvyD7y3DTw__&Key-Pair-Id=APKA-JLOHF5GGSLRBV4ZA

163 Footnote reference: [1]Larson, A. N., & McIntosh, A. L. (2012). The epidemiology of injury in ATV and motocross sports. In *Epidemiology of Injury in Adventure and Extreme Sports* (Vol. 58, pp. 158-172). Karger Publishers. www.karger.com/Article/Abstract/338728

164 Weintraub, R. & Miller, D. (2016). *ATVs Are Dangerous to Children*. Consumer Federation of America. https://consumerfed.org/press_release/atvs-are-dangerous-to-children/#:~:text=ATVs%20are%20one%20of%20the,-for%20Consumer%20Federation%20of%20America

165 Levenson, M. S. (2003). *All-terrain vehicle 2001 injury and exposure studies*. US Consumer Product Safety Commission. https://ruralsafetycenter.org/wp-content/uploads/2017/07/Levenson-2001.pdf

166 Yanchar, N. L., Canadian Paediatric Society, & Injury Prevention Committee. (2012). Preventing injuries from all-terrain vehicles. *Paediatrics & child health, 17*(7), NP-NP. https://academic.oup.com/pch/article/17/7/NP/4560474

167 Rodgers, G. B., & Adler, P. (2001). Risk factors for all-terrain vehicle injuries: a national case-control study. *American Journal of Epidemiology, 153*(11), 1112-1118. https://academic.oup.com/aje/article/153/11/1112/64714

168 Rodgers, G. B., & Adler, P. (2001). Risk factors for all-terrain vehicle injuries: a national case-control study. *American Journal of Epidemiology, 153*(11), 1112-1118. https://academic.oup.com/aje/article/153/11/1112/64714

169 Preventing injuries from all-terrain vehicles. (2004). *Paediatrics & child health, 9*(5), 337–346. www.ncbi.nlm.nih.gov/pmc/articles/PMC2721175/

170 Denning, G., Jennissen, C., Harland, K., Ellis, D., & Buresh, C. (2013). All-terrain vehicles (ATVs) on the road: a serious traffic safety and public health concern. *Traffic injury prevention, 14*(1), 78-85. www.tandfonline.com/doi/abs/10.1080/15389588.2012.675110

171 Hafner, J. W., Hough, S. M., Getz, M. A., Whitehurst, Y., & Pearl, R. H. (2010). All-Terrain Vehicle Safety and Use Patterns in Central Illinois Youth. *The Journal of Rural Health, 26*(1), 67-72. https://onlinelibrary.wiley.com/doi/abs/10.1111/j.1748-0361.2009.00267.x

172 Burgus, S. K., Madsen, M. D., Sanderson, W. T., & Rautiainen, R. H. (2009). Youths operating all-terrain vehicles—implications for safety education. *Journal of agromedicine, 14*(2), 97-104. www.tandfonline.com/doi/abs/10.1080/10599240902751047

173 Campbell, B. T., Kelliher, K. M., Borrup, K., Corsi, J., Saleheen, H., Bourque, M. D., & Lapidus, G. (2010). All-terrain vehicle riding among youth: how do they fair?. *Journal of pediatric surgery, 45*(5), 925-929. https://d1wqtxts1xzle7.cloudfront.net/52081118/j.jpedsurg.2010.02.02120170308-9949-i9934h.pdf?1489020439=&response-content-disposition=inline%3B+filename%3DAll_terrain_vehicle_riding_among_youth_h.pdf&Expires=1615644915&Signature=S4QKkTfe7te7MvS51FoUGhvuR4bSYAaD1jz9dARIr-meN78dl81jdNH1F8utEVx4mmKhn2kljCgyhuptIX06cIs6cinUpmaziCM-MxTElF7yoOyA6bqkYAv1FemsF-dzLmwJoLxIHKuk7bwAETto01Ycz-2Xc2rs6-ZLF-oWI6bjdFNiQ45lB1vc1Q7y-9iPTHw-A6-ajxQ8LIg-TIqrgY0p2BIOvB7sec7qveurWY-929HwZVRe6YdDVll6xOQKVYUdElDw9d2oWnd1vdeYmSak9rS-fOk4hyLfC4NxAeuEgYpoqp1sUHc-SyQQbZy8NKTPaDVKzpLU24qkYvyD7y3DTw__&Key-Pair-Id=APKA-JLOHF5GGSLRBV4ZA

174 Footnote reference: [1] Yanchar, N. L., Canadian Paediatric Society, & Injury Prevention Committee. (2012). Preventing injuries from all-terrain vehicles. *Paediatrics & child health, 17*(7), NP-NP. https://academic.oup.com/pch/article/17/7/NP/4560474

175 *Consumer Federation of America ATVs are dangerous to children.* (2015). Pittsburgh Parent. www.pittsburghparent.com/consumer-federation-of-america-atvs-are-dangerous-to-children/

176 Proskiw, A. (2016). *Vernon teen using ATV crash to teach young people about the frailty of life.* Infonews.ca. https://infotel.ca/newsitem/vernon-teen-using-atv-crash-to-teach-young-people-about-the-frailty-of-life/it28075

177 Mendick, R. (2019). Jaden Moodie: Mother of murdered teenager condemns drug users for fuelling 'killing spree'. *The Telegraph.* www.telegraph.co.uk/news/2019/12/11/jaden-moodie-teenager-guilty-murdering-14-year-old/

178 Pennink, E. (2019). *Wembley teen Ayoub Majdouline gets life for gang murder of Jaden Moodie, 14, during 'killing mission'.* Brent & Kilburn Times. www.kilburntimes.co.uk/news/crime-court/ayoub-majdouline-gets-life-for-murder-of-jaden-moodie-1-6431793

179 Musu-Gillette, L., Zhang, A., Wang, K., Zhang, J., Kemp, J., Diliberti, M., & Oudekerk, B. A. (2018). *Indicators of school crime and safety: 2017.* www.bjs.gov/content/pub/pdf/iscs17.pdf?ed2f26df2d-9c416fbddddd2330a778c6=cbobieglen-cbbigine

180 Cunningham, R. M., Walton, M. A., & Carter, P. M. (2018). The major causes of death in children and adolescents in the United States. *New England Journal of Medicine, 379*(25), 2468-2475. www.nejm.org/doi/10.1056/NEJMsr1804754

181 David-Ferdon, C., & Simon, T. R. (2014). *Preventing Youth Violence: Opportunities for Action.* Centers for Disease Control and Prevention. www.cdc.gov/violenceprevention/youthviolence/pdf/opportunities-for-action.pdf

182 Cunningham, R. M., Walton, M. A., & Carter, P. M. (2018). The major causes of death in children and adolescents in the United States. *New England Journal of Medicine, 379*(25), 2468-2475. www.nejm.org/doi/10.1056/NEJMsr1804754

183 Durkin, M. S., Davidson, L. L., Kuhn, L., O'Connor, P., & Barlow, B. (1994). Low-income neighborhoods and the risk of severe pediatric injury: a small-area analysis in northern Manhattan. *American Journal of Public Health, 84*(4), 587-592. https://ajph.aphapublications.org/doi/pdfplus/10.2105/AJPH.84.4.587

184 Sherman, L. W., Gottfredson, D. C., MacKenzie, D. L., Eck, J., Reuter, P., & Bushway, S. (1997). *Preventing crime: What works, what doesn't, what's promising: A report to the United States Congress.* US Department of Justice, Office of Justice Programs. www.ncjrs.gov/pdffiles1/Digitization/165366NCJRS.pdf

185 *CDC study explores role of drugs, drive-by shootings, and other crimes in gang homicides.* (2012). Office of the Associate Director for Communication, Division of News and Electronic Media, Centers for Disease Control and Prevention. www.cdc.gov/media/releases/2012/p0126_gang_homicides.html

186 Glesmann, C., Krisberg, B., & Marchionna, S. (2009). *Youth in gangs: Who is at risk.* FOCUS. Oakland, CA. http://nccdglobal.org/sites/default/files/publication_pdf/focus-youth-in-gangs.pdf

187 Glesmann, C., Krisberg, B., & Marchionna, S. (2009). *Youth in gangs: Who is at risk.* FOCUS. Oakland, CA. http://nccdglobal.org/sites/default/files/publication_pdf/focus-youth-in-gangs.pdf

188 Melde, C., Taylor, T. J., & Esbensen, F. A. (2009). "I got your back": An examination of the protective function of gang membership in adolescence. *Criminology, 47*(2), 565-594. www.researchgate.net/profile/Chris_Melde/publication/229690609_I_got_your_back_An_examination_of_the_protective_function_of_gang_membership_in_adolescence/links/5afecbf9aca2720c96104313/I-got-your-back-An-examination-of-the-protective-function-of-gang-membership-in-adolescence.pdf

189 Laraque, D., Barlow, B., & Durkin, M. (1999). Prevention of youth injuries. *Journal of the National Medical Association, 91*(10), 557. www.ncbi.nlm.nih.gov/pmc/articles/PMC2608515/pdf/jnma00355-0033.pdf;
Webster, D. W. (1993). The unconvincing case for school-based conflict resolution programs for adolescents. Health Affairs, 12(4), 126-141. www.healthaffairs.org/doi/full/10.1377/hlthaff.12.4.126;
Mytton, J. A., DiGuiseppi, C., Gough, D., Taylor, R. S., & Logan, S. (2006). School-based secondary prevention programmes for preventing violence. Cochrane database of systematic reviews, (3). www.cochranelibrary.com/cdsr/doi/10.1002/14651858.CD004606.pub2/full;
Kellerman AL, Fuqua-Whitley DS, Rivara FP, Mercy J. (1998). Preventing youth violence: what works? *Ann Rev Publ Health 19*(1):271-92. www.annualreviews.org/doi/full/10.1146/annurev.publhealth.19.1.271?amp%3BsearchHistoryKey=%24%7BsearchHistoryKey%7D

190 Smith MD. (1996). Sources of firearm acquisition among a sample of inner-city youths: research results and policy implications. *J Crim Just 24*(4):361-67. www.sciencedirect.com/science/article/pii/0047235296000190

191 Grinshteyn, E., & Hemenway, D. (2016). Violent death rates: the US compared with other high-income OECD countries, 2010. *The American journal of medicine, 129*(3), 266-273. www.amjmed.com/article/S0002-93431501030-X/fulltext

192 *Homicide Mortality by State.* (2019). National Center for Health Statistics, Centers for Disease Control and Prevention. www.cdc.gov/nchs/pressroom/sosmap/homicide_mortality/homicide.htm

193 Rogers, E. (2008). *Another teen drowns in Lake Lanier.* Gainesville Times. www.gainesvilletimes.com/news/another-teen-drowns-in-lake-lanier/

194 Luciew, J. (2019). *Teen boys sneak into Pa. swimming club pool, leave drowning friend to die.* Penn Live. www.pennlive.com/daily-buzz/2019/08/teens-boys-sneaking-into-pa-swimming-pool-leave-drowning-friend-to-die-cops.html

195 Johnson, M. (2019). *Family has questions surrounding drowning death of college student at pool party.* WSB TV Atlanta. www.wsbtv.com/news/local/atlanta/teen-dies-from-apparent-drowning-during-memorial-day-pool-party-police-say/952845727/

196 Quan, L., Bennett, E. E., & Branche, C. M. (2008). Interventions to prevent drowning. In *Handbook of injury and violence prevention* (pp. 81-96). Springer, Boston, MA. https://s3.amazonaws.com/academia.edu.documents/48196822/Dissemination_Implementation_and_Widespr20160820-5814-zgiwgm.pdf?response-content-disposition=inline%3B%20filename%3DDissemination_Implementation_and_Widespr.pdf&X-Amz-Algorithm=AWS4-HMAC-SHA256&X-Amz-Credential=AKIAIWOWYYGZ2Y53UL3A%2F20200217%2Fus-east-1%2Fs3%2Faws4_request&X-Amz-Date=20200217T133404Z&X-Amz-Expires=3600&X-Amz-SignedHeaders=host&X-Amz-Signature=d667cba50c5e98dd60ac39a9da9521999f0fd43a8005bfdbd28f4f3b797b93de#page=108

197 National Center for Health Statistics. *CDC WONDER: Underlying Cause of Death 1999-2016.* Centers for Disease Control and Prevention. http://wonder.cdc.gov/ucd-icd10.html

198 Howland, J., Hingson, R., Mangione, T. W., Bell, N., & Bak, S. M. P. H. (1996). Why are most drowning victims men? Sex differences in aquatic skills and behaviors. *American journal of public health, 86*(1), 93-96. https://ajph.aphapublications.org/doi/pdfplus/10.2105/AJPH.86.1.93

199 Branche, C., Ozanne-Smith, J., Oyebite, K., & Hyder, A. A. (2008). *World report on child injury prevention.* World Health Organization. https://books.google.co.uk/books?hl=en&lr=&id=UeXwoNh8sbwC&oi=fnd&pg=PR7&dq=World+report+on+child+injury+prevention&ots=hH6uXQfz0M&sig=vmVyuC8mg1osvJd8Pwnv3oJ_BZY&redir_esc=y#v=onepage&q=World%20report%20on%20child%20injury%20prevention&f=false

200 Driscoll, T. R., Harrison, J. A., & Steenkamp, M. (2004). Review of the role of alcohol in drowning associated with recreational aquatic activity. *Injury Prevention, 10*(2), 107-113. https://injuryprevention.bmj.com/content/injuryprev/10/2/107.full.pdf

201 Kerry, J. F. (2015). *Country Reports on Human Rights Practices for 2015.* Bureau of Democracy, Human Rights and Labor. Section 6: Children: Early and Forced Marriage. https://2009-2017.state.gov/j/drl/rls/hrrpt/humanrightsreport//index.htm#fndtn-panel1-1

202 U.S. Coast Guard, Department of Homeland Security (US). (2010). *Recreational Boating Statistics – 2010.* www.uscgboating.org/assets/1/workflow_staging/Page/2010_Recreational_Boating_Statistics.pdf

203 Howland, J., Hingson, R., Mangione, T. W., Bell, N., & Bak, S. M. P. H. (1996). Why are most drowning victims men? Sex differences in aquatic skills and behaviors. *American journal of public health, 86*(1), 93-96. https://ajph.aphapublications.org/doi/pdfplus/10.2105/AJPH.86.1.93

204 Pelletier, A. R., Quinlan, K. P., Sacks, J. J., Van Gilder, T. J., Gilchrist, J., & Ahluwalia, H. K. (2000). Injury prevention practices as depicted in G-rated and PG-rated movies. *Archives of pediatrics & adolescent medicine, 154*(3), 283-286. https://jamanetwork.com/journals/jamapediatrics/fullarticle/348875

205 Wallis, B. A., Watt, K., Franklin, R. C., Taylor, M., Nixon, J. W., & Kimble, R. M. (2015). Interventions associated with drowning prevention in children and adolescents: systematic literature review. *Injury prevention, 21*(3), 195-204. https://injuryprevention.bmj.com/content/21/3/195.short

206 Branche, C., Ozanne-Smith, J., Oyebite, K., & Hyder, A. A. (2008). *World report on child injury prevention.* World Health Organization. https://books.google.co.uk/books?hl=en&lr=&id=UeXwoNh8sbwC&oi=fnd&pg=PR7&dq=World+report+on+child+injury+prevention&ots=hH6uXQfz0M&sig=vmVyuC8mg1osvJd8Pwnv3oJ_BZY&redir_esc=y#v=onepage&q=World%20report%20on%20child%20injury%20prevention&f=false

207 Peters, A. (2016). *This Swimsuit Acts Like An Invisible Life Jacket.* Fast Company. www.fastcompany.com/3059757/this-swimsuit-acts-like-an-invisible-life-jacket

208 https://wingmanlifejacket.com/products/buyhydewingman

209 *History of X Games.* (n.d.) X Games. www.xgamesmediakit.com/read-me

210 Gaydos, R. (2019). *Skateboarder makes history with incredible trick at X Games.* Fox News. www.foxnews.com/sports/skateboarder-mitchie-brusco-x-games-minneapolis

211 Templeton, H. (n.d.). *Are the X Games Too Dangerous?* Men's Journal. www.mensjournal.com/adventure/are-x-games-too-dangerous/

212 Mackinnon, J.B. (2016). *The Strange Brain of the World's Greatest Solo Climber.* Nautilus Neuroscience. https://nautil.us/the-strange-brain-of-the-worlds-greatest-solo-climber-5011/

213 Zuckerman, M. (2007). *Sensation seeking and risky behavior.* American Psychological Association. www.amazon.com/dp/B00CO5Y47E/ref=dp-kindle-redirect?_encoding=UTF8&btkr=1#reader_B00CO5Y47E

214 Ebstein, R. P., Novick, O., Umansky, R., Priel, B., Osher, Y., Blaine, D., ... & Belmaker, R. H. (1996). Dopamine D4 receptor (D4DR) exon III polymorphism associated with the human personality trait of novelty seeking. *Nature genetics, 12*(1), 78-80. www.nature.com/articles/ng0196-78;
Thomson, C. J., Hanna, C. W., Carlson, S. R., & Rupert, J. L. (2013). The- 521 C/T variant in the dopamine-4-receptor gene (DRD4) is associated with skiing and snowboarding behavior. *Scandinavian journal of medicine & science in sports, 23*(2), e108-e113. www.ncbi.nlm.nih.gov/pmc/articles/PMC5798939/

215 *FAQs: How do hang gliding and paragliding differ?* (n.d.). Torrey Pines Glideport. www.flytorrey.com/faqs/

216 *FAQs: How do hang gliding and paragliding differ?* (n.d.). Torrey Pines Glideport. www.flytorrey.com/faqs/

217 Base Jumping. (n.d.) *Wikipedia.* https://en.wikipedia.org/wiki/BASE_jumping

218 **Base jumping**: Soreide, K., Ellingsen, C. L., & Knutson, V. (2007). How dangerous is BASE jumping? An analysis of adverse events in 20,850 jumps from the Kjerag Massif, Norway. *Journal of Trauma and Acute Care Surgery, 62*(5), 1113-1117. https://journals.lww.com/jtrauma/Abstract/2007/05000/How_Dangerous_is_BASE_Jumping__An_Analysis_of.6.aspx;
**Paragliding**: Canbek, U., İmerci, A., Akgün, U., Yeşil, M., Aydin, A., & Balci, Y. (2015). Characteristics of injuries caused by paragliding accidents: A cross-sectional study. *World journal of emergency medicine, 6*(3), 221. www.ncbi.nlm.nih.gov/pmc/articles/PMC4566014/; Ekerhovd, K. M., Novomesky, F., Komarekova, I., & Strak,

L. (2013). Descriptive epidemiological study of fatal incidents and injury mechanisms among civilian sport parachutists in Norway from 1963 to 2008. *Rom J Leg Med, 21*, 31-36. www.rjlm.ro/system/revista/25/31-36.pdf; Ellitsgaard, N. (1987). Parachuting injuries: a study of 110,000 sports jumps. *British Journal of Sports Medicine, 21*(1), 13-17. https://bjsm.bmj.com/content/bjsports/21/1/13.full.pdf;
**Hang gliding**: Feletti, F., Aliverti, A., Henjum, M., Tarabini, M., & Brymer, E. (2017). Incidents and injuries in foot-launched flying extreme sports. *Aerospace medicine and human performance, 88*(11), 1016-1023. http://eprints.leedsbeckett.ac.uk/4037/1/Final%20Manuscript.pdf;
**Skydiving**: United States Parachute Association. (n.d.). *How Safe is Skydiving?* https://uspa.org/find/faqs/safety;
**Scuba diving**: Peddie, C. & Watson, J. (2018). *British Sub-Aqua Club Diving Incident Report 2018.* British Sub-Aqua Club. www.bsac.com/document/diving-incident-report-2018-new-format/1bsac-incident-report-2018-new-format.pdf
**Bungee Jumping**: Vanderford, L., & Meyers, M. (1995). Injuries and bungee jumping. *Sports medicine, 20*(6), 369-374. www.researchgate.net/publication/14585316_Injuries_and_Bungee_Jumping;
**Skiing/snowboarding**: National Ski Areas Association (NSAA). (2014-21). *NSAA Fatality Fact Sheet (2020/21, 2019/20); Facts on Skiing Snowboard Safety 2016; Facts on Skiing and Snowboarding (2014, 2013); Facts about Skiing/Snowboarding Safety (2012, 2011).* https://nsaa.org/webdocs/Media_Public/IndustryStats/fatality_fact_sheet_2020-21.pdf

219 Taylor, L. (n.d.). *Why I Do NOT Train Kids.* www-personal.umich.edu/~lpt/kids.htm

220 Taylor, L. (n.d.). *Why I Do NOT Train Kids.* www-personal.umich.edu/~lpt/kids.htm

221 Hawks, T. (2012). *Facts About Skiing/Snowboarding Safety.* National Ski Areas Association. www.nsaa.org/media/68045/NSAA-Facts-About-Skiing-Snowboarding-Safety-10-1-12.pdf

222 Xiang, H., Stallones, L., & Smith, G. A. (2004). Downhill skiing injury fatalities among children. *Injury prevention, 10*(2), 99-102. https://injuryprevention.bmj.com/content/injuryprev/10/2/99.full.pdf

223 US Consumer Product Safety Commission. (1999). *Skiing helmets: an evaluation of the potential to reduce head injury.* US Consumer Product Safety Commission. www.cpsc.gov/s3fs-public/pdfs/skihelm.pdf;
Russell, K., Christie, J., & Hagel, B. E. (2010). The effect of helmets on the risk of head and neck injuries among skiers and snowboarders: a meta-analysis. *Cmaj, 182*(4), 333-340. www.cmaj.ca/content/cmaj/182/4/333.full.pdf;
Sulheim, S., Holme, I., Ekeland, A., & Bahr, R. (2006). Helmet use and risk of head injuries in alpine skiers and snowboarders. *Jama, 295*(8), 919-924. https://jamanetwork.com/journals/jama/fullarticle/202421

224 Zuckerman, M. (2007). *Sensation seeking and risky behavior.* American Psychological Association. www.amazon.com/dp/B00CO5Y47E/ref=dp-kindle-redirect?_encoding=UTF8&btkr=1#reader_B00CO5Y47E

225 Moore, B. (2021). *The Best VR Games for 2021.* PC Magazine. www.pcmag.com/picks/the-best-vr-games-for-2019?test_uuid=001OQhoHLBxsrrrMgWU3gQF&test_variant=b

226 Natale, N. (2018). *5 NFL Athletes Who Had CTE.* Everyday Health. www.everydayhealth.com/concussion/symptoms/nfl-athletes-who-cte/

227 *High School Sports Participation Increases for 29th Consecutive Year.* (2018). National Federation of State High School Associations. www.nfhs.org/articles/high-school-sports-participation-increases-for-29th-consecutive-year/

228 Footnote reference: [1] *Skateboarding FAQ.* (n.d.). Public Skatepark Development Guide. https://publicskateparkguide.org/get-started/working-with-city-staff/city-council-and-parks/

229 US Consumer Product Safety Commission. (2018). *National Electronic Injury Surveillance System (NEISS).*; United States Bureau of Labor Statistics. (n.d.). *American Time Use Survey (ATUS) 2009-2018.*

230 Emergency visits: US Consumer Product Safety Commission. (2018). *National Electronic Injury Surveillance System (NEISS).*;
Concussions: National Research Council, & Committee on Sports-Related Concussions in Youth. (2014). *Sports-related concussions in youth: improving the science, changing the culture.* National Academies Press. www.nap.edu/catalog/18377/sports-related-concussions-in-youth-improving-the-science-changing-the;
Footnote reference: [1] McKee, A. C., Cantu, R. C., Nowinski, C. J., Hedley-Whyte, E. T., Gavett, B. E., Budson, A. E., ... & Stern, R. A. (2009). Chronic traumatic encephalopathy in athletes: progressive tauopathy after repetitive head injury. *Journal of Neuropathology & Experimental Neurology, 68*(7), 709-735. https://europepmc.org/article/PMC/2945234

231 Footnote references:
[1] Gardner, R. C., & Yaffe, K. (2015). Epidemiology of mild traumatic brain injury and neurodegenerative disease. *Molecular and Cellular Neuroscience, 66*, 75-80. www.ncbi.nlm.nih.gov/pmc/articles/PMC4461453/

[2] Sharp, D. J., & Jenkins, P. O. (2015). Concussion is confusing us all. *Practical neurology, 15*(3), 172-186. https://pn.bmj.com/content/15/3/172

232 Kann, L., McManus, T., Harris, W. A., Shanklin, S. L., Flint, K. H., Queen, B., ... & Lim, C. (2018). Youth risk behavior surveillance—United States, 2017. *MMWR Surveillance Summaries, 67*(8), 1. www.ncbi.nlm.nih.gov/pmc/articles/PMC6002027/

233 Sharp, D. J., & Jenkins, P. O. (2015). Concussion is confusing us all. *Practical neurology, 15*(3), 172-186. https://pn.bmj.com/content/15/3/172

234 National Research Council, & Committee on Sports-Related Concussions in Youth. (2014). *Sports-related concussions in youth: Improving the science, changing the culture.* National Academies Press. www.nap.edu/catalog/18377/sports-related-concussions-in-youth-improving-the-science-changing-the

235 McAllister, T. W., Flashman, L. A., Maerlender, A., Greenwald, R. M., Beckwith, J. G., Tosteson, T. D., ... & Grove, M. R. (2012). Cognitive effects of one season of head impacts in a cohort of collegiate contact sport athletes. *Neurology, 78*(22), 1777-1784. www.ncbi.nlm.nih.gov/pmc/articles/PMC3359587/

236 Gardner, R. C., & Yaffe, K. (2015). Epidemiology of mild traumatic brain injury and neurodegenerative disease. *Molecular and Cellular Neuroscience, 66*, 75-80. www.ncbi.nlm.nih.gov/pmc/articles/PMC4461453/

237 Gardner, R. C., & Yaffe, K. (2015). Epidemiology of mild traumatic brain injury and neurodegenerative disease. *Molecular and Cellular Neuroscience, 66*, 75-80. www.ncbi.nlm.nih.gov/pmc/articles/PMC4461453/

238 McKee, A. C., Cantu, R. C., Nowinski, C. J., Hedley-Whyte, E. T., Gavett, B. E., Budson, A. E., ... & Stern, R. A. (2009). Chronic traumatic encephalopathy in athletes: progressive tauopathy after repetitive head injury. *Journal of Neuropathology & Experimental Neurology, 68*(7), 709-735. https://europepmc.org/article/PMC/2945234

239 Stern, R. A., Riley, D. O., Daneshvar, D. H., Nowinski, C. J., Cantu, R. C., & McKee, A. C. (2011). Long-term consequences of repetitive brain trauma: chronic traumatic encephalopathy. *Pm&r, 3*(10), S460-S467. www.bu.edu/cte/files/2011/11/Stern-et-al-2011-PMR-Long-term-Consequences-of-Repetitive-Brain-Trauma1.pdf

240 Concussion Signs and Symptoms. (2019). Centers for Disease Control and Prevention. www.cdc.gov/headsup/basics/concussion_symptoms.html

241 Giza, C. C., Kutcher, J. S., Ashwal, S., Barth, J., Getchius, T. S., Gioia, G. A., ... & McKeag, D. B. (2013). Summary of evidence-based guideline update: evaluation and management of concussion in sports: report of the Guideline Development Subcommittee of the American Academy of Neurology. Neurology, 80(24), 2250-2257. www.ncbi.nlm.nih.gov/pmc/articles/PMC3721093/;
McCrea, M., Kelly, J. P., Randolph, C., Kluge, J., Bartolic, E., Finn, G., & Baxter, B. (1998). Standardized assessment of concussion (SAC): on-site mental status evaluation of the athlete. The Journal of head trauma rehabilitation, 13(2), 27-35. www.academia.edu/download/50010843/Standardized_Assessment_of_Concussion_S20161031-6559-ndhwuy.pdf

242 Footnote references:
[1] Sharp, D. J., & Jenkins, P. O. (2015). Concussion is confusing us all. *Practical neurology, 15*(3), 172-186. https://pn.bmj.com/content/15/3/172

[2] Giza, C. C., Kutcher, J. S., Ashwal, S., Barth, J., Getchius, T. S., Gioia, G. A., ... & McKeag, D. B. (2013). Summary of evidence-based guideline update: evaluation and management of concussion in sports: report of the Guideline Development Subcommittee of the American Academy of Neurology. *Neurology, 80*(24), 2250-2257. www.ncbi.nlm.nih.gov/pmc/articles/PMC3721093/

243 National Research Council, & Committee on Sports-Related Concussions in Youth. (2014). *Sports-related concussions in youth: improving the science, changing the culture.* National Academies Press. www.nap.edu/catalog/18377/sports-related-concussions-in-youth-improving-the-science-changing-the

244 Giza, C. C., Kutcher, J. S., Ashwal, S., Barth, J., Getchius, T. S., Gioia, G. A., ... & McKeag, D. B. (2013). Summary of evidence-based guideline update: evaluation and management of concussion in sports: report of the Guideline Development Subcommittee of the American Academy of Neurology. *Neurology, 80*(24), 2250-2257. www.ncbi.nlm.nih.gov/pmc/articles/PMC3721093/

245 National Research Council, & Committee on Sports-Related Concussions in Youth. (2014). *Sports-related concussions in youth: improving the science, changing the culture.* National Academies Press. www.nap.edu/catalog/18377/sports-related-concussions-in-youth-improving-the-science-changing-the

246 McCrory, P., Meeuwisse, W. H., & Aubry, M. (2012). *Consensus statement on concussion in sport: the 4th International Conference on Concussion in Sport held in Zurich, November 2012.* www.rcsi.ie/files/facultyofsportsexercise/20131031015705_Concussion%20consensus%202013%20BJSM.pdf

247 Stump, S. (2020). *After near-fatal brain injury, former snowboarder reclaims identity 10 years later.* Today. www.today.com/health/former-snowboarder-kevin-pearce-finds-new-identity-10-years-after-t186466?cid=sm_npd_td_fb_ma&fbclid=IwAR2zyJ1ICbnTxamHUI8L50iNyIf-jY0kK7I3JLCeTCIz0XwBWGAUvNu3ST4;
Pierce, K. (2015). *Concussion Blog.* The Invisible Injury. www.theinvisibleinjury.net/blog/2015/10/18/4a-conversation-with-kevin-pearce

248 McCrory, P., Meeuwisse, W. H., & Aubry, M. (2012). *Consensus statement on concussion in sport: the 4th International Conference on Concussion in Sport held in Zurich, November 2012.* www.rcsi.ie/files/facultyofsportsexercise/20131031015705_Concussion%20consensus%202013%20BJSM.pdf;
National Research Council, & Committee on Sports-Related Concussions in Youth. (2014). *Sports-related concussions in youth: improving the science, changing the culture.* National Academies Press. www.nap.edu/catalog/18377/sports-related-concussions-in-youth-improving-the-science-changing-the

249 Giza, C. C., Kutcher, J. S., Ashwal, S., Barth, J., Getchius, T. S., Gioia, G. A., ... & McKeag, D. B. (2013). Summary of evidence-based guideline update: evaluation and management of concussion in sports: report of the Guideline Development Subcommittee of the American Academy of Neurology. *Neurology, 80*(24), 2250-2257. www.ncbi.nlm.nih.gov/pmc/articles/PMC3721093/;
Hollis, S. J., Stevenson, M. R., McIntosh, A. S., Shores, E. A., Collins, M. W., & Taylor, C. B. (2009). Incidence, risk, and protective factors of mild traumatic brain injury in a cohort of Australian nonprofessional male rugby players. *The American journal of sports medicine, 37*(12), 2328-2333. https://journals.sagepub.com/doi/abs/10.1177/0363546509341032

250 Giza, C. C., Kutcher, J. S., Ashwal, S., Barth, J., Getchius, T. S., Gioia, G. A., ... & McKeag, D. B. (2013). Summary of evidence-based guideline update: evaluation and management of concussion in sports: report of the Guideline Development Subcommittee of the American Academy of Neurology. *Neurology, 80*(24), 2250-2257. www.ncbi.nlm.nih.gov/pmc/articles/PMC3721093/

251 Gray, M., Bain, J., & Willis, L. (2009). Protective headgear for soccer players: an overview. *The Sport Journal, 12*(1). http://thesportjournal.org/?s=protective+headgear+soccer+players

252 Maffulli, N., Longo, U. G., Gougoulias, N., Loppini, M., & Denaro, V. (2010). Long-term health outcomes of youth sports injuries. *British journal of sports medicine, 44*(1), 21-25. https://bjsm.bmj.com/content/44/1/21.short;
Caine, D. J., & Golightly, Y. M. (2011). Osteoarthritis as an outcome of paediatric sport: an epidemiological perspective. British journal of sports medicine, 45(4), 298-303. https://bjsm.bmj.com/content/45/4/298.short

253 Maffulli, N., Longo, U. G., Gougoulias, N., Loppini, M., & Denaro, V. (2010). Long-term health outcomes of youth sports injuries. *British Journal of Sports Medicine, 44*(1), 21-25. www.researchgate.net/profile/Nikolaos_Gougoulias/publication/40045399_Long-term_Health_Outcomes_of_Youth_Sports_Injuries/links/0d1c84f906c31011d0000000/Long-term-Health-Outcomes-of-Youth-Sports-Injuries.pdf

254 Lehnhard, R. A., Lehnhard, H. R., Young, R., & Butterfield, S. A. (1996). Monitoring injuries on a college soccer team: the effect of strength training. *The Journal of Strength & Conditioning Research, 10*(2), 115-119. https://journals.lww.com/nsca-jscr/abstract/1996/05000/monitoring_injuries_on_a_college_soccer_team__the.11.aspx

255 Jakobsen, B. W., Kroner, K., Schmidt, S. A., & Kjeldsen, A. (1994). Prevention of injuries in long-distance runners. *Knee Surgery, Sports Traumatology, Arthroscopy, 2*(4), 245-249. https://link.springer.com/article/10.1007/BF01845597

256 Olsen, O. E., Myklebust, G., Engebretsen, L., Holme, I., & Bahr, R. (2005). Exercises to prevent lower limb injuries in youth sports: cluster randomised controlled trial. *Bmj, 330*(7489), 449. www.ncbi.nlm.nih.gov/pmc/articles/PMC549653/

257 Hewett, T. E., Ford, K. R., & Myer, G. D. (2006). Anterior cruciate ligament injuries in female athletes: Part 2, a meta-analysis of neuromuscular interventions aimed at injury prevention. *The American journal of sports medicine, 34*(3), 490-498. www.ncbi.nlm.nih.gov/books/NBK73042/

258 Johnson, C. (2012). *Fighting sporty kids' arthritis risk.* ABC Health and Wellbeing.
www.abc.net.au/health/thepulse/stories/2012/05/23/3503075.htm

259 Footnote references:
[1] Gardner, R. C., & Yaffe, K. (2015). Epidemiology of mild traumatic brain injury and neurodegenerative disease. Molecular and Cellular Neuroscience, 66, 75-80. www.ncbi.nlm.nih.gov/pmc/articles/PMC4461453/

[2] Sharp, D. J., & Jenkins, P. O. (2015). Concussion is confusing us all. *Practical neurology, 15*(3), 172-186. https://pn.bmj.com/content/15/3/172

260 Valovich McLeod, T. C., Decoster, L. C., Loud, K. J., Micheli, L. J., Parker, J. T., Sandrey, M. A., & White, C. (2011). National Athletic Trainers' Association position statement: prevention of pediatric overuse injuries. *Journal of athletic training, 46*(2), 206-220. www.natajournals.org/doi/pdf/10.4085/1062-6050-46.2.206

261 Handoll, H. H., Rowe, B. H., Quinn, K. M., & de Bie, R. (2001). Interventions for preventing ankle ligament injuries. *Cochrane Database of Systematic Reviews*, (3). www.cochranelibrary.com/cdsr/doi/10.1002/14651858.CD000018/pdf/CDSR/CD000018/rel0001/CD000018/CD000018.pdf

262 Wedderkopp, N., Kaltoft, M., Lundgaard, B., Rosendahl, M., & Froberg, K. (1999). Prevention of injuries in young female players in European team handball. A prospective intervention study. *Scandinavian journal of medicine & science in sports*, 9(1), 41-47. https://onlinelibrary.wiley.com/doi/abs/10.1111/j.1600-0838.1999.tb00205.x

263 Tropp, H., Askling, C., & Gillquist, J. A. N. (1985). Prevention of ankle sprains. *The American Journal of Sports Medicine, 13*(4), 259-262. https://journals.sagepub.com/doi/abs/10.1177/036354658501300408

264 Sitler, M., Ryan, C. J., Hopkinson, L. W., Wheeler, L. J., Santomier, J., Kolb, L. R., & Polley, C. D. (1990). The efficacy of a prophylactic knee brace to reduce knee injuries in football: a prospective, randomized study at West Point. *The American journal of sports medicine, 18*(3), 310-315. https://journals.sagepub.com/doi/abs/10.1177/036354659001800315

265 Footnote references: [1] Rome, K., Handoll, H. H., & Ashford, R. L. (2005). Interventions for preventing and treating stress fractures and stress reactions of bone of the lower limbs in young adults. *Cochrane Database of Systematic Reviews*, (2). www.cochranelibrary.com/cdsr/doi/10.1002/14651858.CD000450.pub2/pdf/CDSR/CD000450/CD000450.pdf
[2] Yeung, E. W., & Yeung, S. (2001). Interventions for preventing lower limb soft-tissue injuries in runners. *Cochrane Database of Systematic Reviews*, (3). www.cochranelibrary.com/cdsr/doi/10.1002/14651858.CD001256/full

266 Tropp, H., Askling, C., & Gillquist, J. A. N. (1985). Prevention of ankle sprains. *The American Journal of Sports Medicine, 13*(4), 259-262. https://journals.sagepub.com/doi/abs/10.1177/036354658501300408;
Handoll, H. H., Rowe, B. H., Quinn, K. M., & de Bie, R. (2001). Interventions for preventing ankle ligament injuries. *Cochrane Database of Systematic Reviews*, (3). www.cochranelibrary.com/cdsr/doi/10.1002/14651858.CD000018/full

267 Parkkari, J., Kujala, U. M., & Kannus, P. (2001). Is it possible to prevent sports injuries?. *Sports medicine, 31*(14), 985-995. www.researchgate.net/profile/Jari_Parkkari/publication/11620116_Is_it_possible_to_prevent_sports_injuries_Review_of_controlled_clinical_trials_and_recommendations_for_future_work/links/00463514446531a1c1000000/Is-it-possible-to-prevent-sports-injuries-Review-of-controlled-clinical-trials-and-recommendations-for-future-work.pdf;

268 van Mechelen, W., Hlobil, H., Kemper, H. C., Voorn, W. J., & de Jongh, H. R. (1993). Prevention of running injuries by warm-up, cool-down, and stretching exercises. *The American journal of sports medicine, 21*(5), 711-719. https://journals.sagepub.com/doi/abs/10.1177/036354659302100513

269 Pope, R. P., Herbert, R. D., Kirwan, J. D., & Graham, B. J. (2000). A randomized trial of preexercise stretching for prevention of lower-limb injury. *Medicine and science in sports and exercise, 32*(2), 271-277. https://andrewvs.blogs.com/files/stretching-to-prevent-injury.pdf

270 Rome, K., Handoll, H. H., & Ashford, R. L. (2005). Interventions for preventing and treating stress fractures and stress reactions of bone of the lower limbs in young adults. *Cochrane Database of Systematic Reviews*, (2). www.cochranelibrary.com/cdsr/doi/10.1002/14651858.CD000450.pub2/pdf/CDSR/CD000450/CD000450.pdf;
Pope, R., Herbert, R., & Kirwan, J. (1998). Effects of ankle dorsiflexion range and pre-exercise calf muscle stretching on injury risk in Army recruits. *Australian Journal of Physiotherapy, 44*(3), 165-172.

271 Rose, M. S., Emery, C. A., & Meeuwisse, W. H. (2008). Sociodemographic predictors of sport injury in adolescents. *Medicine & Science in Sports & Exercise, 40*(3), 444-450. www.safetylit.org/citations/index.php?fuseaction=citations.viewdetails&citationIds[]=citjournalarticle_86280_16

272 Rose, M. S., Emery, C. A., & Meeuwisse, W. H. (2008). Sociodemographic predictors of sport injury in adolescents. *Medicine & Science in Sports & Exercise, 40*(3), 444-450. https://journals.lww.com/acsm-msse/Fulltext/2008/03000/Sociodemographic_Predictors_of_Sport_Injury_in.7.aspx

273 Jayanthi, N. A., O'Boyle, J., & Durazo-Arvizu, R. A. (2009). Risk factors for medical withdrawals in United States tennis association junior national tennis tournaments: a descriptive epidemiologic study. *Sports health, 1*(3), 231-235. www.ncbi.nlm.nih.gov/pmc/articles/PMC3445251/

274 Post, E. G., Trigsted, S. M., Riekena, J. W., Hetzel, S., McGuine, T. A., Brooks, M. A., & Bell, D. R. (2017). The association of sport specialization and training volume with injury history in youth athletes. *The American journal of sports medicine, 45*(6), 1405-1412. www.researchgate.net/profile/Eric_Post4/publication/314979249_The_Association_of_Sport_Specialization_and_Training_Volume_With_Injury_History_in_Youth_Athletes/links/59e65268aca2721fc227a5f4/The-Association-of-Sport-Specialization-and-Training-Volume-With-Injury-History-in-Youth-Athletes.pdf

275 Jayanthi, N. A., LaBella, C. R., Fischer, D., Pasulka, J., & Dugas, L. R. (2015). Sports-specialized intensive training and the risk of injury in young athletes: a clinical case-control study. *The American journal of sports medicine, 43*(4), 794-801. www.researchgate.net/profile/Lara_Dugas/publication/272083257_Sports-Specialized_Intensive_Training_and_the_Risk_of_Injury_in_Young_Athletes_A_Clinical_Case-Control_Study/links/55118c230cf270fd7e300ce0.pdf?disableCoverPage=true

276 Loud, K. J., Gordon, C. M., Micheli, L. J., & Field, A. E. (2005). Correlates of stress fractures among preadolescent and adolescent girls. *Pediatrics-English Edition, 115*(4), e399. www.researchgate.net/profile/Alison_Field/publication/7931419_Correlates_of_Stress_Fractures_Among_Preadolescent_and_Adolescent_Girls/links/00b49529cd53a8256a000000/Correlates-of-Stress-Fractures-Among-Preadolescent-and-Adolescent-Girls.pdf

277 Maffulli, N., Longo, U. G., Gougoulias, N., Loppini, M., & Denaro, V. (2010). Long-term health outcomes of youth sports injuries. *British Journal of Sports Medicine, 44*(1), 21-25. www.researchgate.net/profile/Nikolaos_Gougoulias/publication/40045399_Long-term_Health_Outcomes_of_Youth_Sports_Injuries/links/0d1c84f906c31011d0000000/Long-term-Health-Outcomes-of-Youth-Sports-Injuries.pdf

278 Fleisig, G. S., Andrews, J. R., Cutter, G. R., Weber, A., Loftice, J., McMichael, C., ... & Lyman, S. (2011). Risk of serious injury for young baseball pitchers: a 10-year prospective study. *The American journal of sports medicine, 39*(2), 253-257. https://journals.sagepub.com/doi/abs/10.1177/0363546510384224

279 Olsen, S. J., Fleisig, G. S., Dun, S., Loftice, J., & Andrews, J. R. (2006). Risk factors for shoulder and elbow injuries in adolescent baseball pitchers. *The American journal of sports medicine, 34*(6), 905-912. www.researchgate.net/profile/Glenn_Fleisig/publication/7322351_Risk_Factors_for_Shoulder_and_Elbow_Injuries_in_Adolescent_Baseball_Pitchers/links/54d4e1480cf2970e4e63d052/Risk-Factors-for-Shoulder-and-Elbow-Injuries-in-Adolescent-Baseball-Pitchers.pdf

280 Valovich McLeod, T. C., Decoster, L. C., Loud, K. J., Micheli, L. J., Parker, J. T., Sandrey, M. A., & White, C. (2011). National Athletic Trainers' Association position statement: prevention of pediatric overuse injuries. *Journal of athletic training, 46*(2), 206-220. www.natajournals.org/doi/pdf/10.4085/1062-6050-46.2.206

281 Olsen, S. J., Fleisig, G. S., Dun, S., Loftice, J., & Andrews, J. R. (2006). Risk factors for shoulder and elbow injuries in adolescent baseball pitchers. *The American journal of sports medicine, 34*(6), 905-912. www.researchgate.net/profile/Glenn_Fleisig/publication/7322351_Risk_Factors_for_Shoulder_and_Elbow_Injuries_in_Adolescent_Baseball_Pitchers/links/54d4e1480cf2970e4e63d052/Risk-Factors-for-Shoulder-and-Elbow-Injuries-in-Adolescent-Baseball-Pitchers.pdf

282 Valovich McLeod, T. C., Decoster, L. C., Loud, K. J., Micheli, L. J., Parker, J. T., Sandrey, M. A., & White, C. (2011). National Athletic Trainers' Association position statement: prevention of pediatric overuse injuries. *Journal of athletic training, 46*(2), 206-220. www.natajournals.org/doi/pdf/10.4085/1062-6050-46.2.206

283 Artz, R. (2016). *Why I Play Football Despite What I am Learning About Brain Injury.* American Association of Neurological Surgeons. https://aansneurosurgeon.org/feature/play-football-despite-learning-brain-injury/

284 *"Bubble Boy" 40 years later: Look back at heartbreaking case.* (2011). CBS News. www.cbsnews.com/pictures/bubble-boy-40-years-later-look-back-at-heartbreaking-case/

285 *9 Quotes about What It Means to Be a Parent.* (2016). Goodnet. www.goodnet.org/articles/9-quotes-about-what-means-to-be-parent

## 4. Victimization

1 Lockard, R. (2013). *Forgotten Film Gems: Untamed Heart.* Deja Reviewer. https://dejareviewer.com/2013/11/12/forgotten-film-gems-untamed-heart/

2 Warr, M. (1985). Fear of rape among urban women. *Social problems, 32*(3), 238-250. https://heinonline.org/HOL/Page?handle=hein.journals/socprob32&div=32&g_sent=1&casa_token=&collection=journals

3 *Crime > Rape rate: Countries Compared.* (n.d.). NationMaster. www.nationmaster.com/country-info/stats/Crime/Rape-rate

4 Felson, R. B., & Cundiff, P. R. (2014). Sexual assault as a crime against young people. *Archives of sexual behavior, 43*(2), 273-284. https://pdfs.semanticscholar.org/4917/69f1bcb56f43f3cd1fb25b5fb7f2cbc16160.pdf

5 Centers for Disease Control and Prevention. *2017 Youth Risk Behavior Survey Data* [Data set]. www.cdc.gov/yrbs

6 Shackelford, T. K. (2002). Are young women the special targets of rape-murder?. *Aggressive Behavior: Official Journal of the International Society for Research on Aggression, 28*(3), 224-232.

7 Felson, R. B., & Cundiff, P. R. (2012). Age and sexual assault during robberies. *Evolution and Human Behavior, 33*(1), 10-16. www.sciencedirect.com/science/article/pii/S1090513811000419

8 Senn, C. Y., Eliasziw, M., Barata, P. C., Thurston, W. E., Newby-Clark, I. R., Radtke, H. L., & Hobden, K. L. (2015). Efficacy of a sexual assault resistance program for university women. *New England journal of medicine, 372*(24), 2326-2335. www.nejm.org/doi/suppl/10.1056/NEJMsa1411131/suppl_file/nejmsa1411131_appendix.pdf

9 United States Bureau of Justice Statistics. (2014). *National Crime Victimization Survey.* Inter-university Consortium for Political and Social Research. https://doi.org/10.3886/ICPSR36142.v2

10 Senn, C. Y., Eliasziw, M., Barata, P. C., Thurston, W. E., Newby-Clark, I. R., Radtke, H. L., & Hobden, K. L. (2015). Efficacy of a sexual assault resistance program for university women. *New England journal of medicine, 372*(24), 2326-2335. www.nejm.org/doi/suppl/10.1056/NEJMsa1411131;
Sinozich, S., & Langton, L. (2014). *Rape and sexual assault victimization among college-age females, 1995-2013.* US Department of Justice, Office of Justice Programs, Bureau of Justice Statistics. www.bjs.gov/content/pub/pdf/rsavcaf9513.pdf;
Flanagan, A. S., & Furman, W. C. (2000). Sexual victimization and perceptions of close relationships in adolescence. *Child Maltreatment, 5*(4), 350-359. https://journals.sagepub.com/doi/abs/10.1177/1077559500005004006

11 Fisher, B. S., Daigle, L. E., Cullen, F. T., & Turner, M. G. (2003). Reporting sexual victimization to the police and others: Results from a national-level study of college women. *Criminal justice and behavior, 30*(1), 6-38. https://files.eric.ed.gov/fulltext/ED449712.pdf

12 Senn, C. Y., Eliasziw, M., Barata, P. C., Thurston, W. E., Newby-Clark, I. R., Radtke, H. L., & Hobden, K. L. (2015). Efficacy of a sexual assault resistance program for university women. *New England journal of medicine, 372*(24), 2326-2335. www.nejm.org/doi/suppl/10.1056/NEJMsa1411131

13 Hill, R. L., Hesmondhalgh, D., & Megson, M. (2020). Sexual violence at live music events: Experiences, responses and prevention. *International Journal of Cultural Studies, 23*(3), 368-384. https://pure.hud.ac.uk/ws/files/18461041/HILL_HESMONDHALGH_MEGSON_Sexual_violence_at_gigs.pdf

14 2017 Campaign & Survey Report. (2017). *Our Music My Body.* https://drive.google.com/file/d/1TgOGq-mxb26bTjf9plCo2pen9LOp0giBR/view

15 Prescott-Smith, S. (2018). *Two in five young female festival goers have been subjected to unwanted sexual behavior.* YouGov. https://yougov.co.uk/topics/lifestyle/articles-reports/2018/06/21/two-five-young-female-festival-goers-have-been-sub

16 Malamuth, N. M. (1981). Rape proclivity among males. *Journal of social issues, 37*(4), 138-157. www.sscnet.ucla.edu/comm/malamuth/pdf/81Jsi37.pdf

17 Hollander, J. A. (2014). Does self-defense training prevent sexual violence against women?. *Violence Against Women, 20*(3), 252-269. http://impactsafety.org/wp-content/uploads/2016/08/Violence-Against-Women-2014-Hollander-252-69.pdf;
Malamuth, N. M., Huppin, M., & Linz, D. (2018). Sexual assault interventions may be doing more harm than good with high-risk males. *Aggression and violent behavior, 41*, 20-24. www.sciencedirect.com/science/article/abs/pii/S1359178917303646

18 Hopper, J. (2018). *Why It's Time for Sexual Assault Self-Defense Training.* Psychology Today. www.psychologytoday.com/us/blog/sexual-assault-and-the-brain/201809/why-its-time-sexual-assault-self-defense-training;
Hamby, S., Weber, M. C., Grych, J., & Banyard, V. (2016). What difference do bystanders make? The association of bystander involvement with victim outcomes in a community sample. *Psychology of violence, 6*(1), 91. www.lifepathsresearch.org/wp-content/uploads/Hamby-Weber-Grych-Banyard-bystanders-2016.pdf

19 United States Bureau of Justice Statistics. (2014). *National Crime Victimization Survey*. Inter-university Consortium for Political and Social Research. https://doi.org/10.3886/ICPSR36142.v2

20 DeGue, S., Valle, L. A., Holt, M. K., Massetti, G. M., Matjasko, J. L., & Tharp, A. T. (2014). A systematic review of primary prevention strategies for sexual violence perpetration. *Aggression and violent behavior, 19*(4), 346-362. www.ncbi.nlm.nih.gov/pmc/articles/PMC5875446/

21 Kelly, L., & Sharp-Jeffs, N. (2016). *Knowledge and Know-how: the Role of Self-defence in the Prevention of Violence against Women*. www.europarl.europa.eu/RegData/etudes/STUD/2016/571385/IPOL_STU(2016)571385_EN.pdf

22 Brecklin, L. R., & Ullman, S. E. (2005). Self-defense or assertiveness training and women's responses to sexual attacks. *Journal of interpersonal violence, 20*(6), 738-762. https://citeseerx.ist.psu.edu/viewdoc/download?doi=10.1.1.924.9448&rep=rep1&type=pdf;
Orchowski, L. M., Gidycz, C. A., & Raffle, H. (2008). Evaluation of a sexual assault risk reduction and self-defense program: A prospective analysis of a revised protocol. *Psychology of Women Quarterly, 32*(2), 204-218. http://wiki.preventconnect.org/wp-content/uploads/2018/08/Orchowski-2008-Evaluation-of-a-SA.pdf

23 Hollander, J. A. (2014). Does self-defense training prevent sexual violence against women?. *Violence Against Women, 20*(3), 252-269. http://impactsafety.org/wp-content/uploads/2016/08/Violence-Against-Women-2014-Hollander-252-69.pdf

24 Sinclair, J., Sinclair, L., Otieno, E., Mulinge, M., Kapphahn, C., & Golden, N. H. (2013). A self-defense program reduces the incidence of sexual assault in Kenyan adolescent girls. *Journal of Adolescent Health, 53*(3), 374-380. https://static1.squarespace.com/static/586da1dcff7c50a814a5fdd4/t/58c0cf3ae58c62c4d3ab232f/1489030976349/JAH-Article+%283%29.pdf

25 Crime / Violence Prevention. (n.d.). *Social Programs that Work*. https://evidencebasedprograms.org/policy_area/crime-violence-prevention/

26 Senn, C. Y., Eliasziw, M., Barata, P. C., Thurston, W. E., Newby-Clark, I. R., Radtke, H. L., & Hobden, K. L. (2015). Efficacy of a sexual assault resistance program for university women. *New England journal of medicine, 372*(24), 2326-2335. www.nejm.org/doi/full/10.1056/NEJMsa1411131;
Senn, C. Y., Eliasziw, M., Hobden, K. L., Newby-Clark, I. R., Barata, P. C., Radtke, H. L., & Thurston, W. E. (2017). Secondary and 2-Year Outcomes of a Sexual Assault Resistance Program for University Women. *Psychology of Women Quarterly, 41*(2), 147-162. http://journals.sagepub.com/doi/pdf/10.1177/0361684317690119

27 Supplementary Appendix to: Senn, C. Y., Eliasziw, M., Barata, P. C., Thurston, W. E., Newby-Clark, I. R., Radtke, H. L., & Hobden, K. L. (2015). Efficacy of a sexual assault resistance program for university women. *New England journal of medicine, 372*(24), 2326-2335. www.nejm.org/doi/suppl/10.1056/NEJMsa1411131/suppl_file/nejmsa1411131_appendix.pdf

28 Kitzinger, C., & Frith, H. (1999). Just say no? The use of conversation analysis in developing a feminist perspective on sexual refusal. *Discourse & Society, 10*(3), 293-316. https://is.muni.cz/el/1423/podzim2010/GEN144/um/KITZINGER_FRITH_Just_Say_No.pdf

29 Kitzinger, C., & Frith, H. (1999). Just say no? The use of conversation analysis in developing a feminist perspective on sexual refusal. *Discourse & Society, 10*(3), 293-316. https://is.muni.cz/el/1423/podzim2010/GEN144/um/KITZINGER_FRITH_Just_Say_No.pdf

30 McCAW, J. M., & Senn, C. Y. (1998). Perception of cues in conflictual dating situations: A test of the miscommunication hypothesis. *Violence Against Women, 4*(5), 609-624. https://journals.sagepub.com/doi/abs/10.1177/1077801298004005006

31 O'byrne, R., Rapley, M., & Hansen, S. (2006). 'You Couldn't Say "No", Could You?': Young Men's Understandings of Sexual Refusal. *Feminism & Psychology, 16*(2), 133-154. https://www.researchgate.net/profile/Susan_Hansen2/publication/241647583_'You_Couldn't_Say_No_Could_You'_Young_Men's_Understandings_of_Sexual_Refusal/links/55dd975a08aeb41644aeff58/You-Couldnt-Say-No-Could-You-Young-Mens-Understandings-of-Sexual-Refusal.pdf

32 Muehlenhard, C. L., Andrews, S. L., & Beal, G. K. (1996). Beyond "Just Saying No" Dealing with Men's Unwanted Sexual Advances in Heterosexual Dating Contexts. *Journal of Psychology & Human Sexuality, 8*(1-2), 141-168. www.tandfonline.com/doi/abs/10.1300/J056v08n01_10

33 Hopper, J. (2018). *Why It's Time for Sexual Assault Self-Defense Training*. Psychology Today. www.psychologytoday.com/us/blog/sexual-assault-and-the-brain/201809/why-its-time-sexual-assault-self-defense-training

34 Bart, P., & O'Brien, P. H. (1985). *Stopping rape: Successful survival strategies* (pp. 1-10). New York: Pergamon Press. www.ojp.gov/ncjrs/virtual-library/abstracts/stopping-rape-successful-survival-strategies

35 Senn, C. Y., Eliasziw, M., Barata, P. C., Thurston, W. E., Newby-Clark, I. R., Radtke, H. L., & Hobden, K. L. (2015). Efficacy of a sexual assault resistance program for university women. *New England journal of medicine, 372*(24), 2326-2335. www.nejm.org/doi/suppl/10.1056/NEJMsa1411131/suppl_file/nejmsa1411131_appendix.pdf

36 Elsohly, M. A., & Salamone, S. J. (1999). Prevalence of drugs used in cases of alleged sexual assault. *Journal of analytical toxicology, 23*(3), 141-146.

37 Marx, B. P., Gross, A. M., & Adams, H. E. (1999). The effect of alcohol on the responses of sexually coercive and noncoercive men to an experimental rape analogue. *Sexual Abuse, 11*(2), 131-145. https://journals.sagepub.com/doi/abs/10.1177/107906329901100204;
Loiselle, M., & Fuqua, W. R. (2007). Alcohol's effects on women's risk detection in a date-rape vignette. *Journal of American College Health, 55*(5), 261-266. http://citeseerx.ist.psu.edu/viewdoc/download?-doi=10.1.1.494.4194&rep=rep1&type=pdf

38 Abbey, A., McAuslan, P., & Ross, L. T. (1998). Sexual assault perpetration by college men: The role of alcohol, misperception of sexual intent, and sexual beliefs and experiences. *Journal of Social and Clinical Psychology, 17*(2), 167-195. https://guilfordjournals.com/doi/pdfplus/10.1521/jscp.1998.17.2.167

39 Senn, C. Y., Eliasziw, M., Barata, P. C., Thurston, W. E., Newby-Clark, I. R., Radtke, H. L., & Hobden, K. L. (2015). Efficacy of a sexual assault resistance program for university women. *New England journal of medicine, 372*(24), 2326-2335. www.nejm.org/doi/suppl/10.1056/NEJMsa1411131/suppl_file/nejmsa1411131_appendix.pdf

40 Muehlenhard, C. L., Andrews, S. L., & Beal, G. K. (1996). Beyond "Just Saying No" Dealing with Men's Unwanted Sexual Advances in Heterosexual Dating Contexts. *Journal of Psychology & Human Sexuality, 8*(1-2), 141-168. www.tandfonline.com/doi/abs/10.1300/J056v08n01_10

41 Levine-MacCombie, J., & Koss, M. P. (1986). Acquaintance rape: Effective avoidance strategies. *Psychology of Women Quarterly, 10*(4), 311-320. https://journals.sagepub.com/doi/abs/10.1111/j.1471-6402.1986.tb00756.x?-journalCode=pwqa

42 Babor, T., Caetano, R., Casswell, S., Edwards, G., Giesbrecht, N., Graham, K., ... & Homel, R. (2003). Alcohol: no ordinary commodity: research and public policy. *Rev Bras Psiquiatr, 26*(4), 280-3. www.scielo.br/pdf/%0D/rbp/v26n4/a15v26n4.pdf

43 Footnote reference: [1]Ullman, S. E. (1997). Review and critique of empirical studies of rape avoidance. *Criminal Justice and Behavior, 24*(2), 177-204. https://psycnet.apa.org/record/1997-04017-002

44 Bart, P., & O'Brien, P. H. (1985). *Stopping rape: Successful survival strategies* (pp. 1-10). New York: Pergamon Press. www.ncjrs.gov/App/abstractdb/AbstractDBDetails.aspx?id=100014

45 Muehlenhard, C. L., Andrews, S. L., & Beal, G. K. (1996). Beyond "Just Saying No" Dealing with Men's Unwanted Sexual Advances in Heterosexual Dating Contexts. *Journal of Psychology & Human Sexuality, 8*(1-2), 141-168. www.tandfonline.com/doi/abs/10.1300/J056v08n01_10

46 Kleck, G., & Tark, J. (2004). *Draft final technical report: The impact of victim self-protection on rape completion and injury.* National Institute of Justice. www.ncjrs.gov/pdffiles1/nij/grants/211201.pdf

47 Quinsey, V. L., & Upfold, D. (1985). Rape completion and victim injury as a function of female resistance strategy. *Canadian Journal of Behavioural Science/Revue canadienne des sciences du comportement, 17*(1), 40. www.researchgate.net/profile/Vernon_Quinsey/publication/232473912_Rape_completion_and_victim_injury_as_a_function_of_female_resistance_strategy/links/0deec5217ae5db643b000000/Rape-completion-and-victim-injury-as-a-function-of-female-resistance-strategy.pdf

48 Ullman, S. E. (1998). Does offender violence escalate when rape victims fight back?. *Journal of Interpersonal Violence, 13*(2), 179-192. http://journals.sagepub.com/doi/abs/10.1177/088626098013002001;
Ullman, S. E., & Knight, R. A. (1992). Fighting back: Women's resistance to rape. *Journal of Interpersonal Violence, 7*(1), 31-43. https://journals.sagepub.com/doi/abs/10.1177/088626092007001003;
Quinsey, V. L., & Upfold, D. (1985). Rape completion and victim injury as a function of female resistance strategy. *Canadian Journal of Behavioural Science/Revue canadienne des sciences du comportement, 17*(1), 40. www.researchgate.net/profile/Vernon_Quinsey/publication/232473912_Rape_completion_and_victim_injury_as_a_function_of_female_resistance_strategy/links/0deec5217ae5db643b000000/Rape-completion-and-victim-injury-as-a-function-of-female-resistance-strategy.pdf;

Bart, P., & O'Brien, P. H. (1985). *Stopping rape: Successful survival strategies* (pp. 1-10). New York: Pergamon Press. www.ncjrs.gov/App/abstractdb/AbstractDBDetails.aspx?id=100014

49 Ullman, S. E. (2007). A 10-year update of "review and critique of empirical studies of rape avoidance". *Criminal justice and behavior, 34*(3), 411-429. http://citeseerx.ist.psu.edu/viewdoc/download?doi=10.1.1.459.2919&rep=rep1&type=pdf

50 Beebe, D. K. (1991). Emergency management of the adult female rape victim. *American family physician, 43*(6), 2041-2046. www.nc-cm.org/article130.htm

51 Ullman, S. E. (2007). A 10-year update of "review and critique of empirical studies of rape avoidance". *Criminal justice and behavior, 34*(3), 411-429. http://citeseerx.ist.psu.edu/viewdoc/download?doi=10.1.1.459.2919&rep=rep1&type=pdf;
Kilpatrick, D. G., Saunders, B. E., Amick-McMullan, A., Best, C. L., Veronen, L. J., & Resnick, H. S. (1989). Victim and crime factors associated with the development of crime-related post-traumatic stress disorder. *Behavior Therapy, 20*(2), 199-214. www.sciencedirect.com/science/article/abs/pii/S0005789489800693

52 Senn, C. Y., Eliasziw, M., Barata, P. C., Thurston, W. E., Newby-Clark, I. R., Radtke, H. L., & Hobden, K. L. (2015). Efficacy of a sexual assault resistance program for university women. *New England journal of medicine, 372*(24), 2326-2335. www.nejm.org/doi/suppl/10.1056/NEJMsa1411131/suppl_file/nejmsa1411131_appendix.pdf

53 Senn, C. Y., Eliasziw, M., Barata, P. C., Thurston, W. E., Newby-Clark, I. R., Radtke, H. L., & Hobden, K. L. (2015). Efficacy of a sexual assault resistance program for university women. *New England journal of medicine, 372*(24), 2326-2335. www.nejm.org/doi/suppl/10.1056/NEJMsa1411131/suppl_file/nejmsa1411131_appendix.pdf

54 Harrow, S. (2017). *10 Best Tech Devices to Prevent Rape*. Psychology Today. www.psychologytoday.com/gb/blog/the-body-blog/201704/10-best-tech-devices-prevent-rape

55 *Invi bracelet*. (n.d.). Invi. https://invi.world/shop/invi-bracelet/
Tarantola, A. (2018). *The Invi security bracelet repels assailants with a viscous stink*. Engadget. www.engadget.com/2018-01-09-the-invi-security-bracelet-repels-assailants-with-a-viscous-stin.html?guce_referrer=aHR0cHM6Ly93d3cuZ29vZ2xlLmNvbS8&guce_referrer_sig=AQAAAAz-09XI-IV0eI-kYYtcZAFAFwZuJEI7Y00_xDsK-YqpVbzgjQSQnNaXLOglTwdspblFLmouE8Xk8iYyy2c5CJ-g7y9kaVPg25Omhx5YEXarl5Toi6KOXC-qif67KfHvdX7YBZ4Ip-8huzuZiU1FrT-H7Jx8MNqptLwIcDH6nKlWj&_guc_consent_skip=1589718503

56 Mihala, L. (2018). *Sexual assault: Can wearable gadgets ward off attackers?* BBC News. www.bbc.co.uk/news/business-43228311

57 *Indian engineers design electric anti-rape bra*. (n.d.). DW. www.dw.com/en/indian-engineers-design-electric-anti-rape-bra/a-17798277

58 *Beware of the killer tampon*. (2001). News24. www.news24.com/xArchive/Archive/Beware-of-the-killer-tampon-20010111

59 Freeman, D. W. (2010). Anti-Rape Condoms (PICTURE): *Will Jagged Teeth Deter World Cup Sex Assaults? Rape-aXe Hopes So*. CBS News. www.cbsnews.com/news/anti-rape-condoms-picture-will-jagged-teeth-deter-world-cup-sex-assaults-rape-axe-hopes-so/

60 White, D., & McMillan, L. (2020). Innovating the problem away? A critical study of Anti-Rape technologies. *Violence against women, 26*(10), 1120-1140. https://researchonline.gcu.ac.uk/ws/portalfiles/portal/27220392/Innovating_the_problem_away_white_mcmillan.pdf;
Mohan, M. (2017). *Technological interventions to detect, communicate and prevent sexual assault* (Doctoral dissertation, Massachusetts Institute of Technology). https://dspace.mit.edu/bitstream/handle/1721.1/112540/1012944378-MIT.pdf?sequence=1&isAllowed=y

61 #WhyIDidntReport: *Survivors of sexual assault want you to know why they never went to police*. (n.d.). Journal News. www.journal-news.com/news/national/whyididntreport-survivors-sexual-assault-want-you-know-why-they-never-went-police/MlROWH5BgvPKhYFwAgT1SJ/

62 Campbell, R. (2012). *The neurobiology of sexual assault: Implications for first responders in law enforcement, prosecution, and victim advocacy*. In NIJ Research for the Real World Seminar. https://nij.ojp.gov/media/video/24056

63 *Sexual Assault: Committee Opinion Number 777*. (2019). American College of Obstetricians and Gynecologists. www.acog.org/clinical/clinical-guidance/committee-opinion/articles/2019/04/sexual-assault

64 *Sexual Assault: Committee Opinion Number 777.* (2019). American College of Obstetricians and Gynecologists. www.acog.org/clinical/clinical-guidance/committee-opinion/articles/2019/04/sexual-assault

65 Petter, L. M., & Whitehill, D. L. (1998). Management of female sexual assault. *American family physician, 58*(4), 920. www.aafp.org/afp/1998/0915/p920.html

66 Yuan, N. P., Koss, M. P., & Stone, M. (2006). *The psychological consequences of sexual trauma.* http://citeseerx.ist.psu.edu/viewdoc/download?doi=10.1.1.445.6463&rep=rep1&type=pdf

67 Petter, L. M., & Whitehill, D. L. (1998). Management of female sexual assault. *American family physician, 58*(4), 920. www.aafp.org/afp/1998/0915/p920.html;
Dworkin, E. R., & Schumacher, J. A. (2018). Preventing posttraumatic stress related to sexual assault through early intervention: A systematic review. *Trauma, Violence, & Abuse, 19*(4), 459-472. https://journals.sagepub.com/doi/abs/10.1177/1524838016669518?journalCode=tvaa

68 Krug, E. G., Mercy, J. A., Dahlberg, L. L., & Zwi, A. B. (2002). The world report on violence and health. *The Lancet, 360*(9339), 1083-1088. www.who.int/violence_injury_prevention/violence/global_campaign/en/chap6.pdf

69 Foa, E. B., Hearst-Ikeda, D., & Perry, K. J. (1995). Evaluation of a brief cognitive-behavioral program for the prevention of chronic PTSD in recent assault victims. *Journal of consulting and clinical psychology, 63*(6), 948. https://psycnet.apa.org/record/1996-00402-008;
Foa, E. B., & Street, G. P. (2001). Women and traumatic events. *The Journal of clinical psychiatry.* https://psycnet.apa.org/record/2001-11162-005

70 Finn, J., & Hughes, P. (2008). Evaluation of the RAINN national sexual assault online hotline. *Journal of Technology in Human Services, 26*(2-4), 203-222. www.tandfonline.com/doi/abs/10.1080/15228830802094783

71 Finn, J., Garner, M. D., & Wilson, J. (2011). Volunteer and user evaluation of the national sexual assault online hotline. *Evaluation and program planning, 34*(3), 266-272. https://d1wqtxts1xzle7.cloudfront.net/51414889/j.evalprogplan.2010.09.00220170118-13314-1u971yp.pdf?1484772138=&response-content-disposition=inline%3B+filename%3DVolunteer_and_User_Evaluation_of_the_Nat.pdf&Expires=1609281999&Signature=J9QrWEZWIwssB5GqoxVkfZBHnx--NTUMOzlyQrchQsxH5zrCVrwPnDV9l2c8NnjjsUb-5ht91eB7qmubHrzMuIlllSeGpPyLkTlRBrEk3hcb7TuDYL0sYVlFjy-CibUgYOLJ7v4jV-SMf0Yktwhhk2qUT-0m-5d7R6pk6pR7LB-s4HwsXVC-Vc0DXWNgg9nyYKN8slgD6odXreFdmDpO8lqor6Iam5GBDmUdSmeo-E0dm6UNQ7C6-6g2CLbzemioFEKBJKQMvr66IkrLp308Srl1Zddye-cC-wDRreRYS01OOoHZ36hQZ7W-8mUsWGq4b9HkLUJ1m8Nhyod3tRlsSPkxfg__&Key-Pair-Id=APKAJLOHF5GGSLRBV4ZA

72 Hartley, A. (2019). *Rape survivor, support service share tips on how to help a loved one through sexual assault.* ABC News. www.abc.net.au/news/2019-02-24/what-not-to-say-to-someone-who-has-survived-sexual-assault/10843644

73 National Electronic Injury Surveillance System-All Injury Program (NEISS-AIP). (n.d.). *Web-based Injury Statistics Query and Reporting System (WISQARS): Nonfatal Injury Reports, 2001 - 2014.* Centers for Disease Control and Prevention.

74 United States Bureau of Justice Statistics. (2014). *National Crime Victimization Survey.* Inter-university Consortium for Political and Social Research. https://doi.org/10.3886/ICPSR36142.v2

75 Finkelhor, D., & Dziuba-Leatherman, J. (1994). Children as victims of violence: A national survey. *Pediatrics-English Edition, 94*(4), 413-420. www.unh.edu/ccrc/pdf/CV4.pdf

76 United States Bureau of Justice Statistics. (2014). *National Crime Victimization Survey.* Inter-university Consortium for Political and Social Research. https://doi.org/10.3886/ICPSR36142.v2

77 Leach, J. (2004). Why people 'freeze'in an emergency: temporal and cognitive constraints on survival responses. *Aviation, space, and environmental medicine, 75*(6), 539-542. http://citeseerx.ist.psu.edu/viewdoc/download?doi=10.1.1.167.9523&rep=rep1&type=pdf

78 Fusé, T., Forsyth, J. P., Marx, B., Gallup, G. G., & Weaver, S. (2007). Factor structure of the Tonic Immobility Scale in female sexual assault survivors: An exploratory and confirmatory factor analysis. *Journal of anxiety disorders, 21*(3), 265-283. www.sciencedirect.com/science/article/abs/pii/S0887618506000867;
Galliano, G., Noble, L. M., Travis, L. A., & Puechl, C. (1993). Victim reactions during rape/sexual assault: A preliminary study of the immobility response and its correlates. *Journal of Interpersonal Violence, 8*(1), 109-114. www.falserapetimeline.org/false-rape-1573.pdf;
Burgess, A. W., & Holmstrom, L. L. (1976). Coping behavior of the rape victim. *American Journal of Psychiatry, 133*(4), 413-418. http://citeseerx.ist.psu.edu/viewdoc/download?doi=10.1.1.475.1631&rep=rep1&type=pdf;

Möller, A., Söndergaard, H. P., & Helström, L. (2017). Tonic immobility during sexual assault–a common reaction predicting post-traumatic stress disorder and severe depression. *Acta obstetricia et gynecologica Scandinavica, 96*(8), 932-938. https://obgyn.onlinelibrary.wiley.com/doi/pdf/10.1111/aogs.13174

79 Fusé, T., Forsyth, J. P., Marx, B., Gallup, G. G., & Weaver, S. (2007). Factor structure of the Tonic Immobility Scale in female sexual assault survivors: An exploratory and confirmatory factor analysis. *Journal of anxiety disorders, 21*(3), 265-283. www.sciencedirect.com/science/article/abs/pii/S0887618506000867;
Möller, A., Söndergaard, H. P., & Helström, L. (2017). Tonic immobility during sexual assault–a common reaction predicting post-traumatic stress disorder and severe depression. *Acta obstetricia et gynecologica Scandinavica, 96*(8), 932-938. https://obgyn.onlinelibrary.wiley.com/doi/pdf/10.1111/aogs.13174

80 Amir, M. (1975). Forcible rape. Rape victimology, 43-58. https://heinonline.org/HOL/Page?collection=journals&handle=hein.journals/fedpro31&id=55&men_tab=srchresults

81 Mohan, M. (2015). *Technological Interventions to Detect, Communicate and Prevent Sexual Assault.* https://dspace.mit.edu/bitstream/handle/1721.1/112540/1012944378-MIT.pdf?sequence=1&isAllowed=y

82 *UPS driver helps teen robbery victim, beaten for his sneakers.* (2021). KKTV 11 News. www.kktv.com/2021/05/20/ups-driver-helps-teen-robbery-victim-beaten-for-his-sneakers/

83 Gunns, R. E., Johnston, L., & Hudson, S. M. (2002). Victim selection and kinematics: A point-light investigation of vulnerability to attack. *Journal of Nonverbal Behavior, 26*(3), 129-158. www.ffri.hr/~ibrdar/komunikacija/seminari/Gunns,%202002%20-%20Victim%20selection%20and%20kinematics.pdf

84 Block, R., & Skogan, W. G. (1986). Resistance and nonfatal outcomes in stranger-to-stranger predatory crime. *Violence and victims, 1*(4), 241-253. www.skogan.org/files/Resistance_Nonfatal_Outcomes_in_Stranger-to-Stranger_Predatory_Crime.V_V_1986.pdf

85 Block, R., & Skogan, W. G. (1986). Resistance and nonfatal outcomes in stranger-to-stranger predatory crime. *Violence and victims, 1*(4), 241-253. www.skogan.org/files/Resistance_Nonfatal_Outcomes_in_Stranger-to-Stranger_Predatory_Crime.V_V_1986.pdf

86 Tewksbury, R., & Mustaine, E. E. (2003). College students' lifestyles and self-protective behaviors: Further considerations of the guardianship concept in routine activity theory. *Criminal Justice and Behavior, 30*(3), 302-327. https://heinonline.org/HOL/Page?handle=hein.journals/crmjusbhv30&div=21&g_sent=1&casa_token=&collection=journals

87 Quirk, M. B. (2014). *15 Product Trademarks That Have Become Victims Of Genericization.* Consumer Reports. www.consumerreports.org/consumerist/15-product-trademarks-that-have-become-victims-of-genericization/

88 Leu, C. (2017). *What's Inside Triple-Action Mace? Chili Peppers and UV Dye.* Wired. www.wired.com/story/whats-inside-triple-action-mace-chili-peppers-and-uv-dye/

89 Footnote references:
[1] Volokh, E. (2011). Older Minors, the Right to Keep and Bear (Almost Entirely) Nonlethal Arms, and the Right to Defend Life. *Ariz. St. LJ, 43*, 447. www2.law.ucla.edu/Volokh/nonlethalweaponsminors.pdf
[2] Pepper Spray. (2021). *Wikipedia.* https://en.wikipedia.org/wiki/Pepper_spray

90 *Using pepper spray for personal safety.* (2016). WBTV. www.wbtv.com/story/33854239/blog-using-pepper-spray-for-personal-safety/

91 Tewksbury, R., & Mustaine, E. E. (2003). College students' lifestyles and self-protective behaviors: Further considerations of the guardianship concept in routine activity theory. *Criminal Justice and Behavior, 30*(3), 302-327. https://heinonline.org/HOL/Page?handle=hein.journals/crmjusbhv30&div=21&g_sent=1&casa_token=&collection=journals

92 Perkins, C., Beecher, D., Aberg, D. C., Edwards, P., & Tilley, N. (2017). Personal security alarms for the prevention of assaults against healthcare staff. *Crime Science, 6*(1), 11. https://link.springer.com/article/10.1186/s40163-017-0073-1

93 Buck, S. (2016). *Why is pepper spray still the 'best' rape prevention tech?* Timeline. https://timeline.com/why-is-pepper-spray-still-the-best-rape-prevention-tech-6959ce9731dc

94 Tark, J., & Kleck, G. (2004). Resisting crime: The effects of victim action on the outcomes of crimes. *Criminology, 42*(4), 861-910. https://onlinelibrary.wiley.com/doi/abs/10.1111/j.1745-9125.2004.tb00539.x

95 Guerette, R. T., & Santana, S. A. (2010). Explaining victim self-protective behavior effects on crime incident outcomes: A test of opportunity theory. *Crime & Delinquency, 56*(2), 198-226. http://citeseerx.ist.psu.edu/viewdoc/download?doi=10.1.1.827.9947&rep=rep1&type=pdf

96 Taherzadeh, M. (2018). *Effects of a One-day Krav Maga Training: Early Stages of Skill Acquisition of a Krav Maga Kick and Punch.* https://yorkspace.library.yorku.ca/xmlui/bitstream/handle/10315/35497/Taherzadeh_Mehran_2018_MSc.pdf?sequence=2&isAllowed=y
Citing: Angleman, A. J., Shinzato, Y., Van Hasselt, V. B., & Russo, S. A. (2009). Traditional martial arts versus modern self-defense training for women: Some comments. *Aggression and violent behavior, 14*(2), 89-93. www.sciencedirect.com/science/article/abs/pii/S1359178908000827

97 Taherzadeh, M. (2018). *Effects of a One-day Krav Maga Training: Early Stages of Skill Acquisition of a Krav Maga Kick and Punch.* https://yorkspace.library.yorku.ca/xmlui/bitstream/handle/10315/35497/Taherzadeh_Mehran_2018_MSc.pdf?sequence=2&isAllowed=y
Citing: Angleman, A. J., Shinzato, Y., Van Hasselt, V. B., & Russo, S. A. (2009). Traditional martial arts versus modern self-defense training for women: Some comments. *Aggression and violent behavior, 14*(2), 89-93. www.sciencedirect.com/science/article/abs/pii/S1359178908000827

98 Hosie, R. & Sandu, C. (2017). *Self-Defence for Women: Five Krav Maga Moves Everyone Should Know.* www.independent.co.uk/life-style/health-and-families/self-defence-women-five-krav-maga-moves-techniques-attack-israel-defence-force-idf-a7542231.html;
Levine, D., & Whitman, J. (2009). *Complete Krav Maga: The Ultimate Guide to Over 230 Self-Defense and Combative Techniques.* Ulysses Press. https://books.google.co.uk/books?id=5vXW_oGlZ8wC&printsec=frontcover&redir_esc=y&hl=en#v=onepage&q&f=false

99 Levine, D., & Whitman, J. (2009). *Complete Krav Maga: The Ultimate Guide to Over 230 Self-Defense and Combative Techniques.* Ulysses Press. https://books.google.co.uk/books?id=5vXW_oGlZ8wC&printsec=frontcover&redir_esc=y&hl=en#v=onepage&q&f=false

100 Footnote references:
[1] Heffernan, L. (2016). *Not Just Pepper Spray: Apps and Devices to Keep College Students Safe.* NBC News. www.nbcnews.com/feature/college-game-plan/not-just-pepper-spray-apps-devices-keep-college-students-safe-n563356
[2] Heffernan, L. (2016). *Not Just Pepper Spray: Apps and Devices to Keep College Students Safe.* NBC News. www.nbcnews.com/feature/college-game-plan/not-just-pepper-spray-apps-devices-keep-college-students-safe-n563356
[3] Wentling, N. (2019). *New voice-activated phone app strives to prevent military sexual assaults.* Stars and Stripes. www.stripes.com/news/us/new-voice-activated-phone-app-strives-to-prevent-military-sexual-assaults-1.610571
[4] *Safe Schools Hotline - Youth Program.* (2021). CrimeStoppers. www.crimestoppersgno.org/safe-schools-hotline

101 Genuth, I. (n.d.). *No-Contact Jacket.* The Future of Things. https://thefutureofthings.com/5363-no-contact-jacket/; *Best Inventions of 2003: No-Contact Jacket.* (2003). Time. http://content.time.com/time/specials/packages/article/0,28804,1935038_1935081_1935239,00.html

102 Teen dating violence; a survivor's story. (2015). WRC. www.wrcsd.org/blog/teen-dating-violence-a-survivors-story

103 Liz Claiborne, & Education Development Center . *Love is not abuse: A teen dating violence prevention curriculum.* 3 ed. Liz Claiborne, Inc.; New York. www.uen.org/cte/facs_cabinet/downloads/AdultRoles/LINA_Curriculum%2010_07.pdf

104 Vagi, K. J., Olsen, E. O. M., Basile, K. C., & Vivolo-Kantor, A. M. (2015). Teen dating violence (physical and sexual) among US high school students: Findings from the 2013 National Youth Risk Behavior Survey. *JAMA pediatrics, 169*(5), 474-482. http://jamanetwork.com/journals/jamapediatrics/fullarticle/2173573;
Footnote references:
[1] O'Leary, K. D., Slep, A. M. S., Avery-Leaf, S., & Cascardi, M. (2008). Gender differences in dating aggression among multiethnic high school students. *Journal of Adolescent Health, 42*(5), 473-479. www.jahonline.org/article/S1054-139X%2807%2900435-1/fulltext
[2] Malik, S., Sorenson, S. B., & Aneshensel, C. S. (1997). Community and dating violence among adolescents: Perpetration and victimization. *Journal of adolescent health, 21*(5), 291-302. www.researchgate.net/profile/Shaista_Malik2/publication/13871866_Community_and_Dating_Violence_Among_Adolescents_Perpetration_and_Victimization/links/57d7603608ae6399a395aced/Community-and-Dating-Violence-Among-Adolescents-Perpetration-and-Victimization.pdf
[3] Silverman, J. G., Raj, A., Mucci, L. A., & Hathaway, J. E. (2001). Dating violence against adolescent girls and associated substance use, unhealthy weight control, sexual risk behavior, pregnancy, and suicidality. *Jama, 286*(5), 572-579. https://jamanetwork.com/journals/jama/articlepdf/194061/JOC02015.pdf
[4] Barter, C., Stanley, N., Wood, M., Aghtaie, N., Larkins, C., Øverlien, C., & Hellevik, P. (2015). *Safeguarding Teenage Intimate Relationships (STIR): Connecting online and offline contexts and risks.* Research Report. www.bristol.ac.uk/news/2015/february/stir-study.html

[5] Coker, A. L., McKeown, R. E., Sanderson, M., Davis, K. E., Valois, R. F., & Huebner, E. S. (2000). Severe dating violence and quality of life among South Carolina high school students. *American journal of preventive medicine, 19*(4), 220-227. https://d1wqtxts1xzle7.cloudfront.net/49325111/s0749-3797_2800_2900227-020161003-15854-kwyhlc.pdf?1475524226=&response-content-disposition=inline%3B+filename%3DSevere_dating_violence_and_quality_of_li.pdf&Expires=1601554046&Signature=CnZQoBx6I-s4zJy8Yt-3Tv--yah5AsMADhhqC9gVyC1gGyyB9k-m733WjK8a31GQvInopU1X5B7rTEWL34kD-hQeWy2U-iO-aJU6mGs6r7fbETxBVsDVl6eL64zWXAZumyIHnIuKEs1HVrByfNPcu7rFT6gVQSLCwQM6dyKZ-cyqptKan51ZD3MqCY2ne968H8XVWxUBK31kgUWOeEGzpmPPz--GpYrmyK9elGid3rHI-4po3JHR-RqEo5LlwcvVRoG122rGUrkXlwVKi3agIBQvbz3M-5PR71lYhgixciUeHC1lxL-0m7NcSmyqM-3JyV9gzLF79etHXttNOiRL3mXHyvw__&Key-Pair-Id=APKAJLOHF5GGSLRBV4ZA
[6] Foshee, V. A. (1996). Gender differences in adolescent dating abuse prevalence, types and injuries. *Health education research, 11*(3), 275-286. http://citeseerx.ist.psu.edu/viewdoc/download?doi=10.1.1.574.8743&rep=rep1&type=pdf
[7] Roberts, T. A., & Klein, J. (2003). Intimate partner abuse and high-risk behavior in adolescents. *Archives of pediatrics & adolescent medicine, 157*(4), 375-380. https://jamanetwork.com/journals/jamapediatrics/fullarticle/481301
[8] Halpern, C. T., Oslak, S. G., Young, M. L., Martin, S. L., & Kupper, L. L. (2001). Partner violence among adolescents in opposite-sex romantic relationships: Findings from the National Longitudinal Study of Adolescent Health. *American journal of public health, 91*(10), 1679-1685. https://ajph.aphapublications.org/doi/pdfplus/10.2105/AJPH.91.10.1679

105 Teten, A. L., Ball, B., Valle, L. A., Noonan, R., & Rosenbluth, B. (2009). Considerations for the definition, measurement, consequences, and prevention of dating violence victimization among adolescent girls. *Journal of Women's Health, 18*(7), 923-927. www.researchgate.net/profile/Rita_Noonan/publication/26645702_Considerations_for_the_Definition_Measurement_Consequences_and_Prevention_of_Dating_Violence_Victimization_among_Adolescent_Girls/links/0046351dc771784799000000.pdf;
Niolon, P. H., & Centers for Disease Control and Prevention. (2017). *Preventing intimate partner violence across the lifespan: A technical package of programs, policies, and practices.* Government Printing Office. www.cdc.gov/violenceprevention/pdf/ipv-technicalpackages.pdf;
Footnote references:
[1] Foshee, V. A., Bauman, K. E., Ennett, S. T., Linder, G. F., Benefield, T., & Suchindran, C. (2004). Assessing the long-term effects of the Safe Dates program and a booster in preventing and reducing adolescent dating violence victimization and perpetration. *American journal of public health, 94*(4), 619-624. https://ajph.aphapublications.org/doi/pdfplus/10.2105/AJPH.94.4.619
[2] Wolfe, D. A., Wekerle, C., Scott, K., Straatman, A. L., Grasley, C., & Reitzel-Jaffe, D. (2003). Dating violence prevention with at-risk youth: a controlled outcome evaluation. *Journal of consulting and clinical psychology, 71*(2), 279. www.researchgate.net/profile/Christine_Wekerle/publication/10801603_Dating_violence_prevention_with_at-risk_youth_A_controlled_outcome_evaluation_Journal_of_Consulting_and_Clinical_Psychology_71_279-291/links/09e41510d6c9f30e67000000/Dating-violence-prevention-with-at-risk-youth-A-controlled-outcome-evaluation-Journal-of-Consulting-and-Clinical-Psychology-71-279-291.pdf
[3] Niolon, P. H., & Centers for Disease Control and Prevention. (2017). *Preventing intimate partner violence across the lifespan: A technical package of programs, policies, and practices.* Government Printing Office. www.cdc.gov/violenceprevention/pdf/ipv-technicalpackages.pdf
[4] Foshee, V. A., Reyes, H. L. M., Ennett, S. T., Cance, J. D., Bauman, K. E., & Bowling, J. M. (2012). Assessing the effects of Families for Safe Dates, a family-based teen dating abuse prevention program. *Journal of Adolescent Health, 51*(4), 349-356. www.sciencedirect.com/science/article/abs/pii/S1054139X1100718X

106 Jennings, W. G., Okeem, C., Piquero, A. R., Sellers, C. S., Theobald, D., & Farrington, D. P. (2017). Dating and intimate partner violence among young persons ages 15–30: Evidence from a systematic review. *Aggression and violent behavior, 33*, 107-125. https://eprints.kingston.ac.uk/id/eprint/37330/1/Theobald-D-37330-AAM.pdf

107 Footnote references:
[1] *Love Doesn't Have to Hurt Teens.* (2013). American Psychological Association. www.apa.org/pi/families/resources/love-teens
[2] Liz Claiborne, & Education Development Center. *Love is not abuse: A teen dating violence prevention curriculum.* 3 ed. Liz Claiborne, Inc.; New York. www.uen.org/cte/facs_cabinet/downloads/AdultRoles/LINA_Curriculum%2010_07.pdf
[3] O'Donoghue, A. (1999). *A Love that Kills* [Film]. National Film Board of Canada (NFB). www.nfb.ca/film/love_that_kills/#:~:text=A%20Love%20That%20Kills%20is,daughter's%20life%20and%20tragic%20death

108 Liz Claiborne, & Education Development Center. *Love is not abuse: A teen dating violence prevention curriculum.* 3 ed. Liz Claiborne, Inc.; New York. www.uen.org/cte/facs_cabinet/downloads/AdultRoles/LINA_Curriculum%2010_07.pdf

109 Kinsfogel, K. M., & Grych, J. H. (2004). Interparental Conflict and Adolescent Dating Relationships: Integrating Cognitive, Emotional, and Peer Influences. *Journal of family psychology, 18*(3), 505. www.researchgate.net/

profile/John_Grych/publication/8331979_Interparental_Conflict_and_Adolescent_Dating_Relationships_Integrating_Cognitive_Emotional_and_Peer_Influences/links/53ef7f550cf26b9b7dcdeffe.pdf

110 *Teen dating violence; a survivor's story.* (2015). WRC. www.wrcsd.org/blog/teen-dating-violence-a-survivors-story

# 5. Mental Health

1 Wurtzel, E. (2014). *Prozac nation: Young and depressed in America.* Houghton Mifflin Harcourt.

2 Plath, S. (1972). *The Bell Jar.* Faber & Faber.

3 Footnote reference: [1] Bor, W., Dean, A. J., Najman, J., & Hayatbakhsh, R. (2014). Are child and adolescent mental health problems increasing in the 21st century? A systematic review. *Australian & New Zealand Journal of Psychiatry, 48*(7), 606-616. www.researchgate.net/profile/Angela_Dean/publication/262341586_Are_child_and_adolescent_mental_health_problems_increasing_in_the_21st_century_A_systematic_review/links/55e5123808ae2fac4722fa45/Are-child-and-adolescent-mental-health-problems-increasing-in-the-21st-century-A-systematic-review.pdf;
1999: Kann, L., Kinchen, S. A., Williams, B. I., Ross, J. G., Lowry, R., Grunbaum, J. A., & Kolbe, L. J. (2000). Youth risk behavior surveillance—United States, 1999. *Journal of School Health, 70*(7), 271-285. www.cdc.gov/mmwr/preview/mmwrhtml/ss4905a1.htm;
2001: Grunbaum, J. A., Kann, L., Kinchen, S. A., Williams, B., Ross, J. G., Lowry, R., & Kolbe, L. (2002). Youth risk behavior surveillance—United States, 2001. *Journal of School Health, 72*(8), 313-328. https://stacks.cdc.gov/view/cdc/6696/cdc_6696_DS1.pdf;
2003: Grunbaum, J. A., Kann, L., Kinchen, S., Ross, J., Hawkins, J., Lowry, R., ... & Collins, J. (2004). Youth risk behavior surveillance--United States, 2003. *Morbidity and mortality weekly report Surveillance summaries, 53*(2), 1-96. www.cdc.gov/mmwr/preview/mmwrhtml/ss5302a1.htm;
2005: Eaton, D. K., Kann, L., Kinchen, S., Ross, J., Hawkins, J., Harris, W. A., ... & Wechsler, H. (2006). Youth risk behavior surveillance—United States, 2005. *Journal of school health, 76*(7), 353-372. www.cdc.gov/mmwr/preview/mmwrhtml/ss5505a1.htm;
2007: Eaton, D. K., Kann, L., Kinchen, S., Shanklin, S., Ross, J., Hawkins, J., ... & Wechsler, H. (2008). Youth risk behavior surveillance--United States, 2007. *Morbidity and mortality weekly report Surveillance summaries, 57*(4), 1-131. www.cdc.gov/mmwr/preview/mmwrhtml/ss5704a1.htm?s_cid=ss5704a1_e;
2009: Eaton, D. K., Kann, L., Kinchen, S., Shanklin, S., Ross, J., Hawkins, J., ... & Centers for Disease Control and Prevention (CDC). (2010). Youth risk behavior surveillance-United States, 2009. *MMWR Surveill Summ, 59*(5), 1-142. www.cdc.gov/mmwr/preview/mmwrhtml/ss5905a1.htm;
2011: Eaton, D. K., Kann, L., Kinchen, S., Shanklin, S., Flint, K. H., Hawkins, J., ... & Wechsler, H. (2012). Youth risk behavior surveillance—United States, 2011. *Morbidity and mortality weekly report: Surveillance summaries, 61*(4), 1-162. www.cdc.gov/mmwr/preview/mmwrhtml/ss6104a1.htm;
2013: Kann, L., Kinchen, S., Shanklin, S. L., Flint, K. H., Hawkins, J., Harris, W. A., ... & Zaza, S. (2014). Youth risk behavior surveillance—United States, 2013. *Morbidity and Mortality Weekly Report: Surveillance Summaries, 63*(4), 1-168. www.cdc.gov/mmwr/pdf/ss/ss6304.pdf;
2015: Kann, L., McManus, T., Harris, W. A., Shanklin, S. L., Flint, K. H., Hawkins, J., ... & Zaza, S. (2016). Youth risk behavior surveillance—United States, 2015. *Morbidity and Mortality Weekly Report: Surveillance Summaries, 65*(6), 1-174. www.cdc.gov/mmwr/volumes/65/ss/ss6506a1.htm;
2017: Kann, L., McManus, T., Harris, W. A., Shanklin, S. L., Flint, K. H., Queen, B., ... & Ethier, K. A. (2018). Youth risk behavior surveillance—United States, 2017. *MMWR Surveillance Summaries, 67*(8), 1. www.ncbi.nlm.nih.gov/pmc/articles/PMC6002027/

4 Yap, M. B., Pilkington, P. D., Ryan, S. M., Kelly, C. M., & Jorm, A. F. (2014). Parenting strategies for reducing the risk of adolescent depression and anxiety disorders: a Delphi consensus study. *Journal of affective disorders, 156*, 67-75. www.sciencedirect.com/science/article/abs/pii/S0165032713008288

5 Yap, M. B., Pilkington, P. D., Ryan, S. M., Kelly, C. M., & Jorm, A. F. (2014). Parenting strategies for reducing the risk of adolescent depression and anxiety disorders: a Delphi consensus study. *Journal of affective disorders, 156*, 67-75. www.sciencedirect.com/science/article/abs/pii/S0165032713008288

6 *What is Cognitive Behavioral Therapy?* (2017). American Psychological Assocation. www.apa.org/ptsd-guideline/patients-and-families/cognitive-behavioral

7 Merry, S. N., Hetrick, S. E., Cox, G. R., Brudevold-Iversen, T., Bir, J. J., & McDowell, H. (2012). Cochrane Review: Psychological and educational interventions for preventing depression in children and adolescents. Evidence-Based Child Health: *A Cochrane Review Journal, 7*(5), 1409-1685. https://minerva-access.unimelb.edu.au/bitstream/handle/11343/59278/Merry%20et%20al%202011.pdf?sequence=1&isAllowed=y;

Horowitz, J. L., & Garber, J. (2006). The prevention of depressive symptoms in children and adolescents: A meta-analytic review. *Journal of consulting and clinical psychology, 74*(3), 401. http://204.14.132.173/pubs/journals/releases/ccp-743401.pdf;
Clarke, G. N., Hornbrook, M., Lynch, F., Polen, M., Gale, J., Beardslee, W., ... & Seeley, J. (2001). A randomized trial of a group cognitive intervention for preventing depression in adolescent offspring of depressed parents. *Archives of general psychiatry, 58*(12), 1127-1134. https://jamanetwork.com/journals/jamapsychiatry/fullarticle/481868

8 Hofmann, S. G., Asnaani, A., Vonk, I. J., Sawyer, A. T., & Fang, A. (2012). The efficacy of cognitive behavioral therapy: A review of meta-analyses. *Cognitive therapy and research, 36*(5), 427-440. www.ncbi.nlm.nih.gov/pmc/articles/PMC3584580/?_escaped_fragment_=po;
Blenkiron, P. (2015). *Cognitive behavioural therapy.* Royal College of Psychiatrists. www.rcpsych.ac.uk/mental-health/treatments-and-wellbeing/cognitive-behavioural-therapy-(cbt);
Footnote references:
[1] Proudfoot, J., Goldberg, D., Mann, A., Everitt, B., Marks, I., & Gray, J. A. (2003). Computerized, interactive, multimedia cognitive-behavioural program for anxiety and depression in general practice. *Psychological medicine, 33*(2), 217-227. www.cambridge.org/core/journals/psychological-medicine/article/computerized-interactive-multimedia-cognitivebehavioural-program-for-anxiety-and-depression-in-general-practice/6FF75F9283DF2209226D8910921F5307
[2] Davies, E. B., Morriss, R., & Glazebrook, C. (2014). Computer-delivered and web-based interventions to improve depression, anxiety, and psychological well-being of university students: a systematic review and meta-analysis. *Journal of medical Internet research, 16*(5), e130. www.jmir.org/2014/5/e130/
[3] Psiuk, D., Nowak, E., Cholewa, K., Łopuszańska, U., & Samardakiewicz, M. (2021). The Potential Role of Serotonergic Hallucinogens in Depression Treatment. *Life, 11*(8), 765. www.mdpi.com/2075-1729/11/8/765/pdf

9 Hofmann, S. G., Asnaani, A., Vonk, I. J., Sawyer, A. T., & Fang, A. (2012). The efficacy of cognitive behavioral therapy: A review of meta-analyses. *Cognitive therapy and research, 36*(5), 427-440. www.ncbi.nlm.nih.gov/pmc/articles/PMC3584580/?_escaped_fragment_=po

10 Footnote reference: [1] Allen, J., & Allen, C. W. (2009). *Escaping the endless adolescence: How we can help our teenagers grow up before they grow old.* Ballantine Books.

11 Allen, Joseph. *Escaping the Endless Adolescence: How we can help our teenagers grow up before they grow old.* Random House Publishing Group. Kindle Edition. https://books.google.co.uk/books?hl=en&lr=&id=myEHFTWAmjwC&oi=fnd&pg=PR9&dq=Escaping+the+Endless+Adolescence&ots=8yCPQ5RSm7&sig=Zg52iGB3ugS5gz0mW19DUdLsUiA&redir_esc=y#v=onepage&q=Escaping%20the%20Endless%20Adolescence&f=false

12 Langer, E. J., & Rodin, J. (1976). The effects of choice and enhanced personal responsibility for the aged: A field experiment in an institutional setting. *Journal of personality and social psychology, 34*(2), 191. https://uploads-ssl.webflow.com/59faaf5b01b9500001e95457/5bc55fe136f9e490f13c75c4_Langer%20%26%20Rodin%201976.pdf

13 Andersen, C. H. (2021). *Depression Quotes That Capture Exactly What You're Feeling.* The Healthy. www.thehealthy.com/mental-health/depression/depression-quotes/

14 Snow, K. & McFadden, C. (2017). *Generation at risk: America's youngest facing mental health crisis.* NBC News. www.nbcnews.com/health/kids-health/generation-risk-america-s-youngest-facing-mental-health-crisis-n827836

15 Merikangas, K. R., He, J. P., Burstein, M., Swanson, S. A., Avenevoli, S., Cui, L., ... & Swendsen, J. (2010). Lifetime prevalence of mental disorders in US adolescents: results from the National Comorbidity Survey Replication–Adolescent Supplement (NCS-A). *Journal of the American Academy of Child & Adolescent Psychiatry, 49*(10), 980-989. www.ncbi.nlm.nih.gov/pmc/articles/PMC2946114/?_escaped_fragment_=po=2.63158

16 Footnote references:
[1] Merikangas, K. R., He, J. P., Burstein, M., Swanson, S. A., Avenevoli, S., Cui, L., ... & Swendsen, J. (2010). Lifetime prevalence of mental disorders in US adolescents: results from the National Comorbidity Survey Replication–Adolescent Supplement (NCS-A). *Journal of the American Academy of Child & Adolescent Psychiatry, 49*(10), 980-989. www.ncbi.nlm.nih.gov/pmc/articles/PMC2946114/?_escaped_fragment_=po=2.63158
[2] Kessler, R. C., Berglund, P., Demler, O., Jin, R., Merikangas, K. R., & Walters, E. E. (2005). Lifetime prevalence and age-of-onset distributions of DSM-IV disorders in the National Comorbidity Survey Replication. *Archives of general psychiatry, 62*(6), 593-602. https://jamanetwork.com/journals/jamapsychiatry/articlepdf/208678/yoa40305.pdf
[3] Hooley, J. M., Fox, K. R., & Boccagno, C. (2020). Nonsuicidal self-injury: diagnostic challenges and current perspectives. *Neuropsychiatric disease and treatment, 16*, 101. www.dovepress.com/nonsuicidal-self-injury-diagnostic-challenges-and-current-perspectives-peer-reviewed-fulltext-article-NDT
Chart references:

Non-suicidal self-injury: Swannell, S. V., Martin, G. E., Page, A., Hasking, P., & St John, N. J. (2014). Prevalence of non-suicidal self-injury in nonclinical samples: Systematic review, meta-analysis and meta-regression. *Suicide and Life-Threatening Behavior, 44*(3), 273-303. www.researchgate.net/profile/Graham_Martin/publication/259723469_Prevalence_of_Nonsuicidal_Self-Injury_in_Nonclinical_Samples_Systematic_Review_Meta-Analysis_and_Meta-Regression/links/5a307bfcaca27271ec8a0b94/Prevalence-of-Nonsuicidal-Self-Injury-in-Nonclinical-Samples-Systematic-Review-Meta-Analysis-and-Meta-Regression.pdf;
All other disorders: Merikangas, K. R., He, J. P., Burstein, M., Swanson, S. A., Avenevoli, S., Cui, L., ... & Swendsen, J. (2010). Lifetime prevalence of mental disorders in US adolescents: results from the National Comorbidity Survey Replication–Adolescent Supplement (NCS-A). *Journal of the American Academy of Child & Adolescent Psychiatry, 49*(10), 980-989. www.ncbi.nlm.nih.gov/pmc/articles/PMC2946114/?_escaped_fragment_=po=2.63158

17 Anonymous. (n.d.). *I Stopped Cutting Myself: A Story of Self-Harm and Recovery*. Your Teen for Parents. https://yourteenmag.com/health/teenager-mental-health/cutting-teen-story

18 Rader, D. (2010). *Angelina Jolie: Taming Her Wild Heart*. Parade. https://parade.com/131662/dotsonrader/angelina-jolie-taming-her-wild-heart/

19 University of Oxford Centre for Suicide Research. (2018). *Young people who self-harm: A Guide for School Staff.* www.rcpsych.ac.uk/docs/default-source/improving-care/nccmh/suicide-prevention/wave-1-resources/young-people-who-self-harm-a-guide-for-school-staff.pdf?sfvrsn=e6ebf7ca_2

20 Lloyd-Richardson, E. E., Perrine, N., Dierker, L., & Kelley, M. L. (2007). Characteristics and functions of non-suicidal self-injury in a community sample of adolescents. *Psychological medicine, 37*(8), 1183-1192. www.ncbi.nlm.nih.gov/pmc/articles/PMC2538378/

21 Swannell, S. V., Martin, G. E., Page, A., Hasking, P., & St John, N. J. (2014). Prevalence of non-suicidal self-injury in nonclinical samples: Systematic review, meta-analysis and meta-regression. *Suicide and Life-Threatening Behavior, 44*(3), 273-303. www.researchgate.net/profile/Graham_Martin/publication/259723469_Prevalence_of_Nonsuicidal_Self-Injury_in_Nonclinical_Samples_Systematic_Review_Meta-Analysis_and_Meta-Regression/links/5a307bfcaca27271ec8a0b94/Prevalence-of-Nonsuicidal-Self-Injury-in-Nonclinical-Samples-Systematic-Review-Meta-Analysis-and-Meta-Regression.pdf;
Barrocas, A. L., Hankin, B. L., Young, J. F., & Abela, J. R. (2012). Rates of nonsuicidal self-injury in youth: age, sex, and behavioral methods in a community sample. *Pediatrics, 130*(1), 39-45. www.ncbi.nlm.nih.gov/pmc/articles/PMC3382916/

22 Ross, S., & Heath, N. (2002). A study of the frequency of self-mutilation in a community sample of adolescents. *Journal of Youth and Adolescence, 31*(1), 67-77. www.researchgate.net/profile/Nancy_Heath2/publication/225100400_A_Study_of_the_Frequency_of_Self-Mutilation_in_a_Community_Sample_of_Adolescents/links/0c96052c97148d0196000000.pdf

23 *Intentional self-harm among youth in Canada*. (n.d.). The Canadian Institute for Health Information. www.cihi.ca/sites/default/files/info_child_harm_en.pdf

24 Swannell, S. V., Martin, G. E., Page, A., Hasking, P., & St John, N. J. (2014). Prevalence of nonsuicidal self-injury in nonclinical samples: Systematic review, meta-analysis and meta-regression. *Suicide and Life-Threatening Behavior, 44*(3), 273-303. https://s3.amazonaws.com/academia.edu.documents/46703784/Prevalence_of_Nonsuicidal_Self-Injury_in20160622-1847-1fjw2yt.pdf?AWSAccessKeyId=AKIAIWOWYYGZ2Y53UL3A&Expires=1527698203&Signature=U6GcMPFJG1QIEVyAdBiv7lH7agI%3D&response-content-disposition=inline%3B%20filename%3DPrevalence_of_Nonsuicidal_Self_Injury_in.pdf

25 Arendt, F., Scherr, S., & Romer, D. (2019). Effects of exposure to self-harm on social media: Evidence from a two-wave panel study among young adults. *New Media & Society, 21*(11-12), 2422-2442. https://journals.sagepub.com/doi/pdf/10.1177/1461444819850106

26 Moreno, M. A., Ton, A., Selkie, E., & Evans, Y. (2016). Secret Society 123: understanding the language of self-harm on Instagram. *Journal of Adolescent Health, 58*(1), 78-84. www.ncbi.nlm.nih.gov/pmc/articles/PMC5322804/

27 Moreno, M. A., Ton, A., Selkie, E., & Evans, Y. (2016). Secret Society 123: understanding the language of self-harm on Instagram. *Journal of Adolescent Health, 58*(1), 78-84. www.ncbi.nlm.nih.gov/pmc/articles/PMC5322804/

28 Moreno, M. A., Ton, A., Selkie, E., & Evans, Y. (2016). Secret Society 123: understanding the language of self-harm on Instagram. *Journal of Adolescent Health, 58*(1), 78-84. www.ncbi.nlm.nih.gov/pmc/articles/PMC5322804/

29 Livingstone, S., Haddon, L., Görzig, A., & Ólafsson, K. (2011). *Risks and safety on the internet: the perspective of European children: full findings and policy implications from the EU Kids Online survey of 9-16 year olds and their parents in 25 countries.* http://eprints.lse.ac.uk/33731/1/Risks%20and%20safety%20on%20the%20internet(lse-ro).pdf

30 Klonsky, E. D., May, A. M., & Glenn, C. R. (2013). The relationship between nonsuicidal self-injury and attempted suicide: converging evidence from four samples. *Journal of abnormal psychology, 122*(1), 231. https://doi.apa.org/doiLanding?doi=10.1037%2Fa0030278

31 Prinstein, M. J. (2008). Introduction to the special section on suicide and nonsuicidal self-injury: A review of unique challenges and important directions for self-injury science. *Journal of consulting and clinical psychology, 76*(1), 1. www.researchgate.net/profile/Mitchell_Prinstein/publication/5621877_Introduction_to_the_Special_Section_on_Suicide_and_Nonsuicidal_Self-Injury_A_Review_of_Unique_Challenges_and_Important_Directions_for_Self-Injury_Science/links/02bfe50d07166c9b78000000.pdf

32 Lloyd-Richardson, E. E., Perrine, N., Dierker, L., & Kelley, M. L. (2007). Characteristics and functions of non-suicidal self-injury in a community sample of adolescents. *Psychological medicine, 37*(8), 1183-1192. www.ncbi.nlm.nih.gov/pmc/articles/PMC2538378/

33 Laye-Gindhu, A., & Schonert-Reichl, K. A. (2005). Nonsuicidal self-harm among community adolescents: Understanding the "whats" and "whys" of self-harm. *Journal of youth and Adolescence, 34*(5), 447-457. https://d1wqtxts1xzle7.cloudfront.net/35003254/self_harm_0.pdf?1412524417=&response-content-disposition=inline%3B+filename%3DNonsuicidal_Self_Harm_Among_Community_Ad.pdf&Expires=1617400213&Signature=fC-dO7Ru8qgFUxs9GUVvLa1T8D45wP0nufKPfVnyAdce75A5Nn9f4er52gP~z~mGWbfpQXiaura5rHXsyjQjfl4OQ4pLRzyyi9-A1MFbyyrbwHByUV0fLfRPOFwiBeJfBbuI4CoaSN9mq2Pet2uwnk9mgNvH7myVLXNoUgWZPyA85zZmFT1k3Ny4~-WZjHoTxIIj92sI-k-vGvqDDCF7zeZu7XMKmvqZXk6PvdNj08-Oh7re~BIxG9FAyVxnxmmLU2hh3Fj0R2JzQaowoWFJ7iari8jQ01WpdSik4ue-Q47GPCVXOfvFhDgv3Pph-wzTBBLPe6Q6VEzWyK8mNEhy~g__&Key-Pair-Id=APKAJLOHF5GGSLRBV4ZA

34 Gratz, K. L. (2003). Risk factors for and functions of deliberate self-harm: An empirical and conceptual review. *Clinical Psychology: Science and Practice, 10*(2), 192-205. www.nationellasjalvskadeprojektet.se/wp-content/uploads/2017/10/Gratz2003RiskFactorsandFunctionofSelf-HarminCPSP.pdf;
Hawton, K., Witt, K. G., Salisbury, T. L. T., Arensman, E., Gunnell, D., Townsend, E., ... & Hazell, P. (2015). Interventions for self-harm in children and adolescents. *Cochrane database of systematic reviews*, (12). www.cochranelibrary.com/cdsr/doi/10.1002/14651858.CD012013/full

35 Iyengar, U., Snowden, N., Asarnow, J. R., Moran, P., Tranah, T., & Ougrin, D. (2018). A further look at therapeutic interventions for suicide attempts and self-harm in adolescents: An updated systematic review of randomized controlled trials. *Frontiers in psychiatry, 9*, 583. https://pubmed.ncbi.nlm.nih.gov/30532713/

36 Tebbett-Mock, A. A., Saito, E., McGee, M., Woloszyn, P., & Venuti, M. (2020). Efficacy of dialectical behavior therapy versus treatment as usual for acute-care inpatient adolescents. *Journal of the American Academy of Child & Adolescent Psychiatry, 59*(1), 149-156. https://pubmed.ncbi.nlm.nih.gov/30946973/

37 Ferrey, A. E., Hughes, N. D., Simkin, S., Locock, L., Stewart, A., Kapur, N., ... & Hawton, K. (2016). Changes in parenting strategies after a young person's self-harm: a qualitative study. *Child and adolescent psychiatry and mental health, 10*(1), 20. www.ncbi.nlm.nih.gov/pmc/articles/PMC4930574/

38 Moran, P., Coffey, C., Romaniuk, H., Olsson, C., Borschmann, R., Carlin, J. B., & Patton, G. C. (2012). The natural history of self-harm from adolescence to young adulthood: a population-based cohort study. *The Lancet, 379*(9812), 236-243. www.sciencedirect.com/science/article/pii/S0140673611611410

39 *Pink defends self-harming in new video.* (2011). MTV News. www.mtv.co.uk/pink/news/pink-defends-selfharming-in-new-video

40 Shriver, L. (2010). *We need to talk about Kevin.* Profile Books.

41 Loeber, R., Burke, J. D., Lahey, B. B., Winters, A., & Zera, M. (2000). Oppositional defiant and conduct disorder: a review of the past 10 years, part I. *Journal of the American Academy of Child & Adolescent Psychiatry*, 39(12), 1468-1484. http://citeseerx.ist.psu.edu/viewdoc/download?doi=10.1.1.499.8732&rep=rep1&type=pdf

42 Reynolds, C. R., Kamphaus, R. W., & Vannest, K. J. (2015). *BASC3: Behavior assessment system for children.* PscyhCorp. http://images.pearsonclinical.com/images/assets/basc-3/basc3resources/DSM5_DiagnosticCriteria_ConductDisorder.pdf

43 Kessler, R. C., Berglund, P., Demler, O., Jin, R., Merikangas, K. R., & Walters, E. E. (2005). Lifetime prevalence and age-of-onset distributions of DSM-IV disorders in the National Comorbidity Survey Replication. *Archives*

*of general psychiatry, 62*(6), 593-602. https://jamanetwork.com/journals/jamapsychiatry/articlepdf/208678/yoa40305.pdf

44 Burke, J. D., Loeber, R., & Birmaher, B. (2002). Oppositional defiant disorder and conduct disorder: a review of the past 10 years, part II. *Journal of the American Academy of Child & Adolescent Psychiatry, 41*(11), 1275-1293. https://sciences.ucf.edu/psychology/childrenslearningclinic/wp-content/uploads/sites/91/2013/08/Burke-Loeber-Birmaher-ODD-review-Part-II.pdf;
Reid, J. B., Eddy, J. M., Fetrow, R. A., & Stoolmiller, M. (1999). Description and immediate impacts of a preventive intervention for conduct problems. *American journal of community psychology, 27*(4), 483-518. www.researchgate.net/profile/Mike_Stoolmiller/publication/225250006_Description_and_Immediate_Impacts_of_a_Preventive_Intervention_for_Conduct_Problems/links/09e41510a72434486d000000.pdf;
Brestan, E. V., & Eyberg, S. M. (1998). Effective psychosocial treatments of conduct-disordered children and adolescents: 29 years, 82 studies, and 5,272 kids. *Journal of clinical child psychology, 27*(2), 180-189. www.researchgate.net/profile/Sheila_Eyberg/publication/13636801_Effective_Psychosocial_Treatments_of_Conduct-Disordered_Children_and_Adolescents_29_Years_82_Studies_and_5272_Kids/links/5429fad70cf27e39fa8e6e31.pdf

45 Living with Children. (n.d.). Goodreads. www.goodreads.com/book/show/3664559-living-with-children

46 Burke, J. D., Loeber, R., & Birmaher, B. (2002). Oppositional defiant disorder and conduct disorder: a review of the past 10 years, part II. *Journal of the American Academy of Child & Adolescent Psychiatry, 41*(11), 1275-1293. https://sciences.ucf.edu/psychology/childrenslearningclinic/wp-content/uploads/sites/91/2013/08/Burke-Loeber-Birmaher-ODD-review-Part-II.pdf

47 Feindler, E. L., Marriott, S. A., & Iwata, M. (1984). Group anger control training for junior high school delinquents. *Cognitive therapy and research, 8*(3), 299-311. https://d1wqtxts1xzle7.cloudfront.net/54301332/bf0117300020170831-2886-r3ye71.pdf?1504180379=&response-content-disposition=inline%3B+filename%3DGroup_Anger_Control_Training_for_junior.pdf&Expires=1609706460&Signature=Cnrtm3IL-Bw-F2FG0G6keTmiXSYQE1auaxpU9B-gF3b7UK8JlaMWlaEUwnX-lWhr3eYe20T0TaI9c-AHZniom817L-riTvBslsbHUneza1V3w-C2rxB3YEOo-uNl0M3-xhNfZTqaeOv2fVLDH2HYaMN8Xypqm-2Gn1fIIoARVa-J-L0jjwnxgXPDSIEJUcTs11Elj4vFRRRpQKi6-nJpomoAAFR0C8T1X-Wyvu09u9Znw-K2g03351y2zwl7LT-WqhQTlBiacidwJNAI1Uuhu0Ew1CBIF8GJfxY8keOv2rlzI7-4F7PfoHvsHFhqyO4sBBuKqnMWF4Wax-4ip-PKAwQ9QUQ__&Key-Pair-Id=APKAJLOHF5GGSLRBV4ZA;
Schlichter, K. J., & Horan, J. J. (1981). Effects of stress inoculation on the anger and aggression management skills of institutionalized juvenile delinquents. *Cognitive Therapy and Research, 5*(4), 359-365. https://d1wqtxts1xzle7.cloudfront.net/46140645/bf0117368720160601-12414-swrscj.pdf?1464808231=&response-content-disposition=inline%3B+filename%3DEffects_of_stress_inoculation_on_the_ang.pdf&Expires=1609706793&Signature=CHsXocZCEr5X1YRtmr7EKCxEaBBLgd--BuiUBXcNiE8tLBMIyWBRVmdSF9fRpDKMK3-ShhT-CIt05e6FAGW2wLXDu9PmObt82XvdwRS-5Tqiu-S-GrWg9F2oo3oK9zNq7tXTQzWGuURL3ldRLbf0e2h-50BOzPhIRhTRAlT12PSyXw69-dD6Z04Al5sQxow6oAqJJuBdydCAFOQ0HLjkZYMiOvJDyalLuVQiuyeQ-IHVfieungp8jfOJf6AgsJg2pd4xnY0KMYFuamh35Tz1M0J4bx-hUDT4-VGD8ZpZwCV5baBsbpARAXHL-M41ADpr2O0u4Y52n1sCJo-uFTIIh4CHFQ__&Key-Pair-Id=APKAJLOHF5GGSLRBV4ZA

48 Borduin, C. M., Mann, B. J., Cone, L. T., Henggeler, S. W., Fucci, B. R., Blaske, D. M., & Williams, R. A. (1995). Multisystemic treatment of serious juvenile offenders: long-term prevention of criminality and violence. *Journal of consulting and clinical psychology, 63*(4), 569. www.umbc.edu/ereserves/pdffall19/PSYC%20671%20VENAGLIA/Multisystemic%20Treatment,%20Bourduin&Mann%20psyc671%20fa19%20Venaglia.pdf;
Henggeler, S. W., Melton, G. B., & Smith, L. A. (1992). Family preservation using multisystemic therapy: An effective alternative to incarcerating serious juvenile offenders. *Journal of consulting and clinical psychology, 60*(6), 953. https://psycnet.apa.org/fulltext/1993-15201-001.html;
Baruch, G. (2011). *Multisystemic therapy for young people with antisocial behavior*. National Institute for Health and Care Excellence. www.nice.org.uk/sharedlearning/multisystemic-therapy-for-young-people-with-antisocial-behaviour;
Mihalic, S. F., & Irwin, K. (2003). Blueprints for violence prevention: From research to real-world settings—factors influencing the successful replication of model programs. *Youth violence and juvenile justice, 1*(4), 307-329. http://citeseerx.ist.psu.edu/viewdoc/download?doi=10.1.1.218.4497&rep=rep1&type=pdf

49 Block, J. (1978). Effects of a rational–emotive mental health program on poorly achieving, disruptive high school students. *Journal of Counseling Psychology, 25*(1), 61. https://psycnet.apa.org/record/1978-32711-001

50 Brestan, E. V., & Eyberg, S. M. (1998). Effective psychosocial treatments of conduct-disordered children and adolescents: 29 years, 82 studies, and 5,272 kids. *Journal of clinical child psychology, 27*(2), 180-189. www.researchgate.net/profile/Sheila_Eyberg/publication/13636801_Effective_Psychosocial_Treatments_of_Conduct-Disordered_Children_and_Adolescents_29_Years_82_Studies_and_5272_Kids/links/5429fad70cf27e39fa8e6e31.pdf

51 Burke, J. D., Loeber, R., & Birmaher, B. (2002). Oppositional defiant disorder and conduct disorder: a review of the past 10 years, part II. *Journal of the American Academy of Child & Adolescent Psychiatry, 41*(11), 1275-1293.

https://sciences.ucf.edu/psychology/childrenslearningclinic/wp-content/uploads/sites/91/2013/08/Burke-Loeber-Birmaher-ODD-review-Part-II.pdf

52 Lambert, L. (n.d.). *Why Parents Are Silent About Mental Illness.* Child Mind Institute. https://childmind.org/article/why-parents-are-silent-about-mental-illness/

53 Long, L. (2014). *'I Am Adam Lanza's Mother': A Mom's Perspective On The Mental Illness Conversation In America.* HuffPost. www.huffpost.com/entry/i-am-adam-lanzas-mother-mental-illness-conversation_n_2311009

54 Buckwalter, I. (2012). The Impossible Question of 'We Need to Talk About Kevin': Nature or Nurture? *The Atlantic.* www.theatlantic.com/entertainment/archive/2012/01/the-impossible-question-of-we-need-to-talk-about-kevin-nature-or-nurture/251664/

55 Eaves, L., Rutter, M., Silberg, J. L., Shillady, L., Maes, H., & Pickles, A. (2000). Genetic and environmental causes of covariation in interview assessments of disruptive behavior in child and adolescent twins. *Behavior Genetics, 30*(4), 321-334. https://d1wqtxts1xzle7.cloudfront.net/45805233/a_3A102655351827220160520-21492-1cpnmie-with-cover-page-v2.pdf?Expires=1636070975&Signature=IpERqBqxW-YhEZw-rTHIfs-B085hppUhKEvt8EqE7XfxArd3wcOf-ZREhWDTSV-hedF~MiW8iSfgtfEif69S4fhG8yiDeRjDu1rKzfZA5N-LylyhABaxRGXHDG2yjrjBYOo-h6RiXdfLRhGPVEAWiOIM8QxtqjL0DECOmBfgTrzL7agy~udRDzngm-6N7UZSOlWMZrS2GWZhqNtcrbC8IbSkYxWGjVI~9qRTBXJsYxhvFxstJEF3W4Q2zyulB8WiquXTE-O7RLN7X35LtyQf7GbXypl8BUVOsyjgPq-tXa29nCHiJO6K6CbUNYW1KDPrI6SH0fgxR-avQgp8e9A~8X-UfEw__&Key-Pair-Id=APKAJLOHF5GGSLRBV4ZA;
Salvatore, J. E., & Dick, D. M. (2018). Genetic influences on conduct disorder. *Neuroscience & Biobehavioral Reviews, 91*, 91-101. www.ncbi.nlm.nih.gov/pmc/articles/PMC5183514/

56 Lambert, L. (n.d.). *Why Parents Are Silent About Mental Illness.* Child Mind Institute. https://childmind.org/article/why-parents-are-silent-about-mental-illness/

57 O'Malley, K. (2018). Kate Moss Regrets Mantra 'Nothing Tastes As Good As Skinny Feels' Nine Years Later. *Elle.* www.elle.com/uk/life-and-culture/culture/a23113786/kate-moss-regrets-mantra-nothing-tastes-as-good-as-skinny-feels/

58 Alleyne, R. (2008). Kate Moss: Supermodel lifestyle made me too skinny. *The Telegraph.* www.telegraph.co.uk/news/celebritynews/2637438/Kate-Moss-Supermodel-lifestyle-made-me-too-skinny.html

59 Kate Moss On Her "Years Of Crying" Over Johnny Depp—And How She's Still A Total "Hell-Raiser" Behind Closed Doors. (2012). *Vanity Fair.* www.vanityfair.com/news/2012/10/kate-moss-years-of-crying-johnny-depp

60 Turner, S. L., Hamilton, H., Jacobs, M., Angood, L. M., & Dwyer, D. H. (1997). The influence of fashion magazines on the body image satisfaction of college women: An exploratory analysis. *Adolescence, 32*(127), 603-614. http://docshare01.docshare.tips/files/22880/228800868.pdf;
Durkin, S. J., & Paxton, S. J. (2002). Predictors of vulnerability to reduced body image satisfaction and psychological wellbeing in response to exposure to idealized female media images in adolescent girls. *Journal of psychosomatic research, 53*(5), 995-1005. www.jpsychores.com/article/S0022-3999(02)00489-0/abstract;
Stice, E., & Shaw, H. E. (1994). Adverse effects of the media portrayed thin-ideal on women and linkages to bulimic symptomatology. *Journal of social and clinical psychology, 13*(3), 288-308. http://guilfordjournals.com/doi/abs/10.1521/jscp.1994.13.3.288;
Monro, F., & Huon, G. (2005). Media-portrayed idealized images, body shame, and appearance anxiety. *International Journal of Eating Disorders, 38*(1), 85-90. http://citeseerx.ist.psu.edu/viewdoc/download?doi=10.1.1.912.7721&rep=rep1&type=pdf;
Hargreaves, D. A., & Tiggemann, M. (2004). Idealized media images and adolescent body image:"Comparing" boys and girls. *Body image, 1*(4), 351-361. www.sciencedirect.com/science/article/abs/pii/S1740144504000695;
Groesz, L. M., Levine, M. P., & Murnen, S. K. (2002). The effect of experimental presentation of thin media images on body satisfaction: A meta-analytic review. *International Journal of eating disorders, 31*(1), 1-16. http://athena.uwindsor.ca/users/j/jarry/main.nsf/032ecd0df8f83bdf8525699900571a93/aa9ed943e56182b-f85256abe005bc3f6/$FILE/Groesz%20et%20al%20(2002).pdf;
Mills, J. S., Polivy, J., Herman, C. P., & Tiggemann, M. (2002). Effects of exposure to thin media images: Evidence of self-enhancement among restrained eaters. *Personality and Social Psychology Bulletin, 28*(12), 1687-1699. http://web4.uwindsor.ca/users/j/jarry/main.nsf/032ecd0df8f83bdf8525699900571a93/aa9ed943e56182b-f85256abe005bc3f6/$FILE/Mills%20et%20al%20(2002).pdf
Hawkins, N., Richards, P. S., Granley, H. M., & Stein, D. M. (2004). The impact of exposure to the thin-ideal media image on women. *Eating disorders, 12*(1), 35-50. www.tandfonline.com/doi/abs/10.1080/10640260490267751

61 Holland, G., & Tiggemann, M. (2016). A systematic review of the impact of the use of social networking sites on body image and disordered eating outcomes. *Body image, 17*, 100-110. www.researchgate.net/profile/Grace_Holland/publication/298794212_A_systematic_review_of_the_impact_of_the_use_of_social_network-

ing_sites_on_body_image_and_disordered_eating_outcomes/links/59f2994b458515bfd081d9cd/A-systematic-review-of-the-impact-of-the-use-of-social-networking-sites-on-body-image-and-disordered-eating-outcomes.pdf

62 Footnote reference: [1] Jenkinson, A. (2020). *Why We Eat (too Much): The New Science of Appetite.* Penguin UK.

63 Becker, A. E., Burwell, R. A., Herzog, D. B., Hamburg, P., & Gilman, S. E. (2002). Eating behaviours and attitudes following prolonged exposure to television among ethnic Fijian adolescent girls. *The British Journal of Psychiatry, 180*(6), 509-514. www.cambridge.org/core/journals/the-british-journal-of-psychiatry/article/eating-behaviours-and-attitudes-following-prolonged-exposure-to-television-among-ethnic-fijian-adolescent-girls/44470008998A2B5155CE9C9691243D76/core-reader

64 Becker, A. E. (2004). Television, disordered eating, and young women in Fiji: Negotiating body image and identity during rapid social change. *Culture, Medicine and Psychiatry, 28*(4), 533-559. www.asu.edu/lib/tutorials/empirical/narrative.pdf

65 Piper, T. (2006). *Dove Evolution* [Video]. YouTube. www.youtube.com/watch?v=iYhCn0jf46U

66 Halliwell, E., Easun, A., & Harcourt, D. (2011). Body dissatisfaction: Can a short media literacy message reduce negative media exposure effects amongst adolescent girls?. *British Journal of Health Psychology, 16*(2), 396-403. https://pdfs.semanticscholar.org/34ba/a159a69aeeeae80ad60e3320a533203bcd76.pdf

67 Yamamiya, Y., Cash, T. F., Melnyk, S. E., Posavac, H. D., & Posavac, S. S. (2005). Women's exposure to thin-and-beautiful media images: Body image effects of media-ideal internalization and impact-reduction interventions. *Body image, 2*(1), 74-80. https://s3.amazonaws.com/academia.edu.documents/34388627/00463 52261161ed46f000000.pdf?AWSAccessKeyId=AKIAIWOWYYGZ2Y53UL3A&Expires=1526058197&Signature=zFssOsZoasKofbfTBcf0GUpp8IU%3D&response-content-disposition=inline%3B%20filename%3DBrief_research_report_Womens_exposure_to.pdf;
Irving, L. M., DuPen, J., & Berel, S. (1998). A media literacy program for high school females. *Eating Disorders, 6*(2), 119-131. http://psycnet.apa.org/record/1998-04841-003;
Stice, E., Shaw, H., Burton, E., & Wade, E. (2006). Dissonance and healthy weight eating disorder prevention programs: a randomized efficacy trial. *Journal of consulting and clinical psychology, 74*(2), 263. www.ncbi.nlm.nih.gov/pmc/articles/PMC1479305/

68 Holmstrom, A. J. (2004). The effects of the media on body image: A meta-analysis. *Journal of Broadcasting & Electronic Media, 48*(2), 196-217. www.tandfonline.com/doi/abs/10.1207/s15506878jobem4802_3

69 Smink, F. R., Van Hoeken, D., & Hoek, H. W. (2012). Epidemiology of eating disorders: incidence, prevalence and mortality rates. *Current psychiatry reports, 14*(4), 406-414. https://link.springer.com/article/10.1007/s11920-012-0282-y

70 Sundgot-Borgen, J., & Torstveit, M. K. (2004). Prevalence of eating disorders in elite athletes is higher than in the general population. *Clinical journal of sport medicine, 14*(1), 25-32. https://s3.amazonaws.com/academia.edu.documents/42344169/Prevalence_of_Eating_Disorders_in_Elite_20160207-30451-v8y1ii.pdf?response-content-disposition=inline%3B%20filename%3DPrevalence_of_Eating_Disorders_in_Elite.pdf&X-Amz-Algorithm=AWS4-HMAC-SHA256&X-Amz-Credential=AKIAIWOWYYGZ2Y53UL3A%2F20200220%2Fus-east-1%2Fs3%2Faws4_request&X-Amz-Date=20200220T13233 2Z&X-Amz-Expires=3600&X-Amz-SignedHeaders=host&X-Amz-Signature=4662f44249dd64cce2f-b66814c0d5e42838f0762aa77413085c66dbcf33c8ba6;
Smolak, L., Murnen, S. K., & Ruble, A. E. (2000). Female athletes and eating problems: A meta-analysis. *International journal of eating disorders, 27*(4), 371-380. https://onlinelibrary.wiley.com/doi/abs/10.1002/(SICI)1098-108X(200005)27:4%3C371::AID-EAT1%3E3.0.CO;2-Y

71 Eddy, K. T., Tabri, N., Thomas, J. J., Murray, H. B., Keshaviah, A., Hastings, E., ... & Franko, D. L. (2017). Recovery From Anorexia Nervosa and Bulimia Nervosa at 22-Year Follow-Up. *The Journal of clinical psychiatry, 78*(2), 184-189. http://europepmc.org/abstract/med/28002660

72 Swanson, S. A., Crow, S. J., Le Grange, D., Swendsen, J., & Merikangas, K. R. (2011). Prevalence and correlates of eating disorders in adolescents: Results from the national comorbidity survey replication adolescent supplement. *Archives of general psychiatry, 68*(7), 714-723. file:///C:/Users/01DPH/Downloads/yoa15009_714_723.pdf

73 Hofmann, S. G., Asnaani, A., Vonk, I. J., Sawyer, A. T., & Fang, A. (2012). The efficacy of cognitive behavioral therapy: A review of meta-analyses. *Cognitive therapy and research, 36*(5), 427-440. www.ncbi.nlm.nih.gov/pmc/articles/PMC3584580/?_escaped_fragment_=po

74 *Eating Disorders.* (2016). National Institute of Mental Health. www.nimh.nih.gov/health/topics/eating-disorders/index.shtml;

Costa, M. B., & Melnik, T. (2016). Effectiveness of psychosocial interventions in eating disorders: an overview of Cochrane systematic reviews. *Einstein (Sao Paulo), 14*(2), 235-277. www.scielo.br/scielo.php?pid=S1679-45082016000200020&script=sci_arttext;
Linardon, J., Wade, T. D., De la Piedad Garcia, X., & Brennan, L. (2017). The efficacy of cognitive-behavioral therapy for eating disorders: A systematic review and meta-analysis. *Journal of consulting and clinical psychology, 85*(11), 1080. https://psycnet.apa.org/record/2017-48283-005;
*Eating disorders: recognition and treatment.* (2020). National Institute for Health and Care Excellence. www.nice.org.uk/guidance/ng69/resources/eating-disorders-recognition-and-treatment-pdf-1837582159813

75 Vandereycken, W. (2011). Can eating disorders become 'contagious' in group therapy and specialized inpatient care?. *European Eating Disorders Review, 19*(4), 289-295. https://onlinelibrary.wiley.com/doi/abs/10.1002/erv.1087;
Paxton, S. J., Schutz, H. K., Wertheim, E. H., & Muir, S. L. (1999). Friendship clique and peer influences on body image concerns, dietary restraint, extreme weight-loss behaviors, and binge eating in adolescent girls. *Journal of abnormal psychology, 108*(2), 255. https://psycnet.apa.org/record/1999-13982-007;
Dishion, T. J., & Tipsord, J. M. (2011). Peer contagion in child and adolescent social and emotional development. *Annual review of psychology, 62.* www.ncbi.nlm.nih.gov/pmc/articles/PMC3523739/

76 *The Panorama Interview* [Video]. (1995). BBC1. www.bbc.co.uk/news/special/politics97/diana/panorama.html

77 Ellsberg, M. (2011). How I Overcame Bipolar II (And Saved My Own Life). *Forbes.* www.forbes.com/sites/michaelellsberg/2011/07/18/how-i-overcame-bipolar-ii/

78 Kessler, R. C., Berglund, P., Demler, O., Jin, R., Merikangas, K. R., & Walters, E. E. (2005). Lifetime prevalence and age-of-onset distributions of DSM-IV disorders in the National Comorbidity Survey Replication. *Archives of general psychiatry, 62*(6), 593-602. https://jamanetwork.com/journals/jamapsychiatry/articlepdf/208678/yoa40305.pdf;
National Institute of Mental Health. (2020). *Bipolar Disorder.* www.nimh.nih.gov/health/topics/bipolar-disorder/index.shtml

79 Footnote reference: [1] Kowatch, R. A., Fristad, M., Birmaher, B., Wagner, K. D., Findling, R. L., & Hellander, M. (2005). Treatment guidelines for children and adolescents with bipolar disorder. *Journal of the American Academy of Child & Adolescent Psychiatry, 44*(3), 213-235. www.dbsalliance.org/pdfs/BMPN/treatment_guidelines.pdf

80 Kowatch, R. A., Fristad, M., Birmaher, B., Wagner, K. D., Findling, R. L., & Hellander, M. (2005). Treatment guidelines for children and adolescents with bipolar disorder. *Journal of the American Academy of Child & Adolescent Psychiatry, 44*(3), 213-235. www.dbsalliance.org/pdfs/BMPN/treatment_guidelines.pdf

81 Amick, M. (2015). *Things I Wish I'd Known While Raising A Son with Bipolar Disorder.* https://bringchange2mind.org/2015/05/21/things-i-wish-id-known-while-raising-a-son-with-bipolar-disorder-by-madchen-amick/

82 Chakrabarti, R. (2013). *South Korea's schools: Long days, high results.* BBC News. www.bbc.co.uk/news/education-25187993

83 Koo, S. (2014). An Assault Upon Our Children. *The New York Times.* www.nytimes.com/2014/08/02/opinion/sunday/south-koreas-education-system-hurts-students.html

84 American Psychological Association. (2014). *Stress in America: Are teens adopting adults' stress habits.* www.apa.org/news/press/releases/stress/2013/stress-report.pdf

85 American College Health Association. (2009-2018). *American College Health Association-National College Health Assessment II: Reference Group Executive Summaries Fall 2008 – Fall 2018.* www.acha.org/documents/ncha/ACHA-NCHA_Reference_Group_ExecutiveSummary_Fall2008.pdf

86 Dadds, M. R., Spence, S. H., Holland, D. E., Barrett, P. M., & Laurens, K. R. (1997). Prevention and early intervention for anxiety disorders: a controlled trial. *Journal of Consulting and Clinical Psychology, 65*(4), 627. https://d1wqtxts1xzle7.cloudfront.net/30513237/dadds-spence-1997-prevention-and-early-intervention-for-anxiety-disorders_jconsultingclinicalpsychology.pdf?1359686191=&response-content-disposition=inline%3B+-filename%3DPrevention_and_early_intervention_for_an.pdf&Expires=1617466696&Signature=HhUR4z-R6kd7pZxiZ59fx2IYshQFWwpX0BwCNTeKh~swt~k25lLBfD~fqcsfknAzXEY3qQuw83vAf3h9o9UBhBH-6CZ1htGv85c21XJmdMnD9MZ4CPZjg-Yt0Z2rsWNT5Oa3P67~vuVjqPFsgAgeh8EhQcb3twNSba0Ul-CDaOSW0vUwpdB1P~Kan-TS9TUNs9Oqy4sD4qkRTWCbD6Ysh2R~rTbGQWQ7yqZF8jUU-5sMiW-g04w2Dz2kJmg5OBlA1dyfrcPhFSkdDqrmpSTr3Po03UhPjkrwUFUksoqcmseZUW6IHMsGwfsfNvgKkSk-tYTDa5~u6TILq~PtLa-dKHCG5sg__&Key-Pair-Id=APKAJLOHF5GGSLRBV4ZA;
Mayo-Wilson, E., & Montgomery, P. (2013). Media-delivered cognitive behavioural therapy and behavioural therapy (self-help) for anxiety disorders in adults. *Cochrane Database of Systematic Reviews,* (9). www.cochranelibrary.com/cdsr/doi/10.1002/14651858.CD005330.pub4/full;

Footnote reference: [1] Schmidt, N. B., Eggleston, A. M., Woolaway-Bickel, K., Fitzpatrick, K. K., Vasey, M. W., & Richey, J. A. (2007). Anxiety Sensitivity Amelioration Training (ASAT): A longitudinal primary prevention program targeting cognitive vulnerability. *Journal of anxiety disorders, 21*(3), 302-319.

87 Footnote reference: Khan, A., Lee, E. Y., & Horwood, S. (2022). Adolescent screen time: associations with school stress and school satisfaction across 38 countries. *European Journal of Pediatrics*, 1-9. https://link.springer.com/article/10.1007/s00431-022-04420-z

88 Lund, T. J., & Dearing, E. (2013). Is growing up affluent risky for adolescents or is the problem growing up in an affluent neighborhood?. *Journal of Research on Adolescence, 23*(2), 274-282. https://onlinelibrary.wiley.com/doi/abs/10.1111/j.1532-7795.2012.00829.x

89 Luthar, S. S., & D'Avanzo, Karen (1999). Contextual factors in substance use: A study of suburban and inner-city adolescents. *Development and psychopathology, 11*(4), 845-867. www.ncbi.nlm.nih.gov/pmc/articles/PMC3535189/

90 American Psychological Association. (2014). *Stress in America: Are teens adopting adults' stress habits.* www.apa.org/news/press/releases/stress/2013/stress-report.pdf

91 *It's a Lot Harder to Get into a Top School Than It Used to Be.* (2018). Business Student. www.businessstudent.com/topics/college-acceptance-rates-over-time/

92 Sandel, Michael J.. *The Tyranny of Merit.* Farrar, Straus and Giroux. Kindle Edition.

93 American Psychological Association. (2014). *Stress in America: Are teens adopting adults' stress habits.* www.apa.org/news/press/releases/stress/2013/stress-report.pdf

94 McEwen, B. S. (1998). Protective and damaging effects of stress mediators. *New England journal of medicine, 338*(3), 171-179. https://pdfs.semanticscholar.org/ee3c/1a87d21b1865abe72157226e38103b0d95cf.pdf

95 American Psychological Association. (2014). *Stress in America: Are teens adopting adults' stress habits.* www.apa.org/news/press/releases/stress/2013/stress-report.pdf

96 Fredricks, J. A., & Eccles, J. S. (2006). Extracurricular involvement and adolescent adjustment: Impact of duration, number of activities, and breadth of participation. *Applied Developmental Science, 10*(3), 132-146. https://s3.amazonaws.com/academia.edu.documents/45895728/Extracurricular_Involvement_and_Adolesce20160523-6019-v7lq7l.pdf?AWSAccessKeyId=AKIAIWOWYYGZ2Y53UL3A&Expires=1526640854&Signature=WO6jokjdLJzMK7wMX9d33IyRDJ0%3D&response-content-disposition=inline%3B%20filename%3DExtracurricular_involvement_and_adolesce.pdf

97 Melman, S., Little, S. G., & Akin-Little, K. A. (2007). Adolescent overscheduling: The relationship between levels of participation in scheduled activities and self-reported clinical symptomology. *The High School Journal, 90*(3), 18-30. www.researchgate.net/profile/Steven_Little/publication/236707143_Adolescent_Overscheduling_The_Relationship_Between_Levels_of_Participation_in_Scheduled_Activities_and_Self-Reported_Clinical_Symptomology/links/549818200cf2519f5a1db9cb.pdf;
Luthar, S. S., & D'avanzo, K. (1999). Contextual factors in substance use: A study of suburban and inner-city adolescents. *Development and Psychopathology, 11*(4), 845. www.ncbi.nlm.nih.gov/pmc/articles/PMC3535189/

98 Luthar, S. S., Shoum, K. A., & Brown, P. J. (2006). Extracurricular involvement among affluent youth: A scapegoat for" ubiquitous achievement pressures"?. *Developmental Psychology, 42*(3), 583. www.ncbi.nlm.nih.gov/pmc/articles/PMC1852438/

99 Dale, S. B., & Krueger, A. B. (2002). Estimating the payoff to attending a more selective college: An application of selection on observables and unobservables. *The Quarterly Journal of Economics, 117*(4), 1491-1527. www.nber.org/papers/w7322.pdf

100 Marsh, H. W. (1987). The big-fish-little-pond effect on academic self-concept. *Journal of educational psychology, 79*(3), 280. https://files.eric.ed.gov/fulltext/ED278685.pdf

101 Marsh, H. W., Seaton, M., Trautwein, U., Lüdtke, O., Hau, K. T., O'Mara, A. J., & Craven, R. G. (2008). The big-fish–little-pond-effect stands up to critical scrutiny: Implications for theory, methodology, and future research. *Educational psychology review, 20*(3), 319-350. https://link.springer.com/article/10.1007/s10648-008-9075-6

102 Chang, M. J., Cerna, O., Han, J., & Saenz, V. (2008). The contradictory roles of institutional status in retaining underrepresented minorities in biomedical and behavioral science majors. *The Review of Higher Education, 31*(4), 433-464. www.researchgate.net/profile/Mitchell_Chang/publication/236748393_The_Contradictory_Roles_of_Institutional_Status_in_Retaining_Underrepresented_Minorities_in_Biomedical_and_Behavioral_Science_Ma-

jors/links/0046352a20b9065dc9000000/The-Contradictory-Roles-of-Institutional-Status-in-Retaining-Underrepresented-Minorities-in-Biomedical-and-Behavioral-Science-Majors.pdf

103 Elliott, R., Strenta, A. C., Adair, R., Matier, M., & Scott, J. (1996). The role of ethnicity in choosing and leaving science in highly selective institutions. *Research in Higher Education, 37*(6), 681-709. www.researchgate.net/profile/Rogers_Elliott/publication/226287438_The_Role_of_Ethnicity_in_Choosing_and_Leaving_Science_in_Highly_Selective_Institutions/links/5690052108aed0aed810cddc/The-Role-of-Ethnicity-in-Choosing-and-Leaving-Science-in-Highly-Selective-Institutions.pdf
Citing: Thurgood, D. H., & Clarke, J. E. (1995). *Doctorate recipients from United States universities: Summary report 1993.* https://files.eric.ed.gov/fulltext/ED380003.pdf

104 Conley, J. P., & Onder, A. S. (2019). *Replication data for: The Research Productivity of New PhDs in Economics: The Surprisingly High Non-success of the Successful.* www.openicpsr.org/openicpsr/project/113931/version/V1/view;jsessionid=5139C5BABF73E9F52BA504C02E9AAD52;
Conley, J. P., & Onder, A. S. (2013). *An empirical guide to hiring assistant professors in economics* (No. 13-00009). Vanderbilt University Department of Economics. https://ideas.repec.org/p/van/wpaper/vuecon-sub-13-00009.html

105 Karabel, J. (2006). *The chosen: The hidden history of admission and exclusion at Harvard, Yale, and Princeton.* Houghton Mifflin Harcourt. https://books.google.co.uk/books?hl=en&lr=&id=zwf-Ofc--toC&oi=fnd&pg=PA1&dq=The+Chosen:+The+Hidden+History+of+Admission+and+Exclusion+at+Harvard,+Yale,+and+Princeton&ots=dh-W51qmVR0&sig=v_7glCBy5yKL_Eiz3CgLh-5zI8Y&redir_esc=y#v=onepage&q=happy%20bottom&f=false

106 Davis, J. A. (1966). The campus as a frog pond: An application of the theory of relative deprivation to career decisions of college men. *American journal of Sociology, 72*(1), 17-31. http://illinois-online.org/krassa/ps410/Readings/campus%20as%20frogpond.pdf

107 Jacobs, P. (2013). *28% Of People Went To The Same College As Their Spouse.* www.businessinsider.com/28-people-marry-attended-same-college-2013-10

108 Yang, J. (2015). *Do Asian students face too much academic pressure?* CNN. https://edition.cnn.com/2015/07/02/opinions/yang-genius-girl/index.html

109 Leeb, R. T., Bitsko, R. H., Radhakrishnan, L., Martinez, P., Njai, R., & Holland, K. M. (2020). Mental Health–Related Emergency Department Visits Among Children Aged< 18 Years During the COVID-19 Pandemic—United States, January 1–October 17, 2020. *Morbidity and Mortality Weekly Report, 69*(45), 1675. www.cdc.gov/mmwr/volumes/69/wr/mm6945a3.htm

110 Damour, L. (2021). Eating Disorders in Teens Have 'Exploded' in the Pandemic. *The New York Times.* www.nytimes.com/2021/04/28/well/family/teens-eating-disorders.html?referringSource=articleShare

111 *Kids Under Pressure.* (2021). Challenge Success and NBC News. www.challengesuccess.org/wp-content/uploads/2021/02/CS-NBC-Study-Kids-Under-Pressure-PUBLISHED.pdf

112 Radez, J., Reardon, T., Creswell, C., Lawrence, P. J., Evdoka-Burton, G., & Waite, P. (2020). Why do children and adolescents (not) seek and access professional help for their mental health problems? A systematic review of quantitative and qualitative studies. *European child & adolescent psychiatry*, 1-29. https://link.springer.com/article/10.1007/s00787-019-01469-4

113 Mellor, C. (2014). School-based interventions targeting stigma of mental illness: systematic review. *The Psychiatric Bulletin, 38*(4), 164-171. www.cambridge.org/core/journals/the-psychiatric-bulletin/article/schoolbased-interventions-targeting-stigma-of-mental-illness-systematic-review/55725058F3A3789E310E4BF201982B28

114 Calhoun, A. J., & Gold, J. A. (2020). "I Feel Like I Know Them": the Positive Effect of Celebrity Self-disclosure of Mental Illness. *Academic Psychiatry, 44*(2), 237-241. https://link.springer.com/article/10.1007/s40596-020-01200-5

115 Wong, N. C., Lookadoo, K. L., & Nisbett, G. S. (2017). "I'm Demi and I have bipolar disorder": Effect of parasocial contact on reducing stigma toward people with bipolar disorder. *Communication Studies, 68*(3), 314-333. www.researchgate.net/profile/Norman-Wong-3/publication/317781280_I%27m_Demi_and_I_Have_Bipolar_Disorder_Effect_of_Parasocial_Contact_on_Reducing_Stigma_Toward_People_With_Bipolar_Disorder/links/5a871ba1a6fdcc6b1a3abfdc/Im-Demi-and-I-Have-Bipolar-Disorder-Effect-of-Parasocial-Contact-on-Reducing-Stigma-Toward-People-With-Bipolar-Disorder.pdf

116 McNamara, B. (2018). Dwayne "The Rock" Johnson Opened Up About Mental Health. *Teen Vogue.* www.teenvogue.com/story/dwayne-the-rock-johnson-opened-up-about-mental-health

117 *DiCaprio suffers from Compulsive Disorder.* Female First. www.femalefirst.co.uk/celebrity/Leonardo+DiCaprio-1662.html

118 Gevinson, T. (2014). Not A Girl, Not Yet A Woman: The Two Sides Of Miley Cyrus. *Elle*. www.elle.com/culture/celebrities/a12/miley-cyrus-may-cover-story/

119 Chung, G. (2021). Ryan Reynolds Gets Candid About His 'Lifelong' Struggle with Anxiety: 'I Know I'm Not Alone'. *People*. https://people.com/health/ryan-reynolds-gets-candid-about-lifelong-struggle-with-anxiety/

120 Malik, Z. (2016). Zayn Malik: Why I Went Public With My Anxiety Issues. *Time*. https://time.com/4551320/zayn-malik-anxiety/

121 Denicolo, D. (2016). Amanda Seyfried on Her Mental Health, Her Dog, and Those Eyes. *Allure*. www.allure.com/story/amanda-seyfried-ocd-mental-health-stigma?verso=true

122 Milzhoff, R. (2016). Billboard Women In Music 'Trailblazer' Kesha: My New Songs 'Showcase My Vulnerabilities As a Strength, Not a Weakness'. *Billboard*. www.billboard.com/articles/events/women-in-music/7597386/billboard-women-in-music-trailblazer-kesha-my-new-songs

123 Dodero, C. (2015). Billboard Cover: Lady Gaga Gets Personal About Saving Troubled Teens -- 'I've Suffered Through Depression and Anxiety My Whole Life'. *Billboard*. www.billboard.com/articles/news/magazine-feature/6730027/lady-gaga-billboard-cover-born-this-way-foundation-depression-philanthropy

124 Aldridge, D. (2018). *NBA, NBPA taking steps to further address mental wellness issues for players*. NBA. www.nba.com/news/morning-tip-nba-nbpa-addressing-mental-wellness-issues

125 Berlan, E. D., Corliss, H. L., Field, A. E., Goodman, E., & Austin, S. B. (2010). Sexual orientation and bullying among adolescents in the growing up today study. *Journal of Adolescent Health, 46*(4), 366-371. www.ncbi.nlm.nih.gov/pmc/articles/PMC2844864/

126 Kosciw, J. G., Greytak, E. A., Zongrone, A. D., Clark, C. M., & Truong, N. L. (2018). *The 2017 National School Climate Survey: The Experiences of Lesbian, Gay, Bisexual, Transgender, and Queer Youth in Our Nation's Schools. Gay, Lesbian and Straight Education Network (GLSEN).* 121 West 27th Street Suite 804, New York, NY 10001. www.glsen.org/sites/default/files/2019-10/GLSEN-2017-National-School-Climate-Survey-NSCS-Full-Report.pdf

127 Marshal, M. P., Friedman, M. S., Stall, R., King, K. M., Miles, J., Gold, M. A., ... & Morse, J. Q. (2008). Sexual orientation and adolescent substance use: a meta-analysis and methodological review. *Addiction, 103*(4), 546-556. ; Russell, S. T., & Joyner, K. (2001). Adolescent sexual orientation and suicide risk: Evidence from a national study. *American Journal of public health, 91*(8), 1276-1281. https://ajph.aphapublications.org/doi/pdfplus/10.2105/AJPH.91.8.1276;
Robles, R., Fresán, A., Vega-Ramírez, H., Cruz-Islas, J., Rodríguez-Pérez, V., Domínguez-Martínez, T., & Reed, G. M. (2016). Removing transgender identity from the classification of mental disorders: a Mexican field study for ICD-11. *The Lancet Psychiatry, 3*(9), 850-859. www.acthe.fr/upload/1469967618-tlptrans.pdf

128 Centers for Disease Control and Prevention (CDC). *National Center for Health Statistics (NCHS). National Survey of Family Growth Survey Data*. Hyattsville, MD: U.S. Department of Health and Human Services, Centers for Disease Control and Prevention, 2016-2017. www.cdc.gov/nchs/nsfg/nsfg_questionnaires.htm

129 *Transgender no longer recognised as 'disorder' by WHO*. (2019). BBC News. www.bbc.co.uk/news/health-48448804

130 *WMA Statement on Transgender People*. (2015). World Medical Assocation. www.wma.net/policies-post/wma-statement-on-transgender-people/

131 Kaltiala-Heino, R., & Lindberg, N. (2019). Gender identities in adolescent population: methodological issues and prevalence across age groups. *European Psychiatry, 55*, 61-66. https://helda.helsinki.fi/bitstream/handle/10138/308992/1_s2.0_S0924933818301767_main.pdf?sequence=1&isAllowed=y

132 Footnote references: [1] Flores, A. R., Herman, J. L., Gates, G. J., & Brown, T. N. T. (2017). *How Many Adults Identify as Transgender in the United States?* The Williams Institute. https://williamsinstitute.law.ucla.edu/wp-content/uploads/Trans-Adults-US-Aug-2016.pdf
[2] Zucker, K. J. (2017). Epidemiology of gender dysphoria and transgender identity. *Sexual health, 14*(5), 404-411. www.researchgate.net/profile/Kenneth_Zucker3/publication/319301507_Epidemiology_of_gender_dysphoria_and_transgender_identity/links/59c64210a6fdccc7191ea1a1/Epidemiology-of-gender-dysphoria-and-transgender-identity.pdf

133 Beach, R. K., Boulter, S., Felice, M. E., Gotlieb, E. M., Greydanus, D. E., Hoyle, J. C., ... & Leavitt, S. (1993). Homosexuality and adolescence. *Pediatrics, 92*(4), 631-634. https://pediatrics.aappublications.org/content/pediatrics/92/4/631.full.pdf

134 *Position Statement on Conversion Therapy and LGBTQ Patients.* (2018). American Psychiatric Association. www.psychiatry.org/File%20Library/About-APA/Organization-Documents-Policies/Policies/Position-Conversion-Therapy.pdf

135 Coolidge, F. L., Thede, L. L., & Young, S. E. (2002). The heritability of gender identity disorder in a child and adolescent twin sample. *Behavior genetics, 32*(4), 251-257. www.coolidgetests.org/content/CPNI/Coolidge%20et%20al%202002-Heritability%20of%20gender%20identity%20disorder.pdf

136 Power, R. A., & Pluess, M. (2015). Heritability estimates of the Big Five personality traits based on common genetic variants. *Translational psychiatry, 5*(7), e604-e604. www.nature.com/articles/tp201596

137 Hidalgo, M. A., Ehrensaft, D., Tishelman, A. C., Clark, L. F., Garofalo, R., Rosenthal, S. M., ... & Olson, J. (2013). The gender affirmative model: What we know and what we aim to learn. *Human Development, 56*(5), 285-290. www.karger.com/Article/FullText/355235

138 Rothman, E. F., Sullivan, M., Keyes, S., & Boehmer, U. (2012). Parents' supportive reactions to sexual orientation disclosure associated with better health: Results from a population-based survey of LGB adults in Massachusetts. *Journal of homosexuality, 59*(2), 186-200. www.ncbi.nlm.nih.gov/pmc/articles/PMC3313451/;
Ryan, C., Russell, S. T., Huebner, D., Diaz, R., & Sanchez, J. (2010). Family acceptance in adolescence and the health of LGBT young adults. *Journal of Child and Adolescent Psychiatric Nursing, 23*(4), 205-213. https://onlinelibrary.wiley.com/doi/full/10.1111/j.1744-6171.2010.00246.x

139 Ryan, C., Huebner, D., Diaz, R. M., & Sanchez, J. (2009). Family rejection as a predictor of negative health outcomes in white and Latino lesbian, gay, and bisexual young adults. *Pediatrics, 123*(1), 346-352. https://europepmc.org/article/med/19117902

140 Hidalgo, M. A., Ehrensaft, D., Tishelman, A. C., Clark, L. F., Garofalo, R., Rosenthal, S. M., ... & Olson, J. (2013). The gender affirmative model: What we know and what we aim to learn. *Human Development, 56*(5), 285-290. www.karger.com/Article/FullText/355235

141 Hidalgo, M. A., Ehrensaft, D., Tishelman, A. C., Clark, L. F., Garofalo, R., Rosenthal, S. M., ... & Olson, J. (2013). The gender affirmative model: What we know and what we aim to learn. *Human Development, 56*(5), 285-290. www.karger.com/Article/FullText/355235
Citing: Travers, R., Bauer, G., & Pyne, J. (2012). *Impacts of strong parental support for trans youth: A report prepared for Children's Aid Society of Toronto and Delisle Youth Services.* Trans Pulse.

142 Footnote reference: World Professional Association for Transgender Health. (2012). *Standards of Care for the Health of Transsexual, Transgender, and Gender-Conforming People [7th Version].* www.wpath.org/publications/soc

143 *National Coming Out Day Youth Report.* (2012). Human Rights Campaign. https://assets2.hrc.org/files/assets/resources/NCOD-Youth-Report.pdf?_ga=2.248968069.32347066.1609690063-1712924112.1609690063

144 Rosales, C. (2020). *Coming out to their parents is fraught with danger for LGBTQ+ teens.* The Mercury News. www.mercurynews.com/2020/07/03/coming-out-to-their-parents-is-fraught-with-danger-for-lgbtq-teens/

145 Icons: The Finalists. (2019). BBC Two. www.bbc.co.uk/programmes/articles/3Tk2LpLg755Js0LQF7t3TQ2/the-finalists

146 Pylas, P. (2021). *WWII codebreaker Turing honored on UK's new 50-pound note.* Associated Press. https://apnews.com/article/alan-turing-50-pound-bank-note-uk-codebreaker-d965076529b70fc8dbb020d364d88176

147 Royal pardon for codebreaker Alan Turing. (2013). BBC News. www.bbc.com/news/technology-25495315

## 6. Delinquency

1 Sutton, J. R. (1981). Stubborn children: Law and the socialization of deviance in the puritan colonies. *Family Law Quarterly*, 31-64. www.jstor.org/stable/25739276?seq=1

2 *Teen arrested for 'driving like an idiot' and hitting 4 cars.* (2014). NY Daily News. www.nydailynews.com/news/crime/teen-arrested-driving-idiot-video-article-1.1782653

3 Nathanson, M. (2019). *Teen who threw rock off highway overpass, killing man, sentenced to 3-20 years.* https://abcnews.go.com/US/teen-threw-rock-off-highway-overpass-killing-man/story?id=66631347

4 Gingras, B. (2014). *60 Teens Arrested After Senior Pranksters Break Into New Jersey School, Urinate in Hallways.* NBC New York. www.nbcnewyork.com/news/local/Teaneck-High-School-New-Jersey-Senior-Prank-Arrests-Police--257461121.html

5 Parker-Pope, T. (2010). Stupid Teenage Tricks, for a Virtual Audience. *The New York Times.* https://well.blogs.nytimes.com/2010/06/14/teens-take-high-risks-for-a-virtual-audience/?ref=health

6 Centers for Disease Control and Prevention. (2019). *Youth Risk Behavior Survey Data* [Data set]. www.cdc.gov/healthyyouth/data/yrbs/results.htm

7 National Cyber Security Alliance. (n.d.). *Keeping Up With Generation App 2017: NCSA Parent/Teen Online Safety Survey.* www.google.com/url?sa=t&rct=j&q=&esrc=s&source=web&cd=6&ved=2ahUKEwipgP2X9ujgAhWJSBUIHaHYAqUQFjAFegQIAxAC&url=https%3A%2F%2Fwww.stopthinkconnect.org%2Fdownload%2Fdatasets%2F4892%2FFast_Facts_Keeping_Up_With_Generation_App_NCSA_Parent_Teen_Online_Safety_Survey.pdf&usg=AOvVaw3fk1_aAAv6KvguOyRITDVH

8 Young, T. L., & Zimmerman, R. (1998). Clueless: parental knowledge of risk behaviors of middle school students. *Archives of pediatrics & adolescent medicine, 152*(11), 1137-1139. https://jamanetwork.com/journals/jamapediatrics/fullarticle/190069

9 Luthar, S. S., & Sexton, C. C. (2004). The high price of affluence. In *Advances in child development and behavior* (Vol. 32, pp. 125-162). JAI. www.ncbi.nlm.nih.gov/pmc/articles/PMC4358932/

10 Jonsson, P. (2001). A new vandal hits US streets: the bored, rich teen. *Christian Science Monitor, 93*(240), 1. www.csmonitor.com/2001/1106/p1s4-ussc.html

11 Handoll, H. H., Rowe, B. H., Quinn, K. M., & de Bie, R. (2001). Interventions for preventing ankle ligament injuries. *Cochrane Database of Systematic Reviews,* (3). www.cochranelibrary.com/cdsr/doi/10.1002/14651858.CD000018/pdf/CDSR/CD000018/rel0001/CD000018/CD000018.pdf

12 Wedderkopp, N., Kaltoft, M., Lundgaard, B., Rosendahl, M., & Froberg, K. (1999). Prevention of injuries in young female players in European team handball. A prospective intervention study. *Scandinavian journal of medicine & science in sports, 9*(1), 41-47. https://onlinelibrary.wiley.com/doi/abs/10.1111/j.1600-0838.1999.tb00205.x

13 Levitt, S. D., & Lochner, L. (2001). The determinants of juvenile crime. In *Risky behavior among youths: An economic analysis* (pp. 327-374). University of Chicago Press. www.nber.org/chapters/c10692.pdf

14 Livingstone, S., Haddon, L., Görzig, A., & Ólafsson, K. (2011). *Risks and safety on the internet: the perspective of European children: full findings and policy implications from the EU Kids Online survey of 9-16 year olds and their parents in 25 countries.* http://eprints.lse.ac.uk/33731/1/Risks%20and%20safety%20on%20the%20internet(lsero).pdf

15 Steinberg, L. (2008). A social neuroscience perspective on adolescent risk-taking. *Developmental review, 28*(1), 78-106. www.ncbi.nlm.nih.gov/pmc/articles/PMC2396566/

16 Walker, Matthew. *Why We Sleep: Unlocking the Power of Sleep and Dreams* (p. 93). Scribner. Kindle Edition.

17 Holy Bible, New International Version®, Deuteronomy 21:18-21. BibleGateway. www.biblegateway.com/passage/?search=Deuteronomy%2021%3A18-21&version=NIV

18 Schlegel, A., & Barry Iii, H. (1991). *Adolescence: An anthropological inquiry.* Free Press (New York). https://repository.arizona.edu/bitstream/handle/10150/636966/adolescence_anthropological_inquiry.pdf?sequence=1

19 Allen, Joseph. *Escaping the Endless Adolescence: How we can help our teenagers grow up before they grow old.* Random House Publishing Group. Kindle Edition. https://books.google.co.uk/books?hl=en&lr=&id=myEHFTWAmjwC&oi=fnd&pg=PR9&dq=Escaping+the+Endless+Adolescence&ots=8yCPQ5RSm7&sig=Zg52iGB3ugS5gz0mW19DUdLsUiA&redir_esc=y#v=onepage&q=Escaping%20the%20Endless%20Adolescence&f=false

20 Steinberg, L. (2007). Risk taking in adolescence: New perspectives from brain and behavioral science. *Current directions in psychological science, 16*(2), 55-59. pdf http://citeseerx.ist.psu.edu/viewdoc/download?doi=10.1.1.519.7099&rep=rep1&type=pdf

21 Eckert-Lind, C., Busch, A. S., Petersen, J. H., Biro, F. M., Butler, G., Bräuner, E. V., & Juul, A. (2020). Worldwide secular trends in age at pubertal onset assessed by breast development among girls: a systematic review and

meta-analysis. *Jama Pediatrics, 174*(4), e195881-e195881. https://jamanetwork.com/journals/jamapediatrics/article-abstract/2760573

22 Cesario, S. K., & Hughes, L. A. (2007). Precocious puberty: a comprehensive review of literature. *Journal of Obstetric, Gynecologic & Neonatal Nursing, 36*(3), 263-274. https://d1wqtxts1xzle7.cloudfront.net/46769422/j.1552-6909.2007.00145.x20160624-4266-19stx3m.pdf?1466813031=&response-content-disposition=inline%3B+filename%3DPrecocious_Puberty_A_Comprehensive_Revie.pdf&Expires=1609023982&Signature=H-FIYpo487g3eQuoVl2jpRgWN8hGkFYjEz3PX84ZInGeoKaYElhnseZDRNLuorMLr-ekw6sjNNhSQhR7P-kl8B-LakUaczrAnH1NKmLQcmaCIfKtVFm1Ml3mj90wc3sGy55UAMowYSPW9YBtpgsx5je-hdDNZ-tEwa-9iggZ9YNNlwNho9yNg5Kce5f36fq-QoUUslh2iDOBeU6y7--yqfk6V5w-EqIZu3nIwrBmVG8tynnK-cqzhdm57mQvAWc4JYgNdtYNR-hH7ur0ROEFudhsJfnxRwxvIfoIMO0F5oY70knfH4f6FDr6PODrXfK-m9d-2SCEMpTSTEukRFtAS9uZZwg__&Key-Pair-Id=APKAJLOHF5GGSLRBV4ZA

23 Steinberg, L. (2007). Risk taking in adolescence: New perspectives from brain and behavioral science. *Current directions in psychological science, 16*(2), 55-59. pdf http://citeseerx.ist.psu.edu/viewdoc/download?doi=10.1.1.519.7099&rep=rep1&type=pdf;
Steinberg, L. (2008). A social neuroscience perspective on adolescent risk-taking. *Developmental review, 28*(1), 78-106. www.ncbi.nlm.nih.gov/pmc/articles/PMC2396566/;
Footnote reference: [1] Steinberg, L., Icenogle, G., Shulman, E. P., Breiner, K., Chein, J., Bacchini, D., ... & Fanti, K. A. (2018). Around the world, adolescence is a time of heightened sensation seeking and immature self-regulation. *Developmental science, 21*(2), e12532. https://dukespace.lib.duke.edu/dspace/bitstream/handle/10161/15833/Around%20the%20world%2C%20adolescence%20is%20a%20time%20of%20heightened%20sensation%20seeking%20and%20immature%20self-regulation.pdf?sequence=1

24 Steinberg, L. (2007). Risk taking in adolescence: New perspectives from brain and behavioral science. *Current directions in psychological science, 16*(2), 55-59. pdf http://citeseerx.ist.psu.edu/viewdoc/download?doi=10.1.1.519.7099&rep=rep1&type=pdf

25 Steinberg, L., Albert, D., Cauffman, E., Banich, M., Graham, S., & Woolard, J. (2008). Age differences in sensation seeking and impulsivity as indexed by behavior and self-report: evidence for a dual systems model. *Developmental psychology, 44*(6), 1764. www.researchgate.net/profile/Dustin_Albert/publication/23463848_Age_Differences_in_Sensation_Seeking_and_Impulsivity_as_Indexed_by_Behavior_and_Self-Report_Evidence_for_a_Dual_Systems_Model/links/0f3175374e17714bb9000000.pdf;
Steinberg, L., Icenogle, G., Shulman, E. P., Breiner, K., Chein, J., Bacchini, D., ... & Fanti, K. A. (2018). Around the world, adolescence is a time of heightened sensation seeking and immature self-regulation. *Developmental science, 21*(2), e12532. https://dukespace.lib.duke.edu/dspace/bitstream/handle/10161/15833/Around%20the%20world%2C%20adolescence%20is%20a%20time%20of%20heightened%20sensation%20seeking%20and%20immature%20self-regulation.pdf?sequence=1

26 Steinberg, L. (2007). Risk taking in adolescence: New perspectives from brain and behavioral science. *Current directions in psychological science, 16*(2), 55-59. http://citeseerx.ist.psu.edu/viewdoc/download?doi=10.1.1.519.7099&rep=rep1&type=pdf

27 Cauffman, E., Shulman, E. P., Steinberg, L., Claus, E., Banich, M. T., Graham, S., & Woolard, J. (2010). Age differences in affective decision making as indexed by performance on the Iowa Gambling Task. *Developmental psychology, 46*(1), 193. https://pdfs.semanticscholar.org/0dd9/e1fd8e91b8abb90c88af1126cac33e217f8f.pdf

28 Reyna, V. F., & Farley, F. (2006). Risk and rationality in adolescent decision making: Implications for theory, practice, and public policy. *Psychological science in the public interest, 7*(1), 1-44. https://pdfs.semanticscholar.org/1de4/966482722d1f7da8bbef16d108639d9a1c38.pdf

29 Reyna, V. F., & Farley, F. (2006). Risk and rationality in adolescent decision making: Implications for theory, practice, and public policy. *Psychological science in the public interest, 7*(1), 1-44. https://pdfs.semanticscholar.org/1de4/966482722d1f7da8bbef16d108639d9a1c38.pdf

30 Steinberg, L. (2008). A social neuroscience perspective on adolescent risk-taking. *Developmental review, 28*(1), 78-106. www.ncbi.nlm.nih.gov/pmc/articles/PMC2396566/

31 Duncan, J. (2016). *Reckless teenagers risk their lives by lying down on railway tracks and letting a train run over them.* The Daily Mail Online. www.dailymail.co.uk/news/article-3927218/Reckless-teenagers-risk-lives-lying-railway-tracks-letting-train-run-them.html

32 Dobson, R. (2015). The truth behind the biggest liars, adolescents. *Independent.* www.independent.co.uk/news/science/the-truth-behind-the-biggest-liars-adolescents-10432818.html

33 Chilcoat, H. D., & Anthony, J. C. (1996). Impact of parent monitoring on initiation of drug use through late childhood. *Journal of the American Academy of Child & Adolescent Psychiatry, 35*(1), 91-100. www.jaacap.com/article/S0890-8567(09)63409-2/abstract;
Steinberg, L., Fletcher, A., & Darling, N. (1994). Parental monitoring and peer influences on adolescent substance use. *Pediatrics, 93*(6), 1060-1064. http://pediatrics.aappublications.org/content/93/6/1060.short;
DiClemente, R. J., Wingood, G. M., Crosby, R., Sionean, C., Cobb, B. K., Harrington, K., ... & Oh, M. K. (2001). Parental monitoring: Association with adolescents' risk behaviors. *Pediatrics, 107*(6), 1363-1368. www.teappoyo.com/bibliografia/DiClemente,%20R.%20J.,%20Wingood,%20G.%20M.,%20Crosby,%20R.,%20Sionean,%20C.,%20Cobb,%20B.%20K.,%20Harrington,%20K.,%20&%20...%20Oh,%20M.%20K.%20(2001)..pdf;
Rai, A. A., Stanton, B., Wu, Y., Li, X., Galbraith, J., Cottrell, L., ... & Burns, J. (2003). Relative influences of perceived parental monitoring and perceived peer involvement on adolescent risk behaviors: An analysis of six cross-sectional data sets. *Journal of Adolescent Health, 33*(2), 108-118. www.math.wvu.edu/~ywu/Paper_pdf/Alia%20-%202003%20JAH%20%20six%20datasets.pdf;
Baker, J. G., Rosenthal, S. L., Leonhardt, D., Kollar, L. M., Succop, P. A., Burklow, K. A., & Biro, F. M. (1999). Relationship between perceived parental monitoring and young adolescent girls' sexual and substance use behaviors. *Journal of pediatric and adolescent gynecology, 12*(1), 17-22. www.sciencedirect.com/science/article/pii/S1083318800866152

34 Brown, B. B., Mounts, N., Lamborn, S. D., & Steinberg, L. (1993). Parenting practices and peer group affiliation in adolescence. *Child development, 64*(2), 467-482. https://website.education.wisc.edu/prsg/wp-content/uploads/2014/07/Brown-et-al-1993-Par-prac-PG-affil.pdf;
Crouter, A. C., MacDermid, S. M., McHale, S. M., & Perry-Jenkins, M. (1990). Parental monitoring and perceptions of children's school performance and conduct in dual-and single-earner families. *Developmental psychology, 26*(4), 649. http://psycnet.apa.org/buy/1990-29529-001

35 Romer, D., Stanton, B., Galbraith, J., Feigelman, S., Black, M. M., & Li, X. (1999). Parental influence on adolescent sexual behavior in high-poverty settings. *Archives of pediatrics & adolescent medicine, 153*(10), 1055-1062. https://jamanetwork.com/journals/jamapediatrics/fullarticle/347936;
Metzler, C. W., Noell, J., Biglan, A., Ary, D., & Smolkowski, K. (1994). The social context for risky sexual behavior among adolescents. *Journal of behavioral medicine, 17*(4), 419-438. https://link.springer.com/article/10.1007/BF01858012;
DiClemente, R. J., Wingood, G. M., Crosby, R., Sionean, C., Cobb, B. K., Harrington, K., ... & Oh, M. K. (2001). Parental monitoring: Association with adolescents' risk behaviors. *Pediatrics, 107*(6), 1363-1368. www.teappoyo.com/bibliografia/DiClemente,%20R.%20J.,%20Wingood,%20G.%20M.,%20Crosby,%20R.,%20Sionean,%20C.,%20Cobb,%20B.%20K.,%20Harrington,%20K.,%20&%20...%20Oh,%20M.%20K.%20(2001)..pdf;
Yang, H., Stanton, B., Li, X., Cottrel, L., Galbraith, J., & Kaljee, L. (2007). Dynamic association between parental monitoring and communication and adolescent risk involvement among African-American adolescents. *Journal of the National Medical Association, 99*(5), 517. www.ncbi.nlm.nih.gov/pmc/articles/PMC2576073/pdf/jnma00204-0051.pdf;
Crosby, R. A., DiClemente, R. J., Wingood, G. M., Harrington, K., Davies, S., Hook, E. W., & Oh, M. K. (2002). Low parental monitoring predicts subsequent pregnancy among African-American adolescent females. *Journal of Pediatric and Adolescent Gynecology, 15*(1), 43-46. www.jpagonline.org/article/S1083-3188(01)00138-3/abstract

36 Patterson, G. R., & Stouthamer-Loeber, M. (1984). The correlation of family management practices and delinquency. *Child development*, 1299-1307. www.jstor.org/stable/1129999

37 Richardson, J. L., Radziszewska, B., Dent, C. W., & Flay, B. R. (1993). Relationship between after-school care of adolescents and substance use, risk taking, depressed mood, and academic achievement. *Pediatrics, 92*(1), 32-38. http://pediatrics.aappublications.org/content/92/1/32.short;
Li, X., Stanton, B., & Feigelman, S. (2000). Impact of perceived parental monitoring on adolescent risk behavior over 4 years. *Journal of adolescent health, 27*(1), 49-56. http://psycnet.apa.org/record/2000-08468-004;
Li, X., Feigelman, S., & Stanton, B. (2000). Perceived parental monitoring and health risk behaviors among urban low-income African-American children and adolescents. *Journal of Adolescent Health, 27*(1), 43-48. www.jahonline.org/article/S1054-139X(99)00077-4/abstract;
DiClemente, R. J., Wingood, G. M., Crosby, R., Sionean, C., Cobb, B. K., Harrington, K., ... & Oh, M. K. (2001). Parental monitoring: Association with adolescents' risk behaviors. *Pediatrics, 107*(6), 1363-1368. www.teappoyo.com/bibliografia/DiClemente,%20R.%20J.,%20Wingood,%20G.%20M.,%20Crosby,%20R.,%20Sionean,%20C.,%20Cobb,%20B.%20K.,%20Harrington,%20K.,%20&%20...%20Oh,%20M.%20K.%20(2001)..pdf

38 Coleman, J. S. (1988). Social capital in the creation of human capital. *American journal of sociology, 94*, S95-S120. www.crcresearch.org/files-crcresearch/File/coleman_88.pdf

39 Kerr, M., Stattin, H., & Burk, W. J. (2010). A reinterpretation of parental monitoring in longitudinal perspective. *Journal of Research on Adolescence, 20*(1), 39-64. www.researchgate.net/profile/Hakan_Stattin/publication/229794935_A_Reinterpretation_of_Parental_Monitoring_in_Longitudinal_Perspective/links/5451ed8c0cf2bf864cbaaaf6.pdf

40 Dishion, T. J., Nelson, S. E., & Kavanagh, K. (2003). The family check-up with high-risk young adolescents: Preventing early-onset substance use by parent monitoring. *Behavior Therapy, 34*(4), 553-571. https://d1wqtxts1xzle7.cloudfront.net/64171657/s0005-7894_2803_2980035-720200813-16347-159qsqu.pdf?1597326655=&response-content-disposition=inline%3B+filename%3DThe_family_check_up_with_high_risk_young.pdf&Expires=1617556868&Signature=Ox-5gAr95htYYCHdWlqccuMjCBmjcfNETr80QBH7kMGIR3Jhx77PU~F7JKyfsve5GQ40BlZF4mp8Wtly5bBNK-ihx-qaEB3PscB0xWLOp-Pw1GUEvxT3Ou1HnZybAFdBLb-lExG74kjvo6yDU61J~~uH~ztYnBlDs5-kwhEneSN-Mms-AgHI0NBkLAXdZyTVbELn7cLlasEG1JzVT7mZ~c0n4xKCri--MU8J-qorfJUURKflscD9RSq7ioeHMwMx3nX-h7BNNoSiDZ9~4B0Tk37iHBcmOFMDqBHvmSFmFOEM9zulpPAjnGSxXGWOxKANp12V56oq~3WGLUyy-HLmPzGbYBg__&Key-Pair-Id=APKAJLOHF5GGSLRBV4ZA

41 Stanton, B. F., Li, X., Galbraith, J., Cornick, G., Feigelman, S., Kaljee, L., & Zhou, Y. (2000). Parental underestimates of adolescent risk behavior: A randomized, controlled trial of a parental monitoring intervention. *Journal of adolescent health, 26*(1), 18-26. www.jahonline.org/article/S1054-139X(99)00022-1/fulltext

42 Anderson, M. (2016). *Parents, teens and digital monitoring*. Pew Research Center: Internet, Science & Tech. www.pewresearch.org/internet/2016/01/07/parents-teens-and-digital-monitoring/

43 Knorr, C. (2021). *Parents' Ultimate Guide to Parental Controls*. Common Sense Media. www.commonsensemedia.org/blog/parents-ultimate-guide-to-parental-controls

44 Michael, K., McNamee, A., & Michael, M. G. (2006). *The emerging ethics of humancentric GPS tracking and monitoring*. https://ro.uow.edu.au/cgi/viewcontent.cgi?referer=https://scholar.google.com/&httpsredir=1&article=10215&context=infopapers

45 *Missing Leah Croucher: Teen 'lied about Valentine's Day whereabouts'*. (2019). BBC News. www.bbc.co.uk/news/uk-england-beds-bucks-herts-48542818

46 Mayer, R. N. (2003). Technology, families, and privacy: Can we know too much about our loved ones?. *Journal of Consumer Policy, 26*(4), 419-439. https://link.springer.com/article/10.1023/A:1026387109484

47 Chiu, A. (2019). A Teenager didn't come home. An iphne app led her mother to a ravine. *The Washington Post*. www.washingtonpost.com/nation/2019/06/17/teenager-missed-curfew-an-iphone-app-led-her-mother-ravine/

48 Hartmann, D., & Depro, B. (2006). Rethinking sports-based community crime prevention: A preliminary analysis of the relationship between midnight basketball and urban crime rates. *Journal of sport and social issues, 30*(2), 180-196. http://citeseerx.ist.psu.edu/viewdoc/download?doi=10.1.1.455.8208&rep=rep1&type=pdf

49 Farrell, Jr, W. C., Johnson, Jr, J. H., Sapp, M., Pumphrey, R. M., & Freeman, S. (1996). Redirecting the lives of urban black males: An assessment of Milwaukee's midnight basketball league. *Journal of Community Practice, 2*(4), 91-107. www.tandfonline.com/doi/abs/10.1300/J125v02n04_06

50 Hartmann, D., & Depro, B. (2006). Rethinking sports-based community crime prevention: A preliminary analysis of the relationship between midnight basketball and urban crime rates. *Journal of sport and social issues, 30*(2), 180-196. http://citeseerx.ist.psu.edu/viewdoc/download?doi=10.1.1.455.8208&rep=rep1&type=pdf

51 Sherman, L. W., Gottfredson, D. C., MacKenzie, D. L., Eck, J., Reuter, P., & Bushway, S. (1997). *Preventing crime: What works, what doesn't, what's promising: A report to the United States Congress*. US Department of Justice, Office of Justice Programs. www.ncjrs.gov/pdffiles1/Digitization/165366NCJRS.pdf

52 Eccles, J. S., & Barber, B. L. (1999). Student council, volunteering, basketball, or marching band: What kind of extracurricular involvement matters?. *Journal of adolescent research, 14*(1), 10-43. https://deepblue.lib.umich.edu/bitstream/handle/2027.42/67473/10.1177_0743558499141003.pdf?sequence=2&isAllowed=y;
Camp, W. G. (1990). Participation in student activities and achievement: A covariance structural analysis. *The Journal of Educational Research, 83*(5), 272-278. www.tandfonline.com/doi/abs/10.1080/00220671.1990.10885969;
Moore, M. J., & Werch, C. E. (2005). Sport and physical activity participation and substance use among adolescents. *Journal of Adolescent Health, 36*(6), 486-493. www.sciencedirect.com/science/article/abs/pii/S1054139X04002605;
Thorlindsson, T., & Vilhjalmsson, R. (1991). Factors related to cigarette smoking and alcohol use among adolescents. *Adolescence, 26*(102), 399-418. www.researchgate.net/profile/Runar-Vilhjalmsson/publication/21227661_Factors_Related_to_Cigarette_Smoking_and_Alcohol_Use_Among_Adolescents/links/09e4151105bec52df1000000/Factors-Related-to-Cigarette-Smoking-and-Alcohol-Use-Among-Adolescents.pdf;

Thorlindsson, T., & Bernburg, J. G. (2006). Peer groups and substance use: Examining the direct and interactive effect of leisure activity. *Adolescence, 41*(162). www.researchgate.net/profile/Jon-Bernburg/publication/6811940_Peer_groups_and_substance_use_Examining_the_direct_and_interactive_effect_of_leisure_activity/links/564633ad08ae451880aa3bc6/Peer-groups-and-substance-use-Examining-the-direct-and-interactive-effect-of-leisure-activity.pdf;
Bohnert, A. M., Richards, M., Kohl, K., & Randall, E. (2009). Relationships between discretionary time activities, emotional experiences, delinquency and depressive symptoms among urban African American adolescents. *Journal of Youth and Adolescence, 38*(4), 587-601. https://link.springer.com/article/10.1007/s10964-008-9336-1

53 Curriculum Description. (n.d.). TimeWise. www.personal.psu.edu/llc7/curriculum_description.htm;
Witt, P. A., & Caldwell, L. L. (2010). *The rationale for recreation services for youth: An evidenced based approach.* National Recreation and Park Association. www.researchgate.net/profile/Peter_Witt5/publication/280089228_The_rational_for_recreation_services_for_youth_An_Evidenced_Based_Approach/links/55a7bf2508ae8c884951f716/The-rational-for-recreation-services-for-youth-An-Evidenced-Based-Approach.pdf

54 Caldwell, L. L., Baldwin, C. K., Walls, T., & Smith, E. (2004). Preliminary effects of a leisure education program to promote healthy use of free time among middle school adolescents. *Journal of Leisure Research, 36*(3), 310-335. www.personal.psu.edu/faculty/l/l/llc7/Preliminary%20Evidence%20PDF.pdf

55 Kirby, D. (2007). *Emerging Answers: Research findings on programs to reduce teen pregnancy and sexually transmitted diseases.* The National Campaign to Prevent Teen and Unplanned Pregnancy. https://powertodecide.org/what-we-do/information/resource-library/emerging-answers-2007-new-research-findings-programs-reduce;
Footnote references:
[1] Mihalic, S. F., & Irwin, K. (2003). Blueprints for violence prevention: From research to real-world settings—factors influencing the successful replication of model programs. *Youth violence and juvenile justice, 1*(4), 307-329. http://citeseerx.ist.psu.edu/viewdoc/download?doi=10.1.1.218.4497&rep=rep1&type=pdf
[2] *Program Guide: The Quantum Opportunities Best Practice Model.* (2014). The Eisenhower Foundation. http://eisenhowerfoundation.org/docs/Quantum%20Program%20Guide.pdf
[3] United States. Public Health Service, & United States. Public Health Service. Office of the Surgeon General. (2000). *Youth violence: A report of the Surgeon General.* Public Health Service. https://books.google.co.uk/books?id=mbjFIWL2xMMC&pg=PA144&lpg=PA144&dq=The+Quantum+Opportunities+Program+Blueprints+for+Violence+Prevention+Series,+Center+for+the+Study+and+Prevention+of+Violence,&source=bl&ots=2U2_2iYDRM&sig=ACfU3U1atZFetGtvJkjG2MK6CdJPyvMPbA&hl=en&sa=X&ved=2ahUKEwiwrvzW9eTnAhWNQRUIHS7QAp8Q6AEwAnoECAcQAQ#v=onepage&q=The%20Quantum%20Opportunities%20Program%20Blueprints%20for%20Violence%20Prevention%20Series%2C%20Center%20for%20the%20Study%20and%20Prevention%20of%20Violence%2C&f=false
[4] Allen, J. P., Kuperminc, G., Philliber, S., & Herre, K. (1994). Programmatic prevention of adolescent problem behaviors: The role of autonomy, relatedness, and volunteer service in the Teen Outreach Program. *American Journal of Community Psychology, 22*(5), 595-615. http://people.virginia.edu/~psykliff/pubs/publications/AJ7.pdf
[5] Zeiser, K. (n.d.) *Evaluating the Impact of Early College High Schools.* American Institutes for Research. www.air.org/project/evaluating-impact-early-college-high-schools
[6] Berger, A., Turk-Bicakci, L., Garet, M., Song, M., Knudson, J., Haxton, C., ... & Cassidy, L. (2013). *Early College, Early Success: Early College High School Initiative Impact Study.* American institutes for research. https://files.eric.ed.gov/fulltext/ED577243.pdf
[7] Philliber, S., Kaye, J., & Herrling, S. (2001). *The national evaluation of the Children's Aid Society Carrera-Model Program to prevent teen pregnancy.* Accord, NY: Philliber Research Associates. www.ncjrs.gov/App/Publications/abstract.aspx?ID=259293
[8] Philliber, S., Kaye, J. W., Herrling, S., & West, E. (2002). Preventing pregnancy and improving health care access among teenagers: An evaluation of the Children's Aid Society-Carrera Program. *Perspectives on sexual and reproductive health,* 244-251. https://pdfs.semanticscholar.org/bb4a/413d6d10fc710c3e47ff2aebecd9dfd99ac4.pdf

56 Young, E. (2017). *Iceland knows how to stop teen substance abuse - but the rest of the world isn't listening.* Australian Broadcasting Corporation. www.abc.net.au/triplej/programs/hack/iceland-teen-substance-abuse/8208214

57 Milkman, H. B. (2016). *Iceland Succeeds at Reversing Teenage Substance Abuse: The US Should Follow Suit.* The World Post, Huffpost. www.drugfree.org.au/images/pdf-files/library/iceland/Iceland_Succeeds_at_Reversing_Teenage_Substance_Abuse.pdf

58 Young, E. (2017). *Iceland knows how to stop teen substance abuse - but the rest of the world isn't listening.* Australian Broadcasting Corporation. www.abc.net.au/triplej/programs/hack/iceland-teen-substance-abuse/8208214

59 Kristjansson, A. L., Sigfusdottir, I. D., Thorlindsson, T., Mann, M. J., Sigfusson, J., & Allegrante, J. P. (2016). Population trends in smoking, alcohol use and primary prevention variables among adolescents in Iceland, 1997–2014. *Addiction, 111*(4), 645-652.

60 Milkman, H. B. (2016). *Iceland Succeeds at Reversing Teenage Substance Abuse The US Should Follow Suit.* The World Post, Huffpost. www.drugfree.org.au/images/pdf-files/library/iceland/Iceland_Succeeds_at_Reversing_Teenage_Substance_Abuse.pdf

61 Sherman, L. W., Gottfredson, D. C., MacKenzie, D. L., Eck, J., Reuter, P., & Bushway, S. (1997). *Preventing crime: What works, what doesn't, what's promising: A report to the United States Congress.* US Department of Justice, Office of Justice Programs. www.ncjrs.gov/pdffiles1/Digitization/165366NCJRS.pdf

62 Peeples, F., & Loeber, R. (1994). Do individual factors and neighborhood context explain ethnic differences in juvenile delinquency?. *Journal of Quantitative Criminology, 10*(2), 141-157. https://link.springer.com/article/10.1007/BF02221156;
Duncan, G. J., Brooks-Gunn, J., & Klebanov, P. K. (1994). Economic deprivation and early childhood development. *Child development, 65*(2), 296-318. https://files.eric.ed.gov/fulltext/ED356076.pdf;
Brown, E., & Males, M. (2011). Does age or poverty level best predict criminal arrest and homicide rates? A preliminary investigation. *Justice Policy Journal, 8*(1), 1-30. www.cjcj.org/uploads/cjcj/documents/Does_age.pdf

63 Blyth, D. A., & Leffert, N. (1995). Communities as contexts for adolescent development: An empirical analysis. *Journal of Adolescent Research, 10*(1), 64-87. https://journals.sagepub.com/doi/abs/10.1177/0743554895101005;
Brooks-Gunn, J., Duncan, G. J., Klebanov, P. K., & Sealand, N. (1993). Do neighborhoods influence child and adolescent development?. *American journal of sociology, 99*(2), 353-395. www.researchgate.net/profile/Greg_Duncan3/publication/245966380_Do_Neighborhoods_Influence_Child_and_Adolescent_Development/links/58283d7908ae950ace6f7d00/Do-Neighborhoods-Influence-Child-and-Adolescent-Development.pdf;
Farrington, D. P. (1995). The development of offending and antisocial behaviour from childhood: Key findings from the Cambridge Study in Delinquent Development. *Journal of Child psychology and psychiatry, 6*(36), 929-964. www.infona.pl/resource/bwmeta1.element.elsevier-f897c0ba-c249-3122-aa6b-7e29df6ae99f

64 Lund, T. J., Dearing, E., & Zachrisson, H. D. (2017). Is affluence a risk for adolescents in Norway?. *Journal of Research on Adolescence, 27*(3), 628-643. https://fhi.brage.unit.no/fhi-xmlui/bitstream/handle/11250/2562366/Lund_et_al-2017-Journal_of_Research_on_Adolescence.pdf?sequence=2;
Lund, T. J., & Dearing, E. (2013). Is growing up affluent risky for adolescents or is the problem growing up in an affluent neighborhood?. *Journal of Research on Adolescence, 23*(2), 274-282. https://onlinelibrary.wiley.com/doi/abs/10.1111/j.1532-7795.2012.00829.x

65 Coley, R. L., Sims, J., Dearing, E., & Spielvogel, B. (2018). Locating economic risks for adolescent mental and behavioral health: Poverty and affluence in families, neighborhoods, and schools. *Child development, 89*(2), 360-369. https://srcd.onlinelibrary.wiley.com/doi/pdfdirect/10.1111/cdev.12771

66 Coleman, J. S. (1988). Social capital in the creation of human capital. *American journal of sociology, 94*, S95-S120. www.crcresearch.org/files-crcresearch/File/coleman_88.pdf

67 Coleman, J. S. (1988). Social capital in the creation of human capital. *American journal of sociology, 94*, S95-S120. www.crcresearch.org/files-crcresearch/File/coleman_88.pdf

68 Thorlindsson, T., Bjarnason, T., & Sigfusdottir, I. D. (2007). Individual and community processes of social closure: a study of adolescent academic achievement and alcohol use. *Acta sociologica, 50*(2), 161-178. https://d1wqtxts1xzle7.cloudfront.net/29883124/individual_and_community_processes_of_social_closure_acta_sociologica_vol_50_2_2007.pdf?1351861159=&response-content-disposition=inline%3B+filename%3DIndividual_and_Community_Processes_of_So.pdf&Expires=1617821392&Signature=EtC6RhaolIGW5S1hfVswp1KYZh1eIUHdKCA-zBU5LoFjWaTeUpwjytXkRS5vEVZ1ILOU92CiqYMuPH3W9iQ1HHO5x3KHEW1DvWBj6STDEe92TopaQ90hzaBO82KEpcbLHw1rf9cKT7JzNlTWF-Cu1jkXgLqJrWO-2JBAT6Yayj6BZgpWcfgcEH-sqby3dm3f5gSKNWd3OqDyt4jqY-2Ud6afjP9KfbUvR44p8-y9TCOeY-DY-EJbjrzt3zKmTb8Fdbrlsv0IfpiRfGG6Kj2-Ygl83u5tnPshXqrf6d-timNlHdLAZQO9AON0VWmgpkf3u7P58k1xjQ4AXDsu4uxzr2QA__&Key-Pair-Id=APKAJLOHF5GGSLRBV4ZA

69 Fletcher, A. C., Darling, N. E., Steinberg, L., & Dornbusch, S. (1995). The company they keep: Relation of adolescents' adjustment and behavior to their friends' perceptions of authoritative parenting in the social network. *Developmental psychology, 31*(2), 300. www.researchgate.net/profile/Nancy_Darling/publication/232592286_The_Company_They_Keep_Relation_of_Adolescents'_Adjustment_and_Behavior_to_Their_Friends'_Perceptions_of_Authoritative_Parenting_in_the_Social_Network/links/02e7e51c1b377c3ae3000000.pdf

70 Clinton, H. R. (2006). *It takes a village.* Simon and Schuster.;
Goldberg, J. (2016). *It Takes A Village To Determine The Origins Of An African Proverb.* NPR. www.npr.org/sections/goatsandsoda/2016/07/30/487925796/it-takes-a-village-to-determine-the-origins-of-an-african-proverb

71 Coleman, J. S. (1988). Social capital in the creation of human capital. *American journal of sociology, 94*, S95-S120. www.crcresearch.org/files-crcresearch/File/coleman_88.pdf

72 Petrosino, A., Turpin-Petrosino, C., Hollis-Peel, M. E., & Lavenberg, J. G. (2013). 'Scared Straight'and other juvenile awareness programs for preventing juvenile delinquency. *Cochrane database of systematic reviews*, (4). www.cochranelibrary.com/cdsr/doi/10.1002/14651858.CD002796.pub2/full

73 Dishion, T. J., & Tipsord, J. M. (2011). Peer contagion in child and adolescent social and emotional development. *Annual review of psychology, 62.* www.ncbi.nlm.nih.gov/pmc/articles/PMC3523739/;
McCord, J. (2003). Cures that harm: Unanticipated outcomes of crime prevention programs. *The Annals of the American Academy of Political and Social Science, 587*(1), 16-30. www.gwern.net/docs/sociology/2003-mccord.pdf;
Dishion, T. J., & Tipsord, J. M. (2011). Peer contagion in child and adolescent social and emotional development. *Annual review of psychology, 62.* www.ncbi.nlm.nih.gov/pmc/articles/PMC3523739/

74 Mahoney, J. L., Stattin, H., & Magnusson, D. (2001). Youth recreation centre participation and criminal offending: A 20-year longitudinal study of Swedish boys. *International journal of behavioral development, 25*(6), 509-520. http://citeseerx.ist.psu.edu/viewdoc/download?doi=10.1.1.915.4737&rep=rep1&type=pdf

75 Mahoney, J. L., Stattin, H., & Lord, H. (2004). Unstructured youth recreation centre participation and antisocial behaviour development: Selection influences and the moderating role of antisocial peers. *International journal of behavioral development, 28*(6), 553-560. http://citeseerx.ist.psu.edu/viewdoc/download?-doi=10.1.1.884.3057&rep=rep1&type=pdf

76 Roth, J., Brooks-Gunn, J., Murray, L., & Foster, W. (1998). Promoting healthy adolescents: Synthesis of youth development program evaluations. *Journal of research on Adolescence, 8*(4), 423-459. https://psycnet.apa.org/record/1998-03022-002

77 Schlegel, A., & Barry Iii, H. (1991). *Adolescence: An anthropological inquiry.* Free Press. https://repository.arizona.edu/bitstream/handle/10150/636966/adolescence_anthropological_inquiry.pdf?sequence=1

78 National Research Council. (1998). *Protecting youth at work: Health, safety, and development of working children and adolescents in the United States.* National Academies Press. https://books.google.co.uk/books?hl=en&lr=&id=Vw2dAgAAQBAJ&oi=fnd&pg=PT9&dq=Protecting+youth+at+work:+Health,+safety,+and+development+of+working+children+and+adolescents+in+the+United+States&ots=Cr1n3iStNG&sig=4X9A_Suh6IiD_8qcExNjOyeRa5s&redir_esc=y#v=onepage&q=20%20or%20more&f=false

79 Fitzgerald, S. T., & Laidlaw, A. D. (1995). Adolescents and work: Risks and benefits of teenage employment. *AAOHN Journal, 43*(4), 185-189. https://journals.sagepub.com/doi/pdf/10.1177/216507999504300404;
Barling, J., Rogers, K. A., & Kelloway, E. K. (1995). Some effects of teenagers' part-time employment: The quantity and quality of work make the difference. *Journal of organizational behavior, 16*(2), 143-154. https://hosted.smith.queensu.ca/faculty/julianbarling/Articles/1995%20Barling%20et%20al.pdf

80 Dataset includes both attempts to attack and completed attacks; Only includes responses of "Severely" to the question "How distressing was being a victim of this crime to you?"; represents risk in a single year; analysis of incidents from 2009-2016, scaled up to represent population; missing data allocated proportionally

81 Staff, J., & Uggen, C. (2003). The fruits of good work: Early work experiences and adolescent deviance. *Journal of research in crime and delinquency, 40*(3), 263-290. http://citeseerx.ist.psu.edu/viewdoc/download?-doi=10.1.1.550.8661&rep=rep1&type=pdf;
Vazsonyi, A. T., & Snider, J. B. (2008). Mentoring, competencies, and adjustment in adolescents: American part-time employment and European apprenticeships. *International journal of behavioral development, 32*(1), 46-55. https://fam-hes.ca.uky.edu/files/mbs_paper.pdf

82 National Research Council. (1998). *Protecting youth at work: Health, safety, and development of working children and adolescents in the United States.* National Academies Press. https://books.google.co.uk/books?hl=en&lr=&id=Vw2dAgAAQBAJ&oi=fnd&pg=PT9&dq=Protecting+youth+at+work:+Health,+safety,+and+development+of+working+children+and+adolescents+in+the+United+States&ots=Cr1n3iStNG&sig=4X9A_Suh6IiD_8qcExNjOyeRa5s&redir_esc=y#v=onepage&q=20%20or%20more&f=false;
Fitzgerald, S. T., & Laidlaw, A. D. (1995). Adolescents and work: Risks and benefits of teenage employment. *AAOHN Journal, 43*(4), 185-189. https://journals.sagepub.com/doi/pdf/10.1177/216507999504300404;
Baum, C. L., & Ruhm, C. J. (2016). The changing benefits of early work experience. *Southern Economic Journal, 83*(2), 343-363. www.nber.org/papers/w20413.pdf

83 *Our Network by the Numbers.* (n.d.). Big Brothers and Big Sisters of America. www.bbbs.org/national-office/

84 Kellerman AL, Fuqua-Whitley DS, Rivara FP, Mercy J. (1998). Preventing youth violence: what works? *Ann Rev Publ Health, 19*(1):271-92. www.annualreviews.org/doi/full/10.1146/annurev.publhealth.19.1.271?amp%3BsearchHistoryKey=%24%7BsearchHistoryKey%7D

85 DuBois, D. L., Holloway, B. E., Valentine, J. C., & Cooper, H. (2002). Effectiveness of mentoring programs for youth: A meta-analytic review. *American journal of community psychology, 30*(2), 157-197. https://wmich.edu/sites/default/files/attachments/u58/2015/Effectiveness-of-Mentoring-Programs-for-Youth.pdf

86 Warr, M. (1993). Parents/peers, and delinquency. *Social forces, 72*(1), 247-264. https://heinonline.org/HOL/Page?handle=hein.journals/josf72&div=19&g_sent=1&casa_token=2WsZILJBwuAAAAAA:vGW1d0Y-g_77m-2U-MboFYlqR76p1AuYEU6TMDrXZVwj5QuaAM86r1OC4laH90-PrH2QDgFpcOtVd

87 Lilienfeld, S. (2014). How to Turn Around Troubled Teens. *Scientific American.* www.scientificamerican.com/article/how-to-turn-around-troubled-teens/;
Meade, B., & Steiner, B. (2010). The total effects of boot camps that house juveniles: A systematic review of the evidence. *Journal of Criminal Justice, 38*(5), 841-853. www.sciencedirect.com/science/article/pii/S0047235210001315

88 Klenowski, P. M., Bell, K. J., & Dodson, K. D. (2010). An empirical evaluation of juvenile awareness programs in the United States: Can juveniles be "scared straight"?. *Journal of Offender Rehabilitation, 49*(4), 254-272. www.tandfonline.com/doi/abs/10.1080/10509671003716068;
Footnote references:
[1] Nowak, C., & Heinrichs, N. (2008). A comprehensive meta-analysis of Triple P-Positive Parenting Program using hierarchical linear modeling: Effectiveness and moderating variables. *Clinical child and family psychology review, 11*(3), 114. https://pub.uni-bielefeld.de/record/1586515
[2] Salari, R., Ralph, A., & Sanders, M. R. (2014). An efficacy trial: Positive parenting program for parents of teenagers. *Behaviour Change, 31*(1), 34-52. www.researchgate.net/profile/Raziye-Salari/publication/263021310_An_Efficacy_Trial_Positive_Parenting_Program_for_Parents_of_Teenagers/links/577a7c7008ae355e74f06d0d/An-Efficacy-Trial-Positive-Parenting-Program-for-Parents-of-Teenagers.pdf
[3] United Nations Office on Drugs and Crime. (2010). *Compilation of evidence-based family skills training programmes.* www.unodc.org/documents/prevention/family-compilation.pdf
[4] Nowak, C., & Heinrichs, N. (2008). A comprehensive meta-analysis of Triple P-Positive Parenting Program using hierarchical linear modeling: Effectiveness and moderating variables. *Clinical child and family psychology review, 11*(3), 114. http://cssr.berkeley.edu/cwscmsreports/LatinoPracticeAdvisory/PRACTICE_Evidence_Based_Parent_Training/Triple%20P/2008%20Nowak.pdf
[5] United Nations Office on Drugs and Crime. (2010). *Compilation of evidence-based family skills training programmes.* www.unodc.org/documents/prevention/family-compilation.pdf

89 Hartup, W. W. (1996). The company they keep: Friendships and their developmental significance. *Child development, 67*(1), 1-13. https://books.google.co.uk/books?hl=en&lr=&id=gLWnmVbKdLwC&oi=fnd&pg=PA63&ots=0_N5Eypt81&sig=2nM9w68hjkgwDsfgL6n5ZMxN9JQ&redir_esc=y#v=onepage&q&f=false

90 Keenan, K., Loeber, R., Zhang, Q., Stouthamer-Loeber, M., & Van Kammen, W. B. (1995). The influence of deviant peers on the development of boys' disruptive and delinquent behavior: A temporal analysis. *Development and psychopathology, 7*(4), 715-726. www.cambridge.org/core/journals/development-and-psychopathology/article/influence-of-deviant-peers-on-the-development-of-boys-disruptive-and-delinquent-behavior-a-temporal-analysis/FD9A5F1DDD6FB615918CEC2385522D5B

91 Rich, J. (1998). *The nurture assumption.* Bloomsbury.;
Harris, J. R. (1995). Where is the child's environment? A group socialization theory of development. *Psychological review, 102*(3), 458. https://faculty.weber.edu/eamsel/Classes/Child%203000/Lectures/3%20Childhood/SE%20development/JudithHarris.html

92 Obschonka, M., Andersson, H., Silbereisen, R. K., & Sverke, M. (2013). Rule-breaking, crime, and entrepreneurship: A replication and extension study with 37-year longitudinal data. *Journal of Vocational Behavior, 83*(3), 386-396. www.researchgate.net/profile/Martin-Obschonka/publication/259084521_Rule-breaking_crime_and_entrepreneurship_A_replication_and_extension_study_with_37-year_longitudinal_data/links/557817dd08aeacff2000899e/Rule-breaking-crime-and-entrepreneurship-A-replication-and-extension-study-with-37-year-longitudinal-data;
Footnote reference: [1] Obschonka, M., Andersson, H., Silbereisen, R. K., & Sverke, M. (2013). Rule-breaking, crime, and entrepreneurship: A replication and extension study with 37-year longitudinal data. *Journal of Vocational Behavior, 83*(3), 386-396. www.pathwaystoadulthood.org/docs/Obschonka2013Rulebreakingcrimeandentrepreneurship.pdf

93 Posner, R. A. (1995). *Aging and old age.* University of Chicago Press. https://books.google.ca/books?id=sa5yCx-4f3HQC&pg=PA103&lpg=PA103&dq=They+look+at+the+good+side+rather+than+the+bad%E2%80%A6+They+trust+others+readily+%E2%80%A6+They+are+sanguine&source=bl&ots=Qn4ertGhPe&sig=ACfU3U-3vYs4w1D462PANwnZErZPgYbtI9Q&hl=en&sa=X&ved=2ahUKEwi2t8P94NjvAhUCVa0KHYycAEwQ6A-EwBnoECA8QAw#v=onepage&q=They%20look%20at%20the%20good%20side%20rather%20than%20the%20bad%E2%80%A6%20They%20trust%20others%20readily%20%E2%80%A6%20They%20are%20sanguine&f=false

94 Allen, Joseph. *Escaping the Endless Adolescence: How we can help our teenagers grow up before they grow old.* Random House Publishing Group. Kindle Edition. https://books.google.co.uk/books?hl=en&lr=&id=myEH-FTWAmjwC&oi=fnd&pg=PR9&dq=Escaping+the+Endless+Adolescence&ots=8yCPQ5RSm7&sig=Zg52iG-

B3ugS5gz0mW19DUdLsUiA&redir_esc=y#v=onepage&q=Escaping%20the%20Endless%20Adolescence&f=-false

95 Delinquent. (n.d.). *Cambridge Dictionary*. https://dictionary.cambridge.org/dictionary/english/delinquent

96 Kilgannon, C. (2003). Pondering Lost Boaters, Teenagers Call Risk-Taking a Rite of Passage. *The New York Times*. www.nytimes.com/2003/02/02/nyregion/pondering-lost-boaters-teenagers-call-risk-taking-a-rite-of-passage.html

97 Criminal Justice Information Services Division, Federal Bureau of Investigation. (2014). *Proportion of arrests: 2014 Crime in the United States*. U.S. Department of Justice. https://ucr.fbi.gov/crime-in-the-u.s/2014/crime-in-the-u.s.-2014/tables/table-33;
Arrest rates: Brame, R., Bushway, S. D., Paternoster, R., & Turner, M. G. (2014). Demographic patterns of cumulative arrest prevalence by ages 18 and 23. *Crime & Delinquency, 60*(3), 471-486. www.ncbi.nlm.nih.gov/pmc/articles/PMC4443707/

98 *OJJDP Statistical Briefing Book*. (2019). Office of Juvenile Justice and Delinquency Prevention. www.ojjdp.gov/ojstatbb/structure_process/qa04101.asp?qaDate=2019

99 Brame, R., Bushway, S. D., Paternoster, R., & Turner, M. G. (2014). Demographic patterns of cumulative arrest prevalence by ages 18 and 23. *Crime & Delinquency, 60*(3), 471-486. www.ncbi.nlm.nih.gov/pmc/articles/PMC4443707/

100 Pierce, M. W., Runyan, C. W., & Bangdiwala, S. I. (2014). The use of criminal history information in college admissions decisions. *Journal of school violence, 13*(4), 359-376. https://heinonline.org/HOL/Page?collection=-journals&handle=hein.journals/wjsv13&id=359&men_tab=srchresults;
Weissman, M; Rosenthal, A; Warth, P, Wolf, E; and Messina-Yauchzy, M. (2010). *The Use of Criminal History Records in College Admissions Reconsidered*. Center for Community Alternatives, Innovative Solutions for Justice. www.communityalternatives.org/wp-content/uploads/2020/02/use-of-criminal-history-records-reconsidered.pdf

101 Weissman, M; Rosenthal, A; Warth, P, Wolf, E; and Messina-Yauchzy, M. (2010). *The Use of Criminal History Records in College Admissions Reconsidered*. Center for Community Alternatives, Innovative Solutions for Justice. www.communityalternatives.org/wp-content/uploads/2020/02/use-of-criminal-history-records-reconsidered.pdf

102 Rosenberg, T. (2016). Have You Ever Been Arrested? Check Here. *The New York Times*. www.nytimes.com/2016/05/24/opinion/have-you-ever-been-arrested-check-here.html;
Footnote references:
[1] Sherman, L. W., Gottfredson, D. C., MacKenzie, D. L., Eck, J., Reuter, P., & Bushway, S. D. (1998). *Preventing Crime: What Works, What Doesn't, What's Promising*. Research in Brief. National Institute of Justice. http://files.eric.ed.gov/fulltext/ED423321.pdf
[2] Mihalic, S. F., & Irwin, K. (2003). Blueprints for violence prevention: From research to real-world settings—factors influencing the successful replication of model programs. *Youth violence and juvenile justice, 1*(4), 307-329. http://citeseerx.ist.psu.edu/viewdoc/download?doi=10.1.1.218.4497&rep=rep1&type=pdf
[3] Sherman, L. W., Gottfredson, D. C., MacKenzie, D. L., Eck, J., Reuter, P., & Bushway, S. D. (1998). *Preventing Crime: What Works, What Doesn't, What's Promising*. Research in Brief. National Institute of Justice. http://files.eric.ed.gov/fulltext/ED423321.pdf
[4] Sherman, L. W., Gottfredson, D. C., MacKenzie, D. L., Eck, J., Reuter, P., & Bushway, S. D. (1998). *Preventing Crime: What Works, What Doesn't, What's Promising*. Research in Brief. National Institute of Justice. http://files.eric.ed.gov/fulltext/ED423321.pdf
[5] Heller, S. B., Shah, A. K., Guryan, J., Ludwig, J., Mullainathan, S., & Pollack, H. A. (2017). Thinking, fast and slow? Some field experiments to reduce crime and dropout in Chicago. *The Quarterly Journal of Economics, 132*(1), 1-54. www.sesp.northwestern.edu/docs/publications/175011386958b855eeaed17.pdf

103 Gillett, R. (2016). *14 wildly successful high school dropouts*. Business Insider. www.businessinsider.com/highly-successful-high-school-dropouts-2016-6;
Nekilan, G. (2018). *Famous High School Dropouts That Still Found Success*. Education. https://vocal.media/education/famous-high-school-dropouts-that-still-found-success

104 Digest of Education Statistics. (2020). *Table 219.80: Total number 16- to 24-year-old high school dropouts (status dropouts) and percentage of dropouts among persons 16 to 24 years old (status dropout rate), by selected characteristics: 2007 through 2019*. National Center for Education Statistics. https://nces.ed.gov/programs/digest/d20/tables/dt20_219.80.asp

105 Steinberg, L. (2008). A social neuroscience perspective on adolescent risk-taking. *Developmental review, 28*(1), 78-106. www.ncbi.nlm.nih.gov/pmc/articles/PMC2396566/

106 Beyth-Marom, R., Austin, L., Fischhoff, B., Palmgren, C., & Jacobs-Quadrel, M. (1993). Perceived consequences of risky behaviors: adults and adolescents. *Developmental psychology, 29*(3), 549. http://faculty.weber.edu/eamsel/Classes/Child%203000/Adolescent%20Risk%20taking/Lectures/4-5%20-%20Cognitive/Beyth-Maron%20et%20al.%20(1993).pdf

107 Steinberg, L. (2008). A social neuroscience perspective on adolescent risk-taking. *Developmental review, 28*(1), 78-106. www.ncbi.nlm.nih.gov/pmc/articles/PMC2396566/

108 Steinberg, L. (2008). A social neuroscience perspective on adolescent risk-taking. *Developmental review, 28*(1), 78-106. www.ncbi.nlm.nih.gov/pmc/articles/PMC2396566/

109 Reyna, V. F., & Farley, F. (2006). Risk and rationality in adolescent decision making: Implications for theory, practice, and public policy. *Psychological science in the public interest, 7*(1), 1-44. https://pdfs.semanticscholar.org/1de4/966482722d1f7da8bbef16d108639d9a1c38.pdf

110 Steinberg, L. (2008). A social neuroscience perspective on adolescent risk-taking. *Developmental review, 28*(1), 78-106. www.ncbi.nlm.nih.gov/pmc/articles/PMC2396566/;
Reyna, V. F., & Farley, F. (2006). Risk and rationality in adolescent decision making: Implications for theory, practice, and public policy. *Psychological science in the public interest, 7*(1), 1-44. https://pdfs.semanticscholar.org/1de4/966482722d1f7da8bbef16d108639d9a1c38.pdf

111 Steinberg, L. (2008). A social neuroscience perspective on adolescent risk-taking. *Developmental review, 28*(1), 78-106. www.ncbi.nlm.nih.gov/pmc/articles/PMC2396566/

112 Kirby, D. (1984). *Sexuality education: An evaluation of programs and their effects.* http://files.eric.ed.gov/fulltext/ED277955.pdf

113 Howard, M., & McCabe, J. B. (1990). Helping teenagers postpone sexual involvement. *Family planning perspectives*, 21-26. www.jstor.org/stable/2135434?seq=1#page_scan_tab_contents;
Ellickson, P. L., & Robyn, A. E. (1987). Toward More Effective Drug Prevention Programs. http://eric.ed.gov/?id=ED297211

114 Baird, A., Fugelsang, J., & Bennett, C. (2005, April). *What were you thinking: An fMRI study of adolescent decision-making.* Poster presented at Cognitive Neuroscience Society Meeting. www.researchgate.net/profile/A_Baird/publication/268048958_What_were_you_thinking_An_fMRI_study_of_adolescent_decision_making/links/551a85680cf244e9a45882a5.pdf

115 Reyna, V. F., & Farley, F. (2006). Risk and rationality in adolescent decision making: Implications for theory, practice, and public policy. *Psychological science in the public interest, 7*(1), 1-44. https://pdfs.semanticscholar.org/1de4/966482722d1f7da8bbef16d108639d9a1c38.pdf

116 Reyna, V. F., & Farley, F. (2006). Risk and rationality in adolescent decision making: Implications for theory, practice, and public policy. *Psychological science in the public interest,* 7(1), 1-44. https://pdfs.semanticscholar.org/1de4/966482722d1f7da8bbef16d108639d9a1c38.pdf

117 Goldberg, J. H., Halpern-Felsher, B. L., & Millstein, S. G. (2002). Beyond invulnerability: the importance of benefits in adolescents' decision to drink alcohol. *Health psychology, 21*(5), 477. https://files.eric.ed.gov/fulltext/ED464311.pdf;
Katz, E. C., Fromme, K., & D'Amico, E. J. (2000). Effects of outcome expectancies and personality on young adults' illicit drug use, heavy drinking, and risky sexual behavior. *Cognitive Therapy and Research, 24*(1), 1-22. www.researchgate.net/profile/Elizabeth-Katz-2/publication/226805176_Effects_of_Outcome_Expectancies_and_Personality_on_Young_Adults%27_Illicit_Drug_Use_Heavy_Drinking_and_Risky_Sexual_Behavior/links/5b156d2d4585151f91f9cac5/Effects-of-Outcome-Expectancies-and-Personality-on-Young-Adults-Illicit-Drug-Use-Heavy-Drinking-and-Risky-Sexual-Behavior.pdf

118 Albert, D., & Steinberg, L. (2011). Judgment and decision making in adolescence. *Journal of Research on Adolescence, 21*(1), 211-224. https://repository.brynmawr.edu/cgi/viewcontent.cgi?article=1053&context=psych_pubs

119 Burnett, S., Bault, N., Coricelli, G., & Blakemore, S. J. (2010). Adolescents' heightened risk-seeking in a probabilistic gambling task. *Cognitive development, 25*(2), 183-196. www.sciencedirect.com/science/article/pii/S0885201410000201

120 Figner, B., Mackinlay, R. J., Wilkening, F., & Weber, E. U. (2009). Affective and deliberative processes in risky choice: age differences in risk taking in the Columbia Card Task. *Journal of Experimental Psychology: Learning, Memory, and Cognition, 35*(3), 709. http://citeseerx.ist.psu.edu/viewdoc/download?doi=10.1.1.372.3793&rep=rep1&type=pdf

121 Cauffman, E., Shulman, E. P., Steinberg, L., Claus, E., Banich, M. T., Graham, S., & Woolard, J. (2010). Age differences in affective decision making as indexed by performance on the Iowa Gambling Task. *Developmental psychology, 46*(1), 193. https://pdfs.semanticscholar.org/0dd9/e1fd8e91b8abb90c88af1126cac33e217f8f.pdf; Palminteri, S., Kilford, E. J., Coricelli, G., & Blakemore, S. J. (2016). The computational development of reinforcement learning during adolescence. *PLoS computational biology, 12*(6), e1004953. http://journals.plos.org/ploscompbiol/article?id=10.1371/journal.pcbi.1004953

122 Monk, C. S., McClure, E. B., Nelson, E. E., Zarahn, E., Bilder, R. M., Leibenluft, E., ... & Pine, D. S. (2003). Adolescent immaturity in attention-related brain engagement to emotional facial expressions. *Neuroimage, 20*(1), 420-428. https://pdfs.semanticscholar.org/03c2/812a6b531be99b6cfb231be477a06f98afe8.pdf; Somerville, L. H., Hare, T., & Casey, B. J. (2011). Frontostriatal maturation predicts cognitive control failure to appetitive cues in adolescents. *Journal of cognitive neuroscience, 23*(9), 2123-2134. www.ncbi.nlm.nih.gov/pmc/articles/PMC3131482/

123 Gardner, M., & Steinberg, L. (2005). Peer influence on risk taking, risk preference, and risky decision making in adolescence and adulthood: an experimental study. *Developmental psychology, 41*(4), 625. https://pdfs.semanticscholar.org/21d7/8ac40b0a5a9d74f09494c6e63c0f2374a588.pdf

124 Dobbs, D. (2011). Teenage Brains. *National Geographic Magazine.* www.nationalgeographic.com/magazine/2011/10/beautiful-brains/

125 Knoll, L. J., Magis-Weinberg, L., Speekenbrink, M., & Blakemore, S. J. (2015). Social influence on risk perception during adolescence. *Psychological science, 26*(5), 583-592. http://journals.sagepub.com/doi/full/10.1177/0956797615569578; Knoll, L. J., Leung, J. T., Foulkes, L., & Blakemore, S. J. (2017). Age-related differences in social influence on risk perception depend on the direction of influence. *Journal of adolescence, 60*, 53-63. www.sciencedirect.com/science/article/pii/S0140197117301124

126 Rosenberg, T. (2013). The Destructive Influence of Imaginary Peers. *The New York Times.* https://opinionator.blogs.nytimes.com/2013/03/27/the-destructive-influence-of-imaginary-peers/

127 Somerville, L. H., Jones, R. M., Ruberry, E. J., Dyke, J. P., Glover, G., & Casey, B. J. (2013). The medial prefrontal cortex and the emergence of self-conscious emotion in adolescence. *Psychological science, 24*(8), 1554-1562. www.ncbi.nlm.nih.gov/pmc/articles/PMC3742683/

128 O'Brien, S. F., & Bierman, K. L. (1988). Conceptions and perceived influence of peer groups: Interviews with preadolescents and adolescents. *Child development*, 1360-1365. https://s3.amazonaws.com/academia.edu.documents/46638301/Conceptions_and_Perceived_Influence_of_P20160620-2199-5zmyno.pdf?AWSAccessKeyId=AKIAIWOWYYGZ2Y53UL3A&Expires=1528292680&Signature=5V2E5AGaHyNZ2DwDPCth826Y1Po%3D&response-content-disposition=inline%3B%20filename%3DConceptions_and_perceived_influence_of_p.pdf

129 Steinberg, L. (2008). A social neuroscience perspective on adolescent risk-taking. *Developmental review, 28*(1), 78-106. www.ncbi.nlm.nih.gov/pmc/articles/PMC2396566/

130 Zimring, F. E. (2000). *American youth violence.* Oxford University Press on Demand. https://books.google.co.uk/books?hl=en&lr=&id=vjeDkGjypfsC&oi=fnd&pg=PR9&dq=American+youth+violence.&ots=BAT-tA9Y-No&sig=CJD_CyCIHxE17ceRoYBG6KicfuQ&redir_esc=y#v=onepage&q=American%20youth%20violence.&f=false

131 Bryan, C. J., Yeager, D. S., Hinojosa, C. P., Chabot, A., Bergen, H., Kawamura, M., & Steubing, F. (2016). Harnessing adolescent values to motivate healthier eating. *Proceedings of the National Academy of Sciences, 113*(39), 10830-10835. www.pnas.org/content/pnas/113/39/10830.full.pdf

132 Farrelly, M. C., Nonnemaker, J., Davis, K. C., & Hussin, A. (2009). The influence of the national truth® campaign on smoking initiation. *American journal of preventive medicine, 36*(5), 379-384. www.ajpmonline.org/article/S0749-3797(09)00074-9/fulltext

133 Steinberg, L. (2008). A social neuroscience perspective on adolescent risk-taking. *Developmental review, 28*(1), 78-106. www.ncbi.nlm.nih.gov/pmc/articles/PMC2396566/

134 Reyna, V. F., & Farley, F. (2006). Risk and rationality in adolescent decision making: Implications for theory, practice, and public policy. *Psychological science in the public interest, 7*(1), 1-44. https://pdfs.semanticscholar.org/1de4/966482722d1f7da8bbef16d108639d9a1c38.pdf

135 Reyna, V. F., & Farley, F. (2006). Risk and rationality in adolescent decision making: Implications for theory, practice, and public policy. *Psychological science in the public interest, 7*(1), 1-44. https://pdfs.semanticscholar.org/1de4/966482722d1f7da8bbef16d108639d9a1c38.pdf

136 Centers for Disease Control and Prevention. [1991-2019] Youth Risk Behavior Survey Data. www.cdc.gov/healthyyouth/data/yrbs/results.htm

137 Kann, L., McManus, T., Harris, W. A., Shanklin, S. L., Flint, K. H., Hawkins, J., ... & Zaza, S. (2016). Youth risk behavior surveillance—United States, 2015. *Morbidity and Mortality Weekly Report: Surveillance Summaries, 65*(6), 1-174. www.cdc.gov/mmwr/volumes/65/ss/ss6506a1.htm

# 7. Health

1 Khazan, O. (2016). Why Are So Many Americans Dying Young? *The Atlantic*. www.theatlantic.com/health/archive/2016/12/why-are-so-many-americans-dying-young/510455/

2 *Teenagers (15-17 years of age)*. (2021). National Center on Birth Defects and Developmental Disabilities, Centers for Disease Control and Prevention. www.cdc.gov/ncbddd/childdevelopment/positiveparenting/adolescence2.html

3 Garey, J. (n.d.). *Teens and Sleep: The Cost of Sleep Deprivation*. Child Mind Institute. https://childmind.org/article/happens-teenagers-dont-get-enough-sleep/

4 Gao, B., Dwivedi, S., Milewski, M. D., & Cruz, A. I. (2019). Lack of sleep and sports injuries in adolescents: a systematic review and meta-analysis. *Journal of Pediatric Orthopaedics, 39*(5), e324-e333. www.ingentaconnect.com/content/wk/bpo/2019/00000039/00000005/art00011

5 Mah, C. D., Mah, K. E., Kezirian, E. J., & Dement, W. C. (2011). The effects of sleep extension on the athletic performance of collegiate basketball players. *Sleep, 34*(7), 943-950. www.ncbi.nlm.nih.gov/pubmed/21731144

6 Ericsson, K. A., Krampe, R. T., & Tesch-Römer, C. (1993). The role of deliberate practice in the acquisition of expert performance. *Psychological review, 100*(3), 363. https://mrbartonmaths.com/resourcesnew/8.%20Research/Explicit%20Instruction/Deliberate%20Practice.PDF

7 Curcio, G., Ferrara, M., & De Gennaro, L. (2006). Sleep loss, learning capacity and academic performance. *Sleep medicine reviews, 10*(5), 323-337. https://holistic.ort.org.il/wp-content/uploads/2016/02/sleep-loss-learning-capacity-and-academic-performance-2006.pdf

8 Wolfson, A. R., & Carskadon, W. (2003). Understanding adolescents sleep patterns and school performance. *Sleep Med. Rev, 7*, 491-506. http://web.mit.edu/writing/2010/July/Wolfson&Carskadon2003.pdf

9 Wolfson, A. R., & Carskadon, M. A. (1998). Sleep schedules and daytime functioning in adolescents. *Child development*, 875-887. www.personal.psu.edu/students/s/e/seb302/wolfson_carskadon.pdf

10 Gillen-O'Neel, C., Huynh, V. W., & Fuligni, A. J. (2013). To study or to sleep? The academic costs of extra studying at the expense of sleep. *Child development, 84*(1), 133-142. https://pdfs.semanticscholar.org/7e80/ed35a849c983ba25e072016a015da63e37c0.pdf

11 Foster, R. (2015). *Why Do We Need Sleep?* TED Radio Hour, NPR. www.npr.org/transcripts/399800134?storyId=399800134

12 Dahl, R. E. (1999). The consequences of insufficient sleep for adolescents. *Phi Delta Kappan, 80*(5), 354-359. www.spps.org/cms/lib/MN01910242/Centricity/Domain/7352/conseqsleepdep-dahl.pdf

13 Dahl, R. E. (1999). The consequences of insufficient sleep for adolescents. *Phi Delta Kappan, 80*(5), 354-359. www.spps.org/cms/lib/MN01910242/Centricity/Domain/7352/conseqsleepdep-dahl.pdf

14 Fredriksen, K., Rhodes, J., Reddy, R., & Way, N. (2004). Sleepless in Chicago: tracking the effects of adolescent sleep loss during the middle school years. *Child development, 75*(1), 84-95. http://rhodeslab.org/files/sleepless.pdf

15 Walker, Matthew. *Why We Sleep: Unlocking the Power of Sleep and Dreams* (p. 148). Scribner. Kindle Edition.

16 Chaput, J. P., & Dutil, C. (2016). Lack of sleep as a contributor to obesity in adolescents: impacts on eating and activity behaviors. *International Journal of Behavioral Nutrition and Physical Activity, 13*(1), 1-9. https://ijbnpa.biomedcentral.com/articles/10.1186/s12966-016-0428-0;
Spaeth, A. M., Dinges, D. F., & Goel, N. (2013). Effects of experimental sleep restriction on weight gain, caloric intake, and meal timing in healthy adults. *Sleep, 36*(7), 981-990. www.ncbi.nlm.nih.gov/pmc/articles/PMC3669080/;
Markwald, R. R., Melanson, E. L., Smith, M. R., Higgins, J., Perreault, L., Eckel, R. H., & Wright, K. P. (2013). Impact of insufficient sleep on total daily energy expenditure, food intake, and weight gain. *Proceedings of the National Academy of Sciences, 110*(14), 5695-5700. www.pnas.org/content/pnas/110/14/5695.full.pdf?crsi=6624973103;
Taheri, S., Lin, L., Austin, D., Young, T., & Mignot, E. (2004). Short sleep duration is associated with reduced leptin, elevated ghrelin, and increased body mass index. *PLoS Med, 1*(3), e62. https://journals.plos.org/plosmedicine/article?id=10.1371/journal.pmed.0010062

17 Hart, C. N., Carskadon, M. A., Considine, R. V., Fava, J. L., Lawton, J., Raynor, H. A., ... & Wing, R. (2013). Changes in children's sleep duration on food intake, weight, and leptin. *Pediatrics, 132*(6), e1473-e1480. https://pediatrics.aappublications.org/content/132/6/e1473

18 Gupta, N. K., Mueller, W. H., Chan, W., & Meininger, J. C. (2002). Is obesity associated with poor sleep quality in adolescents?. *American Journal of Human Biology, 14*(6), 762-768. https://onlinelibrary.wiley.com/doi/abs/10.1002/ajhb.10093

19 Gupta, N. K., Mueller, W. H., Chan, W., & Meininger, J. C. (2002). Is obesity associated with poor sleep quality in adolescents?. *American Journal of Human Biology, 14*(6), 762-768. https://onlinelibrary.wiley.com/doi/abs/10.1002/ajhb.10093

20 Hirshkowitz, M., Whiton, K., Albert, S. M., Alessi, C., Bruni, O., DonCarlos, L., ... & Hillard, P. J. A. (2015). National Sleep Foundation's sleep time duration recommendations: methodology and results summary. *Sleep health, 1*(1), 40-43. https://doi.org/10.1016/j.sleh.2014.12.010

21 Tremblay, M. S., Carson, V., Chaput, J. P., Connor Gorber, S., Dinh, T., Duggan, M., ... & Janssen, I. (2016). Canadian 24-hour movement guidelines for children and youth: an integration of physical activity, sedentary behaviour, and sleep. *Applied Physiology, Nutrition, and Metabolism, 41*(6), S311-S327. www.nrcresearchpress.com/doi/full/10.1139/apnm-2016-0151#.XbrbfolCemQ

22 Carskadon, M. A., Wolfson, A. R., Acebo, C., Tzischinsky, O., & Seifer, R. (1998). Adolescent sleep patterns, circadian timing, and sleepiness at a transition to early school days. *Sleep, 21*(8), 871-881. https://pdfs.semanticscholar.org/03cb/ca0256e5c169de4c00d9bc0e420a7434f400.pdf;
Roberts, R. E., Roberts, C. R., & Duong, H. T. (2009). Sleepless in adolescence: prospective data on sleep deprivation, health and functioning. *Journal of adolescence, 32*(5), 1045-1057. www.ncbi.nlm.nih.gov/pmc/articles/PMC2735816/

23 Kann, L., McManus, T., Harris, W. A., Shanklin, S. L., Flint, K. H., Queen, B., ... & Lim, C. (2018). Youth risk behavior surveillance—United States, 2017. *MMWR Surveillance Summaries, 67*(8), 1. www.ncbi.nlm.nih.gov/pmc/articles/PMC6002027/;
Wheaton, A. G., Jones, S. E., Cooper, A. C., & Croft, J. B. (2018). Short sleep duration among middle school and high school students—United States, 2015. *Morbidity and Mortality Weekly Report, 67*(3), 85. http://dx.doi.org/10.15585/mmwr.mm6703a1

24 Emsellem, H. A., Knutson, K. L., Hillygus, D. S., Buxton, O. M., Montgomery-Downs, H., LeBourgeois, M. K., & Spilsbury, J. (2014). 2014 sleep in America poll. *Sleep in the modern family. Sleep Health, 1*(2), 13e. www.sleepfoundation.org/sites/default/files/inline-files/2014-NSF-Sleep-in-America-poll-summary-of-findings---FINAL-Updated-3-26-14-.pdf

25 Wolfson, A. R., & Carskadon, M. A. (1998). Sleep schedules and daytime functioning in adolescents. *Child development, 69*(4), 875-887. www.personal.psu.edu/students/s/e/seb302/wolfson_carskadon.pdf

26 Gibson, E. S., Powles, A. P., Thabane, L., O'Brien, S., Molnar, D. S., Trajanovic, N., ... & Chilcott-Tanser, L. (2006). " Sleepiness" is serious in adolescence: two surveys of 3235 Canadian students. *BMC public health, 6*(1), 116. https://bmcpublichealth.biomedcentral.com/articles/10.1186/1471-2458-6-116

27 Warner, S., Murray, G., & Meyer, D. (2008). Holiday and school-term sleep patterns of Australian adolescents. *Journal of adolescence, 31*(5), 595-608. www.semanticscholar.org/paper/Holiday-and-school-term-sleep-patterns-of-Warner-Murray/d8df0a950eba095de498663b8c0ca54dd3c4a084;
Footnote reference: [1]Walker, Matthew. *Why We Sleep: Unlocking the Power of Sleep and Dreams* (p. 20). Scribner. Kindle Edition.

28 Walker, Matthew. Why We Sleep: Unlocking the Power of Sleep and Dreams (p. 93). Scribner. Kindle Edition; Carskadon, M. A., Wolfson, A. R., Acebo, C., Tzischinsky, O., & Seifer, R. (1998). Adolescent sleep patterns, circadian timing, and sleepiness at a transition to early school days. *Sleep, 21*(8), 871-881. https://pdfs.semanticscholar.org/03cb/ca0256e5c169de4c00d9bc0e420a7434f400.pdf

29 Millman, R. P. (2005). Excessive sleepiness in adolescents and young adults: causes, consequences, and treatment strategies. *Pediatrics, 115*(6), 1774-1786. https://pediatrics.aappublications.org/content/pediatrics/115/6/1774.full.pdf

30 National Sleep Foundation. *2006 Sleep in American Poll: Summary Findings*. National Sleep Foundation. www.sleepfoundation.org/sites/default/files/inline-files/2006_summary_of_findings.pdf

31 Owens, J. A. (2001). The practice of pediatric sleep medicine: results of a community survey. *Pediatrics, 108*(3), e51-e51. https://pdfs.semanticscholar.org/83cb/2e9cae1bf7d4199a3c52a66571fed6c4d6cc.pdf

32 Brody, J. E. (2018). An Underappreciated Key to College Success: Sleep. *The New York Times*. www.nytimes.com/2018/08/13/well/an-underappreciated-key-to-college-success-sleep.html

33 Hansen, M., Janssen, I., Schiff, A., Zee, P. C., & Dubocovich, M. L. (2005). The impact of school daily schedule on adolescent sleep. *Pediatrics, 115*(6), 1555-1561. www.researchgate.net/publication/7812349_The_Impact_of_School_Daily_Schedule_on_Adolescent_Sleep

34 Owens, J., & Adolescent Sleep Working Group. (2014). Insufficient sleep in adolescents and young adults: an update on causes and consequences. *Pediatrics, 134*(3), e921-e932. https://pediatrics.aappublications.org/content/pediatrics/134/3/e921.full.pdf;
Marx, R., Tanner-Smith, E. E., Davison, C. M., Ufholz, L. A., Freeman, J., Shankar, R., ... & Hendrikx, S. (2017). Later school start times for supporting the education, health, and well-being of high school students. *Cochrane database of systematic reviews*, (7). www.ncbi.nlm.nih.gov/pmc/articles/PMC6483483/

35 Owens, J., Drobnich, D., Baylor, A., & Lewin, D. (2014). School start time change: an in-depth examination of school districts in the United States. *Mind, Brain, and Education, 8*(4), 182-213. www.dist50.net/cms/lib/IL02213585/Centricity/Domain/1153/School%20Start%20Time%20Change%20InDepth%20Examination%20of%20US%20Districts.pdf

36 Wheaton, A. G., Chapman, D. P., & Croft, J. B. (2016). School start times, sleep, behavioral, health, and academic outcomes: a review of the literature. *Journal of School Health, 86*(5), 363-381. https://teensneedsleep.files.wordpress.com/2014/10/wheaton-et-al-school-start-times-sleep-behavioral-health-and-academic-outcomes.pdf

37 Wahlstrom, K., Dretzke, B., Gordon, M., Peterson, K., Edwards, K., & Gdula, J. (2014). *Examining the impact of later high school start times on the health and academic performance of high school students: A multi-site study.* https://conservancy.umn.edu/bitstream/handle/11299/162769/Impact%20of%20Later%20Start%20Time%20Final%20Report.pdf?sequence=1

38 Footnote references:
[1] Healthy School Start Times. American Sleep Association. www.sleepassociation.org/blog-post/healthy-school-start-times/
[2] Watson, N. F., Martin, J. L., Wise, M. S., Carden, K. A., Kirsch, D. B., Kristo, D. A., ... & Rowley, J. A. (2017). Delaying middle school and high school start times promotes student health and performance: an American Academy of Sleep Medicine position statement. *Journal of Clinical Sleep Medicine, 13*(04), 623-625. https://jcsm.aasm.org/doi/10.5664/jcsm.6558
[3] Adolescent Sleep Working Group. (2014). School start times for adolescents. *Pediatrics, 134*(3), 642-649. https://pediatrics.aappublications.org/content/134/3/642.full
[4] Barnes, M., Davis, K., Mancini, M., Ruffin, J., Simpson, T., & Casazza, K. (2016). Setting adolescents up for success: promoting a policy to delay high school start times. *Journal of school health, 86*(7), 552-557. https://teensneedsleep.files.wordpress.com/2014/10/barnes-et-al-setting-adolescents-up-for-success.pdf
[5] American Medical Association. (2016). *AMA supports delayed school start times to improve adolescent wellness.* www.ama-assn.org/press-center/press-releases/ama-supports-delayed-school-start-times-improve-adolescent-wellness
[6] Kelley, P., & Lee, C. (2015). *Later Education Start Times in Adolescence: Time for Change.* Education Commission of the States. www.ecs.org/clearinghouse/01/12/19/11219.pdf

39 *Healthy School Start Times.* (n.d.). American Sleep Association. www.sleepassociation.org/blog-post/healthy-school-start-times/

40 Watson, N. F., Martin, J. L., Wise, M. S., Carden, K. A., Kirsch, D. B., Kristo, D. A., ... & Rowley, J. A. (2017). Delaying middle school and high school start times promotes student health and performance: an American

Academy of Sleep Medicine position statement. *Journal of Clinical Sleep Medicine, 13*(04), 623-625. https://jcsm.aasm.org/doi/10.5664/jcsm.6558

41 Adolescent Sleep Working Group. (2014). School start times for adolescents. *Pediatrics, 134*(3), 642-649. https://pediatrics.aappublications.org/content/134/3/642.full

42 Barnes, M., Davis, K., Mancini, M., Ruffin, J., Simpson, T., & Casazza, K. (2016). Setting adolescents up for success: promoting a policy to delay high school start times. *Journal of school health, 86*(7), 552-557. https://teensneedsleep.files.wordpress.com/2014/10/barnes-et-al-setting-adolescents-up-for-success.pdf

43 American Medical Association. (2016). AMA supports delayed school start times to improve adolescent wellness. www.ama-assn.org/press-center/press-releases/ama-supports-delayed-school-start-times-improve-adolescent-wellness

44 Kelley, P., & Lee, C. (2015). *Later Education Start Times in Adolescence: Time for Change. Education Commission of the States.* www.ecs.org/clearinghouse/01/12/19/11219.pdf

45 Trevorrow, T., Zhou, E. S., Dietch, J. R., & Gonzalez, B. D. (2019). Position statement: start middle and high schools at 8: 30 am or later to promote student health and learning. *Translational behavioral medicine, 9*(1), 167-169. www.sbm.org/UserFiles/file/late-school-start-statement-FINAL.pdf

46 American Psychological Association (2014). *Later school start times promote adolescent well-being.* www.apa.org/pi/families/resources/school-start-times.pdf

47 Fogg, N., & Johnson, A. (2015). Child and Adolescent Sleep Patterns and Early School Start Times: Recognizing the Role of the Pediatric Nurse. *Journal of pediatric nursing, 30*(4), 628-631. www.pediatricnursing.org/article/S0882-5963(15)00117-7/fulltext

48 National Parent Teacher Association. (2017). *Resolution on Healthy Sleep for Adolescents.* www.pta.org/home/advocacy/ptas-positions/Individual-PTA-Resolutions/Resolution-on-Healthy-Sleep-for-Adolescents

49 Mukherjee, S., Patel, S. R., Kales, S. N., Ayas, N. T., Strohl, K. P., Gozal, D., & Malhotra, A. (2015). An official American Thoracic Society statement: the importance of healthy sleep. Recommendations and future priorities. *American journal of respiratory and critical care medicine, 191*(12), 1450-1458.

50 *Start School Later Position Statement.* (n.d.). American Association of Sleep Technologists. www.aastweb.org/position-statement-start-school-later?fbclid=IwAR1YNLZ69mSuXV3JSJ4u5zSzTZdN_96Nz2riVLWwzZNm4N-4YoDmW3JUFc_w

51 Nicholls, H. (2018). Let Teenagers Sleep In. *The New York Times.* www.nytimes.com/2018/09/20/opinion/sunday/sleep-school-start-time-screens-teenagers.html?action=click&module=Well&pgtype=Homepage&section=SundayReview

52 Clarkson, K. (2013). *Resetting the Clock: High School Start Times.* Washington Parent. As cited in: Volz, A., Higdon, J., & Lidwell, W. (2019). *The Elements of Education for Teachers: 50 Research-based Principles Every Educator Should Know.* Routledge. https://books.google.co.uk/books?id=jJ6RDwAAQBAJ&pg=PT138&lpg=PT138&dq=%22If+you+knew+that+in+your+child%E2%80%99s+school+there+was+a+toxic+substance+that+reduced+the+capacity%22&source=bl&ots=8OaqNXlH_5&sig=ACfU3U0C5cLNbHHITTY-QU9EfGp86gP7-1Q&hl=en&sa=X&ved=2ahUKEwi2muXH0p7uAhWAThUIHQIjAcw4ChDoATABegQIAhAC#v=onepage&q=%22If%20you%20knew%20that%20in%20your%20child%E2%80%99s%20school%20there%20was%20a%20toxic%20substance%20that%20reduced%20the%20capacity%22&f=false

53 Wolfson, A. R., & Carskadon, M. A. (2005). A survey of factors influencing high school starttimes. *NASSP Bulletin, 89*(642), 47-66. http://citeseerx.ist.psu.edu/viewdoc/download?doi=10.1.1.588.8397&rep=rep1&type=pdf

54 Kelley, P., & Lee, C. (2015). *Later Education Start Times in Adolescence: Time for Change.* Education Commission of the States. www.ecs.org/clearinghouse/01/12/19/11219.pdf

55 Nicholls, H. (2018). Let Teenagers Sleep In. *The New York Times.* www.nytimes.com/2018/09/20/opinion/sunday/sleep-school-start-time-screens-teenagers.html?action=click&module=Well&pgtype=Homepage&section=SundayReview

56 Walker, Matthew. *Why We Sleep: Unlocking the Power of Sleep and Dreams* (p. 313). Scribner. Kindle Edition.

57 Sawyer, H., & Taie, S. (2020). *Start Time for US Public High Schools: Data Point.* National Center for Education Statistics. https://files.eric.ed.gov/fulltext/ED602999.pdf

58 Johns, M. (2015). *About the ESS-CHAD. The Epworth Sleepiness Scale.* http://epworthsleepinessscale.com/about-the-ess-chad/

59 Dollman, J., Ridley, K., Olds, T., & Lowe, E. (2007). Trends in the duration of school-day sleep among 10-to 15-year-old South Australians between 1985 and 2004. *Acta Paediatrica, 96*(7), 1011-1014. https://onlinelibrary.wiley.com/doi/abs/10.1111/j.1651-2227.2007.00278.x

60 *Kids Under Pressure.* (2021). Challenge Success and NBC News. www.challengesuccess.org/wp-content/uploads/2021/02/CS-NBC-Study-Kids-Under-Pressure-PUBLISHED.pdf

61 Walker, Matthew. *Why We Sleep: Unlocking the Power of Sleep and Dreams* (p. 154). Scribner. Kindle Edition.

62 Roehrs, T., & Roth, T. (2008). Caffeine: sleep and daytime sleepiness. *Sleep medicine reviews, 12*(2), 153-162. http://w.umfcv.ro/files/c/a/Caffeine%20-%20Sleep%20and%20daytime%20sleepiness.pdf

63 Tran, N. L., Barraj, L. M., Bi, X., & Jack, M. M. (2016). Trends and patterns of caffeine consumption among US teenagers and young adults, NHANES 2003–2012. *Food and Chemical Toxicology, 94,* 227-242. www.sciencedirect.com/science/article/pii/S0278691516301879

64 Owens, J., & Adolescent Sleep Working Group. (2014). Insufficient sleep in adolescents and young adults: an update on causes and consequences. *Pediatrics, 134*(3), e921-e932. https://pediatrics.aappublications.org/content/pediatrics/134/3/e921.full.pdf;

65 James, J. E., Kristjánsson, Á. L., & Sigfúsdóttir, I. D. (2011). Adolescent substance use, sleep, and academic achievement: Evidence of harm due to caffeine. *Journal of adolescence, 34*(4), 665-673. http://lifecourse.is/wp-content/uploads/2017/02/Adolescent-substance-use-sleep-and-academic-achievement-Evidence-of-harm-due-to-caffeine.pdf

66 Miller, K. E., Dermen, K. H., & Lucke, J. F. (2018). Caffeinated energy drink use by US adolescents aged 13–17: A national profile. *Psychology of Addictive Behaviors, 32*(6), 647. www.ncbi.nlm.nih.gov/pmc/articles/PMC6136946/

67 Talpos, S & Undark. (2019). Teens Are Probably Drinking Too Much Caffeine. *The Atlantic.* www.theatlantic.com/health/archive/2019/06/scientists-say-energy-drinks-ads-shouldnt-target-teens/592657/

68 American Academy of Pediatrics. (2011). Clinical Report—Sports drinks and energy drinks for children and adolescents: Are they appropriate. *Pediatrics, 127*(6), 1182-1189. https://pubmed.ncbi.nlm.nih.gov/21624882/

69 Mattson, M. E. (2013). *Update on emergency department visits involving energy drinks: a continuing public health concern.* The CBHSQ Report. www.ncbi.nlm.nih.gov/books/NBK384664/

70 Emsellem, H. A., Knutson, K. L., Hillygus, D. S., Buxton, O. M., Montgomery-Downs, H., LeBourgeois, M. K., & Spilsbury, J. (2014). 2014 sleep in America poll. Sleep in the modern family. *Sleep Health, 1*(2), 13e. www.sleepfoundation.org/sites/default/files/inline-files/2014-NSF-Sleep-in-America-poll-summary-of-findings---FINAL-Updated-3-26-14-.pdf

71 Levenson, J. C., Shensa, A., Sidani, J. E., Colditz, J. B., & Primack, B. A. (2016). The association between social media use and sleep disturbance among young adults. *Preventive medicine, 85,* 36-41. www.ncbi.nlm.nih.gov/pmc/articles/PMC4857587/;
Emsellem, H. A., Knutson, K. L., Hillygus, D. S., Buxton, O. M., Montgomery-Downs, H., LeBourgeois, M. K., & Spilsbury, J. (2014). 2014 sleep in America poll. Sleep in the modern family. *Sleep Health, 1*(2), 13e. www.sleepfoundation.org/sites/default/files/inline-files/2014-NSF-Sleep-in-America-poll-summary-of-findings---FINAL-Updated-3-26-14-.pdf;
Cain, N., & Gradisar, M. (2010). Electronic media use and sleep in school-aged children and adolescents: A review. *Sleep medicine, 11*(8), 735-742. www.researchgate.net/publication/45438547_Electronic_media_use_and_sleep_in_school-aged_children_and_adolescents_A_review;
Buxton, O. M., Chang, A. M., Spilsbury, J. C., Bos, T., Emsellem, H., & Knutson, K. L. (2015). Sleep in the modern family: protective family routines for child and adolescent sleep. *Sleep health, 1*(1), 15-27. www.sleephealthjournal.org/article/S2352-7218(14)00006-0/fulltext

72 Rideout, V., & Robb, M. B. (2018). *Social media, social life: Teens reveal their experiences.* Common Sense Media. www.commonsensemedia.org/sites/default/files/uploads/research/2018_cs_socialmediasociallife_fullreport-final-release_2_lowres.pdf

73 *7 Things You Should Never Do In Bed (And 2 You Definitely Should).* (2015). Hufington Post. www.huffingtonpost.com/2015/04/24/sleep-hygiene-tips_n_5030168.html

74 Council on Communications and Media, & MBE. (2016). Media use in school-aged children and adolescents. *Pediatrics, 138*(5), e20162592. https://pediatrics.aappublications.org/content/138/5/e20162592

75 Walker, Matthew. *Why We Sleep: Unlocking the Power of Sleep and Dreams* (pp. 268-269). Scribner. Kindle Edition.;
Kozaki, T., Koga, S., Toda, N., Noguchi, H., & Yasukouchi, A. (2008). Effects of short wavelength control in polychromatic light sources on nocturnal melatonin secretion. *Neuroscience letters, 439*(3), 256-259. www.researchgate.net/profile/Tomoaki_Kozaki/publication/5322357_Effects_of_short_wavelength_control_in_polychromatic_light_sources_on_nocturnal_melatonin_secretion/links/54add7350cf2828b29fcb611.pdf

76 Walker, Matthew. *Why We Sleep: Unlocking the Power of Sleep and Dreams* (p. 268). Scribner. Kindle Edition.

77 Duraccio, K. M., Zaugg, K. K., Blackburn, R. C., & Jensen, C. D. (2021). Does iPhone night shift mitigate negative effects of smartphone use on sleep outcomes in emerging adults?. *Sleep Health, 7*(4), 478-484. www.sciencedirect.com/science/article/abs/pii/S2352721821000607?dgcid=coauthor

78 Emsellem, H. A., Knutson, K. L., Hillygus, D. S., Buxton, O. M., Montgomery-Downs, H., LeBourgeois, M. K., & Spilsbury, J. (2014). 2014 sleep in America poll. Sleep in the modern family. *Sleep Health, 1*(2), 13e. www.sleepfoundation.org/sites/default/files/inline-files/2014-NSF-Sleep-in-America-poll-summary-of-findings---FINAL-Updated-3-26-14-.pdf;
LeBourgeois, M. K., Giannotti, F., Cortesi, F., Wolfson, A. R., & Harsh, J. (2005). The relationship between reported sleep quality and sleep hygiene in Italian and American adolescents. *Pediatrics, 115*(Supplement 1), 257-265. www.ncbi.nlm.nih.gov/pmc/articles/PMC3928632/

79 Walker, Matthew. *Why We Sleep: Unlocking the Power of Sleep and Dreams*. Scribner. Kindle Edition.

80 Han, J., Huang, R., Yue, L., Cui, N., & Cao, F. (2021). 585 The Relationship between Napping and Behavioral Problems among Vocational High School Students in China. *Sleep, 44*(Supplement_2), A231â€"A231. doi:10.1093/sleep/zsab072.583 https://academic.oup.com/sleep/article-abstract/44/Supplement_2/A231/6260299?redirectedFrom=fulltext;
*Napping can help tired teens' performance in school.* (2018). Science Daily. www.sciencedaily.com/releases/2018/04/180425195621.htm

81 Walker, Matthew. *Why We Sleep: Unlocking the Power of Sleep and Dreams*. Scribner. Kindle Edition.

82 Walker, Matthew. *Why We Sleep: Unlocking the Power of Sleep and Dreams*. Scribner. Kindle Edition.

83 Ji, X., Li, J., & Liu, J. (2019). The relationship between midday napping and neurocognitive function in early adolescents. *Behavioral sleep medicine, 17*(5), 537-551. www.ncbi.nlm.nih.gov/pmc/articles/PMC6669094/

84 Ericsson, K. A., Krampe, R. T., & Tesch-Römer, C. (1993). The role of deliberate practice in the acquisition of expert performance. *Psychological review, 100*(3), 363. https://mrbartonmaths.com/resourcesnew/8.%20Research/Explicit%20Instruction/Deliberate%20Practice.PDF

85 Walker, M. (2017). *Why we sleep: Unlocking the power of sleep and dreams.* Simon and Schuster.

86 Campbell, D. (2001). 'Fat boy' is work-out king. *The Guardian*. www.theguardian.com/world/2001/feb/11/deniscampbell.theobserver

87 Li, K., Haynie, D., Lipsky, L., Iannotti, R. J., Pratt, C., & Simons-Morton, B. (2016). Changes in moderate-to-vigorous physical activity among older adolescents. *Pediatrics, 138*(4). https://pediatrics.aappublications.org/content/138/4/e20161372

88 Lieberman, D. (2020). *Exercised.* Knopf Doubleday Publishing Group. Kindle Edition. Citing: 2018 Physical Activity Guidelines Advisory Committee. (2018). *2018 physical activity guidelines advisory committee scientific report.*

89 Kann, L., McManus, T., Harris, W. A., Shanklin, S. L., Flint, K. H., Queen, B., ... & Lim, C. (2018). Youth risk behavior surveillance—United States, 2017. *MMWR Surveillance Summaries, 67*(8), 1. www.ncbi.nlm.nih.gov/pmc/articles/PMC6002027/

90 Global Health Observatory (GHO) data repository. (2019). *Prevalence of insufficient physical activity among school going adolescents.* World Health Organization. https://apps.who.int/gho/data/view.main.2482ADO?lang=en

91 McNeely, C. & Blanchard, J. (2009). *The Teen Years Explained.* Johns Hopkins Bloomberg School of Public Health. www.jhsph.edu/research/centers-and-institutes/center-for-adolescent-health/_includes/_pre-redesign/Interactive%20Guide.pdf

92 Hollis, J. L., Williams, A. J., Sutherland, R., Campbell, E., Nathan, N., Wolfenden, L., ... & Wiggers, J. (2016). A systematic review and meta-analysis of moderate-to-vigorous physical activity levels in elementary school physical education lessons. *Preventive medicine, 86*, 34-54. https://nova.newcastle.edu.au/vital/access/services/Download/uon:23070/ATTACHMENT02

93 Sattelmair, J., & Ratey, J. J. (2009). Physically Active Play and Cognition: An Academic Matter?. *American journal of play, 1*(3), 365-374. https://files.eric.ed.gov/fulltext/EJ1068997.pdf

94 Sparling, P. B., & Snow, T. K. (2002). Physical activity patterns in recent college alumni. *Research quarterly for exercise and sport, 73*(2), 200-205. www.proquest.com/docview/218558172?pq-origsite=gscholar&fromopenview=true

95 Lieberman, D. (2020). *Exercised.* Knopf Doubleday Publishing Group. Kindle Edition.

96 Mountjoy, M., Andersen, L. B., Armstrong, N., Biddle, S., Boreham, C., Bedenbeck, H. P. B., ... & van Mechelen, W. (2011). International Olympic Committee consensus statement on the health and fitness of young people through physical activity and sport. *British journal of sports medicine, 45*(11), 839-848. https://bjsm.bmj.com/content/45/11/839?utm_source=trendmd&utm_medium=cpc&utm_campaign=bjsm&utm_content=consumer&utm_term=0-A

97 Sallis, J. F., & Patrick, K. (1994). Physical activity guidelines for adolescents: consensus statement. *Pediatric exercise science, 6*(4), 302-314.

98 Mountjoy, M., Andersen, L. B., Armstrong, N., Biddle, S., Boreham, C., Bedenbeck, H. P. B., ... & van Mechelen, W. (2011). International Olympic Committee consensus statement on the health and fitness of young people through physical activity and sport. *British journal of sports medicine, 45*(11), 839-848. https://bjsm.bmj.com/content/45/11/839?utm_source=trendmd&utm_medium=cpc&utm_campaign=bjsm&utm_content=consumer&utm_term=0-A

99 Calfas, K. J., & Taylor, W. C. (1994). Effects of physical activity on psychological variables in adolescents. *Pediatric exercise science, 6*(4), 406-423. https://journals.humankinetics.com/doi/abs/10.1123/pes.6.4.406;
Sallis, J. F., & Patrick, K. (1994). Physical activity guidelines for adolescents: consensus statement. *Pediatric exercise science, 6*(4), 302-314.

100 Bonhauser, M., Fernandez, G., Püschel, K., Yañez, F., Montero, J., Thompson, B., & Coronado, G. (2005). Improving physical fitness and emotional well-being in adolescents of low socioeconomic status in Chile: results of a school-based controlled trial. *Health Promotion International, 20*(2), 113-122. https://academic.oup.com/heapro/article/20/2/113/827446

101 Crews, D. J., Lochbaum, M. R., & Landers, D. M. (2004). Aerobic physical activity effects on psychological well-being in low-income Hispanic children. *Perceptual and motor skills, 98*(1), 319-324. http://journals.sagepub.com/doi/abs/10.2466/pms.98.1.319-324

102 Bonhauser, M., Fernandez, G., Püschel, K., Yañez, F., Montero, J., Thompson, B., & Coronado, G. (2005). Improving physical fitness and emotional well-being in adolescents of low socioeconomic status in Chile: results of a school-based controlled trial. *Health Promotion International, 20*(2), 113-122. https://academic.oup.com/heapro/article/20/2/113/827446;
DiBartolo, P. M., & Shaffer, C. (2002). A comparison of female college athletes and nonathletes: Eating disorder symptomatology and psychological well-being. *Journal of Sport and Exercise Psychology, 24*(1), 33-41. https://journals.humankinetics.com/doi/abs/10.1123/jsep.24.1.33

103 Hillman, C. H., Erickson, K. I., & Kramer, A. F. (2008). Be smart, exercise your heart: exercise effects on brain and cognition. *Nature reviews neuroscience, 9*(1), 58-65. http://drlardon.com/wp-content/uploads/2014/06/Perspectives.pdf;
Sattelmair, J., & Ratey, J. J. (2009). Physically Active Play and Cognition: An Academic Matter?. *American journal of play, 1*(3), 365-374. https://files.eric.ed.gov/fulltext/EJ1068997.pdf

104 Sallis, J. F., & Patrick, K. (1994). Physical activity guidelines for adolescents: consensus statement. *Pediatric exercise science, 6*(4), 302-314. https://journals.humankinetics.com/view/journals/pes/6/4/article-p302.xml

105 Sallis, J. F., & Patrick, K. (1994). Physical activity guidelines for adolescents: consensus statement. *Pediatric exercise science, 6*(4), 302-314. https://journals.humankinetics.com/view/journals/pes/6/4/article-p302.xml

106 Murray, B. (2007). Hydration and physical performance. *Journal of the American College of Nutrition, 26*(sup5), 542S-548S. https://cdn-00.cteonline.org/resources/documents/b0/b0972d53/b0972d5361d9225a561e-305057d2a520e0e7d59e/HydrationArticle2.pdf

107 Butcher, J., Lindner, K. J., & Johns, D. P. (2002). Withdrawal from Competitive Youth Sport: A Retrospective Ten-year Study. *Journal of Sport Behavior, 25*(2). http://static1.1.sqspcdn.com/static/f/1109123/24906774/1400507345587/Withdrawal+from+Competitive+Youth+Sport.pdf?token=ItiOaDQyBe42I16ffOYvPDADQ5A%3D

108 Goodger, K., Gorely, T., Lavallee, D., & Harwood, C. (2007). Burnout in sport: A systematic review. *The sport psychologist, 21*(2), 127-151. https://dspace.stir.ac.uk/bitstream/1893/7644/1/lavalleesportpsych2007.pdf

109 Csikszentmihalyi, M., Rathunde, K., & Whalen, S. (1997). *Talented teenagers: The roots of success and failure.* Cambridge University Press. www.davidsongifted.org/Search-Database/entry/A10049

110 Schnall, S., Harber, K. D., Stefanucci, J. K., & Proffitt, D. R. (2008). Social support and the perception of geographical slant. *Journal of experimental social psychology, 44*(5), 1246-1255. www.ncbi.nlm.nih.gov/pmc/articles/PMC3291107/

111 Patrick, H., Ryan, A. M., Alfeld-Liro, C., Fredricks, J. A., Hruda, L. Z., & Eccles, J. S. (1999). Adolescents' commitment to developing talent: The role of peers in continuing motivation for sports and the arts. *Journal of youth and adolescence, 28*(6), 741-763. www.researchgate.net/profile/Helen_Patrick/publication/225266120_Adolescents%27_Commitment_to_Developing_Talent_The_Role_of_Peers_in_Continuing_Motivation_for_Sports_and_the_Arts/links/0deec5268308d0ff55000000/Adolescents-Commitment-to-Developing-Talent-The-Role-of-Peers-in-Continuing-Motivation-for-Sports-and-the-Arts.pdf

112 Fox 3rd, S. M., & Haskell, W. L. (1968). Physical activity and the prevention of coronary heart disease. *Bulletin of the New York Academy of Medicine, 44*(8), 950. www.ncbi.nlm.nih.gov/pmc/articles/PMC1750298/pdf/bullnyacadmed00245-0064.pdf;
Buford, T. W., Roberts, M. D., & Church, T. S. (2013). Toward exercise as personalized medicine. *Sports medicine, 43*(3), 157-165. www.ncbi.nlm.nih.gov/pmc/articles/PMC3595541/

113 Andrade, J., & Ignaszewski, A. (2007). Exercise and the heart: A review of the early studies, in memory of Dr RS Paffenbarger. *British Columbia Medical Journal, 49*(10), 540. https://bcmj.org/sites/default/files/public/2007_dec_core_andrade%20%281%29.pdf

114 Campbell, D. (2001). 'Fat boy' is work-out king. *The Guardian.* www.theguardian.com/world/2001/feb/11/deniscampbell.theobserver

115 Aubrey, A. (2019). *Blind From A Bad Diet? Teen Who Ate Mostly Potato Chips And Fries Lost His Sight.* All Things Considered, NPR. https://text.npr.org/s.php?sId=757051172

116 Evans, N. (2012). *"This is the last time you'll see me like this": Britain's fattest teen vows to turn her life around.* Mirror. www.mirror.co.uk/news/uk-news/britains-fattest-teenager-vows-this-859790

117 Bernstein, L. (2016). U.S. Life Expectancy Declines For the First Time Since 1993. *The Washington Post.* www.washingtonpost.com/national/health-science/us-life-expectancy-declines-for-the-first-time-since-1993/2016/12/07/7dcdc7b4-bc93-11e6-91ee-1adddfe36cbe_story.html

118 Khazan, O. (2016). Why Are So Many Americans Dying Young? *The Atlantic.* www.theatlantic.com/health/archive/2016/12/why-are-so-many-americans-dying-young/510455/

119 Kann, L., McManus, T., Harris, W. A., Shanklin, S. L., Flint, K. H., Queen, B., ... & Lim, C. (2018). Youth risk behavior surveillance—United States, 2017. *MMWR Surveillance Summaries, 67*(8), 1. www.ncbi.nlm.nih.gov/pmc/articles/PMC6002027

120 Daniels, S. R., Arnett, D. K., Eckel, R. H., Gidding, S. S., Hayman, L. L., Kumanyika, S., ... & Williams, C. L. (2005). Overweight in children and adolescents: pathophysiology, consequences, prevention, and treatment. *Circulation, 111*(15), 1999-2012. www.ahajournals.org/doi/pdf/10.1161/01.CIR.0000161369.71722.10

121 Twig, G., Afek, A., Shamiss, A., Derazne, E., Landau Rabbi, M., Tzur, D., ... & Tirosh, A. (2014). Adolescence BMI and trends in adulthood mortality: a study of 2.16 million adolescents. *The Journal of Clinical Endocrinology & Metabolism, 99*(6), 2095-2103. https://academic.oup.com/jcem/article/99/6/2095/2537727

122 Eisenberg, M. E., Neumark-Sztainer, D., & Story, M. (2003). Associations of weight-based teasing and emotional well-being among adolescents. *Archives of pediatrics & adolescent medicine, 157*(8), 733-738. https://jamanetwork.com/journals/jamapediatrics/articlepdf/481394/poa20333_733_738.pdf;
Goldfield, G., Moore, C., Henderson, K., Buchholz, A., Obeid, N., & Flament, M. (2010). The relation between weight-based teasing and psychological adjustment in adolescents. *Paediatrics & child health, 15*(5), 283-288. www.ncbi.nlm.nih.gov/pmc/articles/PMC2912633/

123 Fredrickson, B. L., & Roberts, T. A. (1997). Objectification theory: Toward understanding women's lived experiences and mental health risks. *Psychology of women quarterly, 21*(2), 173-206. www.researchgate.net/profile/Tomi-Ann_Roberts/publication/258181826_Objectification_Theory_Toward_Understanding_Women%27s_Lived_Experiences_and_Mental_Health_Risks/links/59f375d4aca272607e2912c0/Objectification-Theory-Toward-Understanding-Womens-Lived-Experiences-and-Mental-Health-Risks.pdf

124 Loh, E. S. (1993). *The economic effects of physical appearance.* Social Science Quarterly. https://psycnet.apa.org/record/1994-03712-001

125 Han, E., Norton, E. C., & Stearns, S. C. (2009). Weight and wages: fat versus lean paychecks. *Health economics, 18*(5), 535-548. https://deepblue.lib.umich.edu/bitstream/handle/2027.42/62135/1386_ftp.pdf?sequence=1

126 Jenkinson, A. (2020). *Why We Eat (too Much): The New Science of Appetite.* Penguin UK.

127 Kann, L., McManus, T., Harris, W. A., Shanklin, S. L., Flint, K. H., Queen, B., ... & Lim, C. (2018). Youth risk behavior surveillance—United States, 2017. *MMWR Surveillance Summaries, 67*(8), 1. www.ncbi.nlm.nih.gov/pmc/articles/PMC6002027/

128 Gantz, W., Schwartz, N., & Angelini, J. R. (2007). *Television food advertising to children in the United States.* The Kaiser Family Foundation. www.kff.org/wp-content/uploads/2013/01/7618.pdf

129 Elsey, J. W., & Harris, J. L. (2016). Trends in food and beverage television brand appearances viewed by children and adolescents from 2009 to 2014 in the USA. *Public health nutrition, 19*(11), 1928-1933. https://pdfs.semanticscholar.org/3cfe/fa1d12be07b216c8d33765060c0d730a7942.pdf

130 Moss, M. (2013). *Salt, sugar, fat: How the food giants hooked us.* Random House Publishing Group. Kindle Edition.

131 Pollan, Michael. *In Defense of Food: An Eater's Manifesto* (p. 148). Penguin Publishing Group. Kindle Edition.

132 Bryan, C. J., Yeager, D. S., Hinojosa, C. P., Chabot, A., Bergen, H., Kawamura, M., & Steubing, F. (2016). Harnessing adolescent values to motivate healthier eating. *Proceedings of the National Academy of Sciences, 113*(39), 10830-10835. www.pnas.org/content/113/39/10830

133 Bryan, C. J., Yeager, D. S., & Hinojosa, C. P. (2019). A values-alignment intervention protects adolescents from the effects of food marketing. *Nature human behaviour, 3*(6), 596-603. www.ncbi.nlm.nih.gov/pmc/articles/PMC6784541/

134 Moss, M. (2013). *Salt, sugar, fat: How the food giants hooked us.* Random House.

135 Laney, C., Morris, E. K., Bernstein, D. M., Wakefield, B. M., & Loftus, E. F. (2008). Asparagus, a love story: Healthier eating could be just a false memory away. *Experimental Psychology, 55*(5), 291-300. www.miamikillianhs.com/ourpages/auto/2011/9/28/55941483/Laney.pdf

136 Neumark-Sztainer, D., Wall, M., Larson, N. I., Eisenberg, M. E., & Loth, K. (2011). Dieting and disordered eating behaviors from adolescence to young adulthood: findings from a 10-year longitudinal study. *Journal of the American Dietetic Association, 111*(7), 1004-1011. www.ncbi.nlm.nih.gov/pmc/articles/PMC3140795/

137 Stice, E., Cameron, R. P., Killen, J. D., Hayward, C., & Taylor, C. B. (1999). Naturalistic weight-reduction efforts prospectively predict growth in relative weight and onset of obesity among female adolescents. *Journal of consulting and clinical psychology, 67*(6), 967. www.researchgate.net/profile/Rebecca-Cameron-3/publication/12703934_Naturalistic_Weight-Reduction_Efforts_Prospectively_Predict_Growth_in_Relative_Weight_and_Onset_of_Obesity_Among_Female_Adolescents/links/56296ce308ae22b1702f2c4d/Naturalistic-Weight-Reduction-Efforts-Prospectively-Predict-Growth-in-Relative-Weight-and-Onset-of-Obesity-Among-Female-Adolescents.pdf

138 Rolland-Cachera, M. F., Thibault, H., Souberbielle, J. C., Soulie, D., Carbonel, P., Deheeger, M., ... & Serog, P. (2004). Massive obesity in adolescents: dietary interventions and behaviours associated with weight regain at 2 y follow-up. *International journal of obesity, 28*(4), 514. www.nature.com/articles/0802605

139 Johnston, C. A., Tyler, C., Fullerton, G., Carlos Poston, W. S., Haddock, C. K., McFarlin, B., ... & Foreyt, J. P. (2007). Results of an intensive school-based weight loss program with overweight Mexican American children. *International Journal of Pediatric Obesity, 2*(3), 144-152. www.tandfonline.com/doi/abs/10.1080/17477160701305864;
Johnston, C. A., Tyler, C., McFarlin, B. K., Poston, W. S., Haddock, C. K., Reeves, R., & Foreyt, J. P. (2007). Weight loss in overweight Mexican American children: a randomized, controlled trial. *Pediatrics, 120*(6), e1450-e1457. https://pediatrics.aappublications.org/content/120/6/e1450.short

Gortmaker, S. L., Peterson, K., Wiecha, J., Sobol, A. M., Dixit, S., Fox, M. K., & Laird, N. (1999). Reducing obesity via a school-based interdisciplinary intervention among youth: Planet Health. *Archives of pediatrics & adolescent medicine, 153*(4), 409-418. https://jamanetwork.com/journals/jamapediatrics/fullarticle/346206

140 McNeely, C., & Blanchard, J. (2009). *The teen years explained: A guide to healthy adolescent development.* Johns Hopkins Bloomberg School of Public Health. Center for Adolescent Health. www.jhsph.edu/research/centers-and-institutes/center-for-adolescent-health/_includes/_pre-redesign/Interactive%20Guide.pdf

141 Savoye, M., Shaw, M., Dziura, J., Tamborlane, W. V., Rose, P., Guandalini, C., ... & Caprio, S. (2007). Effects of a weight management program on body composition and metabolic parameters in overweight children: a randomized controlled trial. *Jama, 297*(24), 2697-2704. https://jamanetwork.com/journals/jama/articlepdf/207688/joc70059_2697_2704.pdf

142 Thomas, D., Elliott, E. J., & Baur, L. (2007). Low glycaemic index or low glycaemic load diets for overweight and obesity. *The Cochrane Library.* http://cochranelibrary-wiley.com/doi/10.1002/14651858.CD005105.pub2/full;
Ebbeling, C. B., Leidig, M. M., Sinclair, K. B., Hangen, J. P., & Ludwig, D. S. (2003). A reduced–glycemic load diet in the treatment of adolescent obesity. *Archives of pediatrics & adolescent medicine, 157*(8), 773-779. https://jamanetwork.com/journals/jamapediatrics/fullarticle/481401

143 McNeely, C. & Blanchard, J. (2009). *The Teen Years Explained.* Johns Hopkins Bloomberg School of Public Health. www.jhsph.edu/research/centers-and-institutes/center-for-adolescent-health/_includes/_pre-redesign/Interactive%20Guide.pdf

144 Walker, M. (2017). *Why we sleep: Unlocking the power of sleep and dreams.* Simon and Schuster.

145 McNeely, C. & Blanchard, J. (2009). *The Teen Years Explained.* Johns Hopkins Bloomberg School of Public Health. www.jhsph.edu/research/centers-and-institutes/center-for-adolescent-health/_includes/_pre-redesign/Interactive%20Guide.pdf;
Robinson, E., Aveyard, P., & Jebb, S. A. (2015). Is plate clearing a risk factor for obesity? A cross-sectional study of self-reported data in US adults. *Obesity, 23*(2), 301-304. https://onlinelibrary.wiley.com/doi/pdf/10.1002/oby.20976

146 Summerbell, C. D., Ashton, V., Campbell, K. J., Edmunds, L., Kelly, S., & Waters, E. (2003). Interventions for treating obesity in children. *Cochrane Database Syst Rev, 3*(3), CD001872. http://cochranelibrary-wiley.com/doi/10.1002/14651858.CD001872.pub2/full

147 Stierman, B., Mishra, S., Gahche, J. J., Potischman, N., & Hales, C. M. (2020). Dietary Supplement Use in Children and Adolescents Aged≤ 19 Years—United States, 2017–2018. *Morbidity and Mortality Weekly Report, 69*(43), 1557. www.cdc.gov/mmwr/volumes/69/wr/mm6943a1.htm

148 Golden, N. H., & Abrams, S. A. (2014). Optimizing bone health in children and adolescents. *Pediatrics, 134*(4), e1229-e1243. www.researchgate.net/profile/Neville-Golden/publication/266325183_Optimizing_Bone_Health_in_Children_and_Adolescents/links/5686b1f908ae1e63f1f5a805/Optimizing-Bone-Health-in-Children-and-Adolescents.pdf

149 US Department of Health and Human Services. (2019). *2015–2020 dietary guidelines for Americans.* US Department of Agriculture. https://health.gov/sites/default/files/2019-09/2015-2020_Dietary_Guidelines.pdf

150 Halterman, J. S., Kaczorowski, J. M., Aligne, C. A., Auinger, P., & Szilagyi, P. G. (2001). Iron deficiency and cognitive achievement among school-aged children and adolescents in the United States. *Pediatrics, 107*(6), 1381-1386. www.medicine.mcgill.ca/epidemiology/hanley/c678/iron_deficiency_IQ.pdf;
Bruner, A. B., Joffe, A., Duggan, A. K., Casella, J. F., & Brandt, J. (1996). Randomised study of cognitive effects of iron supplementation in non-anaemic iron-deficient adolescent girls. *The Lancet, 348*(9033), 992-996. https://d1wqtxts1xzle7.cloudfront.net/49102506/Randomised_study_of_cognitive_effects_of20160925-5350-4qdkor-with-cover-page-v2.pdf?Expires=1636027578&Signature=LOU0eycDkpOVT6IZEts1vD-G-MiHTtpvYOxTYC8jUJQ0BdedDtiR-YPIyFRvb0gLnB5zADJLMP1S8CmuSLXHshXPYc13QaRctm1jrsh2P-Mkk5jq4D9MjajOslVzjHIV7Dm7rdnowbTPUyOzUD5FPjvMkEjt336-EtlpU1VEFJP364Lg4A6Pm-k7XvUOxa7GvWk5LRr-V4NcdicWp8G6oiiYOJTnhtoaWlw61jCE-CZswuX7PPdC75lmrEmfsyTRxg-PH8FvWiThfss6Wf5peq4JKYl1hcqGiIr3-JT5kINXviP6v-8xnSqmXr2PQLjSJuW-WuueJP8YfWYsK-rf-HaRi6Q__&Key-Pair-Id=APKAJLOHF5GGSLRBV4ZA

151 Finkelstein, J. L., Herman, H. S., Guetterman, H. M., Peña-Rosas, J. P., & Mehta, S. (2018). Daily iron supplementation for prevention or treatment of iron deficiency anaemia in infants, children, and adolescents. *The Cochrane Database of Systematic Reviews,* 2018(12). www.ncbi.nlm.nih.gov/pmc/articles/PMC6517129/

152 Musick, K., & Meier, A. (2012). Assessing causality and persistence in associations between family dinners and adolescent well-being. *Journal of Marriage and Family, 74*(3), 476-493. www.ncbi.nlm.nih.gov/pmc/articles/PMC3686529/;
Hoffman, J. (2009). The Guilt-Trip Casserole: The Family Dinner. *The New York Times*. www.nytimes.com/2009/10/04/fashion/04dinner.html

153 Ermisch, J., Iacovou, M., & Skew, A. J. (2011). Family relationships. *Understanding society: Early findings from the first wave of the UK's Household Longitudinal Study*. ISER, University of Essex. http://repository.essex.ac.uk/9115/1/Understanding-Society-Early-Findings.pdf

154 The National Center on Addiction and Substance Abuse at Columbia University. (2012). *The Importance of Family Dinners VIII, A CASAColumbiaTM White Paper*. www.fmi.org/docs/default-source/familymeals/2012924familydinnersviii.pdf?sfvrsn=967c676e_2

155 Hofferth, S. L., & Sandberg, J. F. (2001). How American children spend their time. *Journal of Marriage and Family, 63*(2), 295-308. https://onlinelibrary.wiley.com/doi/abs/10.1111/j.1741-3737.2001.00295.x

156 Gibbs, N. (2006). The Magic of the Family Meal. *Time*. http://content.time.com/time/subscriber/article/0,33009,1200760,00.html

157 Fiese, B. H., & Schwartz, M. (2008). Reclaiming the family table: Mealtimes and child health and wellbeing. *Social Policy Report, 22*(4), 1-20. https://srcd.onlinelibrary.wiley.com/doi/pdf/10.1002/j.2379-3988.2008.tb00057.x;
*Project Zero*. (2016). Harvard Graduate School of Education. www.pz.harvard.edu/projects/the-family-dinner-project

158 David, L., & Uhrenholdt, K. (2010). *The family dinner: Great ways to connect with your kids, one meal at a time*. Grand Central Life & Style. www.amazon.co.uk/Family-Dinner-Great-Ways-Connect/dp/0446565466#:~:text=OK-,The%20Family%20Dinner%3A%20Great%20Ways%20to%20Connect%20with%20Your%20Kids,2010&text=The%20producer%20of%20An%20Inconvenient,fun%20tools%20to%20do%20so

159 Luthar, S. S., & Latendresse, S. J. (2005). Children of the affluent: Challenges to well-being. *Current directions in psychological science, 14*(1), 49-53. https://www.ncbi.nlm.nih.gov/pmc/articles/PMC1948879/?_escaped_fragment_=po=32.3529

160 Musick, K., & Meier, A. (2012). Assessing causality and persistence in associations between family dinners and adolescent well-being. *Journal of Marriage and Family, 74*(3), 476-493. www.ncbi.nlm.nih.gov/pmc/articles/PMC3686529/

161 Dwyer, L., Oh, A., Patrick, H., & Hennessy, E. (2015). Promoting family meals: a review of existing interventions and opportunities for future research. *Adolescent health, medicine and therapeutics, 6*, 115. www.ncbi.nlm.nih.gov/pmc/articles/PMC4482375/

162 McNeely, C., & Blanchard, J. (2009). *The teen years explained: A guide to healthy adolescent development*. Johns Hopkins Bloomberg School of Public Health. Center for Adolescent Health. www.jhsph.edu/research/centers-and-institutes/center-for-adolescent-health/_includes/_pre-redesign/Interactive%20Guide.pdf

163 Wickham, S. R., Amarasekara, N. A., Bartonicek, A., & Conner, T. S. (2020). The Big Three Health Behaviors and Mental Health and Well-Being Among Young Adults: A Cross-Sectional Investigation of Sleep, Exercise, and Diet. *Frontiers in psychology, 11*, 3339. www.frontiersin.org/articles/10.3389/fpsyg.2020.579205/full?utm_source=miragenews&utm_medium=miragenews&utm_campaign=news

164 Gilbert, E. (2007). *Eat, pray, love: one woman's search for everything*. A&C Black.

# 8. Achievement

1 Watterson, B. (2005). *The Complete Calvin and Hobbes*. Andrews McMeel Publishing.

2 Dettmers, S., Trautwein, U., & Lüdtke, O. (2009). The relationship between homework time and achievement is not universal: Evidence from multilevel analyses in 40 countries. *School Effectiveness and school improvement, 20*(4), 375-405. https://refubium.fu-berlin.de/bitstream/handle/fub188/135/Dissertation_SDettmers.pdf?sequence=1#page=84

3 Norman, D. A. (Ed.). (1981). *Perspectives on cognitive science*. Greenwood.

4 Haller, E. P., Child, D. A., & Walberg, H. J. (1988). Can comprehension be taught? A quantitative synthesis of "metacognitive" studies. *Educational researcher, 17*(9), 5-8. https://d1wqtxts1xzle7.cloudfront.net/44598933/5.full-with-cover-page-v2.pdf?Expires=1634836196&Signature=GxK5Ftj9HAJw1oMaLVbeH-b0lQYe8eXV2T1dKQFMMWfgRBrSI9tbcxRPOpmhBlaAlUTW9jfBGxTV7kh1-vLRv6T6-iWdLYlgZ-j4H-JwgJPnOx64pdaj66aV9xyNUFIbwCmySOKa4qqaq8HyZs4jNtgdoILjwZjwuybwdQ7X6syWqC4D3megRH-bzMh8ea-GXhQTpkiWX4dqIedM2zgA6mAkagvCBlJSwAvjVC-2zAHxpoh4izEhg-NdbDmFGlAuWBruG-5PEyHZjjLAVIm-AUMH9-AXYzyVPolfsGXOxY6eGVSvWxtPjuX4anaNZj4hnRrjsicGAUsuBPIDxTsJG-D7Olw__&Key-Pair-Id=APKAJLOHF5GGSLRBV4ZA

5 Gurung, R. A. (2005). How do students really study (and does it matter)?. *Education, 39*, 323-340. www.researchgate.net/profile/Regan_Gurung/publication/228786091_How_Do_Students_Really_Study_and_Does_It_Matter/links/004635140972ab064d000000/How-Do-Students-Really-Study-and-Does-It-Matter.pdf

6 Dunlosky, J., Rawson, K. A., Marsh, E. J., Nathan, M. J., & Willingham, D. T. (2013). Improving students' learning with effective learning techniques: Promising directions from cognitive and educational psychology. *Psychological Science in the Public Interest, 14*(1), 4-58. http://marker.to/XVMEI9;
Kornell, N., & Bjork, R. A. (2007). The promise and perils of self-regulated study. *Psychonomic bulletin & review, 14*(2), 219-224. https://link.springer.com/content/pdf/10.3758/BF03194055.pdf;
Hartwig, M. K., & Dunlosky, J. (2012). Study strategies of college students: Are self-testing and scheduling related to achievement?. *Psychonomic bulletin & review, 19*(1), 126-134. https://link.springer.com/article/10.3758/s13423-011-0181-y;
Karpicke, J. D., Butler, A. C., & Roediger III, H. L. (2009). Metacognitive strategies in student learning: do students practise retrieval when they study on their own?. *Memory, 17*(4), 471-479. www.researchgate.net/profile/Andrew-Butler-7/publication/24268097_Metacognitive_strategies_in_student_learning_Do_students_practise_retrieval_when_they_study_on_their_own/links/5772da3908aeeec389541573/Metacognitive-strategies-in-student-learning-Do-students-practise-retrieval-when-they-study-on-their-own.pdf

7 Dunlosky, J., Rawson, K. A., Marsh, E. J., Nathan, M. J., & Willingham, D. T. (2013). Improving students' learning with effective learning techniques: Promising directions from cognitive and educational psychology. *Psychological Science in the Public Interest, 14*(1), 4-58. http://marker.to/XVMEI9

8 Peterson, S. E. (1991). The cognitive functions of underlining as a study technique. *Literacy Research and Instruction, 31*(2), 49-56. www.tandfonline.com/doi/abs/10.1080/19388079209558078

9 Farrington, C. A., Roderick, M., Allensworth, E., Nagaoka, J., Keyes, T. S., Johnson, D. W., & Beechum, N. O. (2012). *Teaching Adolescents to Become Learners: The Role of Noncognitive Factors in Shaping School Performance--A Critical Literature Review*. Consortium on Chicago School Research. https://files.eric.ed.gov/fulltext/ED542543.pdf

10 Dunlosky, J., Rawson, K. A., Marsh, E. J., Nathan, M. J., & Willingham, D. T. (2013). Improving students' learning with effective learning techniques: Promising directions from cognitive and educational psychology. *Psychological Science in the Public Interest, 14*(1), 4-58. http://marker.to/XVMEI9

11 Hartwig, M. K., & Dunlosky, J. (2012). Study strategies of college students: Are self-testing and scheduling related to achievement?. *Psychonomic bulletin & review, 19*(1), 126-134. https://link.springer.com/article/10.3758/s13423-011-0181-y

12 Dunlosky, J. (2013). Strengthening the student toolbox: Study strategies to boost Learning. *American Educator, 37*(3), 12-21. www.aft.org/sites/default/files/periodicals/dunlosky.pdf

13 Dunlosky, J. (2013). Strengthening the student toolbox: Study strategies to boost Learning. *American Educator, 37*(3), 12-21. www.aft.org/sites/default/files/periodicals/dunlosky.pdf

14 Dunlosky, J., Rawson, K. A., Marsh, E. J., Nathan, M. J., & Willingham, D. T. (2013). Improving students' learning with effective learning techniques: Promising directions from cognitive and educational psychology. *Psychological Science in the Public Interest, 14*(1), 4-58. http://marker.to/XVMEI9

15 Taylor, K., & Rohrer, D. (2010). The effects of interleaved practice. *Applied Cognitive Psychology, 24*(6), 837-848. http://uweb.cas.usf.edu/~drohrer/pdfs/Taylor%26Rohrer2010ACP.pdf

16 Loeber, R., Burke, J. D., Lahey, B. B., Winters, A., & Zera, M. (2000). Oppositional defiant and conduct disorder: a review of the past 10 years, part I. *Journal of the American Academy of Child & Adolescent Psychiatry, 39*(12), 1468-1484. http://citeseerx.ist.psu.edu/viewdoc/download?doi=10.1.1.499.8732&rep=rep1&type=pdf

17 Gillen-O'Neel, C., Huynh, V. W., & Fuligni, A. J. (2013). To study or to sleep? The academic costs of extra studying at the expense of sleep. *Child development, 84*(1), 133-142. https://pdfs.semanticscholar.org/7e80/ed35a849c983ba25e072016a015da63e37c0.pdf

18 Dunlosky, J. (2013). Strengthening the student toolbox: Study strategies to boost Learning. *American Educator, 37*(3), 12-21. www.aft.org/sites/default/files/periodicals/dunlosky.pdf;
Kornell, N. (2009). Optimising learning using flashcards: Spacing is more effective than cramming. *Applied Cognitive Psychology, 23*(9), 1297-1317. https://s3.amazonaws.com/academia.edu.documents/34530303/Kornell.2009b.pdf?AWSAccessKeyId=AKIAIWOWYYGZ2Y53UL3A&Expires=1516975899&Signature=hI%2B-vkA%2B2KlwkjH9FWgb5ZoQmVPM%3D&response-content-disposition=inline%3B%20filename%3DOptimising_Learning_Using_Flashcards_Spa.pdf

19 Dunlosky, J., Rawson, K. A., Marsh, E. J., Nathan, M. J., & Willingham, D. T. (2013). Improving students' learning with effective learning techniques: Promising directions from cognitive and educational psychology. I(1), 4-58. http://marker.to/XVMEI9

20 Zimmerman, B. J., & Pons, M. M. (1986). Development of a structured interview for assessing student use of self-regulated learning strategies. *American educational research journal, 23*(4), 614-628. www.researchgate.net/profile/Manuel_Martinez-Pons/publication/233896774_Development_of_a_Structured_Interview_for_Assessing_Student_Use_of_Self-Regulated_Learning_Strategies/links/00b4953caef487a20e000000.pdf

21 Farrington, C. A., Roderick, M., Allensworth, E., Nagaoka, J., Keyes, T. S., Johnson, D. W., & Beechum, N. O. (2012). *Teaching Adolescents to Become Learners: The Role of Noncognitive Factors in Shaping School Performance--A Critical Literature Review*. Consortium on Chicago School Research. https://files.eric.ed.gov/fulltext/ED542543.pdf

22 Farrington, C. A., Roderick, M., Allensworth, E., Nagaoka, J., Keyes, T. S., Johnson, D. W., & Beechum, N. O. (2012). *Teaching Adolescents to Become Learners: The Role of Noncognitive Factors in Shaping School Performance--A Critical Literature Review*. Consortium on Chicago School Research. https://files.eric.ed.gov/fulltext/ED542543.pdf

23 Duckworth, A. L., Grant, H., Loew, B., Oettingen, G., & Gollwitzer, P. M. (2011). Self-regulation strategies improve self-discipline in adolescents: Benefits of mental contrasting and implementation intentions. *Educational Psychology, 31*(1), 17-26. https://kops.uni-konstanz.de/bitstream/handle/123456789/17105/gollwitzer_strategies.pdf?sequence=2;
Farrington, C. A., Roderick, M., Allensworth, E., Nagaoka, J., Keyes, T. S., Johnson, D. W., & Beechum, N. O. (2012). Teaching Adolescents to Become Learners: The Role of Noncognitive Factors in Shaping School Performance--A Critical Literature Review. Consortium on Chicago School Research. https://files.eric.ed.gov/fulltext/ED542543.pdf

24 Farrington, C. A., Roderick, M., Allensworth, E., Nagaoka, J., Keyes, T. S., Johnson, D. W., & Beechum, N. O. (2012). *Teaching Adolescents to Become Learners: The Role of Noncognitive Factors in Shaping School Performance--A Critical Literature Review*. Consortium on Chicago School Research. https://files.eric.ed.gov/fulltext/ED542543.pdf

25 Farrington, C. A., Roderick, M., Allensworth, E., Nagaoka, J., Keyes, T. S., Johnson, D. W., & Beechum, N. O. (2012). *Teaching Adolescents to Become Learners: The Role of Noncognitive Factors in Shaping School Performance--A Critical Literature Review*. Consortium on Chicago School Research. https://files.eric.ed.gov/fulltext/ED542543.pdf

26 Farrington, C. A., Roderick, M., Allensworth, E., Nagaoka, J., Keyes, T. S., Johnson, D. W., & Beechum, N. O. (2012). *Teaching Adolescents to Become Learners: The Role of Noncognitive Factors in Shaping School Performance--A Critical Literature Review*. Consortium on Chicago School Research. https://files.eric.ed.gov/fulltext/ED542543.pdf
Citing: Palincsar, A. S. (1986). Metacognitive strategy instruction. *Exceptional children, 53*(2), 118-124.

27 Dunlosky, J., Rawson, K. A., Marsh, E. J., Nathan, M. J., & Willingham, D. T. (2013). Improving students' learning with effective learning techniques: Promising directions from cognitive and educational psychology. *Psychological Science in the Public Interest, 14*(1), 4-58. http://marker.to/XVMEI9

28 Smith, S. M., & Vela, E. (2001). Environmental context-dependent memory: A review and meta-analysis. *Psychonomic bulletin & review, 8*(2), 203-220. https://link.springer.com/content/pdf/10.3758/BF03196157.pdf

29 Smith, S. M., Glenberg, A., & Bjork, R. A. (1978). Environmental context and human memory. Memory & Cognition, 6(4), 342-353. https://link.springer.com/content/pdf/10.3758/BF03197465.pdf

30 Rosen, L. D., Carrier, L. M., & Cheever, N. A. (2013). Facebook and texting made me do it: Media-induced task-switching while studying. *Computers in Human Behavior, 29*(3), 948-958. www5.csudh.edu/psych/Facebook_and_Texting_Made_Me_Do_It-Media-Induced_Task-Switching_While_Studying-Compuers_in_Human_Behavior-2013-Rosen_Carrier_Cheever.pdf

31 Rideout, V. J. (2015). *The common sense census: Media use by tweens and teens.* Common Sense Media Incorporated. www.commonsensemedia.org/sites/default/files/uploads/research/census_researchreport.pdf

32 Carrier, L. M., Rosen, L. D., Cheever, N. A., & Lim, A. F. (2015). Causes, effects, and practicalities of everyday multitasking. *Developmental Review, 35*, 64-78. www.researchgate.net/profile/Alex_Lim/publication/272788676_Carrier_Rosen_Cheever_Lim_2015/links/54ee15810cf25238f9399878.pdf

33 Wood, E., Zivcakova, L., Gentile, P., Archer, K., De Pasquale, D., & Nosko, A. (2012). Examining the impact of off-task multi-tasking with technology on real-time classroom learning. *Computers & Education, 58*(1), 365-374. https://blogs.ethz.ch/wp-content/blogs.dir/1318/files/2012/03/Multi-tasking.pdf

34 Zimmerman, B. J., & Pons, M. M. (1986). Development of a structured interview for assessing student use of self-regulated learning strategies. *American educational research journal, 23*(4), 614-628. www.researchgate.net/profile/Manuel_Martinez-Pons/publication/233896774_Development_of_a_Structured_Interview_for_Assessing_Student_Use_of_Self-Regulated_Learning_Strategies/links/00b4953caef487a20e000000.pdf

35 Gurung, R. A. (2005). How do students really study (and does it matter)?. *Education, 39*, 323-340. www.researchgate.net/profile/Regan_Gurung/publication/228786091_How_Do_Students_Really_Study_and_Does_It_Matter/links/004635140972ab064d000000/How-Do-Students-Really-Study-and-Does-It-Matter.pdf

36 Jacobsen, W. C., & Forste, R. (2011). The wired generation: Academic and social outcomes of electronic media use among university students. *Cyberpsychology, Behavior, and Social Networking, 14*(5), 275-280. www.researchgate.net/profile/Renata_Forste/publication/47508990_The_Wired_Generation_Academic_and_Social_Outcomes_of_Electronic_Media_Use_Among_University_Students/links/5963abd9458515a35761f7d6/The-Wired-Generation-Academic-and-Social-Outcomes-of-Electronic-Media-Use-Among-University-Students.pdf

37 Council on Communications and Media, & MBE. (2016). Media use in school-aged children and adolescents. *Pediatrics, 138*(5), e20162592. https://pediatrics.aappublications.org/content/138/5/e20162592

38 Alley, T. R., & Greene, M. E. (2008). The relative and perceived impact of irrelevant speech, vocal music and non-vocal music on working memory. *Current Psychology, 27*(4), 277-289. www.researchgate.net/profile/Thomas_Alley/publication/226187507_The_Relative_and_Perceived_Impact_of_Irrelevant_Speech_Vocal_Music_and_Non-vocal_Music_on_Working_Memory/links/542461130cf238c6ea6ebb43.pdf

39 Rideout, V. J. (2015). *The common sense census: Media use by tweens and teens.* Common Sense Media Incorporated. www.commonsensemedia.org/sites/default/files/uploads/research/census_researchreport.pdf

40 Jäncke, L., & Sandmann, P. (2010). Music listening while you learn: No influence of background music on verbal learning. *Behavioral and Brain Functions, 6*(1), 3. https://behavioralandbrainfunctions.biomedcentral.com/articles/10.1186/1744-9081-6-3;
Alley, T. R., & Greene, M. E. (2008). The relative and perceived impact of irrelevant speech, vocal music and non-vocal music on working memory. *Current Psychology, 27*(4), 277-289. www.researchgate.net/profile/Thomas_Alley/publication/226187507_The_Relative_and_Perceived_Impact_of_Irrelevant_Speech_Vocal_Music_and_Non-vocal_Music_on_Working_Memory/links/542461130cf238c6ea6ebb43.pdf;
De Groot, A. (2006). Effects of stimulus characteristics and background music on foreign language vocabulary learning and forgetting. *Language Learning, 56*(3), 463-506. https://s3.amazonaws.com/academia.edu.documents/45966285/j.1467-9922.2006.00374.x20160526-24283-1wtx9w0.pdf?AWSAccessKeyId=AKIAIWOWYYGZ2Y53UL3A&Expires=1552328065&Signature=quTZVRvbQVqOF3pWkZfWtZoCgHA%3D&response-content-disposition=inline%3B%20filename%3DEffects_of_Stimulus_Characteristics_and.pdf

41 De Groot, A. (2006). Effects of stimulus characteristics and background music on foreign language vocabulary learning and forgetting. *Language Learning, 56*(3), 463-506. https://s3.amazonaws.com/academia.edu.documents/45966285/j.1467-9922.2006.00374.x20160526-24283-1wtx9w0.pdf?AWSAccessKeyId=AKIAIWOWYYGZ2Y53UL3A&Expires=1552328065&Signature=quTZVRvbQVqOF3pWkZfWtZoCgHA%3D&response-content-disposition=inline%3B%20filename%3DEffects_of_Stimulus_Characteristics_and.pdf

42 Furnham, A., & Bradley, A. (1997). Music while you work: The differential distraction of background music on the cognitive test performance of introverts and extraverts. Applied Cognitive Psychology: The Official Journal of the Society for Applied *Research in Memory and Cognition, 11*(5), 445-455. http://citeseerx.ist.psu.edu/viewdoc/download?doi=10.1.1.1000.1425&rep=rep1&type=pdf;

Furnham, A., & Allass, K. (1999). The influence of musical distraction of varying complexity on the cognitive performance of extroverts and introverts. *European Journal of Personality, 13*(1), 27-38. www.gwern.net/docs/music-distraction/1999-furnham-2.pdf;
Daoussis, L., & Mc Kelvie, S. J. (1986). Musical preferences and effects of music on a reading comprehension test for extraverts and introverts. *Perceptual and motor skills, 62*(1), 283-289. https://journals.sagepub.com/doi/abs/10.2466/pms.1986.62.1.283;
Dobbs, S., Furnham, A., & McClelland, A. (2011). The effect of background music and noise on the cognitive test performance of introverts and extraverts. *Applied cognitive psychology, 25*(2), 307-313. https://onlinelibrary.wiley.com/doi/full/10.1002/acp.1692

43 Daoussis, L., & Mc Kelvie, S. J. (1986). Musical preferences and effects of music on a reading comprehension test for extraverts and introverts. *Perceptual and motor skills, 62*(1), 283-289. https://journals.sagepub.com/doi/abs/10.2466/pms.1986.62.1.283

44 Bakosh, L. S., Snow, R. M., Tobias, J. M., Houlihan, J. L., & Barbosa-Leiker, C. (2016). Maximizing mindful learning: Mindful awareness intervention improves elementary school students' quarterly grades. *Mindfulness, 7*(1), 59-67. http://openaccess.city.ac.uk/20007/1/Bakosh%20et%20al%202016Mindfulness_Maximising%20Mindful%20Learning.pdf;
Thierry, K. L., Bryant, H. L., Nobles, S. S., & Norris, K. S. (2016). Two-year impact of a mindfulness-based program on preschoolers' self-regulation and academic performance. *Early Education and Development, 27*(6), 805-821. www.tandfonline.com/doi/abs/10.1080/10409289.2016.1141616

45 Quach, D., Mano, K. E. J., & Alexander, K. (2016). A randomized controlled trial examining the effect of mindfulness meditation on working memory capacity in adolescents. *Journal of Adolescent Health, 58*(5), 489-496. www.jahonline.org/article/S1054-139X%2815%2900380-8/fulltext

46 Mrazek, M. D., Franklin, M. S., Phillips, D. T., Baird, B., & Schooler, J. W. (2013). Mindfulness training improves working memory capacity and GRE performance while reducing mind wandering. *Psychological science, 24*(5), 776-781. http://portal.idc.ac.il/he/main/services/studentsdean/develop_study_ability/documents/mrazek.pdf;
Hall, P. D. (1999). The effect of meditation on the academic performance of African American college students. *Journal of black Studies, 29*(3), 408-415. https://cats.estrellamountain.edu/sites/default/files/docs/317/effect-meditation-academic-performance.pdf;
Ramsburg, J. T., & Youmans, R. J. (2014). Meditation in the higher-education classroom: Meditation training improves student knowledge retention during lectures. *Mindfulness, 5*(4), 431-441. https://link.springer.com/article/10.1007/s12671-013-0199-5

47 Creswell, J. D. (2017). *Mindfulness interventions. Annual review of psychology, 68*, 491-516. https://pdfs.semanticscholar.org/01c3/ae46e25f27a692564793d60f7c4779222d32.pdf

48 Zenner, C., Herrnleben-Kurz, S., & Walach, H. (2014). Mindfulness-based interventions in schools—a systematic review and meta-analysis. *Frontiers in psychology, 5*, 603. www.frontiersin.org/articles/10.3389/fpsyg.2014.00603/full;
Calma-Birling, D., & Gurung, R. A. (2017). Does A Brief Mindfulness Intervention Impact Quiz Performance?. *Psychology Learning & Teaching, 16*(3), 323-335. http://scholar.google.co.uk/scholar_url?url=https%3A%2F%2Fwww.researchgate.net%2Fprofile%2FRegan_Gurung%2Fpublication%2F319109863_Mindfulness_CD-Gurung%2Fdata%2F5991c794aca27289539bacd4%2FMindfulness-CD-Gurung.pdf&hl=en&sa=T&oi=gga&ct=gga&cd=10&d=5373957054280706418&ei=ZTyKXI60F9GImwGH04aYBw&scisig=AAGBfm3UIbuZLTdILcjoRqSvunrJ5rgieA&nossl=1&ws=1920x906&at=Does%20A%20Brief%20Mindfulness%20Intervention%20Impact%20Quiz%20Performance%3F&bn=1

49 Friedman, T. (2004). Doing Our Homework. *The New York Times*. www.nytimes.com/2004/06/24/opinion/doing-our-homework.html

50 Gross, E. L. (2018). *Inside the insanely competitive world of elite New York City preschools*. Business Insider India. www.businessinsider.in/inside-the-insanely-competitive-world-of-elite-new-york-city-preschools/articleshow/64594327.cms

51 Westover, Tara. *Educated*. Random House Publishing Group. Kindle Edition.

52 Coleman, J. S. (1988). Social capital in the creation of human capital. *American journal of sociology, 94*, S95-S120. www.crcresearch.org/files-crcresearch/File/coleman_88.pdf

53 Locurto, C. (1990). The malleability of IQ as judged from adoption studies. *Intelligence, 14*(3), 275-292. www.gwern.net/docs/iq/1990-locurto.pdf

54 Rich, J. (1998). *The nurture assumption: Why Children Turn Out the Way They Do*. Bloomsbury.

55 Plomin, R., & Daniels, D. (1987). Why are children in the same family so different from one another?. *Behavioral and brain Sciences, 10*(1), 1-16. https://arch.neicon.ru/xmlui/handle/123456789/929261;
Plomin, R., Chipuer, H. M., & Neiderhiser, J. M. (1994). Behavioral genetic evidence for the importance of nonshared environment. Separate social worlds of siblings: *The impact of nonshared environment on development,* 1-31. https://books.google.co.uk/books?hl=en&lr=&id=ljIU6nRB4woC&oi=fnd&pg=PA1&dq=Behavioral+genetic+evidence+for+the+importance+of+nonshared+environment.+Separate+social+worlds+of+siblings:+The+impact+of+nonshared+environment+on+development&ots=tTieO1migQ&sig=F6J27bYmqXSqN6iHtw-m_CdtuSA&redir_esc=y#v=onepage&q=Behavioral%20genetic%20evidence%20for%20the%20importance%20of%20nonshared%20environment.%20Separate%20social%20worlds%20of%20siblings%3A%20The%20impact%20of%20nonshared%20environment%20on%20development&f=false

56 Plomin, R., Fulker, D. W., Corley, R., & DeFries, J. C. (1997). Nature, nurture, and cognitive development from 1 to 16 years: A parent-offspring adoption study. *Psychological Science, 8*(6), 442-447. https://journals.sagepub.com/doi/abs/10.1111/j.1467-9280.1997.tb00458.x

57 Rich, J. (1998). *The nurture assumption: Why children turn out the way they do.* Bloomsbury.

58 Smith, S. B. (2017). The Lonely Heir: Inside the Isolating Boarding School Days of Prince Charles. *Vanity Fair.* www.vanityfair.com/style/2017/03/the-isolating-boarding-school-days-of-prince-charles

59 Rich, J. (1998). The nurture assumption. London: Bloomsbury.

60 U.S. Department of Education, National Center for Education Statistics. (2018). *Digest of Education Statistics, 2016* (NCES 2017-094), Chapter 2. https://nces.ed.gov/fastfacts/display.asp?id=6

61 *What is value-added and how does it help?* (n.d.). Center for Evaluation and Monitoring (CEM). www.cem.org/what-is-value-added#:~:text=All%20schools%20improve%20their%20pupils,to%20be%20called%20value%2Dadded

62 Footnote reference: [1] *We're measuring educational opportunity in every community in America.* (n.d). The Educational Opportunity Project at Stanford University. https://edopportunity.org/

63 *Digest of Education Statistics: 2018.* (2018). National Center for Education Statistics. https://nces.ed.gov/programs/digest/d18/

64 *NAEP Data Available for Secondary Analysis.* (2018). National Center for Education Statistics. https://nces.ed.gov/nationsreportcard/researchcenter/datatools.aspx

65 Abdulkadiroglu, A., Pathak, P. A., Schellenberg, J., & Walters, C. R. (2017). *Do parents value school effectiveness?.* National Bureau of Economic Research. https://eml.berkeley.edu/~crwalters/papers/apsw_nyc.pdf

66 Footnote reference: [1] Farrington, C. A., Roderick, M., Allensworth, E., Nagaoka, J., Keyes, T. S., Johnson, D. W., & Beechum, N. O. (2012). *Teaching Adolescents to Become Learners: The Role of Noncognitive Factors in Shaping School Performance--A Critical Literature Review.* Consortium on Chicago School Research. https://files.eric.ed.gov/fulltext/ED542543.pdf

67 Bursztyn, L., Egorov, G., & Jensen, R. (2019). Cool to be smart or smart to be cool? Understanding peer pressure in education. *The Review of Economic Studies, 86*(4), 1487-1526. http://home.uchicago.edu/~bursztyn/Bursztyn_Egorov_Jensen_2018_01_12.pdf

68 Kinney, D. A. (1993). From nerds to normals: The recovery of identity among adolescents from middle school to high school. *Sociology of Education,* 21-40. www.mifras.org/know/wp-content/uploads/2014/04/From-Nerds-to-Normals-The-Recovery-of-Identity-among-Adolescents-from-Middle-School-to-High-School.pdf
Citing: Fordham, S., & Ogbu, J. U. (1986). Black students' school success: Coping with the "burden of 'acting white'". *The urban review, 18*(3), 176-206.

69 Jencks, C., & Mayer, S. E. (1990). The social consequences of growing up in a poor neighborhood. *Inner-city poverty in the United States,* 111, 186. www.nap.edu/download/1539#

70 Rosenbaum, J. E. (1995). Changing the geography of opportunity by expanding residential choice: Lessons from the Gautreaux program. *Housing Policy Debate, 6*(1), 231-269. www.grahamimac.com/housingandeducation/pdf/Rosenbaum_1995.pdf

71 Farrington, C. A., Roderick, M., Allensworth, E., Nagaoka, J., Keyes, T. S., Johnson, D. W., & Beechum, N. O. (2012). *Teaching Adolescents to Become Learners: The Role of Noncognitive Factors in Shaping School Performance--A Critical Literature Review.* Consortium on Chicago School Research. https://files.eric.ed.gov/fulltext/ED542543.pdf

72 Footnote references:
[1] CNN Transcripts. (2009). *Continued Coverage: President Obama Holds Town Hall in Missouri. CNN. http://transcripts.cnn.com/TRANSCRIPTS/0904/29/cnr.04.html*
[2] O-Levels. (2016). *The Economist.* www.economist.com/united-states/2016/07/09/o-levels

73 Purnick, J. (1995). METRO MATTERS; It's a Competitive School, Where It's O.K. to Excel. *The New York Times.* www.nytimes.com/1995/01/23/nyregion/metro-matters-it-s-a-competitive-school-where-it-s-ok-to-excel.html?auth=login-email&login=email&searchResultPosition=5

74 Rich, J. (1998). *The nurture assumption: Why children turn out the way they do.* Bloomsbury.

75 Jencks, C., & Mayer, S. E. (1990). The social consequences of growing up in a poor neighborhood. *Inner-city poverty in the United States,* 111, 186. www.nap.edu/download/1539#

76 Vernberg, E. M. (1990). Experiences with peers following relocation during early adolescence. *American Journal of Orthopsychiatry, 60*(3), 466-472. https://onlinelibrary.wiley.com/doi/abs/10.1037/h0079160;
Wood, D., Halfon, N., Scarlata, D., Newacheck, P., & Nessim, S. (1993). Impact of family relocation on children's growth, development, school function, and behavior. *Jama, 270*(11), 1334-1338. https://jamanetwork.com/journals/jama/article-abstract/408450;
Jelleyman, T., & Spencer, N. (2008). Residential mobility in childhood and health outcomes: a systematic review. *Journal of Epidemiology & Community Health, 62*(7), 584-592. www.researchgate.net/profile/Nicholas_Spencer4/publication/5296174_Residential_mobility_in_childhood_and_health_outcomes_A_systematic_review/links/545b4f940cf28779a4daa9be/Residential-mobility-in-childhood-and-health-outcomes-A-systematic-review;
Braver, S. L., Ellman, I. M., & Fabricius, W. V. (2003). Relocation of children after divorce and children's best interests: New evidence and legal considerations. *Journal of Family Psychology, 17*(2), 206. www.researchgate.net/profile/Sanford_Braver/publication/297376586_Relocation_of_children_after_divorce_and_children's_best_interests_New_evidence_and_legal_considerations/links/56e1e49e08aebc9edb19cbc1/Relocation-of-children-after-divorce-and-childrens-best-interests-New-evidence-and-legal-considerations.pdf;
Simmons, R. G., Burgeson, R., Carlton-Ford, S., & Blyth, D. A. (1987). The impact of cumulative change in early adolescence. *Child development,* 1220-1234. www.jstor.org/stable/1130616?read-now=1&seq=1#page_scan_tab_contents

77 Wiseman, A. W. (2008). A culture of (in) equality?: A cross-national study of gender parity and gender segregation in national school systems. *Research in Comparative and International Education, 3*(2), 179-201. https://journals.sagepub.com/doi/pdf/10.2304/rcie.2008.3.2.179

78 Footnote references:
[1] Mael, F., Alonso, A., Gibson, D., Rogers, K., & Smith, M. (2005). *Single-Sex Versus Coeducational Schooling: A Systematic Review.* US Department of Education. https://files.eric.ed.gov/fulltext/ED486476.pdf
[2] Morse, S. (1998). *Separated by sex: A critical look at single-sex education for girls.* Amer Assn of Univ Women. www.ncgs.org/Pdfs/Resources/Separated-By-Sex-A-Critical-Look-at-Single-Sex-Education-for-Girls.pdf
[3] Smithers, A., & Robinson, P. (2006). *The paradox of single-sex and co-educational schooling.* Carmichael Press. www.alansmithers.com/reports/Paradox27Jul2006.pdf
[4] Gill, J. (2004). *Beyond the great divide: Single sex or coeducation?.* UNSW Press. https://books.google.co.uk/books?hl=en&lr=&id=KYPfxrfMSRcC&oi=fnd&pg=PA7&dq=Beyond+the+Great+Divide:+Single-sex+or+-Co-education&ots=mzQI5aiRpY&sig=i0h045Brm77tU--KUOIaotzboOU#v=onepage&q=Beyond%20the%20Great%20Divide%3A%20Single-sex%20or%20Co-education&f=false
[5] Salomone, R. C. (2008). Same, different, equal: Rethinking single-sex schooling. Yale University Press.
[6] Thompson, T., & Ungerleider, C. (2004). *Single-sex schooling: Final report.* Canadian Centre for Knowledge Mobilisation. https://thetyee.ca/Opinion/2012/09/11/Single%20Sex%20Schooling%20report.pdf
[7] Wong, W. I., Shi, S. Y., & Chen, Z. (2018). Students from single-sex schools are more gender-salient and more anxious in mixed-gender situations: Results from high school and college samples. *PloS One, 13*(12), e0208707. www.ncbi.nlm.nih.gov/pmc/articles/PMC6286141/
[8] Cardona, L., & Kaufmann, K. M. (2017). *Gender Peer Effects, Non-Cognitive Skills and Marriage Market Outcomes: Evidence from Single-Sex Schools in the UK. In National Bureau of Economic Research Conference paper.* https://conference.iza.org/conference_files/transatlantic_2018/kaufmann_k3596.pdf

79 Farrington, C. A., Roderick, M., Allensworth, E., Nagaoka, J., Keyes, T. S., Johnson, D. W., & Beechum, N. O. (2012). *Teaching Adolescents to Become Learners: The Role of Noncognitive Factors in Shaping School Performance--A Critical Literature Review.* https://files.eric.ed.gov/fulltext/ED542543.pdf

80 Medina, J. (2007). At Canarsie High, Now Marked for Closing, Loyalty Prevails. *The New York Times.* www.nytimes.com/2007/12/24/nyregion/24canarsie.html?pagewanted=all

81 Schultz, H. (2019). *My Story.* Howard Schultz. www.howardschultz.com/my-story/#playgrounds

Canarsie High School. (2021). *Wikipedia*. https://en.wikipedia.org/wiki/Canarsie_High_School

82 Steele, C. M., & Aronson, J. (1995). Stereotype threat and the intellectual test performance of African Americans. *Journal of personality and social psychology, 69*(5), 797. https://greatergood.berkeley.edu/images/uploads/Claude_Steele_and_Joshua_Aronson,_1995.pdf

83 Davies, P. G., Spencer, S. J., Quinn, D. M., & Gerhardstein, R. (2002). Consuming images: How television commercials that elicit stereotype threat can restrain women academically and professionally. *Personality and Social Psychology Bulletin, 28*(12), 1615-1628. https://uwspace.uwaterloo.ca/bitstream/handle/10012/588/NQ53990.pdf?sequence=1&isAllowed=y;
Davies, P. G., Spencer, S. J., & Steele, C. M. (2005). Clearing the air: identity safety moderates the effects of stereotype threat on women's leadership aspirations. *Journal of personality and social psychology, 88*(2), 276. http://citeseerx.ist.psu.edu/viewdoc/download?doi=10.1.1.576.3037&rep=rep1&type=pdf

84 Fredrickson, B. L., Roberts, T. A., Noll, S. M., Quinn, D. M., & Twenge, J. M. (1998). That swimsuit becomes you: sex differences in self-objectification, restrained eating, and math performance. *Journal of personality and social psychology, 75*(1), 269. www.researchgate.net/profile/Tomi-Ann_Roberts/publication/247434408_That_swimsuit_becomes_you_Sex_differences_in_self-objectification_restrained_eating_and_math_performance_Correction_to_Fredrickson_et_al_1998/links/5540fcb30cf2718618dc9672/That-swimsuit-becomes-you-Sex-differences-in-self-objectification-restrained-eating-and-math-performance-Correction-to-Fredrickson-et-al-1998.pdf

85 Spencer, S. J., Steele, C. M., & Quinn, D. M. (1999). Stereotype threat and women's math performance. *Journal of experimental social psychology, 35*(1), 4-28. https://nuovoeutile.it/wp-content/uploads/2013/07/Stereotype-threat-Spencer-1999.pdf

86 Inzlicht, M., & Ben-Zeev, T. (2000). A threatening intellectual environment: Why females are susceptible to experiencing problem-solving deficits in the presence of males. *Psychological Science, 11*(5), 365-371. https://pdfs.semanticscholar.org/8c2b/99312266e2e47d44c84030b660b14132eff6.pdf?_ga=2.139923443.1520222002.1552561603-1273937781.1527873639

87 Steele, C. M., & Aronson, J. (1995). Stereotype threat and the intellectual test performance of African Americans. *Journal of personality and social psychology, 69*(5), 797. http://mrnas.pbworks.com/f/claude%20steele%20stereotype%20threat%201995.pdf

88 Croizet, J. C., & Claire, T. (1998). Extending the concept of stereotype threat to social class: The intellectual underperformance of students from low socioeconomic backgrounds. *Personality and Social Psychology Bulletin, 24*(6), 588-594. https://journals.sagepub.com/doi/abs/10.1177/0146167298246003

89 Walton, G. M., & Spencer, S. J. (2009). Latent ability: Grades and test scores systematically underestimate the intellectual ability of negatively stereotyped students. *Psychological Science, 20*(9), 1132-1139. https://cpb-us-w2.wpmucdn.com/u.osu.edu/dist/2/43662/files/2017/02/j2E1467-92802E20092E024172Ex-2319zul.pdf

90 Steele, C. M., & Aronson, J. (1995). Stereotype threat and the intellectual test performance of African Americans. *Journal of personality and social psychology, 69*(5), 797. http://mrnas.pbworks.com/f/claude%20steele%20stereotype%20threat%201995.pdf

91 Hebl, M. R., King, E. B., & Lin, J. (2004). The swimsuit becomes us all: Ethnicity, gender, and vulnerability to self-objectification. *Personality and Social Psychology Bulletin, 30*(10), 1322-1331. https://s3.amazonaws.com/academia.edu.documents/43641927/The_Swimsuit_Becomes_Us_All_Ethnicity_Ge20160311-4153-1yu40bt.pdf?AWSAccessKeyId=AKIAIWOWYYGZ2Y53UL3A&Expires=1518024653&Signature=1I%2FzmqUsPkTPQq671x1q6zC1hpY%3D&response-content-disposition=inline%3B%20filename%3DThe_swimsuit_becomes_us_all_Ethnicity_ge.pdf

92 Aronson, J., Lustina, M. J., Good, C., Keough, K., Steele, C. M., & Brown, J. (1999). When white men can't do math: Necessary and sufficient factors in stereotype threat. *Journal of experimental social psychology, 35*(1), 29-46. https://thetestingpsychologist.com/wp-content/uploads/2020/10/Aronson-Lustina-Good-Keough-Steele-Brown-1999.pdf

93 Walton, G. M., & Cohen, G. L. (2011). A brief social-belonging intervention improves academic and health outcomes of minority students. *Science, 331*(6023), 1447-1451. https://pdfs.semanticscholar.org/cca0/3bf7eed-7eac526086853efa37b8f6d7c424d.pdf

94 Walton, G. M., & Cohen, G. L. (2007). A question of belonging: race, social fit, and achievement. *Journal of personality and social psychology, 92*(1), 82. www.goshen.edu/wp-content/uploads/sites/2/2016/08/WaltonCohen2007.pdf

95 Shapiro, J. R., Williams, A. M., & Hambarchyan, M. (2013). Are all interventions created equal? A multi-threat approach to tailoring stereotype threat interventions. *Journal of Personality and Social Psychology, 104*(2), 277. www.ncbi.nlm.nih.gov/pmc/articles/PMC3682115/

96 Cohen, G. L., Garcia, J., Apfel, N., & Master, A. (2006). Reducing the racial achievement gap: A social-psychological intervention. *Science, 313*(5791), 1307-1310. www.researchgate.net/profile/Nancy_Apfel/publication/6842991_Reducing_the_Racial_Achievement_Gap_A_Social-Psychological_Intervention/links/0912f512a710a84f56000000.pdf

97 Johns, M., Schmader, T., & Martens, A. (2005). Knowing is half the battle: Teaching stereotype threat as a means of improving women's math performance. *Psychological Science*, 16(3), 175-179. http://mrnas.pbworks.com/f/16187467.pdf

98 Good, C., Aronson, J., & Harder, J. A. (2008). Problems in the pipeline: Stereotype threat and women's achievement in high-level math courses. *Journal of applied developmental psychology, 29*(1), 17-28. www.researchgate.net/profile/Jayne_Ann_Harder/publication/223920165_Problems_in_the_Pipeline_Stereotype_Threat_and_Women%27s_Achievement_in_High-Level_Math_Courses/links/5aa98e4faca272d39cd5dd87/Problems-in-the-Pipeline-Stereotype-Threat-and-Womens-Achievement-in-High-Level-Math-Courses.pdf

99 McIntyre, R. B., Lord, C. G., Gresky, D. M., Ten Eyck, L. L., Frye, G. J., & Bond Jr, C. F. (2005). A social impact trend in the effects of role models on alleviating women's mathematics stereotype threat. *Current Research in Social Psychology, 10*(9), 116-136. http://citeseerx.ist.psu.edu/viewdoc/download?doi=10.1.1.409.8363&rep=rep1&type=pdf

100 Bagès, C., & Martinot, D. (2011). What is the best model for girls and boys faced with a standardized mathematics evaluation situation: A hardworking role model or a gifted role model?. *British Journal of Social Psychology, 50*(3), 536-543. https://d1wqtxts1xzle7.cloudfront.net/42391338/What_is_the_best_model_for_girls_and_boy20160208-19558-1gen1cl.pdf?1454949653=&response-content-disposition=inline%3B+filename%3DWhat_is_the_best_model_for_girls_and_boy.pdf&Expires=1593456226&Signature=cQSCf-DG-ZIt4~EUg7FJ8jS-I9GMulXfTCXrRMmHrfHsUV8F9dsmxy8fTRdPM1YsYlygVRLrVXY1VUtLhbTQjgmH-p3~vMOabfWdN0hHyFoFRwcsrMJUty-Wonp87hB4ikLlXSjTVMiRAReh9CwikGlyn8ZTX8x7ASzjEwn3qhLB-BHwhG~-4PKGRftniNWPI9e4kQ5T0xF9yZOggdFeZVYV9bQM2w9sMAyL3kz3tYw0R8ubBHGqocDb-JlpZgVFC-GyvMlxMuMkaLQ-mZPC~ML8anFTJEGYILYmu4HnCMDg88Qw43DlJQVCu15elzro-916QXFC64bUp3alrhpSXK1w6Hg__&Key-Pair-Id=APKAJLOHF5GGSLRBV4ZA

101 *Project Implicit.* (2011). Project Implicit. https://implicit.harvard.edu/implicit/selectatest.html

102 Bryner, J. (2007). *Most Students Bored at School.* Live Science. www.livescience.com/1308-students-bored-school.html

103 Paton, G. (2009). School is boring and irrelevant, say teenagers. *The Telegraph*. www.telegraph.co.uk/education/secondaryeducation/4297452/School-is-boring-and-irrelevant-say-teenagers.html

104 Jason, J. (2017). Bored Out of Their Minds. *Harvard Ed. Magazine*. www.gse.harvard.edu/news/ed/17/01/bored-out-their-minds

105 Farrington, C. A., Roderick, M., Allensworth, E., Nagaoka, J., Keyes, T. S., Johnson, D. W., & Beechum, N. O. (2012). *Teaching Adolescents to Become Learners: The Role of Noncognitive Factors in Shaping School Performance--A Critical Literature Review*. Consortium on Chicago School Research. https://files.eric.ed.gov/fulltext/ED542543.pdf

106 Heffernan, L. E. (2014). The Case for Nagging Kids About Their Homework. *The Atlantic*. www.theatlantic.com/education/archive/2014/01/the-case-for-nagging-kids-about-their-homework/282838/;
Hill, N. E., & Tyson, D. F. (2009). Parental involvement in middle school: a meta-analytic assessment of the strategies that promote achievement. *Developmental psychology, 45*(3), 740. www.ncbi.nlm.nih.gov/pmc/articles/PmC2782391/

107 Hulleman, C. S., & Harackiewicz, J. M. (2009). Promoting interest and performance in high school science classes. *Science, 326*(5958), 1410-1412. https://prlsamp.rcse.upr.edu/downloads/bestpractice2015/Harackiewicz_04.pdf

108 Hulleman, C. S., Godes, O., Hendricks, B. L., & Harackiewicz, J. M. (2010). Enhancing interest and performance with a utility value intervention. *Journal of educational psychology, 102*(4), 880. www.researchgate.net/profile/Michael_Moore9/post/What_do_children_know_about_their_own_learning/attachment/59d63035c49f478072ea067e/AS%3A273600710414336%401442242903837/download/Enhancing+Interest+and+Performance+With+a+Utility+Value+Intervention.pdf

109 Harackiewicz, J. M., Rozek, C. S., Hulleman, C. S., & Hyde, J. S. (2012). Helping parents to motivate adolescents in mathematics and science: An experimental test of a utility-value intervention. *Psychological science, 23*(8), 899-906. https://studentsocialsupport.org/files/s3rd/files/harackiewicz2012extrastem.pdf

110 Strogatz, S. (2019). *Infinite powers: how calculus reveals the secrets of the universe.* Eamon Dolan Books.

111 Pliska, B. (2018). *What calculus is used for?* Brigita Pliska. https://medium.com/@brigitaplika/what-calculus-is-used-for-fb319e8c38b6

112 *Whether You Believe You Can Do a Thing or Not, You Are Right.* (2015). Quote Investigator. https://quoteinvestigator.com/2015/02/03/you-can/

113 Dweck, C. S. (2008). *Mindset: The new psychology of success.* Random House Digital, Inc.

114 Dweck, C. (2014). *The Power of Believing that You Can Improve* [Video]. TED. www.ted.com/talks/carol_dweck_the_power_of_believing_that_you_can_improve?language=en

115 Farrington, C. A., Roderick, M., Allensworth, E., Nagaoka, J., Keyes, T. S., Johnson, D. W., & Beechum, N. O. (2012). *Teaching Adolescents to Become Learners: The Role of Noncognitive Factors in Shaping School Performance--A Critical Literature Review.* Consortium on Chicago School Research. https://files.eric.ed.gov/fulltext/ED542543.pdf

116 Wilson, T. D., & Linville, P. W. (1982). Improving the academic performance of college freshmen: attribution therapy revisited. *Journal of personality and social psychology, 42*(2), 367. http://people.virginia.edu/~tdw/wilson.linville.1982.pdf;
Wilson, T. D., & Linville, P. W. (1985). Improving the performance of college freshmen with attributional techniques. *Journal of Personality and Social Psychology, 49*(1), 287. https://uploads-ssl.webflow.com/59faaf5b01b9500001e95457/5bc5515c36f9e4faf33c6d53_Wilson%20%26%20Linville%2C%201985.pdf

117 Aronson, J., Fried, C. B., & Good, C. (2002). Reducing the effects of stereotype threat on African American college students by shaping theories of intelligence. *Journal of experimental social psychology, 38*(2), 113-125. https://research.steinhardt.nyu.edu/scmsAdmin/uploads/004/308/Aronson%20Fried%20%20Good.pdf

118 Good, C., Aronson, J., & Inzlicht, M. (2003). Improving adolescents' standardized test performance: An intervention to reduce the effects of stereotype threat. *Journal of Applied Developmental Psychology, 24*(6), 645-662. https://users.nber.org/~sewp/events/2005.01.14/Bios+Links/Good-rec1-Good_Aronson_&_Inzlicht.pdf;
Blackwell, L. S., Trzesniewski, K. H., & Dweck, C. S. (2007). Implicit theories of intelligence predict achievement across an adolescent transition: A longitudinal study and an intervention. *Child development, 78*(1), 246-263. http://citeseerx.ist.psu.edu/viewdoc/download?doi=10.1.1.884.9797&rep=rep1&type=pdf

119 Foliano, F., Rolfe, H., Buzzeo, J., Runge, J., & Wilkinson, D. (2019). *Changing mindsets: Effectiveness trial.* National Institute of Economic and Social Research. www.niesr.ac.uk/sites/default/files/publications/Changing%20Mindsets_0.pdf#page=43

120 Denworth, L. (2019). Debate Arises over Teaching "Growth Mindsets" to Motivate Students. *Scientific American.* www.scientificamerican.com/article/debate-arises-over-teaching-growth-mindsets-to-motivate-students/

121 Denworth, L. (2019). Debate Arises over Teaching "Growth Mindsets" to Motivate Students. *Scientific American.* www.scientificamerican.com/article/debate-arises-over-teaching-growth-mindsets-to-motivate-students/

122 Yeager, D. S., Hanselman, P., Walton, G. M., Murray, J. S., Crosnoe, R., Muller, C., ... & Paunesku, D. (2019). A national experiment reveals where a growth mindset improves achievement. *Nature, 573*(7774), 364-369. www.nature.com/articles/s41586-019-1466-y?fbclid=IwAR3eSTiOiVc3v8LARTfGwxTzlS-Dz4AiAFpLK-jK4VcJr57wI0eO8zyvwkEc

123 Yeager, D. S., Romero, C., Paunesku, D., Hulleman, C. S., Schneider, B., Hinojosa, C., ... & Trott, J. (2016). Using design thinking to improve psychological interventions: The case of the growth mindset during the transition to high school. *Journal of educational psychology, 108*(3), 374. www.ncbi.nlm.nih.gov/pmc/articles/PMC4981081/

124 *Growth mindset Unit: High school activities.* (2021). Khan Academy. www.khanacademy.org/partner-content/learnstorm-growth-mindset-activities-us/high-school-activities

125 *Study Hacks Blog: Intelligence is Irrelevant: An MIT Alum's Advice to a Struggling Student.* (2012). Cal Newport. www.calnewport.com/blog/2012/01/09/intelligence-is-irrelevant-an-mit-alums-advice-to-a-struggling-student/

126 Agassi, Andre. *Open* (p. 26). Knopf Doubleday Publishing Group. Kindle Edition.

127 Chua, A. (2011). *Battle hymn of the tiger mother.* Bloomsbury Publishing.

128 Gladwell, M. (2008). *Outliers: The story of success.* Little, Brown.

129 Macnamara, B. N., Hambrick, D. Z., & Oswald, F. L. (2014). Deliberate practice and performance in music, games, sports, education, and professions: A meta-analysis. *Psychological science, 25*(8), 1608-1618. https://journals.sagepub.com/doi/abs/10.1177/0956797614535810

130 Ericsson, K. A., & Charness, N. (1994). Expert performance: Its structure and acquisition. *American psychologist, 49*(8), 725. www.researchgate.net/profile/Neil_Charness/publication/232512760_Expert_performance_Its_structure_and_acquisition_Reply/links/551be6bd0cf20d5fbde2207b/Expert-performance-Its-structure-and-acquisition-Reply.pdf

131 Ericsson, K. A., Krampe, R. T., & Tesch-Römer, C. (1993). The role of deliberate practice in the acquisition of expert performance. *Psychological review, 100*(3), 363. http://projects.ict.usc.edu/itw/gel/EricssonDeliberatePracticePR93.PDF

132 Ericsson, K. A., Krampe, R. T., & Tesch-Römer, C. (1993). The role of deliberate practice in the acquisition of expert performance. *Psychological review, 100*(3), 363. http://projects.ict.usc.edu/itw/gel/EricssonDeliberatePracticePR93.PDF

133 Farrington, C. A., Roderick, M., Allensworth, E., Nagaoka, J., Keyes, T. S., Johnson, D. W., & Beechum, N. O. (2012). *Teaching Adolescents to Become Learners: The Role of Noncognitive Factors in Shaping School Performance--A Critical Literature Review.* Consortium on Chicago School Research. https://files.eric.ed.gov/fulltext/ED542543.pdf

134 Footnote reference: [1] Duckworth, A. L., Peterson, C., Matthews, M. D., & Kelly, D. R. (2007). Grit: perseverance and passion for long-term goals. *Journal of personality and social psychology, 92*(6), 1087. https://hezarsarv.com/wp-content/uploads/2019/04/The-Science-of-Developing-DuckworthPetersonMatthewsKelly_2007_PerseveranceandPassion.pdf

135 Ericsson, K. A., & Charness, N. (1994). Expert performance: Its structure and acquisition. American psychologist, 49(8), 725. www.researchgate.net/profile/Neil_Charness/publication/232512760_Expert_performance_Its_structure_and_acquisition_Reply/links/551be6bd0cf20d5fbde2207b/Expert-performance-Its-structure-and-acquisition-Reply.pdf

136 De Bellefonds, C. (2020). *Why Michael Phelps Has the Perfect Body for Swimming.* Biography. www.biography.com/news/michael-phelp-perfect-body-swimming

137 Connick, M. (2018). *The science of elite long distance running.* https://theconversation.com/the-science-of-elite-long-distance-running-94490;
Kolata, G. (2008). Uncommonly Big Hearts May Not Harm Athletes. *The New York Times.* www.nytimes.com/2008/07/07/health/07hearts.html

138 Ericsson, K. A., & Charness, N. (1994). Expert performance: Its structure and acquisition. *American psychologist, 49*(8), 725. www.researchgate.net/profile/Neil_Charness/publication/232512760_Expert_performance_Its_structure_and_acquisition_Reply/links/551be6bd0cf20d5fbde2207b/Expert-performance-Its-structure-and-acquisition-Reply.pdf

139 Ericsson, K. A., Krampe, R. T., & Tesch-Römer, C. (1993). The role of deliberate practice in the acquisition of expert performance. *Psychological review, 100*(3), 363. http://projects.ict.usc.edu/itw/gel/EricssonDeliberatePracticePR93.PDF

140 Ericsson, K. A., & Charness, N. (1994). Expert performance: Its structure and acquisition. *American psychologist, 49*(8), 725. www.researchgate.net/profile/Neil_Charness/publication/232512760_Expert_performance_Its_structure_and_acquisition_Reply/links/551be6bd0cf20d5fbde2207b/Expert-performance-Its-structure-and-acquisition-Reply.pdf

141 Poropat, A. E. (2009). A meta-analysis of the five-factor model of personality and academic performance. *Psychological bulletin, 135*(2), 322. https://d1wqtxts1xzle7.cloudfront.net/55294393/54018_1.pdf?1513302586=&response-content-disposition=inline%3B+filename%3DA_Meta_Analysis_of_1_Running_head_PERSON.pdf&Expires=1619195359&Signature=eEXcFj2m6ASWUlR72bvvbXkdm4YYo~8IwCBEKUEcLKP0fAfejo2FKF-Gyr~4ho81kj5495Ej3wSTFGfBv89PrXDypM6VLs~IzgfHS34DWBk3V1tWJCFfwFU6nrDrQm4coyFEmA-Gu1M4XOPpIVELGr7k~Lpj-2Prm1woZbu4rbe1Uu~~hdk4Lp0KYtRHttIIUV7VWNCdfsaQSK4UmP2D-43mOkdgdBuNUalnKno0A2QOa931sBdbAIgltmalNxwsnEZgkGURLcjb9S8ysBbL8QKz9TFXDtxiQC-5QXVHj~ok4NVwyUNWYONVs1UZ9zVbe4XFg2kDKUKdUbBkWgMspNLLLw__&Key-Pair-Id=APKAJLOHF5GGSLRBV4ZA

142 Farrington, C. A., Roderick, M., Allensworth, E., Nagaoka, J., Keyes, T. S., Johnson, D. W., & Beechum, N. O. (2012). *Teaching Adolescents to Become Learners: The Role of Noncognitive Factors in Shaping School Performance--A Critical Literature Review*. Consortium on Chicago School Research. https://files.eric.ed.gov/fulltext/ED542543.pdf

143 Duckworth, A. (2013). *Grit: The Power of Passion and Perserverance*. TED. www.ted.com/talks/angela_lee_duckworth_grit_the_power_of_passion_and_perseverance

144 Duckworth, A. L., Peterson, C., Matthews, M. D., & Kelly, D. R. (2007). Grit: perseverance and passion for long-term goals. *Journal of personality and social psychology, 92*(6), 1087. https://hezarsarv.com/wp-content/uploads/2019/04/The-Science-of-Developing-DuckworthPetersonMatthewsKelly_2007_PerseveranceandPassion.pdf

145 Farrington, C. A., Roderick, M., Allensworth, E., Nagaoka, J., Keyes, T. S., Johnson, D. W., & Beechum, N. O. (2012). *Teaching Adolescents to Become Learners: The Role of Noncognitive Factors in Shaping School Performance--A Critical Literature Review*. Consortium on Chicago School Research. https://files.eric.ed.gov/fulltext/ED542543.pdf

146 Rich, J. (1998). *The nurture assumption: Why children turn out the way they do*. Bloomsbury.

147 Ericsson, K. A., Krampe, R. T., & Tesch-Römer, C. (1993). The role of deliberate practice in the acquisition of expert performance. *Psychological review, 100*(3), 363. http://projects.ict.usc.edu/itw/gel/EricssonDeliberatePracticePR93.PDF

148 Bloom, B., et al. 1985. *Developing talent in young people*. Ballantine. www.kragen.net/uploads/4/5/4/3/4543087/developing_talent_in_young_people_-_book_review.pdf

149 Gould, D., Tuffey, S., Udry, E., & Loehr, J. (1996). Burnout in competitive junior tennis players: I. A quantitative psychological assessment. *The sport psychologist, 10*(4), 322-340. https://journals.humankinetics.com/doi/abs/10.1123/tsp.10.4.322;
Raedeke, T. D. (1997). Is athlete burnout more than just stress? A sport commitment perspective. *Journal of sport and exercise psychology, 19*(4), 396-417. www.researchgate.net/profile/Thomas_Raedeke/publication/232560222_Is_Athlete_Burnout_More_than_Just_Stress_A_Sport_Commitment_Perspective/links/54cf945c0cf29ca810feee84.pdf

150 Scanlan, T. K., & Lewthwaite, R. (1984). Social psychological aspects of competition for male youth sport participants: I. Predictors of competitive stress. *Journal of sport psychology, 6*(2), 208-226. https://journals.humankinetics.com/doi/abs/10.1123/jsp.6.2.208;
Brustad, R. J. (1988). Affective outcomes in competitive youth sport: The influence of intrapersonal and socialization factors. *Journal of Sport and Exercise Psychology, 10*(3), 307-321. www.researchgate.net/profile/Robert_Brustad/publication/232554529_Affective_Outcomes_in_Competitive_Youth_Sport_The_Influence_of_Intrapersonal_and_Socialization_Factors/links/00b7d5304fb2d1e1f2000000.pdf;
Scanlan, T. K., & Lewthwaite, R. (1986). Social psychological aspects of competition for male youth sport participants: IV. Predictors of enjoyment. *Journal of sport psychology, 8*(1), 25-35. https://pdfs.semanticscholar.org/191e/d7bea0e925d53242a3ff2308dce8ee6787bb.pdf

151 Wiersma, L. D. (2000). Risks and benefits of youth sport specialization: Perspectives and recommendations. *Pediatric exercise science, 12*(1), 13-22. https://pdfs.semanticscholar.org/6b1b/aa5e795346460395d6370e9f44096af1f37e.pdf;
Wall, M., & Côté, J. (2007). Developmental activities that lead to dropout and investment in sport. *Physical education and sport pedagogy, 12*(1), 77-87. www.researchgate.net/profile/Jean_Cote3/publication/43501357_Developmental_activities_that_lead_to_dropout_and_investment_in_sport/links/540b68870cf2f2b29a32f55a.pdf;
Wiersma, L. D. (2000). Risks and benefits of youth sport specialization: Perspectives and recommendations. *Pediatric exercise science, 12*(1), 13-22. https://pdfs.semanticscholar.org/6b1b/aa5e795346460395d6370e9f44096af1f37e.pdf

152 Bloom, B., et al. 1985. *Developing talent in young people*. Ballantine. www.kragen.net/uploads/4/5/4/3/4543087/developing_talent_in_young_people_-_book_review.pdf

153 Ericsson, K. A., Krampe, R. T., & Tesch-Römer, C. (1993). The role of deliberate practice in the acquisition of expert performance. *Psychological review, 100*(3), 363. http://projects.ict.usc.edu/itw/gel/EricssonDeliberatePracticePR93.PDF

154 Vansteenkiste, M., Simons, J., Lens, W., Sheldon, K. M., & Deci, E. L. (2004). Motivating learning, performance, and persistence: the synergistic effects of intrinsic goal contents and autonomy-supportive contexts. *Journal of personality and social psychology, 87*(2), 246. https://selfdeterminationtheory.org/SDT/documents/2004_VansteenkisteSimonsLensSheldonDeci_JPSP.pdf

155 Patrick, H., Ryan, A. M., Alfeld-Liro, C., Fredricks, J. A., Hruda, L. Z., & Eccles, J. S. (1999). Adolescents' commitment to developing talent: The role of peers in continuing motivation for sports and the arts. *Journal of youth and adolescence, 28*(6), 741-763. www.researchgate.net/profile/Helen_Patrick/publication/225266120_Adolescents%27_Commitment_to_Developing_Talent_The_Role_of_Peers_in_Continuing_Motivation_for_Sports_and_the_Arts/links/0deec5268308d0ff55000000/Adolescents-Commitment-to-Developing-Talent-The-Role-of-Peers-in-Continuing-Motivation-for-Sports-and-the-Arts.pdf

156 Callaway, D. (2018). *Skiing in Norwich: From the Rope Tow to the Olympics.* The Norwich Times. https://norwichtimes.com/skiing-in-norwich-from-the-rope-tow-to-the-olympics/

157 *Frequently Asked Questions: Can my child "ski up" in the next age group.* (2021). Ford Sayre Ski Club. www.fordsayre.org/alpine/junior-racing/frequently-asked-questions/;
Crouse, K. (2018). *Norwich: One Tiny Vermont Town's Secret to Happiness and Excellence.* Simon and Schuster.

158 Gould, D., Tuffey, S., Udry, E., & Loehr, J. (1996). Burnout in competitive junior tennis players: I. A quantitative psychological assessment. *The sport psychologist, 10*(4), 322-340. https://journals.humankinetics.com/doi/abs/10.1123/tsp.10.4.322

159 Mattingly, D. J., Prislin, R., McKenzie, T. L., Rodriguez, J. L., & Kayzar, B. (2002). Evaluating evaluations: The case of parent involvement programs. *Review of educational research, 72*(4), 549-576. www.researchgate.net/profile/Brenda_Kayzar/publication/265290186_549_REVIEW_OF_EDUCATIONAL_RESEARCH_Evaluating_Evaluations_The_Case_of_Parent_Involvement_Programsnetsubscriptions_Subscriptionsnet_Downloaded_from/links/54072c6a0cf2c48563b298b3.pdf;
Pomerantz, E. M., Moorman, E. A., & Litwack, S. D. (2007). The how, whom, and why of parents' involvement in children's academic lives: More is not always better. *Review of educational research, 77*(3), 373-410. http://journals.sagepub.com/doi/abs/10.3102/003465430305567

160 Paul, P. (2019). No, Your Kid Shouldn't Get a Gold Star for Reading. *The New York Times.* www.nytimes.com/2019/08/30/sunday-review/children-reading.html?smid=nytcore-ios-share;
Deci, E. L., Vallerand, R. J., Pelletier, L. G., & Ryan, R. M. (1991). Motivation and education: The self-determination perspective. *Educational psychologist, 26*(3-4), 325-346. http://personal.tcu.edu/pwitt/character/persistence/Self-determination%20theory.pdf;
Carlton, M. P., & Winsler, A. (1998). Fostering intrinsic motivation in early childhood classrooms. *Early Childhood Education Journal, 25*(3), 159-166. www.researchgate.net/profile/Adam_Winsler/publication/225914131_Fostering_Intrinsic_Motivation_in_Early_Childhood_Classrooms/links/0fcfd50d7c82a56e2b000000.pdf

161 Gottfried, A. E. (2017). *Academic Intrinsic Motivation and Educational Competence.* CTL on the Cutting Edge. www.csun.edu/sites/default/files/CTL-Cutting-Edge-Academic-Instrinsic-Motivation-Educational-Competence.pdf

162 Deci, E. L., Vallerand, R. J., Pelletier, L. G., & Ryan, R. M. (1991). Motivation and education: The self-determination perspective. *Educational psychologist, 26*(3-4), 325-346. http://personal.tcu.edu/pwitt/character/persistence/Self-determination%20theory.pdf

163 Gottfried, A. E. (2017). *Academic Intrinsic Motivation and Educational Competence.* CTL on the Cutting Edge. www.csun.edu/sites/default/files/CTL-Cutting-Edge-Academic-Instrinsic-Motivation-Educational-Competence.pdf

164 Agassi, Andre. *Open* (p. 1). Knopf Doubleday Publishing Group. Kindle Edition.

165 Chua, A. (2011). *Battle hymn of the tiger mother.* Bloomsbury Publishing.

166 Carter, M. (2009). *Visible learning: A synthesis of over 800 meta-analyses relating to achievement.* https://apprendre.auf.org/wp-content/opera/13-BF-References-et-biblio-RPT-2014/Visible%20Learning_A%20synthesis%20or%20over%20800%20Meta-analyses%20Relating%20to%20Achievement_Hattie%20J%202009%20...pdf

167 Rutchick, A. M., Smyth, J. M., Lopoo, L. M., & Dusek, J. B. (2009). Great expectations: The biasing effects of reported child behavior problems on educational expectancies and subsequent academic achievement. *Journal of Social and Clinical Psychology, 28*(3), 392-413. https://search.proquest.com/docview/224860609?pq-origsite=gscholar&fromopenview=true

168 Farrington, C. A., Roderick, M., Allensworth, E., Nagaoka, J., Keyes, T. S., Johnson, D. W., & Beechum, N. O. (2012). *Teaching Adolescents to Become Learners: The Role of Noncognitive Factors in Shaping School Performance--A Critical Literature Review.* Consortium on Chicago School Research. https://files.eric.ed.gov/fulltext/ED542543.pdf

169 Carter, M. (2009). *Visible learning: A synthesis of over 800 meta-analyses relating to achievement.* https://apprendre.auf.org/wp-content/opera/13-BF-References-et-biblio-RPT-2014/Visible%20Learning_A%20synthesis%20or%20over%20800%20Meta-analyses%20Relating%20to%20Achievement_Hattie%20J%202009%20...pdf

170 Roese, N. J., & Summerville, A. (2005). What we regret most... and why. *Personality and Social Psychology Bulletin, 31*(9), 1273-1285. www.ncbi.nlm.nih.gov/pmc/articles/PMC2394712/;
Kinnier, R. T., & Metha, A. T. (1989). Regrets and priorities at three stages of life. *Counseling and Values, 33*(3), 182-193. https://s3.amazonaws.com/academia.edu.documents/42493219/Regrets_and_priorities_at_three_stages_o20160209-19986-jp5hxr.pdf?AWSAccessKeyId=AKIAIWOWYYGZ2Y53UL3A&Expires=1551723927&Signature=5T0wQfEimN%2BBPw9K0oE3e4tKFj4%3D&response-content-disposition=inline%3B%20filename%3DRegrets_and_Priorities_at_Three_Stages_o.pdf

171 Blagg, D. (2009). *The Parental Involvement Puzzle.* Usable Knowledge. www.gse.harvard.edu/news/uk/09/10/parental-involvement-puzzle;
Hill, N. E., & Tyson, D. F. (2009). Parental involvement in middle school: a meta-analytic assessment of the strategies that promote achievement. *Developmental psychology, 45*(3), 740. www.ncbi.nlm.nih.gov/pmc/articles/PmC2782391/

# 9. Discretionary Time

1 Allen, M. (2017). *Sean Parker unloads on Facebook: "God only knows what it's doing to our children's brains".* Axios. www.axios.com/sean-parker-unloads-on-facebook-god-only-knows-what-its-doing-to-our-childrens-brains-1513306792-f855e7b4-4e99-4d60-8d51-2775559c2671.html

2 Footnote reference: [1] O'Keeffe, G. S., & Clarke-Pearson, K. (2011). The impact of social media on children, adolescents, and families. *Pediatrics, 127*(4), 800-804. www.cooperativa.cl/noticias/site/artic/20110329/asocfile/20110329173752/reporte_facebook.PDF

3 Rideout, V. J., & Robb, M. B. (2019). *The common sense census: Media use by tweens and teens.* Common Sense Media. www.commonsensemedia.org/sites/default/files/uploads/research/2019-census-8-to-18-full-report-updated.pdf

4 Lenhart, A., Duggan, M., Perrin, A., Stepler, R., Rainie, H., & Parker, K. (2015). *Teens, social media & technology overview 2015.* www.pewresearch.org/internet/2015/04/09/teens-social-media-technology-2015/

5 National Cyber Security Alliance. (n.d.). *Keeping Up With Generation App 2017: NCSA Parent/Teen Online Safety Survey.* www.google.com/url?sa=t&rct=j&q=&esrc=s&source=web&cd=6&ved=2ahUKEwipgP2X9ujgAhWJSBUIHaHYAqUQFjAFegQIAxAC&url=https%3A%2F%2Fwww.stopthinkconnect.org%2Fdownload%2Fdatasets%2F4892%2FFast_Facts_Keeping_Up_With_Generation_App_NCSA_Parent_Teen_Online_Safety_Survey.pdf&usg=AOvVaw3fk1_aAAv6KvguOyRITDVH

6 Selkie, E., Adkins, V., Masters, E., Bajpai, A., & Shumer, D. (2020). Transgender Adolescents' Uses of Social Media for Social Support. *Journal of Adolescent Health, 66*(3), 275-280. www.sciencedirect.com/science/article/abs/pii/S1054139X19304215

7 Mundt, M., Ross, K., & Burnett, C. M. (2018). Scaling social movements through social media: The case of black lives matter. *Social Media+ Society, 4*(4), 2056305118807911. https://journals.sagepub.com/doi/pdf/10.1177/2056305118807911

8 Reich, S. M., Subrahmanyam, K., & Espinoza, G. (2012). Friending, IMing, and hanging out face-to-face: overlap in adolescents' online and offline social networks. *Developmental psychology, 48*(2), 356. www.researchgate.net/profile/Stephanie_Reich/publication/221865570_Friending_IMing_and_Hanging_Out_Face-to-Face_Overlap_in_Adolescents'_Online_and_Offline_Social_Networks/links/574fde1008ae1880a8228ea3.pdf

9 Rideout, V., & Robb, M. B. (2018). *Social media, social life: Teens reveal their experiences.* Common Sense Media. www.commonsensemedia.org/sites/default/files/uploads/research/2018_cs_socialmediasociallife_fullreport-final-release_2_lowres.pdf

10 Lenhart, A., Smith, A., Anderson, M., Duggan, M., & Perrin, A. (2015). *Teens, technology & friendship (Vol. 10).* Pew Research Center. www.pewresearch.org/internet/wp-content/uploads/sites/9/2015/08/Teens-and-Friendships-FINAL2.pdf

11 Fardouly, J., Diedrichs, P. C., Vartanian, L. R., & Halliwell, E. (2015). Social comparisons on social media: The impact of Facebook on young women's body image concerns and mood. *Body Image, 13*, 38-45. www.sciencedirect.com/science/article/abs/pii/S174014451400148X;
Shakya, H. B., & Christakis, N. A. (2017). Association of Facebook use with compromised well-being: a longitudinal study. *American journal of epidemiology, 185*(3), 203-211. https://academic.oup.com/aje/article/185/3/203/2915143

12 Kross, E., Verduyn, P., Demiralp, E., Park, J., Lee, D. S., Lin, N., ... & Ybarra, O. (2013). Facebook use predicts declines in subjective well-being in young adults. *PloS one, 8*(8), e69841. https://journals.plos.org/plosone/article?id=10.1371/journal.pone.0069841&mbid=synd_msnhealth%20(https://journals.plos.org/plosone/article?id=10.1371/journal.pone.0069841&mbid=synd_msnhealth)

13 Tromholt, M. (2016). The Facebook experiment: Quitting Facebook leads to higher levels of well-being. *Cyberpsychology, behavior, and social networking, 19*(11), 661-666. https://pdfs.semanticscholar.org/2a13/6b93eb4d98dda97aa93c3ee58fd3230d5b9c.pdf

14 Arad, A., Barzilay, O., & Perchick, M. (2017). *The Impact of Facebook on Social Comparison and Happiness: Evidence from a Natural Experiment.* www.tau.ac.il/~aradayal/Facebook.pdf

15 Hunt, M. G., Marx, R., Lipson, C., & Young, J. (2018). No more FOMO: Limiting social media decreases loneliness and depression. *Journal of Social and Clinical Psychology, 37*(10), 751-768. https://guilfordjournals.com/doi/pdfplus/10.1521/jscp.2018.37.10.751

16 Best, P., Manktelow, R., & Taylor, B. (2014). Online communication, social media and adolescent wellbeing: A systematic narrative review. Children and Youth Services Review, 41, 27-36. www.researchgate.net/profile/Paul-Best-2/publication/260756474_Online_Communication_Social_Media_and_Adolescent_Wellbeing_A_Systematic_Narrative_Review/links/5fb69e10458515b79751b668/Online-Communication-Social-Media-and-Adolescent-Wellbeing-A-Systematic-Narrative-Review.pdf;
Haidt, J., & Twenge, J. (ongoing). Social media and mental health: A collaborative review. Unpublished manuscript, New York University. https://docs.google.com/document/d/1w-HOfseF2wF9YIpXwUUtP65-olnkPyWcgF5BiAtBEy0/edit

17 Moreno, M. A., Parks, M. R., Zimmerman, F. J., Brito, T. E., & Christakis, D. A. (2009). Display of health risk behaviors on MySpace by adolescents: prevalence and associations. *Archives of pediatrics & adolescent medicine, 163*(1), 27-34. https://jamanetwork.com/journals/jamapediatrics/articlepdf/1730319/poa80074_27_34.pdf

18 Rideout, V., & Robb, M. B. (2018). *Social media, social life: Teens reveal their experiences.* Common Sense Media. www.commonsensemedia.org/sites/default/files/uploads/research/2018_cs_socialmediasociallife_fullreport-final-release_2_lowres.pdf

19 Rideout, V., & Robb, M. B. (2018). *Social media, social life: Teens reveal their experiences.* Common Sense Media. www.commonsensemedia.org/sites/default/files/uploads/research/2018_cs_socialmediasociallife_fullreport-final-release_2_lowres.pdf

20 Haidt, J. (2023). *The Case for Phone-Free Schools.* After Babel. https://jonathanhaidt.substack.com/p/phone-free-schools

21 Ward, A. F., Duke, K., Gneezy, A., & Bos, M. W. (2017). Brain drain: The mere presence of one's own smartphone reduces available cognitive capacity. *Journal of the Association for Consumer Research*, 2(2), 140-154. www.journals.uchicago.edu/doi/10.1086/691462

22 Thompson, N. (2018). *When Tech Knows You Better Than You Know Yourself.* Wired. www.wired.com/story/artificial-intelligence-yuval-noah-harari-tristan-harris/

23 Hari, J. (2022). Your attention didn't collapse. It was stolen. *The Guardian.* https://www.theguardian.com/science/2022/jan/02/attention-span-focus-screens-apps-smartphones-social-media

24 US Department of Health and Human Services. (2023). *Social Media and Youth Mental Health: The U.S. Surgeon General's Advisory.* Centers for Disease Control and Prevention. www.hhs.gov/sites/default/files/sg-youth-mental-health-social-media-advisory.pdf

25 Jolliff, A. (n.d.). *Did the Social Dilemma get it right? Thoughts from a social media researcher.* http://smahrtresearch.com/did-the-social-dilemma-get-it-right-thoughts-from-a-social-media-researcher/

26 Hymas, C. (2018). Secondary schools are introducing strict new bans on mobile phones. *The Telegraph.* www.telegraph.co.uk/news/2018/06/24/secondary-schools-introducing-strict-new-bans-mobile-phones/

27 Ross, H. (2018). *What It's Like to Quit Social Media as a Teenager in 2018.* Repeller. https://repeller.com/how-to-quit-social-media/

28 *Digital Culture Critic Abandons 'Fake On The Internet' Column.* (2015). All Things Considered, NPR. www.npr.org/2015/12/21/460602085/digital-culture-critic-abandons-fake-on-the-internet-column

29 Daniels, J. (2008). *Race, civil rights, and hate speech in the digital era.* https://academicworks.cuny.edu/cgi/viewcontent.cgi?referer=https://scholar.google.com/&httpsredir=1&article=1218&context=gc_pubs

30 *New Survey Reveals Teens Get Their News from Social Media and YouTube.* (2019). Common Sense Media. www.commonsensemedia.org/about-us/news/press-releases/new-survey-reveals-teens-get-their-news-from-social-media-and-youtube

31 Wineburg, S., McGrew, S., Breakstone, J., & Ortega, T. (2016). *Evaluating information: The cornerstone of civic online reasoning.* Stanford Digital Repository. https://stacks.stanford.edu/file/druid:fv751yt5934/SHEG%20Evaluating%20Information%20Online.pdf

32 Smith, J. (2020). Opinion: The Amish use tech differently than you think. We should emulate them. *The Washington Post.* www.washingtonpost.com/opinions/to-learn-how-to-practice-humane-technology-look-to-the-amish/2020/02/17/c79fa0ba-36fc-11ea-bf30-ad313e4ec754_story.html

33 Kahneman, D. (2011). *Thinking, fast and slow.* Macmillan.

34 Veritasium. (2014). *Can You Solve This?* [Video]. YouTube. www.youtube.com/watch?v=vKA4w2O61Xo

35 Henley, J. (2020). How Finland starts its fight against fake news in primary schools. *The Guardian.* https://www.theguardian.com/world/2020/jan/28/fact-from-fiction-finlands-new-lessons-in-combating-fake-news

36 Lessenski, M. (2019). *The Media Literacy Index 2019: Just think about it.* Open Society Institute Sophia. https://osis.bg/?p=3356&lang=en

37 Pariser, E. (2011). *Beware online "filter bubbles"* [Video]. TED. www.ted.com/talks/eli_pariser_beware_online_filter_bubbles/transcript?language=en

38 Thompson, N. (2018). *When Tech Knows You Better Than You Know Yourself* [Video]. Wired. www.wired.com/story/artificial-intelligence-yuval-noah-harari-tristan-harris/

39 From www.commonsense.org/education/digital-citizenship/lesson/hoaxes-and-fakes
Jebdogrpm. (2012). *Pig rescues baby goat* [Video]. YouTube. www.youtube.com/watch?v=g7WjrvG1GMk
Comedy Central (2013). *Nathan For You - Petting Zoo Hero* [Video]. YouTube. www.youtube.com/watch?v=_2My_HOP-bw
Comedy Central (2013). *Nathan For You - Petting Zoo Hero Pt. 2* [Video]. YouTube. www.youtube.com/watch?v=bvtJj6HoYHg

40 BBC Newsnight. (2017). *The rise of 'fake news', manipulation and 'alternative facts' - BBC Newsnight* [Video]. YouTube. www.youtube.com/watch?v=1aTApGWVGoI

41 TED. (2018). *Fake videos of real people -- and how to spot them* [Video]. YouTube. www.youtube.com/watch?v=o2DDU4g0PRo

42 *Reality Check: The Game.* (n.d.). Media Smarts. https://mediasmarts.ca/digital-media-literacy/educational-games/reality-check-game

43 Guess, A., Nagler, J., & Tucker, J. (2019). Less than you think: Prevalence and predictors of fake news dissemination on Facebook. *Science advances, 5*(1), eaau4586. https://advances.sciencemag.org/content/5/1/eaau4586?rss=1&fbclid=IwAR0AnmmBOuikMvGya9AUs3Zd0418CI4aeKLocjhhPfZIQJcgXbGyw3Ix-nE

44 Naté, U. (1997). *Free.* On Situation: Critical [album]. Strictly Rhythm.

45 Zick, C. D. (2010). The shifting balance of adolescent time use. *Youth & Society, 41*(4), 569-596. https://journals.sagepub.com/doi/abs/10.1177/0044118x09338506

46 Larson, R. W., & Verma, S. (1999). How children and adolescents spend time across the world: work, play, and developmental opportunities. *Psychological bulletin, 125*(6), 701. https://psycnet.apa.org/record/1999-01567-005;

Larson, R. W. (2001). How US children and adolescents spend time: What it does (and doesn't) tell us about their development. *Current Directions in Psychological Science, 10*(5), 160-164. www.jstor.org/stable/pdf/20182729.pdf

47 United States Bureau of Labor Statistics. (2007). *American Time Use Survey (ATUS).*

48 *Should I let my 15-year-old go to a concert without an adult?* (n.d.). Quora. www.quora.com/Should-I-let-my-15-year-old-go-to-a-concert-without-an-adult

49 *Appropriate age for a teen to go to a concert?* (n.d.). Mumsnet. www.mumsnet.com/Talk/am_i_being_unreasonable/4060126-Appropriate-age-for-a-teen-to-go-to-a-concert

50 DeRosa, A. & Shah, N. (2021). What Happened at Travis Scott's Astroworld Concert? What to Know. *The Wall Street Journal.* www.wsj.com/articles/what-happened-travis-scott-astroworld-tragedy-11636478633

51 Turris, S. A., Jones, T., & Lund, A. (2018). Mortality at music festivals: An update for 2016-2017–Academic and grey literature for case finding. *Prehospital and disaster medicine, 33*(5), 553-557. www.researchgate.net/profile/Tracie-Jones-3/publication/328030209_Mortality_at_Music_Festivals_An_Update_for_2016-2017_-_Academic_and_Grey_Literature_for_Case_Finding/links/5ce5b814299bf14d95b1cebc/Mortality-at-Music-Festivals-An-Update-for-2016-2017-Academic-and-Grey-Literature-for-Case-Finding.pdf

52 *How Dangerous is Lightning?* (n.d.). National Weather Service. www.weather.gov/safety/lightning-odds#:~:text=According%20to%20the%20NWS%20Storm,with%20various%20degrees%20of%20disability

53 Conaboy, K. (2018). *Bradley Cooper's Ear Doctor Tells Us How He Was Cast in A Star Is Born.* The Cut. www.thecut.com/2018/10/bradley-cooper-a-star-is-born-ear-doctor.html

54 Niskar, A. S., Kieszak, S. M., Holmes, A. E., Esteban, E., Rubin, C., & Brody, D. J. (2001). Estimated prevalence of noise-induced hearing threshold shifts among children 6 to 19 years of age: the Third National Health and Nutrition Examination Survey, 1988–1994, United States. *Pediatrics, 108*(1), 40-43. https://pediatrics.aappublications.org/content/108/1/40.short;
Rabinowitz, P. M., Slade, M. D., Galusha, D., Dixon-Ernst, C., & Cullen, M. R. (2006). Trends in the prevalence of hearing loss among young adults entering an industrial workforce 1985 to 2004. *Ear and hearing, 27*(4), 369-375. www.jborak.com/publications/docs/Slade-Rabinowitz.pdf;
Footnote references:
[1] Axelsson, A., Jerson, T., Lindberg, U., & Lindgren, F. (1981). Early noise-induced hearing loss in teenage boys. *Scandinavian Audiology, 10*(2), 91-96. www.tandfonline.com/doi/abs/10.3109/01050398109076167
[2] Peng, J. H., Tao, Z. Z., & Huang, Z. W. (2007). Risk of damage to hearing from personal listening devices in young adults. *Journal of Otolaryngology, 36*(3). http://citeseerx.ist.psu.edu/viewdoc/download?doi=10.1.1.552.8522&rep=rep1&type=pdf

55 Eggemann, C., Koester, M., & Zorowka, P. (2002). Hearing loss due to leisure time noise is on the rise. The ear also needs a rest period. *MMW Fortschritte der Medizin, 144*(49), 30-33. https://europepmc.org/article/med/12577736

56 Metternich, F. U., & Brusis, T. (1999). Acute hearing loss and tinnitus caused by amplified recreational music. *Laryngo-rhino-otologie, 78*(11), 614-619. https://europepmc.org/article/med/10615655

57 Meyer-Bisch, C. (1996). Epidemiological evaluation of hearing damage related to strongly amplified music (personal cassette players, discotheques, rock concerts)-high-definition audiometric survey on 1364 subjects. *Audiology, 35*(3), 121-142. www.tandfonline.com/doi/abs/10.3109/00206099609071936

58 Meyer-Bisch, C. (1996). Epidemiological evaluation of hearing damage related to strongly amplified music (personal cassette players, discotheques, rock concerts)-high-definition audiometric survey on 1364 subjects. *Audiology, 35*(3), 121-142. www.tandfonline.com/doi/abs/10.3109/00206099609071936;
World Health Organization. (2015). *Hearing loss due to recreational exposure to loud sounds: a review.* World Health Organization. www.who.int/pbd/deafness/Hearing_loss_due_to_recreational_exposure_to_loud_sounds.pdf;
Mostafapour, S. P., Lahargoue, K., & Gates, G. A. (1998). Noise-induced hearing loss in young adults: The role of personal listening devices and other sources of leisure noise. *The Laryngoscope, 108*(12), 1832-1839. https://onlinelibrary.wiley.com/doi/abs/10.1097/00005537-199812000-00013

59 Meyer-Bisch, C. (1996). Epidemiological evaluation of hearing damage related to strongly amplified music (personal cassette players, discotheques, rock concerts)-high-definition audiometric survey on 1364 subjects. *Audiology, 35*(3), 121-142. www.tandfonline.com/doi/abs/10.3109/00206099609071936;

Morata, T. C. (2007). *Young people: Their noise and music exposures and the risk of hearing loss.* www.researchgate.net/profile/Thais_Morata/publication/6442366_Young_people_Their_noise_and_music_exposures_and_the_risk_of_hearing_loss_International_Journal_of_Audiology_463_111-112/links/571a53bb08ae7f552a472f36.pdf

60 World Health Organization. (2015). *Hearing loss due to recreational exposure to loud sounds: a review.* World Health Organization. www.who.int/pbd/deafness/Hearing_loss_due_to_recreational_exposure_to_loud_sounds.pdf

61 Rawool, V. W., & Colligon-Wayne, L. A. (2008). Auditory lifestyles and beliefs related to hearing loss among college students in the USA. *Noise and Health, 10*(38), 1. www.noiseandhealth.org/article.asp?issn=1463-1741;year=2008;volume=10;issue=38;spage=1;epage=10;aulast=Rawool

62 Weichbold, V., & Zorowka, P. (2003). Effects of a hearing protection campaign on the discotheque attendance habits of high-school students: Efectos de una campaña de protección auditiva en los hábitos de asistencia a discotecas de estudiantes de educación media. *International journal of audiology, 42*(8), 489-493. www.tandfonline.com/doi/abs/10.3109/14992020309081519

63 Vogel, I., Brug, J., Van der Ploeg, C. P. B., & Raat, H. (2009). Prevention of adolescents' music-induced hearing loss due to discotheque attendance: a Delphi study. *Health education research, 24*(6), 1043-1050. https://academic.oup.com/her/article/24/6/1043/629541

64 *Quick Statistics About Hearing.* (2016). National Institute on Deafness and Other Communication Disorders. www.nidcd.nih.gov/health/statistics/quick-statistics-hearing

65 Owoeye, J. F. A., Ologe, F. E., & Akande, T. M. (2007). Medical students' perspectives of blindness, deafness, and deafblindness. *Disability and rehabilitation, 29*(11-12), 929-933. https://pubmed.ncbi.nlm.nih.gov/17577727/

66 Roberts, J. J. & Chartrand, M. S. (n.d). *Helen Keller On The Psychosocial Challenges Of Not Correcting One's Hearing Loss.* https://palmbayhearingaids.com/our-blog/helen-keller-on-the-psychosocial-challenges-of-not-correcting-ones-hearing-loss

67 Henesey, B. (2015). *Events: Noise exposure at Ministry of Sound.* Safety & Health Practitioner. www.shponline.co.uk/noise-and-vibration/sound-industry-noise-exposure-ministry-sound/

68 Solon, O. (2016). Smartphones Won't Make Your Kids Dumb--We Think. *Scientific American.* www.scientificamerican.com/article/smartphones-won-t-make-your-kids-dumb-we-think/

69 Karpowitz CF, Pope JC. *The American Family Survey, 2018 Summary Report: Identities, opportunities and challenges.* http://csed.byu.edu/wp-content/uploads/2018/11/american-family-survey-final-report_nov2018.pdf

70 Livingstone, S., Haddon, L., Görzig, A., & Ólafsson, K. (2011). *Risks and safety on the internet: the perspective of European children: full findings and policy implications from the EU Kids Online survey of 9-16 year olds and their parents in 25 countries.* http://eprints.lse.ac.uk/33731/1/Risks%20and%20safety%20on%20the%20internet(lse-ro).pdf

71 Wisniewski, P., Xu, H., Rosson, M. B., & Carroll, J. M. (2017, February). Parents just don't understand: Why teens don't talk to parents about their online risk experiences. In *Proceedings of the 2017 ACM conference on computer supported cooperative work and social computing* (pp. 523-540). https://dl.acm.org/doi/pdf/10.1145/2998181.2998236

72 Livingstone, S., Haddon, L., Görzig, A., & Ólafsson, K. (2011). *Risks and safety on the internet: the perspective of European children: full findings and policy implications from the EU Kids Online survey of 9-16 year olds and their parents in 25 countries.* http://eprints.lse.ac.uk/33731/1/Risks%20and%20safety%20on%20the%20internet(lse-ro).pdf

73 Brock, B. J. (2007). *Living outside the box: TV-free families share their secrets.* Eastern Washington University.

74 Peter, L. J. (1977). *Peter's quotations: Ideas for our time.* Bantam Books.

75 Common Sense Media. (2015). *The common sense census: Media use by tweens and teens.* British Columbia Teachers' Federation. www.commonsensemedia.org/sites/default/files/uploads/research/census_researchreport.pdf

76 Rideout, V. J., & Robb, M. B. (2019). *The common sense census: Media use by tweens and teens.* Common Sense Media. www.commonsensemedia.org/sites/default/files/uploads/research/2019-census-8-to-18-full-report-updated.pdf

77 Anderson, M., & Jiang, J. (2018). *Teens, social media & technology 2018*. Pew Research Center. www.pewresearch.org/internet/2018/05/31/teens-social-media-technology-2018/

78 Common Sense Media. (2015). *The common sense census: Media use by tweens and teens*. British Columbia Teachers' Federation. www.commonsensemedia.org/sites/default/files/uploads/research/census_researchreport.pdf; Rideout, V. J., & Robb, M. B. (2019). *The common sense census: Media use by tweens and teens*. Common Sense Media. www.commonsensemedia.org/sites/default/files/uploads/research/2019-census-8-to-18-full-report-updated.pdf

79 Twenge, J. (2017). Have Smartphones Destroyed a Generation? *The Atlantic*. www.theatlantic.com/magazine/archive/2017/09/has-the-smartphone-destroyed-a-generation/534198/

80 Uhls, Y. T., Michikyan, M., Morris, J., Garcia, D., Small, G. W., Zgourou, E., & Greenfield, P. M. (2014). Five days at outdoor education camp without screens improves preteen skills with nonverbal emotion cues. *Computers in Human Behavior, 39*, 387-392. www.sciencedirect.com/science/article/pii/S0747563214003227

81 Twenge, J. M., Haidt, J., Blake, A. B., McAllister, C., Lemon, H., & Le Roy, A. (2021). Worldwide increases in adolescent loneliness. *Journal of Adolescence*. www.sciencedirect.com/science/article/pii/S0140197121000853

82 Twenge, J. M., Martin, G. N., & Campbell, W. K. (2018). Decreases in psychological well-being among American adolescents after 2012 and links to screen time during the rise of smartphone technology. *Emotion, 18*(6), 765. http://moglen.law.columbia.edu/CPC/AdolescentHappinessSmartphones-Emotion-2018.pdf

83 Schmiedeberg, C., & Schröder, J. (2017). Leisure activities and life satisfaction: An analysis with German panel data. *Applied Research in Quality of Life, 12*(1), 137-151. https://link.springer.com/article/10.1007/s11482-016-9458-7

84 Bélanger, R. E., Akre, C., Berchtold, A., & Michaud, P. A. (2011). A U-shaped association between intensity of Internet use and adolescent health. *Pediatrics, 127*(2), e330-e335. https://pediatrics.aappublications.org/content/127/2/e330.short;
Moreno, M. A., Jelenchick, L., Koff, R., & Eickhoff, J. (2012). Depression and Internet use among older adolescents: An experience sampling approach. *Psychology, 3*(09), 743. www.scirp.org/html/22789.html;
Ivie, E. J., Pettitt, A., Moses, L. J., & Allen, N. B. (2020). A meta-analysis of the association between adolescent social media use and depressive symptoms. *Journal of affective disorders*. www.sciencedirect.com/science/article/abs/pii/S0165032720323727

85 Twenge, J. (2018). *Most unhappy people are unhappy for the exact same reason*. Quartz. https://qz.com/1190151/why-am-i-unhappy-a-new-study-explains-americas-unhappiness-epidemic/
Twenge, J. M., Martin, G. N., & Campbell, W. K. (2018). *Decreases in psychological well-being among American adolescents after 2012 and links to screen time during the rise of smartphone technology*. http://moglen.law.columbia.edu/CPC/AdolescentHappinessSmartphones-Emotion-2018.pdf

86 Orben, A. (2020). Teenagers, screens and social media: a narrative review of reviews and key studies. *Social psychiatry and psychiatric epidemiology*, 1-8. https://link.springer.com/article/10.1007/s00127-019-01825-4?ArticleAuthorOnlineFirst_20200111&utm_content=AA_en_06082018&utm_medium=email&utm_source=ArticleAuthorOnlineFirst&wt_mc=Internal.Event.1.SEM.ArticleAuthorOnlineFirst;
Odgers, C. L., & Jensen, M. R. (2020). Annual Research Review: Adolescent mental health in the digital age: facts, fears, and future directions. *Journal of Child Psychology and Psychiatry, 61*(3), 336-348. https://acamh.onlinelibrary.wiley.com/doi/abs/10.1111/jcpp.13190

87 Przybylski, A. K., & Weinstein, N. (2017). A large-scale test of the Goldilocks Hypothesis: Quantifying the relations between digital-screen use and the mental well-being of adolescents. *Psychological science, 28*(2), 204-215. https://orca-mwe.cf.ac.uk/99720/1/0956797616678438.pdf

88 *Screen Time: How Much Is Too Much?* [Video]. (n.d.). Common Sense Education & KQED Education. www.commonsense.org/education/videos/screen-time-how-much-is-too-much

89 Lee, S. J. (2009). Online communication and adolescent social ties: Who benefits more from Internet use?. *Journal of Computer-Mediated Communication, 14*(3), 509-531. https://academic.oup.com/jcmc/article/14/3/509/4583553;
Odgers, C. (2018). Smartphones are bad for some teens, not all. Nature. www.nature.com/articles/d41586-018-02109-8
Citing: Yau, J. C., & Reich, S. M. (2018). Are the qualities of adolescents' offline friendships present in digital interactions?. *Adolescent Research Review, 3*(3), 339-355. https://link.springer.com/article/10.1007/s40894-017-0059-y

90 Gross, E. F. (2009). Logging on, bouncing back: An experimental investigation of online communication following social exclusion. *Developmental Psychology, 45*(6), 1787. www.cdmc.ucla.edu/Research_files/Sheva%20 dissertation.pdf

91 Hoge, E., Bickham, D., & Cantor, J. (2017). Digital media, anxiety, and depression in children. *Pediatrics, 140*(Supplement 2), S76-S80. https://pediatrics.aappublications.org/content/140/Supplement_2/S76

92 Viner, R., Davie, M., & Firth, A. (2019). *The health impacts of screen time: a guide for clinicians and parents.* Royal College of Paediatrics and Child Health. www.rcpch.ac.uk/sites/default/files/2018-12/rcpch_screen_time_guide_-_final.pdf

93 Dickson, K., Richardson, M., Kwan, I., Macdowall, W., Burchett, H., Stansfield, C., & Thomas, J. (2019). *Screen-based activities and children and young people's mental health and psychosocial wellbeing: a systematic map of reviews.* EPPI-Centre, Social Science Research Unit, UCL Institute of Education, University College London. http://eppi.ioe.ac.uk/cms/Portals/0/PDF%20reviews%20and%20summaries/Systematic%20Map%20of%20Reviews%20on%20Screen-based%20activties_08.01.19.pdf

94 Tremblay, M. S., Carson, V., Chaput, J. P., Connor Gorber, S., Dinh, T., Duggan, M., ... & Janssen, I. (2016). Canadian 24-hour movement guidelines for children and youth: an integration of physical activity, sedentary behaviour, and sleep. *Applied Physiology, Nutrition, and Metabolism, 41*(6), S311-S327. www.nrcresearchpress.com/doi/full/10.1139/apnm-2016-0151#.Xbrbfo1CemQ

95 Footnote references:
[1] Meerkerk, G. J. (2007). *Owned by the Internet: Explorative research into the causes and consequences of compulsive Internet use.* http://repository.ubn.ru.nl/bitstream/handle/2066/77299/77299.pdf?sequence=1
[2] Guertler, D., Rumpf, H. J., Bischof, A., Kastirke, N., Petersen, K. U., John, U., & Meyer, C. (2014). Assessment of problematic internet use by the compulsive internet use scale and the internet addiction test: A sample of problematic and pathological gamblers. *European Addiction Research, 20*(2), 75-81. www.karger.com/Article/Fulltext/355076

96 Guertler, D., Rumpf, H. J., Bischof, A., Kastirke, N., Petersen, K. U., John, U., & Meyer, C. (2014). Assessment of problematic internet use by the compulsive internet use scale and the internet addiction test: A sample of problematic and pathological gamblers. *European Addiction Research, 20*(2), 75-81. www.karger.com/Article/FullText/355076

97 Lopez-Fernandez, O., Freixa-Blanxart, M., & Honrubia-Serrano, M. L. (2013). The problematic Internet entertainment use scale for adolescents: prevalence of problem Internet use in Spanish high school students. *CyberPsychology, Behavior, and social networking, 16*(2), 108-118. http://irep.ntu.ac.uk/id/eprint/28423/1/5975_Lopez-Fernandez.pdf;
Liu, T. C., Desai, R. A., Krishnan-Sarin, S., Cavallo, D. A., & Potenza, M. N. (2011). Problematic Internet use and health in adolescents: data from a high school survey in Connecticut. *The Journal of clinical psychiatry, 72*(6), 836. www.ncbi.nlm.nih.gov/pmc/articles/PMC3686276/

98 Maniccia, D. M., Davison, K. K., Marshall, S. J., Manganello, J. A., & Dennison, B. A. (2011). A meta-analysis of interventions that target children's screen time for reduction. *Pediatrics, 128*(1), e193-e210. https://pediatrics.aappublications.org/content/128/1/e193.short

99 Kamenetz, A. (2020). I Was a Screen–Time Expert. Then the Coronavirus Happened. *The New York Times.* www.nytimes.com/2020/07/27/parenting/children-screen-time-games-phones.html?referringSource=articleShare

100 Buck, K. (2018). Girl, 9, in rehab after getting so addicted to Fortnite she wet herself. *Metro.* https://metro.co.uk/2018/06/10/girl-9-in-rehab-after-getting-so-addicted-to-fortnite-she-wet-herself-7619324/

101 Macnamara, B. N., Hambrick, D. Z., & Oswald, F. L. (2014). Deliberate practice and performance in music, games, sports, education, and professions: A meta-analysis. *Psychological science, 25*(8), 1608-1618. https://journals.sagepub.com/doi/abs/10.1177/0956797614535810

102 Gladwell, M. (2008). *Outliers: The story of success.* Little, Brown.

103 Rideout, V. J. (2015). *The common sense census: Media use by tweens and teens.* Common Sense Media Incorporated. www.commonsensemedia.org/sites/default/files/uploads/research/census_researchreport.pdf

104 Anderson, M., & Jiang, J. (2018). *Teens, social media & technology 2018.* Pew Research Center. www.pewresearch.org/internet/2018/05/31/teens-social-media-technology-2018/

105 Rideout, V. J. (2015). *The common sense census: Media use by tweens and teens.* Common Sense Media Incorporated. www.commonsensemedia.org/sites/default/files/uploads/research/census_researchreport.pdf;

Rehbein, F., Psych, G., Kleimann, M., Mediasci, G., & Mößle, T. (2010). Prevalence and risk factors of video game dependency in adolescence: results of a German nationwide survey. *Cyberpsychology, Behavior, and Social Networking, 13*(3), 269-277. www.researchgate.net/profile/Florian_Rehbein/publication/44682033_Prevalence_and_Risk_Factors_of_Video_Game_Dependency_in_Adolescence_Results_of_a_German_Nationwide_Survey/links/02e7e537c92e675a37000000/Prevalence-and-Risk-Factors-of-Video-Game-Dependency-in-Adolescence-Results-of-a-German-Nationwide-Survey.pdf

106 Bediou, B., Adams, D. M., Mayer, R. E., Tipton, E., Green, C. S., & Bavelier, D. (2018). Meta-analysis of action video game impact on perceptual, attentional, and cognitive skills. *Psychological bulletin, 144*(1), 77. www.researchgate.net/profile/Benoit_Bediou/publication/321324846_Meta-Analysis_of_Action_Video_Game_Impact_on_Perceptual_Attentional_and_Cognitive_Skills/links/5bd08c10299bf14eac81d4c5/Meta-Analysis-of-Action-Video-Game-Impact-on-Perceptual-Attentional-and-Cognitive-Skills.pdf

107 Bavelier, D., Achtman, R. L., Mani, M., & Föcker, J. (2012). Neural bases of selective attention in action video game players. *Vision research, 61*, 132-143. www.sciencedirect.com/science/article/pii/S0042698911002872;
Granic, I., Lobel, A., & Engels, R. C. (2014). The benefits of playing video games. *American psychologist, 69*(1), 66. https://ecirtam.net/autoblogs/autoblogs/wwwpsyetgeekcom_b5b05cdb291029679998f4bbf13bf6d0c1b27186/media/affa8d7f.amp-a0034857.pdf;
Green, C. S., & Bavelier, D. (2012). Learning, attentional control, and action video games. *Current biology, 22*(6), R197-R206. www.sciencedirect.com/science/article/pii/S0960982212001303

108 Bavelier, D., Green, C. S., Han, D. H., Renshaw, P. F., Merzenich, M. M., & Gentile, D. A. (2011). Brains on video games. *Nature reviews neuroscience, 12*(12), 763. www.ncbi.nlm.nih.gov/pmc/articles/PMC4633025/

109 Gentile, D. A., Anderson, C. A., Yukawa, S., Ihori, N., Saleem, M., Ming, L. K., ... & Rowell Huesmann, L. (2009). The effects of prosocial video games on prosocial behaviors: International evidence from correlational, longitudinal, and experimental studies. *Personality and Social Psychology Bulletin, 35*(6), 752-763. www.ncbi.nlm.nih.gov/pmc/articles/PMC2678173/

110 Russoniello, C. V., O'Brien, K., & Parks, J. M. (2009). EEG, HRV and Psychological Correlates while Playing Bejeweled II: A Randomized Controlled Study. *Annual review of cybertherapy and telemedicine, 7*(1), 189-192. www.researchgate.net/profile/Brenda_Wiederhold/publication/26661683_Next_generation_stress_inoculation_training_for_life_saving_skills_using_prosthetics/links/569eaee508ae4af525449607/Next-generation-stress-inoculation-training-for-life-saving-skills-using-prosthetics.pdf#page=201

111 Lemola, S., Brand, S., Vogler, N., Perkinson-Gloor, N., Allemand, M., & Grob, A. (2011). Habitual computer game playing at night is related to depressive symptoms. *Personality and individual differences, 51*(2), 117-122. https://s3.amazonaws.com/academia.edu.documents/43409493/Habitual_computer_game_playing_at_night_20160305-9195-1kkb3oz.pdf?response-content-disposition=inline%3B%20filename%3DHabitual_computer_game_playing_at_night.pdf&X-Amz-Algorithm=AWS4-HMAC-SHA256&X-Amz-Credential=AKIAIWOWYYGZ2Y53UL3A%2F20191001%2Fus-east-1%2Fs3%2Faws4_request&X-Amz-Date=20191001T103956Z&X-Amz-Expires=3600&X-Amz-SignedHeaders=host&X-Amz-Signature=d55f611357b24f6605d2ab78a248c2c66c53bdeba97d18a7d4bf98eca0a04e52

112 Bavelier, D., Green, C. S., Han, D. H., Renshaw, P. F., Merzenich, M. M., & Gentile, D. A. (2011). Brains on video games. *Nature reviews neuroscience, 12*(12), 763. www.ncbi.nlm.nih.gov/pmc/articles/PMC4633025/

113 Footnote reference: [1] Rehbein, F., Psych, G., Kleimann, M., Mediasci, G., & Mößle, T. (2010). Prevalence and risk factors of video game dependency in adolescence: results of a German nationwide survey. *Cyberpsychology, Behavior, and Social Networking, 13*(3), 269-277. www.researchgate.net/profile/Florian_Rehbein/publication/44682033_Prevalence_and_Risk_Factors_of_Video_Game_Dependency_in_Adolescence_Results_of_a_German_Nationwide_Survey/links/02e7e537c92e675a37000000/Prevalence-and-Risk-Factors-of-Video-Game-Dependency-in-Adolescence-Results-of-a-German-Nationwide-Survey.pdf

114 Smyth, J. M. (2007). Beyond self-selection in video game play: An experimental examination of the consequences of massively multiplayer online role-playing game play. *CyberPsychology & Behavior, 10*(5), 717-721. https://pdfs.semanticscholar.org/3c30/8a6552694e08c583c15c1fa370f59ef8c7fd.pdf

115 American Psychiatric Association, & American Psychiatric Association. (2013). *Diagnostic and statistical manual of mental disorders: DSM-5.*;
Footnote reference: [1] Gentile, D. A., Bailey, K., Bavelier, D., Brockmyer, J. F., Cash, H., Coyne, S. M., ... & Markle, T. (2017). Internet gaming disorder in children and adolescents. *Pediatrics, 140*(Supplement 2), S81-S85. https://pediatrics.aappublications.org/content/140/Supplement_2/S81

116 Gentile, D. (2009). Pathological video-game use among youth ages 8 to 18: A national study. *Psychological science, 20*(5), 594-602. http://facweb.northseattle.edu/lchaffee/PSY100/Journal%20Articles/Gentile%202009.pdf

117 Lemmens, J. S., Valkenburg, P. M., & Gentile, D. A. (2015). The Internet gaming disorder scale. *Psychological assessment, 27*(2), 567. www.pattivalkenburg.nl/images/artikelen_pdf/2015_Lemmens_Valkenburg_Gentile_InternetGamingDisorderScale-PsychologicalAssessment2015.pdf

118 Thomas, N. J., & Martin, F. H. (2010). Video-arcade game, computer game and Internet activities of Australian students: Participation habits and prevalence of addiction. *Australian Journal of Psychology, 62*(2), 59-66. www.tandfonline.com/doi/abs/10.1080/00049530902748283

119 Rehbein, F., Kliem, S., Baier, D., Mößle, T., & Petry, N. M. (2015). Prevalence of Internet gaming disorder in German adolescents: Diagnostic contribution of the nine DSM-5 criteria in a state-wide representative sample. *Addiction, 110*(5), 842-851. www.ceepal.com.uy/Prevalence%20of%20internet%20gaming%20disorder%20in%20German%20dsm5.pdf;
Rehbein, F., Psych, G., Kleimann, M., Mediasci, G., & Mößle, T. (2010). Prevalence and risk factors of video game dependency in adolescence: results of a German nationwide survey. *Cyberpsychology, Behavior, and Social Networking, 13*(3), 269-277. www.researchgate.net/profile/Florian_Rehbein/publication/44682033_Prevalence_and_Risk_Factors_of_Video_Game_Dependency_in_Adolescence_Results_of_a_German_Nationwide_Survey/links/02e7e537c92e675a37000000/Prevalence-and-Risk-Factors-of-Video-Game-Dependency-in-Adolescence-Results-of-a-German-Nationwide-Survey.pdf

120 Brunborg, G. S., Mentzoni, R. A., & Frøyland, L. R. (2014). Is video gaming, or video game addiction, associated with depression, academic achievement, heavy episodic drinking, or conduct problems?. *Journal of behavioral addictions, 3*(1), 27-32. https://core.ac.uk/download/pdf/52115688.pdf;
Toker, S., & Baturay, M. H. (2016). Antecedents and consequences of game addiction. *Computers in Human Behavior, 55*, 668-679. https://d1wqtxts1xzle7.cloudfront.net/60115223/game_addiction20190725-2039-mol0z4-with-cover-page-v2.pdf?Expires=1629152527&Signature=fOBFZqmn6RrpabKFj6p-CACwZV--NjF--1HkEaA0bG10yZSNGLvR6s4f7gtOLkxJLQxVsrbh9LSRLWGvH5deyfETwR0IVK-T0D8OYgmv4M-dzHXAE6uJQvwXU53e0OxOOrpIVSbydgNq1IoRR3KzbAdOZVekzVSmjmLn-sEav-KEM4ijGbQeDiDKeLOdkX2v4M6mXHgM2p6iXXectH8sqXQL6j7nWETAHROow5N--fh-La5j7lNYiyG-FisW0I0gTWqgjJJJ0mJ73wMhv-1qxhZIL8XxexKRNPH5EcTFlv1Oh1iuxpL61rEikxMDFGX-lmIzw1kEKQVRlK-G3UXtp28oZNw__&Key-Pair-Id=APKAJLOHF5GGSLRBV4ZA

121 Zajac, K., Ginley, M. K., & Chang, R. (2020). Treatments of internet gaming disorder: a systematic review of the evidence. *Expert review of neurotherapeutics, 20*(1), 85-93. www.ncbi.nlm.nih.gov/pmc/articles/PMC6930980/

122 Stevens, M. W., King, D. L., Dorstyn, D., & Delfabbro, P. H. (2019). Cognitive–behavioral therapy for Internet gaming disorder: A systematic review and meta-analysis. *Clinical psychology & psychotherapy, 26*(2), 191-203. https://onlinelibrary.wiley.com/doi/abs/10.1002/cpp.2341

123 Gentile, D. A., Bailey, K., Bavelier, D., Brockmyer, J. F., Cash, H., Coyne, S. M., ... & Markle, T. (2017). Internet gaming disorder in children and adolescents. *Pediatrics, 140*(Supplement 2), S81-S85. https://pediatrics.aappublications.org/content/140/Supplement_2/S81

124 Baig, E. (2019). Epic Games sued for not warning parents 'Fortnite' is allegedly as addictive as cocaine. *USA Today*. www.usatoday.com/story/tech/talkingtech/2019/10/07/fortnite-producer-epic-games-lawsuit-says-addictive-as-cocaine/3900236002/

125 Lehman, J. (n.d.). *When Kids Get Violent: "There's No Excuse for Abuse"*. Empowering Parents. www.empoweringparents.com/article/video-games-and-violence-what-every-parent-should-know/

126 Huston, A. C. (1992). *Big world, small screen: The role of television in American society*. U of Nebraska Press. https://books.google.com/books?hl=en&lr=&id=t0B9n--Zt1sC&oi=fnd&pg=PP9&dq=Big+World,+Small+Screen:+The+Role+of+Television+in+American+Society&ots=TewRFwmmvs&sig=jP-nytuPUB36zUfMKPJZ0ZsxZ-cA#v=onepage&q=acts%20of%20violence&f=false

127 Van den Bulck, J. (2004). Media Use and Dreaming: The Relationship Among Television Viewing, Computer Game Play, and Nightmares or Pleasant Dreams. *Dreaming, 14*(1), 43. https://d1wqtxts1xzle7.cloudfront.net/3167822/dreaming.pdf?response-content-disposition=inline%3B+filename%3DMedia_Use_and_Dreaming_The_Relationship.pdf&Expires=1610292415&Signature=HwU05ccMB0d4az-p1aSwi1s6sz1V-1I14l7007F2vDXNODYFv9SccwYeGjjej9IXk6bdjvC8Sv4Q4MqFRb0SPDCTTHKH8X-nOQB3qMuhkA-Mg86dtD-FcYEAoROuGsvrJBiamQaj4QJt5RSpBWLn6Le1xf1qRtjTwpoOOTxEs-VyHb9IC6OMLcsct4nZlTTJKI9T0C0elNqzfbW5WZEs7nQjJ1rliVQdXKlIiwGSciteHv0m8rkwa0Zv-VBLeSwi0FP-VzdHU4pAIahfmOeNVZuIxJpFsBokBsGoZG4RWoaZ-ob6v0QWAnDcb8qt614PX-2hI8aEEShjBudVPZO13TUReIQ__&Key-Pair-Id=APKAJLOHF5GGSLRBV4ZA

128 Bushman, B. J., Jamieson, P. E., Weitz, I., & Romer, D. (2013). Gun violence trends in movies. *Pediatrics, 132*(6), 1014-1018. http://english2010information.pbworks.com/w/file/fetch/84975094/Gun%20violence%20trends%20in%20movies.pdf

129 Worth, K. A., Chambers, J. G., Nassau, D. H., Rakhra, B. K., & Sargent, J. D. (2008). Exposure of US adolescents to extremely violent movies. Pediatrics, 122(2), 306-312. www.ncbi.nlm.nih.gov/pmc/articles/PMC2778277/

130 Ybarra, M. L., Mitchell, K. J., & Korchmaros, J. D. (2011). National trends in exposure to and experiences of violence on the Internet among children. *Pediatrics, 128*(6), e1376-e1386. www.researchgate.net/profile/Josephine_Korchmaros/publication/51817752_National_Trends_in_Exposure_to_and_Experiences_of_Violence_on_the_Internet_Among_Children/links/56d0702908ae85c823486e47/National-Trends-in-Exposure-to-and-Experiences-of-Violence-on-the-Internet-Among-Children.pdf

131 American Psychological Association. (2015). *Resolution on violent video games.* www.apa.org/about/policy/violent-video-games

132 Anderson, C. A. (2004). An update on the effects of playing violent video games. *Journal of adolescence, 27*(1), 113-122. http://citeseerx.ist.psu.edu/viewdoc/download?doi=10.1.1.668.1647&rep=rep1&type=pdf

133 Bushman, B. J., & Anderson, C. A. (2001). Media violence and the American public: Scientific facts versus media misinformation. *American Psychologist, 56*(6-7), 477. www.researchgate.net/profile/Brad_Bushman/publication/11926062_Media_violence_and_the_American_Public_Scientific_facts_versus_media_misinformation/links/0912f5134dadf83c68000000/Media-violence-and-the-American-Public-Scientific-facts-versus-media-misinformation.pdf

134 Anderson, C. A., & Bushman, B. J. (2001). Effects of violent video games on aggressive behavior, aggressive cognition, aggressive affect, physiological arousal, and prosocial behavior: A meta-analytic review of the scientific literature. *Psychological science, 12*(5), 353-359. http://europepmc.org/abstract/med/11554666;
Anderson, C. A., Berkowitz, L., Donnerstein, E., Huesmann, L. R., Johnson, J. D., Linz, D., ... & Wartella, E. (2003). The influence of media violence on youth. *Psychological science in the public interest, 4*(3), 81-110. https://deepblue.lib.umich.edu/bitstream/handle/2027.42/83429/2003.Anderson_etal.InfluenceofMediaViolenceonYouth.PsychologicalScienceinthePublicInterest.pdf?sequence%3D1;
Anderson, C. A. (2004). An update on the effects of playing violent video games. *Journal of adolescence, 27*(1), 113-122. http://citeseerx.ist.psu.edu/viewdoc/download?doi=10.1.1.668.1647&rep=rep1&type=pdf;
Huesmann, L. R. (2007). The impact of electronic media violence: Scientific theory and research. *Journal of Adolescent Health, 41*(6), S6-S13. www.jahonline.org/article/S1054-139X(07)00391-6/fulltext;
Anderson, C. A., Shibuya, A., Ihori, N., Swing, E. L., Bushman, B. J., Sakamoto, A., ... & Saleem, M. (2010). Violent video game effects on aggression, empathy, and prosocial behavior in Eastern and Western countries: A meta-analytic review. *Psychological bulletin, 136*(2), 151. www.researchgate.net/profile/Hannah_Rothstein/publication/41654696_Violent_Video_Game_Effects_on_Aggression_Empathy_and_Prosocial_Behavior_in_Eastern_and_Western_Countries_A_Meta-Analytic_Review/links/0912f5064ecaa20093000000/Violent-Video-Game-Effects-on-Aggression-Empathy-and-Prosocial-Behavior-in-Eastern-and-Western-Countries-A-Meta-Analytic-Review.pdf

135 American Academy of Pediatrics. (2009). Policy statement--Media violence. *Pediatrics, 124*(5), 1495-1503. https://pediatrics.aappublications.org/content/124/5/1495;
Footnote references:
[1] American Psychological Association. (2015). *Resolution on violent video games.* www.apa.org/about/policy/violent-video-games
[2] *Violence in the media and entertainment.* (2004). American Academy of Family Physicians. www.aafp.org/about/policies/all/violence-media.html

136 Anderson, C. A., Berkowitz, L., Donnerstein, E., Huesmann, L. R., Johnson, J. D., Linz, D., ... & Wartella, E. (2003). The influence of media violence on youth. *Psychological science in the public interest, 4*(3), 81-110. https://deepblue.lib.umich.edu/bitstream/handle/2027.42/83429/2003.Anderson_etal.InfluenceofMediaViolenceonYouth.PsychologicalScienceinthePublicInterest.pdf?sequence%3D1;
Nathanson, A. I. (1999). Identifying and explaining the relationship between parental mediation and children's aggression. *Communication Research, 26*(2), 124-143. https://journals.sagepub.com/doi/abs/10.1177/009365099026002002

137 Huesmann, L. R., Eron, L. D., Klein, R., Brice, P., & Fischer, P. (1983). Mitigating the imitation of aggressive behaviors by changing children's attitudes about media violence. *Journal of personality and social psychology, 44*(5), 899. https://deepblue.lib.umich.edu/bitstream/handle/2027.42/83377/1983.Huesmann_etal.MitigatingtheImitatofAggressBehavbyChangingChildren's.JourofPersonality%26SocialPsych.pdf?sequence=1&isAllowed=y

138 Singer, D. G., & Singer, J. L. (Eds.). (2011). *Handbook of children and the media.* https://books.google.co.uk/books?id=moifZwJHunsC&printsec=frontcover&source=gbs_ge_summary_r&cad=0#v=onepage&q&f=false

139 *Interviews: John Halligan.* (2008). Frontline, PBS. www.pbs.org/wgbh/pages/frontline/kidsonline/interviews/halligan.html;

Reany, P. (2009). *Cyberbullying, more than just "messing around"*. Reuters. https://uk.reuters.com/article/us-cyber-bullying-life/cyberbullying-more-than-just-messing-around-idUKTRE54A2ZK20090511

140 Kowalski, R. M., Giumetti, G. W., Schroeder, A. N., & Lattanner, M. R. (2014). Bullying in the digital age: A critical review and meta-analysis of cyberbullying research among youth. *Psychological bulletin, 140*(4), 1073. www.researchgate.net/profile/Amber_Schroeder/publication/260151324_Bullying_in_the_Digital_Age_A_Critical_Review_and_Meta-Analysis_of_Cyberbullying_Research_Among_Youth/links/546f5b6a0cf2d67fc0310ef5.pdf
Citing: Willard, N. E. (2007). *Cyberbullying and cyberthreats: Responding to the challenge of online social aggression, threats, and distress*. Research press.

141 Crick, N. R., & Grotpeter, J. K. (1995). Relational aggression, gender, and social-psychological adjustment. *Child development, 66*(3), 710-722. http://citeseerx.ist.psu.edu/viewdoc/download?doi=10.1.1.708.4971&rep=rep1&type=pdf

142 Cyberbullying Facts. (n.d.). Cyberbullying Research Center. https://cyberbullying.org/facts;
Kowalski, R. M., Giumetti, G. W., Schroeder, A. N., & Lattanner, M. R. (2014). Bullying in the digital age: A critical review and meta-analysis of cyberbullying research among youth. *Psychological bulletin, 140*(4), 1073. www.researchgate.net/profile/Amber_Schroeder/publication/260151324_Bullying_in_the_Digital_Age_A_Critical_Review_and_Meta-Analysis_of_Cyberbullying_Research_Among_Youth/links/546f5b6a0cf2d67fc0310ef5.pdf;
Lilley, C., Ball, R., & Vernon, H. (2014). *The experiences of 11-16 year olds on social networking sites*. National Society for the Prevention of Cruelty to Children (NSPCC). https://library.nspcc.org.uk/HeritageScripts/Hapi.dll/search2?CookieCheck=43727.5529744907&searchTerm0=9781908055125;
Lasher, S., & Baker, C. (2015). *Bullying: evidence from the longitudinal study of young people in England 2, wave 2*. https://dera.ioe.ac.uk/24730/1/Bullying_evidence_from_the_longitudinal_study_of_young_people_in_England_2__wave_2_brief.pdf;
Mitchell, K. J., Wolak, J., & Finkelhor, D. (2007). Trends in youth reports of sexual solicitations, harassment and unwanted exposure to pornography on the Internet. *Journal of adolescent health, 40*(2), 116-126. www.jahonline.org/article/S1054-139X%2806%2900226-6/fulltext;
Zych, Izabela, Rosario Ortega-Ruiz, and Rosario Del Rey. "Systematic review of theoretical studies on bullying and cyberbullying: Facts, knowledge, prevention, and intervention." *Aggression and violent behavior 23*: 1-21. www.researchgate.net/profile/Izabela-Zych-2/publication/284014260_Systematic_review_of_theoretical_studies_on_bullying_and_cyberbullying_Facts_knowledge_prevention_and_intervention/links/570a62e908ae2eb9421fb23c/Systematic-review-of-theoretical-studies-on-bullying-and-cyberbullying-Facts-knowledge-prevention-and-intervention.pdf

143 Livingstone, S., Haddon, L., Görzig, A., & Ólafsson, K. (2011). *Risks and safety on the internet: the perspective of European children: full findings and policy implications from the EU Kids Online survey of 9-16 year olds and their parents in 25 countries*. http://eprints.lse.ac.uk/33731/1/Risks%20and%20safety%20on%20the%20internet(lsero).pdf;
Modecki, K. L., Minchin, J., Harbaugh, A. G., Guerra, N. G., & Runions, K. C. (2014). Bullying prevalence across contexts: A meta-analysis measuring cyber and traditional bullying. *Journal of Adolescent Health, 55*(5), 602-611. www.jahonline.org/article/S1054-139X(14)00254-7/fulltext

144 Kowalski, R. M., & Limber, S. P. (2013). Psychological, physical, and academic correlates of cyberbullying and traditional bullying. *Journal of Adolescent Health, 53*(1), S13-S20. www.jahonline.org/article/S1054-139X(12)00413-2/fulltext

145 Kowalski, R. M., Giumetti, G. W., Schroeder, A. N., & Lattanner, M. R. (2014). Bullying in the digital age: A critical review and meta-analysis of cyberbullying research among youth. *Psychological bulletin, 140*(4), 1073. www.researchgate.net/profile/Amber_Schroeder/publication/260151324_Bullying_in_the_Digital_Age_A_Critical_Review_and_Meta-Analysis_of_Cyberbullying_Research_Among_Youth/links/546f5b6a0cf2d67fc0310ef5.pdf;
Ybarra, M. L., Diener-West, M., & Leaf, P. J. (2007). Examining the overlap in Internet harassment and school bullying: Implications for school intervention. *Journal of Adolescent Health, 41*(6), S42-S50. www.jahonline.org/article/S1054-139X(07)00369-2/fulltext;
Ybarra, M. L., Mitchell, K. J., Wolak, J., & Finkelhor, D. (2006). Examining characteristics and associated distress related to Internet harassment: findings from the Second Youth Internet Safety Survey. *Pediatrics, 118*(4), e1169-e1177. http://pediatrics.aappublications.org/content/118/4/e1169.short;
Erdur-Baker, Ö. (2010). Cyberbullying and its correlation to traditional bullying, gender and frequent and risky usage of internet-mediated communication tools. *New media & society, 12*(1), 109-125. www.researchgate.net/profile/Ozgur_Erdur-Baker/publication/223956341_Cyberbullying_and_its_correlation_to_traditional_bullying_gender_and_frequent_and_risky_usage_of_Internet-mediated_communication_tools/links/543796fb0cf2027cbb20219c.pdf

146 Heirman, W., & Walrave, M. (2008). Assessing concerns and issues about the mediation of technology in cyberbullying. *Cyberpsychology: Journal of Psychosocial Research on Cyberspace, 2*(2). https://cyberpsychology.eu/article/view/4214/3256

147 Kowalski, R. M., & Limber, S. P. (2007). Electronic bullying among middle school students. Journal of adolescent health, 41(6), S22-S30. www.jahonline.org/article/S1054-139X(07)00361-8/fulltext;
Ybarra, M. L., & Mitchell, K. J. (2004). Online aggressor/targets, aggressors, and targets: A comparison of associated youth characteristics. *Journal of child Psychology and Psychiatry, 45*(7), 1308-1316. www.unh.edu/ccrc/pdf/jvq/CV75.pdf

148 Kowalski, R. M., Giumetti, G. W., Schroeder, A. N., & Lattanner, M. R. (2014). Bullying in the digital age: A critical review and meta-analysis of cyberbullying research among youth. *Psychological bulletin, 140*(4), 1073. www.researchgate.net/profile/Amber_Schroeder/publication/260151324_Bullying_in_the_Digital_Age_A_Critical_Review_and_Meta-Analysis_of_Cyberbullying_Research_Among_Youth/links/546f5b6a0cf2d67fc0310ef5.pdf

149 Kowalski, R. M., Giumetti, G. W., Schroeder, A. N., & Lattanner, M. R. (2014). Bullying in the digital age: A critical review and meta-analysis of cyberbullying research among youth. *Psychological bulletin, 140*(4), 1073. www.researchgate.net/profile/Amber_Schroeder/publication/260151324_Bullying_in_the_Digital_Age_A_Critical_Review_and_Meta-Analysis_of_Cyberbullying_Research_Among_Youth/links/546f5b6a0cf2d67fc0310ef5.pdf

150 *10 years later, 'Star Wars Kid' speaks out.* (2013). Maclean's. www.macleans.ca/news/canada/10-years-later-the-star-wars-kid-speaks-out/

151 Heirman, W., & Walrave, M. (2008). Assessing concerns and issues about the mediation of technology in cyberbullying. *Cyberpsychology: Journal of Psychosocial Research on Cyberspace, 2*(2). https://cyberpsychology.eu/article/view/4214/3256

152 Heirman, W., & Walrave, M. (2008). Assessing concerns and issues about the mediation of technology in cyberbullying. *Cyberpsychology: Journal of Psychosocial Research on Cyberspace, 2*(2). https://cyberpsychology.eu/article/view/4214/3256

153 Suler, J. (2004). The online disinhibition effect. Cyberpsychology & behavior, 7(3), 321-326. http://drleannawolfe.com/Suler-TheOnlineDisinhibitionEffect-2004.pdf

154 Heirman, W., & Walrave, M. (2008). Assessing concerns and issues about the mediation of technology in cyberbullying. *Cyberpsychology: Journal of Psychosocial Research on Cyberspace, 2*(2). https://cyberpsychology.eu/article/view/4214/3256;
Sourander, A., Klomek, A. B., Ikonen, M., Lindroos, J., Luntamo, T., Koskelainen, M., ... & Helenius, H. (2010). Psychosocial risk factors associated with cyberbullying among adolescents: A population-based study. *Archives of general psychiatry, 67*(7), 720-728. https://jamanetwork.com/journals/jamapsychiatry/articlepdf/210833/yoa90114_720_728.pdf

155 Zych, I., Ortega-Ruiz, R., & Del Rey, R. (2015). Systematic review of theoretical studies on bullying and cyberbullying: Facts, knowledge, prevention, and intervention. *Aggression and violent behavior, 23*, 1-21. www.researchgate.net/profile/Izabela-Zych-2/publication/284014260_Systematic_review_of_theoretical_studies_on_bullying_and_cyberbullying_Facts_knowledge_prevention_and_intervention/links/570a62e908ae2eb9421fb23c/Systematic-review-of-theoretical-studies-on-bullying-and-cyberbullying-Facts-knowledge-prevention-and-intervention.pdf

156 Kowalski, R. M., Giumetti, G. W., Schroeder, A. N., & Lattanner, M. R. (2014). Bullying in the digital age: A critical review and meta-analysis of cyberbullying research among youth. *Psychological bulletin, 140*(4), 1073. www.researchgate.net/profile/Amber_Schroeder/publication/260151324_Bullying_in_the_Digital_Age_A_Critical_Review_and_Meta-Analysis_of_Cyberbullying_Research_Among_Youth/links/546f5b6a0cf2d67fc0310ef5.pdf;
Aboujaoude, E., Savage, M. W., Starcevic, V., & Salame, W. O. (2015). Cyberbullying: Review of an old problem gone viral. *Journal of Adolescent Health, 57*(1), 10-18. www.researchgate.net/profile/Vladan_Starcevic/publication/278795569_Cyberbullying_Review_of_an_Old_Problem_Gone_Viral/links/5a043bbca6fdcc1c2f5b8f33/Cyberbullying-Review-of-an-Old-Problem-Gone-Viral.pdf;
Sourander, A., Klomek, A. B., Ikonen, M., Lindroos, J., Luntamo, T., Koskelainen, M., ... & Helenius, H. (2010). Psychosocial risk factors associated with cyberbullying among adolescents: A population-based study. *Archives of general psychiatry, 67*(7), 720-728. https://jamanetwork.com/journals/jamapsychiatry/articlepdf/210833/yoa90114_720_728.pdf;
Ybarra, M. L. (2004). Linkages between depressive symptomatology and Internet harassment among young regular Internet users. *CyberPsychology & Behavior, 7*(2), 247-257. https://innovativepublichealth.org/wp-content/uploads/2004/04/Cyberpsychology_depressive_sxs__internet_harassment.pdf;

Baker, Ö. E., & Tanrıkulu, İ. (2010). Psychological consequences of cyber bullying experiences among Turkish secondary school children. *Procedia-Social and Behavioral Sciences, 2*(2), 2771-2776. www.researchgate.net/profile/Ozgur_Erdur-Baker/publication/248607285_Psychological_consequences_of_cyber_bullying_experiences_among_Turkish_secondary_school_children/links/556424a608ae8c0cab36fd75.pdf;
Perren, S., Dooley, J., Shaw, T., & Cross, D. (2010). Bullying in school and cyberspace: Associations with depressive symptoms in Swiss and Australian adolescents. *Child and adolescent psychiatry and mental health, 4*(1), 28. https://capmh.biomedcentral.com/articles/10.1186/1753-2000-4-28;
Perren, S., Corcoran, L., Cowie, H., Dehue, F., Mc Guckin, C., Sevcikova, A., ... & Völlink, T. (2012). Tackling cyberbullying: Review of empirical evidence regarding successful responses by students, parents, and schools. *International Journal of Conflict and Violence, 6*(2), 283. https://lra.le.ac.uk/bitstream/2381/31446/5/Cyberbullying%20article_ijcv6%282%292012.pdf

157 Notar, C. E., Padgett, S., & Roden, J. (2013). Cyberbullying: A review of the literature. *Universal journal of educational research, 1*(1), 1-9. www.hrpub.org/download/201306/ujer.2013.010101.pdf

Citing: Wong-Lo, M., & Bullock, L. M. (2011). Digital aggression: Cyberworld meets school bullies. *Preventing School Failure: Alternative Education for Children and Youth, 55*(2), 64-70.
Citing: Wong-Lo, M., & Bullock, L. M. (2011). Digital aggression: Cyberworld meets school bullies. *Preventing School Failure: Alternative Education for Children and Youth, 55*(2), 64-70.

158 Cassidy, W., Brown, K., & Jackson, M. (2012). "Making Kind Cool": Parents' Suggestions for Preventing Cyber Bullying and Fostering Cyber Kindness. *Journal of Educational Computing Research, 46*(4), 415-436. http://journals.sagepub.com/doi/abs/10.2190/EC.46.4.f

159 Zhou, Z., Tang, H., Tian, Y., Wei, H., Zhang, F., & Morrison, C. M. (2013). Cyberbullying and its risk factors among Chinese high school students. *School Psychology International, 34*(6), 630-647. http://tweb.cjcu.edu.tw/journal/2013_10_30_08_55_26.160.pdf#page=58;
Lilley, C., Ball, R., & Vernon, H. (2014). *The experiences of 11-16 year olds on social networking sites*. National Society for the Prevention of Cruelty to Children (NSPCC). https://library.nspcc.org.uk/HeritageScripts/Hapi.dll/search2?CookieCheck=43727.5529744907&searchTerm0=9781908055125;
Li, Qing. (2010). Cyberbullying in high schools: A study of students' behaviors and beliefs about this new phenomenon. *Journal of Aggression, Maltreatment & Trauma, 19*(4), 372-392. www.tandfonline.com/doi/full/10.1080/10926771003788979?src=recsys&mobileUi=0

160 Li, Qing. (2010). Cyberbullying in high schools: A study of students' behaviors and beliefs about this new phenomenon. *Journal of Aggression, Maltreatment & Trauma, 19*(4), 372-392. www.tandfonline.com/doi/full/10.1080/10926771003788979?src=recsys&mobileUi=0;
Hutson, E., Kelly, S., & Militello, L. K. (2018). Systematic review of cyberbullying interventions for youth and parents with implications for evidence-based practice. *Worldviews on evidence-based nursing, 15*(1), 72-79. https://sigmapubs.onlinelibrary.wiley.com/doi/full/10.1111/wvn.12257;
Agatston, P. W., Kowalski, R., & Limber, S. (2007). Students' perspectives on cyber bullying. *Journal of Adolescent Health, 41*(6), S59-S60. www.jahonline.org/article/S1054-139X(07)00368-0/fulltext

161 Mesch, G. S. (2009). Parental mediation, online activities, and cyberbullying. *CyberPsychology & Behavior, 12*(4), 387-393. www.dhi.ac.uk/san/waysofbeing/data/communication-zangana-mesch-2009a.pdf

162 Hoff, D. L., & Mitchell, S. N. (2009). Cyberbullying: Causes, effects, and remedies. *Journal of Educational Administration, 47*(5), 652-665. www.emeraldinsight.com/doi/abs/10.1108/09578230910981107?journalCode=jea

163 Garaigordobil, M., & Martínez-Valderrey, V. (2015). Effects of Cyberprogram 2.0 on "face-to-face" bullying, cyberbullying, and empathy. *Psicothema, 27*(1). www.sc.ehu.es/ptwgalam/art_completo/2014/2015/Cyberprogram%20CB_IECA%20Psicotema.pdf;
Williford, A., Elledge, L. C., Boulton, A. J., DePaolis, K. J., Little, T. D., & Salmivalli, C. (2013). Effects of the KiVa antibullying program on cyberbullying and cybervictimization frequency among Finnish youth. *Journal of Clinical Child & Adolescent Psychology, 42*(6), 820-833. www.ingentaconnect.com/content/routledg/hcap20/2013/00000042/00000006/art00007;
Salmivalli, C., Kärnä, A., & Poskiparta, E. (2011). Counteracting bullying in Finland: The KiVa program and its effects on different forms of being bullied. *International Journal of Behavioral Development, 35*(5), 405-411. http://citeseerx.ist.psu.edu/viewdoc/download?doi=10.1.1.945.8603&rep=rep1&type=pdf;
Footnote references:
[1] Garaigordobil, M., & Martínez-Valderrey, V. (2015). Effects of Cyberprogram 2.0 on "face-to-face" bullying, cyberbullying, and empathy. *Psicothema, 27*(1). www.sc.ehu.es/ptwgalam/art_completo/2014/2015/Cyberprogram%20CB_IECA%20Psicotema.pdf
[2] Del Rey, R., Casas, J. A., & Ortega, R. (2016). Impact of the ConRed program on different cyberbulling roles. *Aggressive behavior, 42*(2), 123-135. https://onlinelibrary.wiley.com/doi/abs/10.1002/ab.21608

[3] Garaigordobil, M., & Martínez-Valderrey, V. (2015). Effects of Cyberprogram 2.0 on "face-to-face" bullying, cyberbullying, and empathy. *Psicothema, 27*(1). www.sc.ehu.es/ptwgalam/art_completo/2014/2015/Cyberprogram%20CB_IECA%20Psicotema.pdf
[4] Machimbarrena, J. M., & Garaigordobil, M. (2017). Bullying/Cyberbullying in 5th and 6th grade: differences between public and private schools. *Anales de psicología, 33*(2), 319-326. http://scielo.isciii.es/scielo.php?script=sci_arttext&pid=S0212-97282017000200014
Annex: http://scielo.isciii.es/img/revistas/ap/v33n2/psicologia_desarrollo4_anexo1.jpg
[5] *Whole-School Social and Emotional Wellbeing Initiative for Schools.* (2021). Telethon Kids Institute. http://friendlyschools.com.au/fsp/about/research/
[6] Cross, D., Shaw, T., Hadwen, K., Cardoso, P., Slee, P., Roberts, C., ... & Barnes, A. (2016). Longitudinal impact of the Cyber Friendly Schools program on adolescents' cyberbullying behavior. *Aggressive behavior, 42*(2), 166-180. https://onlinelibrary.wiley.com/doi/abs/10.1002/ab.21609

164 Li, Q. (2010). Cyberbullying in high schools: A study of students' behaviors and beliefs about this new phenomenon. *Journal of Aggression, Maltreatment & Trauma, 19*(4), 372-392. www.tandfonline.com/doi/full/10.1080/10926771003788979?src=recsys&mobileUi=0

165 Ashby, E. (2012). *Cyberbully movie review.* Common Sense Media. www.commonsensemedia.org/movie-reviews/cyberbully

166 Barcellos, K. (2019). *Speaker urges RMS students to take action on bullying.* Rutland Herald. www.rutlandherald.com/news/speaker-urges-rms-students-to-take-action-on-bullying/article_71a9d646-dfda-52b8-a7f5-3007dc9a6aa9.html

167 *Beauty Pageant Origins and Culture.* (n.d.). American Experience, PBS. www.pbs.org/wgbh/americanexperience/features/missamerica-beauty-pageant-origins-and-culture/

168 Coppinger, M. (2020). *Sources: UFC 251 generates around 1.3 million PPV buys, most since 2018.* The Athletic. https://theathletic.com/1926427/2020/07/13/sources-ufc-251-generates-around-1-3-million-ppv-buys-most-since-2018/

169 Malkin, A. R., Wornian, K., & Chrisler, J. C. (1999). Women and weight: Gendered messages on magazine covers. *Sex Roles, 40*(7-8), 647-655. www.researchgate.net/profile/Joan_Chrisler/publication/251375508_Women_and_Weight_Gendered_Messages_on_Magazine_Covers/links/56009b3108aeafc8ac8c77b6.pdf

170 Aubrey, J. S., & Frisby, C. M. (2011). Sexual objectification in music videos: A content analysis comparing gender and genre. *Mass Communication and Society, 14*(4), 475-501. https://d1wqtxts1xzle7.cloudfront.net/47541184/MC_S_music_video_final-with-cover-page-v2.pdf?Expires=1629429301&Signature=Ur1x--thIX7oDioW7JXGupkrIFuBjGwtQ-BqTz1nu80h6HJ-omjO0VnJaNl1qXzAGosy-qRsN3oD9ZSMcFntoYx-3PadOKvmc9tNuXe19KJJn4XWpBGOIhp0Ru2VID4uEpxl65JYa-veFhXOpx9AQhEvlrI6D1GawzvPmQXs-atLkt6-T4quTFj7xZ-1wTUnEZOB0PbOibAxGgZ3ESjj1h37Y94kRnNUBSh332OkcoXXA6VTqC69dQB-1yARwXA2nlzlTaKMcSLX2A4pm-BesnVktj324TXk2usuSyietNTN5yplRwJt5oslzkfT7CwBllzt-de8K-xyMtYzxalNyKw-PiQ__&Key-Pair-Id=APKAJLOHF5GGSLRBV4ZA

171 Bleakley, A., Jamieson, P. E., & Romer, D. (2012). Trends of sexual and violent content by gender in top-grossing US films, 1950–2006. *Journal of Adolescent Health, 51*(1), 73-79. https://d1wqtxts1xzle7.cloudfront.net/46421557/j.jadohealth.2012.02.00620160612-12340-luowl4-with-cover-page-v2.pdf?Expires=1629430887&Signature=Kphr-R66gGvhu-3YJSJY1qGDhv-eBRq6Wl1rQlXZHtlNSmrwA9YghCI4LR76-U7Y-iHjjwnMyJBZ0DA8G-DzMqSH-Lj0iGDSCVg4S5SGaEo6pzeHGEPc8Aw778msEFz29nuLYcUI1QF7kKMk426Ut5UEpKn89EZl6AGSi168fCiZ-jCcO4TOjA6OdyG8lia51RT-gfPtIvVHR8nIZ7ikYmuHsJNKwLMhMzdxJ8c7lqsIA-dGrvLDjKy5PSSoatL-mUf9k-5IuIZHcHxOqS46kq5AeYnPRgSrGm6dwafEcvLJZEBXvOw2Ki-oefP6-Hij-iZRs50w2Cn9QmD9AfQksvS6C-g__&Key-Pair-Id=APKAJLOHF5GGSLRBV4ZA

172 Prieler, M. (2016). Gender stereotypes in Spanish-and English-language television advertisements in the United States. *Mass Communication and Society, 19*(3), 275-300. www.tandfonline.com/doi/abs/10.1080/15205436.2015.1111386

173 Eisend, M. (2010). A meta-analysis of gender roles in advertising. *Journal of the Academy of Marketing Science, 38*(4), 418-440. https://d1wqtxts1xzle7.cloudfront.net/60958288/A_meta-analysis_of_gender_roles_in_advertising20191020-121773-1km3tn4-with-cover-page-v2.pdf?Expires=1629509589&Signature=T7Dywhd-73qfSAxsSs-wokmkudjTYJnLPFJDHZu-6kdOhZIcYCutabnhz9AIX92MGVDQ-w7ToDGaSkWsyQ6Swt-VpPbbWUy3z7YOhP7C4TkIqoR22KLuNjTo59XpWbKvsphBjmwdQbtWqGm8Sct6pyb3cWCJBnAyw1JN-7mCX-F-AUb89OcgNR2s9HZdeD8GGkal5TxsMvufhxOoubNven9h2O0PN3gpcHTQqbBSHk-AdqE4K-PVo5WQ9sCSjhZnsyVzTwmQJUManvbv-vw868nIAE6i3a1LUyUtm4w-60MH5pMGiddgbeKdUNvlTZc-4mCNJALGU41Rc1hbJfl3yPndYkw__&Key-Pair-Id=APKAJLOHF5GGSLRBV4ZA

174 Ward, L. M., Hansbrough, E., & Walker, E. (2005). Contributions of music video exposure to black adolescents' gender and sexual schemas. *Journal of adolescent research, 20*(2), 143-166. http://scholar.google.co.uk/scholar_url?url=https%3A%2F%2Fsites.google.com%2Fsite%2Fbradleybond%2FWardHansbrough.pdf&hl=en&sa=T&oi=gga&ct=gga&cd=0&ei=Hge5Wv6tK4bYmgHT36WIDQ&scisig=AAGBfm1LpIoCvaRu-jrY-9fimy11QKnOUEw&nossl=1&ws=1920x929;
Kalof, L. (1999). The effects of gender and music video imagery on sexual attitudes. *The Journal of Social Psychology, 139*(3), 378-385. www.researchgate.net/profile/Linda_Kalof/publication/12888075_The_Effects_of_Gender_and_Music_Video_Imagery_on_Sexual_Attitudes/links/54c296150cf219bbe4e8caa1.pdf

175 Ward, L. M. (2003). Understanding the role of entertainment media in the sexual socialization of American youth: A review of empirical research. *Developmental Review, 23*(3), 347-388. www.sciencedirect.com/science/article/pii/S0273229703000133;
Ward, L. M., & Friedman, K. (2006). Using TV as a guide: Associations between television viewing and adolescents' sexual attitudes and behavior. *Journal of research on adolescence, 16*(1), 133-156. http://onlinelibrary.wiley.com/doi/10.1111/j.1532-7795.2006.00125.x/full;
Ward, L. M., Hansbrough, E., & Walker, E. (2005). Contributions of music video exposure to black adolescents' gender and sexual schemas. *Journal of adolescent research, 20*(2), 143-166. http://scholar.google.co.uk/scholar_url?url=https%3A%2F%2Fsites.google.com%2Fsite%2Fbradleybond%2FWardHansbrough.pdf&hl=en&sa=T&oi=gga&ct=gga&cd=0&ei=a_u4Wq2gKY2pmAHO9aKIBw&scisig=AAGBfm1LpIoCvaRu-jrY-9fimy11QKnOUEw&nossl=1&ws=1920x929

176 Ward, L. M. (2002). Does television exposure affect emerging adults' attitudes and assumptions about sexual relationships? Correlational and experimental confirmation. *Journal of youth and adolescence, 31*(1), 1-15. https://deepblue.lib.umich.edu/bitstream/handle/2027.42/45292/10964_2004_Article_364602.pdf?sequence=1&isAllowed=y

177 Johnson, J. D., Adams, M. S., Ashburn, L., & Reed, W. (1995). Differential gender effects of exposure to rap music on African American adolescents' acceptance of teen dating violence. *Sex Roles, 33*(7-8), 597-605. https://link.springer.com/article/10.1007/BF01544683

178 Milburn, M. A., Mather, R., & Conrad, S. D. (2000). The effects of viewing R-rated movie scenes that objectify women on perceptions of date rape. *Sex Roles, 43*(9-10), 645-664. www.ncdsv.org/images/r-rated_movies.pdf

179 Lanis, K., & Covell, K. (1995). Images of women in advertisements: Effects on attitudes related to sexual aggression. *Sex roles, 32*(9-10), 639-649. www.researchgate.net/profile/Katherine_Covell/publication/226599870_Images_of_Women_in_Advertisements_Effects_on_Attitudes_Related_to_Sexual_Aggression/links/568c39f308ae197e4268a4a6.pdf;
MacKay, N. J., & Covell, K. (1997). The impact of women in advertisements on attitudes toward women. *Sex roles, 36*(9-10), 573-583. https://link.springer.com/article/10.1023/A:1025613923786

180 Fisher, D. A., Hill, D. L., Grube, J. W., Bersamin, M. M., Walker, S., & Gruber, E. L. (2009). Televised sexual content and parental mediation: Influences on adolescent sexuality. *Media psychology, 12*(2), 121-147. www.ncbi.nlm.nih.gov/pmc/articles/PMC3086268/

181 Kaling, M. (2011). Flick Chicks: A guide to women in the movies. *The New Yorker*. www.newyorker.com/magazine/2011/10/03/flick-chicks

182 Hesse, C., & Pedersen, C. L. (2017). Porn sex versus real sex: How sexually explicit material shapes our understanding of sexual anatomy, physiology, and behaviour. *Sexuality & Culture, 21*(3), 754-775. www.researchgate.net/profile/Cory_Pedersen/publication/313418046_Porn_Sex_Versus_Real_Sex_How_Sexually_Explicit_Material_Shapes_Our_Understanding_of_Sexual_Anatomy_Physiology_and_Behaviour/links/5ac86f73aca272abdc5e9ccb/Porn-Sex-Versus-Real-Sex-How-Sexually-Explicit-Material-Shapes-Our-Understanding-of-Sexual-Anatomy-Physiology-and-Behaviour.pdf

183 Sabina, C., Wolak, J., & Finkelhor, D. (2008). The nature and dynamics of Internet pornography exposure for youth. *CyberPsychology & Behavior, 11*(6), 691-693. http://scholars.unh.edu/cgi/viewcontent.cgi?article=1283&context=soc_facpub

184 Sabina, C., Wolak, J., & Finkelhor, D. (2008). The nature and dynamics of Internet pornography exposure for youth. *CyberPsychology & Behavior, 11*(6), 691-693. https://scholars.unh.edu/cgi/viewcontent.cgi?article=1283&context=soc_facpub

185 Chen, A. S., Leung, M., Chen, C. H., & Yang, S. C. (2013). Exposure to internet pornography among Taiwanese adolescents. *Social behavior and personality: An international journal, 41*(1), 157-164. www.ingentaconnect.com/content/sbp/sbp/2013/00000041/00000001/art00015;

Mitchell, K. J., Wolak, J., & Finkelhor, D. (2007). Trends in youth reports of sexual solicitations, harassment and unwanted exposure to pornography on the Internet. *Journal of adolescent health, 40*(2), 116-126. www.jahonline.org/article/S1054-139X%2806%2900226-6/fulltext

186 Sabina, C., Wolak, J., & Finkelhor, D. (2008). The nature and dynamics of Internet pornography exposure for youth. *CyberPsychology & Behavior, 11*(6), 691-693. https://scholars.unh.edu/cgi/viewcontent.cgi?article=1283&context=soc_facpub

187 Sabina, C., Wolak, J., & Finkelhor, D. (2008). The nature and dynamics of Internet pornography exposure for youth. *CyberPsychology & Behavior, 11*(6), 691-693. https://scholars.unh.edu/cgi/viewcontent.cgi?article=1283&context=soc_facpub

188 Mitchell, K. J., Wolak, J., & Finkelhor, D. (2007). Trends in youth reports of sexual solicitations, harassment and unwanted exposure to pornography on the Internet. *Journal of adolescent health, 40*(2), 116-126. www.jahonline.org/article/S1054-139X%2806%2900226-6/fulltext;
Livingstone, S., Davidson, J., Bryce, J., Batool, S., Haughton, C., & Nandi, A. (2017). *Children's online activities, risks and safety: a literature review by the UKCCIS evidence group*. http://eprints.lse.ac.uk/84956/1/Literature%20Review%20Final%20October%202017.pdf

189 Stranden, A. L. (2014). *Adolescents regret having watched porn.* Science Nordway. http://sciencenordic.com/adolescents-regret-having-watched-porn

190 Livingstone, S., & Bober, M. (2004). *UK children go online: Surveying the experiences of young people and their parents.* http://eprints.lse.ac.uk/395/1/UKCGOsurveyreport.pdf

191 *We need to talk about pornography: Children, parents and age verification.* (n.d.). Internet Matters. www.internetmatters.org/wp-content/uploads/2019/06/WeNeedToTalkAboutPornography-LowRes.pdf;
Lauricella, A. R., Cingel, D. P., Beaudoin-Ryan, L., Robb, M. B., Saphir, M., & Wartella, E. A. (2016). *The Common Sense census: Plugged-in parents of tweens and teens.* Common Sense Media. www.commonsensemedia.org/sites/default/files/uploads/research/common-sense-parent-census_whitepaper_for-web.pdf

192 Cameron, D. (2013). *The internet and pornography: Prime Minister calls for action.* Gov.UK. www.gov.uk/government/speeches/the-internet-and-pornography-prime-minister-calls-for-action

193 Martellozzo, E., Monaghan, A., Adler, J. R., Davidson, J., Leyva, R., & Horvath, M. A. (2016). *"I wasn't sure it was normal to watch it..." A quantitative and qualitative examination of the impact of online pornography on the values, attitudes, beliefs and behaviours of children and young people.* www.mdx.ac.uk/__data/assets/pdf_file/0021/223266/MDX-NSPCC-OCC-pornography-report.pdf

194 Wright, P. J., Herbenick, D., & Paul, B. (2019). Adolescent Condom Use, Parent-adolescent Sexual Health Communication, and Pornography: Findings from a US Probability Sample. *Health Communication*, 1-7. www.tandfonline.com/doi/abs/10.1080/10410236.2019.1652392

195 Weaver, J. B., Masland, J. L., & Zillmann, D. (1984). Effect of erotica on young men's aesthetic perception of their female sexual partners. *Perceptual and Motor Skills, 58*(3), 929-930.

196 Zillmann, D., & Bryant, J. (1988). Pornography's impact on sexual satisfaction 1. *Journal of Applied Social Psychology, 18*(5), 438-453. https://s3.amazonaws.com/academia.edu.documents/51881424/ZILLMANN._Pornographys_impact_on_sexual_satisfaction.pdf?response-content-disposition=inline%3B%20filename%3DZILLMANN._Pornographys_impact_on_sexual.pdf&X-Amz-Algorithm=AWS4-HMAC-SHA256&X-Amz-Credential=AKIAIWOWYYGZ2Y53UL3A%2F20190824%2Fus-east-1%2Fs3%2Faws4_request&X-Amz-Date=20190824T104218Z&X-Amz-Expires=3600&X-Amz-SignedHeaders=host&X-Amz-Signature=36ef4e557f443c672f12c0bab1368371dd207aa3f4794e3f47fe9020905a7d02;
Footnote references:
[1] Landripet, I., & Štulhofer, A. (2015). Is pornography use associated with sexual difficulties and dysfunctions among younger heterosexual men?. *The journal of sexual medicine, 12*(5), 1136-1139. www.bib.irb.hr/756533?rad=756533
[2] Prause, N., & Pfaus, J. (2015). Viewing sexual stimuli associated with greater sexual responsiveness, not erectile dysfunction. *Sexual medicine, 3*(2), 90-98. www.sciencedirect.com/science/article/pii/S205011611530057X
[3] Laumann, E. O., Paik, A., & Rosen, R. C. (1999). Sexual dysfunction in the United States: prevalence and predictors. *Jama, 281*(6), 537-544. www.fact.on.ca/newpaper/joc80785.htm
[4] Mitchell, K. R., Mercer, C. H., Ploubidis, G. B., Jones, K. G., Datta, J., Field, N., ... & Clifton, S. (2013). Sexual function in Britain: findings from the third National Survey of Sexual Attitudes and Lifestyles (Natsal-3). *The Lancet, 382*(9907), 1817-1829. www.sciencedirect.com/science/article/pii/S0140673613623661

197 Footnote references:

[1] Laumann, E. O., Gagnon, J. H., Michael, R. T., & Michaels, S. (1994). *The social organization of sexuality: Sexual practices in the United States.* University of Chicago press. https://books.google.co.uk/books?hl=en&lr=&id=3RbyuQAYsdMC&oi=fnd&pg=PR19&dq=The+Social+Organization+of+Sexuality:+Sexual+Practices+in+the+United+States&ots=B7tqUGXM6-&sig=5CjAv5uGx2hD2IuLEXa15Pc_Bes&redir_esc=y#v=onepage&q=table%203.6&f=false
[2] Herbenick, D., Reece, M., Schick, V., Sanders, S. A., Dodge, B., & Fortenberry, J. D. (2010). Sexual behavior in the United States: Results from a national probability sample of men and women ages 14–94. *The journal of sexual medicine, 7,* 255-265. hwww.researchgate.net/profile/Debby_Herbenick/publication/47674626_Sexual_Behavior_in_the_United_States_Results_from_a_National_Probability_Sample_of_Men_and_Women_Ages_14-94/links/5a37a00f0f7e9b7c486e2380/Sexual-Behavior-in-the-United-States-Results-from-a-National-Probability-Sample-of-Men-and-Women-Ages-14-94.pdf
[3] Ryan, K. M., & Mohr, S. (2005). Gender differences in playful aggression during courtship in college students. *Sex Roles, 53*(7-8), 591-601. www.researchgate.net/profile/Kathryn-Ryan-2/publication/225505843_Gender_Differences_in_Playful_Aggression_During_Courtship_in_College_Students/links/00b4953360c97b7c26000000/Gender-Differences-in-Playful-Aggression-During-Courtship-in-College-Students.pdf
[4] Herbenick, D., Fu, T. C., Wright, P., Paul, B., Gradus, R., Bauer, J., & Jones, R. (2020). Diverse sexual behaviors and pornography use: Findings from a nationally representative probability survey of Americans aged 18 to 60 years. *The journal of sexual medicine, 17*(4), 623-633. https://altsexnycconference.org/wp-content/uploads/2020/06/Herbenick-Fu-Wright-Paul-Gradus-Bauer-Jones-2020.pdf

198 Ybarra, M. L., Finkelhor, D., Mitchell, K. J., & Wolak, J. (2009). Associations between blocking, monitoring, and filtering software on the home computer and youth-reported unwanted exposure to sexual material online. *Child Abuse & Neglect, 33*(12), 857-869. https://innovativepublichealth.org/wp-content/uploads/2012/02/CAN_YISS2-filtering-paper.pdf;
Przybylski, A. K., & Nash, V. (2018). Internet filtering and adolescent exposure to online sexual material. *Cyberpsychology, Behavior, and Social Networking, 21*(7), 405-410. www.liebertpub.com/doi/pdf/10.1089/cyber.2017.0466

199 Rothman, E. F., Daley, N., & Alder, J. (2020). A Pornography Literacy Program for Adolescents. *American Journal of Public Health, 110*(2), 154-156. www.ncbi.nlm.nih.gov/pmc/articles/PMC6951388/

200 Livingstone, S., & Helsper, E. J. (2008). Parental mediation of children's internet use. *Journal of broadcasting & electronic media, 52*(4), 581-599. http://eprints.lse.ac.uk/25723/1/Parental_mediation_and_children's_internet_use_(LSERO_version).pdf

201 Gallop, C. (2009). *Make Love not Porn* [Video]. TED Conferences. www.ted.com/talks/cindy_gallop_make_love_not_porn

202 Grooming. (n.d.). *Oxford's English dictionaries.* Oxford University Press. www.google.com/search?q=definition+of+grooming&rlz=1C1GCEB_enGB922GB922&oq=definition+of+grooming&aqs=-chrome..69i57j0i512l9.2821j0j15&sourceid=chrome&ie=UTF-8

203 Bowles, N. & Keller, M.H. (2020). Video Games and Online Chats Are 'Hunting Grounds' for Sexual Predators. *The New York Times.* www.nytimes.com/interactive/2019/12/07/us/video-games-child-sex-abuse.html?mtrref=undefined&assetType=REGIWALL

204 Madden, M., Cortesi, S., Gasser, U., Lenhart, A., & Duggan, M. (2012). *Parents, Teens, and Online Privacy.* Pew internet & American life project. www.pewinternet.org/2012/11/20/parents-teens-and-online-privacy/

205 Eurobarometer, F. (2008). *Towards a safer use of the Internet for children in the EU–a parents' perspective.* European Commission, 3-144. http://uploadi.www.ris.org/editor/1234951358za%20222.pdf

206 *Carly's Law.* (2017). The Carly Ryan Foundation. www.carlyryanfoundation.com/posts/2017/05/10/carlys-law

207 *'Cyber-grooming': Germany toughens law on online predators.* (2019). The Local. www.thelocal.de/20190626/cyber-grooming-germany-toughens-law-on-online-predators

208 Dedkova, L. (2015). Stranger is not always danger: The myth and reality of meetings with online strangers. *Living in the digital age,* 78. www.researchgate.net/profile/Anna_Sevcikova/publication/279572823_The_Educational_Dimension_of_Pornography_Adolescents'_Use_of_New_Media_for_Sexual_Purposes/links/5596f00e08ae99aa62c8c7d1/The-Educational-Dimension-of-Pornography-Adolescents-Use-of-New-Media-for-Sexual-Purposes.pdf#page=79;
Wolak, J., Finkelhor, D., & Mitchell, K. (2004). Internet-initiated sex crimes against minors: Implications for prevention based on findings from a national study. *Journal of adolescent health, 35*(5), 424-e11. www.jahonline.org/article/S1054-139X(04)00171-5/fulltext

209 Livingstone, S., Haddon, L., Görzig, A., & Ólafsson, K. (2011). *Risks and safety on the internet: the perspective of European children: full findings and policy implications from the EU Kids Online survey of 9-16 year olds and their parents in 25 countries.* http://eprints.lse.ac.uk/33731/1/Risks%20and%20safety%20on%20the%20internet(lse-ro).pdf

210 Dedkova, L. (2015). Stranger is not always danger: The myth and reality of meetings with online strangers. *Living in the digital Aage, 78.* www.researchgate.net/profile/Anna_Sevcikova/publication/279572823_The_Educational_Dimension_of_Pornography_Adolescents'_Use_of_New_Media_for_Sexual_Purposes/links/5596f00e08ae99aa62c8c7d1/The-Educational-Dimension-of-Pornography-Adolescents-Use-of-New-Media-for-Sexual-Purposes.pdf#page=79

211 Livingstone, S., Haddon, L., Görzig, A., & Ólafsson, K. (2011). *Risks and safety on the internet: the perspective of European children: full findings and policy implications from the EU Kids Online survey of 9-16 year olds and their parents in 25 countries.* http://eprints.lse.ac.uk/33731/1/Risks%20and%20safety%20on%20the%20internet(lse-ro).pdf;
Barbovschi, M., Marinescu, V., Velicu, A., & Laszlo, E. (2012). *Meeting new contacts online.* Children, risk and safety on the internet, 177-189. https://books.google.co.uk/books?hl=en&lr=&id=R__hfWbE3Dw-C&oi=fnd&pg=PA177&dq=Barbovschi,+Marinescu,+Velicu,+%26+Laszlo&ots=xiFZ_JYAAB&sig=Nf-nGWgoZzqD4Z4A4nhp1XVUh5_M&redir_esc=y#v=onepage&q=Barbovschi%2C%20Marinescu%2C%20Velicu%2C%20%26%20Laszlo&f=false

212 Livingstone, S., Haddon, L., Görzig, A., & Ólafsson, K. (2011). *Risks and safety on the internet: the perspective of European children: full findings and policy implications from the EU Kids Online survey of 9-16 year olds and their parents in 25 countries.* http://eprints.lse.ac.uk/33731/1/Risks%20and%20safety%20on%20the%20internet(lse-ro).pdf

213 Livingstone, S., Haddon, L., Görzig, A., & Ólafsson, K. (2011). *Risks and safety on the internet: the perspective of European children: full findings and policy implications from the EU Kids Online survey of 9-16 year olds and their parents in 25 countries.* http://eprints.lse.ac.uk/33731/1/Risks%20and%20safety%20on%20the%20internet(lse-ro).pdf;
Barbovschi, M., Marinescu, V., Velicu, A., & Laszlo, E. (2012). *Meeting new contacts online.* Children, risk and safety on the internet, 177-189. https://books.google.co.uk/books?hl=en&lr=&id=R__hfWbE3Dw-C&oi=fnd&pg=PA177&dq=Barbovschi,+Marinescu,+Velicu,+%26+Laszlo&ots=xiFZ_JYAAB&sig=Nf-nGWgoZzqD4Z4A4nhp1XVUh5_M&redir_esc=y#v=onepage&q=Barbovschi%2C%20Marinescu%2C%20Velicu%2C%20%26%20Laszlo&f=false

214 Wolak, J., Finkelhor, D., & Mitchell, K. (2004). Internet-initiated sex crimes against minors: Implications for prevention based on findings from a national study. *Journal of adolescent health, 35*(5), 424-e11. www.jahonline.org/article/S1054-139X(04)00171-5/fulltext

215 Walsh, W. A., Wolak, J., & Mitchell, K. J. (2013). Close relationships with people met online in a national US sample of adolescents. *Cyberpsychology: Journal of Psychosocial Research on Cyberspace, 7*(3). https://cyberpsychology.eu/article/view/4289/3334

216 Livingstone, S., Haddon, L., Görzig, A., & Ólafsson, K. (2011). *Risks and safety on the internet: the perspective of European children: full findings and policy implications from the EU Kids Online survey of 9-16 year olds and their parents in 25 countries.* http://eprints.lse.ac.uk/33731/1/Risks%20and%20safety%20on%20the%20internet(lse-ro).pdf;
Liau, A. K., Khoo, A., & Hwaang, P. (2005). Factors influencing adolescents engagement in risky internet behavior. CyberPsychology & Behavior, 8(6), 513-520. https://repository.nie.edu.sg/bitstream/10497/4525/3/CPB-8-6-513.pdf;
Wolak, J., Mitchell, K. J., & Finkelhor, D. (2002). Close online relationships in a national sample of adolescents. *Adolescence, 37,* 441-456. www.researchgate.net/profile/Kimberly_Mitchell6/publication/11011068_Close_online_relationships_in_a_national_sample_of_adolescents/links/553652da0cf218056e93ca62/Close-online-relationships-in-a-national-sample-of-adolescents.pdf

217 Child Trends. (2018). *Violent Crime Victimization.* www.childtrends.org/wp-content/uploads/2015/12/71_Violent-Crime_Appendix1.xlsx

218 Wolak, J., Finkelhor, D., Mitchell, K. J., & Ybarra, M. L. (2010). *Online "predators" and their victims: Myths, realities, and implications for prevention and treatment.* https://cyber.harvard.edu/sites/cyber.law.harvard.edu/files/amp%20final.pdf

219 Mitchell, K. J., Jones, L. M., Finkelhor, D., & Wolak, J. (2014). *Trends in unwanted online experiences and sexting.* www.unh.edu/ccrc/pdf/Full%20Trends%20Report%20Feb%202014%20with%20tables.pdf;

Jones, L. M., Mitchell, K. J., & Finkelhor, D. (2012). Trends in youth internet victimization: Findings from three youth internet safety surveys 2000–2010. *Journal of adolescent Health, 50*(2), 179-186. www.jahonline.org/article/S1054-139X(11)00338-7/fulltext;
Ybarra, M. L., & Mitchell, K. J. (2008). How risky are social networking sites? A comparison of places online where youth sexual solicitation and harassment occurs. *Pediatrics, 121*(2), e350-e357. www.unh.edu/ccrc/pdf/CV167.pdf

220 Mitchell, K. J., Finkelhor, D., & Wolak, J. (2001). Risk factors for and impact of online sexual solicitation of youth. *Jama, 285*(23), 3011-3014. https://jamanetwork.com/journals/jama/fullarticle/193923;
Mitchell, K. J., Wolak, J., & Finkelhor, D. (2007). Trends in youth reports of sexual solicitations, harassment and unwanted exposure to pornography on the Internet. *Journal of adolescent health, 40*(2), 116-126. www.jahonline.org/article/S1054-139X%2806%2900226-6/fulltext

221 Wolak, J., Mitchell, K. J., & Finkelhor, D. (2006). *Online Victimization of Youth: Five Years Later.* https://scholars.unh.edu/cgi/viewcontent.cgi?referer=http://scholar.google.com/&httpsredir=1&article=1053&context=ccrc

222 Priebe, G., Mitchell, K. J., & Finkelhor, D. (2013). To tell or not to tell? Youth's responses to unwanted internet experiences. *Cyberpsychology.* https://scholars.unh.edu/cgi/viewcontent.cgi?article=1247&context=psych_facpub;
Livingstone, S., Davidson, J., Bryce, J., Batool, S., Haughton, C., & Nandi, A. (2017). *Children's online activities, risks and safety: a literature review by the UKCCIS evidence group.* http://eprints.lse.ac.uk/84956/1/Literature%20Review%20Final%20October%202017.pdf

223 Wolak, J., Mitchell, K. J., & Finkelhor, D. (2006). *Online Victimization of Youth: Five Years Later.* https://scholars.unh.edu/cgi/viewcontent.cgi?referer=http://scholar.google.com/&httpsredir=1&article=1053&context=ccrc;
Livingstone, S., Haddon, L., Görzig, A., & Ólafsson, K. (2011). *Risks and safety on the internet: the perspective of European children: full findings and policy implications from the EU Kids Online survey of 9-16 year olds and their parents in 25 countries.* http://eprints.lse.ac.uk/33731/1/Risks%20and%20safety%20on%20the%20internet(lsero).pdf

224 Wolak, J., Mitchell, K. J., & Finkelhor, D. (2006). *Online Victimization of Youth: Five Years Later.* https://scholars.unh.edu/cgi/viewcontent.cgi?referer=http://scholar.google.com/&httpsredir=1&article=1053&context=ccrc

225 Lenhart, A., & Madden, M. (2007). *Teens, privacy and online social networks: How teens manage their online identities and personal information in the age of MySpace.* www.pewresearch.org/internet/2007/04/18/teens-privacy-and-online-social-networks/

226 Wolak, J., Finkelhor, D., Mitchell, K. J., & Ybarra, M. L. (2010). *Online "predators" and their victims: Myths, realities, and implications for prevention and treatment.* https://cyber.harvard.edu/sites/cyber.law.harvard.edu/files/amp%20final.pdf

227 Mitchell, K. J., Finkelhor, D., & Wolak, J. (2001). Risk factors for and impact of online sexual solicitation of youth. *Jama, 285*(23), 3011-3014. https://jamanetwork.com/journals/jama/fullarticle/193923

228 Wolak, J., Finkelhor, D., Mitchell, K. J., & Ybarra, M. L. (2010). *Online "predators" and their victims: Myths, realities, and implications for prevention and treatment.* https://cyber.harvard.edu/sites/cyber.law.harvard.edu/files/amp%20final.pdf

229 Berson, I. R., Berson, M. J., & Ferron, J. M. (2002). Emerging risks of violence in the digital age: Lessons for educators from an online study of adolescent girls in the United States. *Journal of School Violence, 1*(2), 51-71. http://citeseerx.ist.psu.edu/viewdoc/download?doi=10.1.1.475.5923&rep=rep1&type=pdf;
Mitchell, K. J., Finkelhor, D., & Wolak, J. (2001). Risk factors for and impact of online sexual solicitation of youth. *Jama, 285*(23), 3011-3014. https://jamanetwork.com/journals/jama/fullarticle/193923

230 Mishna, F., Cook, C., Saini, M., Wu, M. J., & MacFadden, R. (2011). Interventions to prevent and reduce cyber abuse of youth: A systematic review. *Research on Social Work Practice, 21*(1), 5-14. http://citeseerx.ist.psu.edu/viewdoc/download?doi=10.1.1.981.5581&rep=rep1&type=pdf

231 Inbar, M. (2009). *'Sexting' bullying cited in teen's suicide.* Today.com. www.today.com/news/sexting-bullying-cited-teens-suicide-1C9013027

232 Kristof, N. (2021). Why Do We Let Corporations Profit From Rape Videos? *The New York Times.* www.nytimes.com/2021/04/16/opinion/sunday/companies-online-rape-videos.html

233 Lee, M., & Crofts, T. (2015). Gender, pressure, coercion and pleasure: Untangling motivations for sexting between young people. *British Journal of Criminology, 55*(3), 454-473. https://d1wqtxts1xzle7.cloudfront.net/47930278/454.full-libre.pdf?1470795918=&response-content-disposition=inline%3B+filename%3DGENDER_PRESSURE_COERCION_AND_PLEASURE_UN.pdf&Expires=1680717998&Signature=KE1WZ-

flDj82PCp5-bQCDoWDK6WTnkpnGo6vvbW9SYMnkz5hCKGX5ItFiXCYGj0TLkqt3EZwLNuxdALCd4G-4ixAM0420TJ-erElaQImLFjrui2O3eLpsrI9DTOcYemE0CnHwr18Gufm-FF6zkYXIDC1wlkEm8u0pC8t-gt1DGD9tq0o3oTKWVwSxTpAnw-7Q-8HuYsaQ6WRgNnlHr7K6YidIMsRDo3FKK-Y9ZfpgYUGn-QgysSgB93AK-D58wr-DRn-hDRMnOzs95yXOlrVMexg3Bx41Ea2gZSp-OClSI72h1FgzMdpAvug6roY-iH-FImVrSzJ3uLlK68-tHjeGVGXu2Q__&Key-Pair-Id=APKAJLOHF5GGSLRBV4ZA

234 Strasburger, V. C., Zimmerman, H., Temple, J. R., & Madigan, S. (2019). Teenagers, sexting, and the law. *Pediatrics, 143*(5), e20183183. https://pediatrics.aappublications.org/content/143/5/e20183183;
O'Connor, K., Drouin, M., Yergens, N., & Newsham, G. (2017). Sexting legislation in the United States and abroad: a call for uniformity. *International Journal of Cyber Criminology, 11*(2). www.cybercrimejournal.com/O%27Connoretalvol11issue2IJCC2017.pdf;
*Sexting Laws Across America.* (n.d.). CyberBullying Research Center. https://cyberbullying.org/sexting-laws;
*Sexting.* (n.d.). Child Law Advice. https://childlawadvice.org.uk/information-pages/sexting/;
*Sexting.* (n.d.). Get the Facts. www.getthefacts.health.wa.gov.au/keeping-safe/sexting

235 O'Connor, K., Drouin, M., Yergens, N., & Newsham, G. (2017). Sexting legislation in the United States and abroad: a call for uniformity. *International Journal of Cyber Criminology, 11*(2). www.cybercrimejournal.com/O%27Connoretalvol11issue2IJCC2017.pdf

236 Lenhart, A. (2009). Teens and sexting. *Pew internet & American life project, 1*, 1-26. http://ncdsv.org/images/PewInternet_TeensAndSexting_12-2009.pdf

237 Madigan, S., Ly, A., Rash, C. L., Van Ouytsel, J., & Temple, J. R. (2018). Prevalence of multiple forms of sexting behavior among youth: A systematic review and meta-analysis. *JAMA pediatrics, 172*(4), 327-335. https://jamanetwork.com/journals/jamapediatrics/article-abstract/2673719?redirect=true

238 Madigan, S., Ly, A., Rash, C. L., Van Ouytsel, J., & Temple, J. R. (2018). Prevalence of multiple forms of sexting behavior among youth: A systematic review and meta-analysis. *JAMA pediatrics, 172*(4), 327-335. https://jamanetwork.com/journals/jamapediatrics/article-abstract/2673719?redirect=true;
Region, M. (2015). *Highlights from the MetroWest Adolescent Health Survey.* www.doversherborn.org/uploaded/Our_Schools/HighSchool/Z_Publications_Other_HS/MetroWest_Adolescent_Health_Survey_Highlights_for_MetroWest_Region.pdf;
Strassberg, D. S., McKinnon, R. K., Sustaíta, M. A., & Rullo, J. (2013). Sexting by high school students: An exploratory and descriptive study. *Archives of Sexual behavior, 42*(1), 15-21. https://jordanrullo.com/wp-content/uploads/2017/08/Strassberg_2013_Sexting-by-High-School-Students.pdf;
Fleschler Peskin, M., Markham, C. M., Addy, R. C., Shegog, R., Thiel, M., & Tortolero, S. R. (2013). Prevalence and patterns of sexting among ethnic minority urban high school students. *Cyberpsychology, Behavior, and Social Networking, 16*(6), 454-459. www.liebertpub.com/doi/full/10.1089/cyber.2012.0452;
Temple, J. R., Paul, J. A., Van Den Berg, P., Le, V. D., McElhany, A., & Temple, B. W. (2012). Teen sexting and its association with sexual behaviors. *Archives of pediatrics & adolescent medicine, 166*(9), 828-833. https://jamanetwork.com/journals/jamapediatrics/fullarticle/1212181;
Temple, J. R., & Choi, H. (2014). Longitudinal association between teen sexting and sexual behavior. *Pediatrics, 134*(5), e1287-e1292. www.ncbi.nlm.nih.gov/pmc/articles/PMC4210802/;
Stanley, N., Barter, C., Wood, M., Aghtaie, N., Larkins, C., Lanau, A., & Överlien, C. (2018). Pornography, sexual coercion and abuse and sexting in young people's intimate relationships: A European study. *Journal of interpersonal violence, 33*(19), 2919-2944. http://clok.uclan.ac.uk/13319/1/Nicky%20Stanley%20Pornography%20Sexual%20Coercion.pdf

239 Gordon-Messer, D., Bauermeister, J. A., Grodzinski, A., & Zimmerman, M. (2013). Sexting among young adults. *Journal of adolescent health, 52*(3), 301-306. www.ncbi.nlm.nih.gov/pmc/articles/PMC3580013/;
Benotsch, E. G., Snipes, D. J., Martin, A. M., & Bull, S. S. (2013). Sexting, substance use, and sexual risk behavior in young adults. *Journal of adolescent health, 52*(3), 307-313. www.ncbi.nlm.nih.gov/pmc/articles/PMC3580005/

240 Livingstone, S., Haddon, L., Görzig, A., & Ólafsson, K. (2011). *Risks and safety on the internet: the perspective of European children: full findings and policy implications from the EU Kids Online survey of 9-16 year olds and their parents in 25 countries.* http://eprints.lse.ac.uk/33731/1/Risks%20and%20safety%20on%20the%20internet(lse-ro).pdf

241 Madigan, S., Ly, A., Rash, C. L., Van Ouytsel, J., & Temple, J. R. (2018). Prevalence of multiple forms of sexting behavior among youth: A systematic review and meta-analysis. *JAMA pediatrics, 172*(4), 327-335. https://jamanetwork.com/journals/jamapediatrics/article-abstract/2673719?redirect=true;
Footnote references:
Branch, K., Hilinski-Rosick, C. M., Johnson, E., & Solano, G. (2017). Revenge porn victimization of college students in the United States: An exploratory analysis. *International Journal of Cyber Criminology, 11*(1), 128-142. www.cybercrimejournal.com/Branchetalvol11issue1IJCC2017.pdf;

Dir, A. L., & Cyders, M. A. (2015). Risks, risk factors, and outcomes associated with phone and internet sexting among university students in the United States. *Archives of sexual behavior, 44*(6), 1675-1684. www.ncbi.nlm.nih.gov/pmc/articles/PMC6834346/;
Dir, A. L., & Cyders, M. A. (2015). Risks, risk factors, and outcomes associated with phone and internet sexting among university students in the United States. *Archives of sexual behavior, 44*(6), 1675-1684. www.ncbi.nlm.nih.gov/pmc/articles/PMC6834346/;
Klettke, B., Hallford, D. J., & Mellor, D. J. (2014). Sexting prevalence and correlates: A systematic literature review. *Clinical psychology review, 34*(1), 44-53. www.researchgate.net/profile/David_Hallford/publication/259473730_Sexting_prevalence_and_correlates_A_systematic_literature_review/links/57418ebf08aea45ee8490fce.pdf;
Wood, M., Barter, C., Stanley, N., Aghtaie, N., & Larkins, C. (2015). Images across Europe: The sending and receiving of sexual images and associations with interpersonal violence in young people's relationships. *Children and Youth Services Review, 59*, 149-160. http://clok.uclan.ac.uk/13214/8/13214%20Image%20accross%20Europe%20article%20CYSR%20Final%203%2011%2015.pdf

242 Eaton, A., Jacobs, H., & Ruvalcaba, Y. (2017). *2017 Nationwide Online Study of Nonconsensual Porn Victimization and Perpetration.* www.cybercivilrights.org/wp-content/uploads/2017/06/CCRI-2017-Research-Report.pdf

243 Klettke, B., Hallford, D. J., & Mellor, D. J. (2014). Sexting prevalence and correlates: A systematic literature review. *Clinical psychology review, 34*(1), 44-53. www.researchgate.net/profile/David_Hallford/publication/259473730_Sexting_prevalence_and_correlates_A_systematic_literature_review/links/57418ebf08aea45ee8490fce.pdf
Citing: *MTV Digital Abuse Survey, Executive Summary.* (2009). Associated Press and MTV.;
Eaton, A., Jacobs, H., & Ruvalcaba, Y. (2017). *2017 Nationwide Online Study of Nonconsensual Porn Victimization and Perpetration.* www.cybercivilrights.org/wp-content/uploads/2017/06/CCRI-2017-Research-Report.pdf

244 Eaton, A., Jacobs, H., & Ruvalcaba, Y. (2017). *2017 Nationwide Online Study of Nonconsensual Porn Victimization and Perpetration.* www.cybercivilrights.org/wp-content/uploads/2017/06/CCRI-2017-Research-Report.pdf;
Short, E., Brown, A., Pitchford, M., & Barnes, J. (2017). Revenge Porn: Findings from the Harassment and Revenge Porn (HARP) Survey–Preliminary Results. *Annual Review of CyberTherapy and Telemedicine, 15*, 161-166. https://pure.uvt.nl/ws/portalfiles/portal/24446962/Annual_Review_of_CyberTherapy_and_Telemedicine_2017.pdf;
Millner, C. (2013). Public humiliation over private photos. SFGate. www.sfgate.com/opinion/article/Public-humiliation-over-private-photos-4264155.php

245 Lenhart, A. (2009). Teens and sexting. *Pew internet & American life project, 1*, 1-26. http://ncdsv.org/images/PewInternet_TeensAndSexting_12-2009.pdf

246 Kashner, S. (2014). Both Huntress and Prey. *Vanity Fair.* www.vanityfair.com/hollywood/2014/10/jennifer-lawrence-photo-hacking-privacy

247 Maher, B. (2002). *Just for Laughs Festival.* The Toronto Sun.

248 Calvert, S. L. (2008). Children as consumers: Advertising and marketing. *The future of children*, 205-234. https://files.eric.ed.gov/fulltext/EJ795864.pdf

249 Potvin Kent, M., Pauzé, E., Roy, E. A., de Billy, N., & Czoli, C. (2019). Children and adolescents' exposure to food and beverage marketing in social media apps. *Pediatric obesity, 14*(6), e12508. https://onlinelibrary.wiley.com/doi/pdf/10.1111/ijpo.12508

250 Logicalis, U. K. (2016). *The age of digital enlightenment.* www.uk.logicalis.com/globalassets/united-kingdom/microsites/real-time-generation/realtime-generation-2016-report.pdf

251 Boyland, E., & Tatlow-Golden, M. (2017). Exposure, power and impact of food marketing on children: evidence supports strong restrictions. *European Journal of Risk Regulation, 8*(2), 224-236. https://oro.open.ac.uk/55643/7/55643.pdf

252 Boyland, E., & Tatlow-Golden, M. (2017). Exposure, power and impact of food marketing on children: evidence supports strong restrictions. *European Journal of Risk Regulation, 8*(2), 224-236. https://oro.open.ac.uk/55643/7/55643.pdf

253 Livingstone, S. (2006). *Television advertising of food and drink products to children. New research on advertising foods to children: an updated review of the literature.* Research Annex, 9. http://eprints.lse.ac.uk/21758/1/Television_advertising_of_food_and_drink_products_to_children.pdf

254 Boyland, E., & Tatlow-Golden, M. (2017). Exposure, power and impact of food marketing on children: evidence supports strong restrictions. *European Journal of Risk Regulation, 8*(2), 224-236. https://oro.open.ac.uk/55643/7/55643.pdf

255 *9 Strategies to Help Cater Your Digital Marketing to the Youth Under-24 Generation Z.* (2020). Unlimited Exposure. https://unlimitedexposure.com/basic-digital-marketing/1123-9-strategies-to-help-cater-your-digital-marketing-to-the-youth-under-24-generation-z.html

256 *Heineken's New Online Marketing Deal to Reach 103 Million Minors Monthly.* (2018). European Centre for Monitoring Alcohol Marketing (EUCAM). https://eucam.info/2011/07/05/heinekens-new-online-marketing-deal-to-reach-103-million-minors-monthly/

257 Livingstone, S., & Helsper, E. J. (2006). Does advertising literacy mediate the effects of advertising on children? A critical examination of two linked research literatures in relation to obesity and food choice. *Journal of communication, 56*(3), 560-584. http://eprints.lse.ac.uk/1018/1/Advertising_literacy_mediate_effects_children_2007.pdf;
Rozendaal, E., Lapierre, M. A., Van Reijmersdal, E. A., & Buijzen, M. (2011). Reconsidering advertising literacy as a defense against advertising effects. *Media psychology, 14*(4), 333-354. www.tandfonline.com/doi/abs/10.1080/15213269.2011.620540

258 Rozendaal, E., Buijzen, M., & Valkenburg, P. (2009). *Do children's cognitive advertising defenses reduce their desire for advertised products?.* www.degruyter.com/document/doi/10.1515/COMM.2009.018/html

259 Kuglich, D. (n.d.). *Art of Rhetoric* [Video]. Read Write Think. www.readwritethink.org/video/art-rhetoric

260 Lorenz, T. (2018). Posting Instagram Sponsored Content Is the New Summer Job. *The Atlantic.* www.theatlantic.com/technology/archive/2018/08/posting-instagram-sponsored-content-is-the-new-summer-job/568108/

261 Dobrin, I. (2017). *To Protect Children From Identity Theft, Parents Must Be Proactive.* NPR. www.npr.org/2017/10/18/556237149/to-protect-children-from-identity-theft-parents-must-be-proactive

262 Weisbaum, H. (2018). *More than 1 million children were victims of ID theft last year.* NBC News. www.nbcnews.com/business/consumer/more-1-million-children-were-victims-id-theft-last-year-n885351

263 Hinduja, S., & Patchin, J. W. (2008). Personal information of adolescents on the Internet: A quantitative content analysis of MySpace. *Journal of adolescence, 31*(1), 125-146. www.researchgate.net/profile/Sameer-Hinduja/publication/6232464_Personal_Information_of_Adolescents_on_the_Internet_A_Quantitative_Content_Analysis_of_MySpace/links/59dc9bf10f7e9b1460038015/Personal-Information-of-Adolescents-on-the-Internet-A-Quantitative-Content-Analysis-of-MySpace.pdf

264 Lenhart, A., & Madden, M. (2007). *Teens, privacy and online social networks: How teens manage their online identities and personal information in the age of MySpace.* www.pewresearch.org/internet/2007/04/18/teens-privacy-and-online-social-networks/

265 Livingstone, S., Haddon, L., Görzig, A., & Ólafsson, K. (2011). *Risks and safety on the internet: the perspective of European children: full findings and policy implications from the EU Kids Online survey of 9-16 year olds and their parents in 25 countries.* http://eprints.lse.ac.uk/33731/1/Risks%20and%20safety%20on%20the%20internet(lse-ro).pdf

266 Harrell, E. (2019). Victims of Identity Theft, 2016: Bulletin. www.bjs.gov/content/pub/pdf/vit16.pdf

267 *Child Identity Theft.* (n.d.). Federal Trade Commission, Consumer Information. www.consumer.ftc.gov/articles/0040-child-identity-theft#:~:text=general%20for%20details.-,When%20Your%20Child%20Turns%2016,needs%20to%20rent%20an%20apartment

268 *How do I check to see if my child has a credit report?* (2018). Consumer Financial Protection Bureau. www.consumerfinance.gov/ask-cfpb/how-do-i-check-to-see-if-my-child-has-a-credit-report-en-1865/

269 *Identity Theft and Your Social Security Number.* (n.d.). Social Security Administration. www.ssa.gov/pubs/EN-05-10064.pdf

270 Martinez, J. A., Rutledge, P. C., & Sher, K. J. (2007). Fake ID ownership and heavy drinking in underage college students: Prospective findings. *Psychology of addictive behaviors, 21*(2), 226. www.ncbi.nlm.nih.gov/pmc/articles/PMC2711502/

271 Ball, J. (2014). *How a team of students beat the casinos.* BBC News. www.bbc.com/news/magazine-27519748

272 YouTube Movies. (2013). *21 – Trailer.* [Video]. YouTube. www.youtube.com/watch?v=kCEhvQ6bZAo

273 Gambling Age. (2022.) *Wikipedia.* https://en.wikipedia.org/wiki/Gambling_age

274 Calado, F., Alexandre, J., & Griffiths, M. D. (2017). Prevalence of adolescent problem gambling: A systematic review of recent research. *Journal of Gambling Studies, 33*(2), 397-424. www.ncbi.nlm.nih.gov/pmc/articles/PMC5445143/

275 Footnote reference: [1] American Psychiatric Association. (2013). *Diagnostic and statistical manual of mental disorders: DSM-5.* http://repository.poltekkes-kaltim.ac.id/657/1/Diagnostic%20and%20statistical%20manual%20of%20mental%20disorders%20_%20DSM-5%20%28%20PDFDrive.com%20%29.pdf

276 Shaffer, H. J., Hall, M. N., & Vander Bilt, J. (1999). Estimating the prevalence of disordered gambling behavior in the United States and Canada: a research synthesis. *American journal of public health, 89*(9), 1369-1376. https://ajph.aphapublications.org/doi/pdfplus/10.2105/AJPH.89.9.1369;
Derevensky, J. L. (2015). Youth gambling: Some current misconceptions. Austin *J. Psychiatr. Behav. Sci, 2,* 1-9. https://austinpublishinggroup.com/psychiatry-behavioral-sciences/fulltext/ajpbs-v2-id1039.php

277 Gambling Commission. (2018). *Young people and gambling 2018. A research study among, 11-16.* www.gamblingcommission.gov.uk/PDF/survey-data/Young-People-and-Gambling-2018-Report.pdf;
Calado, F., Alexandre, J., & Griffiths, M. D. (2017). Prevalence of adolescent problem gambling: A systematic review of recent research. *Journal of Gambling Studies, 33*(2), 397-424. www.ncbi.nlm.nih.gov/pmc/articles/PMC5445143/

278 Campbell, C., Derevensky, J., Meerkamper, E., & Cutajar, J. (2011). Parents' perceptions of adolescent gambling: A Canadian national study. *Journal of Gambling Issues,* (25), 36-53. http://jgi.camh.net/jgi/index.php/jgi/article/viewFile/3837/3878

279 Gambling Commission. (2018). *Young people and gambling 2018. A research study among, 11-16.* www.gamblingcommission.gov.uk/PDF/survey-data/Young-People-and-Gambling-2018-Report.pdf

280 Temcheff, C. E., Derevensky, J. L., St-Pierre, R. A., Gupta, R., & Martin, I. (2014). Beliefs and attitudes of mental health professionals with respect to gambling and other high risk behaviors in schools. *International Journal of Mental Health and Addiction, 12*(6), 716-729. www.researchgate.net/profile/Renee_St-Pierre/publication/269039372_Beliefs_and_Attitudes_of_Mental_Health_Professionals_with_Respect_to_Gambling_and_Other_High_Risk_Behaviors_in_Schools/links/55c908a208aeca747d670cce/Beliefs-and-Attitudes-of-Mental-Health-Professionals-with-Respect-to-Gambling-and-Other-High-Risk-Behaviors-in-Schools.pdf

281 Derevensky, J. L., & Gilbeau, L. (2015). Adolescent gambling: twenty-five years of research. *Canadian Journal of Addiction, 6*(2), 4-12. www.csam-smca.org/wp-content/uploads/2015/09/CJAM-Vol6No2-Double.pdf#page=4;
Ladouceur, R., Goulet, A., & Vitaro, F. (2013). Prevention programmes for youth gambling: a review of the empirical evidence. *International Gambling Studies, 13*(2), 141-159. www.tandfonline.com/doi/abs/10.1080/14459795.2012.740496

282 Grande-Gosende, A., López-Núñez, C., García-Fernández, G., Derevensky, J., & Fernández-Hermida, J. R. (2020). Systematic review of preventive programs for reducing problem gambling behaviors among young adults. *Journal of gambling studies, 36*(1), 1-22. www.greo.ca/Modules/EvidenceCentre/files/Grande-Gosende%20et%20al%20(2019)_Systematic%20review%20of%C2%A0preventive%20programs_Final.pdf

283 Delfabbro, P. H., Winefield, A. H., & Anderson, S. (2009). Once a gambler–always a gambler? A longitudinal analysis of gambling patterns in young people making the transition from adolescence to adulthood. *International Gambling Studies, 9*(2), 151-163. www.tandfonline.com/doi/abs/10.1080/14459790902755001

284 Hughes, V. (2018). *A teenager in the UK has lost £80,000 by gambling online with his parents' credit cards.* BestBettingSites.com. www.bestbettingsites.uk/news/society/teenager-loses-80000-gambling-online.html

285 Bowling, L. (2015). *How I overcame a shopping addiction + the 6 tricks I used to get better.* Financial Best Life. https://financialbestlife.com/how-i-knew-i-had-a-shopping-addiction/

286 De La Cretaz, B. (2016). My Shopping Addiction Nearly Destroyed My Life. *Elle.* www.elle.com/life-love/a33022/my-shopping-addiction-nearly-destroyed-my-life/

287 The Story of Stuff Project. (2009). The Story of Stuff [Video]. YouTube. www.youtube.com/watch?v=9GorqroigqM

288 Kellett, S., & Bolton, J. V. (2009). Compulsive buying: A cognitive–behavioural model. *Clinical Psychology & Psychotherapy: An International Journal of Theory & Practice, 16*(2), 83-99. https://d1wqtxts1xzle7.cloudfront.net/49308216/cpp.58520161002-1760-1f9tou2-with-cover-page-v2.pdf?Expires=1632779618&Signature=L-

W7U80-pcEauJKCztp-8tv3hTpQR1LCn7Q4EiacD53SzfBP1ak4FOBQDeYc1B89-vBvRp5JtoRUqPh-QHlBtn3oFJUItdRaa6E9QXg-AQxixwMF0YM2aUthhGsoA1l93mrOA49tXomrURzEPw8qegX1bTsRG-cLa2gBeB-PPYvF27Y-IW11QShAnxHCO0TzwapGaZDcnj34dPR-3Gvbfl83eff1pgDo7w6IhVnt8by8s-3fRl8Naty6eZXc5gLRgAUpwh60IXAuJAOKb3DAbEYBQtdT5ExxgoWuE-3xt0QsNN1tqyr3et8iXCAkQb-zH9RSWfUUfved3tZfmH0SxUcnfmg__&Key-Pair-Id=APKAJLOHF5GGSLRBV4ZA

289 Piquet-Pessôa, M., Ferreira, G. M., Melca, I. A., & Fontenelle, L. F. (2014). DSM-5 and the decision not to include sex, shopping or stealing as addictions. *Current Addiction Reports, 1*(3), 172-176. https://link.springer.com/article/10.1007/s40429-014-0027-6

290 Horváth, C., Adigüzel, F., & Herk, H. V. (2013). *Cultural aspects of compulsive buying in emerging and developed economies: A cross cultural study in compulsive buying.* https://repository.ubn.ru.nl/bitstream/handle/2066/121943/121943.pdf

291 Maraz, A., Griffiths, M. D., & Demetrovics, Z. (2016). The prevalence of compulsive buying: a meta-analysis. *Addiction, 111*(3), 408-419. http://irep.ntu.ac.uk/id/eprint/27158/1/PubSub4615_Griffiths.pdf

292 Footnote reference: [1] Ridgway, N. M., Kukar-Kinney, M., & Monroe, K. B. (2008). An expanded conceptualization and a new measure of compulsive buying. *Journal of consumer Research, 35*(4), 622-639. https://scholarship.richmond.edu/cgi/viewcontent.cgi?article=1006&context=marketing-faculty-publications

293 Horváth, C., Adigüzel, F., & Herk, H. V. (2013). *Cultural aspects of compulsive buying in emerging and developed economies: A cross cultural study in compulsive buying.* https://repository.ubn.ru.nl/bitstream/handle/2066/121943/121943.pdf

294 Mitchell, J. E., Burgard, M., Faber, R., Crosby, R. D., & de Zwaan, M. (2006). Cognitive behavioral therapy for compulsive buying disorder. *Behaviour research and therapy, 44*(12), 1859-1865. www.sciencedirect.com/science/article/abs/pii/S0005796705002767

295 De La Cretaz, B. (2016). My Shopping Addiction Nearly Destroyed My Life. *Elle.* www.elle.com/life-love/a33022/my-shopping-addiction-nearly-destroyed-my-life/

296 Stanley-Becker, I. (2019). What leads Harvard to rescind admission? Racism, plagiarism — and killing your mom. *The Washington Post.* www.washingtonpost.com/nation/2019/06/18/what-leads-harvard-rescind-admission-racism-plagiarism-killing-your-mom/

297 *Plagiarism.* (n.d.). University of Oxford. www.ox.ac.uk/students/academic/guidance/skills/plagiarism

298 BavaHarji, M., Chetty, T. N., Ismail, Z. B., & Letchumanan, K. (2016). A Comparison of the Act and Frequency of Plagiarism between Technical and Non-Technical Programme Undergraduates. *English Language Teaching, 9*(4), 106-118. https://files.eric.ed.gov/fulltext/EJ1095601.pdf

299 Mawsdley, R. D. (2009). The tangled web of plagiarism litigation: Sorting out the legal issues. *BYU Educ. & LJ,* 245. https://digitalcommons.law.byu.edu/cgi/viewcontent.cgi?article=1259&context=elj

300 Curtis, G. J., & Vardanega, L. (2016). Is plagiarism changing over time? A 10-year time-lag study with three points of measurement. *Higher Education Research & Development, 35*(6), 1167-1179. https://researchrepository.murdoch.edu.au/id/eprint/35573/1/10-year_time_lag_study_of_plagiarism.pdf

301 McCabe, D. L. (2005). Cheating among college and university students: A North American perspective. *International Journal for Educational Integrity, 1*(1). http://citeseerx.ist.psu.edu/viewdoc/download?doi=10.1.1.465.9927&rep=rep1&type=pdf

302 Brimble, M., & Stevenson-Clarke, P. (2006). Managing academic dishonesty in Australian universities: Implications for teaching, learning and scholarship. *Accounting, Accountability & Performance, 12*(1), 32. https://research-repository.griffith.edu.au/bitstream/handle/10072/11264/39372_1.pdf?sequence=1

303 Shabe, L. (2018). *What are the consequences of plagiarism in college?* Scribbr. www.scribbr.com/plagiarism/consequences-of-plagiarism/

304 Curtis, G. J., & Vardanega, L. (2016). Is plagiarism changing over time? A 10-year time-lag study with three points of measurement. *Higher Education Research & Development, 35*(6), 1167-1179. https://researchrepository.murdoch.edu.au/id/eprint/35573/1/10-year_time_lag_study_of_plagiarism.pdf

305 *Teenager gets damages reduced after copyright ignorance claim.* (2008). Pinsent Masons Out-Law. www.pinsentmasons.com/out-law/news/teenager-gets-damages-reduced-after-copyright-ignorance-claim

306 Palfrey, J. G., Gasser, U., Simun, M., & Barnes, R. (2009). *Youth, creativity, and copyright in the digital age.* Berkman Center Research Publication, (2009-05). https://dash.harvard.edu/bitstream/handle/1/3128762/Palfrey+-+Youth,+Creativity,+and+Copyright+in+the+Digital+Age.pdf?sequence=2

307 Palfrey, J. G., Gasser, U., Simun, M., & Barnes, R. (2009). *Youth, creativity, and copyright in the digital age.* Berkman Center Research Publication, (2009-05). https://dash.harvard.edu/bitstream/handle/1/3128762/Palfrey+-+Youth,+Creativity,+and+Copyright+in+the+Digital+Age.pdf?sequence=2

308 Perkins, M., Gezgin, U. B., & Roe, J. (2020). Reducing plagiarism through academic misconduct education. *International Journal for Educational Integrity, 16*, 1-15. https://edintegrity.biomedcentral.com/articles/10.1007/s40979-020-00052-8

309 *Teaching Copyright.* (n.d.). Electronic Frontier Foundation. www.eff.org/teachingcopyright

310 *Photos for Class.* (2021). Storyboard That. www.photosforclass.com/

311 *Use & remix.* (n.d.). Creative Commons. https://creativecommons.org/use-remix/

312 Park, C. (2003). In other (people's) words: Plagiarism by university students--literature and lessons. *Assessment & evaluation in higher education, 28*(5), 471-488. www.lancaster.ac.uk/people/gyaccp/caeh_28_5_02lores.pdf
Citing: Kruse, H. H. (1990). Mark Twain's A Connecticut Yankee: reconsiderations and revisions. American Literature, 62(3), 464-483. www.jstor.org/stable/2926742?seq=1
; Rose, J. (1992). The invisible sources of Nineteen Eighty-Four. *Journal of Popular Culture, 26*(1), 93.; https://search.proquest.com/openview/51ac09d2def06b936d6885fb8f58cb58/1?cbl=1819044&pq-origsite=gscholar ; Acheson, J. (1978). Beckett, Proust, and Schopenhauer. Contemporary Literature, 19(2), 165-179. www.jstor.org/stable/1207953?seq=1

313 *Syria girls: First missing London schoolgirl named.* (2015). BBC News. www.bbc.co.uk/news/uk-31886146

314 *Hate speech.* (n.d.) Oxford Languages & Google.

315 Oksanen, A., Hawdon, J., Holkeri, E., Näsi, M., & Räsänen, P. (2014). Exposure to online hate among young social media users. *Sociological studies of children & youth, 18*(1), 253-273. https://books.google.co.uk/books?hl=en&lr=&id=k2StBAAAQBAJ&oi=fnd&pg=PA253&dq=internet+teens+danger+hate+speech&ots=qe-4B9EOqAm&sig=0q_rGXzCxRNFna-vZ3scv5rKcXo#v=onepage&q&f=false;
Bond, D. (2016). One-third of young teenagers encounter 'hate speech' online. *Financial Times.* www.ft.com/content/a48174f4-ab87-11e6-ba7d-76378e4fef24

316 *Social Media, Social Life: Teens Reveal their Experiences.* (2018). Common Sense Media. www.commonsensemedia.org/sites/default/files/uploads/research/2018_cs_socialmediasociallife_fullreport-final-release_2_lowres.pdf

317 Gagliardone, I., Gal, D., Alves, T., & Martinez, G. (2015). *Countering online hate speech.* Unesco Publishing. https://unesdoc.unesco.org/ark:/48223/pf0000233231

318 Collins, B, Toomey, M. (2018). *MartinLutherKing.Org is Owned by Neo-Nazis.* Daily Beast. www.thedailybeast.com/martinlutherkingorg-is-owned-by-neo-nazis;
Tynes, B. (2005). Children, adolescents and the culture of online hate. *Handbook of children, culture and violence*, 267-89. https://books.google.co.uk/books?hl=en&lr=&id=U5p1AwAAQBAJ&oi=fnd&pg=PA267&dq=Children,+adolescents,+and+the+culture+of+online+hate&ots=xRsPzBsf-t&sig=62jN22W7DVSeDMvmx-eMITpSgbYE&redir_esc=y#v=onepage&q=Children%2C%20adolescents%2C%20and%20the%20culture%20of%20online%20hate&f=false

319 Daniels, J. (2008). *Race, civil rights, and hate speech in the digital era.* https://academicworks.cuny.edu/cgi/viewcontent.cgi?referer=https://scholar.google.com/&httpsredir=1&article=1218&context=gc_pubs

320 Davies, G., Bouchard, M., Wu, E., Joffres, K., & Frank, R. (2015). Terrorist and extremist organizations' use of the Internet for recruitment. *Social networks, terrorism and counter-terrorism: Radical and connected,* 105-127. http://opac.lib.idu.ac.id/unhan-ebook/assets/uploads/files/8c981-036.social-networks-terrorism-and-counter-terrorism.pdf#page=124

321 Daniels, J. (2008). *Race, civil rights, and hate speech in the digital era.* https://academicworks.cuny.edu/cgi/viewcontent.cgi?referer=https://scholar.google.com/&httpsredir=1&article=1218&context=gc_pubs

322 *Syria girls: First missing London schoolgirl named.* (2015). BBC News. www.bbc.co.uk/news/uk-31886146

323 Daw, S. (2020). A Complete Timeline of Kevin Hart's Oscar-Hosting Controversy, From Tweets to Apologies. *Billboard.* www.billboard.com/articles/events/oscars/8492982/kevin-hart-oscar-hosting-controversy-timeline

324 Joseph, A. (2019). *Nick Bosa liked Instagram posts featuring racist and homophobic slurs.* USA Today Sports. https://ftw.usatoday.com/2019/04/nick-bosa-instagram-racist-n-word-posts-twitter-social-media-nfl-draft

325 Jaschik, S. (2018). *Social Media as 'Fair Game' in Admissions.* Inside Higher Ed. www.insidehighered.com/admissions/article/2018/04/23/new-data-how-college-admissions-officers-view-social-media-applicants

326 *Kaplan Test Prep Survey Finds Colleges And Applicants Agree: Social Media is Fair Game in the Admissions Process.* (2018). Kaplan. www.kaptest.com/blog/press/2018/04/17/kaplan-test-prep-survey-finds-colleges-applicants-agree-social-media-fair-game-admissions-process/

327 Natanson, H. (2017). Harvard Rescinds Acceptances for At Least Ten Students for Obscene Memes. *The Harvard Crimson.* www.thecrimson.com/article/2017/6/5/2021-offers-rescinded-memes/

328 Shugerman, E. (2017). 10 students have Harvard acceptances withdrawn over Facebook memes. *The Independent.* www.independent.co.uk/news/world/americas/harvard-facebook-memes-student-acceptance-taken-away-withdrawn-university-a7775991.html

329 Peters, B. & Curbelo, C. (2017). *Google To Kids: 'Don't Post Anything You Wouldn't Want Grandma To See'.* CBS Miami. https://miami.cbslocal.com/2017/02/09/google-goes-to-middle-schoolers-to-cover-internet-safety/

330 Adams, D. (2002). *The salmon of doubt: Hitchhiking the universe one last time (Vol. 3).* Harmony. https://books.google.co.uk/books?id=7QaIdP69jrIC&printsec=frontcover&source=gbs_ge_summary_r&cad=0#v=onepage&q=set%20of%20rules&f=false

331 O'Connor, R. (2015). *Rewire: change your brain to break bad habits, overcome addictions, conquer self-destructive behavior.* Penguin. www.michaeldpollock.com/quotes-tv-addiction/

332 Knorr, C. (2021). *Parents' Ultimate Guide to Parental Controls.* Common Sense Media. www.commonsensemedia.org/blog/parents-ultimate-guide-to-parental-controls

333 Ghosh, A. K., Badillo-Urquiola, K., Guha, S., LaViola Jr, J. J., & Wisniewski, P. J. (2018). *Safety vs. surveillance: what children have to say about mobile apps for parental control.* In Proceedings of the 2018 CHI Conference on Human Factors in Computing Systems (pp. 1-14). http://eecs.ucf.edu/isuelab/publications/pubs/pn1838-ghoshA.pdf

334 Knorr, C. (2021). *Parents' Ultimate Guide to Parental Controls.* Common Sense Media. www.commonsensemedia.org/blog/parents-ultimate-guide-to-parental-controls

335 O'Keeffe, G. S., & Clarke-Pearson, K. (2011). The impact of social media on children, adolescents, and families. Pediatrics, 127(4), 800-804. www.cooperativa.cl/noticias/site/artic/20110329/asocfile/20110329173752/reporte_facebook.PDF

336 *Family Media Plan.* (n.d.). Healthy Children.org, American Academy of Pediatrics. www.healthychildren.org/English/media/Pages/default.aspx#home

337 Smith, J. (2020). Opinion: The Amish use tech differently than you think. We should emulate them. *The Washington Post.* www.washingtonpost.com/opinions/to-learn-how-to-practice-humane-technology-look-to-the-amish/2020/02/17/c79fa0ba-36fc-11ea-bf30-ad313e4ec754_story.html

# 10. Character

1 Redfort, R. (n.d.). *Ruby Redfort > Quotes > Quotable Quote.* Goodreads. www.goodreads.com/quotes/76-64736-sticks-and-stones-may-break-my-bones-but-words-can#:~:text=Quotes%20%3E%20Quotable%20Quote-,%E2%80%9CSticks%20and%20stones%20may%20break%20my%20bones%2C%20but,words%20can%20also%20hurt%20me.&text=Bats%20and%20bricks%20may%20ache,it's%20words%20that%20I%20remember.%E2%80%9D

2 Abadi, M. (2017). 9 wildly successful people who were bullied as kids. *Business Insider.* www.businessinsider.com/successful-people-who-were-bullied-2017-12?r=US&IR=T#rihanna-1

3 Abadi, M. (2017). 9 wildly successful people who were bullied as kids. *Business Insider.* www.businessinsider.com/successful-people-who-were-bullied-2017-12?r=US&IR=T#rihanna-1

4 Modecki, K. L., Minchin, J., Harbaugh, A. G., Guerra, N. G., & Runions, K. C. (2014). Bullying prevalence across contexts: A meta-analysis measuring cyber and traditional bullying. *Journal of Adolescent Health, 55*(5), 602-611.;
Giannini, S. (2019). *Behind the numbers: ending school violence and bullying.* United Nations Educational, Scientific and Cultural Organization. https://unesdoc.unesco.org/ark:/48223/pf0000366483;
Zych, I., Ortega-Ruiz, R., & Del Rey, R. (2015). Systematic review of theoretical studies on bullying and cyberbullying: Facts, knowledge, prevention, and intervention. *Aggression and violent behavior, 23*, 1-21. www.researchgate.net/profile/Izabela-Zych-2/publication/284014260_Systematic_review_of_theoretical_studies_on_bullying_and_cyberbullying_Facts_knowledge_prevention_and_intervention/links/570a62e908ae2eb9421fb23c/Systematic-review-of-theoretical-studies-on-bullying-and-cyberbullying-Facts-knowledge-prevention-and-intervention.pdf

5 Craig, W. M., & Harel, Y. (2001). *Bullying, physical fighting and victimization.* Young people's health in context: International report from the HBSC, 2, 133-144. www.biu.ac.il/SOC/hbsc/books/2.pdf

6 Centers for Disease Control and Prevention. (n.d.). *High School Youth Risk Behavior Survey 1991-2019 Results.* https://nccd.cdc.gov/youthonline/App/Results.aspx?TT=K&OUT=0&SID=HS&QID=H59&LID=LL&YID=YY&LID2=&YID2=&COL=T&ROW1=N&ROW2=N&HT=QQ&LCT=LL&FS=S1&FR=R1&FG=G1&FA=A1&FI=I1&FP=P1&FSL=S1&FRL=R1&FGL=G1&FAL=A1&FIL=I1&FPL=P1&PV=&TST=&C1=&C2=&QP=G&DP=1&VA=CI&CS=Y&SYID=&EYID=&SC=DEFAULT&SO=ASC;
Centers for Disease Control and Prevention. (n.d.). *Middle School Youth Risk Behavior Survey 1991-2019 Results.* https://nccd.cdc.gov/youthonline/App/Results.aspx?TT=K&OUT=0&SID=MS&QID=M12&LID=LL&YID=YY&LID2=&YID2=&COL=T&ROW1=N&ROW2=N&HT=QQ&LCT=LL&FS=S1&FR=R1&FG=G1&FA=A1&FI=I1&FP=P1&FSL=S1&FRL=R1&FGL=G1&FAL=A1&FIL=I1&FPL=P1&PV=&TST=&C1=&C2=&QP=G&DP=1&VA=No&CS=Y&SYID=&EYID=&SC=DEFAULT&SO=ASC

7 Zych, I., Ortega-Ruiz, R., & Del Rey, R. (2015). Systematic review of theoretical studies on bullying and cyberbullying: Facts, knowledge, prevention, and intervention. *Aggression and violent behavior, 23*, 1-21. www.researchgate.net/profile/Izabela-Zych-2/publication/284014260_Systematic_review_of_theoretical_studies_on_bullying_and_cyberbullying_Facts_knowledge_prevention_and_intervention/links/570a62e908ae2eb9421fb23c/Systematic-review-of-theoretical-studies-on-bullying-and-cyberbullying-Facts-knowledge-prevention-and-intervention.pdf

8 Fuligni, A. J., Telzer, E. H., Bower, J., Cole, S. W., Kiang, L., & Irwin, M. R. (2009). A preliminary study of daily interpersonal stress and C-reactive protein levels among adolescents from Latin American and European backgrounds. *Psychosomatic medicine, 71*(3), 329. www.ncbi.nlm.nih.gov/pmc/articles/PMC2715831/

9 Sijtsema, J. J., Veenstra, R., Lindenberg, S., & Salmivalli, C. (2009). Empirical test of bullies' status goals: Assessing direct goals, aggression, and prestige. *Aggressive Behavior: Official Journal of the International Society for Research on Aggression, 35*(1), 57-67. https://core.ac.uk/reader/232377360

10 Salmivalli, C. (2010). Bullying and the peer group: A review. *Aggression and violent behavior, 15*(2), 112-120. https://pdfs.semanticscholar.org/5997/ad572810ed42b64bafa45b85e4c8487a32b6.pdf;
Sijtsema, J. J., Veenstra, R., Lindenberg, S., & Salmivalli, C. (2009). Empirical test of bullies' status goals: Assessing direct goals, aggression, and prestige. *Aggressive Behavior: Official Journal of the International Society for Research on Aggression, 35*(1), 57-67. https://core.ac.uk/reader/232377360

11 Juvonen, J., Graham, S., & Schuster, M. A. (2003). Bullying among young adolescents: The strong, the weak, and the troubled. *Pediatrics, 112*(6), 1231-1237. http://citeseerx.ist.psu.edu/viewdoc/download?doi=10.1.1.905.9523&rep=rep1&type=pdf

12 Pellegrini, A. D. (2002). Affiliative and aggressive dimensions of dominance and possible functions during early adolescence. *Aggression and Violent Behavior, 7*(1), 21-31. www.sciencedirect.com/science/article/abs/pii/S1359178900000331

13 Russell, S. T., Sinclair, K. O., Poteat, V. P., & Koenig, B. W. (2012). Adolescent health and harassment based on discriminatory bias. *American journal of public health, 102*(3), 493-495. www.ncbi.nlm.nih.gov/pmc/articles/PMC3487669/

14 Salmivalli, C. (2010). Bullying and the peer group: A review. *Aggression and violent behavior, 15*(2), 112-120. https://pdfs.semanticscholar.org/5997/ad572810ed42b64bafa45b85e4c8487a32b6.pdf

15 Tenenbaum, L. S., Varjas, K., Meyers, J., & Parris, L. (2011). Coping strategies and perceived effectiveness in fourth through eighth grade victims of bullying. *School Psychology International, 32*(3), 263-287. http://citeseerx.ist.psu.edu/viewdoc/download?doi=10.1.1.878.3646&rep=rep1&type=pdf

16 Murray-Harvey, R., Skrzypiec, G., & Slee, P. T. (2012). Effective and ineffective coping with bullying strategies as assessed by informed professionals and their use by victimised students. *Journal of Psychologists and Counsellors in Schools, 22*(1), 122-138. www.researchgate.net/profile/Phillip_Slee/publication/259424093_Effective_and_Ineffective_Coping_With_Bullying_Strategies_as_Assessed_by_Informed_Professionals_and_Their_Use_by_Victimised_Students/links/57d5077008ae0c0081e6feeb/Effective-and-Ineffective-Coping-With-Bullying-Strategies-as-Assessed-by-Informed-Professionals-and-Their-Use-by-Victimised-Students.pdf

17 Robison, K., & Schools, M. P. (2010). *Bullies and victims: A primer for parents.* National Association of School Psychologists. www.nasponline.org/x33033.xml;
Fekkes, M., Pijpers, F. I., & Verloove-Vanhorick, S. P. (2005). Bullying: Who does what, when and where? Involvement of children, teachers and parents in bullying behavior. *Health education research, 20*(1), 81-91. https://academic.oup.com/her/article/20/1/81/632611

18 Prinstein, M. J., & Dodge, K. A. (Eds.). (2008). *Understanding peer influence in children and adolescents.* Guilford Press. https://books.google.com/books?hl=en&lr=&id=n2Cr7GC0QX4C&oi=fnd&pg=PA1&dq=Understanding+Peer+Influence+in+Children+and+Adolescents&ots=ZAwS1_CdRk&sig=cHC3qq-vOsWjUHy1mnq-8N_0-rTY#v=onepage&q=bullying&f=false
Citing: Juvonen, J., & Cadigan, R. J. (2002). *Social Determinants of Public Behavior of Middle School Youth: Perceived Peer Norms and Need To Be Accepted.* https://eric.ed.gov/?id=ED471690

19 Footnote reference: [1] Robison, K., & Schools, M. P. (2010). *Bullies and victims: A primer for parents.* National Association of School Psychologists. www.nasponline.org/x33033.xml

20 Salmivalli, C. (2010). Bullying and the peer group: A review. *Aggression and violent behavior, 15*(2), 112-120. https://pdfs.semanticscholar.org/5997/ad572810ed42b64bafa45b85e4c8487a32b6.pdf
Citing: Kärnä, A., Voeten, M., Poskiparta, E., & Salmivalli, C. (2010). Vulnerable children in different classrooms: Classroom-level factors moderate the effect of individual risk on victimization. *Merrill-Palmer Quarterly, 56,* 261-282. Citing: Kärnä, A., Salmivalli, C., Poskiparta, E., & Voeten, M. J. M. (2008, May). *Do bystanders influence the frequency of bullying in a classroom.* In The XIth EARA conference, Turin, Italy.

21 Miller, N. T. (2020). *Bystander Motivation in Bullying Situations* (Doctoral dissertation, Adler University). https://search.proquest.com/openview/6a6f2a0dac09659eef8de62c683adb80/1?pq-origsite=gscholar&cbl=18750&diss=y
Citing: Salmivalli, C., Lappalainen, M., & Lagerspetz, K. M. (1998). Stability and change of behavior in connection with bullying in schools: A two-year follow-up. *Aggressive Behavior: Official Journal of the International Society for Research on Aggression, 24*(3), 205-218. https://onlinelibrary.wiley.com/doi/abs/10.1002/(SICI)1098-2337(1998)24:3%3C205::AID-AB5%3E3.0.CO;2-J

22 Prinstein, M. J., & Dodge, K. A. (Eds.). (2008). *Understanding peer influence in children and adolescents.* Guilford Press. https://books.google.com/books?hl=en&lr=&id=n2Cr7GC0QX4C&oi=fnd&pg=PA1&dq=Understanding+Peer+Influence+in+Children+and+Adolescents&ots=ZAwS1_CdRk&sig=cHC3qq-vOsWjUHy1mnq-8N_0-rTY#v=onepage&q=bullying&f=false
Citing: Juvonen, J., & Cadigan, R. J. (2002*). Social Determinants of Public Behavior of Middle School Youth: Perceived Peer Norms and Need To Be Accepted.* https://eric.ed.gov/?id=ED471690

23 Lynn Hawkins, D., Pepler, D. J., & Craig, W. M. (2001). Naturalistic observations of peer interventions in bullying. *Social development, 10*(4), 512-527. www.mac-cura.ca/download%20docs/Papers%20for%20Site/Interventions/Hawkins%20et%20al.,%202001.pdf;
Miller, N. T. (2020). *Bystander Motivation in Bullying Situations* (Doctoral dissertation, Adler University). https://search.proquest.com/openview/6a6f2a0dac09659eef8de62c683adb80/1?pq-origsite=gscholar&cbl=18750&diss=y

24 Sainio, M., Veenstra, R., Huitsing, G., & Salmivalli, C. (2011). Victims and their defenders: A dyadic approach. *International journal of behavioral development, 35*(2), 144-151. https://journals.sagepub.com/doi/pdf/10.1177/0165025410378068

25 Miller, N. T. (2020). *Bystander Motivation in Bullying Situations* (Doctoral dissertation, Adler University). https://search.proquest.com/openview/6a6f2a0dac09659eef8de62c683adb80/1?pq-origsite=gscholar&cbl=18750&diss=y;
Perkins, H. W., Craig, D. W., & Perkins, J. M. (2011). Using social norms to reduce bullying: A research intervention among adolescents in five middle schools. *Group Processes & Intergroup Relations, 14*(5), 703-722. http://journals.sagepub.com/doi/abs/10.1177/1368430210398004

26 Salmivalli, C., Lappalainen, M., & Lagerspetz, K. M. (1998). Stability and change of behavior in connection with bullying in schools: A two-year follow-up. *Aggressive Behavior: Official Journal of the International Society for Research on Aggression, 24*(3), 205-218. https://onlinelibrary.wiley.com/doi/abs/10.1002/(SICI)1098-2337(1998)24:3%3C205::AID-AB5%3E3.0.CO;2-J

27 Miller, N. T. (2020). *Bystander Motivation in Bullying Situations* (Doctoral dissertation, Adler University). https://search.proquest.com/openview/6a6f2a0dac09659eef8de62c683adb80/1?pq-origsite=gscholar&cbl=18750&diss=y
Citing: Rigby, K., & Johnson, B. (2005). Student bystanders in Australian schools. *Pastoral Care in Education, 23*(2), 10-16. www.tandfonline.com/doi/pdf/10.1111/j.0264-3944.2005.00326.x?needAccess=true

28 Lynn Hawkins, D., Pepler, D. J., & Craig, W. M. (2001). Naturalistic observations of peer interventions in bullying. *Social development, 10*(4), 512-527. www.mac-cura.ca/download%20docs/Papers%20for%20Site/Interventions/Hawkins%20et%20al.,%202001.pdf

29 Farrington, D. P., & Ttofi, M. M. (2009). School-based programs to reduce bullying and victimization. *Campbell systematic reviews, 5*(1), i-148. https://onlinelibrary.wiley.com/doi/pdf/10.4073/csr.2009.6

30 Paluck, E. L., Shepherd, H., & Aronow, P. M. (2016). Changing climates of conflict: A social network experiment in 56 schools. *Proceedings of the National Academy of Sciences, 113*(3), 566-571. www.pnas.org/content/113/3/566.long

31 Footnote references:
[1] Ttofi, M. M., & Farrington, D. P. (2011). Effectiveness of school-based programs to reduce bullying: A systematic and meta-analytic review. *Journal of Experimental Criminology, 7*(1), 27-56. http://sinohacesnadasosparte.org/Download/english/02_METAANALISIS_2011.pdf
[2] Olweus, D. (1994). Bullying at school: basic facts and effects of a school based intervention program. *Journal of child psychology and psychiatry, 35*(7), 1171-1190. www.researchgate.net/profile/Dan_Olweus/publication/15391812_Bullying_at_School_Basic_Facts_and_Effects_of_a_School_Based_Intervention_Program/links/59ddf4a3aca272204c2bca5d/Bullying-at-School-Basic-Facts-and-Effects-of-a-School-Based-Intervention-Program.pdf
[3] Mihalic, S. F., & Irwin, K. (2003). Blueprints for violence prevention: From research to real-world settings—factors influencing the successful replication of model programs. *Youth violence and juvenile justice, 1*(4), 307-329. http://citeseerx.ist.psu.edu/viewdoc/download?doi=10.1.1.218.4497&rep=rep1&type=pdf
[4] Kraft, E. M., & Wang, J. (2009). Effectiveness of cyber bullying prevention strategies: A study on students' perspectives. *International Journal of Cyber Criminology, 3*(2). https://search.proquest.com/docview/763181751?pq-origsite=gscholar&fromopenview=true

32 Farrington, D. P., & Ttofi, M. M. (2009). School-based programs to reduce bullying and victimization. *Campbell systematic reviews, 5*(1), i-148. https://onlinelibrary.wiley.com/doi/pdf/10.4073/csr.2009.6;
Ttofi, M. M., & Farrington, D. P. (2011). Effectiveness of school-based programs to reduce bullying: A systematic and meta-analytic review. *Journal of Experimental Criminology, 7*(1), 27-56. http://sinohacesnadasosparte.org/Download/english/02_METAANALISIS_2011.pdf

33 Chen, S. A. (2015). *A Girl Like Her Movie Review*. Common Sense Media. www.commonsensemedia.org/movie-reviews/a-girl-like-her

34 Rich, J. (1998). *The nurture assumption: Why children turn out the way they do*. Bloomsbury.

35 Abadi, M. (2017). 9 wildly successful people who were bullied as kids. *Business Insider*. www.businessinsider.com/successful-people-who-were-bullied-2017-12?r=US&IR=T#rihanna-1

36 Sales, Nancy Jo. American Girls: Social Media and the Secret Lives of Teenagers (p. 271). Knopf Doubleday Publishing Group. Kindle Edition.

37 Smith, D. (2001). *Harassment in the hallways*. American Psychological Association. www.apa.org/monitor/sep01/harassment

38 Hill, C., & Kearl, H. (2011). *Crossing the line: Sexual harassment at school*. American Association of University Women. http://files.eric.ed.gov/fulltext/ED525785.pdf

39 Lipson, J. (2001). *Hostile Hallways: Bullying, Teasing, and Sexual Harassment in School*. AAUW Educational Foundation. https://files.eric.ed.gov/fulltext/ED454132.pdf

40 Hill, C., & Kearl, H. (2011). *Crossing the line: Sexual harassment at school*. American Association of University Women. http://files.eric.ed.gov/fulltext/ED525785.pdf

41 Hill, C., & Kearl, H. (2011). *Crossing the line: Sexual harassment at school*. American Association of University Women. http://files.eric.ed.gov/fulltext/ED525785.pdf

42 Hill, C., & Kearl, H. (2011). *Crossing the line: Sexual harassment at school*. American Association of University Women. http://files.eric.ed.gov/fulltext/ED525785.pdf

43 Hlavka, H. R. (2014). Normalizing sexual violence: Young women account for harassment and abuse. *Gender & Society, 28*(3), 337-358. www.jstor.org/stable/43669888?read-now=1&seq=1#page_scan_tab_contents

44 Busby, E. (2018). One in three girls sexually harassed in public while wearing school uniforms, report finds. *Independent.* www.independent.co.uk/news/education/education-news/sexual-harassment-school-uniforms-me-too-plan-international-uk-girls-a8571031.html
Citing: *Two Thirds of Girls Have Been Sexually Harassed in Public, New Survey Finds.* (2018). Plan International UK. https://plan-uk.org/media-centre/two-thirds-of-girls-have-been-sexually-harassed-in-public-new-survey-finds

45 Weissbourd, R., Anderson, T. R., Cashin, A., & McIntyre, J. (2017). The talk: How adults can promote young people's healthy relationships and prevent misogyny and sexual harassment. *Harvard Graduate School of Education, 16*(8), 1-46. https://static1.squarespace.com/static/5b7c56e255b02c683659fe43/t/5bd51a0324a69425bd079b59/1540692500558/mcc_the_talk_final.pdf

46 Hill, C., & Kearl, H. (2011). *Crossing the line: Sexual harassment at school.* American Association of University Women.. http://files.eric.ed.gov/fulltext/ED525785.pdf

47 Hlavka, H. R. (2014). Normalizing sexual violence: Young women account for harassment and abuse. *Gender & Society, 28*(3), 337-358. www.jstor.org/stable/43669888?read-now=1&seq=1#page_scan_tab_contents

48 Hill, C., & Kearl, H. (2011). *Crossing the line: Sexual harassment at school.* American Association of University Women. http://files.eric.ed.gov/fulltext/ED525785.pdf;
Weale, S. (2017). Sexual harassment 'rife' in schools but largely unreported, study says. *The Guardian.* www.theguardian.com/world/2017/dec/12/sexual-harassment-rife-in-schools-but-largely-unreported-study-says

49 Lipson, J. (2001). Hostile Hallways: Bullying, Teasing, and Sexual Harassment in School. American Association of University Women. https://files.eric.ed.gov/fulltext/ED454132.pdf

50 Lichty, L. F., Torres, J. M., Valenti, M. T., & Buchanan, N. T. (2008). Sexual Harassment Policies in K-12 Schools: Examining Accessibility to Students and Content. *Journal of School Health, 78*(11), 607-614. https://deepblue.lib.umich.edu/bitstream/handle/2027.42/75026/j.1746-1561.2008.00353.x.pdf%3Bjsessionid%3D491D89E6A4A8739D653E6677800FE623?sequence%3D1

51 Lichty, L. F., Torres, J. M., Valenti, M. T., & Buchanan, N. T. (2008). Sexual Harassment Policies in K-12 Schools: Examining Accessibility to Students and Content. *Journal of School Health, 78*(11), 607-614. https://deepblue.lib.umich.edu/bitstream/handle/2027.42/75026/j.1746-1561.2008.00353.x.pdf%3Bjsessionid%3D491D89E6A4A8739D653E6677800FE623?sequence%3D1

52 Katherine. (2020). *#MeToo in Middle School: Talking About Sexual Harassment and Boundaries with Tweens.* A Mighty Girl. www.amightygirl.com/blog?p=28874

53 Weissbourd, R., Anderson, T. R., Cashin, A., & McIntyre, J. (2017). The talk: How adults can promote young people's healthy relationships and prevent misogyny and sexual harassment. *Harvard Graduate School of Education, 16*(8), 1-46. https://static1.squarespace.com/static/5b7c56e255b02c683659fe43/t/5bd51a0324a69425bd079b59/1540692500558/mcc_the_talk_final.pdf

54 Hill, C., & Kearl, H. (2011). *Crossing the line: Sexual harassment at school.* American Association of University Women. http://files.eric.ed.gov/fulltext/ED525785.pdf

55 Higginson, N. M. (1993). *Addressing Sexual Harassment in the Classroom. Educational Leadership.* www.ascd.org/publications/educational-leadership/nov93/vol51/num03/Addressing-Sexual-Harassment-in-the-Classroom.aspx

56 *6 Tips for Reducing and Preventing Misogyny and Sexual Harassment Among Teens and Young Adults.* (2018). Making Caring Common Project, Harvard Graduate School of Education. https://mcc.gse.harvard.edu/resources-for-families/6-tips-parents-reducing-preventing-misogyny-sexual-harassment

57 Ruiz, S. (n.d.). *Not Your Baby.* SusanaRuiz.org. https://susanaruiz.org/takeactiongames-notyourbaby

58 Hill, C., & Kearl, H. (2011). *Crossing the line: Sexual harassment at school.* American Association of University Women. http://files.eric.ed.gov/fulltext/ED525785.pdf

59 Balick, D. (2004). *Harassment-Free Hallways: How to Stop Sexual Harassment in School. A Guide for Students, Parents, and Schools.* American Association of University Women Educational Foundation. https://files.eric.ed.gov/fulltext/ED534504.pdf

60 Balick, D. (2004). *Harassment-Free Hallways: How to Stop Sexual Harassment in School. A Guide for Students, Parents, and Schools.* American Association of University Women Educational Foundation. https://files.eric.ed.gov/fulltext/ED534504.pdf

61 Balick, D. (2004). *Harassment-Free Hallways: How to Stop Sexual Harassment in School. A Guide for Students, Parents, and Schools.* American Association of University Women Educational Foundation. https://files.eric.ed.gov/fulltext/ED534504.pdf

62 Lichty, L. F., Torres, J. M., Valenti, M. T., & Buchanan, N. T. (2008). Sexual Harassment Policies in K-12 Schools: Examining Accessibility to Students and Content. *Journal of School Health, 78*(11), 607-614. https://deepblue.lib.umich.edu/bitstream/handle/2027.42/75026/j.1746-1561.2008.00353.x.pdf%3Bjsessionid%3D491D89E6A4A8739D653E6677800FE623?sequence%3D1

63 Pinker, Steven. The Better Angels of Our Nature: Why Violence Has Declined . Penguin Publishing Group. Kindle Edition.

64 Dey, T. (2006). *Failure to launch* [Film]. Paramount Pictures. www.imdb.com/title/tt0427229/characters/nm0177896; www.imdb.com/title/tt0427229/characters/nm0000572

65 Twenge, J. M. (2017). *IGen: Why today's super-connected kids are growing up less rebellious, more tolerant, less happy--and completely unprepared for adulthood--and what that means for the rest of us.* Simon and Schuster. https://books.google.co.uk/books?hl=en&lr=&id=HiKaDQAAQBAJ&oi=fnd&pg=PT7&dq=%2218-year-old-s+now+act+like+15-year-olds+used+to%22&ots=aQTTiYhKYY&sig=Ya9a68U6s85WUgioBYbpXTD-UD-w&redir_esc=y#v=onepage&q=%2218-year-olds%20now%20act%20like%2015-year-olds%20used%20to%22&f=false

66 *Highway Statistics 1998.* (2014). Office of Highway Policy Information, Federal Highway Administration. www.fhwa.dot.gov/policyinformation/statistics/1998/dl20.cfm;
*Highway Statistics 2018.* (2020). Office of Highway Policy Information, Federal Highway Administration. www.fhwa.dot.gov/policyinformation/statistics/2018/dl20.cfm

67 Hofer, B. K., Thebodo, S. W., Meredith, K., Kaslow, Z., & Saunders, A. (2016). The Long Arm of the Digital Tether: Communication with Home during Study Abroad. Frontiers: *The Interdisciplinary Journal of Study Abroad, 28*, 24-41. https://files.eric.ed.gov/fulltext/EJ1123178.pdf

68 Yelowitz, A. (2007). *Young adults leaving the nest: The role of the cost of living.* The price of independence: The economics of early adulthood, 170-207. https://books.google.co.uk/books?hl=en&lr=&id=0fQWAwAAQBAJ&oi=fnd&pg=PA170&dq=Young+adults+leaving+the+nest:+The+role+of+cost-of-living&ots=UkpX-D9htqw&sig=ngtHN_dqrIMBJissxAfbzI8WoX4&redir_esc=y#v=onepage&q=Young%20adults%20leaving%20the%20nest%3A%20The%20role%20of%20cost-of-living&f=false

69 Wightman, P. D., Patrick, M. E., Schoeni, R. F., & Schulenberg, J. E. (2013). *Historical trends in parental financial support of young adults.* Population Studies Center Research Report, (13-801). https://pdfs.semanticscholar.org/dacd/f19eff3be9fbb9ebed0b511ce2feaedb0040.pdf

70 Allen, Joseph. *Escaping the Endless Adolescence: How we can help our teenagers grow up before they grow old.* Random House Publishing Group. Kindle Edition. https://books.google.co.uk/books?hl=en&lr=&id=myEHFTWAm-jwC&oi=fnd&pg=PR9&dq=Escaping+the+Endless+Adolescence&ots=8yCPQ5RSm7&sig=Zg52iGB3ugS-5gz0mW19DUdLsUiA&redir_esc=y#v=onepage&q=Escaping%20the%20Endless%20Adolescence&f=false

71 Larson, R. W. (2001). How US children and adolescents spend time: What it does (and doesn't) tell us about their development. *Current Directions in Psychological Science, 10*(5), 160-164. https://pdfs.semanticscholar.org/b4ee/0859d49f18629dc865c1ac6f9ca6537dc862.pdf

72 Schulz, F. (2019). Trends in Children's Gendered Housework Performance. Time Use Evidence from Germany, 1991–2013. *Child Indicators Research*, 1-22. https://link.springer.com/article/10.1007/s12187-019-09702-x

73 Wallace, J. (2015). Why Children Need Chores. *The Wall Street Journal.* www.wsj.com/articles/why-children-need-chores-1426262655

74 Larson, R. W. (2001). How US children and adolescents spend time: What it does (and doesn't) tell us about their development. *Current Directions in Psychological Science, 10*(5), 160-164. https://pdfs.semanticscholar.org/b4ee/0859d49f18629dc865c1ac6f9ca6537dc862.pdf

Citing: Goodnow, J. J. (1988). Children's household work: Its nature and functions. *Psychological Bulletin, 103*(1), 5. http://psycnet.apa.org/buy/1988-10303-001

75 Riggio, H. R., Valenzuela, A. M., & Weiser, D. A. (2010). Household responsibilities in the family of origin: Relations with self-efficacy in young adulthood. *Personality and Individual Differences, 48*(5), 568-573. http://parented.wdfiles.com/local--files/chores-allowances/Household%20Responsibilities%20in%20the%20Family%20of%20Origin.pdf

76 Vaillant, G. E., & Vaillant, C. O. (1981). Natural history of male psychological health: X. Work as a predictor of positive mental health. *The American journal of psychiatry*. www.ncbi.nlm.nih.gov/pubmed/7294211

77 *Child labour.* (2019). Unicef. https://data.unicef.org/topic/child-protection/child-labour/

78 Frank, A. (1952). *Anne Frank: The Diary of a young girl.* DoubleDay & Company.

79 Power, R. A., & Pluess, M. (2015). Heritability estimates of the Big Five personality traits based on common genetic variants. *Translational psychiatry, 5*(7), e604-e604. www.nature.com/articles/tp201596

80 Jang, K. L., Livesley, W. J., & Vemon, P. A. (1996). Heritability of the big five personality dimensions and their facets: A twin study. *Journal of personality, 64*(3), 577-592. https://andymatuschak.org/files/papers/Jang%20et%20al.%20-%201996%20-%20Heritability%20of%20the%20Big%20Five%20Personality%20Dimension.pdf; Loehlin, J. C., McCrae, R. R., Costa Jr, P. T., & John, O. P. (1998). Heritabilities of common and measure-specific components of the Big Five personality factors. *Journal of research in personality, 32*(4), 431-453. http://socionics.org/forums/storage/9/421602/hedirity.pdf

81 Harris, J. R. (1995). Where is the child's environment? A group socialization theory of development. *Psychological review, 102*(3), 458. https://faculty.weber.edu/eamsel/Classes/Child%203000/Lectures/3%20Childhood/SE%20development/JudithHarris.html

82 Harris, J. R. (1995). Where is the child's environment? A group socialization theory of development. *Psychological review, 102*(3), 458. https://faculty.weber.edu/eamsel/Classes/Child%203000/Lectures/3%20Childhood/SE%20development/JudithHarris.html

83 Sapolsky, Robert M.. *Behave.* Penguin Publishing Group. Kindle Edition.

84 Mesoudi, A., Magid, K., & Hussain, D. (2016). How do people become WEIRD? Migration reveals the cultural transmission mechanisms underlying variation in psychological processes. *PloS one, 11*(1), e0147162. https://journals.plos.org/plosone/article?id=10.1371/journal.pone.0147162;
Phinney, J. S., Ong, A., & Madden, T. (2000). Cultural values and intergenerational value discrepancies in immigrant and non-immigrant families. *Child development, 71*(2), 528-539. https://srcd.onlinelibrary.wiley.com/doi/epdf/10.1111/1467-8624.00162

85 Rand, D. G., & Epstein, Z. G. (2014). Risking your life without a second thought: Intuitive decision-making and extreme altruism. *Plos one, 9*(10), e109687. https://journals.plos.org/plosone/article?id=10.1371/journal.pone.0109687

86 Greene, J. D., & Paxton, J. M. (2009). Patterns of neural activity associated with honest and dishonest moral decisions. *Proceedings of the National Academy of Sciences, 106*(30), 12506-12511. www.pnas.org/doi/full/10.1073/pnas.0900152106

87 Malesky, A., Grist, C., Poovey, K., & Dennis, N. (2022). The effects of peer influence, honor codes, and personality traits on cheating behavior in a university setting. *Ethics & Behavior, 32*(1), 12-21. www.tandfonline.com/doi/abs/10.1080/10508422.2020.1869006; McCabe, D. L., Treviño, L. K., & Butterfield, K. D. (2001). Cheating in academic institutions: A decade of research. *Ethics &Behavior, 11*(3), 219-232. www.tandfonline.com/doi/abs/10.1207/S15327019EB1103_2?journalCode=hebh20

88 Bekkers, R., & Wiepking, P. (2011). Who gives? A literature review of predictors of charitable giving part one: Religion, education, age and socialisation. *Voluntary Sector Review, 2*(3), 337-365. https://repub.eur.nl/pub/32755/metis_172194.pdf

## 11. Appearance

1 Foreman, A. (2015). Why Footbinding Persisted in China for a Millennium. *Smithsonian Magazine.* www.smithsonianmag.com/history/why-footbinding-persisted-china-millennium-180953971/

2 Atropa belladonna (Deadly Nightshade), in Meriney, S. D., & Fanselow, E. (2019). *Synaptic transmission.* Academic Press. www.sciencedirect.com/topics/neuroscience/atropa-belladonna

3 Killgrove, K. (2015). Here's How Corsets Deformed The Skeletons Of Victorian Women. *Forbes*. www.forbes.com/sites/kristinakillgrove/2015/11/16/how-corsets-deformed-the-skeletons-of-victorian-women/#350e632e799c

4 Korzhov, N. & Kovalenko, A. (2013). *Myanmar's neck ring women*. Aljazeera. www.aljazeera.com/gallery/2013/9/17/myanmars-neck-ring-women#:~:text=Among%20the%20Kayan%20tribe%20the,life%20is%20on%20the%20decline.&text=Pan%20Pat%2C%20Myanmar%20%E2%80%93%20Women%20of,the%20more%20beautiful%20the%20woman

5 Rizzo, J. (2017). Striking Photos of Cultural Fashions You Have to See. *National Geographic*. www.nationalgeographic.com/travel/travel-interests/arts-and-culture/style-culture-fashion-around-world/#close

6 Harper, B. (2000). Beauty, stature and the labour market: A British cohort study. *Oxford Bulletin of Economics and Statistics, 62*, 771-800. http://citeseerx.ist.psu.edu/viewdoc/download?doi=10.1.1.200.4097&rep=rep1&type=pdf

7 Fredrickson, B. L., & Roberts, T. A. (1997). Objectification theory: Toward understanding women's lived experiences and mental health risks. *Psychology of women quarterly, 21*(2), 173-206. www.researchgate.net/profile/Tomi-Ann_Roberts/publication/258181826_Objectification_Theory_Toward_Understanding_Women%27s_Lived_Experiences_and_Mental_Health_Risks/links/59f375d4aca272607e2912c0/Objectification-Theory-Toward-Understanding-Womens-Lived-Experiences-and-Mental-Health-Risks.pdf

8 Harper, B. (2000). Beauty, stature and the labour market: A British cohort study. *Oxford Bulletin of Economics and Statistics, 62*, 771-800. http://citeseerx.ist.psu.edu/viewdoc/download?doi=10.1.1.200.4097&rep=rep1&type=pdf;
Hamermesh, D. S., & Biddle, J. E. (1993). *Beauty and the labor market* (No. w4518). National Bureau of Economic Research. www.nber.org/papers/w4518.pdf;
Von Bose, C. M. (2013). *The economics of beautification and beauty*. https://repositories.lib.utexas.edu/bitstream/handle/2152/21180/VONBOSE-DISSERTATION-2013.pdf?sequence=1;
Hosoda, M., Stone-Romero, E. F., & Coats, G. (2003). The effects of physical attractiveness on job-related outcomes: A meta-analysis of experimental studies. *Personnel psychology, 56*(2), 431-462. https://search.proquest.com/docview/220134042?pq-origsite=gscholar&fromopenview=true;
Biddle, J. E., & Hamermesh, D. S. (1998). Beauty, productivity, and discrimination: Lawyers' looks and lucre. *Journal of labor Economics, 16*(1), 172-201. https://d1wqtxts1xzle7.cloudfront.net/33971/22anjvmdu18xgh4bncss.pdf?1425064483=&response-content-disposition=inline%3B+filename%3DPDF_Version.pdf&Expires=1611061347&Signature=TqiBa7hUOeVuVVIiOz8KWb6Mue1VTyqVeuyWfef~jZ-4-vxCjtAbYlZprQxiSGsXYcqpM9hJPD1IrfLwWx0aaOz6Rz5~rJl9FMYfFpbUESu~5ucvjTIdaPBUOnmyJMrMpBtzRmhZDS-ZBJ0-Z3UueYNgcsv5uWnkPykXhCtDiKAjXXtf6wQaLgyHX4pMdNMKJ9vur-cCnt4rI7T0lzQzsLsR53CQgM9Ip~SYPLWkxqr6TPcibwSpMPW8ppywiz6i3GpA9g4B-uumH6B1yN~p9ppnFjSjbil4HdboTX8ZLXyitWJhCNZ9OuqDEWlIY9pdPECSAuvA-88D2~AIIwZgoQ__&Key-Pair-Id=APKAJLOHF5GGSLRBV4ZA

9 Von Bose, C. M. (2013). *The economics of beautification and beauty*. https://repositories.lib.utexas.edu/bitstream/handle/2152/21180/VONBOSE-DISSERTATION-2013.pdf?sequence=1

10 Clifford, M. M., & Walster, E. (1973). The effect of physical attractiveness on teacher expectations. *Sociology of education*, 248-258. http://math.coe.uga.edu/prime/Methods/Expectations.pdf

11 Rich, J. (1975). Effects of children's physical attractiveness on teachers' evaluations. *Journal of Educational Psychology, 67*(5), 599. https://psycnet.apa.org/record/1976-05620-001

12 Hamermesh, D. S., & Parker, A. (2005). Beauty in the classroom: Instructors' pulchritude and putative pedagogical productivity. *Economics of Education Review, 24*(4), 369-376. www.nber.org/system/files/working_papers/w9853/w9853.pdf

13 Langlois, J. H., Kalakanis, L., Rubenstein, A. J., Larson, A., Hallam, M., & Smoot, M. (2000). Maxims or myths of beauty? A meta-analytic and theoretical review. *Psychological bulletin, 126*(3), 390. http://beauty-review.nl/wp-content/uploads/2014/04/Maxims-or-myths-of-beauty-A-meta-analytic-and-theoretical-review.pdf;
Hamermesh, D. S. (2011). Beauty pays: Why attractive people are more successful. Princeton University Press.;
Hope, D. A., & Mindell, J. A. (1994). Global social skill ratings: Measures of social behavior or physical attractiveness?. *Behaviour research and therapy, 32*(4), 463-469. www.sciencedirect.com/science/article/abs/pii/0005796794900116;
Rhode, D. L. (2010). *The beauty bias: The injustice of appearance in life and law*. Oxford University Press. https://books.google.com/books?hl=en&lr=&id=zDXRCwAAQBAJ&oi=fnd&pg=PR5&dq=%22The+Beauty+Bias%22&ots=GOMxHy_lUw&sig=JtGSxo79QAytPOSScp-AokDG8WY#v=onepage&q=%22The%20Beauty%20Bias%22&f=false

14 Dahl, M. (2014). *Stop obsessing: Women spend 2 weeks a year on their appearance, TODAY survey shows.* Today. www.today.com/health/stop-obsessing-women-spend-2-weeks-year-their-appearance-today-2D12104866

15 Hamermesh, D. S., Meng, X., & Zhang, J. (2002). Dress for success—does primping pay?. *Labour Economics, 9*(3), 361-373. www.nber.org/system/files/working_papers/w7167/w7167.pdf

16 Albino, J. E., Lawrence, S. D., & Tedesco, L. A. (1994). Psychological and social effects of orthodontic treatment. *Journal of behavioral medicine, 17*(1), 81-98. https://deepblue.lib.umich.edu/bitstream/handle/2027.42/44814/10865_2005_Article_BF01856884.pdf?sequence=1;
Kerr, W. J. S., & O'donnell, J. M. (1990). Panel perception of facial attractiveness. *British Journal of Orthodontics, 17*(4), 299-304. www.tandfonline.com/doi/abs/10.1179/bjo.17.4.299

17 Olsen, J. A., & Inglehart, M. R. (2011). Malocclusions and perceptions of attractiveness, intelligence, and personality, and behavioral intentions. *American Journal of Orthodontics and Dentofacial Orthopedics, 140*(5), 669-679. www.sciencedirect.com/science/article/abs/pii/S0889540611006780

18 Von Bose, C. M. (2013). *The economics of beautification and beauty.* https://repositories.lib.utexas.edu/bitstream/handle/2152/21180/VONBOSE-DISSERTATION-2013.pdf?sequence=1

19 Von Bose, C. M. (2013). *The economics of beautification and beauty.* https://repositories.lib.utexas.edu/bitstream/handle/2152/21180/VONBOSE-DISSERTATION-2013.pdf?sequence=1

20 Bartolini, T., Kresge, J., McLennan, M., Windham, B., Buhr, T. A., & Pryor, B. (1988). Perceptions of personal characteristics of men and women under three conditions of eyewear. *Perceptual and Motor Skills, 67*(3), 779-782. https://journals.sagepub.com/doi/abs/10.2466/pms.1988.67.3.779

21 Jellesma, F. C. (2013). Do glasses change children's perceptions? Effects of eyeglasses on peer-and self-perception. *European Journal of Developmental Psychology, 10*(4), 449-460. www.tandfonline.com/doi/abs/10.1080/17405629.2012.700199

22 Walline, J. J., Gaume, A., Jones, L. A., Rah, M. J., Manny, R. E., Berntsen, D. A., ... & Quinn, N. (2007). Benefits of contact lens wear for children and teens. *Eye & contact lens, 33*(6), 317-321. https://journals.lww.com/claojournal/Abstract/2007/11000/Benefits_of_Contact_Lens_Wear_for_Children_and.10.aspx

23 Elliott, J. (2008). *'Acne drove me to try to take my life.'* BBC News. http://news.bbc.co.uk/1/hi/health/7293961.stm

24 McCarthy, J. (2015). *This man's severe acne left him on the verge of suicide but now he has set up his own skincare business and he's thriving.* Wales Online. www.walesonline.co.uk/news/wales-news/mans-severe-acne-left-him-10550344

25 *Acne: Types of Acne.* (2020). National Institutes of Health. www.niams.nih.gov/health-topics/acne/advanced#tab-types

26 Coghan, A. (2016). *How lack of oxygen makes bacteria cause acne and how to stop it.* New Scientist. www.newscientist.com/article/2110826-how-lack-of-oxygen-makes-bacteria-cause-acne-and-how-to-stop-it/

27 Hui, R. W. (2017). Common misconceptions about acne vulgaris: A review of the literature. *Clinical Dermatology Review, 1*(2), 33. www.cdriadvlkn.org/article.asp?issn=2542-551X;year=2017;volume=1;issue=2;spage=33;epage=36;aulast=Hui;
Law, M. P. M., Chuh, A. A. T., Lee, A., & Molinari, N. (2010). Acne prevalence and beyond: acne disability and its predictive factors among Chinese late adolescents in Hong Kong. *Clinical and Experimental Dermatology: Clinical dermatology, 35*(1), 16-21. https://onlinelibrary.wiley.com/doi/abs/10.1111/j.1365-2230.2009.03340.x;
Yahya, H. (2009). Acne vulgaris in Nigerian adolescents–prevalence, severity, beliefs, perceptions, and practices. *International journal of dermatology, 48*(5), 498-505. https://onlinelibrary.wiley.com/doi/pdf/10.1111/j.1365-4632.2009.03922.x;
Rademaker, M., Garioch, J. J., & Simpson, N. B. (1989). Acne in schoolchildren: no longer a concern for dermatologists. *British Medical Journal, 298*(6682), 1217-1219. www.ncbi.nlm.nih.gov/pmc/articles/PMC1836257/pdf/bmj00230-0025.pdf;
Pearl, A., Arroll, B., Lello, J., & Birchall, N. M. (1998). The impact of acne: a study of adolescents' attitudes, perception and knowledge. *The New Zealand Medical Journal, 111*(1070), 269-271. https://europepmc.org/article/med/9734528

28 Bhate, K., & Williams, H. C. (2013). Epidemiology of acne vulgaris. *British Journal of Dermatology, 168*(3), 474-485. https://onlinelibrary.wiley.com/doi/full/10.1111/bjd.12149

29 Williams, H. C., Dellavalle, R. P., & Garner, S. (2012). Acne vulgaris. *The Lancet, 379*(9813), 361-372. http://beauty-review.nl/wp-content/uploads/2015/01/Acne-Vulgaris.pdf

30 Cordain, L., Lindeberg, S., Hurtado, M., Hill, K., Eaton, S. B., & Brand-Miller, J. (2002). Acne vulgaris: a disease of Western civilization. *Archives of dermatology, 138*(12), 1584-1590. https://jamanetwork.com/journals/jamadermatology/fullarticle/479093

31 Law, M. P. M., Chuh, A. A. T., Lee, A., & Molinari, N. (2010). Acne prevalence and beyond: acne disability and its predictive factors among Chinese late adolescents in Hong Kong. *Clinical and Experimental Dermatology: Clinical dermatology, 35*(1), 16-21. https://onlinelibrary.wiley.com/doi/abs/10.1111/j.1365-2230.2009.03340.x

32 Mallon, E., Newton, J. N., Klassen, A., Stewart-Brown, S. L., Ryan, T. J., & Finlay, A. Y. (1999). The quality of life in acne: a comparison with general medical conditions using generic questionnaires. *The British journal of dermatology, 140*(4), 672-676. https://europepmc.org/article/med/10233319

33 Pearl, A., Arroll, B., Lello, J., & Birchall, N. M. (1998). The impact of acne: a study of adolescents' attitudes, perception and knowledge. *The New Zealand Medical Journal, 111*(1070), 269-271. https://europepmc.org/article/med/9734528

34 Kubota, Y., Shirahige, Y., Nakai, K., Katsuura, J., Moriue, T., & Yoneda, K. (2010). Community-based epidemiological study of psychosocial effects of acne in Japanese adolescents. *The Journal of dermatology, 37*(7), 617-622. https://onlinelibrary.wiley.com/doi/abs/10.1111/j.1346-8138.2010.00855.x;
Hahm, B. J., Min, S. U., Yoon, M. Y., Shin, Y. W., Kim, J. S., Jung, J. Y., & Suh, D. H. (2009). Changes of psychiatric parameters and their relationships by oral isotretinoin in acne patients. *The Journal of dermatology, 36*(5), 255-261. https://onlinelibrary.wiley.com/doi/abs/10.1111/j.1346-8138.2009.00635.x;
Samuels, D. V., Rosenthal, R., Lin, R., Chaudhari, S., & Natsuaki, M. N. (2020). Acne vulgaris and risk of depression and anxiety: A meta-analytic review. *Journal of the American Academy of Dermatology*. www.sciencedirect.com/science/article/abs/pii/S0190962220302796

35 Halvorsen, J. A., Stern, R. S., Dalgard, F., Thoresen, M., Bjertness, E., & Lien, L. (2011). Suicidal ideation, mental health problems, and social impairment are increased in adolescents with acne: a population-based study. *Journal of Investigative Dermatology, 131*(2), 363-370. www.sciencedirect.com/science/article/pii/S0022202X15351496

36 Zaidi, Z. (2009). Dispelling the myths and misconceptions of acne. JPMA. *The Journal of the Pakistan Medical Association, 59*(5), 264. www.jpma.org.pk/PdfDownload/1684.pdf

37 Levitt, S. (2016). *Before You Pop a Pimple*. WebMD. www.webmd.com/skin-problems-and-treatments/features/pop-a-zit#1

38 Marcoux, D. (1999, September). Cosmetics, skin care, and appearance in teenagers. In *Seminars in cutaneous medicine and surgery* (Vol. 18, No. 3, pp. 244-249). WB Saunders. https://d1wqtxts1xzle7.cloudfront.net/58193385/s1085-5629_2899_2980022-420190115-10800-vrizg.pdf?1547607114=&response-content-disposition=inline%3B+-filename%3DCosmetics_skin_care_and_appearance_in_te.pdf&Expires=1592579640&Signature=PYQAyNb3MTH-tR4zG4vCcsIpIXxyS5kzMNNQF0AQN81j-Bx37N~Fxb~-GOpipv5~5stT~Q06gLvDQ3vixjNpaV4~QHaBN-bqmML3QsoxCBABsCMLjo96Lpz6vMM~pS4cRUAaGgaTOc8duNs80ZFf5KRW73zWbC~9GUmtuW-zMU2H-dQMhFH7w4f8njBhOo4jmhVBcQIlhylP96uBV5foXx3qhvtwge3xstaZjKbGcZzMCwrij6NQ5dJHKJsyilm-Mvpy9rzCyTNFXx0tadFmr2LSwFeJ0Mubg~vaT1CLcyC5DXk2WJMlJwiAy49Qre-2EDpGwY9EJYS2QTgzhqAjP-3GusA__&Key-Pair-Id=APKAJLOHF5GGSLRBV4ZA

39 Magin, P., Pond, D., Smith, W., & Watson, A. (2005). A systematic review of the evidence for 'myths and misconceptions' in acne management: diet, face-washing and sunlight. *Family practice, 22*(1), 62-70. https://academic.oup.com/fampra/article/22/1/62/440463;
Hui, R. W. (2017). Common misconceptions about acne vulgaris: A review of the literature. *Clinical Dermatology Review, 1*(2), 33. www.cdriadvlkn.org/article.asp?issn=2542-551X;year=2017;volume=1;issue=2;spage=33;epage=36;aulast=Hui

40 Williams, H. C., Dellavalle, R. P., & Garner, S. (2012). Acne vulgaris. *The Lancet, 379*(9813), 361-372. http://beauty-review.nl/wp-content/uploads/2015/01/Acne-Vulgaris.pdf

41 Leyden, J. J. (1997). Therapy for acne vulgaris. *New England Journal of Medicine, 336*(16), 1156-1162. http://jacobimed.org/public/Ambulatory_files/mlove/CurriculumConsult%20and%20Specialties/Dermatology/acne.pdf;
Williams, H. C., Dellavalle, R. P., & Garner, S. (2012). Acne vulgaris. *The Lancet, 379*(9813), 361-372. http://beauty-review.nl/wp-content/uploads/2015/01/Acne-Vulgaris.pdf;
*Overview, Acne*. (2019). UK National Health Service. www.nhs.uk/conditions/acne/

42 Metrus, L. (2021). *The 7-Day Meal Plan to Banish Acne, According to a Nutritionist.* Byrdie.

43 Leyden, J. J. (1997). Therapy for acne vulgaris. *New England Journal of Medicine, 336*(16), 1156-1162. http://jacobimed.org/public/Ambulatory_files/mlove/CurriculumConsult%20and%20Specialties/Dermatology/acne.pdf;
Davidovici, B. B., & Wolf, R. (2010). The role of diet in acne: facts and controversies. *Clinics in dermatology, 28*(1), 12-16. www.beauty-review.nl/wp-content/uploads/2015/01/The-role-of-diet-in-acne-facts-and-controversies.pdf;
Williams, H. C., Dellavalle, R. P., & Garner, S. (2012). Acne vulgaris. *The Lancet, 379*(9813), 361-372. http://beauty-review.nl/wp-content/uploads/2015/01/Acne-Vulgaris.pdf;
Gollnick, H., Cunliffe, W., Berson, D., Dreno, B., Finlay, A., Leyden, J. J., ... & Thiboutot, D. (2003). Management of acne: a report from a Global Alliance to Improve Outcomes in Acne. *Journal of the American Academy of Dermatology, 49*(1), S1-S37. www.alessandrolivistudiomedico.it/wp-content/uploads/2020/02/traumi.pdf

44 Hui, R. W. (2017). Common misconceptions about acne vulgaris: A review of the literature. Clinical Dermatology Review, 1(2), 33. www.cdriadvlkn.org/article.asp?issn=2542-551X;year=2017;volume=1;issue=2;spage=33;epage=36;aulast=Hui

45 Strauss, J. S., Krowchuk, D. P., Leyden, J. J., Lucky, A. W., Shalita, A. R., Siegfried, E. C., ... & Bhushan, R. (2007). Guidelines of care for acne vulgaris management. *Journal of the American Academy of Dermatology, 56*(4), 651-663. www.mediskin.cn/uploadfiles/file/20130424/20130424111431_1837.pdf

46 Green, J., & Sinclair, R. D. (2001). Perceptions of acne vulgaris in final year medical student written examination answers. *Australasian Journal of Dermatology, 42*(2), 98-101. https://westerndermatology.com.au/wp-content/uploads/2019/11/Acne-perceptions.pdf;
Brajac, I., Bilić-Zulle, L., Tkalčić, M., Lončarek, K., & Gruber, F. (2004). Acne vulgaris: myths and misconceptions among patients and family physicians. *Patient education and counseling, 54*(1), 21-25. www.sciencedirect.com/science/article/abs/pii/S073839910300168X

47 Gollnick, H., Cunliffe, W., Berson, D., Dreno, B., Finlay, A., Leyden, J. J., ... & Thiboutot, D. (2003). Management of acne: a report from a Global Alliance to Improve Outcomes in Acne. *Journal of the American Academy of Dermatology, 49*(1), S1-S37. www.alessandrolivistudiomedico.it/wp-content/uploads/2020/02/traumi.pdf;
Sagransky, M., Yentzer, B. A., & Feldman, S. R. (2009). Benzoyl peroxide: a review of its current use in the treatment of acne vulgaris. *Expert opinion on pharmacotherapy, 10*(15), 2555-2562. www.tandfonline.com/doi/abs/10.1517/14656560903277228;
Footnote reference: [1] Williams, H. C., Dellavalle, R. P., & Garner, S. (2012). Acne vulgaris. *The Lancet, 379*(9813), 361-372. http://beauty-review.nl/wp-content/uploads/2015/01/Acne-Vulgaris.pdf

48 Williams, H. C., Dellavalle, R. P., & Garner, S. (2012). Acne vulgaris. *The Lancet, 379*(9813), 361-372. http://beauty-review.nl/wp-content/uploads/2015/01/Acne-Vulgaris.pdf

49 Henry, R. E. (2009). Prioritizing healthcare resources to keep the baby boomers out of nursing homes. *American health & drug benefits, 2*(4), 152. www.ncbi.nlm.nih.gov/pmc/articles/PMC4106529/;
*Appendix C: Comparative Effectiveness Research Priorities: IOM Recommendations (2009).* (2009). NCBI. www.ncbi.nlm.nih.gov/books/NBK64788/

50 Gollnick, H. P., & Zouboulis, C. C. (2014). Not all acne is acne vulgaris. *Deutsches Ärzteblatt International, 111*(17), 301. www.ncbi.nlm.nih.gov/pmc/articles/PMC4098044/

51 Troeth, S. (2018). How I found light at the end of the very dark tunnel that acne plunged me into. *The Guardian.* www.theguardian.com/commentisfree/2018/dec/28/how-i-found-light-at-the-end-of-the-very-dark-tunnel-that-acne-plunged-me-into

52 Rich, J. (1998). *The nurture assumption: Why children turn out the way they do.* Bloomsbury.

53 Conti, G., Galeotti, A., Mueller, G., & Pudney, S. (2013). Popularity. *Journal of Human Resources, 48*(4), 1072-1094. www.nber.org/papers/w18475.pdf

54 Persico, N., Postlewaite, A., & Silverman, D. (2004). The effect of adolescent experience on labor market outcomes: The case of height. *Journal of Political Economy, 112*(5), 1019-1053. www.nber.org/papers/w10522.pdf

55 Persico, N., Postlewaite, A., & Silverman, D. (2004). The effect of adolescent experience on labor market outcomes: The case of height. *Journal of Political Economy, 112*(5), 1019-1053. www.nber.org/papers/w10522.pdf

56 Senior, J. (2013). Why You Truly Never Leave High School. *New York Magazine.* https://nymag.com/news/features/high-school-2013-1/

57 Mullin, G. (2019). Horrific photos of teen's severe sunburn serves as warning that sunscreen is not enough. *New York Post.* https://nypost.com/2019/07/26/horrific-photos-of-teens-severe-sunburn-serves-as-warning-that-sunscreen-is-not-enough/

58 Zinman, R., Schwartz, S., Gordon, K., Fitzpatrick, E., & Camfield, C. (1995). Predictors of sunscreen use in childhood. *Archives of pediatrics & adolescent medicine, 149*(7), 804-807. https://jamanetwork.com/journals/jamapediatrics/article-abstract/517609

59 Dusza, S. W., Halpern, A. C., Satagopan, J. M., Oliveria, S. A., Weinstock, M. A., Scope, A., ... & Geller, A. C. (2012). Prospective study of sunburn and sun behavior patterns during adolescence. *Pediatrics, 129*(2), 309-317. www.ncbi.nlm.nih.gov/pmc/articles/PMC3269110/

60 Davis, K. J., Cokkinides, V. E., Weinstock, M. A., O'Connell, M. C., & Wingo, P. A. (2002). Summer sunburn and sun exposure among US youths ages 11 to 18: national prevalence and associated factors. *Pediatrics, 110*(1), 27-35. http://citeseerx.ist.psu.edu/viewdoc/download?doi=10.1.1.491.7451&rep=rep1&type=pdf

61 Elwood, J. M., & Jopson, J. (1997). Melanoma and sun exposure: an overview of published studies. *International journal of cancer, 73*(2), 198-203. https://onlinelibrary.wiley.com/doi/pdf/10.1002/%28SICI%291097-0215%2819971009%2973%3A2%3C198%3A%3AAID-IJC6%3E3.0.CO%3B2-R;
Dennis, L. K., Vanbeek, M. J., Freeman, L. E. B., Smith, B. J., Dawson, D. V., & Coughlin, J. A. (2008). Sunburns and risk of cutaneous melanoma: does age matter? A comprehensive meta-analysis. *Annals of epidemiology, 18*(8), 614-627. www.ncbi.nlm.nih.gov/pmc/articles/PMC2873840/

62 Kyle, R. G., MacMillan, I., Forbat, L., Neal, R. D., O'Carroll, R. E., Haw, S., & Hubbard, G. (2014). Scottish adolescents' sun-related behaviours, tanning attitudes and associations with skin cancer awareness: a cross-sectional study. *BMJ open, 4*(5), e005137. https://bmjopen.bmj.com/content/bmjopen/4/5/e005137.full.pdf

63 Kann, L., McManus, T., Harris, W. A., Shanklin, S. L., Flint, K. H., Queen, B., ... & Lim, C. (2018). Youth risk behavior surveillance—United States, 2017. *MMWR Surveillance Summaries, 67*(8), 1. www.ncbi.nlm.nih.gov/pmc/articles/PMC6002027/

64 Boldeman, C., Beitner, H., Jansson, B., Nilsson, B., & Ullen, H. (1996). Sunbed use in relation to phenotype, erythema, sunscreen use and skin diseases. A questionnaire survey among Swedish adolescents. *British Journal of Dermatology, 135*(5), 712-716. https://onlinelibrary.wiley.com/doi/abs/10.1046/j.1365-2133.1996.d01-1067.x

65 Hillhouse, J. J., & Turrisi, R. (2002). Examination of the efficacy of an appearance-focused intervention to reduce UV exposure. *Journal of behavioral medicine, 25*(4), 395-409. https://link.springer.com/article/10.1023/A:1015870516460;
Jones, J. L., & Leary, M. R. (1994). Effects of appearance-based admonitions against sun exposure on tanning intentions in young adults. *Health Psychology, 13*(1), 86. https://psycnet.apa.org/doiLanding?doi=10.1037/0278-6133.13.1.86

66 Olson, A. L., Gaffney, C. A., Starr, P., & Dietrich, A. J. (2008). The impact of an appearance-based educational intervention on adolescent intention to use sunscreen. *Health education research, 23*(5), 763-769. https://academic.oup.com/her/article/23/5/763/625699

67 Colwell, A. & Eaton, J. (2018). *Head to head: Should girls ever be sent home from school because their skirts are too short?* The Good Schools Guide. www.goodschoolsguide.co.uk/digital-media/chalk-and-chat/issue-seven/head-to-head-short-skirts

68 Mbabazi, J. & Niwe, L. (2018). *The long and short of the mini skirt debate.* The New Times. www.newtimes.co.rw/lifestyle/long-and-short-mini-skirt-debate

69 *Indicator 19: Safety and Security Practices at Public Schools.* (2020). Indicators of School Crime and Safety, National Center for Education Statistics. https://nces.ed.gov/programs/crimeindicators/ind_19.asp

70 Gentile, E., & Imberman, S. A. (2012). Dressed for success? The effect of school uniforms on student achievement and behavior. *Journal of Urban Economics, 71*(1), 1-17. www.nber.org/system/files/working_papers/w17337/w17337.pdf;
Sanchez, J. E., Yoxsimer, A., & Hill, G. C. (2012). Uniforms in the middle school: Student opinions, discipline data, and school police data. *Journal of School Violence, 11*(4), 345-356. https://heinonline.org/HOL/Page?handle=hein.journals/wjsv11&div=25&g_sent=1&casa_token=yE2oBx2j5-IAAAAA:1G7NtamEGaAPoiq86N0GvikuOUpgjprroYgAdKW_tZ3zpEi7nDHoqS1cvtCW6dsX3ROmZmB7W6co&collection=journals

71 Bell, E. L. (1991). Adult's perception of male garment styles. *Clothing and Textiles Research Journal, 10*(1), 8-12. http://citeseerx.ist.psu.edu/viewdoc/download?doi=10.1.1.852.2586&rep=rep1&type=pdf;

Paek, S. L. (1986). Effect of garment style on the perception of personal traits. *Clothing and Textiles Research Journal, 5*(1), 10-16. https://journals.sagepub.com/doi/abs/10.1177/0887302X8600500102

72 Lennon, S. J. (1990). Effects of clothing attractiveness on perceptions. *Home Economics Research Journal, 18*(4), 303-310. www.researchgate.net/profile/Sharron_Lennon/publication/229503548_Effects_of_Clothing_Attractiveness_on_Perceptions/links/004635324be57d134b000000.pdf

73 Glick, P., Larsen, S., Johnson, C., & Branstiter, H. (2005). Evaluations of sexy women in low-and high-status jobs. *Psychology of women quarterly, 29*(4), 389-395. https://journals.sagepub.com/doi/abs/10.1111/j.1471-6402.2005.00238.x;
Gille-Knauf, T. R., & Mittag, R. M. (2008). Smart and sexy? Major and Clothing's influence on perceptions of intelligence. *UW-L Journal of Undergraduate Research, 6*, 1-9. http://citeseerx.ist.psu.edu/viewdoc/download?doi=10.1.1.507.1639&rep=rep1&type=pdf;
Graff, K., Murnen, S. K., & Smolak, L. (2012). Too sexualized to be taken seriously? Perceptions of a girl in childlike vs. sexualizing clothing. *Sex roles, 66*(11-12), 764-775. www.researchgate.net/profile/Sarah_Murnen/publication/256403145_Too_Sexualized_to_be_Taken_Seriously_Perceptions_of_a_Girl_in_Childlike_vs_Sexualizing_Clothing/links/0c96052273803cb803000000/Too-Sexualized-to-be-Taken-Seriously-Perceptions-of-a-Girl-in-Childlike-vs-Sexualizing-Clothing.pdf

74 Behling, D. (1995). Influence of dress on perception of intelligence and scholastic achievement in urban schools with minority populations. *Clothing and Textiles Research Journal, 13*(1), 11-16. https://journals.sagepub.com/doi/abs/10.1177/0887302X9501300102

75 Behling, D. U., & Williams, E. A. (1991). Influence of dress on perception of intelligence and expectations of scholastic achievement. *Clothing and Textiles Research Journal, 9*(4), 1-7. www.bxscience.edu/ourpages/auto/2007/6/12/1181662648192/Dress%20and%20Intelligence.pdf

76 Rosenthal, R., & Jacobson, L. (1968). Pygmalion in the classroom. *The urban review, 3*(1), 16-20. https://uploads-ssl.webflow.com/59faaf5b01b9500001e95457/5bc54cd6eb16de0ec3199a67_Rosenthal%2C%20R.%2C%20%26%20Jacobson%2C%20L.%201968.pdf

77 Allen, C. D., & Eicher, J. B. (1973). *Adolescent girls' acceptance and rejection based on appearance.* https://conservancy.umn.edu/bitstream/handle/11299/162781/Adolescent%201973%20vol%208.pdf?sequence=1

78 Hendricks, S. H., Kelley, E. A., & Eicher, J. B. (1968). *Senior girls' appearance and social acceptance.* https://conservancy.umn.edu/bitstream/handle/11299/162564/Senior%20girls%20appearance.pdf?sequence=1&isAllowed=y

79 Piacentini, M., & Mailer, G. (2004). Symbolic consumption in teenagers' clothing choices. *Journal of Consumer Behaviour: An International Research Review, 3*(3), 251-262. https://onlinelibrary.wiley.com/doi/abs/10.1002/cb.138

80 Bowes, L., Carnegie, R., Pearson, R., Mars, B., Biddle, L., Maughan, B., ... & Heron, J. (2015). Risk of depression and self-harm in teenagers identifying with goth subculture: a longitudinal cohort study. *The Lancet Psychiatry, 2*(9), 793-800. www.sciencedirect.com/science/article/pii/S2215036615001649

81 Rutledge, C. M., Rimer, D., & Scott, M. (2008). Vulnerable Goth teens: The role of schools in this psychosocial high-risk culture. *Journal of school health, 78*(9), 459-464. https://onlinelibrary.wiley.com/doi/abs/10.1111/j.1746-1561.2008.00331.x

82 Abbey, A., Cozzarelli, C., McLaughlin, K., & Harnish, R. J. (1987). The Effects of Clothing and Dyad Sex Composition on Perceptions of Sexual Intent: Do Women and Men Evaluate These Cues Differently. *Journal of Applied Social Psychology, 17*(2), 108-126. www.researchgate.net/profile/Richard_Harnish/publication/229726203_The_Effects_of_Clothing_and_Dyad_Sex_Composition_on_Perceptions_of_Sexual_Intent_Do_Women_and_Men_Evaluate_These_Cues_Differently1/links/5b040e4d0f7e9be94bdb2b82/The-Effects-of-Clothing-and-Dyad-Sex-Composition-on-Perceptions-of-Sexual-Intent-Do-Women-and-Men-Evaluate-These-Cues-Differently1.pdf
Citing: Zellman, G. L., & Goodchilds, J. D. (1983). *Becoming sexual in adolescence.* Changing boundaries: Gender roles and sexual behavior, 49-63.

83 Abbey, A., Cozzarelli, C., McLaughlin, K., & Harnish, R. J. (1987). The Effects of Clothing and Dyad Sex Composition on Perceptions of Sexual Intent: Do Women and Men Evaluate These Cues Differently. *Journal of Applied Social Psychology, 17*(2), 108-126. www.researchgate.net/profile/Richard_Harnish/publication/229726203_The_Effects_of_Clothing_and_Dyad_Sex_Composition_on_Perceptions_of_Sexual_Intent_Do_Women_and_Men_Evaluate_These_Cues_Differently1/links/5b040e4d0f7e9be94bdb2b82/The-Effects-of-Clothing-and-Dyad-Sex-Composition-on-Perceptions-of-Sexual-Intent-Do-Women-and-Men-Evaluate-These-Cues-Differently1.pdf
Citing: Zellman, G. L., & Goodchilds, J. D. (1983). *Becoming sexual in adolescence.* Changing boundaries: Gender roles and sexual behavior, 49-63.

84 Abbey, A., Cozzarelli, C., McLaughlin, K., & Harnish, R. J. (1987). The Effects of Clothing and Dyad Sex Composition on Perceptions of Sexual Intent: Do Women and Men Evaluate These Cues Differently. *Journal of Applied Social Psychology, 17*(2), 108-126. www.researchgate.net/profile/Richard_Harnish/publication/229726203_The_Effects_of_Clothing_and_Dyad_Sex_Composition_on_Perceptions_of_Sexual_Intent_Do_Women_and_Men_Evaluate_These_Cues_Differently1/links/5b040e4d0f7e9be94bdb2b82/The-Effects-of-Clothing-and-Dyad-Sex-Composition-on-Perceptions-of-Sexual-Intent-Do-Women-and-Men-Evaluate-These-Cues-Differently1.pdf
Citing: Zellman, G. L., & Goodchilds, J. D. (1983). *Becoming sexual in adolescence.* Changing boundaries: Gender roles and sexual behavior, 49-63.;
Edmonds, E. M., Cahoon, D. D., & Hudson, E. (1992). Male-female estimates of feminine assertiveness related to females' clothing styles. *Bulletin of the Psychonomic Society, 30*(2), 143-144. https://link.springer.com/content/pdf/10.3758/BF03330422.pdf;
Cahoon, D. D., & Edmonds, E. M. (1989). Male-female estimates of opposite-sex first impressions concerning females' clothing styles. *Bulletin of the Psychonomic Society, 27*(3), 280-281. https://link.springer.com/content/pdf/10.3758/BF03334607.pdf;
Koukounas, E., & Itsou, S. (2018). Alcohol, women's clothing, and the perception of sexual intent. Journal of Substance Use, 23(2), 206-210. www.tandfonline.com/doi/abs/10.1080/14659891.2017.1378744

85 Bernard, P., Hanoteau, F., Gervais, S., Servais, L., Bertolone, I., Deltenre, P., & Colin, C. (2019). Revealing clothing does not make the object: ERP evidences that cognitive objectification is driven by posture suggestiveness, not by revealing clothing. *Personality and Social Psychology Bulletin, 45*(1), 16-36. https://journals.sagepub.com/doi/full/10.1177/0146167218775690

86 Niesta Kayser, D., Elliot, A. J., & Feltman, R. (2010). Red and romantic behavior in men viewing women. *European Journal of Social Psychology, 40*(6), 901-908. https://onlinelibrary.wiley.com/doi/pdf/10.1002/ejsp.757

87 Cahoon, D. D., & Edmonds, E. M. (1989). Male-female estimates of opposite-sex first impressions concerning females' clothing styles. *Bulletin of the Psychonomic Society, 27*(3), 280-281. https://link.springer.com/content/pdf/10.3758/BF03334607.pdf;
Terry, R. L., & Doerge, S. (1979). Dress, posture, and setting as additive factors in subjective probabilities of rape. *Perceptual and Motor Skills, 48*(3), 903-906. https://journals.sagepub.com/doi/abs/10.2466/pms.1979.48.3.903;
Cahoon, D. D., & Edmonds, E. M. (1989). Male-female estimates of opposite-sex first impressions concerning females' clothing styles. *Bulletin of the Psychonomic Society, 27*(3), 280-281. https://link.springer.com/content/pdf/10.3758/BF03334607.pdf;
Workman, J. E., & Orr, R. L. (1996). Clothing, sex of subject, and rape myth acceptance as factors affecting attributions about an incident of acquaintance rape. *Clothing and Textiles Research Journal, 14*(4), 276-284. https://journals.sagepub.com/doi/abs/10.1177/0887302X9601400407;
Lewis, L., & Johnson, K. K. (1989). Effect of Dress, Cosmetics, Sex of Subject, and Causal Inference on Attribution of Victim Responsibility. *Clothing and Textiles Research Journal, 8*(1), 22-27. http://citeseerx.ist.psu.edu/viewdoc/download?doi=10.1.1.962.1119&rep=rep1&type=pdf

88 *Rule 412. Sex-Offense Cases: The Victim.* (n.d.). Cornell Law School. www.law.cornell.edu/rules/fre/rule_412

89 *What to Wear in Saudi Arabia; Dress code advice for tourists.* (2020). Family Travel in the Middle East. www.familytravel-middleeast.com/what-to-wear-saudi-arabia/#8-what-should-children-wear-in-saudi-arabia;
Quinn, B. (2016). French police make woman remove clothing on Nice beach following burkini ban. *The Guardian.* www.theguardian.com/world/2016/aug/24/french-police-make-woman-remove-burkini-on-nice-beach

90 Marogly. (2011). Go Beyond The Cover (Dermablend) Rick Genest. YouTube. www.youtube.com/watch?v=iBXdxt34LIU;
Padnani, A. (2018). Rick Genest, Tattooed 'Zombie Boy' in Lady Gaga Video, Dies at 32. *The New York Times.* www.nytimes.com/2018/08/03/obituaries/rick-genest-tattooed-model-known-as-zombie-boy-dies-at-32.html

91 Rosentiel, T. (2010). Portrait of the Millennials. Pew Research Center. www.pewresearch.org/files/old-assets/ppt/Paul-Taylor-Portrait-of-the-Millennials.ppt

92 Shannon-Missal, L. (2016). *Tattoo Takeover: Three in Ten Americans Have Tattoos, and Most Don't Stop at Just One.* The Harris Poll. https://theharrispoll.com/tattoos-can-take-any-number-of-forms-from-animals-to-quotes-to-cryptic-symbols-and-appear-in-all-sorts-of-spots-on-our-bodies-some-visible-in-everyday-life-others-not-so-much-but-one-thi/

93 McElroy, J. C., Summers, J. K., & Moore, K. (2014). The effect of facial piercing on perceptions of job applicants. *Organizational Behavior and Human Decision Processes, 125*(1), 26-38. www.sciencedirect.com/science/article/abs/pii/S0749597814000442

94 Jibuti, D. (2018). *Discrimination against Workers with Visible Tattoos: Experimental Evidence from Germany.* CERGE-EI Working Paper Series, (628). www.researchgate.net/profile/Daviti_Jibuti/publication/329117986_

Discrimination_against_Workers_with_Visible_Tattoos_Experimental_Evidence_from_Germany/links/5bf679d092851c6b27d19f59/Discrimination-against-Workers-with-Visible-Tattoos-Experimental-Evidence-from-Germany.pdf

95 Oosterzee, A. F. (2009). Are you regretting your Tattoo?: *The effects of demographical variables, initial motivations, impulsiveness, tattoo characteristics, daily events and the decision-making process on having regrets about a tattoo* (Bachelor's thesis, University of Twente). https://essay.utwente.nl/59660/1/scriptie_A_Oosterzee.pdf

96 Shannon-Missal, L. (2016). *Tattoo Takeover: Three in Ten Americans Have Tattoos, and Most Don't Stop at Just One*. The Harris Poll. https://theharrispoll.com/tattoos-can-take-any-number-of-forms-from-animals-to-quotes-to-cryptic-symbols-and-appear-in-all-sorts-of-spots-on-our-bodies-some-visible-in-everyday-life-others-not-so-much-but-one-thi/

97 Dukes, R. L. (2016). Regret among tattooed adolescents. *The Social Science Journal, 53*(4), 455-458. www.sciencedirect.com/science/article/abs/pii/S0362331916300453

98 Shannon-Missal, L. (2016). *Tattoo Takeover: Three in Ten Americans Have Tattoos, and Most Don't Stop at Just One*. The Harris Poll. https://theharrispoll.com/tattoos-can-take-any-number-of-forms-from-animals-to-quotes-to-cryptic-symbols-and-appear-in-all-sorts-of-spots-on-our-bodies-some-visible-in-everyday-life-others-not-so-much-but-one-thi/

99 Klein, A., Rittmann, I., Hiller, K. A., Landthaler, M., & Bäumler, W. (2014). An Internet-based survey on characteristics of laser tattoo removal and associated side effects. *Lasers in medical science, 29*(2), 729-738. https://link.springer.com/article/10.1007/s10103-013-1395-1

100 *Hepatitis C Questions and Answers for the Public.* (2020). Centers for Disease Control and Prevention. www.cdc.gov/hepatitis/hcv/cfaq.htm;
Tohme, R. A., & Holmberg, S. D. (2012). Transmission of hepatitis C virus infection through tattooing and piercing: a critical review. *Clinical Infectious Diseases, 54*(8), 1167-1178. www.ncbi.nlm.nih.gov/pmc/articles/PMC4613802/

101 Legal Status of tattooing in the United States. (n.d.) Wikipedia. https://en.wikipedia.org/wiki/Legal_status_of_tattooing_in_the_United_States

102 Brady, B. G., Gold, H., Leger, E. A., & Leger, M. C. (2015). Self-reported adverse tattoo reactions: a New York City C entral Park study. *Contact Dermatitis, 73*(2), 91-99. www.researchgate.net/profile/Elizabeth_Leger/publication/277336901_Self-reported_adverse_tattoo_reactions_a_New_York_City_Central_Park_study/links/5a7e1c7caca272a73765cb14/Self-reported-adverse-tattoo-reactions-a-New-York-City-Central-Park-study.pdf

103 Klügl, I., Hiller, K. A., Landthaler, M., & Bäumler, W. (2010). Incidence of health problems associated with tattooed skin: a nation-wide survey in German-speaking countries. *Dermatology, 221*(1), 43-50. www.karger.com/Article/Abstract/292627

104 Piccinini, P., Pakalin, S., Contor, L., Bianchi, I., & Senaldi, C. (2016). *Safety of tattoos and permanent make-up: Final report.* EUR27947. https://ec.europa.eu/jrc/en/publication/eur-scientific-and-technical-research-reports/safety-tattoos-and-permanent-make-final-report;
Laux, P., Tralau, T., Tentschert, J., Blume, A., Al Dahouk, S., Bäumler, W., ... & de Cuyper, C. (2016). A medical-toxicological view of tattooing. *The Lancet, 387*(10016), 395-402. https://estpresearch.org/fileadmin/user_upload/ESTP/Publications/A_medical-toxicological_view_of_tattooing_Lancet_Laux_tat_review_2015.pdf

105 Rich, J. (1998). *The nurture assumption: Why children turn out the way they do*. Bloomsbury.

106 *Johnny Depp denies slapping ex-wife for laughing at his tattoo.* (2020). BBC News. www.bbc.com/news/uk-53332148

107 Cocozza, P. (2019). How young is too young to wear makeup? *The Guardian*. www.theguardian.com/fashion/shortcuts/2019/aug/07/makeup-children-john-lewis-mac-beauty-cosmetics-masterclass-cancelled-lipstick

108 TLC. (2011). *Toddlers & Tiaras - Airbrush Makeup for a 1-year-old* [Video]. YouTube. www.youtube.com/watch?v=Tad4IYhdHiQ

109 *Girls as Young as Six Ask to Wear Makeup, Due to Social Media, Bullying and 'Feeling Ugly'.* (2019). Cosmetify. www.cosmetify.com/press/girls-as-young-as-six-ask-to-wear-makeup-due-to-social-media-bullying-and-feeling-ugly/

110 *Beauty is Child's Play: 80% of US Tweens use Beauty and Personal Care Products.* (2016). Mintel Press Office. www.mintel.com/press-centre/beauty-and-personal-care/beauty-is-childs-play-80-of-us-tweens-use-beauty-and-personal-care-products

111 Cash, T. F., Dawson, K., Davis, P., Bowen, M., & Galumbeck, C. (1989). Effects of cosmetics use on the physical attractiveness and body image of American college women. *The Journal of social psychology, 129*(3), 349-355.; Workman, J. E., & Johnson, K. K. (1991). The role of cosmetics in impression formation. *Clothing and Textiles Research Journal, 10*(1), 63-67. https://journals.sagepub.com/doi/abs/10.1177/0887302X9101000109; Guéguen, N., & Jacob, C. (2011). Enhanced female attractiveness with use of cosmetics and male tipping behavior in restaurants. *Journal of Cosmetic Science, 62*(3), 283. https://pdfs.semanticscholar.org/0281/6278ba8e-4c1d69ae9b056057f1206455b709.pdf

112 Mulhern, R., Fieldman, G., Hussey, T., Lévêque, J. L., & Pineau, P. (2003). Do cosmetics enhance female Caucasian facial attractiveness?. *International journal of cosmetic science, 25*(4), 199-205. http://scholar.google.com/scholar_url?url=http%3A%2F%2Fwww.academia.edu%2Fdownload%2F39536441%2FInternational_Journal_of_Cosmetic_Science.doc&hl=en&sa=T&oi=gga&ct=gga&cd=0&d=5902967005924781804&ei=81pOXtGfMIvJsQKjkKHYCg&scisig=AAGBfm0tGUNpkRQQMkhXyBv7Wo0iMf5IWg&nossl=1&ws=1670x-809&at=Do%20cosmetics%20enhance%20female%20Caucasian%20facial%20attractiveness%3F

113 Guéguen, N., & Jacob, C. (2011). Enhanced female attractiveness with use of cosmetics and male tipping behavior in restaurants. *Journal of Cosmetic Science, 62*(3), 283. https://pdfs.semanticscholar.org/0281/6278ba8e-4c1d69ae9b056057f1206455b709.pdf
Citing: Graham, J. A., & Jouhar, A. J. (1981). The effects of cosmetics on person perception. *International journal of cosmetic science, 3*(5), 199-210. https://onlinelibrary.wiley.com/doi/abs/10.1111/j.1467-2494.1981.tb00283.x

114 Etcoff, N. L., Stock, S., Haley, L. E., Vickery, S. A., & House, D. M. (2011). Cosmetics as a feature of the extended human phenotype: Modulation of the perception of biologically important facial signals. *PloS one, 6*(10), e25656. https://journals.plos.org/plosone/article?id=10.1371/journal.pone.0025656

115 Nash, R., Fieldman, G., Hussey, T., Lévêque, J. L., & Pineau, P. (2006). Cosmetics: They influence more than Caucasian female facial attractiveness. *Journal of applied social psychology, 36*(2), 493-504. http://femininebeauty.info/f/makeup.pdf;
Guéguen, N., & Jacob, C. (2011). Enhanced female attractiveness with use of cosmetics and male tipping behavior in restaurants. *Journal of Cosmetic Science, 62*(3), 283. https://pdfs.semanticscholar.org/0281/6278ba8e-4c1d69ae9b056057f1206455b709.pdf

116 Guéguen, N., & Jacob, C. (2011). Enhanced female attractiveness with use of cosmetics and male tipping behavior in restaurants. *Journal of Cosmetic Science, 62*(3), 283. https://pdfs.semanticscholar.org/0281/6278ba8e-4c1d69ae9b056057f1206455b709.pdf

117 Yoo, J. J., & Kim, H. Y. (2010). Use of beauty products among US adolescents: An exploration of media influence. *Journal of Global Fashion Marketing, 1*(3), 172-181. www.tandfonline.com/doi/abs/10.1080/20932685.2010.10593069

118 Environmental Working Group. (2008). *Teen girls' body burden of hormone-altering cosmetics chemicals.* www.ewg.org/research/teen-girls-body-burden-hormone-altering-cosmetics-chemicals/detailed-findings

119 Narayan, P. (2018). *The cosmetics industry has avoided strict regulation for over a century; Now rising health concerns has FDA inquiring.* CNBC. www.cnbc.com/2018/08/01/fda-begins-first-inquiry-of-lightly-regulated-cosmetics-industry.html;
Harley, K. G., Kogut, K., Madrigal, D. S., Cardenas, M., Vera, I. A., Meza-Alfaro, G., ... & Eskenazi, B. (2016). Reducing phthalate, paraben, and phenol exposure from personal care products in adolescent girls: findings from the HERMOSA intervention study. *Environmental health perspectives, 124*(10), 1600-1607. https://ehp.niehs.nih.gov/doi/full/10.1289/ehp.1510514

120 Narayan, P. (2018). *The cosmetics industry has avoided strict regulation for over a century; Now rising health concerns has FDA inquiring.* CNBC. www.cnbc.com/2018/08/01/fda-begins-first-inquiry-of-lightly-regulated-cosmetics-industry.html

121 Kwa, M., Welty, L. J., & Xu, S. (2017). Adverse events reported to the US Food and Drug Administration for cosmetics and personal care products. *JAMA internal medicine, 177*(8), 1202-1204. www.ncbi.nlm.nih.gov/pmc/articles/PMC5818793/

122 Narayan, P. (2018). *The cosmetics industry has avoided strict regulation for over a century; Now rising health concerns has FDA inquiring.* CNBC. www.cnbc.com/2018/08/01/fda-begins-first-inquiry-of-lightly-regulated-cosmetics-industry.html

123 Little, B. (2016). Arsenic Pills and Lead Foundation: The History of Toxic Makeup. *National Geographic*. www.nationalgeographic.com/news/2016/09/ingredients-lipstick-makeup-cosmetics-science-history/

124 *Three selfie-crazy teens crushed by train*. (2019). New Straits Times. www.nst.com.my/world/2019/05/484588/three-selfie-crazy-teens-crushed-train

125 *'Selfie' named by Oxford Dictionaries as word of 2013*. (2013). BBC News. www.bbc.co.uk/news/uk-24992393

126 Katz, J. E., & Crocker, E. T. (2015). Selfies| selfies and photo messaging as visual conversation: Reports from the United States, United Kingdom and China. *International Journal of Communication, 9*, 12. https://ijoc.org/index.php/ijoc/article/viewFile/3180/1405

127 Baron, J. (2019). Does Editing Your Selfies Make You More Likely To Want Plastic Surgery? *Forbes*. www.forbes.com/sites/jessicabaron/2019/06/27/plastic-surgeons-ask-if-selfie-editing-is-related-to-a-desire-for-plastic-surgery/#37060c031e02

128 The American Society for Aesthetic Plastic Surgery. (1997). *ASAPS 1997 Statistics on Cosmetic Surgery*. www.surgery.org/sites/default/files/ASAPS1997Stats_0.pdf;
The American Society for Aesthetic Plastic Surgery. (2002). *2002 Age Distribution for Cosmetic Procedures*. www.surgery.org/sites/default/files/age.pdf;
The American Society for Aesthetic Plastic Surgery. (2007). *Cosmetic Surgery National Data Bank Statistics 2007*. www.surgery.org/sites/default/files/2007stats.pdf;
The American Society for Aesthetic Plastic Surgery. (2012). *Cosmetic Surgery National Data Bank Statistics 2012*. www.surgery.org/sites/default/files/ASAPS-2012-Stats.pdf;
The American Society for Aesthetic Plastic Surgery. (2017). *Cosmetic Surgery National Data Bank Statistics 2017*. https://surgery.org/sites/default/files/ASAPS-Stats2017.pdf

129 Simis, K. J., Hovius, S. E., de Beaufort, I. D., Verhulst, F. C., Koot, H. M., & Adolescence Plastic Surgical Research Group. (2002). After plastic surgery: adolescent-reported appearance ratings and appearance-related burdens in patient and general population groups. *Plastic and reconstructive surgery, 109*(1), 9-17. https://core.ac.uk/download/pdf/15457585.pdf

# 12. Relationships

1 Waters, M. (Director). (2004). *Mean Girls* [Film]. Paramount Pictures. www.imdb.com/title/tt0377092/characters/nm0688132

2 *The World's Strictest Parents* [Video]. BBC. www.bbc.co.uk/programmes/b00nd2f3

3 Robin, A. L., & Foster, S. L. (2002). *Negotiating parent-adolescent conflict: A behavioral-family systems approach*. Guilford Press.

4 Riesch, S. K., Bush, L., Nelson, C. J., Ohm, B. J., Portz, P. A., Abell, B., ... & Jenkins, P. (2000). Topics of conflict between parents and young adolescents. *Journal for specialists in pediatric nursing, 5*(1), 27-40.

5 Riesch, S. K., Bush, L., Nelson, C. J., Ohm, B. J., Portz, P. A., Abell, B., ... & Jenkins, P. (2000). Topics of conflict between parents and young adolescents. *Journal for specialists in pediatric nursing, 5*(1), 27-40.

6 Cusk, R. (2015). Raising Teenagers: The Mother of All Problems. *The New York Times*. www.nytimes.com/2015/03/22/magazine/raising-teenagers-the-mother-of-all-problems.html

7 Committee on Psychosocial Aspects of Child and Family Health. (1998). Guidance for effective discipline. *Pediatrics, 101*(4), 723-728. https://pediatrics.aappublications.org/content/101/4/723

8 Nieman, P., Shea, S., Canadian Paediatric Society, & Community Paediatrics Committee. (2004). Effective discipline for children. *Paediatrics & Child Health, 9*(1), 37-41. www.ncbi.nlm.nih.gov/pmc/articles/PMC2719514/

9 Deroma, V. M., Lassiter, K. S., & Davis, V. A. (2004). Adolescent involvement in discipline decision making. *Behavior modification, 28*(3), 420-437. https://journals.sagepub.com/doi/abs/10.1177/0145445503258993

10 Allen, Joseph. *Escaping the Endless Adolescence: How we can help our teenagers grow up before they grow old*. Random House Publishing Group. Kindle Edition. https://books.google.co.uk/books?hl=en&lr=&id=myEHFTWAmjwC&oi=fnd&pg=PR9&dq=Escaping+the+Endless+Adolescence&ots=8yCPQ5RSm7&sig=Zg52iG-

B3ugS5gz0mW19DUdLsUiA&redir_esc=y#v=onepage&q=Escaping%20the%20Endless%20Adolescence&f=-false

11 Silverberg, S. B., & Steinberg, L. (1987). Adolescent autonomy, parent-adolescent conflict, and parental well-being. *Journal of youth and adolescence, 16*(3), 293-312. https://link.springer.com/article/10.1007/BF02139096

12 Steinberg, L. (2001). We know some things: Parent–adolescent relationships in retrospect and prospect. *Journal of research on adolescence, 11*(1), 1-19. http://ss1.spletnik.si/4_4/000/000/349/967/steinberg-2001.pdf;
McNeely, C. & Blanchard, J. (2009). *The Teen Years Explained: A Guide to Healthy Adolescent Development.* Johns Hopkins Bloomberg School of Public Health. www.jhsph.edu/research/centers-and-institutes/center-for-adolescent-health/_includes/_pre-redesign/Interactive%20Guide.pdf;
Laursen, B. (1993). The perceived impact of conflict on adolescent relationships. *Merrill-Palmer Quarterly* (1982-), 535-550. www.researchgate.net/profile/Brett-Laursen/publication/232523532_The_Perceived_Impact_of_Conflict_on_Adolescent_Relationships/links/00b7d521b4c1abcc2a000000/The-Perceived-Impact-of-Conflict-on-Adolescent-Relationships.pdf

13 *Review of Divergent realities: The emotional lives of mothers, fathers, and adolescents.* (2010). Kirkus. www.kirkusreviews.com/book-reviews/reed-larson/divergent-realities/;
Silverberg, S. B., & Steinberg, L. (1990). Psychological well-being of parents with early adolescent children. *Developmental psychology, 26*(4), 658. https://psycnet.apa.org/record/1990-28113-001

14 Tew, J., & Nixon, J. (2010). Parent abuse: Opening up a discussion of a complex instance of family power relations. *Social Policy and Society, 9*(4), 579-589. http://pure-oai.bham.ac.uk/ws/files/17448657/Tew-S1474746410000291a.pdf

15 Hunter, C., Nixon, J., & Parr, S. (2010). Mother abuse: a matter of youth justice, child welfare or domestic violence?. *Journal of Law and Society, 37*(2), 264-284. https://heinonline.org/HOL/Page?handle=hein.journals/jlsocty37&div=19&g_sent=1&casa_token=KpIfVxDm8l0AAAAA:m_Ik9myjFrEif2doPMWRMH3NUOYlVkmkd8AA9kkGu7qBjPXG4Tn9mUZ3k7lurhMvVol8X1XTSaK0&collection=journals

16 Cottrell, B., & Finlayson, M. (2001). *Parent abuse: The abuse of parents by their teenage children.* Ottawa, Canada: Family Violence Prevention Unit, Health Canada. http://publications.gc.ca/collections/Collection/H72-21-180-2000E.pdf

17 Larson, R. W., Richards, M. H., Moneta, G., Holmbeck, G., & Duckett, E. (1996). Changes in adolescents' daily interactions with their families from ages 10 to 18: Disengagement and transformation. *Developmental Psychology, 32*(4), 744. https://books.google.co.uk/books?hl=en&lr=&id=Do1EAgAAQBAJ&oi=fnd&pg=PA118&ots=4QRent-eSI&sig=hrsHDD1HteVAyXnxfx4wGxa8kdU#v=onepage&q&f=false

18 Larson, R. W., Richards, M. H., Moneta, G., Holmbeck, G., & Duckett, E. (1996). Changes in adolescents' daily interactions with their families from ages 10 to 18: Disengagement and transformation. *Developmental Psychology, 32*(4), 744. https://books.google.co.uk/books?hl=en&lr=&id=Do1EAgAAQBAJ&oi=fnd&pg=PA118&ots=4QRent-eSI&sig=hrsHDD1HteVAyXnxfx4wGxa8kdU#v=onepage&q&f=false

19 Larson, R. W., Richards, M. H., Moneta, G., Holmbeck, G., & Duckett, E. (1996). Changes in adolescents' daily interactions with their families from ages 10 to 18: Disengagement and transformation. *Developmental Psychology, 32*(4), 744. https://books.google.co.uk/books?hl=en&lr=&id=Do1EAgAAQBAJ&oi=fnd&pg=PA118&ots=4QRent-eSI&sig=hrsHDD1HteVAyXnxfx4wGxa8kdU#v=onepage&q&f=false

20 Allen, Joseph. *Escaping the Endless Adolescence: How we can help our teenagers grow up before they grow old.* Random House Publishing Group. Kindle Edition. https://books.google.co.uk/books?hl=en&lr=&id=myEHFTWAmjwC&oi=fnd&pg=PR9&dq=Escaping+the+Endless+Adolescence&ots=8yCPQ5RSm7&sig=Zg52iGB3ugS5gz0mW19DUdLsUiA&redir_esc=y#v=onepage&q=Escaping%20the%20Endless%20Adolescence&f=-false

21 *Talking With Teens: The YMCA Parent and Teen Survey Final Report.* (2000). Global Strategy Group Inc. https://clintonwhitehouse3.archives.gov/WH/EOP/First_Lady/html/teens/survey.html

22 American Psychological Association. (2002). *Developing adolescents: A reference for professionals.* www.apa.org/pi/families/resources/develop.pdf

23 *9 Quotes about What It Means to Be a Parent: Celebrating all types of moms and dads in honor of the Global Day of Parents.* (2015). Goodnet. www.goodnet.org/articles/9-quotes-about-what-means-to-be-parent

24 Brontë, C. (1847). *Jane Eyre.* Smith, Elder and Co.

25 Krakauer, J. (2018). *Into the wild.* Pan Macmillan. Citing Christopher McCandless who is said to have written this phrase in the margin of a book

26 Proust, M. (1957). *Pleasures and days: and other writings.* Doubleday.

27 Lempers, J. D., & Clark-Lempers, D. S. (1992). Young, middle, and late adolescents' comparisons of the functional importance of five significant relationships. *Journal of youth and adolescence, 21*(1), 53-96. https://link.springer.com/content/pdf/10.1007/BF01536983.pdf

28 *21 Things I Wish I Could Tell My Teenage Self.* (n.d.). Mad Love. https://mad-love.com/21-things-i-wish-i-could-tell-my-teenage-self/

29 Rich, J. (1998). The nurture assumption: Why children turn out the way they do. Bloomsbury.

30 LaFontana, K. M., & Cillessen, A. H. (2010). Developmental changes in the priority of perceived status in childhood and adolescence. *Social Development, 19*(1), 130-147. https://digitalcommons.sacredheart.edu/cgi/viewcontent.cgi?article=1023&context=psych_fac

31 Rosenberg, F. R., & Simmons, R. G. (1975). Sex differences in the self-concept in adolescence. *Sex roles, 1*(2), 147-159. https://link.springer.com/article/10.1007%252FBF00288008

32 Parkhurst, J. T., & Hopmeyer, A. (1998). Sociometric popularity and peer-perceived popularity: Two distinct dimensions of peer status. *The Journal of Early Adolescence, 18*(2), 125-144. https://journals.sagepub.com/doi/abs/10.1177/0272431698018002001

33 Gavin, L. A., & Furman, W. (1989). Age differences in adolescents' perceptions of their peer groups. *Developmental Psychology, 25*(5), 827. www.du.edu/ahss/psychology/relationship-center/media/documents/publications/gavin-fuhrman-1989.pdf

34 Prinstein, M. J., & Cillessen, A. H. (2003). Forms and functions of adolescent peer aggression associated with high levels of peer status. *Merrill-Palmer Quarterly* (1982-), 310-342. http://mitch.web.unc.edu/files/2013/10/Prinstein-Cillessen-2003-MPQ.pdf

35 Eder, D. (1985). The cycle of popularity: Interpersonal relations among female adolescents. *Sociology of education,* 154-165. www.researchgate.net/profile/Donna_Eder/publication/247823949_The_Cycle_of_Popularity_Interpersonal_Relations_Among_Female_Adolescents/links/567afb7008ae1e63f1df7f60.pdf

36 Mayeux, L., Sandstrom, M. J., & Cillessen, A. H. (2008). Is being popular a risky proposition?. *Journal of research on adolescence, 18*(1), 49-74. https://onlinelibrary.wiley.com/doi/abs/10.1111/j.1532-7795.2008.00550.x

37 Gavin, L. A., & Furman, W. (1989). Age differences in adolescents' perceptions of their peer groups. *Developmental Psychology, 25*(5), 827. www.du.edu/ahss/psychology/relationship-center/media/documents/publications/gavin-fuhrman-1989.pdf

38 Brown, B. B., Von Bank, H., & Steinberg, L. (2008). Smoke in the looking glass: Effects of discordance between self-and peer rated crowd affiliation on adolescent anxiety, depression and self-feelings. *Journal of Youth and Adolescence, 37*(10), 1163-1177. https://prsg.education.wisc.edu/wp-content/uploads/2014/07/brown-et-al-08-Smoke-in-looking-glass.pdf

39 Bowker, J. C. (2011). Examining two types of best friendship dissolution during early adolescence. *The Journal of Early Adolescence, 31*(5), 656-670. www.researchgate.net/profile/Julie-Bowker/publication/230887284_Examining_Two_Types_of_Best_Friendship_Dissolution_During_Early_Adolescence/links/0c96052b6043ee35b6000000/Examining-Two-Types-of-Best-Friendship-Dissolution-During-Early-Adolescence.pdf

40 Bowker, A. (2004). Predicting friendship stability during early adolescence. *The Journal of Early Adolescence, 24*(2), 85-112. https://citeseerx.ist.psu.edu/viewdoc/download?doi=10.1.1.828.2049&rep=rep1&type=pdf; Chan, A., & Poulin, F. (2007). Monthly changes in the composition of friendship networks in early adolescence. *Merrill-Palmer Quarterly* (1982-), 578-602.www.researchgate.net/profile/Francois-Poulin/publication/224975832_Monthly_Changes_in_the_Composition_of_Friendship_Networks_in_Early_Adolescence/links/0deec53206177a2aac000000/Monthly-Changes-in-the-Composition-of-Friendship-Networks-in-Early-Adolescence.pdf

41 Hartl, A. C., Laursen, B., & Cillessen, A. H. (2015). A survival analysis of adolescent friendships: The downside of dissimilarity. *Psychological Science, 26*(8), 1304-1315. www.ncbi.nlm.nih.gov/pmc/articles/PMC4529362/

42 Hardy, C. L., Bukowski, W. M., & Sippola, L. K. (2002). Stability and change in peer relationships during the transition to middle-level school. *The Journal of Early Adolescence, 22*(2), 117-142. http://citeseerx.ist.psu.edu/viewdoc/download?doi=10.1.1.1019.2746&rep=rep1&type=pdf

43 Değirmencioğlu, S. M., Urberg, K. A., Tolson, J. M., & Richard, P. (1998). Adolescent friendship networks: Continuity and change over the school year. *Merrill-Palmer Quarterly* (1982-), 313-337. www.researchgate.net/profile/Serdar-Degirmencioglu/publication/279894180_Adolescent_friendship_networks_Continuity_and_change_over_the_school_year/links/57f0286308ae280dd0aea7b0/Adolescent-friendship-networks-Continuity-and-change-over-the-school-year.pdf

44 Rich, J. (1998). *The nurture assumption: Why children turn out the way they do.* Bloomsbury. Hollingworth, L. S. (1942). *Children above 180 IQ Stanford-Binet; origin and development.* World Book. https://psycnet.apa.org/record/1942-03833-000;
Terman, L. M. (1947). *Genetic Studies of Genius, 4 vols.* Vol. I, Mental and physical traits of one thousand gifted children, 1925; Vol. II, The early mental traits of three hundred geniuses, 1926; Vol. III, The promise of youth, 1930; Vol. IV, The gifted child grows up, 1947.

45 Reijntjes, A., Stegge, H., Terwogt, M. M., Kamphuis, J. H., & Telch, M. J. (2006). Emotion regulation and its effects on mood improvement in response to an in vivo peer rejection challenge. *Emotion, 6*(4), 543. https://pdfs.semanticscholar.org/c0b8/40db0a6c4c847b4ec1c3bb7f7e7d8594331c.pdf;
Abrams, D., Weick, M., Thomas, D., Colbe, H., & Franklin, K. M. (2011). On-line ostracism affects children differently from adolescents and adults. *British Journal of Developmental Psychology, 29*(1), 110-123. https://kar.kent.ac.uk/27493/1/Abrams_et_al_Cyberostracism_BJDP_2011_Manuscript.pdf;
Sebastian, C., Viding, E., Williams, K. D., & Blakemore, S. J. (2010). Social brain development and the affective consequences of ostracism in adolescence. *Brain and cognition, 72*(1), 134-145. https://pdfs.semanticscholar.org/4fab/82c0e8a03e7a1b61660c4f7c95ec9584046c.pdf

46 Salvy, S. J., Bowker, J. C., Nitecki, L. A., Kluczynski, M. A., Germeroth, L. J., & Roemmich, J. N. (2011). Impact of simulated ostracism on overweight and normal-weight youths' motivation to eat and food intake. *Appetite, 56*(1), 39-45. www.ncbi.nlm.nih.gov/pmc/articles/PMC3030642/

47 Williams, K. D. (2002). *Ostracism: The power of silence.* Guilford Press. https://books.google.co.uk/books?hl=en&lr=&id=M0flM4dgpDUC&oi=fnd&pg=PA1&dq=Ostracism:+The+power+of+silence&ots=NRG-FuUiPDs&sig=TKwnJ714FCTfKenDBNeNuE7Y1v0&redir_esc=y#v=onepage&q=Ostracism%3A%20The%20power%20of%20silence&f=false

48 Timeo, S., Riva, P., & Paladino, M. P. (2019). Learning to cope with everyday instances of social exclusion: A review of emotional and cognitive strategies for children and adolescents. *Journal of Applied Biobehavioral Research, 24*(4), e12173. www.researchgate.net/profile/Paolo_Riva2/publication/336259105_Learning_to_cope_with_everyday_instances_of_social_exclusion_A_review_of_emotional_and_cognitive_strategies_for_children_and_adolescents/links/5ddbfd0f458515dc2f4daf99/Learning-to-cope-with-everyday-instances-of-social-exclusion-A-review-of-emotional-and-cognitive-strategies-for-children-and-adolescents.pdf

49 Barber, B.L., Stone, M.R., & Eccles, J.S. (1999). *Peer crowd-based identities and adjustment: Pathways of jocks, princesses, brains, basket-cases, and criminals.* http://education-webfiles.s3-website-us-west-2.amazonaws.com/arp/garp/articles/eccles99v.pdf

50 Heckerling, A. (1995). *Clueless* [Film]. Paramount Pictures.

51 Carver, K., Joyner, K., & Udry, J. R. (2003). National estimates of adolescent romantic relationships. In *Adolescent romantic relations and sexual behavior* (pp. 37-70). Psychology Press. https://books.google.co.uk/books?hl=en&lr=&id=QX6g7LMOLhIC&oi=fnd&pg=PT8&dq=Adolescent+Romantic+Relationships+and+-Sexual+Behavior:+Theory,+Research,+and+Practical+Implications&ots=44egCCqHzP&sig=E8jb4Bnmtlh_8CD-M8M8HQshq8xA&redir_esc=y#v=onepage&q=national%20estimates&f=false

52 O'Sullivan, L. F., & Meyer-Bahlburg, H. F. (2003). African-American and Latina inner-city girls' reports of romantic and sexual development. *Journal of Social and Personal Relationships, 20*(2), 221-238. http://citeseerx.ist.psu.edu/viewdoc/download?doi=10.1.1.903.9120&rep=rep1&type=pdf

53 Thomas, R. J., & Hausen, S. (2019). *Disintermediating your friends: How Online Dating in the United States displaces other ways of meeting.* https://web.stanford.edu/~mrosenfe/Rosenfeld_et_al_Disintermediating_Friends.pdf

54 This is the age you're most likely to meet 'The One'. (2016). *Marie Claire.* www.marieclaire.co.uk/news/the-age-you-are-most-likely-to-meet-the-one-plus-statistics-for-relationship-milestones-20898

55 Magnusson, D., & Stattin, H. (2018). *Pubertal maturation in female development.* Routledge. https://books.google.co.uk/books?hl=en&lr=&id=sHp0DwAAQBAJ&oi=fnd&pg=PT6&dq=Pubertal+maturation+in+female+de-

velopment.&ots=25aFBU5LKP&sig=_n70sIGnAOcq2R8Ef42cSr098Gk&redir_esc=y#v=onepage&q=Pubertal%20maturation%20in%20female%20development.&f=false

56 Barber, B., & Eccles, J. (2003). The joy of romance: Healthy adolescent relationships as an educational agenda. *Adolescent romantic relations and sexual behavior: Theory, research, and practical implications*, 355-370. www.researchgate.net/publication/233895997_The_Joy_of_Romance_Healthy_Adolescent_Relationships_as_an_Educational_Agenda

57 Collins, W. A., Welsh, D. P., & Furman, W. (2009). Adolescent romantic relationships. *Annual review of psychology, 60*, 631-652. www.researchgate.net/profile/Deborah_Welsh/publication/23499643_Adolescent_Romantic_Relationships/links/00b49526fd73b237cb000000.pdf

58 Rodgers, J. L. (1996). *Sexual transitions in adolescence.* https://books.google.co.uk/books?hl=en&lr=&id=Ind0DwAAQBAJ&oi=fnd&pg=PT6&dq=ransitions+through+adolescence:+Interpersonal+domains+and+context&ots=5JAmSIsgex&sig=q73AosgVO7KkMsVBwlh0OYui6oc&redir_esc=y#v=onepage&q=modal%20reason&f=false

59 Rodgers, J. L. (1996). *Sexual transitions in adolescence.* https://books.google.co.uk/books?hl=en&lr=&id=Ind0DwAAQBAJ&oi=fnd&pg=PT6&dq=ransitions+through+adolescence:+Interpersonal+domains+and+context&ots=5JAmSIsgex&sig=q73AosgVO7KkMsVBwlh0OYui6oc&redir_esc=y#v=onepage&q=modal%20reason&f=false

60 Smiler, A. P. (2008). "I wanted to get to know her better": Adolescent boys' dating motives, masculinity ideology, and sexual behavior. *Journal of adolescence, 31*(1), 17-32. https://d1wqtxts1xzle7.cloudfront.net/31268283/smiler_2008.pdf?1368779686=&response-content-disposition=inline%3B+filename%3DI_wanted_to_get_to_know_her_better_Adol.pdf&Expires=1603213548&Signature=bxCzmbNB9TTC6Rpg3Yfoo-cjt8pY3NRdPUqZoXtyqZVcJGdZLZ3j7O1fnQTWuoGb98Y~RwRh7RG2fcZf0qsbL4UT1rOMpE0kvhvvwPsNz~u6on1vhWZMvrwmTRIaEkL1OwXa6fQfMJno758miHqWE2UsN0tBfexgG1NcihJQthu7xF-kR8~6rtEwvwpGmotnoC0cp3mePkk3ehxp-SIFNV8wovSXjDcc~Ng65uTQtCihY0~Gq0SS-1Wrmld8wXRdE7NcUDcoswrP8aejqmUjLlp6nwAIf1QjxcquNK2pnBXIBXbnMXZc72fMqP2N~BBH-C4AUNqaI6hKmyhbJa6v6uCQ__&Key-Pair-Id=APKAJLOHF5GGSLRBV4ZA

61 Parker-Pope, T. (2008). Peeking Inside the Mind of the Boy Dating Your Daughter. *The New York Times.* www.nytimes.com/2008/02/24/weekinreview/24parker.html

62 Monroe, S. M., Rohde, P., Seeley, J. R., & Lewinsohn, P. M. (1999). Life events and depression in adolescence: Relationship loss as a prospective risk factor for first onset of major depressive disorder. *Journal of abnormal psychology, 108*(4), 606. www.researchgate.net/profile/Paul_Rohde/publication/51355648_Life_events_and_depression_in_adolescence_Relationship_loss_as_a_prospective_risk_factor_for_first_onset_of_major_depressive_disorder/links/545aa0bb0cf2c46f664385a5.pdf;
Joyner, K., & Udry, J. R. (2000). You don't bring me anything but down: Adolescent romance and depression. *Journal of Health and Social Behavior*, 369-391. www.jstor.org/stable/2676292?seq=1

63 Luciano, E. C., & Orth, U. (2017). Transitions in romantic relationships and development of self-esteem. *Journal of personality and Social Psychology, 112*(2), 307. https://boris.unibe.ch/95490/7/Luciano%20and%20Orth%202017%20JPSP.pdf

64 Langeslag, S. J., & Sanchez, M. E. (2018). Down-regulation of love feelings after a romantic break-up: Self-report and electrophysiological data. *Journal of experimental psychology: general, 147*(5), 720. https://psycnet.apa.org/doiLanding?doi=10.1037%2Fxge0000360

65 Wood, E., Senn, C. Y., Desmarais, S., Park, L., & Verberg, N. (2002). Sources of information about dating and their perceived influence on adolescents. *Journal of adolescent research, 17*(4), 401-417. https://d1wqtxts1xzle7.cloudfront.net/43313664/2002_-_Eileen_Wood_-_SourcesofInformationaboutDatingandTheirPerceivedIn_retrieved-2016-03-03_.pdf?1457017040=&response-content-disposition=inline%3B+filename%3DSources_of_Information_about_Dating_and.pdf&Expires=1603124467&Signature=TQvp-6WXat17v4242ltkXuFsCx7ejQxxmUYEfOV12nLIHm7jDMomGBh6vNYMRYu-U8PD6MVGxFHR4izOy-mX2wiLt-Uet1jv2xv5u5T4fXlY2yly6Z--i59oVFHCjtQoVtV8dDwLy5XGSlsq0iYE5z4a8ypsjS4kgO4u-VSh6Qvs4cSmPYmO7GWj5RT2hTBcmDk889bg2kTLt0MYF057FwN82cBZrAfHQLgNoI~tEawYD-1kNnkn7yH4kxFQBntU23QZ5rqEL3K04jkIa3zHsYppsyeyWjR17iu2DAlWmTQiHTLQkYhSlEweKI-KE8IKXs0p2gBsG6nhEuYYsZoyM9bwOkQ__&Key-Pair-Id=APKAJLOHF5GGSLRBV4ZA

66 Weissbourd, R., Anderson, T. R., Cashin, A., & McIntyre, J. (2017). The talk: How adults can promote young people's healthy relationships and prevent misogyny and sexual harassment. *Harvard Graduate School of Education, 16*(8), 1-46. https://static1.squarespace.com/static/5b7c56e255b02c683659fe43/t/5bd51a0324a69425bd079b59/1540692500558/mcc_the_talk_final.pdf

67 Ramadurai, Ch. (2020). *Indian Matchmaking: The reality show that's divided viewers.* BBC Culture. www.bbc.com/culture/article/20200806-indian-matchmaking-the-reality-show-that-s-divided-viewers

68 Cleopatra summary. (n.d.). *Britannica.com.* www.britannica.com/summary/Cleopatra-queen-of-Egypt

69 de Diez Canseco, M. R., & Murra, J. V. (1960). Succession, Coöption to Kingship, and Royal Incest among the Inca. *Southwestern Journal of Anthropology, 16*(4), 417-427. www.journals.uchicago.edu/doi/abs/10.1086/soutjanth.16.4.3628886?journalCode=soutjanth

70 Lippe-McGraw, J. (2020). 12 Famous Sibling Rivalries Throughout History. *Reader's Digest.* www.rd.com/list/famous-sibling-rivalries/

71 Raffaelli, M. (1992). Sibling conflict in early adolescence. *Journal of Marriage and the Family,* 652-663. https://digitalcommons.unl.edu/cgi/viewcontent.cgi?article=1129&context=psychfacpub

72 Tucker, C. J., & Finkelhor, D. (2017). The state of interventions for sibling conflict and aggression: A systematic review. *Trauma, Violence, & Abuse, 18*(4), 396-406. www.researchgate.net/profile/Corinna-Tucker/publication/287326582_The_State_of_Interventions_for_Sibling_Conflict_and_Aggression_A_Systematic_Review/links/569e2ff608aed27a70326f28/The-State-of-Interventions-for-Sibling-Conflict-and-Aggression-A-Systematic-Review.pdf

73 Raffaelli, M. (1992). Sibling conflict in early adolescence. *Journal of Marriage and the Family,* 652-663. https://digitalcommons.unl.edu/cgi/viewcontent.cgi?article=1129&context=psychfacpub

74 Feinberg, M. E., Sakuma, K. L., Hostetler, M., & McHale, S. M. (2013). Enhancing sibling relationships to prevent adolescent problem behaviors: Theory, design and feasibility of Siblings Are Special. *Evaluation and Program Planning, 36*(1), 97-106. www.ncbi.nlm.nih.gov/pmc/articles/PMC3513510/

75 Perlman, M., & Ross, H. S. (1997). The benefits of parent intervention in children's disputes: An examination of concurrent changes in children's fighting styles. *Child development,* 690-700. www.jstor.org/stable/1132119?seq=1

76 Bennett, J. C. (1990). Nonintervention into siblings' fighting as a catalyst for learned helplessness. *Psychological Reports, 66*(1), 139-145. https://journals.sagepub.com/doi/abs/10.2466/pr0.1990.66.1.139

77 Laursen, B., & Collins, W. A. (1994). Interpersonal conflict during adolescence. *Psychological bulletin, 115*(2), 197. www.researchgate.net/profile/Brett-Laursen/publication/15034527_Interpersonal_Conflict_During_Adolescence/links/00b495192421476f80000000/Interpersonal-Conflict-During-Adolescence.pdf;
Tucker, C. J., & Finkelhor, D. (2017). The state of interventions for sibling conflict and aggression: A systematic review. *Trauma, Violence, & Abuse, 18*(4), 396-406. www.researchgate.net/profile/Corinna-Tucker/publication/287326582_The_State_of_Interventions_for_Sibling_Conflict_and_Aggression_A_Systematic_Review/links/569e2ff608aed27a70326f28/The-State-of-Interventions-for-Sibling-Conflict-and-Aggression-A-Systematic-Review.pdf

78 Feinberg, M. E., Sakuma, K. L., Hostetler, M., & McHale, S. M. (2013). Enhancing sibling relationships to prevent adolescent problem behaviors: Theory, design and feasibility of Siblings Are Special. *Evaluation and Program Planning, 36*(1), 97-106. www.ncbi.nlm.nih.gov/pmc/articles/PMC3513510/;
Feinberg, M. E., Solmeyer, A. R., Hostetler, M. L., Sakuma, K. L., Jones, D., & McHale, S. M. (2013). Siblings are special: Initial test of a new approach for preventing youth behavior problems. *Journal of Adolescent Health, 53*(2), 166-173. www.jahonline.org/article/S1054-139X(12)00402-8/fulltext

79 Smith, J., & Ross, H. (2007). Training parents to mediate sibling disputes affects children's negotiation and conflict understanding. *Child development, 78*(3), 790-805. https://srcd.onlinelibrary.wiley.com/doi/abs/10.1111/j.1467-8624.2007.01033.x;
Siddiqui, A., & Ross, H. (2004). Mediation as a method of parent intervention in children's disputes. *Journal of Family Psychology, 18*(1), 147. https://psycnet.apa.org/record/2004-11293-013;
Kennedy, D. E., & Kramer, L. (2008). Improving emotion regulation and sibling relationship quality: The more fun with sisters and brothers program. *Family Relations, 57*(5), 567-578. www.researchgate.net/profile/Denise-Kennedy-2/publication/230074230_Improving_Emotion_Regulation_and_Sibling_Relationship_Quality_The_More_Fun_With_Sisters_and_Brothers_Program/links/5b5e3f47a6fdccf0b200653f/Improving-Emotion-Regulation-and-Sibling-Relationship-Quality-The-More-Fun-With-Sisters-and-Brothers-Program.pdf;
Perlman, M., & Ross, H. S. (1997). The benefits of parent intervention in children's disputes: An examination of concurrent changes in children's fighting styles. *Child development,* 690-700. www.jstor.org/stable/1132119?seq=1

80 Kennedy, D. E., & Kramer, L. (2008). Improving emotion regulation and sibling relationship quality: The more fun with sisters and brothers program. *Family Relations, 57*(5), 567-578. www.researchgate.net/profile/Denise-Kennedy-2/publication/230074230_Improving_Emotion_Regulation_and_Sibling_Relationship_Quality_The_More_Fun_With_Sisters_and_Brothers_Program/links/5b5e3f47a6fdccf0b200653f/Improving-Emotion-Regulation-and-Sibling-Relationship-Quality-The-More-Fun-With-Sisters-and-Brothers-Program.pdf

81 Kramer, L. (2010). The essential ingredients of successful sibling relationships: An emerging framework for advancing theory and practice. *Child Development Perspectives, 4*(2), 80-86. https://srcd.onlinelibrary.wiley.com/doi/abs/10.1111/j.1750-8606.2010.00122.x

82 Johnson, D. W., & Johnson, R. T. (2001). *Teaching students to be peacemakers: A meta-analysis.* https://files.eric.ed.gov/fulltext/ED460178.pdf

83 Buhrmester, D., & Furman, W. (1990). Perceptions of sibling relationships during middle childhood and adolescence. *Child development, 61*(5), 1387-1398. https://citeseerx.ist.psu.edu/viewdoc/download?doi=10.1.1.951.3039&rep=rep1&type=pdf;
Furman, W., & Buhrmester, D. (1992). Age and sex differences in perceptions of networks of personal relationships. *Child development, 63*(1), 103-115. www.sadieandco.com/ahss/psychology/relationship-center/media/documents/publications/burhmester-fuhrman-1992.pdf

84 Scharf, M., Shulman, S., & Avigad-Spitz, L. (2005). Sibling relationships in emerging adulthood and in adolescence. *Journal of Adolescent Research, 20*(1), 64-90. https://journals.sagepub.com/doi/pdf/10.1177/0743558404271133

85 Eckel, S. (2019). *Why Do Adult Siblings Stop Speaking? The Psychology Behind Family Estrangement and Sibling Rivalries.* Reader's Digest. www.rd.com/article/adult-sibling-estrangement/

86 Diener, E., & Oishi, S. (2005). The nonobvious social psychology of happiness. *Psychological Inquiry, 16*(4), 162-167. www.researchgate.net/profile/Shigehiro_Oishi/publication/233103138_The_Nonobvious_Social_Psychology_of_Happiness/links/5727a6d308aee491cb414aab/The-Nonobvious-Social-Psychology-of-Happiness.pdf

87 *Gwyneth Paltrow stunned by derision over her 'conscious uncoupling' announcement.* (2020). Reuters. www.reuters.com/article/us-people-gwyneth-paltrow/gwyneth-paltrow-stunned-by-derision-over-her-conscious-uncoupling-announcement-idUSKCN252346

88 *Gwyneth Paltrow stunned by derision over her 'conscious uncoupling' announcement.* (2020). Reuters. www.reuters.com/article/us-people-gwyneth-paltrow/gwyneth-paltrow-stunned-by-derision-over-her-conscious-uncoupling-announcement-idUSKCN252346

89 *Marriage & divorce.* (n.d.). American Psychological Association. www.apa.org/topics/divorce-child-custody#:~:text=They%20are%20also%20good%20for,subsequent%20marriages%20is%20even%20higher;
Pelley, V. (2021). What Is the Divorce Rate in America? Fatherly. www.fatherly.com/love-money/what-is-divorce-rate-america/

90 Emery, R. E., Sbarra, D., & Grover, T. (2005). Divorce mediation: Research and reflections. *Family Court Review, 43*(1), 22-37. https://heinonline.org/HOL/Page?handle=hein.journals/fmlcr43&div=7&g_sent=1&casa_token=LYjDxOJCNhMAAAAA:BPko_WadarwNu2casZkoXl3rFBwOYKnN0faxg6MLVGnxOWd-1uNFDZudKQK-6D8HWW58uCS3C1Kzs&collection=journals;
Kelly, J. B., & Emery, R. E. (2003). Children's adjustment following divorce: Risk and resilience perspectives. Family Relations, 52(4), 352-362. https://thefamilysite.info/demo/files/2011/08/Children%E2%80%99s-Adjustment-Following-Divorce-Risk-and-Resilience-Perspectives.pdf

91 Amato, P. R. (2014). The consequences of divorce for adults and children: An update. *Društvena istraživanja: časopis za opća društvena pitanja, 23*(1), 5-24. http://scholar.google.com/scholar_url?url=https%3A%2F%2Fhrcak.srce.hr%2Ffile%2F180281&hl=en&sa=T&oi=gga&ct=gga&cd=1&d=11466852713798013366&ei=-fu2uXY2VO8HRsQLT4ZSIBQ&scisig=AAGBfm1VgPQRGuWmeSwBXq8P3OsOzJ39Fw&nossl=1&ws=1813x868&at=The%20consequences%20of%20divorce%20for%20adults%20and%20children%3A%20An%20update&bn=1

92 Pollet, S. L., & Lombreglia, M. (2008). A nationwide survey of mandatory parent education. *Family Court Review, 46*(2), 375-394. https://heinonline.org/HOL/Page?collection=journals&handle=hein.journals/fmlcr46&id=380&men_tab=srchresults

93 Erickson, S., & Ver Steegh, N. (2001). *Mandatory divorce education classes: What do the parents say.* Wm. Mitchell L. Rev., 28, 889. https://open.mitchellhamline.edu/cgi/viewcontent.cgi?referer=https://scholar.google.com/&httpsredir=1&article=1658&context=wmlr;
Thoennes, N., & Pearson, J. (1999). Parent education in the domestic relations court: A multisite assessment. *Family Court Review, 37*(2), 195-218. https://heinonline.org/HOL/Page?handle=hein.journals/fmlcr37&div=16&g_sent=1&casa_token=FdKXtbZc7zgAAAAA:2cRjQigywtXUV9Ls-aljNrt6gzOCy1wnuY2vwW3ky0x-x9bklyXTEIdHfAzJvHAeX32x-EhjnDCS

94 Zimmerman, D. K., Brown, J. H., & Portes, P. R. (2004). Assessing custodial mother adjustment to divorce: The role of divorce education and family functioning. *Journal of Divorce & Remarriage, 41*(1-2), 1-24. www.tandfonline.com/doi/abs/10.1300/J087v41n01_01;
Criddle Jr, M. N., Allgood, S. M., & Piercy, K. W. (2003). The relationship between mandatory divorce education and level of post-divorce parental conflict. *Journal of Divorce & Remarriage, 39*(3-4), 99-111. www.tandfonline.com/doi/abs/10.1300/J087v39n03_05

95 Amato, P. R. (2014). The consequences of divorce for adults and children: An update. *Društvena istraživanja: časopis za opća društvena pitanja, 23*(1), 5-24. http://scholar.google.com/scholar_url?url=https%3A%2F%2Fhrcak.srce.hr%2Ffile%2F180281&hl=en&sa=T&oi=gga&ct=gga&cd=1&d=11466852713798013366&ei=-fu2uXY2VO8HRsQLT4ZSIBQ&scisig=AAGBfm1VgPQRGuWmeSwBXq8P3OsOzJ39Fw&nossl=1&ws=1813x868&at=The%20consequences%20of%20divorce%20for%20adults%20and%20children%3A%20An%20update&bn=1

96 Kelly, J. B., & Emery, R. E. (2003). Children's adjustment following divorce: Risk and resilience perspectives. *Family Relations, 52*(4), 352-362. https://thefamilysite.info/demo/files/2011/08/Children%E2%80%99s-Adjustment-Following-Divorce-Risk-and-Resilience-Perspectives.pdf

97 Amato, P. R. (2014). The consequences of divorce for adults and children: An update. *Društvena istraživanja: časopis za opća društvena pitanja, 23*(1), 5-24. http://scholar.google.com/scholar_url?url=https%3A%2F%2Fhrcak.srce.hr%2Ffile%2F180281&hl=en&sa=T&oi=gga&ct=gga&cd=1&d=11466852713798013366&ei=-fu2uXY2VO8HRsQLT4ZSIBQ&scisig=AAGBfm1VgPQRGuWmeSwBXq8P3OsOzJ39Fw&nossl=1&ws=1813x868&at=The%20consequences%20of%20divorce%20for%20adults%20and%20children%3A%20An%20update&bn=1

98 Petrie, J., Bunn, F., & Byrne, G. (2006). Parenting programmes for preventing tobacco, alcohol or drugs misuse in children <18: a systematic review. *Health education research, 22*(2), 177-191. https://academic.oup.com/her/article/22/2/177/622709;
*Focus on Kids*. (n.d.). Extension University of Missouri. https://extension.missouri.edu/programs/focus-on-kids

99 Pedro-Carroll, J. L. (2005). Fostering resilience in the aftermath of divorce: The role of evidence-based programs for children. *Family Court Review, 43*(1), 52-64. https://webtest.childrensinstitute.net/sites/default/files/documents/children-resilience-family-court-review.pdf

100 Amato, P. R. (2014). The consequences of divorce for adults and children: An update. *Društvena istraživanja: časopis za opća društvena pitanja, 23*(1), 5-24. http://scholar.google.com/scholar_url?url=https%3A%2F%2Fhrcak.srce.hr%2Ffile%2F180281&hl=en&sa=T&oi=gga&ct=gga&cd=1&d=11466852713798013366&ei=-fu2uXY2VO8HRsQLT4ZSIBQ&scisig=AAGBfm1VgPQRGuWmeSwBXq8P3OsOzJ39Fw&nossl=1&ws=1813x868&at=The%20consequences%20of%20divorce%20for%20adults%20and%20children%3A%20An%20update&bn=1

101 Rowen, J., & Emery, R. (2018). Parental denigration: A form of conflict that typically backfires. *Family Court Review, 56*(2), 258-268. https://indigo.uic.edu/articles/journal_contribution/Parental_Denigration_A_Form_of_Conflict_that_Typically_Backfire/10766771/files/19279211.pdf

102 Fabricius, W. V., & Hall, J. A. (2000). Young Adults' Perspectives on Divorce Living Arrangements. *Family Court Review, 38*(4), 446-461. https://heinonline.org/hol-cgi-bin/get_pdf.cgi?handle=hein.journals/fmlcr38&section=38&casa_token=GGYIW9NyqlsAAAAA:8fAjrs5VWsifpSbz_i_iYPTv_w0z5xMdagYguH1C6jjBPRmF-34w6EgZZ5Kk_OxcyMs3c__vwBrNP

103 Sadeghi, H. & Sami, S. (n.d.). *Conscious Uncoupling*. Goop. https://goop.com/wellness/relationships/conscious-uncoupling-2/

104 *Gwyneth Paltrow stunned by derision over her 'conscious uncoupling' announcement*. (2020). Reuters. www.reuters.com/article/us-people-gwyneth-paltrow/gwyneth-paltrow-stunned-by-derision-over-her-conscious-uncoupling-announcement-idUSKCN252346

## *Final thoughts*

1 Scherfig, L. (Director). (2009). *An Education* [Film]. BBC Films.

2 Robledo, S. J. (2009). *An Education Movie review*. Common Sense Media. www.commonsensemedia.org/movie-reviews/an-education

3 Ortved, T. (2022). That Cloud of Smoke Is Not a Mirage. *The New York Times*. www.nytimes.com/2022/01/12/style/smoking-cigarettes-comeback.html

4 Senior, J. (2013). Why You Truly Never Leave High School. *New York Magazine*. https://nymag.com/news/features/high-school-2013-1/;
Janssen, S. M., Murre, J. M., & Meeter, M. (2008). Reminiscence bump in memory for public events. *European Journal of Cognitive Psychology, 20*(4), 738-764. https://research.vu.nl/ws/portalfiles/portal/2340857/Janssen++European+Journal+of+Cognitive+Psychology+20%284%29+2008+u.pdf;
Rubin, D. C., & Schulkind, M. D. (1997). The distribution of autobiographical memories across the lifespan. *Memory & cognition, 25*(6), 859-866. https://link.springer.com/content/pdf/10.3758/BF03211330.pdf

5 Conway, M. A., Wang, Q., Hanyu, K., & Haque, S. (2005). A cross-cultural investigation of autobiographical memory: On the universality and cultural variation of the reminiscence bump. *Journal of Cross-Cultural Psychology, 36*(6), 739-749. https://journals.sagepub.com/doi/abs/10.1177/0022022105280512;
Janssen, S. M., & Murre, J. M. (2008). Reminiscence bump in autobiographical memory: Unexplained by novelty, emotionality, valence, or importance of personal events. *The Quarterly Journal of Experimental Psychology, 61*(12), 1847-1860. www.researchgate.net/profile/Steve_Janssen/publication/23495035_Reminiscence_bump_in_autobiographical_memory_Unexplained_by_novelty_emotionality_valence_or_importance_of_personal_events/links/548118a40cf263ee1adfae94.pdf;
Murre, J. M., Janssen, S. M., Rouw, R., & Meeter, M. (2013). The rise and fall of immediate and delayed memory for verbal and visuospatial information from late childhood to late adulthood. *Acta psychologica, 142*(1), 96-107. www.ikleeranders.nl/wp-content/uploads/2016/06/Wetenschappelijk-onderzoek.pdf

6 Johnson, K. M. (2017). *If I Could Give My Teenage Self Some Advice, I Would Tell Her This*. Odyssey. www.theodysseyonline.com/advice-should-have-given-myself

7 Jones, K. (2014). *8 Things I Wish I Could Tell My Teenage Self*. Kristen Jones. www.kristinjones.co/8-things-i-wish-i-could-tell-my-teenage-self/

8 McCallum, L. (2016). *30 Adults Confess The Biggest Regrets Of Their Teenage Years*. Tickld. www.tickld.com/wow/2164270/fbkda30-adults-confess-the-biggest-regrets-of-their-teenage-years/

9 McLanahan, S., & Adams, J. (1987). Parenthood and psychological well-being. *Annual review of sociology, 13*(1), 237-257. www.annualreviews.org/doi/abs/10.1146/annurev.so.13.080187.001321

10 Rich, J. (1998). The nurture assumption: Why children turn out the way they do. Bloomsbury.

11 Thornton, A., Orbuch, T. L., & Axinn, W. G. (1995). Parent-child relationships during the transition to adulthood. *Journal of Family issues, 16*(5), 538-564. https://deepblue.lib.umich.edu/bitstream/handle/2027.42/67343/10.1177_019251395016005003.pdf?sequence=2

12 Becker, C., Kirchmaier, I., & Trautmann, S. T. (2019). Marriage, parenthood and social network: Subjective well-being and mental health in old age. *PloS one, 14*(7), e0218704. https://journals.plos.org/plosone/article?id=10.1371/journal.pone.0218704;
Wolfinger, N. H. (2018). *Does Having Children Make People Happier in the Long Run?* Institute for Family Studies. https://ifstudies.org/blog/does-having-children-make-people-happier-in-the-long-run

13 White, L., & Edwards, J. N. (1990). Emptying the nest and parental well-being: An analysis of national panel data. *American sociological review*, 235-242. www.jstor.org/stable/2095629?seq=1;
Footnote reference: [1] Mazzuco, S. (2006). The impact of children leaving home on the parents' wellbeing: A comparative analysis of France and Italy. *Genus*, 35-52. www.jstor.org/stable/29789324?seq=1

14 Pollmann-Schult, M. (2014). Parenthood and life satisfaction: Why don't children make people happy?. *Journal of Marriage and Family, 76*(2), 319-336. www.researchgate.net/profile/Matthias_Pollmann-Schult/publication/260532341_Parenthood_and_Life_Satisfaction_Why_Don%27t_Children_Make_People_Happy/links/5e54db6992851c1dcb8bcb7f/Parenthood-and-Life-Satisfaction-Why-Dont-Children-Make-People-Happy.pdf

15 Hansen, T. (2012). Parenthood and happiness: A review of folk theories versus empirical evidence. *Social Indicators Research, 108*(1), 29-64. https://oda-hioa.archive.knowledgearc.net/bitstream/handle/10642/2428/995951post.pdf?sequence=1

# Appendix I: Promising drug programs

1 Office of the Surgeon General. (2016). *Facing Addiction in America: The Surgeon General's Report on Alcohol, Drugs, and Health.* U.S. Department of Health and Human Services (HHS). https://addiction.surgeongeneral.gov/sites/default/files/chapter-3-prevention.pdf;
Mihalic, S. F., & Irwin, K. (2003). Blueprints for violence prevention: From research to real-world settings—factors influencing the successful replication of model programs. *Youth violence and juvenile justice, 1*(4), 307-329. http://citeseerx.ist.psu.edu/viewdoc/download?doi=10.1.1.218.4497&rep=rep1&type=pdf;
Lipp, A. (2011). Universal school-based prevention programmes for alcohol misuse in young people. *International Journal of Evidence-Based Healthcare, 9*(4), 452-453. www.cochranelibrary.com/cdsr/doi/10.1002/14651858.CD009113/full;
Crime / Violence Prevention. (n.d.). *Social Programs that Work.* https://evidencebasedprograms.org/policy_area/crime-violence-prevention/;
Faggiano, F., Minozzi, S., Versino, E., & Buscemi, D. (2014). Universal school-based prevention for illicit drug use. *Cochrane Database of Systematic Reviews,* (12). www.cochranelibrary.com/cdsr/doi/10.1002/14651858.CD003020.pub3/full

2 Gottfredson, D. C., Wilson, D. B., & Najaka, S. S. (2002). School-based crime prevention. *Evidence-based crime prevention, 56,* 164. www.ncjrs.gov/works/chapter5.htm;
Botvin, G. J., Griffin, K. W., & Nichols, T. D. (2006). Preventing youth violence and delinquency through a universal school-based prevention approach. *Prevention science, 7*(4), 403-408. https://bobcat.militaryfamilies.psu.edu/sites/default/files/placed-programs/LST%20Botvin%202006.pdf

3 Botvin, G. J., & Griffin, K. W. (2004). Life skills training: Empirical findings and future directions. *Journal of primary prevention, 25*(2), 211-232. www.researchgate.net/profile/Gilbert_Botvin/publication/226086316_Life_Skills_Training_Empirical_Findings_and_Future_Directions/links/02bfe5144a7a6b238f000000/Life-Skills-Training-Empirical-Findings-and-Future-Directions.pdf;
Spoth, R. L., Clair, S., Shin, C., & Redmond, C. (2006). Long-term effects of universal preventive interventions on methamphetamine use among adolescents. *Archives of pediatrics & adolescent medicine, 160*(9), 876-882. http://scholar.google.co.uk/scholar_url?url=https%3A%2F%2Fjamanetwork.com%2Fjournals%2Fjamapediatrics%2Farticlepdf%2F205447%2Fpoa60033_876_882.pdf&hl=en&sa=T&oi=gga&ct=gga&cd=0&d=7435542823641563589&ei=VOX_XNTPLouemgHkjbeAAQ&scisig=AAGBfm25VTIorDspNE-2ABHILvW8x23Metg&nossl=1&ws=1920x906&at=Long-term%20effects%20of%20universal%20preventive%20interventions%20on%20methamphetamine%20use%20among%20adolescents&bn=1

4 Botvin, G. J., Griffin, K. W., & Nichols, T. D. (2006). Preventing youth violence and delinquency through a universal school-based prevention approach. *Prevention science, 7*(4), 403-408. https://bobcat.militaryfamilies.psu.edu/sites/default/files/placed-programs/LST%20Botvin%202006.pdf

5 Botvin LifeSkills Training High School Program. (n.d.). *Botvin LifeSkills Training.* www.lifeskillstraining.com/botvin-lifeskills-training-high-school-program/

6 Lipp, A. (2011). Universal school-based prevention programmes for alcohol misuse in young people. *International Journal of Evidence-Based Healthcare, 9*(4), 452-453. www.cochranelibrary.com/cdsr/doi/10.1002/14651858.CD009113/full;
Faggiano, F., Minozzi, S., Versino, E., & Buscemi, D. (2014). Universal school-based prevention for illicit drug use. *Cochrane Database of Systematic Reviews,* (12). www.cochranelibrary.com/cdsr/doi/10.1002/14651858.CD003020.pub3/full

7 Faggiano, F., Vigna-Taglianti, F., Burkhart, G., Bohrn, K., Cuomo, L., Gregori, D., ... & van der Kreeft, P. (2010). The effectiveness of a school-based substance abuse prevention program: 18-month follow-up of the EU-Dap cluster randomized controlled trial. *Drug and alcohol dependence, 108*(1), 56-64. https://expertise.hogent.be/files/6002252/The_effectiveness_of_a_school_based_substance_abuse_prevention_program_18_Month_follow_up_of_the_EU_Dap_cluster_randomized_controlled_trial._Drug_and_Alcohol_Dependence.pdf

8 Office of the Surgeon General. (2016). *Facing Addiction in America: The Surgeon General's Report on Alcohol, Drugs, and Health.* U.S. Department of Health and Human Services (HHS). https://addiction.surgeongeneral.gov/sites/default/files/chapter-3-prevention.pdf;
Hecht, M. L., Marsiglia, F. F., Elek, E., Wagstaff, D. A., Kulis, S., Dustman, P., & Miller-Day, M. (2003). Culturally grounded substance use prevention: An evaluation of the keepin'it REAL curriculum. *Prevention Science, 4*(4), 233-248. www.researchgate.net/profile/Flavio_Marsiglia/publication/9025296_Culturally_Grounded_Substance_Use_Prevention_An_Evaluation_of_the_keepin'_it_REAL_Curriculum/links/09e415086ea5386a81000000.pdf

9 Mihalic, S. F., & Irwin, K. (2003). Blueprints for violence prevention: From research to real-world settings—factors influencing the successful replication of model programs. *Youth violence and juvenile justice, 1*(4), 307-329. http://citeseerx.ist.psu.edu/viewdoc/download?doi=10.1.1.218.4497&rep=rep1&type=pdf

10 McBride, N., Farringdon, F., Midford, R., Meuleners, L., & Phillips, M. (2003). Early unsupervised drinking–reducing the risks. The school health and alcohol harm reduction project. *Drug and Alcohol Review, 22*(3), 263-276. www.tandfonline.com/doi/abs/10.1080/09595230310001544409;
McBride, N., Farringdon, F., Midford, R., Meuleners, L., & Phillips, M. (2004). Harm minimization in school drug education: final results of the School Health and Alcohol Harm Reduction Project (SHAHRP). *Addiction, 99*(3), 278-291. www.hri.global/files/2011/07/21/06.5_McBride_-_Harm_Minimization_in_School_Education_%28SHAHRP%2C_USA%29_.pdf

11 Neighbors, C., Larimer, M. E., Lostutter, T. W., & Woods, B. A. (2006). Harm reduction and individually focused alcohol prevention. *International Journal of Drug Policy, 17*(4), 304-309. www.ncbi.nlm.nih.gov/pmc/articles/PMC1797804/;
Shope, J. T., Copeland, L. A., Marcoux, B. C., & Kamp, M. E. (1996). Effectiveness of a school-based substance abuse prevention program. *Journal of Drug Education, 26*(4), 323-337. https://journals.sagepub.com/doi/abs/10.2190/E9HH-PBUH-802D-XD6U

12 Conrod, P. J., O'Leary-Barrett, M., Newton, N., Topper, L., Castellanos-Ryan, N., Mackie, C., & Girard, A. (2013). Effectiveness of a selective, personality-targeted prevention program for adolescent alcohol use and misuse: a cluster randomized controlled trial. *JAMA psychiatry, 70*(3), 334-342. https://jamanetwork.com/journals/jamapsychiatry/fullarticle/1558064

13 Kumpfer, K. L., & Alvarado, R. (2003). Family-strengthening approaches for the prevention of youth problem behaviors. *American Psychologist, 58*(6-7), 457. https://pdfs.semanticscholar.org/ce21/3721a35299e9fc3902b2dee16acee861178c.pdf

14 Gilligan, C., Wolfenden, L., Foxcroft, D. R., Williams, A. J., Kingsland, M., Hodder, R. K., ... & Rae, J. (2019). Family-based prevention programmes for alcohol use in young people. *Cochrane database of systematic reviews*, (3). www.cochranelibrary.com/cdsr/doi/10.1002/14651858.CD012287.pub2/full

15 Kumpfer, K. L., & Alvarado, R. (1998). *Effective family strengthening interventions.* US Department of Justice, Office of Justice Programs, Office of Juvenile Justice and Delinquency Prevention. https://pdfs.semanticscholar.org/2a2e/4c1628d55289fbc94e45718c7582d7bb50a7.pdf;
Office of the Surgeon General. (2016). *Facing Addiction in America: The Surgeon General's Report on Alcohol, Drugs, and Health.* U.S. Department of Health and Human Services (HHS). https://addiction.surgeongeneral.gov/sites/default/files/chapter-3-prevention.pdf
United Nations Office on Drugs and Crime. (2010). *Compilation of evidence-based family skills training programmes.* United Nations. www.unodc.org/documents/prevention/family-compilation.pdf

16 US Department of Health and Human Services. (2012). *Preventing tobacco use among youth and young adults: a report of the Surgeon General.* US Department of Health and Human Services, Centers for Disease Control and Prevention, National Center for Chronic Disease Prevention and Health Promotion, Office on Smoking and Health, 3.www.cdc.gov/tobacco/data_statistics/sgr/2012/index.htm

Citing: Kumpfer, K. L., Molgaard, V., & Spoth, R. (1996). The Strengthening Families Program for the prevention of delinquency and drug use. In R. D. Peters & R. J. McMahon (Eds.), *Preventing childhood disorders, substance abuse, and delinquency* (pp. 241–267). Sage Publications, Inc. https://psycnet.apa.org/record/1996-98466-011

17 Kumpfer, K. L., Molgaard, V., & Spoth, R. (1996). The Strengthening Families Program for the prevention of delinquency and drug use. In R. D. Peters & R. J. McMahon (Eds.), *Preventing childhood disorders, substance abuse, and delinquency* (pp. 241–267). Sage Publications, Inc. https://psycnet.apa.org/record/1996-98466-011

18 Spoth, R. L., Redmond, C., & Shin, C. (2001). Randomized trial of brief family interventions for general populations: adolescent substance use outcomes 4 years following baseline. *Journal of consulting and clinical psychology, 69*(4), 627. www.researchgate.net/profile/Richard-Spoth/publication/11796284_Randomized_Trial_of_Brief_Family_Interventions_for_General_Populations_Adolescent_Substance_Use_Outcomes_4_Years_Following_Baseline/links/0f31752f3f4d67866a000000/Randomized-Trial-of-Brief-Family-Interventions-for-General-Populations-Adolescent-Substance-Use-Outcomes-4-Years-Following-Baseline.pdf;
Foxcroft, D. R., Ireland, D., Lister-Sharp, D. J., Lowe, G., & Breen, R. (2003). Longer-term primary prevention for alcohol misuse in young people: a systematic review. *Addiction, 98*(4), 397-411. https://pdfs.semanticscholar.org/5d39/d229bc5c200dee28fcb066419dc63e8aa0f8.pdf;
Spoth, R. L., Clair, S., Shin, C., & Redmond, C. (2006). Long-term effects of universal preventive interventions on methamphetamine use among adolescents. *Archives of pediatrics & adolescent medicine, 160*(9), 876-882. http://scholar.google.co.uk/scholar_url?url=https%3A%2F%2Fjamanetwork.com%2Fjournals%2Fja-

mapediatrics%2Farticlepdf%2F205447%2Fpoa60033_876_882.pdf&hl=en&sa=T&oi=gga&ct=gga&cd=0&d=7435542823641563589&ei=VOX_XNTPLouemgHkjbeAAQ&scisig=AAGBfm25VTIorDspNE-2ABHILvW8x23Metg&nossl=1&ws=1920x906&at=Long-term%20effects%20of%20universal%20preventive%20interventions%20on%20methamphetamine%20use%20among%20adolescents&bn=1;
Spoth, R., Trudeau, L., Shin, C., Ralston, E., Redmond, C., Greenberg, M., & Feinberg, M. (2013). Longitudinal effects of universal preventive intervention on prescription drug misuse: three randomized controlled trials with late adolescents and young adults. *American Journal of Public Health, 103*(4), 665-672. www.ncbi.nlm.nih.gov/pmc/articles/PMC3673263/;
Spoth, R., Redmond, C., Shin, C., & Azevedo, K. (2004). Brief family intervention effects on adolescent substance initiation: school-level growth curve analyses 6 years following baseline. *Journal of consulting and clinical psychology, 72*(3), 535. https://www.researchgate.net/profile/Kari_Azevedo/publication/8429495_Brief_Family_Intervention_Effects_on_Adolescent_Substance_Initiation_School-Level_Growth_Curve_Analyses_6_Years_Following_Baseline/links/0912f50eb6199b259f000000/Brief-Family-Intervention-Effects-on-Adolescent-Substance-Initiation-School-Level-Growth-Curve-Analyses-6-Years-Following-Baseline.pdf;
Gates, S., McCambridge, J., Smith, L. A., & Foxcroft, D. (2006). Interventions for prevention of drug use by young people delivered in non-school settings. *Cochrane Database of Systematic Reviews*, (1). www.cochranelibrary.com/cdsr/doi/10.1002/14651858.CD005030.pub2/full

19 Connell, A. M., Dishion, T. J., Yasui, M., & Kavanagh, K. (2007). An adaptive approach to family intervention: linking engagement in family-centered intervention to reductions in adolescent problem behavior. *Journal of consulting and clinical psychology, 75*(4), 568. www.researchgate.net/profile/Thomas_Dishion/publication/6174767_An_Adaptive_Approach_to_Family_Intervention_Linking_Engagement_in_Family-Centered_Intervention_to_Reductions_in_Adolescent_Problem_Behavior/links/0fcfd50a419c8c3d79000000/An-Adaptive-Approach-to-Family-Intervention-Linking-Engagement-in-Family-Centered-Intervention-to-Reductions-in-Adolescent-Problem-Behavior.pdf;
Dishion, T. J., Nelson, S. E., & Kavanagh, K. (2003). The family check-up with high-risk young adolescents: Preventing early-onset substance use by parent monitoring. *Behavior Therapy, 34*(4), 553-571. https://bobcat.militaryfamilies.psu.edu/sites/default/files/placed-programs/Family%20check%20up%20Dishion%20et%20al%202003.pdf

20 United Nations Office on Drugs and Crime. (2010). *Compilation of evidence-based family skills training programmes.* www.unodc.org/documents/prevention/family-compilation.pdf

21 United Nations Office on Drugs and Crime. (2010). *Compilation of evidence-based family skills training programmes.* www.unodc.org/documents/prevention/family-compilation.pdf

22 Bauman, K. E., Foshee, V. A., Ennett, S. T., Pemberton, M., Hicks, K. A., King, T. S., & Koch, G. G. (2001). The influence of a family program on adolescent tobacco and alcohol use. *American journal of public health, 91*(4), 604. www.ncbi.nlm.nih.gov/pmc/articles/PMC1446646/pdf/11291373.pdf;
Griffin, K. W., & Botvin, G. J. (2010). Evidence-based interventions for preventing substance use disorders in adolescents. *Child and adolescent psychiatric clinics of North America, 19*(3), 505-526. www.ncbi.nlm.nih.gov/pmc/articles/PMC2916744/

23 Griffin, K. W., & Botvin, G. J. (2010). Evidence-based interventions for preventing substance use disorders in adolescents. *Child and adolescent psychiatric clinics of North America, 19*(3), 505-526. www.ncbi.nlm.nih.gov/pmc/articles/PMC2916744/

24 U.S. Department of Health and Human Services (HHS), Office of the Surgeon General. (2016). Facing Addiction in America: The Surgeon General's Report on Alcohol, Drugs, and Health. HHS. https://addiction.surgeongeneral.gov/sites/default/files/chapter-3-prevention.pdf

25 Pantin, H., Prado, G., Lopez, B., Huang, S., Tapia, M. I., Schwartz, S. J., ... & Branchini, J. (2009). A randomized controlled trial of Familias Unidas for Hispanic adolescents with behavior problems. *Psychosomatic medicine, 71*(9), 987. www.ncbi.nlm.nih.gov/pmc/articles/PMC2805119/

26 Forgatch, M. S., & Gewirtz, A. H. (2017). The evolution of the Oregon Model of parent management training. *Evidence-based psychotherapies for children and adolescents*, 85. https://books.google.co.uk/books?hl=en&lr=&id=vvfKDgAAQBAJ&oi=fnd&pg=PA85&dq=The+evolution+of+the+Oregon+Model+of+Parent+Management&ots=4vU0pZbfMm&sig=K4Hbwdt8_kiAD13U0p0p3NwufHI#v=onepage&q=The%20evolution%20of%20the%20Oregon%20Model%20of%20Parent%20Management&f=false

27 United Nations Office on Drugs and Crime. (2010). *Compilation of evidence-based family skills training programmes.* www.unodc.org/documents/prevention/family-compilation.pdf

28 Spoth, R., Redmond, C., Shin, C., & Azevedo, K. (2004). Brief family intervention effects on adolescent substance initiation: school-level growth curve analyses 6 years following baseline. *Journal of consulting and clinical psychology, 72*(3), 535. www.researchgate.net/profile/Kari_Azevedo/publication/8429495_Brief_Family_Interven-

tion_Effects_on_Adolescent_Substance_Initiation_School-Level_Growth_Curve_Analyses_6_Years_Following_Baseline/links/0912f50eb6199b259f000000/Brief-Family-Intervention-Effects-on-Adolescent-Substance-Initiation-School-Level-Growth-Curve-Analyses-6-Years-Following-Baseline.pdf;
Spoth, R. L., Redmond, C., & Shin, C. (2001). Randomized trial of brief family interventions for general populations: adolescent substance use outcomes 4 years following baseline. *Journal of consulting and clinical psychology, 69*(4), 627. www.researchgate.net/profile/Richard_Spoth/publication/11796284_Randomized_Trial_of_Brief_Family_Interventions_for_General_Populations_Adolescent_Substance_Use_Outcomes_4_Years_Following_Baseline/links/0f31752f3f4d67866a000000.pdf;
Park, J., Kosterman, R., Hawkins, J. D., Haggerty, K. P., Duncan, T. E., Duncan, S. C., & Spoth, R. (2000). Effects of the "Preparing for the Drug Free Years" curriculum on growth in alcohol use and risk for alcohol use in early adolescence. *Prevention Science, 1*(3), 125-138. https://bobcat.militaryfamilies.psu.edu/sites/default/files/placed-programs/park%20et%202000.pdf

29 Wu, Y., Stanton, B. F., Galbraith, J., Kaljee, L., Cottrell, L., Li, X., ... & Burns, J. M. (2003). Sustaining and broadening intervention impact: a longitudinal randomized trial of 3 adolescent risk reduction approaches. *Pediatrics, 111*(1), e32-e38. https://pdfs.semanticscholar.org/eba2/789641d5cd468881eb068408a184629729f3.pdf;
Ichiyama, M. A., Fairlie, A. M., Wood, M. D., Turrisi, R., Francis, D. P., Ray, A. E., & Stanger, L. A. (2009). A randomized trial of a parent-based intervention on drinking behavior among incoming college freshmen. *Journal of Studies on Alcohol and Drugs, Supplement,* (16), 67-76. www.ncbi.nlm.nih.gov/pmc/articles/PMC2701098/;
LaBrie, J. W., Earle, A. M., Boyle, S. C., Hummer, J. F., Montes, K., Turrisi, R., & Napper, L. E. (2016). A parent-based intervention reduces heavy episodic drinking among first-year college students. *Psychology of addictive behaviors, 30*(5), 523. www.ncbi.nlm.nih.gov/pmc/articles/PMC5103706/

30 Office of the Surgeon General. (2016). *Facing Addiction in America: The Surgeon General's Report on Alcohol, Drugs, and Health.* U.S. Department of Health and Human Services (HHS). https://addiction.surgeongeneral.gov/sites/default/files/chapter-3-prevention.pdf

31 Schinke, S. P., Schwinn, T. M., Di Noia, J., & Cole, K. C. (2004). Reducing the risks of alcohol use among urban youth: three-year effects of a computer-based intervention with and without parent involvement. *Journal of studies on alcohol, 65*(4), 443-449. www.ncbi.nlm.nih.gov/pmc/articles/PMC2795165/

32 Schinke, S. P., Fang, L., & Cole, K. C. (2009). Preventing substance use among adolescent girls: 1-year outcomes of a computerized, mother–daughter program. *Addictive behaviors, 34*(12), 1060-1064. www.ncbi.nlm.nih.gov/pmc/articles/PMC2741484/;
Schinke, S. P., Fang, L., & Cole, K. C. (2009). Computer-delivered, parent-involvement intervention to prevent substance use among adolescent girls. *Preventive medicine, 49*(5), 429-435. www.ncbi.nlm.nih.gov/pmc/articles/PMC2783411/;
Fang, L., & Schinke, S. P. (2013). Two-year outcomes of a randomized, family-based substance use prevention trial for Asian American adolescent girls. *Psychology of Addictive Behaviors, 27*(3), 788. www.ncbi.nlm.nih.gov/pmc/articles/PMC4135055/

33 Office of the Surgeon General. (2016). *Facing Addiction in America: The Surgeon General's Report on Alcohol, Drugs, and Health.* U.S. Department of Health and Human Services (HHS). https://addiction.surgeongeneral.gov/sites/default/files/chapter-3-prevention.pdf;
Walton, M. A., Resko, S., Barry, K. L., Chermack, S. T., Zucker, R. A., Zimmerman, M. A., ... & Blow, F. C. (2014). A randomized controlled trial testing the efficacy of a brief cannabis universal prevention program among adolescents in primary care. *Addiction, 109*(5), 786-797. www.ncbi.nlm.nih.gov/pmc/articles/PMC3984620/

34 Foxcroft, D. R., Ireland, D., Lister-Sharp, D. J., Lowe, G., & Breen, R. (2003). Longer-term primary prevention for alcohol misuse in young people: a systematic review. *Addiction, 98*(4), 397-411. https://pdfs.semanticscholar.org/5d39/d229bc5c200dee28fcb066419dc63e8aa0f8.pdf

35 Foxcroft, D. R., Ireland, D., Lister-Sharp, D. J., Lowe, G., & Breen, R. (2003). Longer-term primary prevention for alcohol misuse in young people: a systematic review. *Addiction, 98*(4), 397-411. https://pdfs.semanticscholar.org/5d39/d229bc5c200dee28fcb066419dc63e8aa0f8.pdf;
Gottfredson, D. C., Wilson, D. B., & Najaka, S. S. (2002). School-based crime prevention. *Evidence-based crime prevention,* 56, 164. www.ncjrs.gov/works/chapter5.htm;
Ellickson, P. L., Bell, R. M., & McGuigan, K. (1993). Preventing adolescent drug use: long-term results of a junior high program. *American journal of public health, 83*(6), 856-861. https://ajph.aphapublications.org/doi/pdfplus/10.2105/AJPH.83.6.856

36 Foxcroft, D. R., Ireland, D., Lister-Sharp, D. J., Lowe, G., & Breen, R. (2003). Longer-term primary prevention for alcohol misuse in young people: a systematic review. *Addiction, 98*(4), 397-411. https://pdfs.semanticscholar.org/5d39/d229bc5c200dee28fcb066419dc63e8aa0f8.pdf;
Sherman, L. W., Gottfredson, D. C., MacKenzie, D. L., Eck, J., Reuter, P., & Bushway, S. D. (1998). *Preventing Crime: What Works, What Doesn't, What's Promising. Research in Brief.* National Institute of Justice. http://files.eric.ed.gov/fulltext/ED423321.pdf

# Appendix II: Other drugs


1 Cooper, R., Naclerio, F., Allgrove, J., & Jimenez, A. (2012). Creatine supplementation with specific view to exercise/sports performance: an update. *Journal of the International Society of Sports Nutrition, 9*(1), 1-11. www.ncbi.nlm.nih.gov/pmc/articles/PMC3407788/

2 Jagim, A. R., Stecker, R. A., Harty, P. S., Erickson, J. L., & Kerksick, C. M. (2018). Safety of Creatine Supplementation in Active Adolescents and Youth: A Brief Review. *Frontiers in nutrition*, 5, 115. www.frontiersin.org/articles/10.3389/fnut.2018.00115/full

3 Smith, J., & Dahm, D. L. (2000, December). Creatine use among a select population of high school athletes. In *Mayo Clinic Proceedings* (Vol. 75, No. 12, pp. 1257-1263). Elsevier. https://citeseerx.ist.psu.edu/viewdoc/download?doi=10.1.1.571.8695&rep=rep1&type=pdf

4 Herriman, M., Fletcher, L., Tchaconas, A., Adesman, A., & Milanaik, R. (2017). Dietary supplements and young teens: misinformation and access provided by Retailers. *Pediatrics, 139*(2). https://pediatrics.aappublications.org/content/139/2/e20161257

5 Cooper, R., Naclerio, F., Allgrove, J., & Jimenez, A. (2012). Creatine supplementation with specific view to exercise/sports performance: an update. *Journal of the International Society of Sports Nutrition, 9*(1), 1-11. www.ncbi.nlm.nih.gov/pmc/articles/PMC3407788/;
Jagim, A. R., Stecker, R. A., Harty, P. S., Erickson, J. L., & Kerksick, C. M. (2018). Safety of Creatine Supplementation in Active Adolescents and Youth: A Brief Review. *Frontiers in nutrition*, 5, 115. www.frontiersin.org/articles/10.3389/fnut.2018.00115/full

6 Gomez, J. (2005). American Academy of Pediatrics Committee on Sports Medicine and Fitness. Use of performance-enhancing substances. *Pediatrics, 115*(4), 1103-1106. https://pubmed.ncbi.nlm.nih.gov/15805399/

7 Terjung, R. L., Clarkson, P., Eichner, E. R., Greenhaff, P. L., Hespel, P. J., Israel, R. G., ... & Williams, M. H. (2000). American College of Sports Medicine roundtable. The physiological and health effects of oral creatine supplementation. *Medicine and science in sports and exercise, 32*(3), 706-717. https://journals.lww.com/acsm-msse/Fulltext/2000/03000/Physiological_and_Health_Effects_of_Oral_Creatine.24.aspx

8 Herriman, M., Fletcher, L., Tchaconas, A., Adesman, A., & Milanaik, R. (2017). Dietary supplements and young teens: misinformation and access provided by Retailers. *Pediatrics, 139*(2). https://pediatrics.aappublications.org/content/139/2/e20161257

9 Smith, J., & Dahm, D. L. (2000, December). Creatine use among a select population of high school athletes. In *Mayo Clinic Proceedings* (Vol. 75, No. 12, pp. 1257-1263). Elsevier. https://citeseerx.ist.psu.edu/viewdoc/download?doi=10.1.1.571.8695&rep=rep1&type=pdf

10 Cooper, E. R., McGrath, K. C., Li, X., Akram, O., Kasz, R., Kazlauskas, R., ... & Heather, A. K. (2017). The use of tandem yeast and mammalian cell in vitro androgen bioassays to detect androgens in internet-sourced sport supplements. *Drug testing and analysis, 9*(4), 545-552. https://analyticalsciencejournals.onlinelibrary.wiley.com/doi/abs/10.1002/dta.2000

11 Geyer, H., Parr, M. K., Mareck, U., Reinhart, U., Schrader, Y., & Schänzer, W. (2004). Analysis of non-hormonal nutritional supplements for anabolic-androgenic steroids-results of an international study. *International journal of sports medicine, 25*(02), 124-129. www.koelnerliste.com/fileadmin/user_upload/Downloads/PDF/DE/IOC_Studie_2004.pdf

12 *Supplements in Sport: Supplement Advice for Athletes and Sports*. (n.d.). Sports Integrity Australia. www.sportintegrity.gov.au/what-we-do/anti-doping/supplements-sport

13 Bezrutczyk, D. (2020). *Diet Pills*. Rehab Spot. www.rehabspot.com/drugs/diet-pills/

14 Hampp, C., Kang, E. M., & Borders-Hemphill, V. (2013). Use of prescription antiobesity drugs in the United States. Pharmacotherapy: *The Journal of Human Pharmacology and Drug Therapy, 33*(12), 1299-1307. www.ncbi.nlm.nih.gov/pmc/articles/PMC4740913/

15 Cumella, E., Hahn, J. & Woods, B. K. (2007). *Weighing Alli's impact: eating disorder patients might be tempted to abuse the first FDA-approved nonprescription diet pill.* Gale Onfile. https://go.gale.com/ps/anonymous?id=GALE%7CA166565729&sid=googleScholar&v=2.1&it=r&linkaccess=abs&issn=19317093&p=HRCA&sw=w

16 Chanoine, J. P., Hampl, S., Jensen, C., Boldrin, M., & Hauptman, J. (2005). Effect of orlistat on weight and body composition in obese adolescents: a randomized controlled trial. *Jama, 293*(23), 2873-2883. https://jamanetwork.com/journals/jama/article-abstract/201079

17 Maahs, D., Serna, D. G. D., Kolotkin, R. L., Ralston, S., Sandate, J., Qualls, C., & Schade, D. S. (2006). Randomized, double-blind, placebo-controlled trial of orlistat for weight loss in adolescents. *Endocrine Practice, 12*(1), 18-28. www.endocrinepractice.org/article/S1530-891X(20)40691-3/fulltext

18 Wilson, K. M., Klein, J. D., Sesselberg, T. S., Yussman, S. M., Markow, D. B., Green, A. E., ... & Gray, N. J. (2006). Use of complementary medicine and dietary supplements among US adolescents. *Journal of adolescent health, 38*(4), 385-394. www.jahonline.org/article/S1054-139X(05)00075-3/fulltext

19 Bezrutczyk, D. (2020). *Diet Pills.* Rehab Spot. www.rehabspot.com/drugs/diet-pills/

20 Bray, G. A. (1993). Use and abuse of appetite-suppressant drugs in the treatment of obesity. *Annals of internal medicine, 119*(7_Part_2), 707-713. www.acpjournals.org/doi/abs/10.7326/0003-4819-119-7_part_2-199310011-00016

21 Bezrutczyk, D. (2020). *Diet Pills.* Rehab Spot. www.rehabspot.com/drugs/diet-pills/

22 Woodard, K., Louque, L., & Hsia, D. S. (2020). Medications for the treatment of obesity in adolescents. *Therapeutic Advances in Endocrinology and Metabolism,* 11, 2042018820918789. https://journals.sagepub.com/doi/full/10.1177/2042018820918789

23 White, B., Jamieson, L., Clifford, S., Shield, J. P. H., Christie, D., Smith, F., ... & Viner, R. M. (2015). Adolescent experiences of anti-obesity drugs. *Clinical obesity, 5*(3), 116-126. https://pubmed.ncbi.nlm.nih.gov/25974187/

24 McDuffie, J. R., Calis, K. A., Booth, S. L., Uwaifo, G. I., & Yanovski, J. A. (2002). Effects of orlistat on fat-soluble vitamins in obese adolescents. Pharmacotherapy: *The Journal of Human Pharmacology and Drug Therapy, 22*(7), 814-822. https://accpjournals.onlinelibrary.wiley.com/doi/abs/10.1592/phco.22.11.814.33627

25 Wilson, K. M., Klein, J. D., Sesselberg, T. S., Yussman, S. M., Markow, D. B., Green, A. E., ... & Gray, N. J. (2006). Use of complementary medicine and dietary supplements among US adolescents. *Journal of adolescent health, 38*(4), 385-394. www.jahonline.org/article/S1054-139X(05)00075-3/fulltext

26 Golden, N. H., Schneider, M., & Wood, C. (2016). Preventing obesity and eating disorders in adolescents. *Pediatrics, 138*(3). https://pediatrics.aappublications.org/content/early/2016/08/18/peds.2016-1649

27 European Monitoring Centre for Drugs and Drug Addiction. (n.d.). *Lysergide (LSD) drug profile.* www.emcdda.europa.eu/publications/drug-profiles/lsd

28 European Monitoring Centre for Drugs and Drug Addiction. (n.d.). *Lysergide (LSD) drug profile.* www.emcdda.europa.eu/publications/drug-profiles/lsd;
Jenkins, J. P. (2006). LSD. Britannica. www.britannica.com/science/LSD

29 European Monitoring Centre for Drugs and Drug Addiction. (n.d.). *Lysergide (LSD) drug profile.* www.emcdda.europa.eu/publications/drug-profiles/lsd

30 Delphi Behavioral Health Group. (2019). *Is Buying LSD Online Dangerous?* https://delphihealthgroup.com/online-drug-dangers/lsd/;
Winstock, A., Barratt, M., Ferris, J., & Maier, L. (2019). Global drug survey. *MixMag,* 251, 68-73. www.drugsandalcohol.ie/30537/1/Exec-Summary.pdf;
Teen*ager charged by police over 'largest seizure ever' of LSD in SA, allegedly bought on the dark web.* (2019). Australian Broadcasting Corporation News. www.abc.net.au/news/2019-07-04/police-bust-teen-for-trafficking-largest-ever-quantity-of-lsd/11279144;
European Monitoring Centre for Drugs and Addiction. (2017). *Drugs and the darknet: perspectives for enforcement, research and policy.* www.emcdda.europa.eu/system/files/publications/6585/TD0417834ENN.pdf

31 Passie, T., Halpern, J. H., Stichtenoth, D. O., Emrich, H. M., & Hintzen, A. (2008). The pharmacology of lysergic acid diethylamide: a review. *CNS neuroscience & therapeutics, 14*(4), 295-314. https://onlinelibrary.wiley.com/doi/pdf/10.1111/j.1755-5949.2008.00059.x

32 Passie, T., Halpern, J. H., Stichtenoth, D. O., Emrich, H. M., & Hintzen, A. (2008). The pharmacology of lysergic acid diethylamide: a review. *CNS neuroscience & therapeutics, 14*(4), 295-314. https://onlinelibrary.wiley.com/doi/pdf/10.1111/j.1755-5949.2008.00059.x

33 Strassman, R. J. (1984). Adverse reactions to psychedelic drugs. A review of the literature. *J Nerv Ment Dis, 172*(10), 577-595. https://wiki.dmt-nexus.me/w/images/5/5c/psychedelic_adverse_effects.pdf

34 Rubinow, D. R., & Cancro, R. (1977). The bad trip: An epidemiological survey of youthful hallucinogen use. *Journal of youth and adolescence, 6*(1), 1-9. https://link.springer.com/article/10.1007/BF02138920

35 Passie, T., Halpern, J. H., Stichtenoth, D. O., Emrich, H. M., & Hintzen, A. (2008). The pharmacology of lysergic acid diethylamide: a review. *CNS neuroscience & therapeutics, 14*(4), 295-314. https://onlinelibrary.wiley.com/doi/pdf/10.1111/j.1755-5949.2008.00059.x

36 Ungerleider, J. (1968). The acute side effects from LSD. *The problems and prospects of LSD*, 61-68. www.cista.net/tomes/Somagetics/J.%20Thomas%20Ungerleider,%20M.D.%20(Ed.)%20-%20The%20Problems%20and%20Prospects%20of%20LSD.pdf#page=71

37 Strassman, R. J. (1984). Adverse reactions to psychedelic drugs. A review of the literature. *J Nerv Ment Dis, 172*(10), 577-595. https://wiki.dmt-nexus.me/w/images/5/5c/psychedelic_adverse_effects.pdf

38 Ungerleider, J. (1968). The acute side effects from LSD. *The problems and prospects of LSD*, 61-68. www.cista.net/tomes/Somagetics/J.%20Thomas%20Ungerleider,%20M.D.%20(Ed.)%20-%20The%20Problems%20and%20Prospects%20of%20LSD.pdf#page=71

39 Strassman, R. J. (1984). Adverse reactions to psychedelic drugs. A review of the literature. *J Nerv Ment Dis, 172*(10), 577-595. https://wiki.dmt-nexus.me/w/images/5/5c/psychedelic_adverse_effects.pdf

40 Baggott, M. J., Coyle, J. R., Erowid, E., Erowid, F., & Robertson, L. C. (2011). Abnormal visual experiences in individuals with histories of hallucinogen use: A web-based questionnaire. *Drug and alcohol dependence, 114*(1), 61-67. www.sciencedirect.com/science/article/abs/pii/S0376871610003200

41 Passie, T., Halpern, J. H., Stichtenoth, D. O., Emrich, H. M., & Hintzen, A. (2008). The pharmacology of lysergic acid diethylamide: a review. *CNS neuroscience & therapeutics, 14*(4), 295-314. tps://onlinelibrary.wiley.com/doi/pdf/10.1111/j.1755-5949.2008.00059.x;
Halpern, J. H., & Pope, H. G. (2003). Hallucinogen persisting perception disorder: what do we know after 50 years?. *Drug and alcohol dependence, 69*(2), 109-119. http://chemistry.mdma.ch/hiveboard/rhodium/pdf/hppd.review.pdf

42 Footnote references:
[1]Johnston, L., Miech, R., O'Malley, P., Bachman, J., Schulenberg, J., & Patrick, M. (2020). *Monitoring the Future national survey results on drug use, 1975-2019: Overview, key findings on adolescent drug use.* https://deepblue.lib.umich.edu/bitstream/handle/2027.42/162579/FINAL.pdf?sequence=1
[2] Gable, R. S. (2004). Comparison of acute lethal toxicity of commonly abused psychoactive substances. *Addiction, 99*(6), 686-696. http://chemistry.mdma.ch/hiveboard/rhodium/pdf/psychoactives.acute.lethal.toxicity.pdf

43 National Institute on Drug Abuse; National Institutes of Health; U.S. Department of Health and Human Services. (2011). *What are inhalants?* Drugabuse.gov. www.drugabuse.gov/publications/research-reports/inhalants/what-are-inhalants

44 Johnston, L., Miech, R., O'Malley, P., Bachman, J., Schulenberg, J., & Patrick, M. (2020). *Monitoring the Future national survey results on drug use, 1975-2019: Overview, key findings on adolescent drug use.* https://deepblue.lib.umich.edu/bitstream/handle/2027.42/162579/FINAL.pdf?sequence=1

45 National Institute on Drug Abuse. (2011). *What are the short- and long-term effects of inhalant use?* National Institutes of Health; U.S. Department of Health and Human Services. www.drugabuse.gov/publications/research-reports/inhalants/what-are-short-long-term-effects-inhalant-use

46 National Institute on Drug Abuse. (2011). *What are the other medical consequences of inhalant abuse?* National Institutes of Health; U.S. Department of Health and Human Services. www.drugabuse.gov/publications/research-reports/inhalants/what-are-other-medical-consequences-inhalant-abuse

47 National Institute on Drug Abuse. (2017). *MDMA (Ecstasy) Abuse Research Report: What is the history of MDMA?* National Institutes of Health; U.S. Department of Health and Human Services. www.drugabuse.gov/publications/research-reports/mdma-ecstasy-abuse/what-is-the-history-of-mdma#:~:text=MDMA%20was%20developed%20by%20a,as%20is%20often%20incorrectly%20cited

48 National Institute on Drug Abuse. (2017). *What is MDMA?* National Institutes of Health; U.S. Department of Health and Human Services. www.drugabuse.gov/publications/research-reports/mdma-ecstasy-abuse/what-mdma

49 Drug Inforcement Administration. (2017). *Drugs of Abuse: A DEA Resource Guide*. U.S. Department of Justice. www.dea.gov/sites/default/files/2018-06/drug_of_abuse.pdf

50 National Drug Intelligence Center. (2005). *National Drug Threat Assessment 2005, MDMA*. U.S. Department of Justice. www.justice.gov/archive/ndic/pubs11/12620/mdma.htm

51 Verheyden, S. L., Henry, J. A., & Curran, H. V. (2003). Acute, sub-acute and long-term subjective consequences of 'ecstasy'(MDMA) consumption in 430 regular users. *Human Psychopharmacology: Clinical and Experimental, 18*(7), 507-517. http://onlinelibrary.wiley.com/doi/10.1002/hup.529/full

52 Gouzoulis-Mayfrank, E., & Daumann, J. (2006). Neurotoxicity of methylenedioxyamphetamines (MDMA; ecstasy) in humans: how strong is the evidence for persistent brain damage?. *Addiction, 101*(3), 348-361. http://citeseerx.ist.psu.edu/viewdoc/download?doi=10.1.1.670.2384&rep=rep1&type=pdf;
Parrott, A. C., Lees, A., Garnham, N. J., Jones, M., & Wesnes, K. (1998). Cognitive performance in recreational users of MDMA or'ecstasy': Evidence for memory deficits. *Journal of psychopharmacology, 12*(1), 79-83. https://journals.sagepub.com/doi/abs/10.1177/026988119801200110

53 Parrott, A. C. (2013). Human psychobiology of MDMA or 'Ecstasy': an overview of 25 years of empirical research. Human Psychopharmacology: *Clinical and Experimental, 28*(4), 289-307. www.researchgate.net/profile/Andrew_Parrott/publication/259223663_Parrott2013HumPsych25yearRev/data/595ceb66a6fdcc8623299b75/parrott2013HumPsychopharm25yearReview.pdf

54 McCann, U. D., & Ricaurte, G. A. (2007). Effects of (±) 3, 4-methylenedioxymethamphetamine (MDMA) on sleep and circadian rhythms. *TheScientificWorldJournal, 7*, 231-238. https://downloads.hindawi.com/journals/tswj/2007/159317.pdf

55 Schilt, T., de Win, M. M., Koeter, M., Jager, G., Korf, D. J., van den Brink, W., & Schmand, B. (2007). Cognition in novice ecstasy users with minimal exposure to other drugs: a prospective cohort study. *Archives of General Psychiatry, 64*(6), 728-736. http://jamanetwork.com/journals/jamapsychiatry/fullarticle/482306

56 National Institute on Drug Abuse. (2020). *MDMA (Ecstasy/Molly) DrugFacts*. National Institutes of Health; U.S. Department of Health and Human Services. www.drugabuse.gov/publications/drugfacts/mdma-ecstasymolly

57 Grigg, J. (2019). *'My friends are taking MDMA at raves and music festivals. Is it safe?'* The Conversation. https://theconversation.com/my-friends-are-taking-mdma-at-raves-and-music-festivals-is-it-safe-122128

58 Measham, F. C. (2019). Drug safety testing, disposals and dealing in an English field: Exploring the operational and behavioural outcomes of the UK's first onsite 'drug checking'service. *International Journal of Drug Policy, 67*, 102-107. https://dro.dur.ac.uk/27159/1/27159.pdf

59 American School Health Association, Association for the Advancement of Health Education (US), Society for Public Health Education, United States. (1989). *The National Adolescent Student Health Survey: A report on the health of America's youth*. Office of Disease Prevention, Health Promotion, & Centers for Disease Control (US). https://books.google.co.uk/books?id=nmFlxoUeX9EC&pg=PA166&lpg=PA166&dq=adolescent+%22stay-awake+pills%22&source=bl&ots=QRgU6bQn0M&sig=ACfU3U0j_Hl9n3EDtK83La2b_Ot-VpSHxNg&hl=en&sa=X&ved=2ahUKEwios7randjuAhUdUhUIHUixBfQ4ChDoATAEegQICBAC#v=onepage&q=adolescent%20%22stay-awake%20pills%22&f=false

60 Mitler, M. M., & O'Malley, M. B. (2005). Wake-promoting medications: efficacy and adverse effects. *Principles and practice of sleep medicine, 4th ed.*, Kryger MH, Roth T and Dement WC (Eds.), 484-98. www.researchgate.net/publication/285518182_Wake-Promoting_Medications_Efficacy_and_Adverse_Effects

61 Burke, L. M. (2008). Caffeine and sports performance. Applied physiology, nutrition, and metabolism, 33(6), 1319-1334. https://pdfs.semanticscholar.org/8a99/789e74876808e5e66d4d411593be7e7f02b1.pdf;
Grgic, J., Grgic, I., Pickering, C., Schoenfeld, B. J., Bishop, D. J., & Pedisic, Z. (2020). Wake up and smell the coffee: caffeine supplementation and exercise performance—an umbrella review of 21 published meta-analyses. *British journal of sports medicine, 54*(11), 681-688. https://bjsm.bmj.com/content/bjsports/early/2019/03/29/bjsports-2018-100278.full.pdf?hootPostID=95f8555cf5e11b89088d991f4fe0e17e

62 Higgins, J. P., Babu, K., Deuster, P. A., & Shearer, J. (2018). Energy drinks: A contemporary issues paper. *Current sports medicine reports, 17*(2), 65-72. https://journals.lww.com/acsm-csmr/Fulltext/2018/02000/Energy_Drinks___A_Contemporary_Issues_Paper.9.aspx

63 Sport Science Institute. (2014). *Caffeine and Athletic Performance*. National Collegiate Athletic Association, www.ncaa.org/sites/default/files/Caffeine%20and%20Athletic%20Performance.pdf

64 Higgins, J. P., Babu, K., Deuster, P. A., & Shearer, J. (2018). Energy drinks: A contemporary issues paper. *Current sports medicine reports, 17*(2), 65-72. https://journals.lww.com/acsm-csmr/Fulltext/2018/02000/Energy_Drinks___A_Contemporary_Issues_Paper.9.aspx

65 Nawrot, P., Jordan, S., Eastwood, J., Rotstein, J., Hugenholtz, A., & Feeley, M. (2003). Effects of caffeine on human health. *Food Additives & Contaminants, 20*(1), 1-30. www.researchgate.net/profile/Mark_Feeley/publication/10957470_Effect_of_caffeine_on_human_health/links/09e41508e60e522c2a000000.pdf;
Seifert, S. M., Schaechter, J. L., Hershorin, E. R., & Lipshultz, S. E. (2011). Health effects of energy drinks on children, adolescents, and young adults. *Pediatrics, 127*(3), 511-528. https://pediatrics.aappublications.org/content/pediatrics/127/3/511.full.pdf?source=post_page---------------------------;
*Health Canada Reminds Canadians to Manage Caffeine Consumption.* (2010). Government of Canada. www.healthycanadians.gc.ca/recall-alert-rappel-avis/hc-sc/2010/13484a-eng.php#:~:text=Health%20Canada%20recommends%20that%20healthy,caffeine%20can%20be%20more%20severe

66 Committee on Nutrition and the Council on Sports Medicine and Fitness. (2011). Sports drinks and energy drinks for children and adolescents: are they appropriate?. *Pediatrics, 127*(6), 1182-1189. https://pediatrics.aappublications.org/content/pediatrics/127/6/1182.full.pdf

67 National Institute on Drug Abuse. (n.d.). *Spice.* National Institutes of Health; U.S. Department of Health and Human Services. https://teens.drugabuse.gov/drug-facts/spice

68 van Amsterdam, J., Nutt, D., & van den Brink, W. (2013). Generic legislation of new psychoactive drugs. *Journal of psychopharmacology, 27*(3), 317-324. www.researchgate.net/profile/Wim_Van_den_Brink/publication/235003818_Van_Amsterdam_Legislation_NPDs_J_psychopharm_2013/links/0912f5103ade4a74a1000000.pdf

69 House, S. (2018). *Tailoring Regimes for a Designer Drug: Developing Civil Liability for Retailers of Synthetic Marijuana.* Vlex. https://law-journals-books.vlex.com/vid/tailoring-regimes-for-designer-704400137

70 What is Synthetic Marijuana? (2018). *The Boston Globe.* www.bostonglobe.com/metro/2018/08/16/what-synthetic-marijuana/YmVpBPEKPDhmdMjOTyvzjN/story.html

71 van Amsterdam, J., Nutt, D., & van den Brink, W. (2013). Generic legislation of new psychoactive drugs. *Journal of psychopharmacology, 27*(3), 317-324. www.researchgate.net/profile/Wim_Van_den_Brink/publication/235003818_Van_Amsterdam_Legislation_NPDs_J_psychopharm_2013/links/0912f5103ade4a74a1000000.pdf

72 Zawilska, J. B., & Wojcieszak, J. (2014). Spice/K2 drugs–more than innocent substitutes for marijuana. *International journal of neuropsychopharmacology, 17*(3), 509-525. http://ijnp.oxfordjournals.org/content/17/3/509.abstract

73 Cohen, M. R. (2013). *10 over-the-counter medicines abused by teens.* The Philadelphia Inquirer. www.inquirer.com/philly/blogs/healthcare/10-over-the-counter-medicines-abused-by-teens.html;
National Institute on Drug Abuse. (2017). *Over-the-Counter Medicines DrugFacts.* National Institutes of Health; U.S. Department of Health and Human Services. www.drugabuse.gov/publications/drugfacts/over-counter-medicines

74 Abraham, O., & Chmielinski, J. (2018). Adolescents' Misuse of Over-The-Counter Medications: The Need for Pharmacist-led Intervention. *Innovations in pharmacy, 9*(3), 4-4. https://pubs.lib.umn.edu/index.php/innovations/article/download/979/1312

75 Schwartz, R. H. (2005). Adolescent abuse of dextromethorphan. *Clinical pediatrics, 44*(7), 565-568. www.researchgate.net/profile/Richard_Schwartz6/publication/7610241_Adolescent_Abuse_of_Dextromethorphan/links/5557338d08aeaaff3bf7281d/Adolescent-Abuse-of-Dextromethorphan.pdf

76 Mutschler, J., Koopmann, A., Grosshans, M., Hermann, D., Mann, K., & Kiefer, F. (2010). Dextromethorphan withdrawal and dependence syndrome. *Deutsches Ärzteblatt International, 107*(30), 537. www.ncbi.nlm.nih.gov/pmc/articles/PMC2925345/

77 Abraham, O., & Chmielinski, J. (2018). Adolescents' Misuse of Over-The-Counter Medications: The Need for Pharmacist-led Intervention. *Innovations in pharmacy, 9*(3), 4-4. https://pubs.lib.umn.edu/index.php/innovations/article/download/979/1312

78 *Cocaine: A Short History.* (n.d.). Foundation for a Drug Free World. www.drugfreeworld.org/drugfacts/cocaine/a-short-history.html

79 National Institute on Drug Abuse. (2021). *Cocaine DrugFacts*. National Institutes of Health; U.S. Department of Health and Human Services. www.drugabuse.gov/publications/drugfacts/cocaine

80 Riezzo, I., Fiore, C., De Carlo, D., Pascale, N., Neri, M., Turillazzi, E., & Fineschi, V. J. C. M. C. (2012). Side effects of cocaine abuse: multiorgan toxicity and pathological consequences. *Current medicinal chemistry, 19*(33), 5624-5646. www.researchgate.net/profile/Guillermo_Bizantino/project/Cocaine-and-cardiovascular-disease/attachment/59370eda1042bfac89186187/AS:502348009009152@1496780506091/download/Toxicidad+multiorga%CC%81nica+por+cocai%CC%81na+riezzo2012.pdf?context=ProjectUpdatesLog

81 United Nations Office on Drugs and Crime (UNODC). (2010). *World Drug Report 2010: United Nations Publication*. United Nations. www.unodc.org/documents/wdr/WDR_2010/1.3_The_globa_cocaine_market.pdf

82 McCrystal, P., & Percy, A. (2009). A profile of adolescent cocaine use in Northern Ireland. International Journal of Drug Policy, 20(4), 357-364. https://d1wqtxts1xzle7.cloudfront.net/50509111/j.drugpo.2008.09.00520161123-1754-10o06fi.pdf?1479937644=&response-content-disposition=inline%3B+filename%3DA_profile_of_adolescent_cocaine_use_in_N.pdf&Expires=1612809212&Signature=ZcLuYOYjzFVwTOOoIi3SWD1y7hsZZ2O3h5p19JOkdpa1NVhmkhqHlzFq4JahJ-rCtfIYfXkonnWADekHjwlM-KRPfQQ0O8E1YLzPCwCHiiXXLtQSJLSwv1UCT5b1LasnP8SVP7hq7h8k3OEl1uCof-YuWxiud9uL-PHh278awUC4-In5xwGmOrpjIlfSBUb3AeJ--n8OQsSYoN5ReFKVcHSJ-H2WU9nYrDeHAQonAcA-MmCvieXxewDZhkVc-pMEm6v-Ec9zph6MpOt1DA0VTfcinIKBS8JPOOC7xwGphLVNh95SW08aBcmZ-JAsoxPmgDK4VfJfZTEyj9XXh0rJma03JA__&Key-Pair-Id=APKAJLOHF5GGSLRBV4ZA

83 Moyle, L., Childs, A., Coomber, R., & Barratt, M. J. (2019). # Drugsforsale: An exploration of the use of social media and encrypted messaging apps to supply and access drugs. *International Journal of Drug Policy, 63*, 101-110. www.researchgate.net/profile/Leah_Moyle/publication/330060775_Drugsforsale_An_exploration_of_the_use_of_social_media_and_encrypted_messaging_apps_to_supply_and_access_drugs/links/5cd92b2092851c4eab9a0ad5/Drugsforsale-An-exploration-of-the-use-of-social-media-and-encrypted-messaging-apps-to-supply-and-access-drugs.pdf

84 McCrystal, P., & Percy, A. (2009). A profile of adolescent cocaine use in Northern Ireland. *International Journal of Drug Policy, 20*(4), 357-364. https://d1wqtxts1xzle7.cloudfront.net/50509111/j.drugpo.2008.09.00520161123-1754-10o06fi.pdf?1479937644=&response-content-disposition=inline%3B+filename%3DA_profile_of_adolescent_cocaine_use_in_N.pdf&Expires=1612809212&Signature=ZcLuYOYjzFVwTOOoIi3SWD1y7hsZZ2O3h5p19JOkdpa1NVhmkhqHlzFq4JahJ-rCtfIYfXkonnWADekHjwlM-KRPfQQ0O8E1YLzPCwCHiiXXLtQSJLSwv1UCT5b1LasnP8SVP7hq7h8k3OEl1uCof-YuWxiud9uL-PHh278awUC4-In5xwGmOrpjIlfSBUb3AeJ--n8OQsSYoN5ReFKVcHSJ-H2WU9nYrDeHAQonAcA-MmCvieXxewDZhkVc-pMEm6v-Ec9zph6MpOt1DA0VTfcinIKBS8JPOOC7xwGphLVNh95SW08aBcmZ-JAsoxPmgDK4VfJfZTEyj9XXh0rJma03JA__&Key-Pair-Id=APKAJLOHF5GGSLRBV4ZA

85 Riezzo, I., Fiore, C., De Carlo, D., Pascale, N., Neri, M., Turillazzi, E., & Fineschi, V. J. C. M. C. (2012). Side effects of cocaine abuse: multiorgan toxicity and pathological consequences. *Current medicinal chemistry, 19*(33), 5624-5646. www.researchgate.net/profile/Guillermo_Bizantino/project/Cocaine-and-cardiovascular-disease/attachment/59370eda1042bfac89186187/AS:502348009009152@1496780506091/download/Toxicidad+multiorga%CC%81nica+por+cocai%CC%81na+riezzo2012.pdf?context=ProjectUpdatesLog

86 Shannon, M. (1988). Clinical toxicity of cocaine adulterants. *Annals of emergency medicine, 17*(11), 1243-1247. www.sciencedirect.com/sdfe/pdf/download/eid/1-s2.0-S0196064488800787/first-page-pdf

87 National Institute on Drug Abuse. (n.d.). *Cocaine*. National Institutes of Health; U.S. Department of Health and Human Services. www.drugabuse.gov/drug-topics/cocaine

88 O'Brien, M. S., & Anthony, J. C. (2005). Risk of becoming cocaine dependent: epidemiological estimates for the United States, 2000–2001. *Neuropsychopharmacology, 30*(5), 1006-1018. www.nature.com/articles/1300681

89 National Institute on Drug Abuse. (2016). *How is cocaine addiction treated?* National Institutes of Health; U.S. Department of Health and Human Services. www.drugabuse.gov/publications/research-reports/cocaine/what-treatments-are-effective-cocaine-abusers

90 National Institute on Drug Abuse. (2018). *Anabolic Steroids DrugFacts*. National Institutes of Health; U.S. Department of Health and Human Services. https://nida.nih.gov/publications/drugfacts/anabolic-steroids

91 Committee on Sports Medicine and Fitness. (1997). Adolescents and anabolic steroids: a subject review. *Pediatrics, 99*(6), 904-908. https://pediatrics.aappublications.org/content/99/6/904

92 Piacentino, D., D Kotzalidis, G., Del Casale, A., Rosaria Aromatario, M., Pomara, C., Girardi, P., & Sani, G. (2015). Anabolic-androgenic steroid use and psychopathology in athletes. A systematic review. *Current neuropharmacology, 13*(1), 101-121. www.ncbi.nlm.nih.gov/pmc/articles/PMC4462035/

93 Harmer, P. A. (2010). Anabolic-androgenic steroid use among young male and female athletes: is the game to blame? *British journal of sports medicine, 44*(1), 26-31. https://bjsm.bmj.com/content/44/1/26

94 Laure, P., & Binsinger, C. (2005). Adolescent athletes and the demand and supply of drugs to improve their performance. *Journal of sports science & medicine, 4*(3), 272. www.ncbi.nlm.nih.gov/pmc/articles/PMC3887330/ Citing: Tanner, S. M., Miller, D. W., & Alongi, C. (1995). Anabolic steroid use by adolescents: prevalence, motives, and knowledge of risks. *Clinical journal of sport medicine: official journal of the Canadian Academy of Sport Medicine, 5*(2), 108-115. https://europepmc.org/article/med/7882111

95 U.S. Food and Drug Administration. (2017). *Teens and Steroids: A Dangerous Combo.* www.fda.gov/consumers/consumer-updates/teens-and-steroids-dangerous-combo

96 Cramer, R. J. (2005). *Anabolic steroids are easily purchased without a prescription and present significant challenges to law enforcement officials.* US Government Accountability Office. www.gao.gov/assets/100/93845.pdf

97 McBride, J. A., Carson III, C. C., & Coward, R. M. (2018). The availability and acquisition of illicit anabolic androgenic steroids and testosterone preparations on the Internet. *American journal of men's health, 12*(5), 1352-1357. www.ncbi.nlm.nih.gov/pmc/articles/PMC6142130/

98 Goldberg, L., Bents, R., Bosworth, E., Trevisan, L., & Elliot, D. L. (1991). Anabolic steroid education and adolescents: do scare tactics work?. *Pediatrics, 87*(3), 283-286. https://pediatrics.aappublications.org/content/87/3/283

99 U.S. Government Accountability Office. (2007). *Anabolic steroid abuse: Federal efforts to prevent and reduce anabolic steroid abuse among teenagers.* www.gao.gov/new.items/d0815.pdf

100 U.S. Government Accountability Office. (2007). *Anabolic steroid abuse: Federal efforts to prevent and reduce anabolic steroid abuse among teenagers.* www.gao.gov/new.items/d0815.pdf;
Committee on Sports Medicine and Fitness. (1997). Adolescents and anabolic steroids: a subject review. *Pediatrics, 99*(6), 904-908. https://pediatrics.aappublications.org/content/99/6/904

101 Wichstrøm, L., & Pedersen, W. (2001). Use of anabolic-androgenic steroids in adolescence: winning, looking good or being bad?. *Journal of studies on alcohol, 62*(1), 5-13. https://citeseerx.ist.psu.edu/viewdoc/download?-doi=10.1.1.488.6146&rep=rep1&type=pdf

102 Pope, H. G., & Katz, D. L. (1994). Psychiatric and medical effects of anabolic-androgenic steroid use: a controlled study of 160 athletes. *Archives of general psychiatry, 51*(5), 375-382. https://jamanetwork.com/journals/jamapsychiatry/article-abstract/496600

103 U.S. Government Accountability Office. (2007). *Anabolic steroid abuse: Federal efforts to prevent and reduce anabolic steroid abuse among teenagers.* www.gao.gov/new.items/d0815.pdf

104 U.S. Government Accountability Office. (2007). *Anabolic steroid abuse: Federal efforts to prevent and reduce anabolic steroid abuse among teenagers.* www.gao.gov/new.items/d0815.pdf

105 Kanayama, G., Brower, K. J., Wood, R. I., Hudson, J. I., & Pope Jr, H. G. (2009). Anabolic–androgenic steroid dependence: an emerging disorder. *Addiction, 104*(12), 1966-1978. www.ncbi.nlm.nih.gov/pmc/articles/PMC2780436/

106 National Institute on Drug Abuse. (2018). *What are the risks of anabolic steroid use in teens?* National Institutes of Health; U.S. Department of Health and Human Services. www.drugabuse.gov/publications/research-reports/steroids-other-appearance-performance-enhancing-drugs-apeds/what-are-risks-anabolic-steroid-use-in-teens

107 U.S. Government Accountability Office. (2007). *Anabolic steroid abuse: Federal efforts to prevent and reduce anabolic steroid abuse among teenagers.* www.gao.gov/new.items/d0815.pdf

108 Committee on Sports Medicine and Fitness. (1997). Adolescents and anabolic steroids: a subject review. *Pediatrics, 99*(6), 904-908. https://pediatrics.aappublications.org/content/99/6/904

109 American College of Sports Medicine. (1984). Position statement on anabolic/androgenic steroids. *Sports Med Bull, 19*, 8-12. Revised April 2012. www.mshsaa.org/resources/pdf/anabolicSteroids.pdf

110 American College of Sports Medicine. (2010). *The use of anabolic-androgenic steroids in sports.* www.medscape.com/viewarticle/716339

# Appendix III: Sexually transmitted diseases


1 Division of STD Prevention, National Center for HIV/AIDS, Viral Hepatitis, STD, and TB Prevention. (2021). *Sexually Transmitted Diseases (STDs) Data & Statistics*. Centers for Disease Control and Prevention. www.cdc.gov/std/stats15/other.htm

2 Division of STD Prevention, National Center for HIV/AIDS, Viral Hepatitis, STD, and TB Prevention. (2016). *Human Papillomavirus (HPV) Treatment and Care*. Centers for Disease Control and Prevention. www.cdc.gov/std/hpv/treatment.htm

3 Winer, R. L., Hughes, J. P., Feng, Q., O'Reilly, S., Kiviat, N. B., Holmes, K. K., & Koutsky, L. A. (2006). Condom use and the risk of genital human papillomavirus infection in young women. *New England Journal of Medicine, 354*(25), 2645-2654. www.nejm.org/doi/full/10.1056/NEJMoa053284

4 Kavanagh, K., Pollock, K. G., Cuschieri, K., Palmer, T., Cameron, R. L., Watt, C., ... & Robertson, C. (2017). Changes in the prevalence of human papillomavirus following a national bivalent human papillomavirus vaccination programme in Scotland: a 7-year cross-sectional study. *The Lancet Infectious Diseases, 17*(12), 1293-1302. http://scholar.google.com/scholar_url?url=http%3A%2F%2Faura.abdn.ac.uk%2Fbitstream%2F-handle%2F2164%2F10254%2FHPV_LID_Uni_Repository_version.docx%3Fsequence%3D1%26isAl-lowed%3Dy&hl=en&sa=T&oi=gga&ct=gga&cd=0&d=12923925713806101433&ei=cB1jW5KDJ4_emgHZsJjABQ&scisig=AAGBfm1Z3Z2XurdQSQLV6Zu_IJo3IynYnw&nossl=1&ws=1920x901;
Huh, W. K., Joura, E. A., Giuliano, A. R., Iversen, O. E., de Andrade, R. P., Ault, K. A., ... & Mayrand, M. H. (2017). Final efficacy, immunogenicity, and safety analyses of a nine-valent human papillomavirus vaccine in women aged 16–26 years: a randomised, double-blind trial. *The Lancet, 390*(10108), 2143-2159. http://scholar.google.com/scholar_url?url=https%3A%2F%2Fqmro.qmul.ac.uk%2Fxmlui%2Fbitstream%2Fhan-dle%2F123456789%2F25830%2FFinal%2520efficacy%2520HPV%2520vaccine%2520Cuzick%25202017.docx%3Fsequence%3D1&hl=en&sa=T&oi=gga&ct=gga&cd=0&d=9021357415894081406&ei=AB5jW4-zKI-jmmgGspY7oCQ&scisig=AAGBfm1xNGEjQ2vv6l1tSB0Vr8Fdm_Cy8A&nossl=1&ws=1920x901;
Gargano, J. W., Unger, E. R., Liu, G., Steinau, M., Meites, E., Dunne, E., & Markowitz, L. E. (2017). Prevalence of genital human papillomavirus in males, United States, 2013–2014. *The Journal of infectious diseases, 215*(7), 1070-1079. https://academic.oup.com/jid/article/215/7/1070/2972752

5 Ho, G. Y., Bierman, R., Beardsley, L., Chang, C. J., & Burk, R. D. (1998). Natural history of cervicovaginal papillomavirus infection in young women. *New England Journal of Medicine, 338*(7), 423-428. www.nejm.org/doi/full/10.1056/NEJM199802123380703

6 Garland, S. M., Steben, M., Sings, H. L., James, M., Lu, S., Railkar, R., ... & Joura, E. A. (2009). Natural history of genital warts: analysis of the placebo arm of 2 randomized phase III trials of a quadrivalent human papillomavirus (types 6, 11, 16, and 18) vaccine. *The Journal of infectious diseases, 199*(6), 805-814. https://academic.oup.com/jid/article/199/6/805/2192034;
Gissmann, L., Wolnik, L., Ikenberg, H., Koldovsky, U., Schnürch, H. G., & Zur Hausen, H. (1983). Human papillomavirus types 6 and 11 DNA sequences in genital and laryngeal papillomas and in some cervical cancers. *Proceedings of the National Academy of Sciences, 80*(2), 560-563. www.pnas.org/content/pnas/80/2/560.full.pdf

7 Footnote references:
[1] Markowitz, L. E., Liu, G., Hariri, S., Steinau, M., Dunne, E. F., & Unger, E. R. (2016). Prevalence of HPV after introduction of the vaccination program in the United States. *Pediatrics*, peds-2015. https://pediatrics.aappublications.org/content/137/3/e20151968
[2] Daugherty, M., & Byler, T. (2018). Genital Wart and Human Papillomavirus Prevalence in Men in the United States From Penile Swabs: Results From National Health and Nutrition Examination Surveys. *Sexually transmitted diseases, 45*(6), 412-416. www.ncbi.nlm.nih.gov/pubmed/29750774
[3] Markowitz, L. E., Liu, G., Hariri, S., Steinau, M., Dunne, E. F., & Unger, E. R. (2016). Prevalence of HPV after introduction of the vaccination program in the United States. *Pediatrics*, peds-2015. https://pediatrics.aappublications.org/content/137/3/e20151968
[4] Gargano, J. W., Unger, E. R., Liu, G., Steinau, M., Meites, E., Dunne, E., & Markowitz, L. E. (2017). Prevalence of genital human papillomavirus in males, United States, 2013–2014. *The Journal of infectious diseases, 215*(7), 1070-1079. https://academic.oup.com/jid/article/215/7/1070/2972752
[5] Hillman, R. J., Giuliano, A. R., Palefsky, J. M., Goldstone, S., Moreira, E. D., Vardas, E., ... & Marshall, J. B. (2011). The Immunogenicity of Quadrivalent Hpv (Types 6/11/16/18) Vaccine in Males Aged 16-26. *Clinical and Vaccine Immunology*, CVI-05208.

8 Division of STD Prevention, National Center for HIV/AIDS, Viral Hepatitis, STD, and TB Prevention. (2015). *2015 Sexually Transmitted Diseases Treatment Guidelines: Anogenital Warts*. Centers for Disease Control and Prevention. www.cdc.gov/std/tg2015/warts.htm

9 Division of STD Prevention, National Center for HIV/AIDS, Viral Hepatitis, STD, and TB Prevention. (2016). *Human Papillomavirus (HPV) Treatment and Care*. Centers for Disease Control and Prevention. www.cdc.gov/std/hpv/treatment.htm;
Division of STD Prevention, National Center for HIV/AIDS, Viral Hepatitis, STD, and TB Prevention. (2015). *2015 Sexually Transmitted Diseases Treatment Guidelines: Anogenital Warts*. Centers for Disease Control and Prevention. www.cdc.gov/std/tg2015/warts.htm

10 Division of STD Prevention, National Center for HIV/AIDS, Viral Hepatitis, STD, and TB Prevention. (2015). *2015 Sexually Transmitted Diseases Treatment Guidelines: Anogenital Warts*. Centers for Disease Control and Prevention. www.cdc.gov/std/tg2015/warts.htm

11 Graziottin, A., & Serafini, A. (2009). HPV infection in women: psychosexual impact of genital warts and intraepithelial lesions. *The journal of sexual medicine, 6*(3), 633-645. https://m.alessandragraziottin.it/ew/ew_voceall/37/1948%20-%20HPV%20infection%20in%20women.pdf;
Maw, R. D., Reitano, M., & Roy, M. (1998). An international survey of patients with genital warts: perceptions regarding treatment and impact on lifestyle. *International journal of STD & AIDS, 9*(10), 571-578. http://journals.sagepub.com/doi/abs/10.1258/0956462981921143

12 Meijer, C. J., Snijders, P. J., & Brule, A. (2000). Screening for cervical cancer: should we test for infection with high-risk HPV?. *Canadian Medical Association Journal, 163*(5), 535-538. www.ncbi.nlm.nih.gov/pmc/articles/PMC80460/

13 Saraiya, M., Unger, E. R., Thompson, T. D., Lynch, C. F., Hernandez, B. Y., Lyu, C. W., ... & Copeland, G. (2015). US assessment of HPV types in cancers: implications for current and 9-valent HPV vaccines. *JNCI: Journal of the National Cancer Institute, 107*(6). https://academic.oup.com/jnci/article/107/6/djv086/872092;
Walboomers, J. M., Jacobs, M. V., Manos, M. M., Bosch, F. X., Kummer, J. A., Shah, K. V., ... &
Muñoz, N. (1999). Human papillomavirus is a necessary cause of invasive cervical cancer worldwide.
*The Journal of pathology, 189*(1), 12-19. https://onlinelibrary.wiley.com/doi/abs/10.1002/(SICI)1096-9896(199909)189:1%3C12::AID-PATH431%3E3.0.CO;2-F

14 Footnote references:
[1] National Cancer Institute. (2018). *SEER Cancer Statistics Review 1975-2015*. https://seer.cancer.gov/csr/1975_2015/results_single/sect_01_table.01.pdf
[2] American Cancer Society. (2020). *Lifetime Risk of Developing or Dying From Cancer*. www.cancer.org/cancer/cancer-basics/lifetime-probability-of-developing-or-dying-from-cancer.html
[3] United States Cancer Statistics Data Brief. (2020). *HPV and Cancer*. Centers for Disease Control and Prevention. www.cdc.gov/cancer/hpv/statistics/cases.htm
[4] Viens, L. J. (2016). Human papillomavirus–associated cancers—United States, 2008–2012. MMWR. *Morbidity and mortality weekly report, 65*. www.cdc.gov/mmwr/volumes/65/wr/mm6526a1.htm
[5] Markowitz, L. E., Liu, G., Hariri, S., Steinau, M., Dunne, E. F., & Unger, E. R. (2016). Prevalence of HPV after introduction of the vaccination program in the United States. *Pediatrics*, peds-2015. https://pediatrics.aappublications.org/content/137/3/e20151968
[6] Giuliano, A. R., Lu, B., Nielson, C. M., Flores, R., Papenfuss, M. R., Lee, J. H., ... & Harris, R. B. (2008). Age-specific prevalence, incidence, and duration of human papillomavirus infections in a cohort of 290 US men. *The Journal of infectious diseases, 198*(6), 827-835. https://pubmed.ncbi.nlm.nih.gov/18657037/
[7] Markowitz, L. E., Liu, G., Hariri, S., Steinau, M., Dunne, E. F., & Unger, E. R. (2016). Prevalence of HPV after introduction of the vaccination program in the United States. *Pediatrics*, peds-2015. https://pediatrics.aappublications.org/content/137/3/e20151968
[8] Gargano, J. W., Unger, E. R., Liu, G., Steinau, M., Meites, E., Dunne, E., & Markowitz, L. E. (2017). Prevalence of genital human papillomavirus in males, United States, 2013–2014. *The Journal of infectious diseases, 215*(7), 1070-1079. https://academic.oup.com/jid/article/215/7/1070/2972752
[9] Hillman, R. J., Giuliano, A. R., Palefsky, J. M., Goldstone, S., Moreira, E. D., Vardas, E., ... & Marshall, J. B. (2011). The Immunogenicity of Quadrivalent Hpv (Types 6/11/16/18) Vaccine in Males Aged 16-26. *Clinical and Vaccine Immunology*, CVI-05208.

15 Markowitz, L. E., Dunne, E. F., Saraiya, M., Chesson, H. W., Curtis, C. R., Gee, J., ... & Unger, E. R. (2014). Human papillomavirus vaccination: recommendations of the Advisory Committee on Immunization Practices (ACIP). *Morbidity and Mortality Weekly Report: Recommendations and Reports, 63*(5), 1-30. https://stacks.cdc.gov/view/cdc/25363/cdc_25363_DS1.pdf

16 Forhan, S. E., Gottlieb, S. L., Sternberg, M. R., Xu, F., Datta, S. D., McQuillan, G. M., ... & Markowitz, L. E. (2009). Prevalence of sexually transmitted infections among female adolescents aged 14 to 19 in the United States. *Pediatrics, 124*(6), 1505-1512. https://pdfs.semanticscholar.org/5852/b4b3a7a856cd0f9ad7551a07f4ff6fd0d9e9.pdf

17 Walker, T. Y., Elam-Evans, L. D., Singleton, J. A., Yankey, D., Markowitz, L. E., Fredua, B., ... & Stokley, S. (2017). National, regional, state, and selected local area vaccination coverage among adolescents aged 13–17

years—United States, 2016. MMWR. *Morbidity and mortality weekly report, 66*(33), 874. www.ncbi.nlm.nih.gov/pmc/articles/PMC5687818/

18 Division of STD Prevention, National Center for HIV/AIDS, Viral Hepatitis, STD, and TB Prevention. (2021). *Chlamydia - CDC Fact Sheet (Detailed)*. Centers for Disease Control and Prevention. www.cdc.gov/std/chlamydia/stdfact-chlamydia-detailed.htm;
Cates Jr, W., & Wasserheit, J. N. (1991). Genital chlamydial infections: epidemiology and reproductive sequelae. *American journal of obstetrics and gynecology, 164*(6), 1771-1781. www.sciencedirect.com/science/article/pii/000293789190559A

19 Low, N., Redmond, S., Alexander, K., van Bergen, J., Ward, H., Uüskula, A., ... & Woodhall, S. (2014). *Chlamydia control in Europe: literature review*. https://ecdc.europa.eu/en/publications-data/chlamydia-control-europe-literature-review;
Haggerty, C. L., Gottlieb, S. L., Taylor, B. D., Low, N., Xu, F., & Ness, R. B. (2010). Risk of sequelae after Chlamydia trachomatis genital infection in women. *The Journal of infectious diseases, 201*(Supplement_2), S134-S155. www.researchgate.net/profile/Nicola_Low/publication/44599438_Risk_of_Sequelae_after_Chlamydia_trachomatis_Genital_Infection_in_Women/links/0912f5136fe20a1743000000/Risk-of-Sequelae-after-Chlamydia-trachomatis-Genital-Infection-in-Women.pdf

20 Haggerty, C. L., Gottlieb, S. L., Taylor, B. D., Low, N., Xu, F., & Ness, R. B. (2010). Risk of sequelae after Chlamydia trachomatis genital infection in women. *The Journal of infectious diseases, 201*(Supplement_2), S134-S155. www.researchgate.net/profile/Nicola_Low/publication/44599438_Risk_of_Sequelae_after_Chlamydia_trachomatis_Genital_Infection_in_Women/links/0912f5136fe20a1743000000/Risk-of-Sequelae-after-Chlamydia-trachomatis-Genital-Infection-in-Women.pdf;
Low, N., Redmond, S., Alexander, K., van Bergen, J., Ward, H., Uüskula, A., ... & Woodhall, S. (2014). *Chlamydia control in Europe: literature review*. https://ecdc.europa.eu/en/publications-data/chlamydia-control-europe-literature-review;
Woodhall, S., Ong, K. J., Hartney, T., Pitt, R., Chandra, N., Soldan, K., & Dunbaret, K. (2014). *Opportunistic chlamydia screening of young adults in england: an evidence summary*. Public Health England. https://assets.publishing.service.gov.uk/government/uploads/system/uploads/attachment_data/file/740182/Opportunistic_Chlamydia_Screening_Evidence_Summary_April_2014.pdf

21 Land, J. A., Van Bergen, J. E. A. M., Morre, S. A., & Postma, M. J. (2009). Epidemiology of Chlamydia trachomatis infection in women and the cost-effectiveness of screening. *Human reproduction update, 16*(2), 189-204. https://academic.oup.com/humupd/article/16/2/189/737223;
Kavanagh, K., Wallace, L. A., Robertson, C., Wilson, P., & Scoular, A. (2013). Estimation of the risk of tubal factor infertility associated with genital chlamydial infection in women: a statistical modelling study. *International journal of epidemiology, 42*(2), 493-503. https://academic.oup.com/ije/article/42/2/493/735968

22 Centers for Disease Control and Prevention. (2014). *Chlamydia - CDC Fact Sheet*. www.cdc.gov/std/chlamydia/stdfact-chlamydia.htm;
Wood, H., & Gudka, S. (2018). Pharmacist-led screening in sexually transmitted infections: current perspectives. *Integrated pharmacy research & practice, 7*, 67. www.ncbi.nlm.nih.gov/pmc/articles/PMC6007388/

23 Farley, T. A., Cohen, D. A., & Elkins, W. (2003). Asymptomatic sexually transmitted diseases: the case for screening. *Preventive medicine, 36*(4), 502-509. www.sciencedirect.com/science/article/pii/S0091743502000580

24 Haggerty, C. L., Gottlieb, S. L., Taylor, B. D., Low, N., Xu, F., & Ness, R. B. (2010). Risk of sequelae after Chlamydia trachomatis genital infection in women. *The Journal of infectious diseases, 201*(Supplement_2), S134-S155. www.researchgate.net/profile/Nicola_Low/publication/44599438_Risk_of_Sequelae_after_Chlamydia_trachomatis_Genital_Infection_in_Women/links/0912f5136fe20a1743000000/Risk-of-Sequelae-after-Chlamydia-trachomatis-Genital-Infection-in-Women.pdf

25 Low, N., Redmond, S., Alexander, K., van Bergen, J., Ward, H., Uüskula, A., ... & Woodhall, S. (2014). *Chlamydia control in Europe: literature review*. https://ecdc.europa.eu/en/publications-data/chlamydia-control-europe-literature-review

26 van Valkengoed, I. G., Morré, S. A., van den Brule, A. J., Meijer, C. J., Bouter, L. M., & Boeke, A. J. P. (2004). Overestimation of complication rates in evaluations of Chlamydia trachomatis screening programmes—implications for cost-effectiveness analyses. *International Journal of Epidemiology, 33*(2), 416-425. https://academic.oup.com/ije/article/33/2/416/715875

27 Eng, T. R., & Butler, W. T. (Eds.). (1997). *The hidden epidemic: Confronting sexually transmitted diseases*. National Academies Press. www.ncbi.nlm.nih.gov/books/NBK232938/
Citing: Cates, J. W. (1990). The epidemiology and control of sexually transmitted diseases in adolescents. *Adolescent medicine, 1*(3), 409-428. https://europepmc.org/abstract/med/10350724

28 Sedlecki, K., Markovic, M., & Rajic, G. (2001). Risk factors for Clamydia infections of the genital organs in adolescent females. *Srpski arhiv za celokupno lekarstvo, 129*(7-8), 169-174. https://pubmed.ncbi.nlm.nih.gov/11797445/

29 Division of STD Prevention, National Center for HIV/AIDS, Viral Hepatitis, STD, and TB Prevention. (2016). *Chlamydia Treatment and Care.* Centers for Disease Control and Prevention. www.cdc.gov/std/chlamydia/treatment.htm

30 Hillis, S. D., Joesoef, R., Marchbanks, P. A., Wasserheit, J. N., Cates Jr, W., & Westrom, L. (1993). Delayed care of pelvic inflammatory disease as a risk factor for impaired fertility. *American journal of obstetrics and gynecology, 168*(5), 1503-1509. www.sciencedirect.com/science/article/pii/S000293781190790X;
Low, N., Redmond, S., Alexander, K., van Bergen, J., Ward, H., Uüskula, A., ... & Woodhall, S. (2014). *Chlamydia control in Europe: literature review.* https://ecdc.europa.eu/en/publications-data/chlamydia-control-europe-literature-review;
Oakeshott, P., Kerry, S., Aghaizu, A., Atherton, H., Hay, S., Taylor-Robinson, D., ... & Hay, P. (2010). Randomised controlled trial of screening for Chlamydia trachomatis to prevent pelvic inflammatory disease: the POPI (prevention of pelvic infection) trial. *Bmj, 340,* c1642.;
Scholes, D., Stergachis, A., Heidrich, F. E., Andrilla, H., Holmes, K. K., & Stamm, W. E. (1996). Prevention of pelvic inflammatory disease by screening for cervical chlamydial infection. *New England Journal of Medicine, 334*(21), 1362-1366. www.nejm.org/doi/full/10.1056/nejm199605233342103

31 National Center for HIV/AIDS, Viral Hepatitis, STD, and TB Prevention. (2021). *Chlamydia - CDC Fact Sheet (Detailed).* Division of STD Prevention, Centers for Disease Control and Prevention. www.cdc.gov/std/chlamydia/stdfact-chlamydia-detailed.htm;
Workowski, K. A., & Berman, S. M. (2006). *Sexually transmitted diseases treatment guidelines, 2006.* Centers for Disease Control and Prevention. www.cdc.gov/mmwr/PDF/rr/rr5511.pdf

32 United States Preventive Services Task Force. (2014). *The guide to clinical preventive services 2014: recommendations of the US Preventive Services Taskforce.* Agency for Healthcare Research and Quality. www.ahrq.gov/prevention/guidelines/guide/section2a.html#Chlamydia

33 Woodhall, S., Ong, K. J., Hartney, T., Pitt, R., Chandra, N., Soldan, K., & Dunbaret, K. (2014). *Opportunistic chlamydia screening of young adults in england: an evidence summary.* Public Health England. https://assets.publishing.service.gov.uk/government/uploads/system/uploads/attachment_data/file/740182/Opportunistic_Chlamydia_Screening_Evidence_Summary_April_2014.pdf

34 Fleming, D. T., McQuillan, G. M., Johnson, R. E., Nahmias, A. J., Aral, S. O., Lee, F. K., & St. Louis, M. E. (1997). Herpes simplex virus type 2 in the United States, 1976 to 1994. *New England Journal of Medicine, 337*(16), 1105-1111. www.nejm.org/doi/full/10.1056/NEJM199710163371601

35 World Health Organization. (2015). *Globally, an estimated two-thirds of the population under 50 are infected with herpes simplex virus type 1.* www.who.int/news-room/detail/28-10-2015-globally-an-estimated-two-thirds-of-the-population-under-50-are-infected-with-herpes-simplex-virus-type-1;
Langenberg, A., Benedetti, J., Jenkins, J., Ashley, R., Winter, C., & Corey, L. (1989). Development of clinically recognizable genital lesions among women previously identified as having asymptomatic herpes simplex virus type 2 infection. *Annals of Internal Medicine, 110*(11), 882-887. http://citeseerx.ist.psu.edu/viewdoc/download?doi=10.1.1.933.2565&rep=rep1&type=pdf;
Cowan, F. M., Johnson, A. M., Ashley, R., Corey, L., & Mindel, A. (1994). Antibody to herpes simplex virus type 2 as serological marker of sexual lifestyle in populations. *Bmj, 309*(6965), 1325-1329. www.ncbi.nlm.nih.gov/pmc/articles/PMC2541869/pdf/bmj00466-0017.pdf;
Xu, F., Sternberg, M. R., Gottlieb, S. L., Berman, S. M., Markowitz, L. E., Forhan, S. E., & Taylor, L. D. (2010). Seroprevalence of herpes simplex virus type 2 among persons aged 14-49 years-United States, 2005-2008. *Morbidity and Mortality Weekly Report, 59*(15), 456-459. www.cdc.gov/mmwr/preview/mmwrhtml/mm5915a3.htm;
Guinan, M. E., Wolinsky, S. M., & Reichman, R. C. (1985). Epidemiology of genital herpes simplex virus infection. *Epidemiologic reviews, 7*(1), 127-146. http://citeseerx.ist.psu.edu/viewdoc/download?doi=10.1.1.874.7788&rep=rep1&type=pdf;
Cowan, F. M., Johnson, A. M., Ashley, R., Corey, L., & Mindel, A. (1994). Antibody to herpes simplex virus type 2 as serological marker of sexual lifestyle in populations. *Bmj, 309*(6965), 1325-1329. www.ncbi.nlm.nih.gov/pmc/articles/PMC2541869/pdf/bmj00466-0017.pdf

36 Mertz, G. J., Benedetti, J., Ashley, R., Selke, S. A., & Corey, L. (1992). Risk factors for the sexual transmission of genital herpes. *Annals of internal medicine, 116*(3), 197-202. https://annals.org/aim/article-abstract/705283/risk-factors-sexual-transmission-genital-herpes

37 Division of STD Prevention, National Center for HIV/AIDS, Viral Hepatitis, STD, and TB Prevention. (2021). *Genital Herpes - CDC Fact Sheet (Detailed)*. Centers for Disease Control and Prevention. www.cdc.gov/std/herpes/stdfact-herpes-detailed.htm

38 McGill, F., Griffiths, M. J., Bonnett, L. J., Geretti, A. M., Michael, B. D., Beeching, N. J., ... & Jung, A. (2018). Incidence, aetiology, and sequelae of viral meningitis in UK adults: a multicentre prospective observational cohort study. *The Lancet Infectious Diseases, 18*(9), 992-1003. www.thelancet.com/journals/laninf/article/PIIS1473-3099(18)30245-7/fulltext

39 Tunkel, A. R. (2018). Aseptic meningitis in adults. *UpToDate*. www.uptodate.com/contents/aseptic-meningitis-in-adults

40 Kropp, R. Y., Wong, T., Cormier, L., Ringrose, A., Burton, S., Embree, J. E., & Steben, M. (2006). Neonatal herpes simplex virus infections in Canada: results of a 3-year national prospective study. *Pediatrics, 117*(6), 1955-1962. http://pediatrics.aappublications.org/content/117/6/1955.short;
Brown, Z. A., Benedetti, J., Ashley, R., Burchett, S., Selke, S., Berry, S., ... & Corey, L. (1991). Neonatal herpes simplex virus infection in relation to asymptomatic maternal infection at the time of labor. *New England Journal of Medicine, 324*(18), 1247-1252. www.nejm.org/doi/full/10.1056/NEJM199105023241804

41 Footnote reference: [1] Kropp, R. Y., Wong, T., Cormier, L., Ringrose, A., Burton, S., Embree, J. E., & Steben, M. (2006). Neonatal herpes simplex virus infections in Canada: results of a 3-year national prospective study. *Pediatrics, 117*(6), 1955-1962. http://pediatrics.aappublications.org/content/117/6/1955.short

42 United States Preventive Services Task Force. (2014). *The guide to clinical preventive services 2014: recommendations of the US Preventive Services Taskforce*. Agency for Healthcare Research and Quality. www.ahrq.gov/prevention/guidelines/guide/section2b.html#Herpes

43 Xu, F., Schillinger, J. A., Sternberg, M. R., Johnson, R. E., Lee, F. K., Nahmias, A. J., & Markowitz, L. E. (2002). Seroprevalence and coinfection with herpes simplex virus type 1 and type 2 in the United States, 1988–1994. *The Journal of infectious diseases, 185*(8), 1019-1024. https://pdfs.semanticscholar.org/3a54/5e5f31a018c-f472a06694cab3f8b9e0fa7dc.pdf

44 Division of STD Prevention, National Center for HIV/AIDS, Viral Hepatitis, STD, and TB Prevention. (2017). *Genital Herpes - CDC Fact Sheet*. Centers for Disease Control and Prevention. www.cdc.gov/std/herpes/stdfact-herpes.htm

45 Division of STD Prevention, National Center for HIV/AIDS, Viral Hepatitis, STD, and TB Prevention. (2017). *Genital Herpes - CDC Fact Sheet*. Centers for Disease Control and Prevention. www.cdc.gov/std/herpes/stdfact-herpes.htm

46 Nahmias, A. J., Lee, F. K., & Beckman-Nahmias, S. U. S. A. (1990). Sero-epidemiological and-sociological patterns of herpes simplex virus infection in the world. *Scand J Infect Dis Suppl, 69*, 19-36. www.ncbi.nlm.nih.gov/pubmed/2175939/%EF%BF%BD%C3%9C

47 Division of STD Prevention, National Center for HIV/AIDS, Viral Hepatitis, STD, and TB Prevention. (2017). *Genital Herpes - CDC Fact Sheet*. Centers for Disease Control and Prevention. www.cdc.gov/std/herpes/stdfact-herpes.htm

48 Farley, T. A., Cohen, D. A., & Elkins, W. (2003). Asymptomatic sexually transmitted diseases: the case for screening. *Preventive medicine, 36*(4), 502-509. www.sciencedirect.com/science/article/pii/S0091743502000580;
Handsfield, H. H., Lipman, T. O., Harnisch, J. P., Tronca, E., & Holmes, K. K. (1974). Asymptomatic gonorrhea in men: diagnosis, natural course, prevalence and significance. *New England Journal of Medicine, 290*(3), 117-123. www.nejm.org/doi/full/10.1056/nejm197401172900301;
Hein, K., Marks, A., & Cohen, M. I. (1977). Asymptomatic gonorrhea: Prevalence in apopulation of urban adolescents. *The Journal of pediatrics, 90*(4), 634-635. www.ncbi.nlm.nih.gov/pubmed/839383

49 LeFevre, M. L. (2014). Screening for chlamydia and gonorrhea: US Preventive Services Task Force recommendation statement. *Annals of internal medicine, 161*(12), 902-910. https://annals.org/acp/content_public/journal/aim/931809/0000605-201412160-00009.pdf

50 Division of STD Prevention, National Center for HIV/AIDS, Viral Hepatitis, STD, and TB Prevention. (2014). *Gonorrhea - CDC Fact Sheet*. Centers for Disease Control and Prevention. www.cdc.gov/std/gonorrhea/stdfact-gonorrhea.htm

51 Division of STD Prevention, National Center for HIV/AIDS, Viral Hepatitis, STD, and TB Prevention. (2014). *Gonorrhea - CDC Fact Sheet*. Centers for Disease Control and Prevention. www.cdc.gov/std/gonorrhea/stdfact-gonorrhea.htm;

Platt, R., Rice, P. A., & McCormack, W. M. (1983). Risk of acquiring gonorrhea and prevalence of abnormal adnexal findings among women recently exposed to gonorrhea. *Jama, 250*(23), 3205-3209. https://jamanetwork.com/journals/jama/article-abstract/389055

52 Division of STD Prevention, National Center for HIV/AIDS, Viral Hepatitis, STD, and TB Prevention. (2020). *Gonorrhea Treatment and Care*. Centers for Disease Control and Prevention. www.cdc.gov/std/gonorrhea/treatment.htm

53 The initial reproductive health visit. Committee Opinion No. 598. American College of Obstetricians and Gynecologists. *Obstet Gynecol 2014*;123:1143–7. www.acog.org/clinical/clinical-guidance/committee-opinion/articles/2014/05/the-initial-reproductive-health-visit

54 American Family Physician. (2012). *Gonorrhea*. www.aafp.org/afp/2012/1115/p931-s1.html

55 US Preventive Services Task Force. (2005). Screening for gonorrhea: recommendation statement. *The Annals of Family Medicine, 3*(3), 263-267. www.annfammed.org/content/3/3/263.full.pdf

56 Division of STD Prevention, National Center for HIV/AIDS, Viral Hepatitis, STD, and TB Prevention. (2021). *Trichomoniasis - CDC Fact Sheet*. Centers for Disease Control and Prevention. www.cdc.gov/std/trichomonas/STDFact-Trichomoniasis.htm

57 Workowski, K. A., & Berman, S. M. (2010). *Sexually transmitted diseases treatment guidelines, 2010*. Centers for Disease Control and Prevention. https://stacks.cdc.gov/view/cdc/6119/cdc_6119_DS1.pdf

58 Schweitzer, A., Horn, J., Mikolajczyk, R. T., Krause, G., & Ott, J. J. (2015). Estimations of worldwide prevalence of chronic hepatitis B virus infection: a systematic review of data published between 1965 and 2013. *The Lancet, 386*(10003), 1546-1555. http://bibliobase.sermais.pt:8008/BiblioNET/Upload/PDF13/009845%20Lancet%202015%20386%201003%201546-1555.pdf

59 Centers for Disease Control and Prevention. (2015). *Viral hepatitis surveillance United States*. www.cdc.gov/hepatitis/statistics/2015surveillance/pdfs/2015HepSurveillanceRpt.pdf

60 Nelson, N. P., Easterbrook, P. J., & McMahon, B. J. (2016). Epidemiology of hepatitis B virus infection and impact of vaccination on disease. *Clinics in liver disease, 20*(4), 607-628. www.ncbi.nlm.nih.gov/pmc/articles/PMC5582972/

61 Schweitzer, A., Horn, J., Mikolajczyk, R. T., Krause, G., & Ott, J. J. (2015). Estimations of worldwide prevalence of chronic hepatitis B virus infection: a systematic review of data published between 1965 and 2013. *The Lancet, 386*(10003), 1546-1555. http://bibliobase.sermais.pt:8008/BiblioNET/Upload/PDF13/009845%20Lancet%202015%20386%201003%201546-1555.pdf

62 National Center for HIV/AIDS, Viral Hepatitis, STD, and TB Prevention. (2015). *HIV Surveillance Report: Diagnoses of HIV Infection in the United States and Dependent Areas, 2015*. Centers for Disease Control and Prevention. www.cdc.gov/hiv/pdf/library/reports/surveillance/cdc-hiv-surveillance-report-2015-vol-27.pdf

63 Rangel, M. C., Gavin, L., Reed, C., Fowler, M. G., & Lee, L. M. (2006). Epidemiology of HIV and AIDS among adolescents and young adults in the United States. *Journal of Adolescent Health, 39*(2), 156-163. www.jahonline.org/article/S1054-139X(06)00077-2/fulltext

64 Division of STD Prevention, National Center for HIV/AIDS, Viral Hepatitis, STD, and TB Prevention. (2019). *Sexually transmitted disease surveillance 2018*. Centers for Disease Control and Prevention. www.cdc.gov/std/stats18/tables/34.htm

65 Ghanem, K. G., & Tuddenham, S. (2018). Screening for sexually transmitted infections. *UpToDate*. www.uptodate.com/contents/screening-for-sexually-transmitted-infections

## Appendix V: Fatality rates of extreme sports

1 Appendix V: Fatality rates of extreme sports
United States Consumer Product Safety Commission. (n.d.). *NEISS Frequently Asked Questions*. www.cpsc.gov/Research--Statistics/NEISS-Injury-Data/Neiss-Frequently-Asked-Questions

2 Rogers, A. (1977). The perilous skateboard. *British medical journal, 2*(6093), 1026. www.ncbi.nlm.nih.gov/pmc/articles/PMC1631772/pdf/brmedj00485-0062c.pdf

3 National Ski Areas Association (NSAA). (2020). *NSAA Fatality Fact Sheet.* NSAA Journal. https://nsaa.org/webdocs/Media_Public/IndustryStats/fatality_fact_sheet_2020-21.pdf;
National Ski Areas Association (NSAA). (2019). *NSAA Fatality Fact Sheet.* NSAA Journal. www.nsaa.org/media/348423/fatality_fact_sheet_1920.pdf;
National Ski Areas Association (NSAA). (2016). *Facts on Skiing and Snowboard Safety.* NSAA Journal. www.nsaa.org/media/276230/Facts_on_Skiing__Snowboard_Safety_2016.pdf;
National Ski Areas Association (NSAA). (2014). *Facts on Skiing and Snowboard Safety.* NSAA Journal. www.nsaa.org/media/215062/Facts_on_Skiing__Snowboard_2014.pdf;
National Ski Areas Association (NSAA). (2013). *Facts on Skiing and Snowboard Safety.* NSAA Journal. www.nsaa.org/media/175091/Facts_on_Skiing_and_Snowboarding_10_4_13.pdf;
National Ski Areas Association (NSAA). (2012). *Facts on Skiing and Snowboard Safety.* NSAA Journal. www.nsaa.org/media/68045/NSAA-Facts-About-Skiing-Snowboarding-Safety-10-1-12.pdf;
National Ski Areas Association (NSAA). (2011). *Facts on Skiing and Snowboard Safety.* NSAA Journal. www.yumpu.com/en/document/read/3318565/nsaa-fact-sheet-national-ski-areas-association

4 Bianchi, G., Brügger, O., & Niemann, S. (2017). Skiing and snowboarding in Switzerland: Trends in injury and fatality rates over time. In Scher, I. S., Greenwald, R. M., & Petrone, N. (2017). *Snow sports trauma and safety: conference proceedings of the International Society for Skiing Safety: 21st volume.* Springer Nature. http://library.oapen.org/bitstream/id/b53e4b26-211a-49e6-8029-51af53d692f4/1002289.pdf#page=38

5 Isaac, A. (2020). *NSAA Fatality Fact Sheet.* National Ski Areas AssociatioN Journal. https://nsaa.org/webdocs/Media_Public/IndustryStats/fatality_fact_sheet_2020-21.pdf

6 Isaac, A. (2019). *NSAA Fatality Fact Sheet.* National Ski Areas Association Journal. www.nsaa.org/media/348423/fatality_fact_sheet_1920.pdf

7 Macnab, A. J., & Cadman, R. (1996). Demographics of alpine skiing and snowboarding injury: lessons for prevention programs. *Injury Prevention, 2*(4), 286-289. www.researchgate.net/publication/13883079_Demographics_of_alpine_skiing_and_snowboarding_injury_Lessons_for_prevention_programs

8 National Ski Areas Association (NSAA). (2011). *NSAA FACT SHEET: Facts About Skiing/Snowboarding Safety.* NSAA Journal. www.missionridge.com/sites/default/files/NSAA%20Facts%20About%20Skiing%20%26%20Snowboarding%20Safety%209.1.11.pdf

9 Belin, D & Becher, D. (2017). *2016-17 NSAA National Demographic Study.* NSAA Journal. www.rrcassociates.com/wp-content/uploads/2018/08/DemographicResults.EW1617.compressed.pdf

10 Belin, D. & Becher, D. (2017). *2016-2017 NSAA National Demographic Study.* NSAA Journal. www.rrcassociates.com/wp-content/uploads/2018/08/DemographicResults.EW1617.compressed.pdf

11 Søreide, K. (2012). The epidemiology of injury in bungee jumping, BASE jumping, and skydiving. *Epidemiology of Injury in Adventure and Extreme Sports, 58,* 112-129. www.karger.com/Article/Abstract/338720

12 Vanderford, L., & Meyers, M. (1995). Injuries and bungee jumping. *Sports medicine, 20*(6), 369-374. www.researchgate.net/publication/14585316_Injuries_and_Bungee_Jumping

13 Peddie, C. & Watson, J. (2018). *British Sub-Aqua Club Diving Incident Report 2018.* British Sub-Aqua Club. www.bsac.com/document/diving-incident-report-2018-new-format/1bsac-incident-report-2018-new-format.pdf

14 Spiegelhalter, D. (2014). *Extreme sports: What are the risks?* BBC. www.bbc.com/future/story/20120302-extreme-sports-a-risky-business

15 Buzzacott, P., Schiller, D., Crain, J., & Denoble, P. J. (2018). Epidemiology of morbidity and mortality in US and Canadian recreational scuba diving. *Public health, 155,* 62-68. www.sciencedirect.com/science/article/abs/pii/S0033350617303864

16 United States Parachute Association. (n.d.). *Skydiving Safety.* https://uspa.org/find/faqs/safety

17 Canbek, U., İmerci, A., Akgün, U., Yeşil, M., Aydin, A., & Balci, Y. (2015). Characteristics of injuries caused by paragliding accidents: A cross-sectional study. *World journal of emergency medicine, 6*(3), 221. www.ncbi.nlm.nih.gov/pmc/articles/PMC4566014/

18 Ekerhovd, K. M., Novomesky, F., Komarekova, I., & Strak, L. (2013). Descriptive epidemiological study of fatal incidents and injury mechanisms among civilian sport parachutists in Norway from 1963 to 2008. *Rom J Leg Med, 21*, 31-36. www.rjlm.ro/system/revista/25/31-36.pdf

19 Ellitsgaard, N. (1987). Parachuting injuries: a study of 110,000 sports jumps. *British Journal of Sports Medicine, 21*(1), 13-17. https://bjsm.bmj.com/content/bjsports/21/1/13.full.pdf

20 White, R. C., Schreyer, R., & Downing, K. (1980). Trends in emerging and high risk activities. In In: LaPage, Wilbur F., ed. *Proceedings 1980 National Outdoor Recreation Trends Symposium. Gen. Tech. Rep. NE-57. Vols. I and II.* US Department of Agriculture, Forest Service, Northeastern Forest Experimental Station: 199-204. (Vol. 57). www.nrs.fs.fed.us/pubs/gtr/gtr_ne57/gtr_ne57_1_199.pdf

21 Klein, E. (2017). *The risks and rewards of hang gliding: pilots' desire to fly like birds often outweighs the dangers of the sport.* USC StorySpace Students. https://uscstoryspace.com/2017-2018/erikajkl/Fall_Midterm/HangGliding/; Glenshaw, P. (2019). *Born in the 1960s, The Sport of Hang Gliding Still Hangs On.* Air & Space Magazine. www.airspacemag.com/airspacemag/rise-and-fall-of-hang-gliding-180972601/

22 Feletti, F., Aliverti, A., Henjum, M., Tarabini, M., & Brymer, E. (2017). Incidents and injuries in foot-launched flying extreme sports. *Aerospace medicine and human performance, 88*(11), 1016-1023. http://eprints.leedsbeckett.ac.uk/4037/1/Final%20Manuscript.pdf

23 SBK Base. (n.d.). *Our History*. https://sbkbase.com/our-history/;
Spiegelhalter, D. (2014). *Extreme sports: What are the risks?* BBC. www.bbc.com/future/story/20120302-extreme-sports-a-risky-business

24 Soreide, K., Ellingsen, C. L., & Knutson, V. (2007). How dangerous is BASE jumping? An analysis of adverse events in 20,850 jumps from the Kjerag Massif, Norway. *Journal of Trauma and Acute Care Surgery, 62*(5), 1113-1117. https://journals.lww.com/jtrauma/Abstract/2007/05000/How_Dangerous_is_BASE_Jumping__An_Analysis_of.6.aspx

# Appendix VI: Recommended media

1 Niederdeppe, J., Farrelly, M. C., & Haviland, M. L. (2004). Confirming "truth": more evidence of a successful tobacco countermarketing campaign in Florida. *American journal of public health, 94*(2), 255-257. https://ajph.aphapublications.org/doi/pdfplus/10.2105/AJPH.94.2.255

2 Holtgrave, D. R., Wunderink, K. A., Vallone, D. M., & Healton, C. G. (2009). Cost–utility analysis of the national truth® campaign to prevent youth smoking. *American journal of preventive medicine, 36*(5), 385-388. www.ajpmonline.org/article/S0749-3797%2809%2900075-0/pdf

3 Evans, W. D., Rath, J. M., Hair, E. C., Snider, J. W., Pitzer, L., Greenberg, M., ... & Vallone, D. (2018). Effects of the truth FinishIt brand on tobacco outcomes. *Preventive medicine reports, 9*, 6-11. www.ncbi.nlm.nih.gov/pmc/articles/PMC5724797/

4 Huang, L. L., Lazard, A. J., Pepper, J. K., Noar, S. M., Ranney, L. M., & Goldstein, A. O. (2017). Impact of The Real Cost campaign on adolescents' recall, attitudes, and risk perceptions about tobacco use: a national study. *International journal of environmental research and public health, 14*(1), 42. www.mdpi.com/1660-4601/14/1/42/pdf

5 Footnote references:
[1] U.S. Food & Drug Administration. (2021). *Fresh Empire Campaign*. www.fda.gov/tobacco-products/fresh-empire-campaign
[2] U.S. Food and Drug Administration. (n.d.). *Fresh Empire Research & Evaluation*. www.fda.gov/media/94558/download
[3] Uncited Guillory, J., Crankshaw, E., Farrelly, M. C., Alam, I., Fiacco, L., Curry, L., ... & Delahanty, J. (2020). LGBT young adults' awareness of and receptivity to the This Free Life tobacco public education campaign. *Tobacco Control*. https://tobaccocontrol.bmj.com/content/tobaccocontrol/early/2020/01/14/tobaccocontrol-2019-055239.full.pdf
[4] U.S. Food and Drug Administration. (2021). *This Free Life Campaign*. www.fda.gov/tobacco-products/free-life-campaign
[5] Lantz, P. M., Jacobson, P. D., Warner, K. E., Wasserman, J., Pollack, H. A., Berson, J., & Ahlstrom, A. (2000). Investing in youth tobacco control: a review of smoking prevention and control strategies. *Tobacco control, 9*(1), 47-63. http://tobaccocontrol.bmj.com/content/9/1/47.full

[6] Thomas, R. E., McLellan, J., & Perera, R. (2013). School-based programmes for preventing smoking. *Evidence-Based Child Health: A Cochrane Review Journal, 8*(5), 1616-2040. www.prevencionbasadaenlaevidencia.com/uploads/PDF/RP_Cochrane_School_SmokingPrev_2013.pdf

6 Birnbaum, S.(2017). *6 Types of Technology to Track Your Teen Driver.* Tech.Co. https://tech.co/news/technology-track-teen-driver-2017-02

7 Cars.com. (2017). *TrueMotion App Moves to Make Driving Safer.* www.cars.com/articles/truemotion-app-moves-to-make-driving-safer-1420693277580/

8 Safety and Children with Disabilities. (2019). *Self-Directed Violence and Other Forms of Self-Injury.* Centers for Disease Control and Prevention. www.cdc.gov/ncbddd/disabilityandsafety/self-injury.html;
Morris, P. (2021). I Don't Want Another Family to Lose a Child the Way We Did. *The New York Times.* www.nytimes.com/2021/03/25/opinion/suicide-prevention.html?action=click&module=Opinion&pgtype=Homepage

9 Cohen, J. (2016). *New App Eyeballs Distracted Pedestrians.* Next City. https://nextcity.org/daily/entry/look-up-app-walking-city-sights-distracted-walking

10 Dehnart, A. (2020). *16 and Recovering: a powerful look at addiction that's MTV's best reality show in years.* Reality Blurred. www.realityblurred.com/realitytv/2020/09/16-recovering-mtv-review/

11 Finn, J., & Hughes, P. (2008). Evaluation of the RAINN national sexual assault online hotline. *Journal of Technology in Human Services, 26*(2-4), 203-222. www.tandfonline.com/doi/abs/10.1080/15228830802094783

12 Finn, J., Garner, M. D., & Wilson, J. (2011). Volunteer and user evaluation of the national sexual assault online hotline. *Evaluation and program planning, 34*(3), 266-272. https://d1wqtxts1xzle7.cloudfront.net/51414889/j.evalprogplan.2010.09.00220170118-13314-1u971yp.pdf?1484772138=&response-content-disposition=inline%3B+filename%3DVolunteer_and_User_Evaluation_of_the_Nat.pdf&Expires=1609281999&Signature=J9QrWEZWIwssB5GqoxVkfZBHnx--NTUMOzlyQrchQsxH5zrCVrwPnDV9l2c8NnjjsUb-5ht91eB7qmubHrzMuIlllSeGpPyLkTlRBrEk3hcb7TuDYL0sYVlFjy-CibUgYOLJ7v4jV-SMf0Yktwhhk2qUT-0m-5d7R6pk6pR7LB-s4HwsXVC-Vc0DXWNgg9nyYKN8slgD6odXreFdmDpO8lqor6Iam5GBDmUdSmeo-E0dm6UNQ7C6-6g2CLbzemioFEKBJKQMvr66IkrLp308Srl1Zddye-cC-wDRreRYS01OOoHZ36hQZ7W-8mUsWGq4b9HkLUJ1m8Nhyod3tRlsSPkxfg__&Key-Pair-Id=APKAJLOHF5GGSLRBV4ZA

13 American Psychological Association. (2013). *Love Doesn't Have to Hurt Teens.* www.apa.org/pi/families/resources/love-teens

14 Liz Claiborne, & Education Development Center . *Love is not abuse: A teen dating violence prevention curriculum.* 3 ed. Liz Claiborne, Inc.; New York. www.uen.org/cte/facs_cabinet/downloads/AdultRoles/LINA_Curriculum%2010_07.pdf

15 O'Donoghue, A. (1999). *A Love that Kills.* National Film Board of Canada (NFB). www.nfb.ca/film/love_that_kills/#:~:text=A%20Love%20That%20Kills%20is,daughter's%20life%20and%20tragic%20death

16 Piper, T. (2006). *Dove Evolution* [video]. YouTube. www.youtube.com/watch?v=iYhCn0jf46U

17 Savoye, M., Shaw, M., Dziura, J., Tamborlane, W. V., Rose, P., Guandalini, C., ... & Caprio, S. (2007). Effects of a weight management program on body composition and metabolic parameters in overweight children: a randomized controlled trial. *Jama, 297*(24), 2697-2704. https://jamanetwork.com/journals/jama/articlepdf/207688/joc70059_2697_2704.pdf

18 Project Implicit. (2011). *Project Implicit.* https://implicit.harvard.edu/implicit/selectatest.html

19 Ashby, E. (2012). *Cyberbully movie review.* Common Sense Media. www.commonsensemedia.org/movie-reviews/cyberbully

20 Gallop, C. (2009). *Make Love not Porn* [Video]. TED Conferences. www.ted.com/talks/cindy_gallop_make_love_not_porn

21 Pariser, E. (2011). *Beware online "filter bubbles"* [Video]. TED. www.ted.com/talks/eli_pariser_beware_online_filter_bubbles/transcript?language=en

22 Thompson, N. (2018). *When Tech Knows You Better Than You Know Yourself* [Video]. Wired. www.wired.com/story/artificial-intelligence-yuval-noah-harari-tristan-harris/

23 Jolliff, A. (2020). *Did the Social Dilemma get it right? Thoughts from a social media researcher.* SMAHRT Researcher. http://smahrtresearch.com/did-the-social-dilemma-get-it-right-thoughts-from-a-social-media-researcher/

24 From www.commonsense.org/education/digital-citizenship/lesson/hoaxes-and-fakes.
Jebdogrpm. (2012). *Pig rescues baby goat* [Video]. YouTube. www.youtube.com/watch?v=g7WjrvG1GMk
Comedy Central (2013). *Nathan For You - Petting Zoo Hero* [Video]. YouTube. www.youtube.com/watch?v=_2My_HOP-bw
Comedy Central (2013). *Nathan For You - Petting Zoo Hero Pt. 2* [Video]. YouTube. www.youtube.com/watch?v=bvtJj6HoYHg

25 BBC Newsnight. (2017). *The rise of 'fake news', manipulation and 'alternative facts' - BBC Newsnight* [Video]. YouTube. www.youtube.com/watch?v=1aTApGWVGoI

26 TED. (2018). *Fake videos of real people -- and how to spot them | Supasorn Suwajanakorn* [Video]. YouTube. www.youtube.com/watch?v=o2DDU4g0PRo

27 Media Smarts. (n.d.). *Reality Check: The Game.* https://mediasmarts.ca/digital-media-literacy/educational-games/reality-check-game

28 Chen, S. A. (2015). *A Girl Like Her Movie Review.* Common Sense Media. www.commonsensemedia.org/movie-reviews/a-girl-like-her

29 Ruiz, S. (n.d.). *Not Your Baby.* SusanaRuiz.org. https://susanaruiz.org/takeactiongames-notyourbaby

# Appendix VII: Threat score calculations

1 National Center for Health Statistics. (2020). *CDC WONDER: Underlying Cause of Death 1999-2016.* Centers for Disease Control and Prevention. http://wonder.cdc.gov/ucd-icd10.html

2 National Center for Injury Prevention and Control. (2014). *Web-based Injury Statistics Query and Reporting System (WISQARS)* [Data set]. Centers for Disease Control and Prevention.

3 Davenport, S & Matthews, K. (2018). *Opioid use disorder in the United States: Diagnosed prevalence by payer, age, sex, and state.* Milliman. www.milliman.com/en/insight/opioid-use-disorder-in-the-united-states-diagnosed-prevalence-by-payer-age-sex-and-sta

4 National Center for Statistics and Analysis. (2021). *Alcohol impaired driving: 2019 data* (Traffic Safety Facts. Report No. DOT HS 813 120). National Highway Traffic Safety Administration. https://crashstats.nhtsa.dot.gov/Api/Public/Publication/813120

5 National Center for Statistics and Analysis. (2021). *Alcohol impaired driving: 2019 data* (Traffic Safety Facts. Report No. DOT HS 813 120). National Highway Traffic Safety Administration. https://crashstats.nhtsa.dot.gov/Api/Public/Publication/813120

6 Lira, M. C., Heeren, T. C., Buczek, M., Blanchette, J. G., Smart, R., Pacula, R. L., & Naimi, T. S. (2021). Trends in cannabis involvement and risk of alcohol involvement in motor vehicle crash fatalities in the United States, 2000–2018. *American journal of public health, 111*(11), 1976-1985. https://ajph.aphapublications.org/doi/10.2105/AJPH.2021.306466

7 National Center for Health Statistics. (2020). *CDC WONDER: Underlying Cause of Death 1999-2016.* Centers for Disease Control and Prevention. http://wonder.cdc.gov/ucd-icd10.html

8 National Center for Injury Prevention and Control. (2014). *Web-based Injury Statistics Query and Reporting System (WISQARS)* [Data set]. Centers for Disease Control and Prevention.

9 National Center for Health Statistics. (2020). *CDC WONDER: Underlying Cause of Death 1999-2016.* Centers for Disease Control and Prevention. http://wonder.cdc.gov/ucd-icd10.html

10 National Center for Injury Prevention and Control. (2014). *Web-based Injury Statistics Query and Reporting System (WISQARS)* [Data set]. Centers for Disease Control and Prevention.

11 Criminal Justice Information Services Division. (2018). *2018 Crime in the United States, Table 38.* U.S. Department of Justice. https://ucr.fbi.gov/crime-in-the-u.s/2018/crime-in-the-u.s.-2018/topic-pages/tables/table-38

12 United States Census Bureau. (2021). *National Population by Characteristics: 2010-2019.* www.census.gov/data/tables/time-series/demo/popest/2010s-national-detail.html

13 National Center for Health Statistics. (2020). *CDC WONDER: Underlying Cause of Death 1999-2016.* Centers for Disease Control and Prevention. http://wonder.cdc.gov/ucd-icd10.html

14 National Center for Injury Prevention and Control. (2014). *Web-based Injury Statistics Query and Reporting System (WISQARS)* [Data set]. Centers for Disease Control and Prevention.

15 National Center for Health Statistics. (2020). *CDC WONDER: Underlying Cause of Death 1999-2016.* Centers for Disease Control and Prevention. http://wonder.cdc.gov/ucd-icd10.html

16 National Center for Injury Prevention and Control. (2014). *Web-based Injury Statistics Query and Reporting System (WISQARS)* [Data set]. Centers for Disease Control and Prevention.

17 National Center for Health Statistics. (2020). *CDC WONDER: Underlying Cause of Death 1999-2016.* Centers for Disease Control and Prevention. http://wonder.cdc.gov/ucd-icd10.html

18 National Center for Injury Prevention and Control. (2014). *Web-based Injury Statistics Query and Reporting System (WISQARS)* [Data set]. Centers for Disease Control and Prevention.

19 National Center for Health Statistics. (2020). *CDC WONDER: Underlying Cause of Death 1999-2016.* Centers for Disease Control and Prevention. http://wonder.cdc.gov/ucd-icd10.html

20 National Center for Health Statistics. (2020). *CDC WONDER: Underlying Cause of Death 1999-2016.* Centers for Disease Control and Prevention. http://wonder.cdc.gov/ucd-icd10.html

21 National Center for Injury Prevention and Control. (2014). *Web-based Injury Statistics Query and Reporting System (WISQARS)* [Data set]. Centers for Disease Control and Prevention.

22 National Center for Health Statistics. (2020). *CDC WONDER: Underlying Cause of Death 1999-2016.* Centers for Disease Control and Prevention. http://wonder.cdc.gov/ucd-icd10.html

23 National Center for Injury Prevention and Control. (2014). *Web-based Injury Statistics Query and Reporting System (WISQARS)* [Data set]. Centers for Disease Control and Prevention.

24 National Center for Health Statistics. (2020). *CDC WONDER: Underlying Cause of Death 1999-2016.* Centers for Disease Control and Prevention. http://wonder.cdc.gov/ucd-icd10.html

25 National Center for Injury Prevention and Control. (2014). *Web-based Injury Statistics Query and Reporting System (WISQARS)* [Data set]. Centers for Disease Control and Prevention.

26 Davenport, S & Matthews, K. (2018). *Opioid use disorder in the United States: Diagnosed prevalence by payer, age, sex, and state.* Milliman. www.milliman.com/en/insight/opioid-use-disorder-in-the-united-states-diagnosed-prevalence-by-payer-age-sex-and-sta

27 National Center for Health Statistics. (2020). *CDC WONDER: Underlying Cause of Death 1999-2016.* Centers for Disease Control and Prevention. http://wonder.cdc.gov/ucd-icd10.html

28 National Center for Injury Prevention and Control. (2014). *Web-based Injury Statistics Query and Reporting System (WISQARS)* [Data set]. Centers for Disease Control and Prevention.

29 Davenport, S & Matthews, K. (2018). *Opioid use disorder in the United States: Diagnosed prevalence by payer, age, sex, and state.* Milliman. www.milliman.com/en/insight/opioid-use-disorder-in-the-united-states-diagnosed-prevalence-by-payer-age-sex-and-sta

30 National Center for Health Statistics. (2020). *CDC WONDER: Underlying Cause of Death 1999-2016.* Centers for Disease Control and Prevention. http://wonder.cdc.gov/ucd-icd10.html

31 National Center for Injury Prevention and Control. (2014). *Web-based Injury Statistics Query and Reporting System (WISQARS)* [Data set]. Centers for Disease Control and Prevention.

32 Inter-university Consortium for Political and Social Research. *National Crime Victimization Survey, [United States], 2009-2016.* United States Bureau of Justice Statistics. https://doi.org/10.3886/ICPSR36142.v2

33 National Center for Health Statistics. (2020). *CDC WONDER: Underlying Cause of Death 1999-2016.* Centers for Disease Control and Prevention. http://wonder.cdc.gov/ucd-icd10.html

34 National Center for Injury Prevention and Control. (2014). *Web-based Injury Statistics Query and Reporting System (WISQARS)* [Data set]. Centers for Disease Control and Prevention.

35 Inter-university Consortium for Political and Social Research. *National Crime Victimization Survey, [United States], 2009-2016*. United States Bureau of Justice Statistics. https://doi.org/10.3886/ICPSR36142.v2

36 National Center for Health Statistics. (2020). *CDC WONDER: Underlying Cause of Death 1999-2016*. Centers for Disease Control and Prevention. http://wonder.cdc.gov/ucd-icd10.html

37 National Center for Injury Prevention and Control. (2014). *Web-based Injury Statistics Query and Reporting System (WISQARS)* [Data set]. Centers for Disease Control and Prevention.

38 Hingson, R. W., Heeren, T., & Winter, M. R. (2006). Age at drinking onset and alcohol dependence: age at onset, duration, and severity. *Archives of pediatrics & adolescent medicine, 160*(7), 739-746. https://jamanetwork.com/journals/jamapediatrics/articlepdf/205204/poa60009_739_746.pdf

39 Merikangas, K. R., He, J. P., Burstein, M., Swanson, S. A., Avenevoli, S., Cui, L., ... & Swendsen, J. (2010). Lifetime prevalence of mental disorders in US adolescents: results from the National Comorbidity Survey Replication–Adolescent Supplement (NCS-A). *Journal of the American Academy of Child & Adolescent Psychiatry, 49*(10), 980-989. www.ncbi.nlm.nih.gov/pmc/articles/PMC2946114/?_escaped_fragment_=po=2.63158

40 Stahre, M., Roeber, J., Kanny, D., Brewer, R. D., & Zhang, X. (2014). Peer reviewed: contribution of excessive alcohol consumption to deaths and years of potential life lost in the United States. *Preventing chronic disease, 11*. www.ncbi.nlm.nih.gov/pmc/articles/PMC4075492/

41 National Center for Health Statistics. (2020). *CDC WONDER: Underlying Cause of Death 1999-2016*. Centers for Disease Control and Prevention. http://wonder.cdc.gov/ucd-icd10.html

42 National Center for Injury Prevention and Control. (2014). *Web-based Injury Statistics Query and Reporting System (WISQARS)* [Data set]. Centers for Disease Control and Prevention.

43 Calabria, B., Degenhardt, L., Hall, W., & Lynskey, M. (2010). Does cannabis use increase the risk of death? Systematic review of epidemiological evidence on adverse effects of cannabis use. *Drug and alcohol review, 29*(3), 318-330. http://citeseerx.ist.psu.edu/viewdoc/download?doi=10.1.1.660.1986&rep=rep1&type=pdf;
Hall, W., & Solowij, N. (1998). Adverse effects of cannabis. *The Lancet, 352*(9140), 1611-1616. https://dickkeslerphd.com/wp-content/uploads/2019/01/Adverse-Effects-of-Cannabis-pot-1.pdf

44 Hasin, D. S., Kerridge, B. T., Saha, T. D., Huang, B., Pickering, R., Smith, S. M., ... & Grant, B. F. (2016). Prevalence and correlates of DSM-5 cannabis use disorder, 2012-2013: findings from the National Epidemiologic Survey on Alcohol and Related Conditions–III. *American Journal of Psychiatry, 173*(6), 588-599. https://pubmed.ncbi.nlm.nih.gov/26940807/

45 Han, B., Compton, W. M., Blanco, C., & Jones, C. M. (2019). Time since first cannabis use and 12-month prevalence of cannabis use disorder among youth and emerging adults in the United States. *Addiction, 114*(4), 698-707. https://onlinelibrary.wiley.com/doi/abs/10.1111/add.14511

46 Johnston, L., Miech, R., O'Malley, P., Bachman, J., Schulenberg, J., & Patrick, M. (2020). *Monitoring the Future national survey results on drug use, 1975-2019: Overview, key findings on adolescent drug use*. Institute for Social Research. https://deepblue.lib.umich.edu/bitstream/handle/2027.42/162579/FINAL.pdf?sequence=1

47 Hasin, D. S., Kerridge, B. T., Saha, T. D., Huang, B., Pickering, R., Smith, S. M., ... & Grant, B. F. (2016). Prevalence and correlates of DSM-5 cannabis use disorder, 2012-2013: findings from the National Epidemiologic Survey on Alcohol and Related Conditions–III. *American Journal of Psychiatry, 173*(6), 588-599. https://pubmed.ncbi.nlm.nih.gov/26940807/

48 Johnston, L., Miech, R., O'Malley, P., Bachman, J., Schulenberg, J., & Patrick, M. (2020). *Monitoring the Future national survey results on drug use, 1975-2019: Overview, key findings on adolescent drug use*. Institute for Social Research. https://deepblue.lib.umich.edu/bitstream/handle/2027.42/162579/FINAL.pdf?sequence=1

49 Johnston, L., Miech, R., O'Malley, P., Bachman, J., Schulenberg, J., & Patrick, M. (2020). *Monitoring the Future national survey results on drug use, 1975-2019: Overview, key findings on adolescent drug use*. Institute for Social Research. https://deepblue.lib.umich.edu/bitstream/handle/2027.42/162579/FINAL.pdf?sequence=1

50 US Department of Health and Human Services. (2014). *The health consequences of smoking—50 years of progress: a report of the Surgeon General*. (Table 12.2.2, p.790). Centers for Disease Control and Prevention. www.ncbi.nlm.nih.gov/books/NBK179276/pdf/Bookshelf_NBK179276.pdf

51 Anthony, J. C., Warner, L. A., & Kessler, R. C. (1997). *Comparative epidemiology of dependence on tobacco, alcohol, controlled substances, and inhalants: basic findings from the National Comorbidity Survey*. American Psychological Association. www.researchgate.net/profile/Lynn_Warner2/publication/232545123_Comparative_Epide-

miology_of_Dependence_on_Tobacco_Alcohol_Controlled_Substances_and_Inhalants_Basic_Findings_From_the_National_Comorbidity_Survey/links/0fcfd5124debe9ee41000000.pdf

52 Johnston, L., Miech, R., O'Malley, P., Bachman, J., Schulenberg, J., & Patrick, M. (2020). *Monitoring the Future national survey results on drug use, 1975-2019: Overview, key findings on adolescent drug use.* Institute for Social Research. https://deepblue.lib.umich.edu/bitstream/handle/2027.42/162579/FINAL.pdf?sequence=1

53 US Department of Health and Human Services. (2014). *The health consequences of smoking—50 years of progress: a report of the Surgeon General.* (Table 12.2.2, p.790) Centers for Disease Control and Prevention. www.ncbi.nlm.nih.gov/books/NBK179276/pdf/Bookshelf_NBK179276.pdf

54 Anthony, J. C., Warner, L. A., & Kessler, R. C. (1997). *Comparative epidemiology of dependence on tobacco, alcohol, controlled substances, and inhalants: basic findings from the National Comorbidity Survey.* American Psychological Association. www.researchgate.net/profile/Lynn_Warner2/publication/232545123_Comparative_Epidemiology_of_Dependence_on_Tobacco_Alcohol_Controlled_Substances_and_Inhalants_Basic_Findings_From_the_National_Comorbidity_Survey/links/0fcfd5124debe9ee41000000.pdf

55 Office on Smoking and Health, National Center for Chronic Disease Prevention and Health Promotion. (2021). *Outbreak of Lung Injury Associated with the Use of E-Cigarette, or Vaping, Products.* Centers for Disease Control and Prevention. www.cdc.gov/tobacco/basic_information/e-cigarettes/severe-lung-disease.html

56 United States Census Bureau. (2021). *2017 National Population Projections Tables: Main Series.* Census.gov. www.census.gov/data/tables/2017/demo/popproj/2017-summary-tables.html

57 Johnston, L., Miech, R., O'Malley, P., Bachman, J., Schulenberg, J., & Patrick, M. (2020). *Monitoring the Future national survey results on drug use, 1975-2019: Overview, key findings on adolescent drug use.* Institute for Social Research. https://deepblue.lib.umich.edu/bitstream/handle/2027.42/162579/FINAL.pdf?sequence=1

58 Institute for Social Research, the University of Michigan. (2017). *Monitoring the Future Study.* National Institutes of Health, National Institute on Drug Abuse. www.cdc.gov/nchs/hus/contents2017.htm#051

59 Hammond, D., Reid, J. L., Rynard, V. L., O'Connor, R. J., Goniewicz, M. L., Piper, M. E., & Bansal-Travers, M. (2021). *Indicators of dependence and efforts to quit vaping and smoking among youth in Canada, England and the USA.* Tobacco Control. http://davidhammond.ca/wp-content/uploads/2021/02/2021_ITCYouth_EcigDependenceCessation_Hammond.pdf

60 Johnston, L. D., O'Malley, P. M., Bachman, J. G., & Schulenberg, J. E. (2013). *Monitoring the Future national survey results on drug use, 1975-2012. Volume I: Secondary school students.* Institute for Social Research. https://deepblue.lib.umich.edu/bitstream/handle/2027.42/137921/mtf-vol1_2012.pdf?sequence=1a

61 Anthony, J. C., Warner, L. A., & Kessler, R. C. (1997). *Comparative epidemiology of dependence on tobacco, alcohol, controlled substances, and inhalants: basic findings from the National Comorbidity Survey.* American Psychological Association. https://d1wqtxts1xzle7.cloudfront.net/45949452/Comparative_epidemiology_of_dependence_o20160525-10037-184ph73-with-cover-page-v2.pdf?Expires=1640667915&Signature=RkzTtbaBxJ034f-0pAxQXQ1MS2dS5WiI1ULg9DV-WEpjLGKq0CeV-hnpS3Vt64XutKJTNvwy1DEn7xXFa1VgJA77fGe-p0Y0yri8nd9b-W4Y6vXx-TcdD5UF1MwanF1tm-CYtwDp45xjZXswFqMu6PLBbNNAidri1WAjHd52o-luc27JHaVPtnpxWablcm8MCnWEWzHv5OoeEglC1rSG76gw3CXaqtaJ-C-bZLdeuivzxriDcny1kYTJT-K6n0Ugx4u9sPnsImp-rud9MQTw2ROLv6MlNUcqfEtVWDQJpuHDaaqK5pnx4ChzE3bQVnAxpKb-ZylYw7m5U6eYJ9GkPmgaZLQ__&Key-Pair-Id=APKAJLOHF5GGSLRBV4ZAa

62 Johnston, L. D., O'Malley, P. M., Bachman, J. G., & Schulenberg, J. E. (2013). *Monitoring the Future national survey results on drug use, 1975-2012. Volume I: Secondary school students.* Institute for Social Research. https://deepblue.lib.umich.edu/bitstream/handle/2027.42/137921/mtf-vol1_2012.pdf?sequence=1a

63 Anthony, J. C., Warner, L. A., & Kessler, R. C. (1997). *Comparative epidemiology of dependence on tobacco, alcohol, controlled substances, and inhalants: basic findings from the National Comorbidity Survey.* American Psychological Association. https://d1wqtxts1xzle7.cloudfront.net/45949452/Comparative_epidemiology_of_dependence_o20160525-10037-184ph73-with-cover-page-v2.pdf?Expires=1640667915&Signature=RkzTtbaBxJ034f0pAxQXQ1MS2dS5WiI1ULg9DV-WEpjLGKq0CeV-hnpS3Vt64XutKJTNvwy1DEn7xXFa1VgJA77f-Gep0Y0yri8nd9b-W4Y6vXx-TcdD5UF1MwanF1tm-CYtwDp45xjZXswFqMu6PLBbNNAidri1WAjH-d52oluc27JHaVPtnpxWablcm8MCnWEWzHv5OoeEglC1rSG76gw3CXaqtaJ-C-bZLdeuivzxriDcny1kYT-JTK6n0Ugx4u9sPnsImp-rud9MQTw2ROLv6MlNUcqfEtVWDQJpuHDaaqK5pnx4ChzE3bQVnAxpKb-ZylYw7m5U6eYJ9GkPmgaZLQ__&Key-Pair-Id=APKAJLOHF5GGSLRBV4ZAa

64 National Center for Health Statistics. (2020). *CDC WONDER: Underlying Cause of Death 1999-2016.* Centers for Disease Control and Prevention. http://wonder.cdc.gov/ucd-icd10.html

65 National Center for Injury Prevention and Control. (2014). *Web-based Injury Statistics Query and Reporting System (WISQARS)* [Data set]. Centers for Disease Control and Prevention.

66 Johnston, L., Miech, R., O'Malley, P., Bachman, J., Schulenberg, J., & Patrick, M. (2020). *Monitoring the Future national survey results on drug use, 1975-2019: Overview, key findings on adolescent drug use.* Institute for Social Research. https://deepblue.lib.umich.edu/bitstream/handle/2027.42/162579/FINAL.pdf?sequence=1

67 Anthony, J. C., Warner, L. A., & Kessler, R. C. (1997). *Comparative epidemiology of dependence on tobacco, alcohol, controlled substances, and inhalants: basic findings from the National Comorbidity Survey.* American Psychological Association. https://d1wqtxts1xzle7.cloudfront.net/45949452/Comparative_epidemiology_of_dependence_o20160525-10037-184ph73-with-cover-page-v2.pdf?Expires=1640667915&Signature=RkzTtbaBx-J034f0pAxQXQ1MS2dS5WiI1ULg9DV~WEpjLGKq0CeV~hnpS3Vt64XutKJTNvwy1DEn7xXFa1VgJA77f-Gep0Y0yri8nd9b~W4Y6vXx~TcdD5UF1MwanF1tm-CYtwDp45xjZXswFqMu6PLBbNNAidri1WAjH-d52oluc27JHaVPtnpxWablcm8MCnWEWzHv5OoeEglC1rSG76gw3CXaqtaJ~C-bZLdeuivzxriDcny1kYT-JTK6n0Ugx4u9sPnsImp~rud9MQTw2ROLv6MlNUcqfEtVWDQJpuHDaaqK5pnx4ChzE3bQVnAxpKb-ZylYw7m5U6eYJ9GkPmgaZLQ__&Key-Pair-Id=APKAJLOHF5GGSLRBV4ZA

68 National Center for Health Statistics. (2020). *CDC WONDER: Underlying Cause of Death 1999-2016.* Centers for Disease Control and Prevention. http://wonder.cdc.gov/ucd-icd10.html

69 National Center for Injury Prevention and Control. (2014). *Web-based Injury Statistics Query and Reporting System (WISQARS)* [Data set]. Centers for Disease Control and Prevention.

70 Johnston, L., Miech, R., O'Malley, P., Bachman, J., Schulenberg, J., & Patrick, M. (2020). *Monitoring the Future national survey results on drug use, 1975-2019: Overview, key findings on adolescent drug use.* Institute for Social Research. https://deepblue.lib.umich.edu/bitstream/handle/2027.42/162579/FINAL.pdf?sequence=1

71 Anthony, J. C., Warner, L. A., & Kessler, R. C. (1997). *Comparative epidemiology of dependence on tobacco, alcohol, controlled substances, and inhalants: basic findings from the National Comorbidity Survey.* American Psychological Association. https://d1wqtxts1xzle7.cloudfront.net/45949452/Comparative_epidemiology_of_dependence_o20160525-10037-184ph73-with-cover-page-v2.pdf?Expires=1640667915&Signature=RkzTtbaBx-J034f0pAxQXQ1MS2dS5WiI1ULg9DV~WEpjLGKq0CeV~hnpS3Vt64XutKJTNvwy1DEn7xXFa1VgJA77f-Gep0Y0yri8nd9b~W4Y6vXx~TcdD5UF1MwanF1tm-CYtwDp45xjZXswFqMu6PLBbNNAidri1WAjH-d52oluc27JHaVPtnpxWablcm8MCnWEWzHv5OoeEglC1rSG76gw3CXaqtaJ~C-bZLdeuivzxriDcny1kYT-JTK6n0Ugx4u9sPnsImp~rud9MQTw2ROLv6MlNUcqfEtVWDQJpuHDaaqK5pnx4ChzE3bQVnAxpKb-ZylYw7m5U6eYJ9GkPmgaZLQ__&Key-Pair-Id=APKAJLOHF5GGSLRBV4ZA

72 American Cancer Society. (2020). *Lifetime Risk of Developing or Dying From Cancer.* www.cancer.org/cancer/cancer-basics/lifetime-probability-of-developing-or-dying-from-cancer.html

73 National Cancer Institute. (2018). *SEER Cancer Statistics Review 1975-2015.* https://seer.cancer.gov/csr/1975_2015/results_single/sect_01_table.01.pdf

74 HPV and Cancer. (2021). Centers for Disease Control and Prevention. www.cdc.gov/cancer/hpv/statistics/cases.htm

75 Giuliano, A. R., Lu, B., Nielson, C. M., Flores, R., Papenfuss, M. R., Lee, J. H., ... & Harris, R. B. (2008). Age-specific prevalence, incidence, and duration of human papillomavirus infections in a cohort of 290 US men. *The Journal of infectious diseases, 198*(6), 827-835. https://watermark.silverchair.com/198-6-827.pdf?token=AQECAHi208BE49Ooan9kkhW_Ercy7Dm3ZL_9Cf3qfKAc485ysgAAAakwggGlBgkqhkiG9w0BB-wagggGWMIIBkgIBADCCAYsGCSqGSIb3DQEHATAeBglghkgBZQMEAS4wEQQM5nZyRcRu62esB_uJAgEQgIIBXGb0ZSIoSHzbjWYzcvpWMWdMrW5ysZzgMOEupOSP10YIZuPyrcuIPj_aceT150Fh5m_KZw6Lt8DTxkIYrxCXzmzEp2R76QvSMujMVE88bg2JDRMovieNRHMLdIXWuKu-QezJFFy4i6tgJZDW_Lp-23DKzBkTwxybCmNQ1HKWBiY9Xc_3N7wblTxM3FpIOM7LPRSINKeuPWAfURGexBlkDXU43OzjP4nN-L3SerCnbtCJcJoHM02o2oa2I_JUOywo-RGZG-k1TsA8jeiRos-fD_ZsoDNDAumY47r1oFKE4EVNwU_jzHujB-z1S3h0qCJ5rVxlNEeehlqJgR0BbJ4-CeMYNRk3INMrIhF739pXs4re4CzRB1fvz4PJx_jSeo21nv6zAQ8XdwLW-MQR2R8jG-xEvHfEHiMVTuqS5kRjlKVZWpa41h3WWwvlYZRwn12pAc_w6dv5thjkPLiPFxKxAA

76 Markowitz, L. E., Liu, G., Hariri, S., Steinau, M., Dunne, E. F., & Unger, E. R. (2016). Prevalence of HPV after introduction of the vaccination program in the United States. *Pediatrics, 137*(3). http://pediatrics.aappublications.org/content/early/2016/02/19/peds.2015-1968?sso=1&sso_redirect_count=2&nfstatus=401&nftoken=00000000-0000-0000-0000-000000000000&nfstatusdescription=ERROR:%20No%20local%20token&nfstatus=401&nftoken=00000000-0000-0000-0000-000000000000&nfstatusdescription=ERROR:+No+local+token

77 Viens, L. J. (2016). Human papillomavirus–associated cancers—United States, 2008–2012. MMWR. *Morbidity and mortality weekly report,* 65. www.cdc.gov/mmwr/volumes/65/wr/mm6526a1.htm

78 Centers for Disease Control and Prevention. (2021). *Sexually Transmitted Diseases (STDs).* www.cdc.gov/std/stats15/other.htm

79 Markowitz, L. E., Liu, G., Hariri, S., Steinau, M., Dunne, E. F., & Unger, E. R. (2016). Prevalence of HPV after introduction of the vaccination program in the United States. *Pediatrics, 137*(3). https://pediatrics.aappublications.org/content/137/3/e20151968

80 Daugherty, M., & Byler, T. (2018). Genital Wart and Human Papillomavirus Prevalence in Men in the United States From Penile Swabs: Results From National Health and Nutrition Examination Surveys. *Sexually transmitted diseases, 45*(6), 412-416. www.ncbi.nlm.nih.gov/pubmed/29750774

81 Gargano, J. W., Unger, E. R., Liu, G., Steinau, M., Meites, E., Dunne, E., & Markowitz, L. E. (2017). Prevalence of genital human papillomavirus in males, United States, 2013–2014. *The Journal of infectious diseases, 215*(7), 1070-1079. https://academic.oup.com/jid/article/215/7/1070/2972752

82 Markowitz, L. E., Liu, G., Hariri, S., Steinau, M., Dunne, E. F., & Unger, E. R. (2016). Prevalence of HPV after introduction of the vaccination program in the United States. *Pediatrics, 137*(3). https://pediatrics.aappublications.org/content/137/3/e20151968

83 American Academy of Pediatrics. (2020). *CDC: 54% of teens fully vaccinated against HPV.* https://publications.aap.org/aapnews/news/8085

84 Land, J. A., Van Bergen, J. E. A. M., Morre, S. A., & Postma, M. J. (2009). Epidemiology of Chlamydia trachomatis infection in women and the cost-effectiveness of screening. *Human reproduction update, 16*(2), 189-204. https://academic.oup.com/humupd/article/16/2/189/737223;
Kavanagh, K., Wallace, L. A., Robertson, C., Wilson, P., & Scoular, A. (2013). Estimation of the risk of tubal factor infertility associated with genital chlamydial infection in women: a statistical modelling study. *International journal of epidemiology, 42*(2), 493-503. https://academic.oup.com/ije/article/42/2/493/735968

85 Farley, T. A., Cohen, D. A., & Elkins, W. (2003). Asymptomatic sexually transmitted diseases: the case for screening. *Preventive medicine, 36*(4), 502-509. www.sciencedirect.com/science/article/pii/S0091743502000580

86 van Valkengoed, I. G., Morré, S. A., van den Brule, A. J., Meijer, C. J., Bouter, L. M., & Boeke, A. J. P. (2004). Overestimation of complication rates in evaluations of Chlamydia trachomatis screening programmes—implications for cost-effectiveness analyses. *International Journal of Epidemiology, 33*(2), 416-425. https://academic.oup.com/ije/article/33/2/416/715875

87 Maddow-Zimet I., Kost, K. & Finn, S. (2020). *Pregnancies, Births and Abortions in the United States, 1973–2016: National and State Trends by Age.* Guttmacher Institute. www.guttmacher.org/report/pregnancies-births-abortions-in-united-states-1973-2016
https://data.guttmacher.org/states/trend?state=US&topics=170&dataset=data

Printed in Great Britain
by Amazon

42118986R00304